GRAPHICS FOR ENGINEERS

BY THE SAME AUTHORS

Basic Drawing for Engineering Technology, 1964

GRAPHICS FOR ENGINEERS
Visualization, Communication, and Design

Randolph P. Hoelscher

*Professor and Head of the Department
of General Engineering, Emeritus*

Clifford H. Springer

Professor of General Engineering, Emeritus

Jerry S. Dobrovolny

*Professor and Head of the Department
of General Engineering*

UNIVERSITY OF ILLINOIS

John Wiley and Sons, Inc.   *New York · London · Sydney*

4 5 6 7 8 9 10

Copyright ©️ 1968 by John Wiley & Sons, Inc.

All rights reserved. No part of this book may be reproduced
by any means, nor transmitted, nor translated into a machine
language without the written permission of the publisher.

Library of Congress Catalog Card Number: 67-29722
Printed in the United States of America
ISBN 0 471 40558 2

Preface

Engineers, designers, draftsmen, and technicians must work together to build the many products and projects, both large and small, that are necessary for our modern life. Teamwork and an intercommunication of ideas are essential in this task.

The language used in engineering drawing, together with supporting graphical systems for computation and representation, must be thoroughly understood by all who carry on the work of engineering. This book has been designed so as to enable the student who plans to enter the field of engineering or production can learn this language and use it proficiently. It contains the latest standards that have been nationally and internationally accepted by the various national standardization bodies. It therefore serves as an excellent reference book in engineering offices.

This is the latest of a series of books based on the successful organization and teaching methods of a department that has been in existence for over sixty years. During these years it has had conservative overlapping leadership of experienced men, all of them graduate engineers. It represents a philosophy of teaching in engineering drawing and graphic sciences that is in harmony with the current trend in engineering education practice. The same sound and valid objectives that guided the preparation of *Engineering Drawing and Geometry* by Hoelscher and Springer have been followed in this book.

In keeping with the current semantics of engineering science, the title has been changed to *Graphics for Engineers*. Graphical expression or graphics is a much more inclusive term than drawing since it covers all forms of art from painting to printing, including line work from etching to charts and diagrams. The term is therefore well adapted to this book, especially when modified by the term "for Engineers."

A subtitle, *Visualization, Communication, and Design,* has been added, which is in accord with our objectives in preparing this book. These objectives are as follows:

1. To provide a textbook so clear in its verbal discussion and pictorial illustration that it can be readily understood by the student. To accomplish this, more step-by-step illustrations and explanations have been given.

2. To make a textbook that presents the best in drafting practice, but emphasizes the development of the reasoning process in its theoretical discussion rather than manual skill.

3. To provide the necessary material in one textbook to cover adequately the work in basic drawing courses, fundamental descriptive geometry, advanced courses for sophomores in professional fields, and fundamental work in graphical computation.

4. To present the material in such a way that it will (*a*) stimulate creative imagination, (*b*) develop visual perception in three dimensions and (*c*) promote original thinking, useful in engineering design.

5. To eliminate all material that is not essential for engineering students or useful in a reference work on drawing for practicing engineers. Thus it serves both as learning and reference material.

6. To adhere rigorously to third-quadrant projection, not only for the three principal views but for auxiliary views as well, which is the basis for the unification of drawing practice among the United States, Great Britain, and Canada. Thus the plane of projection is always between the object and the viewer. Consequently, the reference line, if used, is always between the adjacent views.

7. To facilitate understanding of the material by a strategic use of color. In some chapters color is used not only to distinguish planes of projection, but also for the more functional purpose of aiding the student in differentiating between auxiliary planes, cutting planes, and other surfaces. In the chapter on Auxiliary Projections, reference lines between the various views and the projecting lines to them are also drawn in color. This makes the construction for each view stand out clearly.

The organization of Part One of this book has been changed from that of its predecessor to conform more closely with current teaching practice. Since many teachers wish to coordinate some descriptive geometry with their drawing courses, the four fundamental operations of projection theory have been placed in Chapter 6 on orthographic projection. The chapter on Auxiliary Projection follows immediately, thus laying the foundation for an understanding of the advanced projection in Part Two.

Chapters on Sectional Views, Fasteners, and Shop Terms and Processes have been placed ahead of Basic Dimensioning, since the information in those chapters is necessary for the shape description on any engineering part before size dimensions can be applied. While this order seems logical, each chapter is self-contained, and the instructor can change the assignment schedule to suit his own objectives.

On the subject of dimensioning, two chapters have been presented. This is the area in which the greatest advancement has been made in recent years. The first chapter on Basic Dimensioning covers all of the material needed by students in such fields as civil engineering, architecture, and in general engineering practice. The second chapter on Dimensioning for Interchangeable Assembly is quite essential for students who will go into mass-production industries, such as the automotive industries, aeronautics, and space vehicles.

In Part Two, "Advanced Projection Systems," all the theory in descriptive geometry that is necessary for the successful solution of problems in design and drafting has been included. This part covers all of the material normally given in a descriptive geometry course. It has been so arranged that it may be used in a combined and integrated course in both drawing and descriptive geometry or in separate courses if so desired. One textbook with a uniform system of nomenclature has a distinct advantage over two books with different systems. All forms of pictorial drawing have been presented on an exact theoretical basis as well as by conventional constructions where these are appropriate.

In the chapters on Axonometric and Oblique, conventional methods of construction have been placed first. The exact theory of projection has been presented at the end of each chapter, for those who wish to give a more rigorous course. Considerable proficiency in making these two types of pictorial drawings can be attained by the conventional methods. Many schools will not have time for more thorough study.

The five chapters in Part Three, "Technical Charts and Graphic Computation," contain enough material for a two-credit-hour course in graphical computation. This material has been presented in logical sequence. The chapters are independent of one another. Any of the chapters can conveniently be introduced in a drawing course. This is commonly done with the chapter on Charts and Diagrams.

The chapters in Part Four, "Professional Applications," have been designed for technical courses in the professional fields. The treatment is thorough and sufficiently detailed in character and explanation, so that the student may do problems of a professional character without entering into theoretical design work. The problems that have been included in each of these chapters are not merely copy work but offer an excellent opportunity for the development of clear thinking and good judgment. Few other texts present problems in this area.

The pictures at the opening of each chapter are intended to give the student some idea of the development of engineering from the earliest times to the present. This should provide both a motive and an inspiration to participate in this advancing area of human knowledge and service.

The number of problems has been increased in most chapters. They have been selected to emphasize design based on good judgement. Open-ended problems, that is, those with more than one possible solution, have been included to give the student a situation similar to that in engineering practice, although on a simpler scale.

These problems simulate to a degree, suitable for younger students, the "case method" of approach to problems that occur in daily engineering work.

To meet the problem situation we have provided sixteen workbooks, with the aid of staff members at the University of Illinois, to cover a variety of courses. These are available from the Stipes Publishing Company, 10 Chester Street, Champaign, Illinois 61820. At present there are:

(a) Five workbooks for straight drawing courses, designated Series A, B, C, D, and E;

(b) Four workbooks for straight descriptive geometry courses, designated Series 1, 2, 3, and 4;

(c) Five workbooks for combination courses, designated Series 11, 12, 13, 15, and 16;

(d) Two workbooks for advanced drawing and geometry courses with application to design, designated Series 21 and 22.

Full-scale solution files are available to instructors for Workbooks, Series A, B, C, D, and E; Series 1, 2, 3, and 4, and also Series 11, 12, 13, 15, and 16. Workbooks save a great deal of the student's time since the layout for the solution is printed and the student can forego the labor of making it.

Acknowledgements

We are indebted to several of our colleagues for valuable assistance in the development of this book. The chapter on Architectural Drawing was prepared by Professor Wayne L. Shick, the chapter on Pipe Drawing by Professor Leonard D. Walker. The chapter on Computer Drawing was prepared by Mr. Robert J. Tatem of the Bell Telephone Laboratories. The chapter on Tooling for Production was prepared by Mr. Gerald W. Gladden, Supervisor of Technical Occupations, State of Illinois, Division of Vocational and Technical Education. We wish to thank Mr. David C. O'Bryant and Mr. Ronald H. Hausch for their assistance in preparing illustrations; and to Mrs. Marilyn Butler for typing the manuscript. To each of these persons we express our appreciation for their contribution to the usefulness of this book. Our thanks go also to Professor H. H. Jordan, the originator of a long series of books of which this one is the culmination. We also express our appreciation of Professor Howard Nelson and to Professor Grace Wilson for assistance in several sections of the book. Many valuable suggestions and criticisms were received from members of the staff of the University of Illionis, both at Urbana and at the Chicago Circle campus. To these men and many others at other schools we express our gratitude. Many industrial concerns have contributed drawings for illustration purposes, for which credit is given at the appropriate places.

Urbana, Illinois   *R. P. Hoelscher*
January 1969   *C. H. Springer*
                                                                                       J. S. Dobrovolny

Contents

PART ONE

Basic Drawing

An Introduction to Engineering Drawing

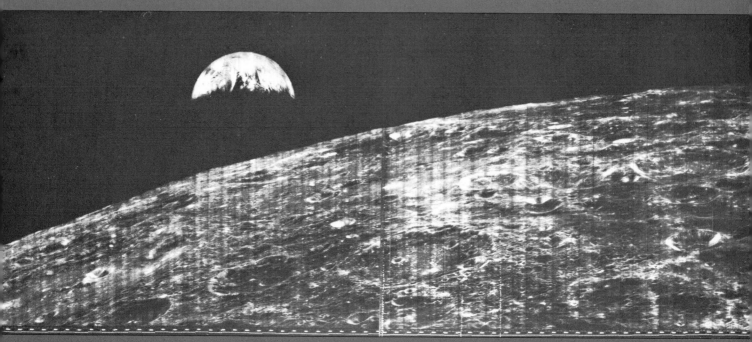

World's first view of the earth taken by a spacecraft, Lunar Orbiter I, taken from vicinity of the moon. (Courtesy of NASA.)

Communication satellite INTELSAT II. (Courtesy of COMSAT.)

Chapter 1 An Introduction to Engineering Drawing

1.1 ORIGIN OF PROJECTION DRAWING. The representation of three-dimensional objects on two-dimensional surfaces by means of geometric drawings, such as plans and elevations, has involved a gradual change. Through the centuries drawings developed from crude pictorials of prehistoric man, such as that in Fig. 1.1, through a period of highly artistic drawings to the present well-developed types of industrial drawing. In Mesopotamia, maps were made on clay tablets such as that shown in Fig. 1.2. In the early Middle Ages, most of the construction work was concerned with buildings. During the Roman period drawings of building plans were made before construction was undertaken. Frequently construction problems were worked out by the mason or builder from general specifications as the work progressed. However, very few examples of these drawings have been preserved.

One early Egyptian drawing made on papyrus which shows two views of a shrine without dimensions has been found. Pictorial drawings seemed to have been quite common during the Middle Ages. See Fig. 1.3.

Two elevations are in existence of the west front of the Cathedral of Orvieto, supposed to have been made by Lorenzo del Maitano of Siena soon after 1310. These are not true front views, since each is in slight perspective. By the end of the fifteenth century, there were draftsmen who could make true elevations. One of the earliest examples of the use of plan and elevation is included in an album of drawings in the Vatican Library, drawn by Giuliano da Sangallo. The date on the title page is 1465, but the book was not actually completed until 1490.

The drawings of early architects and engineers contained the basic idea of the theory that was to be developed into our modern forms of geometric projection. The system of right-angle projection on planes set up perpendicular to each other was first completely worked out by Gaspard Monge in the eighteenth cen-

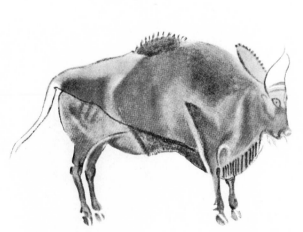

Fig. 1.1   Late Palaeolithic representation of a bison. (From Singer, Holmyard, and Hall, *A History of Technology,* **Vol. 1, University Press, Oxford, England.)**

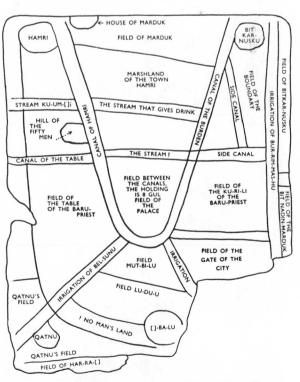

Fig. 1.2   Map of fields and canals near Nippur. (From Singer, Holmyard, and Hall, *A History of Technology,* **Vol. 1, University Press, Oxford, England.)**

tury and was used to solve geometric problems. See Fig. 1.4. The work of Monge is the basis of descriptive geometry, which is the fundamental theory underlying all modern industrial drawing.

1.2 FUNCTION OR PURPOSE OF ENGINEERING DRAWING. In order that the student may understand the reason for studying engineering drawing, this chapter gives a brief overall view of the scope of the subject and its place in engineering practice.

The ideas for all the works of man are conceived in some person's mind. These ideas may require extensive computations. But they do not end there. Inevitably what is sometimes referred to as "hardware" must be produced. This hardware can rarely be produced without drawings. Even though computers are being designed to make drawings, some kind of preliminary drawing or layout is necessary to program the computer.

Some of the more common uses of drawings are stated in the following paragraphs.

1.2.1 Design of machines. In designing machines, and other structures, the engineer or technician must first form a clear mental picture of the thing to be made. He must then convey this idea to others. This cannot be done by the written word alone. But it can be done by drawings combined with verbal instructions or specifications.

1.2.2 Fabrication details. Most machines require a number of separate parts. These parts are then assembled, either permanently or in a definite position as moving parts. In either event the parts must fit together exactly. This requires that the size and location of parts be held to very close tolerances. See Chapter 12.

1.2.3 Design of buildings. The basic drawings for buildings consist of floor plans for each story, elevations for each side, and numerous sectional views and large scale detail drawings of various parts. Even a relatively simple home will require a considerable amount of such drawings. For examples see Chapter 24.

Fig. 1.3 First stages in the excavation of a mine. (From Agricola, *De re metallica*, 1556.)

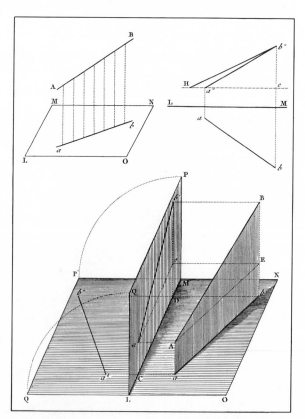

Fig. 1.4 Typical illustration from *Descriptive Geometrie* by Gaspard Monge.

1.2.4 Detail drawings. Larger structures will require separate sets of steel or reinforced concrete framing plans, plumbing plans, heating and ventilating plans, as well as drawings for elevators, electrical wiring, and any special equipment that may be involved.

1.2.5 Cost estimates. Before any contracts for construction or manufacturing can be made, cost estimates must be prepared. Such estimates are made from drawings and specifications. The drawing must delineate the exact size and shape of all parts. The kind and quality of materials to be used must be clearly stated.

1.2.6 Highway and railroad construction plans. In order to construct highways or railroads, maps must be made showing the exact location of the center line of the road, the "right of way" lines, and the boundary lines of adjacent property.

In addition to the plan, a profile showing the elevation of the ground along the center line must be made. This drawing also shows the grade line for the finished road. At frequent intervals along the road cross-sectional views must be made showing the "cut" or "fill" required. See Chapter 23.

Other details such as drainage, culverts, bridges, and viaducts must also be supplied before any contracts for construction can be entered into.

1.2.7 Department of defense. Drawings for military equipment must be made to the specification and standards required by the Department of Defense. Thousands of such drawings are made annually. Thus a battleship or submarine will require 40 to 50 thousand drawings.

1.2.8 Aerospace applications. A very large amount of complex mathematics is necessary to place a satellite in orbit. Many sciences are also involved. But nothing happens until "hardware" is designed and produced. Satellites, missiles, and space platforms require thousands of drawings. Some of these parts involve close and very accurate tolerances in order to function properly.

1.2.9 Sales presentations. In many projects companies will submit "proposals" as a part of the sales promotion. These are very frequently printed booklets describing in detail what the company proposes to furnish or supply. The proposals are illustrated with many kinds of drawings including those of a pictorial character such as isometric, oblique, or perspective.

1.3 MEANING OF TERMS. In the area of drawing, a number of terms have been used, such as mechanical drawing, engineering drawing, technical drawing, engineering graphics, and graphic science. Many of these terms are used loosely to mean the same thing. Some are misnomers. To clarify the meanings of terms as used in this book, the following paragraphs explain the terms and the contents of the field of drawing as used in industry and science.

1.3.1 Instrumental and freehand drawing. The older term mechanical drawing is really a misnomer since it seems to imply the drawing of mechanical things. It really means drawings made with instruments or instrumental drawings, as contrasted with freehand drawing, which is done without the aid of instruments. Hence we have two comprehensive types of drawings: instrumental and freehand. Drawings of any kind may be made by either method, although it should be quite clear that where very accurate line work is required, instruments must be used.

1.3.2 Engineering graphics. This is the most inclusive term now applied to drawings of all varieties made with pen or pencil, except those that may be classified as pure art. It ranges from the simple three-view drawing of a machine part to the most complex graphical layout of nomographs or graphical calculus computations.

This extensive group of drawings divides itself quite naturally into two major groups: *projection drawings* or drawings based on a geometrical theory of projection, and *nonprojection drawings* having a fundamental basis of algebraic mathematics. An outline of these two major categories is given in the paragraphs that follow.

1.4 PROJECTION DRAWING. This type includes drawings based on a fundamental geometric theory of projection. It includes the major portion of drawings made in industry. Some kinds of projection drawing, particularly in the pictorial area, may be made by "rule of thumb," but the underlying theoretical construction on which all rules are based is orthographic projection. *This term simply means that the projecting lines from the object to the plane of projection are at right angles to that plane.*

1.4.1 Orthographic multiview drawing. Drawings of this variety involve one, two, three, or more views based on right-angle projection. The planes on which the views are made are also at right angles to each other. This is the type most commonly used in industry. Figure 1.5 shows such a three-view drawing. For complete discussion see Chapter 6.

1.4.2 Pictorial projections. These drawings show

three faces of an object in one view. Since they look like photographs, they are called pictorial drawings. Many types of pictorial drawings can be made by rule-of-thumb methods. In all cases these methods are based on orthographic projection theory. The fact that the underlying basis for all forms of projection is orthographic projection should become clear to the student as he proceeds through the text.

1.4.2.1 Axonometric projection. All axonometric projections are purely orthographic. Three types of axonometric drawings are possible, depending on the position of the object relative to the plane of projection.

a. *Isometric projection* results when the plane of projection makes equal angles with the three principal faces of the object or when the axes of the object make equal angles with the plane of projection. See Fig. 1.6(a). For a complete discussion see Chapter 15.

b. *Dimetric projection* results when two axes of the object make equal angles with the plane of projection and the third axis has a different value. This type of drawing gives a more pleasing appearance, as shown in Fig. 1.6(b). See also Chapter 15.

c. *Trimetric projection* is produced when the three axes of the object each make different angles with the plane of projection. These should always be made in true projection because rule-of-thumb methods are too slow. See Fig. 1.6(c) and Chapter 15.

1.4.2.2 Oblique projection. An oblique projection results when parallel projecting lines make an angle other than 90° with the plane of projection. Obviously, many types of oblique projection can be made. A few of these have been given special names.

a. *Cavalier projection.* When the projecting lines make an angle of 45° with the plane of projection the drawing is called a Cavalier projection or drawing. An example is shown in Fig. 1.7(a). For further details see Chapter 16.

b. *Cabinet projection.* When the angle that the projecting lines make with the plane of projection is such that the scale on the receding axis in the drawing is just one-half as long as the other two axes the result is called a Cabinet drawing. See Fig. 1.7(b); also Chapter 16.

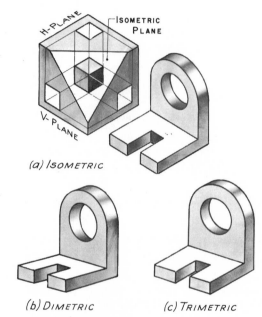

(a) ISOMETRIC

(b) DIMETRIC   *(c) TRIMETRIC*

Fig. 1.6   Axonometric projection.

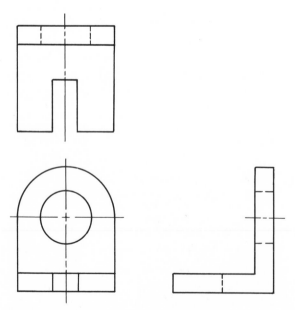

Fig. 1.5   Three-view orthographic projection.

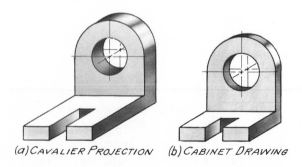

(a) CAVALIER PROJECTION   *(b) CABINET DRAWING*

Fig. 1.7   Oblique projection.

c. Clinographic projection. In Cavalier and Cabinet projection the principal face of the object is made parallel to the plane of projection. For some purposes, however, it may be desirable to turn the object at an angle with the plane of projection. In the fields of minerology and crystallography such a system is used. The angles are shown in Fig. 1.8. For further discussion see Chapter 16.

1.4.2.3   Perspective. When the projecting lines converge to a point the drawing is called a perspective. Three kinds of perspectives may be made to serve different purposes. If the principal face of the object is parallel to the plane of projection and there is only one vanishing point, the drawing is called a parallel or one-point perspective. See Fig. 1.9(*a*).

If two faces of the object are at an angle with the plane of projection, while the third face is perpendicular to it, two principal vanishing points occur and the

drawing is called an angular or two-point perspective. See Fig. 1.9(*b*).

When all three principal faces of the object are inclined to the plane of projection, the drawing is called an oblique or three-point perspective. See Fig. 1.9(*c*).

1.4.3   Descriptive geometry. This is the science of orthographic projection theory underlying all types of projection. It may be noted here that the geometric construction for the kinds of projection mentioned in the preceding paragraphs is based on orthographic projection. The study of descriptive geometry provides a method for solving the problem's relation to points, lines, planes, and other surfaces in space. Fig. 1.10 illustrates a problem of this kind. See Chapter 13.

1.4.3.1   Space relationships. Descriptive geometry can be used to solve the relationship between parts of an object, such as the distance from a point to a plane or the true shape of the face of an object. Clearance

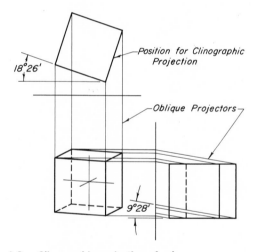

Fig. 1.8   Clinographic projection of cube.

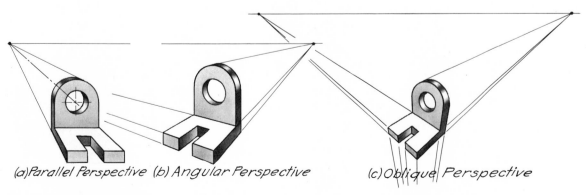

(a)Parallel Perspective (b) Angular Perspective   (c)Oblique Perspective

Fig. 1.9   Types of perspective.

problems such as the relationship between moving parts or the access to bolts and screws can best be solved by descriptive geometry.

1.4.3.2 Problems of motion. By means of kinematics, a graphical method closely related to descriptive geometry, the problems of motion can be readily solved on the drawing board. For example, the need to change the rotary motion of a motor to reciprocating linear motion at various speeds and accelerations is a common one.

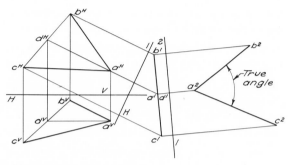

Fig. 1.10 Descriptive geometry.

1.5 SUMMARY. The kinds of projection discussed in this chapter, the relationships of the geometric elements entering into each type of projection, and the classification and name of each special form of projection are summarized in Table 1.1. Each type is discussed in detail in later chapters.

1.6 SHOP AND CONSTRUCTION METHODS. Before he can proceed very far in his profession the young engineer or technician must become familiar with methods of manufacture in the shop or construction in the field. It is clearly a waste of time and money to make a drawing, however beautiful and accurate, of a part that cannot be made economically in the shop. Since shop courses have almost disappeared from engineering education, the technical student as a part of his training in graphic expression should learn the simpler fundamentals of shop and construction methods as presented in several chapters of this book.

1.7 DIMENSIONING. A shape description of a part shown by one or more projected views is totally inadequate unless dimensions are given showing the exact

TABLE 1.1   TYPES OF PROJECTIONS

Major Classifications	Subdivision	Number of Planes of Projection	Relation of Lines of Sight to Plane of Projection	Relation of Lines of Sight to Each Other	Location of Point of Sight in Relation to Plane of Projection	Position of Enclosing Cube with Relation to Plane of Projection
Orthographic	Multiple view	As many as necessary	Perpendicular	Parallel	Infinite distance	Faces parallel to planes
	Isometric	One	Perpendicular	Parallel	Infinite distance	Faces equally inclined to plane
	Dimetric	One	Perpendicular	Parallel	Infinite distance	Two faces equally inclined to plane
	Trimetric	One	Perpendicular	Parallel	Infinite distance	Three faces at different angles to plane
Oblique	Cavalier	One	45°	Parallel	Infinite distance	Principal face parallel to plane
	Cabinet	One	63° 26′	Parallel	Infinite distance	Principal face parallel to plane
	Clinographic	One	80° 32′	Parallel	Infinite distance	Principal face at angle of 18° 26′
	General	One	Any angle except those above	Parallel	Infinite distance	Principal face parallel to plane
Perspective	One-point	One	Various angles	Converge at a point	Finite distance	Principal face parallel to plane
	Two-point	One	Various angles	Converge at a point	Finite distance	Two faces inclined and one face perpendicular to plane
	Three-point	One	Various angles	Converge at a point	Finite distance	Three faces inclined to plane

size of each part and the location of parts in relation to each other. It is this phase of drawing that requires the greatest care and study. Engineers are giving a great deal of attention to the standardization of dimensioning so that there may be no ambiguity. The dimensioning practice given in this book represents the most recently adopted American standards, as set forth in the latest USASI Y14–5 standard. The letters USASI mean United States of America Standards Institute. This was formerly the American Standards Association.

1.8 PROFESSIONAL ASPECTS OF DRAWING. The young man who plans to enter a technical industry will frequently find his work in one of the specialized fields, such as civil engineering, mechanical engineering, or architecture. In the larger industries and in research institutions the work tends to cross over professional lines. In any event, the fundamental principles of drawings as explained in this book will be the same in all these areas. After training in basic drawing, the student may wish to go further in specialized fields.

As a result of professional specialization we now have the following varieties of technical drawing.

1. Machine drawing
2. Map drawing
3. Structural drawing
4. Welding drawing
5. Architectural drawing
6. Pipe drawing
7. Electrical drawing
8. Charts and diagrams
9. Nomographs
10. Graphical mathematics
11. Empirical equations

The difference between these areas of special drawing practices lies in the symbols, conventional practices, standards, and dimensioning methods used in each area. These areas are covered in later chapters.

1.9 STANDARDIZATION OF DRAFTING. In order to establish drafting practice throughout the country on a firm basis so that drawings made anywhere will have clear and unmistakable meaning everywhere, engineers have established standards in drafting. Those standards were set up first in industrial companies, later in engineering societies, and finally in a collective effort through the American Standards Association. The drafting procedures shown and recommended in this book reflect the latest revision of these American Standards, which are in general agreement with those of Great Britian and Canada.

The student should become familiar with the work of the American Standards Association (USASI) and that of the professional engineering society with which he is most concerned, for it is only through this standardization that modern mass production is possible.

1.10 NONPROJECTION DRAWING. The following phases of engineering graphics are algebraic in character, rather than geometric, except for certain parts of the first class. The theory of projection is not involved in any of the others.

1.10.1 Charts and diagrams. These are drawings used to show graphically the relationship between facts. Two variables are usually involved, as shown in Fig. 1.11. A chart involving three variables in pictorial form is shown in Fig. 1.12. Three-dimensional charts of this kind follow the rules for axonometric projection. A three-variable chart may also be made as a plane figure instead of being pictorial in form. In this situation the third variable is shown by a series of curves.

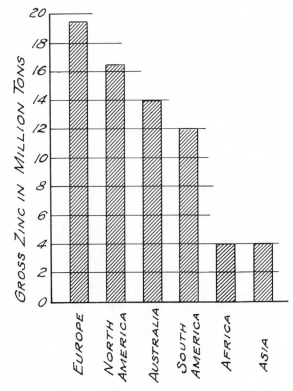

Fig. 1.11 Bar diagram.

1.10.2   Vector diagrams. Problems involving the relationship between quantities that have direction as well as size may be solved graphically as shown in Fig. 1.13. This is a stress diagram for a roof truss. The graphical method is rapid, sufficiently accurate for all practical purposes, and self-checking.

1.10.3   Nomographs. These two-dimensional charts may be used to make repeated solutions of an equation with three or more variables. The simpler kinds may be constructed by means of plane geometry. The more complicated ones require the use of determinants or other algebraic computation. A simple illustration is shown in Fig. 1.14.

1.10.4   Empirical equations. When it is difficult to derive a rational equation by a logical reasoning process, the data may be plotted on various types of co-ordinate paper until a straight line is obtained. Figure 1.15 shows the data from an experiment, which when plotted on rectangular coordinate paper give a curve, as in Fig. 1.15(*a*), while the same data plotted on semi-log paper result in a straight line, as in Fig. 1.15(*b*). The equation of the straight line can be readily determined.

1.10.5   Graphical calculus. Certain problems in the calculus can be solved graphically. The graphical method is most useful when it is difficult or impossible to determine a rational equation for a curve. See Fig. 1.16.

1.11   LEGAL ASPECTS. The drawings for buildings, bridges, dams, and other major construction projects have always been the basis for legal contracts in which the builder agrees to erect the structure in accordance with the plans prepared by the engineer for the owner. Such drawings must always be clear and unmistakable in meaning. The drawing, in fact, becomes a legal document. If it is subject to more than one interpretation, litigation may arise causing unnecessary delay and expense.

In the machine industry, modern mass production has brought with it the letting of contracts for the manufacture of machine parts in large quantity. Machine parts, for interchangeable assembly, must be finished very accurately to the dimensions specified. The engineer can seldom go into his own shop and tell the foreman what he wants since the part may be pro-

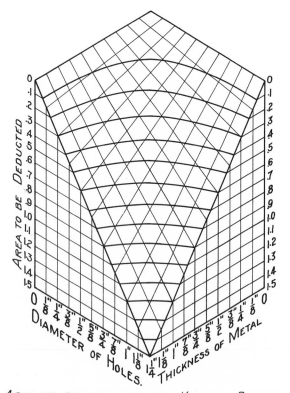

Fig. 1.12   Three-variable chart in pictorial form.

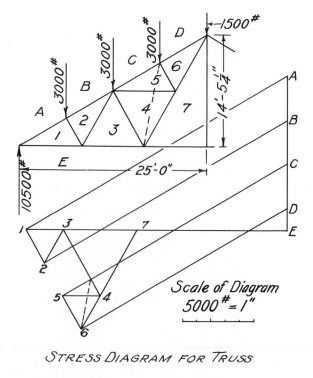

Fig. 1.13   Vector diagram.

duced in a plant hundreds of miles away. The drawing itself must tell the whole story. It must be made not merely so that it can be understood, but it must be so

clear in its meaning that it cannot be misunderstood or misinterpreted either by accident or intention.

This places on the technical man who makes the drawing or directs the work of producing it a heavy responsibility to understand thoroughly both the fundamental theory and the conventional practice of drafting that he studies in his engineering graphics courses.

1.12   ENGINEERING DESIGN. Engineering design is the process of creating something new. It may be a new product to be manufactured and sold. It may be a new component that is a part of an old product which will make that product perform more efficiently. Or it may be a new system of some kind such as the complete water and sanitary system of a large building which involves new ideas. Essentially, engineering design is a problem-solving process. This may involve mathematical and graphical methods. Ingenuity and imagination are essential in the development of an engineering design. It also involves a familiarity with materials of all kinds, as well as new processes in computation and production.

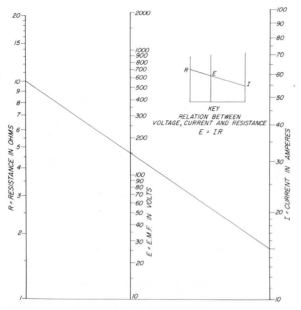

Fig. 1.14   Three-variable nomograph.

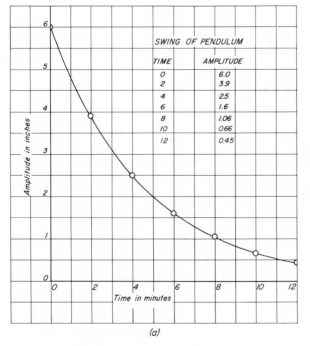

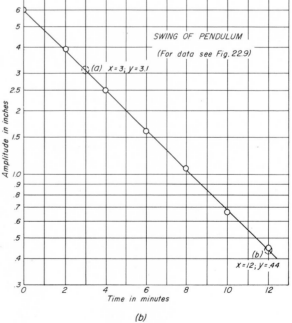

Fig. 1.15   Charts for derivation of empirical equation.

1.13 ENGINEERING METHOD. The term "engineering method" refers to the manner in which engineers solve the problems presented to them. There is no single standard set of steps that the engineer must follow in solving all of his problems, but certain broad principles are usually employed in a manner and sequence which are chosen to fit the problem to be solved. A list of these general principles has been outlined in the following paragraphs.

1.13.1 Statement of the problem. The problem may be clearly stated in the contract that an engineer signs or in the instructions that he is given by an employer. If such a statement is not made, the engineer must formulate the problem in his own mind with a clear vision of what the end product of his work is to be. This may or may not be "spelled out" verbally.

1.13.2 Scientific principles. After the problem has been clearly stated, the next step is to identify the laws of physical science that might apply to the problem. This is done by a careful analysis breaking the problem down into its component parts and setting up the necessary mathematical equations that apply to the problem.

1.13.3 Proposed solution. Most engineering prob-

lems have more than one solution. In the solution stage of the engineering method, it is necessary to make some assumptions, determine the limiting conditions of the problem, and make the calculations that will produce the answer. Such items as factors of safety, building code requirements, and the economics of the situation have to be taken into consideration.

1.13.4 Evaluation. When more than one solution is feasible, the various solutions must be compared and a selection made of the solution that best fits all of the conditions of the problem. For larger engineering projects the scope is often too wide to be considered here.

1.13.5 Checking. After a solution has been chosen, the entire problem must be checked from beginning to end:

a. To see that all limiting conditions have been satisfied.
b. To see that any public laws that may apply have been duly met.
c. To see that all computations are correct.
d. To see that all drawings involved are correct and cannot be misinterpreted.
e. To see that the latest development in new materials, especially suited for the project, have been employed.
f. To see that the best methods of production can be used.

1.13.6 Report. Finally, a report of some kind must be presented. This may require written specifications and detailed drawings or it may be an informal discussion, with drawings submitted, by a younger man to his superior officer in a company.

1.14 ENGINEERING GRAPHICS AND DESIGN. The student should realize that engineering graphics is an integral part of the whole process of engineering design from the point where computation begins to the end result of the project represented by drawings. Many computations can be made graphically and the end product is almost always described by one or more drawings.

For the beginner, drawing is an excellent tool for testing and developing the imagination. Many problems in engineering graphics can have more than one solution. These are sometimes referred to as open-ended problems. A number of problems of this type have been included in this text to stimulate the imagination.

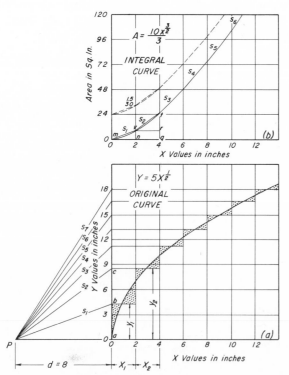

Fig. 1.16 Graphical integration.

CHAPTER 2
Lettering

OLD: The Rosetta Stone with text in hieroglyphics, demotic, and Greek. (The Bettmann Archive.)

NEW: Plaque in the United Nations Plaza. (Albert Mozell, Photo Researchers.)

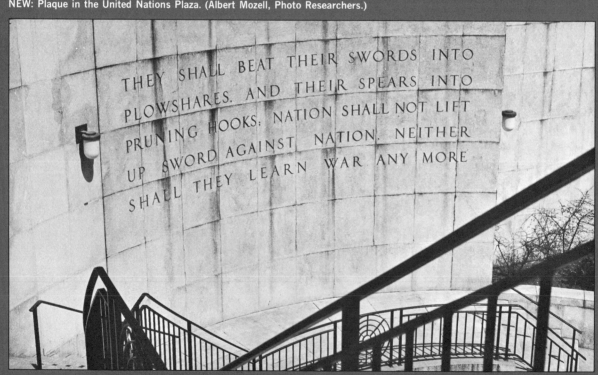

Chapter 2   Lettering

2.1   INTRODUCTION. Lettering is used on engineering drawings because it is more uniform and more easily read than script. If one word or one dimension should be misinterpreted on an engineering drawing, the entire part might be ruined. In a few plants typing is used instead of lettering, but the majority use free-hand lettering. The type of drawing determines the style of lettering used.

2.2   STYLE IN LETTERING. To designate the style of lettering desired it is necessary to prescribe several characteristics.

a. Original or basic form (Gothic, roman, Text such as Old English).

b. Character of stroke (single, double, or filled in).

c. Slant or vertical.

d. Capitals or small letters (upper or lower case).

2.3   GOTHIC STYLE. When making drawings of machine parts, the style of lettering used by the majority of engineers is single-stroke, vertical, Gothic capitals. Occasionally the slant letters are used. Some engineers use a combination of capitals and lower-case or small letters. The vertical and slant alphabets of this style are illustrated in Figs. 2.1 and 2.2.

2.4   USES OF OTHER STYLES. The civil engineer is more likely to use the slant, single-stroke, Gothic, upper and lower case as shown in Fig. 2.2. On maps he sometimes uses the more decorative style known as Modern Roman. This style is illustrated in Fig. 2.26. The use of an ellipse guide in lettering is illustrated in Fig. 2.27.

The architect uses a variation of the single-stroke Gothic that is distinguished by the addition of curves and seraphs. This is shown in Fig. 2.3.

ABCDEFGHIJKLMNOPQRS
TUVWXYZ
abcdefghijklmnopqrstuvwxyz

Fig. 2.1   The single-stroke vertical alphabet.

*ABCDEFGHIJKLMNOPQRS
TUVWXYZ
abcdefghijklmnopqrstuvwxyz*

Fig. 2.2   The single-stroke slant alphabet.

*ABCDEFGHIJKLMN
OPQRSTUVWXYZ&
1234567890
abcdefghijklmnop
qrstuvwxyz*

Reserved and pleasing in appearance, yet simple enough for occasional use on engineering drawings.

ABCDEFGHIJKLMN
OPQRSTUVWXYZ&
1234567890
abcdefghijklmnopqr
stuvwxyz

Fig. 2.3   A style used in architectural drawing.

For signs, inscriptions, diplomas and the like, the double-stroke or filled-in letters are frequently used. The double-stroke Gothic is shown in Fig. 2.28. The most decorative and the most difficult to make is the Old English, shown in Fig. 2.29. These alphabets are shown for reference so that an engineer can learn to make them if the occasion should arise. It is not intended that the young engineer learn anything but the single-stroke Gothic.

2.5   SIZE OF LETTERS. When the size of any lettering is given, it means the height of the capital letters. When used in engineering lettering, the small letters have their bodies two-thirds the height of the capitals. Such small letters as b, d, h have stems called ascenders, which are made the same height as the capitals. Such letters as g, j, p have descenders that extend one-third the height of the capital letters below the lower guideline.

Numerals have the same height as the capital letters. Fractions are at least one and one-half times the height of the capital letters. The numbers in the numerator and denominator are each two-thirds the height of the capital letters.

On a drawing that is to be microfilmed, the size of the lettering must be large enough to stand the great reduction that is necessary. No letters should be less than ⅛ inch and even larger letters are frequently preferred.

2.6   GUIDELINES. Lettering should never be done without guidelines. These guidelines consist of three parallel lines, one for the base line of the lettering, one for the top of the capital letters, and one for the top of the small letters. See Fig. 2.4.

The Braddock lettering triangle, illustrated in Fig. 2.5, gives a convenient method of drawing these lines. There are several columns of holes in the triangle by means of which guidelines for various sizes of letters may be made. The height of letter for each column is given below the column in thirty-seconds of an inch. Thus number 4 will give guidelines for letters ⁴⁄₃₂ or ⅛ inch high. The pencil point is inserted in each hole successively and a line drawn by sliding the triangle along a T-square, as shown in Fig. 2.5.

The Ames lettering guide can also be used to draw guide lines, using only one set of holes. The size is changed by rotating the center disk to the desired index number. The sizes are also specified in thirty seconds of an inch. See Fig. 2.6. Uniformly spaced lines for cross-hatching may also be done with this instrument.

Fig. 2.4   Guidelines and height of letters.

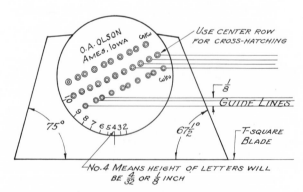

Fig. 2.6   The Ames lettering instrument.

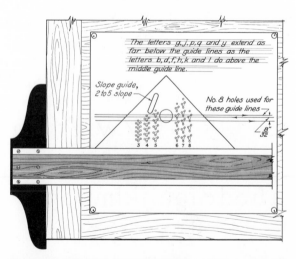

Fig. 2.5 The Braddock lettering triangle.

All guidelines should be made lightly so that they may be erased and so that they will not show on a print. A sharp 4H pencil should be used for drawing guidelines.

2.7 SLOPE OF LETTERS. Whether using vertical or slant lettering, it is important that the stems of all letters have the same slope. To accomplish this, light parallel lines may be drawn across the guidelines as shown in Fig. 2.7. For slant letters those lines may vary from 65 to 75° with the horizontal. For vertical lettering it is important that the letters be as nearly vertical as possible, because the eye can easily pick up errors in the slope of vertical lines.

2.8 ELEMENTS OF LETTERS. In engineering lettering each letter is composed of two elements or combinations of them. These elements are the straight line or stem and the oval.

2.8.1 Stems. The stems are the straight lines, vertical or slant, that form a part of more than four fifths of the letters of the alphabet. The horizontal lines in such letters as E, F, and H are not classified as stems but must be made as carefully and neatly as the stems.

The following rules are applicable in forming all stems:

a. The stems must be uniform in weight, thickness and height.

b. The stems must be perfectly straight without hooks or curls at either end.

c. The slopes of stems must be uniform. The stems must be parallel to each other throughout any piece of lettering.

Examples of good and bad stems are shown in Fig. 2.8.

2.8.2 Ovals. The oval forms the curved parts of the letters. Although the ovals should be five-sixths as wide as they are high, it is better to make them too broad than too narrow. The oval is formed inside a parallelogram, and is tangent at the center point at each side. Parallelogram and oval are shown in Fig. 2.9. The standard width is indicated on the drawing. The ovals are usually made with two strokes beginning at the top and meeting at the bottom without a perceptible joint. However, for small letters when using the pencil the ovals are often made with a single stroke.

In vertical lettering the slope line coincides with the major axis of the ellipse. In slant lettering the slope line will be about 65°, while the major axis of the ellipse will be nearer 45° with the horizontal. See Fig. 2.9.

2.9 COMBINATION OF STEM AND OVAL. In letters in which the stem and oval are combined, the stem is always tangent to the oval. This is illustrated in Fig. 2.10. The weight of the stroke for the stem and the oval must be the same. There must be no enlargement at the point of tangency. In letters such as small a, b, and d the oval must be a complete ellipse. The weight of the stroke will vary directly with the size of the lettering.

2.10 TECHNIQUE OF LETTERING. To attain the proper technique for lettering, it is necessary to consider the following:

a. The selection of the proper pencil or pen.

b. The position of the hand for lettering.

c. The proper direction of the strokes.

Fig. 2.7 Slope guidelines.

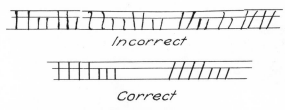

Fig. 2.8 Stems of single-stroke letters.

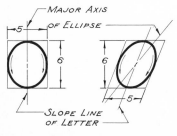

Fig. 2.9 Direction of strokes in making the oval.

Fig. 2.10 Joining stems and ovals.

2.10.1 Selection and sharpening of the pencil. The most important technique in lettering is the making of a good solid black line. This depends on selecting a pencil that has the proper hardness and on keeping it well sharpened. To make a good black line a soft pencil should be selected. This should be 2H or softer depending on the purpose of the drawing and the method of reproduction. If a blacker line is desired, it is better to select a softer pencil than to use more pressure on the pencil.

To get a good clean-cut line requires that the pencil be sharpened properly and frequently. A conical point slightly rounded should be used.

2.10.2 Selection and use of a pen. In inking lettering the thickness of the line depends on the pen used rather than the pressure. Figure 2.11 shows a variety of pen points and the weight of line that can be obtained from each. Many of these are special-purpose pens that can be used for shading or block lettering. For general-purpose lettering, Gillott, Easterbrook, or Leonardt pen points are available in a variety of sizes. The ball-point pen makes it easier to maintain a uniform weight of line. The Payzant pen or the tube pens of the proper size will insure a uniform weight of stroke. The Rapidograph pens shown in Fig. 2.12 are used extensively at the present time. The speed ball

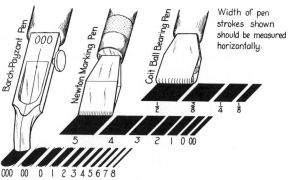
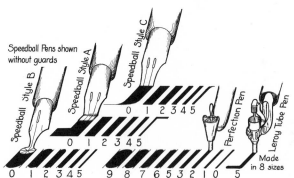

Fig. 2.11 Special lettering pens.

Fig. 2.12 Rapidograph pens. (Courtesy of Dietzgen.)

pen is used for a shaded stroke.

In using any kind of freehand pen it is best to fill the pen by using the quill or tube in the stopper. Do not dip the pen in the bottle. Do not overfill the pen or it may run out and make a blot on the drawing.

When in use, the pen must be cleaned frequently to avoid carbon deposits on the point. Whenever lettering is discontinued, even for a short time, the pen must be cleaned thoroughly.

2.10.3 Position of the hand. For good lettering the hand must hold the pencil or pen firmly, but there should be no tension caused by gripping too tightly. The best way to hold the pencil is shown in Fig. 2.13.

The following rules, if carefully followed, will give a good foundation for improving the ability to letter.

a. The forearm should rest on the desk.
b. The index finger should be kept as straight as possible along the pencil. This will help to avoid tension in the hand.
c. The strokes should be made with as little bending of the finger as possible.
d. The forearm should be at an angle of 75 to 80° with the line of lettering. The paper may be located in any convenient position.
e. All strokes should be made from top to bottom and left to right.

With the exception of the last two, these rules apply

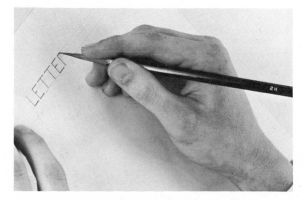

Fig. 2.13   Position of hand for lettering.

to either right-handed or left-handed lettering. Some left-handed people prefer to get the hand completely above the lettering, while others work with the arm at an angle of about 45° with the lettering.

2.11   THE ART OF LETTERING. The art of good lettering depends on obtaining uniformity in six items:

a. Uniformity of shape.
b. Uniformity of style.
c. Uniformity of size.
d. Uniformity of weight.
e. Uniformity of slope.
f. Uniformity of spacing.

Without uniformity in these six fundamentals, the lettering will not look well and may even be difficult to read.

2.11.1   Uniformity of shape. This requires thorough familiarity with the proper shape of the letters and that each letter be made the same every time.

2.11.2   Uniformity of style. Gothic, roman, and Old English letters should not be mixed in the same piece of lettering. Also, capitals and small letters should not be mixed except for purposes of capitalization of proper nouns. This is the most common error and should be carefully avoided. Such an error is not likely to occur when all capitals are being used.

2.11.3   Uniformity of size. Uniformity of size requires that guidelines be drawn for all lettering and that they be faithfully followed. A slight overrunning or failure to touch guidelines is very noticeable when the guidelines have been removed. The width of the letters must also be uniform. It is better to have the ovals too wide than too narrow.

2.11.4   Uniformity of weight. All straight strokes and ovals must have the same weight and must maintain that weight throughout their entire length. See Fig. 2.10.

2.11.5   Uniformity of slope. The stems and the axes of all letters must be parallel, whether they are vertical or inclined. Light slope guidelines drawn across the horizontal guidelines at the proper angle will help to keep the letters at the proper slope.

2.11.6   Uniformity of spacing. This is the basis of good composition and requires that the letters in the words and the words in the sentences be properly spaced so that they can be easily read. Figure 2.14 shows the effect of poor spacing. *As a general rule it is best to make the letters broad and the space between them small.* The spacing between words should be sufficient for the letter N to be lettered there. Because of the great variety in the shape of the letters, no actual spacing can be recommended. *If the white spaces between the letters appear equal and the white spaces between the words are made to appear equal, the lettering will read well.* This results in making letters with straight sides farther apart and letters with included space closer together. See Fig. 2.15.

When the space available for lettering is smaller than normal or larger than normal, the letters may be compressed or expanded, as illustrated in Fig. 2.16. In each case the change is made in the letters themselves rather than the spacing between letters.

2.12   THE MECHANICS OF LETTERING. The engineer should be thoroughly familiar with the shape and characteristics of every letter of the alphabet. Figure 2.17 illustrates these letters in both vertical and slant form. It gives the approved width of each letter, the number of strokes and direction of each stroke for the easiest and most rapid construction. *These strokes should always be made with one continuous motion rather than by using an overlapping sketch stroke.* The strokes must not be hurried, but with practice they can be made rapidly and with confidence to give the best-appearing letters. The unique characteristics of each letter, together with hints for forming them, are given in Fig. 2.17.

The letters and numerals divide themselves naturally into three groups:

a. Those made entirely with straight lines.
b. Those made entirely with ovals.
c. Those made by using a combination of straight lines and ovals.

2.12.1   Capital letters made entirely with straight lines. Letters such as H, F, E, I, L, N, T, and the numeral 1 form this group. In each of these letters the stems lie on the slope line. Figure 2.17 indicates the width of each letter and the desirable position of the crosslines.

Such letters as A, V, M, W, K, Y, X, Z, and the numerals 4 and 7 are also made with straight lines, but each has some characteristic that must be carefully observed to obtain the correct letters. For many of them the principal characteristic is the fact that the slope line bisects the angle between the two strokes. In others, such as K, special hints for the construction are given.

2.12.2   Letters made entirely with curves. Included in this group are such letters as O, Q, C, G, S, and the numerals 3, 6, 8, 9, and 0. In making these letters it is usually best to follow the direction and order of the strokes given. However, for small letters being made with pencil, many engineers prefer to use one complete stroke for an oval. This cannot be done when inking. See Fig. 2.17.

2.12.3   Letters made with a combination of curves and straight lines. Such letters as B, D, J, P, R, U, and

(continued on page 26)

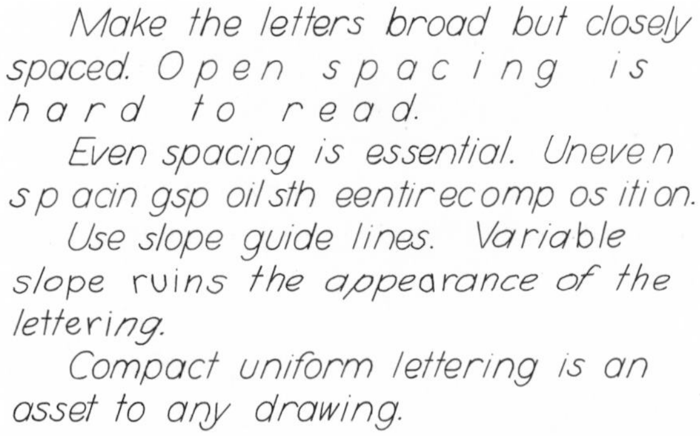

Fig. 2.14   Study of composition of lettering.

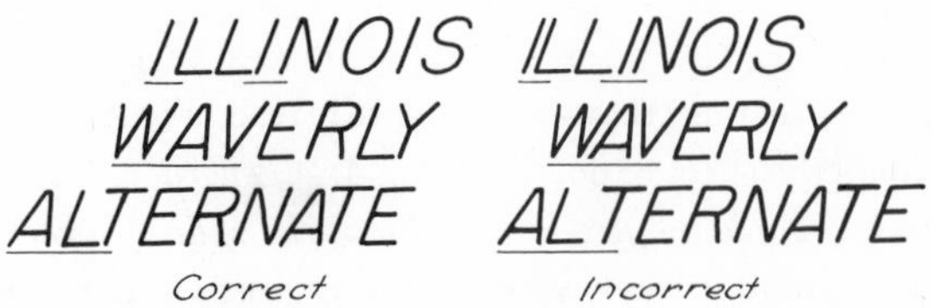

Correct   Incorrect

Fig. 2.15   Spacing of letters.

Fig. 2.16   Compressed and expanded alphabets.

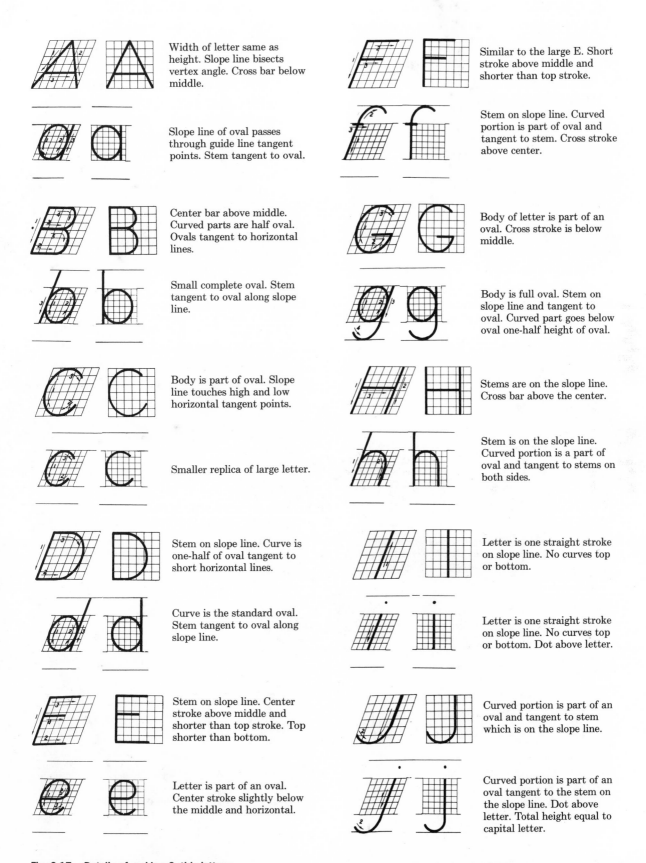

Width of letter same as height. Slope line bisects vertex angle. Cross bar below middle.

Slope line of oval passes through guide line tangent points. Stem tangent to oval.

Center bar above middle. Curved parts are half oval. Ovals tangent to horizontal lines.

Small complete oval. Stem tangent to oval along slope line.

Body is part of oval. Slope line touches high and low horizontal tangent points.

Smaller replica of large letter.

Stem on slope line. Curve is one-half of oval tangent to short horizontal lines.

Curve is the standard oval. Stem tangent to oval along slope line.

Stem on slope line. Center stroke above middle and shorter than top stroke. Top shorter than bottom.

Letter is part of an oval. Center stroke slightly below the middle and horizontal.

Similar to the large E. Short stroke above middle and shorter than top stroke.

Stem on slope line. Curved portion is part of oval and tangent to stem. Cross stroke above center.

Body of letter is part of an oval. Cross stroke is below middle.

Body is full oval. Stem on slope line and tangent to oval. Curved part goes below oval one-half height of oval.

Stems are on the slope line. Cross bar above the center.

Stem is on the slope line. Curved portion is a part of oval and tangent to stems on both sides.

Letter is one straight stroke on slope line. No curves top or bottom.

Letter is one straight stroke on slope line. No curves top or bottom. Dot above letter.

Curved portion is part of an oval and tangent to stem which is on the slope line.

Curved portion is part of an oval tangent to the stem on the slope line. Dot above letter. Total height equal to capital letter.

Fig. 2.17   Details of making Gothic letters.

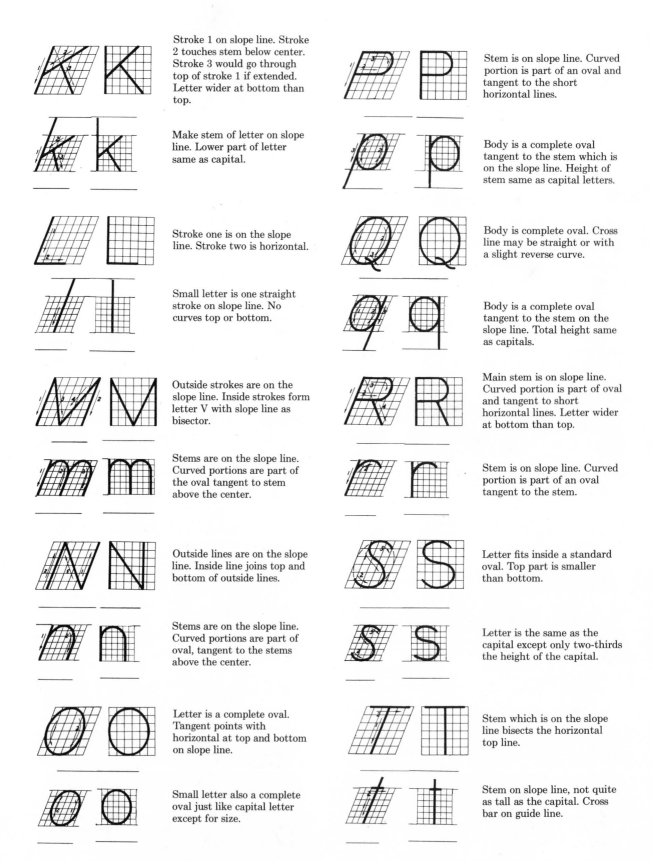

Stroke 1 on slope line. Stroke 2 touches stem below center. Stroke 3 would go through top of stroke 1 if extended. Letter wider at bottom than top.

Make stem of letter on slope line. Lower part of letter same as capital.

Stroke one is on the slope line. Stroke two is horizontal.

Small letter is one straight stroke on slope line. No curves top or bottom.

Outside strokes are on the slope line. Inside strokes form letter V with slope line as bisector.

Stems are on the slope line. Curved portions are part of the oval tangent to stem above the center.

Outside lines are on the slope line. Inside line joins top and bottom of outside lines.

Stems are on the slope line. Curved portions are part of oval, tangent to the stems above the center.

Letter is a complete oval. Tangent points with horizontal at top and bottom on slope line.

Small letter also a complete oval just like capital letter except for size.

Stem is on slope line. Curved portion is part of an oval and tangent to the short horizontal lines.

Body is a complete oval tangent to the stem which is on the slope line. Height of stem same as capital letters.

Body is complete oval. Cross line may be straight or with a slight reverse curve.

Body is a complete oval tangent to the stem on the slope line. Total height same as capitals.

Main stem is on slope line. Curved portion is part of oval and tangent to short horizontal lines. Letter wider at bottom than top.

Stem is on slope line. Curved portion is part of an oval tangent to the stem.

Letter fits inside a standard oval. Top part is smaller than bottom.

Letter is the same as the capital except only two-thirds the height of the capital.

Stem which is on the slope line bisects the horizontal top line.

Stem on slope line, not quite as tall as the capital. Cross bar on guide line.

Fig. 2.17 *(continued)*   **Details of making Gothic letters.**

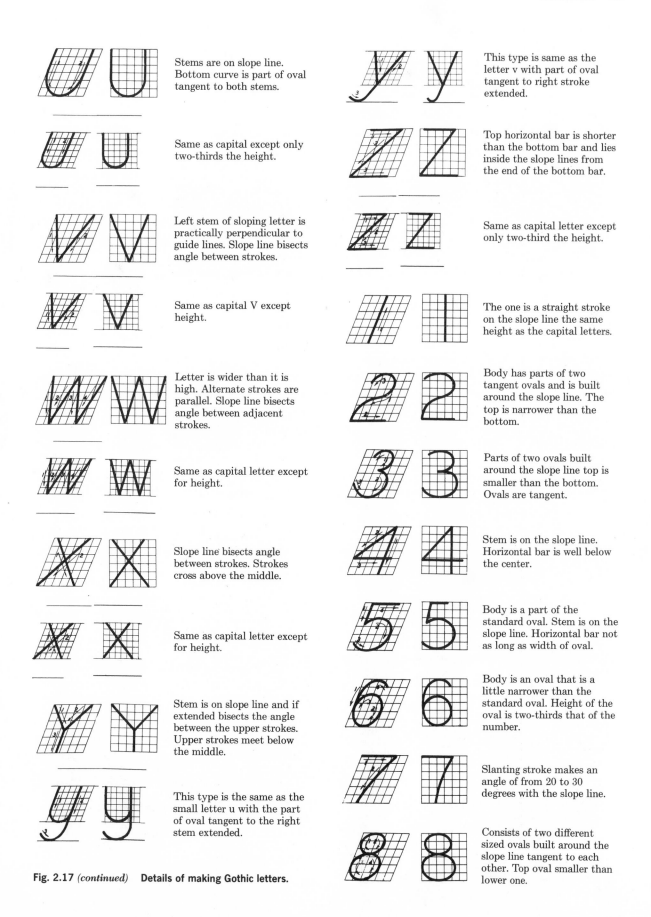

Stems are on slope line. Bottom curve is part of oval tangent to both stems.

Same as capital except only two-thirds the height.

Left stem of sloping letter is practically perpendicular to guide lines. Slope line bisects angle between strokes.

Same as capital V except height.

Letter is wider than it is high. Alternate strokes are parallel. Slope line bisects angle between adjacent strokes.

Same as capital letter except for height.

Slope line bisects angle between strokes. Strokes cross above the middle.

Same as capital letter except for height.

Stem is on slope line and if extended bisects the angle between the upper strokes. Upper strokes meet below the middle.

This type is the same as the small letter u with the part of oval tangent to the right stem extended.

This type is same as the letter v with part of oval tangent to right stroke extended.

Top horizontal bar is shorter than the bottom bar and lies inside the slope lines from the end of the bottom bar.

Same as capital letter except only two-third the height.

The one is a straight stroke on the slope line the same height as the capital letters.

Body has parts of two tangent ovals and is built around the slope line. The top is narrower than the bottom.

Parts of two ovals built around the slope line top is smaller than the bottom. Ovals are tangent.

Stem is on the slope line. Horizontal bar is well below the center.

Body is a part of the standard oval. Stem is on the slope line. Horizontal bar not as long as width of oval.

Body is an oval that is a little narrower than the standard oval. Height of the oval is two-thirds that of the number.

Slanting stroke makes an angle of from 20 to 30 degrees with the slope line.

Consists of two different sized ovals built around the slope line tangent to each other. Top oval smaller than lower one.

Fig. 2.17 (*continued*)   **Details of making Gothic letters.**

the numerals 2 and 5 are included in this group. The direction and number of strokes indicated in Fig. 2.17 should be followed rigorously. The straight lines must be tangent to the ellipse in every case.

2.12.4   The rule of stability. The stability of several letters indicates another classification of capital letters. Letters such as A, B, E, H, R, X, and Y require special consideration because of the placing of the crossbar. *In each case the crossing or the crossbar is arranged to make the white spaces within the letter appear equal.* Instruction is given in Fig. 2.17, showing the best method of doing this in each case.

2.12.5   Lower-case or small letters. These may be divided into the same groups as the capitals. Complete instructions for forming them are listed and illustrated in Fig. 2.17. One of the major differences between capitals and small letters lies in the fact that some of the small letters have ascenders and some have descenders. The body of the lower-case letter is two-thirds the height of the capital letters. The ascenders go up to the full height of the capital letters, except that of t which may be made a little lower. The descenders go one-third of the height of the capitals below the lower guideline. Special instructions are given in Fig. 2.17 when needed.

2.12.6   Fractions. Fractions frequently occur when dimensioning a drawing. *They should be made large.* The most common error is making them too small to be easily read. The fractions should extend above and below the capitals or integers. They should be at least one and one-half the height of the numeral or capital letter. *The numerator and denominator must each be at least two-thirds as high as the capital letter.* The line between them is horizontal and neither the numerator nor the denominator may touch this line. To obtain the proper slope of a fraction, a slope guideline should be placed through the center of the fraction, and both numerator and denominator must be built around the slope line. See Fig. 2.18.

2.13   LARGE AND SMALL CAPITALS. In a sentence or a paragraph of lettering, large and small capital letters may be combined, just as capitals and small letters are used together. The large and small capitals are usually easier to read than capital and lower-case letters. See Fig. 2.19.

2.14   TITLES. In most industrial drafting rooms, printed title blocks are used. Therefore, the draftsman does not have to design the title, but merely letter in a few words in the appropriate place.

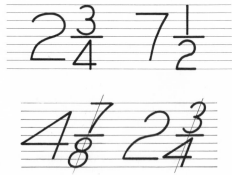

Fig. 2.18   Integers and fractions.

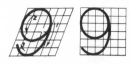

Body of figure is an oval similar to the bottom of the 6. The lower curve is part of a similar oval.

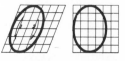

The complete oval for the zero is narrower than the oval for the letters. All other ovals used in numerals are based on this.

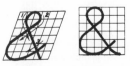

Symbols are based on ovals and straight lines balanced around the slope line.

Fig. 2.17 *(continued)*   **Details of making Gothic letters.**

LARGE AND SMALL CAPITALS ARE FREQUENTLY USED INSTEAD OF UPPER AND LOWER CASE LETTERS.

EITHER VERTICAL OR SLANT LETTERS MAY BE USED.

Fig. 2.19   Composition with capital letters.

Figure 2.20 shows the dimensions of a title block specified by the Department of Defense. It is placed in the lower right-hand corner of the drawing. The information to be placed in each block is listed as follows:

a. Signatures or initials of persons preparing, checking, and approving the drawing. The initials should be accompanied by a date.
b. Drawing title.
c. Name and address of design activity.
d. Approval by design activity.

e. Approval by other than design activity.
f. Code identification number.
g. Drawing size.
h. Drawing number.
j. Scale.
k. Weight.
l. Sheet number and number of sheets. Thus: sheet number 2 of 5.

The information necessary in a parts list is shown in Fig. 2.21. This is frequently placed above the title. The

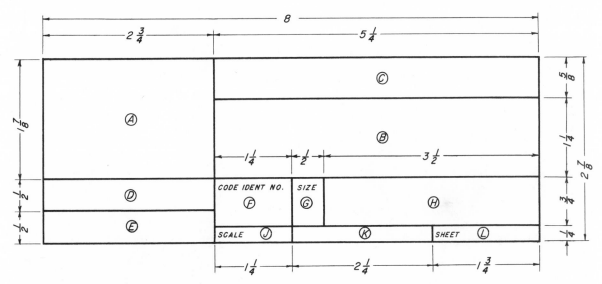

Fig. 2.20   Title-block layout.

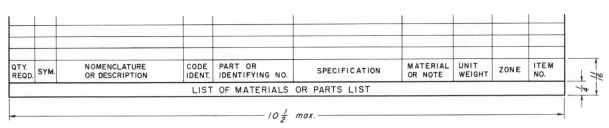

Fig. 2.21   Parts list.

revision block showing all changes may be placed in the upper right-hand corner of the drawing. Figure 2.22 shows a sample revision block. Capital letters should be used throughout in all of these forms.

2.15   MECHANICAL LETTERING. When perfection in lettering is desired and time is available, several kinds of lettering devices are available. These have a template and a tube pen by means of which the letters can be copied. One of the first to be used was the Wrico, which consisted of a template in which holes had been cut in the shape of the letters. Two settings were necessary for most of the letters. See Fig. 2.23.

The one most commonly used today is the Leroy guide. This guide has the letters engraved in the template. While one point follows the letters on the template, the tube pen inks the letters on the drawing. See Fig. 2.24.

A third instrument known as the Varigraph is similar to the Leroy in operation, but is so constructed that the size of the letter can be changed. It also allows a change in the relation of the width to the height, thus making it possible to construct compressed or expanded letters. A wide variety of stencils can be obtained, including Text or Old English. See Fig. 2.25.

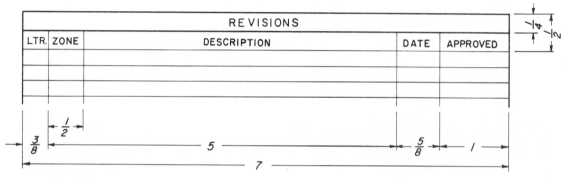

Fig. 2.22   Format for revisions.

Fig. 2.23   Wrico lettering instruments. (Courtesy of Wood-Regan Instrument Co.)

Fig. 2.24   Leroy lettering guides. (Courtesy Keuffel and Esser Co.)

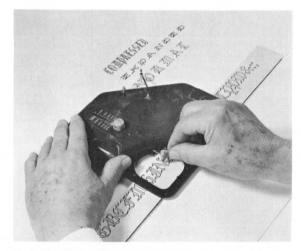

Fig. 2.25   Varigraph.

Fig. 2.26 Modern roman slant letters.

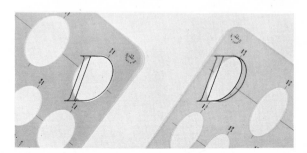

Fig. 2.27 Use of ellipse guides in making roman lettering.

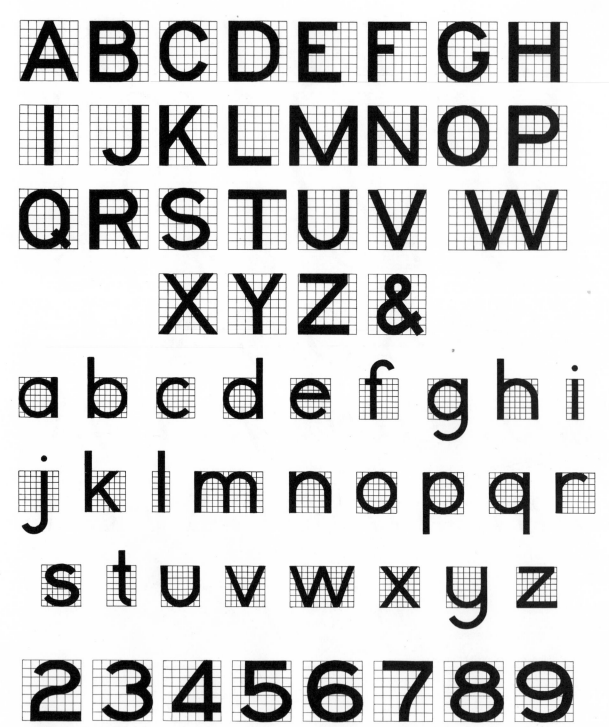

Fig. 2.28 Gothic letters.

Fig. 2.29   Old English Text alphabet. (Courtesy Ross F. George.)

Fig. 2.30   Ovals and straight lines.

SELF-STUDY QUESTIONS

Before trying to answer these questions, read the chapter carefully. Then, without reference to the text, answer as many questions as possible. For those that cannot be answered, the number in parentheses following the question number, gives the article in which the answer can be found. Look it up and write down the answer. Check the answers that you did give to see that they are correct.

2.1 **(2.4)** The style of lettering most frequently used for engineering drawings is _____.

2.2 **(2.5)** The height of the _____ letters is accepted as the height of a line of lettering.

2.3 **(2.5)** The body of the lower-case letters is _____ the height of the capital letters.

2.4 **(2.5)** The height of the ascenders in lower case lettering is _____ the height of the capital letters.

2.5 **(2.5)** The length of the descenders in lower case lettering is _____ the height of the capital letters.

2.6 **(2.7)** The accepted slope for slant lettering is approximately _____ degrees.

2.7 **(2.6)** To maintain uniformity of size _____ should always be used.

2.8 **(2.8)** The two elements that are used to form all engineering letters are the _____ and the _____ .

2.9 **(2.8.2)** In the two parallelograms shown below, sketch an inclined and a vertical letter O. Show the major axes of the ellipses by a center line (long, short, long dashes).

2.10 **(2.8.2)** In the guidelines shown below, sketch an inclined and a vertical letter *O*. Show the slope line of each by a center line.

2.11 **(2.12.4)** The rule of stability states that, for certain letters having two parts, the white spaces within the letter should _____ equal.

2.12 **(2.12.1)** In the guidelines shown below, sketch the slant letters M, A, N, L, Y, Z and X. Show direction of the slope line of each letter by a center line.

2.13 **(2.11.6)** Is it true that the spacing between letters should always be uniform? _____

2.14 **(2.11.6)** Words should be spaced so that the white spaces between words _____ uniform.

2.15 **(2.11.6)** When the space available for lettering is small, the lettering can be compressed by reducing the width of the _____ .

2.16 **(2.11)** In good lettering there should be uniformity of style, _____ , shape, size, and weight of letters.

2.17 **(2.15)** The most commonly used aid for mechanical lettering is the _____ lettering guide.

2.18 **(2.5)** The smallest size of lettering that should be used for microfilming is _____ inch.

2.19 **(2.14)** Important items of information that should be included in a title are drawing title, _____,

date, signature of designer, and drawing number.

2.20 **(2.14)** The revision block is used to show _____ that have been made on the drawing.

PROBLEMS

All lettering problems are to be done on 8½″ x 11″ standard sheets unless otherwise directed by the instructor.

Divide the space inside the borderline of the selected sheet into four equal rectangles by means of horizontal and vertical center lines. Inside these spaces, rule guidelines as directed, and then do the exercises assigned from the following problems. Allow a margin of ½″ at the top and on each side of the lettering space and a margin at the bottom as near ½″ as the guideline layout will permit. It is recommended that the Braddock lettering triangle or Ames lettering instrument be used for ruling guidelines that are within the limits of these instruments.

Where the term "guidelines" occurs in the following problems, it means a set of three lines (see Fig. 2.4) whose overall height is that specified in the problem. The space between sets of guidelines will be as produced by the lettering triangle, or two-thirds the overall height of the guidelines if a lettering instrument is not available. It is recommended that lettering drills be of not more than 10 to 20 minutes' duration.

2.1 Rule guidelines ⅜″ high and make an alternate series of smooth ovals and straight stems, as shown in Fig. 2.30. Make either slant or vertical style, as assigned.

2.2 Same as Problem 2.1, using guidelines of any height assigned by your instructor.

2.3 Rule guidelines 3⁄16″ high, and then execute the group of lower-case letters or numerals assigned from Fig. 2.17. Make approximately the same number of each letter to fill out the line, using the vertical or slant style, as assigned. Do not draw the coordinate background.

2.4 Same as Problem 2.3, using guidelines of any height as assigned by your instructor.

2.5 Rule guidelines 3⁄16″ high, and then execute the group of capital letters assigned from Fig. 2.17. Make approximately the same number of each letter to fill out the line, using vertical or slant style, as assigned.

2.6 Same as Problem 2.5, using guidelines of any height as assigned by your instructor.

2.7 Rule guidelines 3⁄16″ high, and then execute the letters of the alphabet in the order of their occurrence, as shown in Fig. 2.17. Fill out each line by repeating the alphabet as much as may be necessary.

2.8 Rule guidelines 3⁄16″ high, and then make the numerals shown in Fig. 2.17. Repeat the numerals, and add additional fractions to fill out the space. Use vertical or slant style, as assigned.

2.9 Same as Problem 2.8, using guidelines of a height assigned by your instructor.

2.10 Rule guidelines 5⁄32″ high, and then letter the material in one of the paragraphs assigned from the following group. The material is to be well balanced within the area reserved for it, whether done on regular lettering sheets or in connection with other drawing work. Use all capitals or initial capitals and lower-case letters as assigned.

a. In order that a piece of composition may look well, it must have uniformity in slope, weight, size, and spacing of the letters and words.

b. Control of the hand in lettering is best accomplished through short daily drills of 10 to 20 minutes' duration. The work should be deliberately and critically done.

c. The pen should be suited to the size and character of the work being done. A ball-point pen can hardly be used for fine letters; a fine-point pen should not be used for heavy work.

d. Keep the points of the pen free from dried ink, and clean thoroughly at the end of each piece of work. Fill the pen by means of the quill in the stopper of the ink bottle instead of dipping it in the bottle itself.

e. Triangles and T-square should be kept clean and free from dust and soot to prevent the drawing paper and tracing cloth from becoming soiled and unfit to work upon. Perspiration from the hands soon injures the surface qualities of the tracing cloth.

f. Plan the location of all the views of a drawing before beginning any. Reserve space for the title the very first thing. Allow generous space for dimensions and notes. Place these, as far as possible, between views.

g. Omit no dimension that may be needed for clearness, but do not repeat unnecessarily. Always give the overall dimension, and place it outside the detail dimensions. Do not hesitate to give explanatory notes.

2.11 Rule a title block similar to Fig. 2.20 and fill in all the spaces with assumed lettering that might apply to the manufacture of some commercial casting.

2.12 Rule a block for a parts list similar to Fig. 2.21 and letter a parts list for your fountain pen.

2.13 Rule a revision block similar to Fig. 2.22 and letter the following changes: *A*, zone B6, change diameter from 1″ to 1⅛″; *B*, zone C4 change distance from 7⁄16″ to 9⁄16″; *C*, zone D2, change tolerance from 0.001 to 0.002; *D*, zone B3, change 32° to 31° 30′.

Use and Care of Instruments

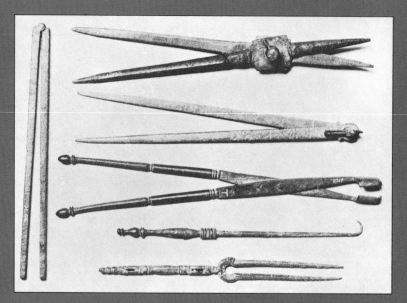

OLD: Roman mathematical instruments (The Bettman Archive)

NEW: Auto-flow drafting machine. (Keuffel and Esser Co.)

Chapter 3 Use and Care of Instruments

3.1 INTRODUCTION. There are two fundamental purposes for an engineering graphics course. The first of these is to give the student an understanding of the principles on which engineering drawing is based. The second purpose is to give him instruction and practice in the use of his instruments so that he may acquire a workmanlike facility in their manipulation. The engineer's objective is not to produce a drawing that will just "get by" but rather to secure the best results. In doing this, he must keep in mind correctness, accuracy, and appearance while producing the drawing in the least possible time.

To learn the correct form of handling instruments, one should study the proper use of them as explained in this chapter, so that awkward and useless movements may be avoided. No attempt is made here to illustrate the hundreds of pieces of special drafting tools on the market. The engineer who learns to use the regular equipment discussed in this chapter can use the special tools without further instruction.

3.2 REGULAR EQUIPMENT. The following list of equipment constitutes what is called a set or kit of instruments. The case of instruments is illustrated in Fig. 3.1.

Case of Instruments
1 Large compass
1 Pen attachment
1 Beam compass with attachments
1 Hairspring divider
1 Ruling pen
1 Box of leads
1 Screwdriver

Other Equipment
1 T-square
1 Architect's scale
1 Engineer's scale
1 12″ 30–60° triangle
1 8″ 30–60° triangle
1 6″ 45° Braddock lettering triangle
2 Irregular curves
1 6″ protractor
1 Erasing shield
1 Eraser
Assorted pencils and pen points

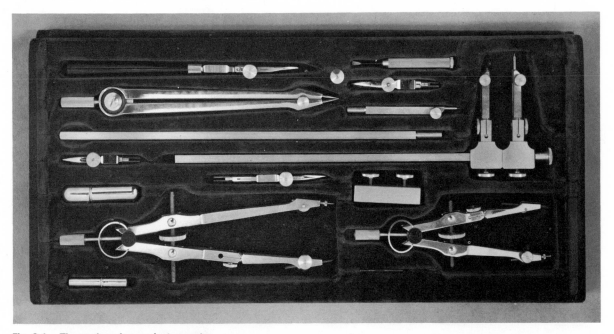

Fig. 3.1 The engineer's case instruments.

3.3 PENCILS. Special pencils are used for drawing. They are of uniform size, hexagonal in shape, with varying size of lead as shown in Fig. 3.2. Eighteen degrees of hardness are supplied by the manufacturer, ranging from 7B, the softest and blackest, to 9H which is the hardest.

Although all manufacturers use the same system of marking their pencils, it will be found that the pencils from different manufacturers having the same hardness number do not actually have the same hardness. It is for this reason that most draftsmen usually prefer to use only one brand of pencil. Refill pencils, shown in Fig. 3.3, are also on the market together with refill leads of the varying degrees of hardness for the entire range.

For general layout work in drawing, the 4H and 5H pencils are the most useful. The harder varieties are used in graphic statics and other graphical computation methods where fine lines and extreme accuracy are required. For making a finished pencil drawing the H and 2H are more desirable since they give a sharp black line. For sketching and artwork, the softer grades are used. The draftsman should learn to choose the quality of pencil appropriate to the work he has in hand.

More important than the quality of the pencil is the condition in which it is kept. The proper shape for a pencil point is shown in Fig. 3.4. The tapered wood portion should be about ⅞ inch long, and ⅜ inch of lead should be exposed. The lead should be brought to a point by means of a file or sandpaper. For a conical point as in Fig. 3.4(*a*), the pencil should be rotated slowly while it is rubbed back and forth. The pencil should be inclined to the direction of motion, as shown in Fig. 3.5. To produce the wedge point, as in Fig. 3.4(*b*), the opposite sides must be filed down. The bevel point, as in Fig. 3.4(*c*), is made by filing on one side. In refill pencils, the lead should be filed down to a good point just as frequently as in the regular pencil.

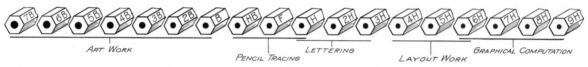

Fig. 3.2   Grades of drawing pencils.

Fig. 3.3   Refill drawing pencil.

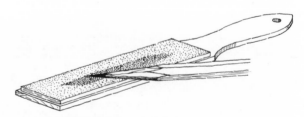

Fig. 3.5   Sharpening the drawing pencil.

Fig. 3.4   Correct pencil point shapes.

The wedge point is limited in use to drawing long straight lines since it does not wear down so rapidly. The conical point may be used for all general drafting purposes and always should be used for lettering. The bevel point is recommended for use in the compass, as it has the same advantages there as the wedge point has for straight lines, as well as making it possible to draw very small circles. It is also used with the softer pencils for purposes of shading.

In drawing a straight line, the pencil should be held in a plane perpendicular to the paper along the edge of the T-square or triangle, and should be inclined in the direction of motion at an angle of 60 to 75° with the paper. See Fig. 3.6. Note that the pencil is held in a somewhat different manner from that used in lettering. The pencil should not be allowed to rock back and forth transversely to the direction of motion. For preliminary work, just enough pressure should be applied to the pencil to make a firm light line that can be readily seen, but not enough pressure to make a groove in the paper. A groove cannot be erased and spoils the appearance of a drawing. The importance of clean-cut pencil work cannot be overemphasized; it tends toward both speed and accuracy. The proper direction for drawing lines in various positions is shown in Figs. 3.7 and 3.8. The general criterion is to draw away from the body.

3.4 ERASERS AND ERASING TOOLS. Only a pencil eraser should be used to remove lines made in error or to change lines because of an alteration in design. This applies to both pencil and ink lines. A grit eraser, a razor blade or other sharp instrument will destroy the surface of the paper and ruin the drawing.

When there are many lines close together and only one line needs to be removed or changed, the others may be protected by using an erasing shield, as shown

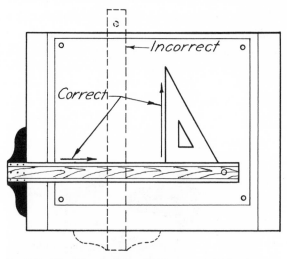
Fig. 3.7   Direction of ruling with T-square and triangle.

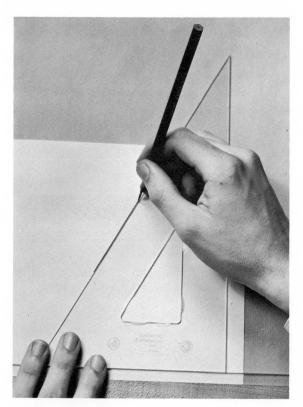
Fig. 3.6   Drawing with the pencil.

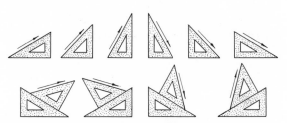
Fig. 3.8   Direction of drawing inclined lines.

in Fig. 3.9. One of the openings is placed over the line to be removed in such a way that other lines do not show, and then the erasure is made through this opening.

The razor blade and erasing knife or point shown in Fig. 3.10 have their legitimate use in checking a drawing to remove ink lines when they may have overrun a bit and to remove small amounts of ink in places where it will not be necessary to ink the spot again.

For large erasures a motor-driven eraser saves time and energy. It must be used carefully with a light touch or the surface may be damaged. See Fig. 3.9.

When extensive changes are required, a new tracing may be made by reproduction methods, masking out any desired portions of the original drawing. Photographic drawings are used in some instances when changes are to be made in an existing plant facility. Their use is discussed in Chapter 31.

Art gum, which is a softer variety of rubber, should be used to clean the drawing. When cleaning is necessary, it should be done before the drawing is inked. Pencil drawings, finished with a soft pencil that makes a deep black line, cannot be successfully cleaned with art gum since the pencil lines smudge very easily. It is far better to keep the drawing clean than to try to scrub it with art gum after it has been soiled. The following suggestions, if observed, will help to keep the drawing clean:

a. In moving the T-square, bear down on the head so that the blade is raised slightly from the paper.
b. The hands are always somewhat oily—keep them off the paper.
c. Use a hard pencil for layout work.
d. Pick up the triangles rather than sliding them.
e. When finishing a drawing with a soft pencil, cover all views, except the one you are working on, with a clean sheet of paper.
f. Blow graphite particles, which flake off the soft pencil, from the sheet.
g. Use a brush or soft cloth to brush erasing crumbs off the sheet rather than the flat of the hand.
h. Use a hard, smooth-surfaced paper, if it is suitable for the type of drawing being made.
i. Use of a finely ground cleansing material on the drawing during work will keep both the drawing and instruments clean. Several varieties of this material may be purchased.

Fig. 3.9   Use of the erasing shield and motor eraser.

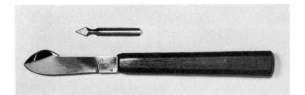

Fig. 3.10   Knife and penscratcher.

3.5 LETTERING PENS. Although some drafts-men use the ruling pen for lettering, it is not a good practice. The regular penholder with pen points similar to those used in writing should be used. A full discussion of lettering pens is given in Art. 2.10.2.

3.6 DRAWING BOARDS. Drawing boards vary greatly in size, from small ones 12 inches by 15 inches to large vertical boards 6 or 7 feet high by 10 or 12 feet long. Regardless of size, the surface should be free from cracks and it should be a plane. Soft white pine or bass wood is a most suitable material since this will take thumbtacks or other fasteners. At least one edge should be straight as a base for the T-square.

3.7 T-SQUARE. The common T-square consists of two parts, the blade and the head, which should be rigidly fastened together. A variety of kinds and sizes may be obtained from the vendors. Various lengths may be obtained, ranging from 18 inches to 72 inches.

To keep the T-square in good condition, careful handling is required. It should not be used as a hammer nor be allowed to drop to the floor. The upper or drawing edge should not be used as a guide for the knife in cutting paper. If the head should become loose, the screws must be removed and the two parts glued together. The screws may then be replaced, and the T-square is ready for use again.

3.8 PARALLEL RULES. On large drawing boards, of both the horizontal and vertical type, a parallel rule permanently attached to the table is used in place of a T-square. It is a large straight edge that operates by means of a wire-cable arrangement. It always remains parallel to its previous position as it is moved up and down the board, as shown in Fig. 3.11. On the vertical boards there is a ledge at the bottom of the board to hold drafting tools.

3.9 DRAFTING MACHINE. In many offices a drafting machine similar to the one shown in Fig. 3.12 is used in place of the T-square, triangles, and scales. In operation, this device keeps the two blades always parallel to their original position no matter where they are moved on the sheet. The two blades, which may be simple straight edges or straight edges with scales along them, are accurately set at right angles to each other. The blades are removable, hence a variety of scales may be used. The adjusting head has a protractor with vernier attachment so that the blades may be set and clamped at any desired angle. Considerable saving of time results from the use of this machine. For larger drafting operations, the drafting machine shown in Fig. 3.12 is used.

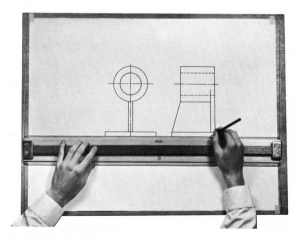

Fig. 3.11 Parallel rule.

Fig. 3.12 Drafting machine.

3.10   TRIANGLES. Triangles are the instruments used by the draftsman in connection with the T-square to draw lines at various angles with the horizontal. The two most common varieties that every draftsman should possess are the 30–60° and the 45° triangles. With these two triangles, angles of 15, 30, 45, 60, 75, and 90° with the horizontal can be drawn as shown in Fig. 3.13. The pencil or pen should be moved in the direction indicated by the arrows. Triangles range in size from 4 to 18 inches. The length of the long leg of the triangle determines the size. A thickness of about 0.08 of an inch is recommended.

3.11   USE OF TRIANGLES. Besides drawing lines of various angles as indicated in Fig. 3.13, the triangles may be used in pairs or singly with a T-square to draw one line parallel to another as shown in Fig. 3.14.

A good method of drawing a line perpendicular to another line is the following:

a. Place the hypotenuse of one triangle along the original line as shown in the first position in Fig. 3.15(a).

b. Support this triangle with another triangle as in Fig. 3.15(a) or with the blade of the T-square.

c. Rotate the first triangle through 90° into the second position as shown in Fig. 3.15(a).

d. Draw the line along the rotated position of the hypotenuse to obtain a line perpendicular to the original line.

Another method is illustrated in Fig. 3.15(b), using the following steps:

a. Align one leg of a triangle with the original line.

b. Support the hypotenuse of the triangle with the blade of the T-square or another triangle.

c. Slide the triangle along the hypotenuse to the second position.

d. Draw a line along the other leg of the triangle, thereby making a line perpendicular to the original line.

In drawing a line in any direction, the general rule may be laid down that the direction of motion of the

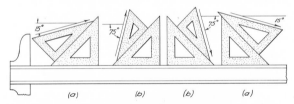

Fig. 3.13   Drawing angles of 15 and 75°.

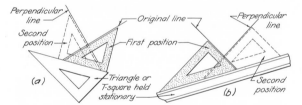

Fig. 3.15   Drawing perpendicular lines.

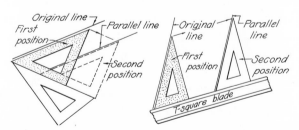

Fig. 3.14   Drawing parallel lines.

pen or pencil should be away from the body of the draftsman and not toward it. To draw a straight line between any two points (not horizontal or vertical), place the pencil on one point, bring the triangle up to it, and then rotate the triangle about the pencil point as a pivot until the edge touches the other point. Then draw the line.

3.12 STANDARD DRAWING SHEET SIZES. Two series of drawing sheet sizes are recommended by the United States of America Standards Institute, Sectional Committee Y-14—1957 as listed:

Multiples of 8½ x 11		Multiples of 9 x 12	
Size	Letter Designation	Size	Letter Designation
8½ x 11	A	9 x 12	A
11 x 17	B	12 x 18	B
17 x 22	C	18 x 24	C
22 x 34	D	24 x 36	D
34 x 44	E	36 x 48	E

Both drawing paper and cloth can be obtained in cut sheets of these sizes as well as in rolls, varying in width from 24 to 54 inches by 6-inch increments.

3.13 DRAWING MEDIA. The type of drawing media used in industry varies from company to company and with the use that will be made of the drawings. Some companies use a buff-colored detailing paper for their original layouts. A 25 per cent rag stock paper is normally used when good erasing quality is required.

Many industrial drawings are made directly on tracing paper. The drawing is finished with a medium pencil (H or F). These drawings can then be used for making "prints" directly from the drawings without any intermediate operations such as tracing or microfilming. Tracing paper may be obtained in several weights and with corresponding transparency. A paper that has been oil-treated is called vellum.

3.13.1 Tracing cloth. There are two types of tracing cloth that can be used when greater permanence is required. One is called a pencil tracing cloth, which has been treated to make the surface white so that the pencil lines show more clearly.

Regular tracing cloth has a bluish color and is quite transparent. It should be used exclusively for ink drawing since pencil lines do not show up well on this cloth. However, some companies do use pencil on ink tracing cloth. The cloth has a dull side, and the other side is extremely glossy. The glossy side does not take ink well, and it is recommended that the dull side be used for inking. Erasures of ink or pencil lines should

be made only with a pencil eraser.

When the making of a tracing is to extend over several days, it is recommended that one view at a time be fully completed rather than working over the entire area. The cloth is quite responsive to changes in the moisture content of the air and will expand or shrink a great deal from one day to the next.

3.13.2 Glass cloth. In recent years a great variety of plastic materials have been introduced for use as drawing media. Some of these are Mylar, Kronaflex, glass cloth, and drafting film. These materials have the advantage of not shrinking or expanding because of temperature and humidity. They hold their size and are dimensionally stable. Both pencil and ink can be used to draw on them.

A specially coated film is used for undimensioned drawings. The drawings are scribed onto the film with a metal scriber. The pointed metal scriber removes the opaque coating on the film. The aircraft industry uses this method of producing many of its drawings. This process is also used in making electronic circuitry layouts. These drawings are so accurate that they can be used as a template directly.

Photographic reproductions of drawings on a film base are used widely when making revisions on drawings. The parts of the drawing to be revised can be removed and the new revision can be drawn onto the same film master, thereby creating a new drawing. This saves a considerable amount of time by not having to redraw the parts of the drawing that do not require any changes.

3.14 PAPER FASTENERS. The drawing paper may be held on the board by means of fine wire staples. These are driven into the board by a special stapler. The staples are quite fine and do not damage the board as much as thumbtacks, and they offer little obstruction to the T-square and triangles.

Masking tape is used extensively in fastening papers to the board by sticking small pieces of it across the corners of the paper.

3.15 SCALES. Drawings of large objects must be made smaller than the object because of the limited paper size. Some objects can be drawin full-size. Thus, if 1 inch on the drawing represents 2 inches on the object, the drawing is said to be half-size or half-scale and should be marked: Scale ½″ = 1″. If 1 inch on the drawing represents ½ inch on the object, it is said to be double-size and should be marked: Scale 2″ = 1″.

There are four basic scales in common use. They are so calibrated that they can be used directly without making any arithmetic computation for reduction. The four scales are: architect's, civil engineer's, mechanical engineer's, and the decimal scale. They can be obtained in either triangular or flat shapes as shown in Fig. 3.16. The reductions available are listed below:

Architect's Scales		Civil Engineer's Scales
Full-size	$1'' = 0'1''$	$1'' = 10.0'$*
Quarter-size	$3'' = 1'0''$	$1'' = 20.0'$
One-eighth	$1\frac{1}{2}'' = 1'0''$	$1'' = 30.0'$
One-twelfth	$1'' = 1'0''$	$1'' = 40.0'$
	$\frac{3}{4}'' = 1'0''$	$1'' = 50.0'$
	$\frac{1}{2}'' = 1'0''$	$1'' = 60.0'$
	$\frac{3}{8}'' = 1'0''$	$1'' = 80.0'$
	$\frac{1}{4}'' = 1'0''$	$1'' = 100.0'$
	$\frac{3}{16}'' = 1'0''$	
	$\frac{1}{8}'' = 1'0''$	
	$\frac{3}{32}'' = 1'0''$	

* Or some integral power of 10' as, for example, 100' or 1000'. The civil engineer's scales are convenient for scaling forces in a vector diagram.

3.15.1 The architect's scale.

The basic unit at the end of the scale represents one foot and is subdivided into twelve parts to represent inches. See Fig. 3.17. On the larger scales, such as $3'' = 1'0''$, the inch division is further subdivided so that the smallest subdivision may represent $\frac{1}{8}$ of an inch. The smaller scales, on the other hand, do not have the basic unit divided into so many divisions. The smallest subdivision on the $\frac{1}{8}'' = 1'0''$ scale represents 2 inches.

3.15.2 The civil engineer's scale.

The civil engineer's scale marked 10 has each inch subdivided into

Mechanical Engineer's Scales	Decimal Scale
$2'' = 1''$	$1.00'' = 1.00''$
$1\frac{1}{2}'' = 1''$	$0.50'' = 1.00''$
$1'' = 1''$	$0.375'' = 1.00''$
$\frac{3}{4}'' = 1''$	$0.25'' = 1.00''$
$\frac{1}{2}'' = 1''$	
$\frac{1}{4}'' = 1''$	
$\frac{1}{8}'' = 1''$	

tenths. Figure 3.18 shows a 20 and 40 scale. These scales are fully divided and are used on map drawings as well as various other works in civil engineering. The scales available have the inch divided into 10, 20, 30, 40, 50, and 60 parts. These scales are also useful in graphic statics and nomography where the units may represent feet, pounds, stress, or pounds per square inch.

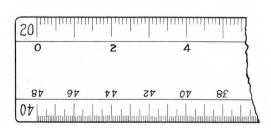

Fig. 3.16 **Types of scales.**

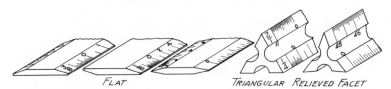

Fig. 3.17 **Architect's scale.**

Fig. 3.18 **Civil engineer's scale.**

3.15.3 The mechanical engineer's scale. On these scales the major end unit represents 1 inch and the subdivisions represent the commonly used fractions of an inch, ½, ¼, ⅛, 1/16, etc., as shown in Fig. 3.19. These scales may be obtained either open- or full-divided. Fractions used in industry are always multiples of ½, such as ¼, ⅛, 1/16. Such fractions as ⅓, ⅕, ⅙, 1/7, or other odd numbers are never used.

3.15.4 Decimal scale. Throughout industry in general there is a strong tendency toward decimal dimensioning rather than fractional. When parts are dimensioned in decimals, two-place decimals are used. These are made in even numbers, that is, fiftieths of an inch, so that when halved (diameters to radii) a two-place decimal results. A scale with graduations in fiftieths of an inch is shown in Fig. 3.20. Half-size and quarter-size decimal scales may be used in the drafting room. For additional information about these decimal scales, see American Standard USASI-Z75.1—1955.

3.16 USE OF SCALES. In Fig. 3.21 two illustrations show the use of scales. Note that in all cases the inner end of the first subdivided unit is marked 0 and the numbering goes from that point toward the other

end of the scale. There are two lines of numbers, one of which applies to the scale at one end and the other to the scale at the opposite end. The larger of these scales is always just twice the smaller. To mark off 4 feet 3½ inches, set the scale with the division numbered 4 at one end and count off the 3½ inches in the subdivided unit at the other end, as shown in Fig. 3.21(a). Or, again, to mark off 4 7/16 inches, set the mark numbered 4 at one end and count off the 7/16-inch division in the opposite direction from the 0 as shown in Fig. 3.21(b). To lay off a number of equal spaces, a scale rather than a divider should be used, since a minute error in setting a divider may result in a large cumulative error.

When a number of unequal distances are to be set off, the total of which lies within the length of the scale, it is best to add these distances arithmetically and then mark off the distances with the scale always at the same beginning or reference point. This avoids cumulative errors of setting.

To use the scale properly, one should place the scale on the paper with the working edge farthest from him and then, looking down over it, mark off the required dimensions with a very sharp, conical-pointed pencil

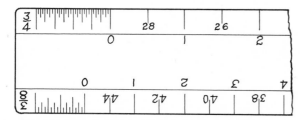

Fig. 3.19　Mechanical engineer's scale.

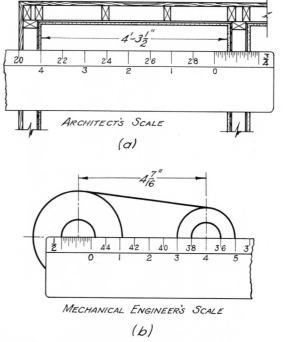

ARCHITECT'S SCALE

(a)

MECHANICAL ENGINEER'S SCALE

(b)

Fig. 3.21　Use of scales.

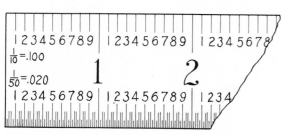

Fig. 3.20　Decimal scale.

or a needle point, as shown in Fig. 3.22. Note that a blunt pencil is of little value for this purpose, since the draftsman cannot see where the point actually touches the paper. The pencil or needle point should be held in a vertical position.

3.17   CASE OF INSTRUMENTS. Instruments may be purchased singly or in groups, in cases designed to hold them. An adequate set for general drafting purposes should contain approximately the items illustrated in Fig. 3.1.

The following paragraphs make clear the proper methods for handling the various pieces of the set, what to look for in selecting them, and how to care for

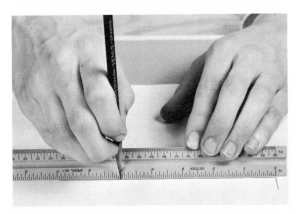

Fig. 3.22   Laying off dimensions with a scale.

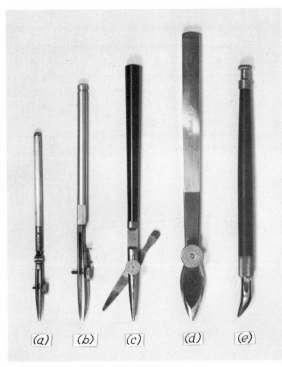

Fig. 3.23   Ruling pens.

them and keep them in proper working order. The use to which they are subjected and the care they receive, when not in use, determine to a large extent how long they will last.

3.18   RULING PENS. Ruling pens are supplied with two general types of points and several kinds of handles as shown in Fig. 3.23. The wide-pointed pens serve best for drawing long, heavy borderlines since they hold more ink. Pens come in various lengths, and when buying a single pen the individual can choose one that suits his hand.

The nibs of the pen, as the two blades are called, can be opened and closed by means of a screw. The spring pressure of the blades should be positive, but not too strong so as to reduce unnecessary wear on the threads.

3.18.1   Care of ruling pens. When the nibs are too pointed, as illustrated in Fig. 3.24(*a*), the ink will not flow well since the high capillary action on the ink holds it from the point of the pen. After the pen is used for some time, it will have a flat spot worn on one side as shown in Fig. 3.24(*b*). Both of these conditions can be corrected by properly sharpening the nibs to the proper profile as shown in Fig. 3.24(*c*). To sharpen a pen, an oil stone is used in the following manner:

a. Close the nibs of the pen and rub it on the stone, holding it in a plane perpendicular to the surface of the stone as shown in Fig. 3.25(*a*).

b. Grind the nibs down to an even length and to a parabolic profile as shown in Fig. 3.24(*c*) by rocking the pen back and forth in the direction of motion as grinding proceeds.

c. The nibs are sharpened by grinding on the outside as shown in Fig. 3.25(*b*). Care must be taken to maintain equal length of the nibs and prevent shiny flat spots.

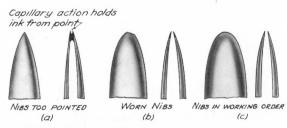

Fig. 3.24   Ruling pen nibs.

3.18.2   Using a ruling pen. The ruling pen should be held in the same manner as the drawing pencil, that is, slightly inclined in the direction of motion and in a plane perpendicular to the paper through the line being drawn. Great care must be exercised to get and keep the correct position of the pen, since only a slight deviation is necessary to bring disastrous results. Figure 3.26 shows the right and wrong relations between the ruling pen and the triangle or T-square together with the type of line that results from such handling. Both nibs of the pen must touch the paper and, when held perpendicular to the paper, the bevel of the nibs keeps the point at the proper distance from

the triangle. A white space should always show between the line and the T-square.

The pen should be filled by placing the quill, which is in the stopper of the small ink bottle, between the nibs of the pen and letting the ink run into the pen as shown in Fig. 3.27. The ink should not stand more than ¼ inch high in the pen, as the weight of a higher column will frequently cause the ink to run out and make a blot.

Long lines should always be drawn in an arm movement, coming to rest near the end of the line and finishing with a finger movement. Short lines, of course, are always drawn with a finger movement.

Fig. 3.25   Sharpening the ruling pen.

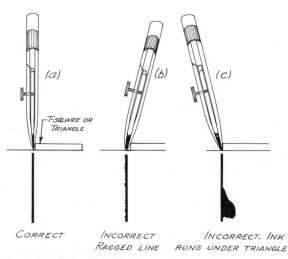

Fig. 3.26   Using the ruling pen.

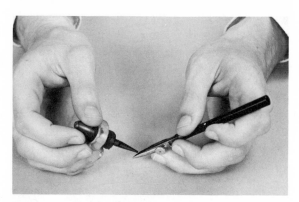

Fig. 3.27   Filling the ruling pen.

3.19   INKING. In inking straight lines and curves that join each other, the curve should be inked first and then care taken to stop the arc exactly at the tangent point as shown in Fig. 3.28. The ruling pen should then be lined up with the end of the arc by looking down squarely over the pen, as shown in Fig. 3.28, before actually touching it to the paper. In order that the arc and straight line may have exactly the same width, which is absolutely necessary, a few sample arcs are made on scratch paper, which should be of the same kind as that on which the drawing is made. Then the width of the ruling pen is adjusted by drawing lines to these arcs and changing until a perfect match is secured. In all cases the ink line should straddle the pencil line over which it is drawn.

For convenience, a line gage may be made up, with the weights of lines in proper proportion drawn on a piece of heavy paper. This can be used as a standard to maintain uniformity in the weight of lines from one drawing to the next. For larger drawing a heavier set of lines should be used.

One of the common faults of beginners is that of running the lines beyond their proper stopping points. It should be remembered that the ink flows just a little ahead of the pen; therefore, when the line being drawn is to end upon another line, the pen must be stopped at the near side of the line. A little practice will enable the draftsman to determine just when to stop his pen to avoid overrunning.

3.20   DRAWING INK. One cannot discuss the use of the ruling pen without giving consideration to drawinks because the ink has a decided influence on the results produced. Drawing inks may be obtained in black and a wide variety of colors. The black ink is a combination of carbon and a solvent. The carbon, however, is in suspension and not in solution; consequently it is a very thick ink. The solvent contains alcohol and evaporates very readily. The ink bottle should therefore always be kept tightly closed, except when filling the pen. This practice also avoids upsetting an open ink bottle with the consequent spoiling of drawings and equipment. Most of the colored inks are true solu-

tions and are much thinner than the black india ink. One must be particularly careful not to fill the pen too full with colored inks because the ink will run out of the pen much more readily when it touches the paper.

Since india ink dries very rapidly, it forms little cakes of carbon on the inside of the nibs; therefore, the pen must be cleaned frequently while in use. It must be always cleaned before it is put away. The pen is cleaned by inserting a piece of chamois or soft cloth between the nibs while the ink is still moist and then pulling the cloth out. A clogged pen is one of the most common causes of poor lines. It should be noted also that due to evaporation the ink gradually thickens in the bottle. It then dries out very rapidly in the pen and is difficult to use. Ammonia may be used to thin the ink. Normally, it is best to purchase a fresh bottle. Another cause of poor lines is the presence of lint, dust, and dirt on the paper. The ruling pen will pick these up and cause a sudden widening of the line.

3.21   QUALITY OF INK LINE. In order to give a drawing "life and vigor" there must be a variation in the weight of the different lines employed. The outline of the object should stand out sharply, with the hidden lines somewhat less prominent. Dimension lines, auxiliary lines, center lines, and crosshatching should be still lighter. The weight and character of lines shown in Fig. 3.29 are those recommended by the United States of America Standards Institute. These

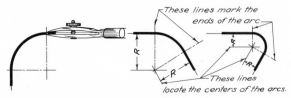
Fig. 3.28   Joining arcs and straight lines.

Border Lines	Extra Thick
Visible Lines	Thick
Invisible Lines	Medium
Section Lines	Thin
Center Lines	Thin
Extension Line / Dimension Lines	Thin
Cutting Plane Lines	Thick
Cutting Plane Lines	Thick
Break Line (short)	Thick
Break Line (long)	Thin
Phantom Line	Thin

Fig. 3.29   Proper weight of lines. (Courtesy United States of America Standards Institute.)

weights of lines may be varied somewhat in accordance with the size and nature of the drawing, but in any event three distinct weights should be maintained.

In drawing hidden lines or any other line of an interrupted character, the pen should be brought to a full stop before it is lifted from the paper. This will produce a square-ended line as shown in Fig. 3.30, whereas lifting the pen while it is in motion causes the line to fade out with a ragged end. The secret of making good-looking hidden lines lies in making the dashes of uniform length and the spaces between them also uniform but very small, say about 1/32 of an inch.

When a number of lines converge to a point, the best practice is to run only the two outside lines to the point and stop all intermediate lines along the arc of a circle just large enough to prevent the lines from touching. If the converging lines are very numerous as in charts, two arcs may be used and alternate lines may be stopped on the inner and outer arcs as illustrated in Fig. 3.31.

3.22 ORDER OF INKING. In inking a drawing or making a tracing, a certain order or procedure should be followed to give the best results in the least time. A good drawing must have uniformity and contrast. That is, there must be uniformity among lines of any one kind and contrast between lines of different kinds. To obtain this result, the lines should be inked in the following order:

a. Visible outlines, all of the same weight.
  1. Circles and arcs of circles and other curved lines.
  2. Horizontal lines beginning at the top.
  3. Vertical lines beginning at the left.
  4. Inclined lines.
b. Invisible outlines in the same order as in (a) above.
c. Center lines in the same order as in (a) above. Some draftsmen prefer to ink center lines first.
d. Crosshatching light lines, evenly spaced.
e. Dimension lines in the same order as in (a) above.
f. Dimensions, arrowheads, and other lettering.
g. Borderlines, title box, trim lines.

The importance of drawing arcs and circles first should not be overlooked for one can always make a straight line tangent to one or two arcs, but it is extremely difficult to make an arc or curve tangent to two straight lines, particularly if one of them should be just slightly out of place.

3.23 COMPASS. The large compass is one of the most important instruments in the draftsman's kit. It should be adjusted before it is used for the first time and then maintained in that condition. One leg is arranged to hold either a lead or a pen. The pen should be put in the compass first and then the needle point adjusted so that it is about 1/32 of an inch longer than the pen, as shown in Fig. 3.32. Thus when the needle point sinks into the paper the pen will be perpendicular to the paper and just touch it when the compass is held

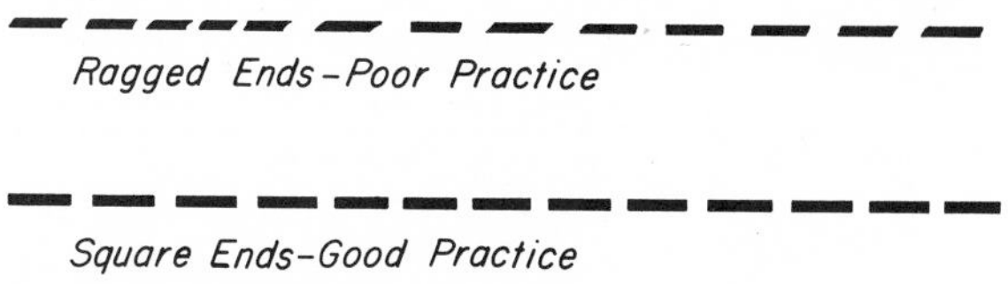

Ragged Ends – Poor Practice

Square Ends – Good Practice

Fig. 3.30 Hidden-line technique.

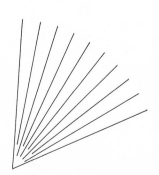

Fig. 3.31 Drawing converging lines.

Fig. 3.32 Adjustment of compass points.

in a vertical position. The needle point, once adjusted, should not be changed. The length of the lead should be adjusted to match the needle point.

The lead for the compass should be of the same hardness as that used in pencil work. The lead should be sharpened to a bevel point on the outside as shown in Fig. 3.33, since it is easier to sharpen in this manner and permits the drawing of smaller circles.

In drawing small circles, the legs of the compass may be kept straight; but for the larger ones, one or both legs should be bent as in Fig. 3.34 in order that the pen may be perpendicular to and have both nibs touching the paper. When drawing circles in ink, it is best to move the pen clockwise and to go around the circle only once. However, to secure good black pencil lines it may be necessary to go over the circle several times. When a number of concentric circles are to be drawn, a horn center is very convenient. It prevents wearing a large hole in the paper.

For circles larger than the compass will accommodate, the beam compass should be used. This requires more skill since both hands must be employed, one to hold the needle point at the center and the other to move the pencil or pen point as shown in Fig. 3.35.

3.24 DIVIDERS. Dividers are used chiefly for transferring distances and occasionally for dividing spaces into equal parts. To set the divider it should be held as shown in Fig. 3.36. If the distance to be set permits, the second and third fingers are placed inside to help control the movement of the points. If the space to be set is small, the divider must first be opened wider than the space and then closed down to the proper measurement by pressure from the thumb and

fingers; or the hairspring adjustment may be used.

To step off distances, grasp the knurled top of the divider between the thumb and first finger and rotate first in one direction and then in the other. This avoids taking a new hold on the instrument, which would be necessary if it were always turned in the same direction. The points of the instrument should not be

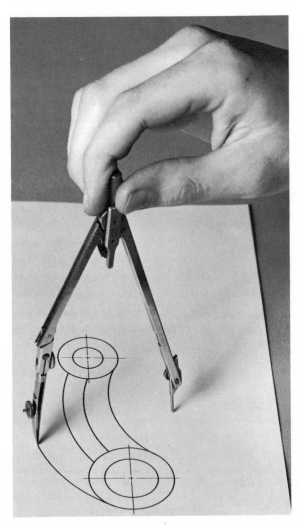

Fig. 3.34 Drawing with compass.

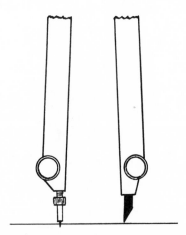

Fig. 3.33 Sharpening compass lead.

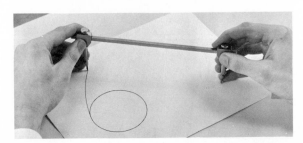

Fig. 3.35 Drawing with beam compass.

pushed through the paper, but instead only dents need be made. These may be identified by immediately touching them with a sharp, soft pencil to make a dot or by lightly encircling them, after which they readily can be found.

3.25 BOW INSTRUMENTS. Bow instruments are small instruments that are used for drawing small arcs and circles and they can be obtained in a number of styles. Those with the adjusting screw on the outside are called side-adjusting, whereas those with the screw nut in the center are called center-adjusting. Which type to use is a matter of preference among draftsmen.

The most common fault with these instruments is the wearing and stripping of the threads on the adjusting screw. If the spring pressure is too great, they will wear rapidly. One of their chief advantages is the accuracy with which they may be set and the fact that they can be laid aside temporarily without danger of losing the setting.

3.26 IRREGULAR CURVES. There is such a wide variety of irregular or French curves produced that it is impossible to give more than a sampling of the different kinds within the limits of this book. In Fig. 3.37

are shown a few curves of common usefulness which are simply designated as irregular curves.

The irregular curve is one of the most difficult instruments to use skillfully, especially when doing ink work. The skill required lies not only in the handling of the pen, but also to a considerable extent in the placing of the curve. The irregular curve should be made to fit as many of the points as possible at one time. In no case should the line be drawn when the curve does not fit at least three points and have the proper curvature with regard to the next points on both sides. Then when the curve is moved forward the last two points should be rematched and a portion of the curve that was previously drawn can be retraced to avoid humps in the final curve.

Figure 3.38 shows how the curve may be set several times to complete one curved line. In this figure two curves are used. Curve No. 1 fits the central part of the sine curve up to the point b. Curve No. 2 fits the upper part down to the point a^1. An overlap occurs between the points a and b, and each curve should be used to the center of the space between these points. Note that points a^1 and b^1 on curve No. 2 if reversed would co-

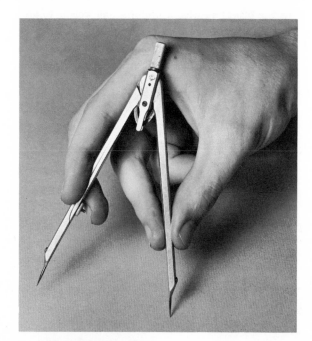

Fig. 3.36 Setting the divider.

Fig. 3.37 Irregular curves.

incide with *a* and *b* and the upper portion of the curved line under curve No. 1. Figure 3.38 shows that curve No. 2 comes tangent to the horizontal construction line at the top. Points of tangency should always be used as guides in setting the curve.

The ruling pen should be held perpendicular to the paper in drawing an irregular curve. This is particularly true on curves of sharp radius where the pen must also be rotated between the fingers so that the same spot on the nibs remains in contact with the curve.

3.27 TECHNIQUE OF DRAFTING. *The primary essentials of good drafting techniques are speed, accuracy, and neatness.* A few basic rules to help achieve these qualities are as follows:

a. Do not sharpen pencil over the drawing board.
b. Knock excess graphite off file or sandpaper pad on the leg of table or chair at a point near the floor. Do this immediately after sharpening pencil.
c. Always keep pencil sharp.
d. Do not fill ruling pen or compass over the drawing board.
e. Do not have ink bottle on drawing board.
f. Put stopper in ink bottle immediately after filling pen.
g. Time will be saved by using a scale guard on the triangular scales to indicate the scale in use. Otherwise, a good deal of time is lost hunting for the correct scale.

3.28 PENCIL TECHNIQUE. In making a pencil drawing it is important to maintain a good, sharp point on the pencil. Generally a harder pencil such as a 4H or 5H is used to lay out the problem. Then a 3H or softer pencil is used to draw in the detail of the drawing. Some of the things to consider in making a drawing look "sharp" are as follows:

a. Do not overrun corners.
b. Do not press hard on the pencil to cause grooves.
c. Maintain proper weight distinction between different types of lines.
d. Remove all construction lines.
e. Do not make center lines or projection lines too long.

3.29 MICROFILM TECHNIQUE. Many companies are using microfilming methods to produce shop prints of their drawings. Often the drawings are reduced as much as 30 to 1 when they are photographed onto microfilm. Therefore, the techniques discussed in Arts. 3.22 and 3.28 must be adapted to take into consideration the allowances for reductions.

At the present time no USASI standard has been prepared for use as a guide. However, many companies have developed their own standard for use on their drawings. Extra care must be taken to insure good spacing of letters with a uniform line weight to produce consistently good results on microfilm. The size of the letters must not be too small, as discussed in Art. 2.5.

Fig. 3.38 Use of irregular curves.

The line work must be sharp and uniform in weight. It is better to make the lines heavier than normal to insure their being reproduced. In the case of crosshatching, the lines must not be too close together. A more complete discussion of the use of microfilming in a drafting and design room appears in Chapter 31.

3.30   SECTION LINERS. For small areas the draftsman spaces his crosshatching by eye. When the area is large or when the work is very important and is to be reproduced, the crosshatching can be spaced with section liners.

The draftsman may construct devices of his own that will aid in the even spacing of crosshatching lines. By scratching a line on the triangle, say ¹⁄₁₆ of an inch from the edge and parallel to it, this line can be used as a guide in doing the pencil work. The first crosshatching line is drawn and then the triangle is moved up so that the line on the triangle is over the one on the drawing and a second line is drawn. Two or more

lines can be made on the triangle to give different spacings or different spacings can be made on the various edges as illustrated in Fig. 3.39.

A small piece of heavy cardboard or thin veneer can be cut to the shape of the hole in the triangle but slightly smaller. By shifting the triangle and block alternately, accurate spacing may be obtained. For small areas the middle line of holes in the Ames lettering instrument may be used.

3.31   PROTRACTORS. Protractors may be obtained in small sizes, made of thin brass or plastic, or in the more expensive varieties of polished steel having vernier attachments for accurate setting of the ruling edge. A steel vernier is shown in Fig. 3.40(*a*), a plastic protractor in Fig. 3.40(*b*). They are used to measure angles and are particularly useful in map work. The usual divisions are in degrees and fractions thereof, though other divisions such as percentage parts of a circle may be obtained.

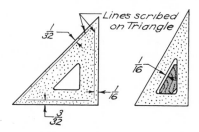

Fig. 3.39   Aids in section lining.

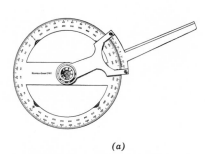

(*a*)

(*b*)

Fig. 3.40   Protractors. (Courtesy of Dietzgen Co.)

3.32 SPECIAL CELLULOID TOOLS. A variety of special celluloid forms are on the market whose purpose and usefulness is self-evident. A number of these are shown in Fig. 3.41. Ellipse guides, which may be obtained in a wide variety of sizes, are particularly useful in pictorial drawing. Circle guides are valuable time savers.

3.33 DROP PEN. The drop pen shown in Fig. 3.42 is used for drawing very small circles. The pencil or pen point spins around the central axis. The top is held with the thumb and index finger, and the pen is raised and lowered with the third finger. The third finger is then used to give it a spin when in place. This instrument is particularly useful to structural engineers in drawing rivet holes or heads.

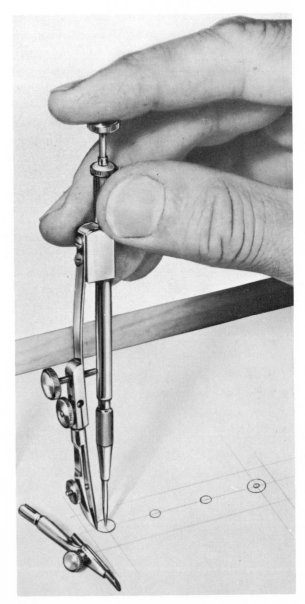

Fig. 3.42   Use of drop pen. (Courtesy of Dietzgen Co.)

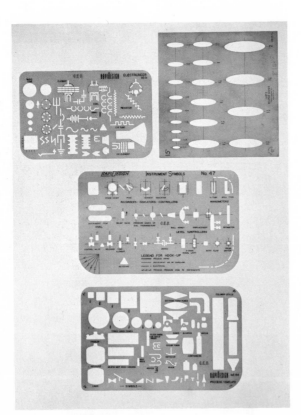

Fig. 3.41   Special drafting tools.

3.34 CONTOUR PEN. The contour pen shown in Fig. 3.43 is used by map draftsmen in drawing contour lines that are quite irregular in shape. The pen swivels very freely on the axis that passes up through the handle. By holding it almost vertical, it can be made to follow any curved line no matter how sharply it turns.

3.35 SPECIAL EQUIPMENT. There are many specialized pieces of equipment available to aid the draftsman in his work. Figure 3.44 is a picture of an ellipsograph that is used for making an ellipse of any size using pencil or ink. For other types of special equipment the draftsman should contact the instrument companies. In using this type of equipment the same care and techniques are to be used as described in the previous articles in this chapter.

Fig. 3.43   Contour pen.

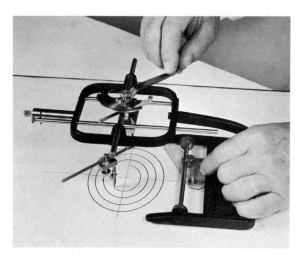

Fig. 3.44   Ellipsograph.

SELF-STUDY QUESTIONS

Before trying to answer these questions, read the chapter carefully. Then, without reference to the text, answer as many questions as possible. For those that cannot be answered, the number, in parentheses following the question number, gives the article in which the answer can be found. Look it up and write down the answer. Check the answers that you did give to see that they are correct.

3.1 **(3.1)** In many cases a _____ can be used as well as a drawing made with instruments.

3.2 **(3.1)** To make an accurate drawing _____ are used.

3.3 **(3.3)** The softest drawing pencil is _____.

3.4 **(3.3)** The hardest drawing pencil is _____.

3.5 **(3.3)** For layout work, a good pencil to use would be _____.

3.6 **(3.3)** For sketching the _____ pencils are used.

3.7 **(3.3)** For finishing the drawing a _____ pencil could be used.

3.8 **(3.3)** For general purpose work the _____ point is used.

3.9 **(3.3)** In drawing a line the pencil should be _____ in the direction of motion.

3.10 **(3.3)** The _____ point is used for drawing long lines.

3.11 **(3.3)** The bevel point is used in the _____.

3.12 **(3.4)** To remove lines the _____ should be used.

3.13 **(3.4)** To protect the surrounding parts of the drawing an _____ should be used.

3.14 **(3.16)** To avoid cumulative errors a _____ should be used in laying off a series of equal distances along a line.

3.15 **(3.17)** A _____ is used for inking straight lines.

3.16 **(3.17)** The _____ of a ruling pen must be properly sharpened.

3.17 **(3.19)** The _____ should be inked first and then the tangent lines.

3.18 **(3.23)** The _____ is used to draw arcs and circles.

3.19 **(3.23)** The _____ _____ is used for drawing very large circles.

3.20 **(3.24)** The _____ are used to transfer distances.

3.21 **(3.26)** In drawing curves representing test data, the _____ is often used.

3.22 **(3.28)** To keep the drawing neat, do not _____ corners.

3.23 **(3.28)** In finishing a drawing remove all _____.

3.24 **(3.22)** In inking a drawing the _____ lines should be inked first.

3.25 **(3.31)** To measure angles on a drawing the _____ is used.

3.26 **(3.33)** For inking a large number of small circles the _____ is used.

3.27 **(3.34)** To draw contour lines on a map the _____ is used.

3.28 **(3.7)** The two parts of the T-square are the _____ and the _____.

3.29 **(3.9)** The drafting machine takes the place of the _____, _____, and _____.

3.30 **(3.10)** The two most common triangles in use are the _____ and the _____.

3.31 **(3.11)** Two triangles can be used to draw one line _____ to another line.

3.32 **(3.13)** For reproduction purposes many industrial drawings are made directly on _____ paper.

3.33 **(3.13.2)** Mylar has the advantage over tracing cloth of being _____ .

3.34 **(3.15)** When a drawing is made to the scale of $2'' = 1''$, it is said to be _____ .

3.35 **(3.15.2)** The _____ scale is divided into tenths.

3.36 **(3.15.3)** The mechanical engineer's scale is calibrated in _____ .

3.37 **(3.15.1)** The _____ scale is divided into twelfths.

3.38 **(3.15.4)** When fractional dimensioning is not used, the _____ scale should be used.

PROBLEMS

Some individuals prefer to teach the use of instruments by exercises that allow the student to concentrate his entire attention on acquiring skill. For those persons Problems 3.1 to 3.5 have been presented. Others prefer to have the student learn to use his instruments on regular drawing problems. Problems 3.6 to 6.10 will supply this need, as well as problems chosen from other parts of the text.

In all cases the student should arrange the problems to form a well-balanced sheet. The scale is to be full-size ($8\frac{1}{2} \times 11''$ or $9 \times 12''$ sheets) unless otherwise specified by the instructor. Show clearly the construction in all problems where construction is involved. Ink problems, unless otherwise directed.

Accuracy of construction is the primary aim. Geometrical problems are therefore very excellent material for training in accuracy. All problems should be constructed with a hard pencil sharpened to produce a hairline. In all tangency problems, exact tangency is to be secured even though this requires a slight shifting of the center of a circle from its geometrical location. Geometrical constructions will be found in Chapter 4.

3.1 On an A-size sheet of paper ($8\frac{1}{2} \times 11''$) draw four rectangles of the size shown in Fig. 3.45 well balanced inside the borderline of your sheet. In the rectangles reproduce the patterns shown in Fig. 3.45(a), (b), (c), and (d). Repeat the patterns to cover the entire rec-

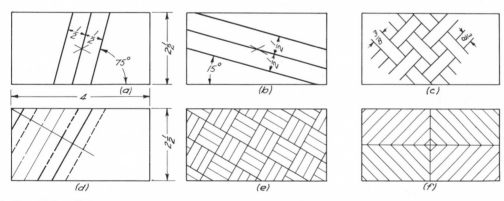

Fig. 3.45   Geometric patterns.

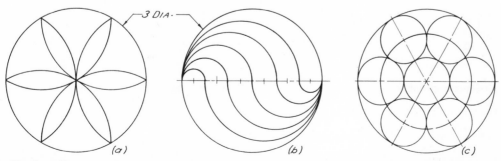

Fig. 3.46   Circular patterns.

tangle. Make all lines of thickness used for visible outlines except in *d* where the proper weight for each type
of line should be used. See Fig. 3.29.

3.2 Same as Problem 3.1. Copy patterns of Fig. 3.45(*b*), (*d*),
(*e*), and (*f*).

3.3 Same as Problem 3.1. Copy patterns of Fig. 3.45(*a*), (*c*),
(*d*), and (*f*).

3.4 Reproduce the patterns of Fig. 3.46(*a*) and (*b*). Have
circles well balanced on your sheet. Thickness of lines
to be that of section lines in Fig. 3.29.

3.5 Same as Problem 3.4. Copy patterns of Fig. 3.46(*a*) and
(*c*).

3.6 Draw the valve gasket of Fig. 3.47. Scale full-size unless
otherwise specified.

3.7 Draw the heavy-duty gasket of Fig. 3.48. Scale full-size
unless otherwise specified.

3.8 Reproduce the pipe gasket of Fig. 3.49 to the scale
specified by your instructor. Show construction for the
location of centers of the 1″ radius arcs, and mark
tangency points of these arcs with the other circular
arcs.

3.9 Reproduce the pump gasket of Fig. 3.50. Locate centers
of small arcs and locate tangency points with other arcs.

3.10 Reproduce one or more geometrical layout problems
as assigned from the illustrations of Chapter 4.

3.11 Design an insignia incorporating your initials using
only straight lines, circles, or arcs of circles.

3.12 Design a new hood ornament using straight lines and
circles.

3.13 Design an ornamental hub cap for a new automobile.

3.14 Design a new display sign for a major oil company using
straight lines and circles.

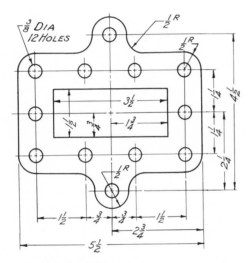

Fig. 3.47   Valve gasket.

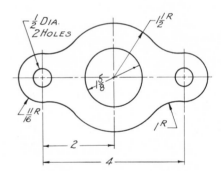

Fig. 3.49   Pipe gasket.

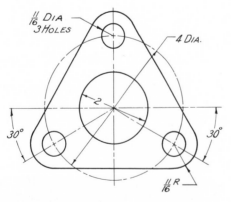

Fig. 3.48   Heavy-duty gasket.

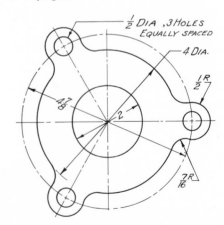

Fig. 3.50   Pump gasket.

CHAPTER 4
Geometrical Construction

NEW: New York State Thruway. (Philip Gendreau)

OLD: Roman Road in 1736. Engraved by B. Picard. (Bettman Archive)

Chapter 4   Geometrical Construction

4.1   INTRODUCTION. To be successful in drafting or engineering design and in engineering practice in general, the engineer must have at his command many of the simpler geometrical constructions shown in this chapter. A great variety of some of the more common as well as some of the more difficult constructions are presented. These constructions make this book an excellent reference for use in subsequent courses as well as in engineering practice. The draftsman, technician, and engineer have a wide variety of drafting equipment available to aid them in making various geometric constructions. By using combinations of these drafting tools, many shortcuts are possible to make work simpler. Where possible, a practical application of the particular geometric construction is shown in the same figure in which the construction procedure is outlined.

4.2   LINES. It is often necessary to divide lines or spaces into a given number of parts and to draw lines parallel or perpendicular to each other. The following paragraphs deal with a number of simple geometrical constructions that can be used by the draftsman and engineer in his work.

4.2.1   Bisect a line—compass method. A line can be bisected by using a compass and straight edge as shown in Fig. 4.1. The construction detail is as follows:

a. Set the compass using a radius r larger than half the length of the line segment AB to be bisected.

b. Using points A and B respectively, draw two arcs with radius r from each point as indicated in Fig. 4.1(*b*). It is important to have a good sharp point on the lead in the compass and to be certain that the steel point is placed at the exact end points of the line.

c. At the intersections C and D of the construction arcs, draw a line between them using a straight edge or triangle as is shown in Fig. 4.1(*c*). Line CD is the perpendicular bisector of the line AB and divides the line into two equal parts.

4.2.2.   Bisect a line—triangle method. A line can be bisected by using a triangle and the T-square as shown in Fig. 4.2. The construction details are outlined below.

a. Through the two end points of line AB, draw two lines through each of the points as shown in Fig. 4.2(*b*). Care must be taken to have the line pass through points A and B and to have the construction lines each make the same angle with given line AB.

b. Points C and D determined by the intersections of the four construction lines are used to draw line CD as shown in Fig. 4.2(*c*). This line is the perpendicular bisector of the line segment AB.

4.2.3   Line parallel to another line through a given point—compass method. By definition, parallel lines meet at infinity. This means that they are constantly a uniform distance apart. In the case of drawing a line

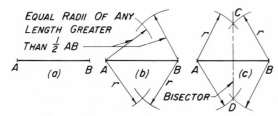

Fig. 4.1   Bisecting a line using a compass.

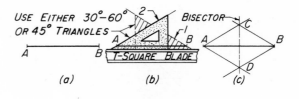

Fig. 4.2   Bisecting a line with a triangle.

through a point parallel to a given line, the uniform distance is the shortest distance from the point to the line. This is the perpendicular distance from the point to the line. Figure 4.3 shows the steps in drawing a line through point A parallel to line AB. The steps are as follows:

a. Set the compass with radius R which is the shortest distance from point A to line CD as shown in Fig. 4.3(b). The shortest distance R is the perpendicular distance from A to CD.

b. Using the radius R, strike two or more arcs with centers on the given line BC as shown in Fig. 4.3(c).

c. Through point A draw a line tangent to the construction arcs. This line is parallel to line BC.

4.2.4   Line parallel to another line through a given point—triangle method. Figure 4.4 shows the procedure that can be used to construct a line parallel to another line a given distance apart by using two triangles or a triangle and T-square. The construction is performed as follows:

a. Place a triangle in position *1* along line BC as shown in Fig. 4.4(b).

b. Place a second triangle or the T-square in contact with the first triangle as shown in Fig. 4.4(b).

c. Move the first triangle along the second triangle from position *1* to position *2*, making sure that in position *2* it lines up with point A as shown in Fig. 4.4(c).

d. Through point A draw a line along the edge of the

first triangle in position *2*. This line is parallel to the given line BC and passes through point A.

4.2.5   Line parallel to a curved line. Figure 4.5 shows the compass method applied to drawing a curved line parallel to another curved line a given distance r apart. The compass is set at radius r as in Fig. 4.5. A series of arcs are drawn from points along the given curved line. A sufficient number of arcs must be drawn close enough to each other so that a smooth curve can be drawn tangent to these arcs as shown in Fig. 4.5. This method breaks down when the curve is too sharply concave.

4.2.6   Line perpendicular to another line through a given point—triangle method. In Arts. 4.2.1 and 4.2.2 two construction methods are discussed by which a perpendicular bisector of a line segment is obtained. Many times it is necessary merely to draw a line through a point perpendicular or at 90° to a line. The most convenient method of doing this is shown in Fig. 4.6 by using a triangle and a T-square or two triangles. The construction is as follows:

a. Place triangle in position *1* aligning one edge along line AB as shown in Fig. 4.6(b).

b. Place a T-square or another triangle in contact with the first triangle as shown in Fig. 4.6(b).

c. Keeping the T-square in place, rotate the triangle 90° into position *2* passing through point C as shown in Fig. 4.6(c).

d. Draw a line through point C along the edge of the triangle to line AB.

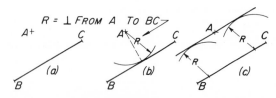

Fig. 4.3   Drawing a line through a point parallel to a line.

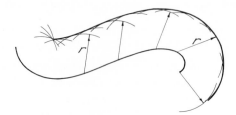

Fig. 4.5   Drawing a curved line parallel to another.

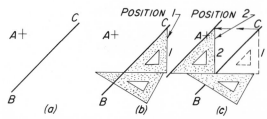

Fig. 4.4   Drawing a line through a point parallel to a line.

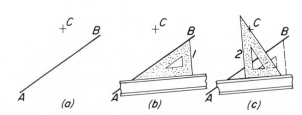

Fig. 4.6   Drawing one line perpendicular to another.

This construction not only provides a method for constructing a perpendicular line through a point to a line, but also enables the determination of the shortest distance from a point to a line.

4.2.7   Divide a line or space into a given number of equal parts—even parts and even lengths. When a line must be divided into an equal number of parts, a number of methods are available. When the line is an even dimension so that it can be readily divided into easily measurable units or a scale, the points are merely marked off on the line along the scale.

As an example, if a 2-inch line is to be divided into four equal parts, lay off ½-inch increments along the line with a scale and a good sharp-pointed pencil. A construction method for dividing a line in halves, fourths, eighths, etc. is described in Art. 4.2.11 and shown in Fig. 4.10. This is based on the principle discusssed in Art. 4.2.2.

4.2.8   Divide a line or space into a given number of equal parts—odd number of parts. To divide a line into an odd number of equal parts, a construction similar to that shown in Fig. 4.7 is used. Thus in Fig. 4.7(a) the 2-inch line AB is to be divided into 5 equal parts. Proceed as follows:

a. Draw a line AC through point A making a convenient angle with line AB as in Fig. 4.7(a).
b. Lay off 5 equal spaces along line AC as shown in Fig. 4.7(b).
c. Draw a construction line from point 5 to point B.
d. Draw lines parallel to line 5-B through points 4, 3, 2, and 1 respectively, as shown in Fig. 4.7(c). The

points at which these parallel lines intersect the given line AB determine the 5 equal segments on line AB.

Figure 4.7(d) illustrates the application of this principle to practical problems.

4.2.9   Divide a line or space into proportional parts—parallel line principle. Figure 4.8 shows how the principle of Fig. 4.7 can be applied to divide a line into any type of proportional parts. To construct a single scale, as in Fig. 4.8, proceed as follows:

a. From either end of line AB draw a line like AC at any convenient angle.
b. Mark off on this line the desired units.
c. For a scale of squares mark the significant points of the squares desired as in Fig. 4.8, for example 1, 4, 9, 16, and 25.
d. Connect the end point 25 for squares to B.
e. From the other points 1, 4, 9, and 16 draw lines parallel to 25-B.
f. Mark the points on line AB as 1, 2, 3, 4, and 5 thus making a scale of the squares of these numbers.

For the logarithmic scale use as many points on the original scale as desired. To construct a logarithmic scale proceed in the same manner, marking off logarithms of numbers on the line AC.

4.2.10   Construction of logarithmic scales—triangle principle. It is often desirable to have available a series of scales of different lengths for some function such as logarithms. This can be accomplished as shown in Fig. 4.9.

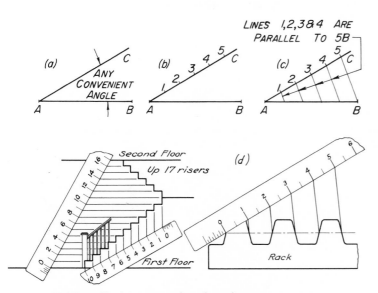

Fig. 4.7   Dividing a line into any number of equal spaces.

a. Construct the original scale or use one already made and fasten it to the drawing paper.

b. Select a point *A* approximately opposite the center of the original scale and at a perpendicular distance equal to the length of the scale. This distance is for convenience only. Thus if the original scale is 5 inches long and point *A* is 5 inches from the scale, as shown in Fig. 4.9, a line 4 inches from *A* will give a 4-inch scale.

c. Draw lines from the significant points on the original scale to point *A*.

d. For a 3-inch scale, fold the drawing paper along the 3-inch line.

4.2.11 Divide a line or space into fractional parts. The construction for dividing a line into fractional parts is shown in Fig. 4.10. Assume that line *AB* in Fig. 4.10(*a*) is to be divided. The procedures is as follows:

a. Construct a rectangle of any convenient size on line *AB*.

b. Draw both diagonals.

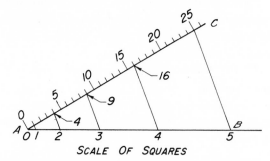

SCALE OF SQUARES

Fig. 4.8 Proportional functional scales.

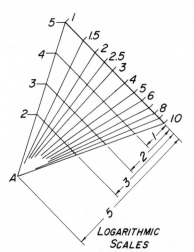

Fig. 4.9 Functional scale of different lengths.

c. A vertical line from intersection *E* divides *AB* into two equal parts at *M*.

d. For a one-third part of *AB* draw a line from *D* to *M*.

e. Where line *DM* crosses the original diagonal at *F*, draw a vertical line to *AB*, thus locating *G* the one-third point.

f. Further subdivision can be made in a similar manner, as shown in Fig. 4.10(*b*).

4.2.12 Line through a point *P* making a common intersection with two other lines *AB* and *CD* when their intersection is inaccessible. The steps in the construction of a line passing through a given point intersecting two other lines when their intersection is inaccessible are shown in Fig. 4.11 and are as follows:

a. With *P* as one vertex, draw any convenient triangle *1* as shown in Fig. 4.11(*b*), having the other vertices on the two given lines.

b. At any other convenient place draw a similar triangle *2*.

c. The line through *P* and the corresponding point

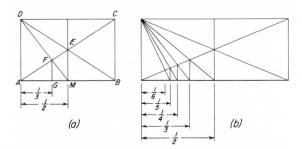

Fig. 4.10 Dividing a line or space into fractional parts.

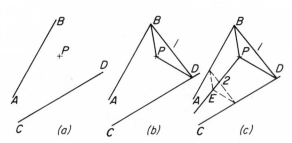

Fig. 4.11 Intersecting lines when intersection is inaccessible.

E will meet the given lines in a common intersection.

4.3 ANGLES, DEFINITION OF TERMS. The meanings of terms used in discussing angles are shown and defined in Fig. 4.12. The construction of angles of various sizes are commonly required in an engineering office.

4.3.1 Bisect an angle. Figure 4.13 illustrates the method of bisecting any given angle.

a. With any convenient radius *R* and the center at *A*, draw an arc *1* across angle *BAC* intersecting *AC* at *N* and *AB* at *M*, as shown in Fig. 4.13(*a*).

b. With any radius greater than one-half the arc *MN* and centers at *M* and *N*, draw arcs *2* and *3* intersecting at point *P* as in Fig. 4.13(*b*).

c. A line from *A* through this intersection *P* divides angle *BAC* into two equal parts, as shown in Fig. 4.13(*c*).

4.3.2 Layout an angle equal to a given angle. One angle can be constructed equal to another as shown in Fig. 4.14.

a. With *A* as a center, draw an arc of any convenient

radius *R* across the angle, thus locating *m* and *n*. Fig. 4.14(*b*).

b. With *m* as a center, set the compass to radius *r*, so that the arc will pass through *n*.

c. At the new location on *A′ B′* reconstruct the angle using the same radius *R* to draw arc *1*, then with radius *r* and center at *m′* draw arc *2*. The intersection of arcs *1* and *2* locates *n′*. Draw *A′n′* to make the required angle, as in Fig. 4.14(*c*).

4.3.3 Line perpendicular (90°) to another line at the end of the line. One line may be drawn at right angles (90°) to another line as shown in Fig. 4.15. The construction is as follows:

a. Bisect the given line *AB* as shown in Fig. 4.15(*a*).

b. At any point *C* on the bisector and a radius *CB*, draw an arc through *B* greater than a semicircle. Fig. 4.15(*b*).

c. Draw the diameter *BCD*.

d. Draw line *DA*, which is at right angles to line *AB*. Fig. 4.15(*c*).

The geometric principle used in this construction is that lines drawn from the ends of a diameter of a circle to any point on the circumference of it form a right angle with each other.

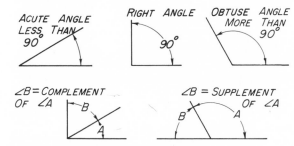

Fig. 4.12   Definition of terms for angles.

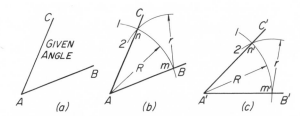

Fig. 4.14   Constructing an angle equal to a given angle.

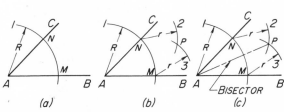

Fig. 4.13   Bisecting an angle.

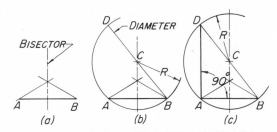

Fig. 4.15   Perpendicular to a line at the end of the line.

4.3.4 Line perpendicular (90°) to another line by the *3, 4, 5* **method.** For constructing a *3-4-5* right triangle, the steps are as follows:

a. On the given line *AD* in Fig. 4.16(*a*) lay off three equal spaces from *B* to *C* of any convenient length.

b. At *B* draw a line in a convenient direction and on it lay off four spaces from *B* to *E* each equal to those between *B* and *C*. Figure 4.16(*b*).

c. At *C* draw another line and on it lay off five equal spaces from *C* to *F* of the same length as the others, as in Fig. 4.16(*c*).

d. With *B* as a center and *BE* as a radius, draw an arc to the right.

e. With *C* as a center and *CF* as a radius, draw an arc intersecting the first one at *G*. Figure 4.16(*c*).

f. Draw the line *GB*, which will be at right angles to line *AD*.

This method is used in the field to lay out right angles in construction. It was used in ancient times by the Egyptians.

4.3.5 Lay out any given angle with a protractor. Assume that any angle is to be constructed at *B* on line *AC*, as shown in Fig. 4.17.

a. Place the protractor along line *AC* with its center at *B*.

b. Mark a point *D* at the required angle (59.5° clockwise from *A* in this case).

c. Remove the protractor and draw line *BD*.

4.3.6 Lay out an angle by the tangent method. Assume that the angle (35°) is to be laid out at *A* on line *AB* as shown in Fig. 4.18.

a. On the given line *AB* measure off ten spaces to *x*, at any convenient scale.

b. Look up the tangent of the required angle in a table of tangents in the appendix (35° in this case = 0.700) and multiply it by 10. The tangent of an angle is the ratio of the opposite side over the adjacent side in a right angle triangle.

c. Measure this distance on a line perpendicular to *AB*, from *x* thus locating *y* as shown in Fig. 4.18(*b*).

d. Connect *A* with point *y*, thus making angle *BAC* equal to 35°.

4.3.7 Lay out an angle by the sine method. For laying any angle by the sine method such as 35°, the construction is shown in Fig. 4.19 and the steps are as follows:

a. Lay out ten equal spaces, to any convenient scale, from *A* to *x* on line *AB* as shown in Fig. 4.19(*a*).

b. Multiply the sine of the angle by 10. The sine of 35° = 0.574. Therefore 0.574 × 10 = 5.74.

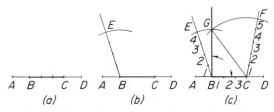

Fig. 4.16 Perpendicular to a line by the *3, 4, 5* method.

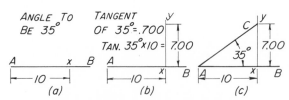

Fig. 4.18 Plotting angles by the tangent method.

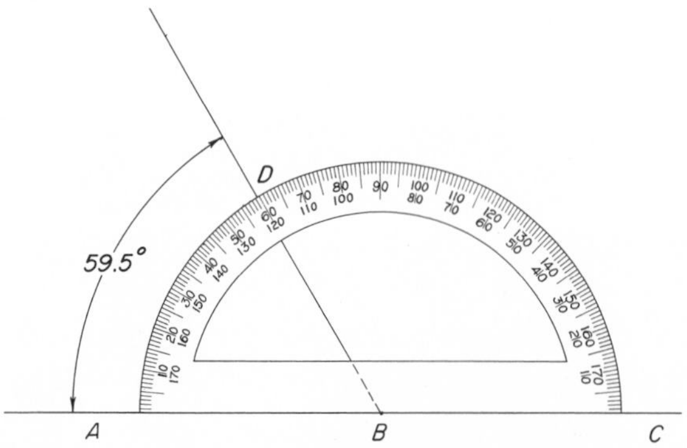

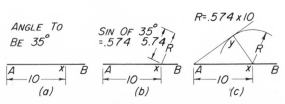

Fig. 4.17 Plotting angles by the protractor method.

Fig. 4.19 Plotting angles by the sine method.

c. With *x* as a center and 5.74 as a radius, draw an arc.

d. Draw a line from *A* tangent to the arc as shown in Fig. 4.19(*c*), thus constructing the required angle. This construction is based on the definition of the sine of an angle, namely, the opposite side over the hypotenuse in a right triangle.

4.4 CONSTRUCTION OF POLYGONS. Any geometric figure enclosed entirely by straight lines may be called a polygon. Regular polygons have their sides and interior angles equal. The more common polygons are shown in Fig. 4.20.

4.5 OTHER TYPES OF POLYGONS. Other plane figures, with their proper names, are illustrated in Fig. 4.21. In the case of the last two figures the term trapezium is sometimes applied to either as a generic term for all irregular four-sided figures.

4.6 CONSTRUCTION OF TRIANGLES. To construct a triangle, three parts must be known; for example:

a. Three sides.

b. Two sides and included angle.

c. Two angles and the side between them.

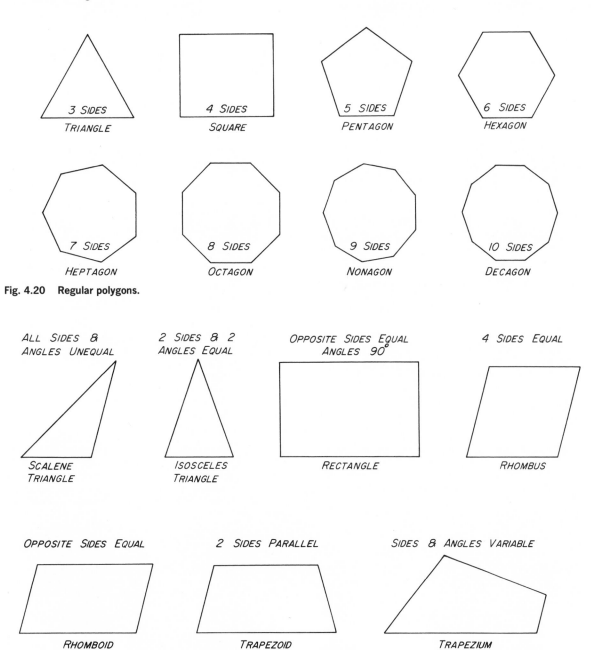

Fig. 4.20 Regular polygons.

Fig. 4.21 Other common geometric plane figures.

4.6.1 Construct a triangle with three sides given. The construction of a triangle with three sides given is shown in Fig. 4.22 and is as follows:

a. Lay out the longest *side a* as a base.
b. With the ends *A* and *B* of this line as centers, draw two arcs having radii equal to the lengths of the other two *sides b* and *c* as shown in Fig. 4.22(*c*).
c. From *A* and *B* draw lines to *x*, thus completing the triangle.

4.6.2 Construct a triangle with two sides and the included angle given. To construct a triangle with two sides and an included angle given, proceed as shown in Fig. 4.23.

a. Lay out longest side *AB* equal to *a* as a base.
b. At the end *A* construct the given angle (by any method).
c. With center *A* and a radius equal to *side b*, draw an arc cutting the second side of the angle and locating the end *x* of the side.
d. Draw a line from *B* to *x*, thus completing the triangle. Figure 4.23(*c*).

4.6.3 Lay out a triangle with two angles and the included side given. To lay out a triangle with one side and two angles given, proceed as shown in Fig. 4.24(*a*).

a. Lay out the given *side a* as a base.
b. At one end *A* lay out one of the given angles—45° in this case. See Fig. 4.24(*b*).
c. At the other end of the base lay out the second given angle, 30° in this case.

d. Extend the sides of the two angles until they intersect at *C* as in Fig. 4.24(*c*). *ABC* is the required triangle.

4.7 CONSTRUCT A SQUARE. A square can be designated by having the length of one of its sides given or by having the length of its diagonal specified, as indicated in Fig. 4.25. With this basic information given, the square can be constructed by several methods that are discussed in the following paragraphs.

4.7.1 Square with length of side given—first method. Figure 4.25(*a*) shows the construction of the square *ABCD* when side *AB* is given. The steps are as follows:

a. Erect a perpendicular to *AB* at *A* as shown in Fig. 4.25(*a*).
b. With *A* as a center, draw an arc having a radius *AB* until it crosses the perpendicular at *C*.
c. With *B* and *C* as centers and with the same radius, draw two arcs intersecting at *D*.
d. Draw *CD* and *BD*, thus completing the square.

4.7.2 Square with length of side given—second method. Figure 4.25(*b*) shows another construction of a square, with the length of one of the sides given as *AB*. The steps are as follows:

a. Bisect line *AB* to determine the midpoint of the line at *x*.
b. With *x* as the center and *Ax* as a radius, draw a circle with *AB* as diameter.
c. Draw the four sides of the square by drawing a line tangent to the circle at points *A*, *B*, and the two

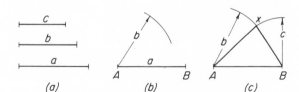

(a)   (b)   (c)

Fig. 4.22   To construct a triangle. Three sides given.

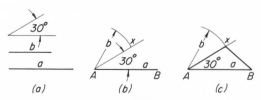

(a)   (b)   (c)

Fig. 4.23   To construct a triangle. Two sides and included angle given.

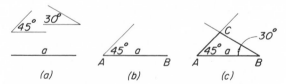

(a)   (b)   (c)

Fig. 4.24   To construct a triangle. Two angles and side between given.

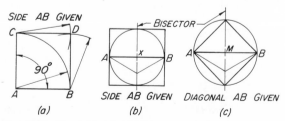

(a)   (b)   (c)

Fig. 4.25   To construct a square.

points at which the bisector intersects the circle.

4.7.3   Square with length of diagonal given. Figure 4.25(*c*) shows the construction of a square with the diagonal *AB* given. The steps are as follows:

a. Bisect the diagonal *AB* as shown in Fig. 4.25(*c*).
b. At the center *M* draw a circle with *AB* as a diameter.
c. With *AB* as one diagonal and the bisector as the other, draw the inscribed square using a T-square and 45° triangle.

4.8   CONSTRUCT A PENTAGON INSCRIBED IN A GIVEN CIRCLE. The construction of a pentagon in a given circle with *AB* as the diameter is shown in Fig. 4.26. The steps are as follows:

a. Bisect the radius *CB* and locate point *D*.
b. Locate point *E* on the circle directly above point *C* as in Fig. 4.26(*b*).
c. Strike an arc with *D* as the center and *DE* as the radius. The intersection where the arc strikes the diameter *AB* locates point *F*.

d. With *E* as a center and a radius *EF*, swing an arc intersecting the circle at *G*.
e. *EG* is one side of the pentagon.
f. Step this side off five times around the circle. Figure 4.26(*c*).

For other methods of construction see Arts. 4.10.1 and 4.10.2.

4.9   CONSTRUCT A HEXAGON. A hexagon may be specified and constructed in three different ways, as shown in Fig. 4.27.

4.9.1   Hexagon with length of side *AB* given. The steps in constructing a hexagon with one side given are as follows:

a. Draw a circle with the length of a side as a radius, as in Fig. 4.27(*a*).
b. Step off the radius six times around the circle.
c. Connect the six points to form the hexagon.

4.9.2   Hexagon with distance across corners given. To draw a hexagon with the distance across corners given, the following steps are used:

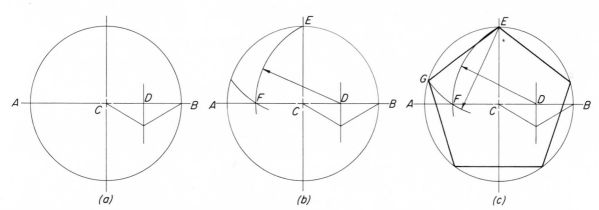

Fig. 4.26   To construct a pentagon within a given circle.

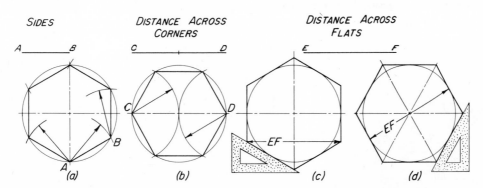

Fig. 4.27   Constructing a hexagon.

a. Draw a circle with the distance across corners as a diameter.

b. With the ends of the diameter as centers, draw two arcs as shown in Fig. 4.27(*b*), thus locating six points including the ends of the diameter.

c. Connect the six points to form the hexagon.

4.9.3   Hexagon with distance across flats given. Figures 4.27(*c*) and (*d*) illustrate two ways of drawing a hexagon when the distance across flats is given.

a. Draw a circle with the distance across flats, *EF*, as a diameter.

b. Circumscribe a hexagon tangent to the circle in either the position of Fig. 4.27(*c*) or (*d*) using a T-square and 30–60° triangles as shown.

4.10   CONSTRUCT A REGULAR POLYGON HAVING ANY GIVEN NUMBER OF SIDES. Regular polygons having any specified number of equal sides may be specified and constructed in several ways, as

illustrated in Figs. 4.28 and 4.29.

4.10.1   Inscribe a polygon within a given circle. The steps in constructing a polygon within a given circle are as follows:

a. Draw the circle and divide its diameter into the specified number of equal parts; five parts in the illustration in Fig. 4.28(*a*).

b. With ends of the diameter *A* and *B* as centers and a radius equal to the diameter, draw two arcs intersecting at *C*, as shown in Fig. 4.28(*b*).

c. From point *C* draw a line through the second division point of the diameter until it crosses the circle at *D*, as in Fig. 4.28(*c*).

d. The chord *AD* is one side of the polygon.

e. Step off the distance *AD* the proper number of times around the circle to complete the polygon.

This method is empirical. It gives exact results for the square and hexagon and is only very slightly in error for other polygons.

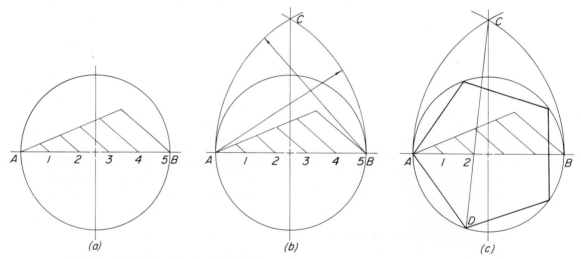

Fig. 4.28   To construct any regular polygon within a circle.

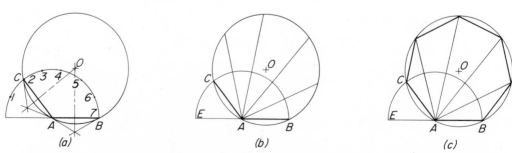

Fig. 4.29   To construct any regular polygon with length of side given.

4.10.2 Polygon with length of side given. In Fig. 4.29 a second method of constructing regular polygons is shown.

a. Lay out AB equal to the given side.

b. With A as a center, draw a semicircle with AB as a radius.

c. Divide the semicircle into the required number of equal parts by trial.

d. Through point A and the second division point C draw a line AC forming the second side of the polygon.

e. Bisect AB and AC and find the intersection O of these bisectors.

f. With O as a center, draw a circle through A, B, and C. This circle contains all the corners of the polygon.

g. From A draw lines through the other division points of the semicircle until they intersect the larger circle, as shown in Fig. 4.29(b).

h. These points are corners of the polygon. See Fig. 4.29(c).

4.11 CONSTRUCT A REGULAR OCTAGON. A regular octagon may be specified in two ways, as shown in Fig. 4.30. Either the distance across flats or the distance across corners may be given.

4.11.1 Octagon with distance across flats given. To construct an octagon with the distance across flats given, see Fig. 4.30.

a. Draw a circle having the distance across flats as a diameter, as shown in Fig. 4.30(a).

b. With a T-square and 45° triangle, draw lines tangent to the circle, first horizontally, then vertically,

and finally at 45° in each direction, as shown in Fig. 4.30(a) and (b).

4.11.2 Octagon with distance across corners given. To construct an octagon with the distance across corners given, as shown in Fig. 4.30, by being inscribed in a circle, take the following steps:

a. Draw a circle having a diameter equal to the distance across corners.

b. Draw the horizontal and vertical center lines as in Fig. 4.30(c).

c. Draw 45° center lines in each direction.

d. Connect all points where the center lines cross the circle as in Fig. 4.30(d).

4.12 REPRODUCE A GIVEN PLANE FIGURE. Plane figures may be composed of either straight lines, curved lines, or combinations thereof, as shown in Figs. 4.31 and 4.32.

4.12.1 Plane figure with straight sides only. The construction for duplicating a plane figure with straight sides is shown in Fig. 4.31.

a. Select one corner, for example A in Fig. 4.31(a), and draw straight lines from A through all other corners.

b. With A as a center, draw an arc across the lines radiating from A and have the arc completely outside the figure, as shown in Fig. 4.31(b).

c. Draw a line $A'B'$ for the new figure in the position desired.

d. Draw a new arc with radius R' equal to R.

e. Draw new arcs $2'$, $3'$, and $4'$ to locate radial lines.

f. With A as a center and arcs successively equal to AC, AD, and AE, reconstruct the plane figure as shown in Fig. 4.31(c).

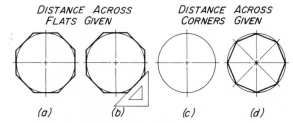

DISTANCE ACROSS FLATS GIVEN   DISTANCE ACROSS CORNERS GIVEN

(a)   (b)   (c)   (d)

Fig. 4.30 Constructing an octagon.

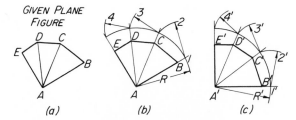

GIVEN PLANE FIGURE

(a)   (b)   (c)

Fig. 4.31 Reproducing a given plane figure.

4.12.2 Plane figure with straight lines and irregular curves. The construction for making figures with straight lines and irregular curves is as follows:

a. With the longest straight side AB as a base, draw a rectangle $ABCD$ just enclosing the figure, as in Fig. 4.32(a).
b. Carefully select points on the contour of the figure and draw coordinates through them as shown in Fig. 4.32(b).
c. Reproduce the entire set of coordinates in the required new position and draw the figure through the relocated points as in Fig. 4.32(c).

4.13 CIRCLES AND LINES TANGENT TO THEM. In order to think correctly about circles and lines tangent to them, one must remember the definition of a circle. It is the locus of points, lying in a plane, at a given distance from a point.

4.13.1 Construct a circle through three points. To construct a circle through three points, the following steps are used:

a. Connect points A, B, and C with two intersecting lines as in Fig. 4.33(a).
b. Find the perpendicular bisector of each line.
c. The intersection of the bisectors is the center of the circle.

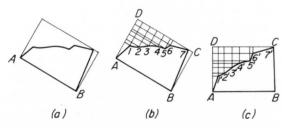

Fig. 4.32 Reproducing a given plane figure having irregular curves

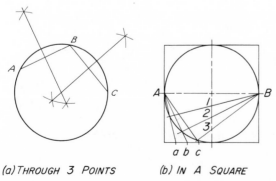

(a) THROUGH 3 POINTS   (b) IN A SQUARE

Fig. 4.33 To draw a circle. (a) Through three points; (b) in a square.

4.13.2 Construct a circle within a square. A circle may be constructed within a square by the following steps, as shown in Fig. 4.33(b):

a. Divide either center line of the square (in this case the vertical one) into any number of equal parts.
b. Divide the side that is perpendicular to the center line used in step one into the same number of equal parts.
c. Draw line $B1$ to intersect line Aa, line $B2$ to intersect Ab, and so on.
d. These intersections are points on the circle. Draw a smooth curve through them.

4.13.3 Draw a circle of radius r through a point and tangent to a straight line. To draw a circle through a point and tangent to a straight line, the following steps are used:

a. Draw an arc 1 with radius r with point A as the center, as in Fig. 4.34(a).
b. Draw a line 2 parallel to the given line BC at a distance r from it.
c. The intersection of arc 1 and line 2 is the center of the tangent arc. The center of the arc is on a perpendicular to the line at the point of tangency.

An application to a drawing problem is shown in Fig. 4.34(b).

4.13.4 Draw a circle with a given radius r through a point and tangent to a circle. The steps in drawing a circle through a given point and tangent to a given circle as shown in Fig. 4.35(a) are as follows:

a. Draw an arc 1 with radius r and the center at A.
b. Draw a second arc 2 with the center of the circle C as a center and a radius $R + r$.
c. The intersection of these arcs is the center of the tangent circle or arc.

A practical application is shown in Fig. 4.35(b).

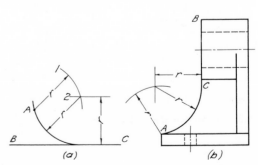

(a)   (b)

Fig. 4.34 Constructing a circle through a point and tangent to a line.

4.13.5   Draw a circle of radius _r_ tangent to two straight lines. The construction for drawing a circle tangent to two intersecting straight lines is shown in Fig. 4.36.

_a._ Draw two lines parallel to the given lines at the distance _r_ as in Figs. 4.36(_a_) and (_b_). The intersec-

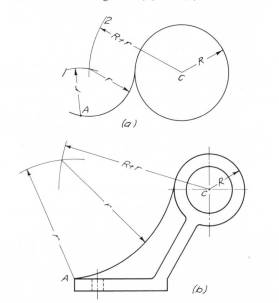

Fig. 4.35   Constructing a circle through a point and tangent to a circle.

tion of these construction lines determine the center of the arc at _O_.

_b._ Determine the tangent points of the arc by constructing perpendicular lines through point _O_ to the given lines as in Figs. 4.36(_a_), (_b_), and (_c_).

_c._ Set the compass with the radius _r_ and _O_ as the center and draw the arc, being careful to stop the arc at the predetermined tangent points.

4.13.6   Draw a circle of radius _r_ tangent to a straight line and another circle. To draw a circle tangent to a line and a circle, the following steps are used:

_a._ Draw a line parallel to the given line a distance _r_ from it as shown in Fig. 4.37(_a_).

_b._ Draw an arc of radius _R + r_ concentric with the given circle.

_c._ The intersection of the line and arc is the required center. A practical application is shown in Fig. 4.37(_b_).

4.13.7   Circle tangent to two other circles—external tangent _r_ radius. To draw a circle tangent externally to two other circles, perform the following steps:

_a._ Using the center of the small circle and the radius _R + r_, draw arc _1_ as in Fig. 4.38.

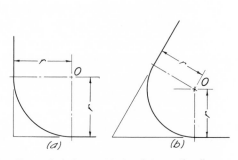

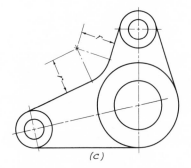

Fig. 4.36   Constructing a circle tangent to two intersecting lines.

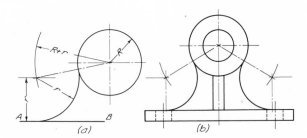

Fig. 4.37   Constructing a circle tangent to a straight line and a circle.

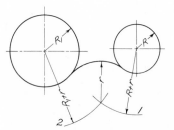

Fig. 4.38   Constructing a circle tangent to two circles.

b. Using the center of the large circle and the radius $R_1 + r$, draw arc *2* as in Fig. 4.38. The intersection of arc *1* and arc *2* determines the center of the tangent circle to be drawn.

c. Set the compass at the radius r and, using the center determined in (*b*) above, draw the required circle. The tangent points are on a line joining the center of the arc with the center of each circle.

4.13.8   Circle tangent to two other circles—internal tangent and radius r. In drawing a circle tangent to two other circles, both given circles will be inside of the tangent arc or circle. See Fig. 4.39. The radius of the tangent circle must be greater than that of either of the given circles.

a. Draw arc *1* with the radius $r - R$, using the center of the circle with radius R as in Fig. 4.39(*a*).

b. Draw arc *2* with the radius $r - R_1$, using the center of the circle with radius R_1 as in Fig. 4.39(*a*). The intersection of arc *1* and arc *2* determines the center of the tangency circle.

c. Through the point of the intersection of arcs *1* and *2*, draw the tangent circle with radius r.

d. The tangent points are on the line joining the centers of the circle and arc.

A practical application of this construction is shown in Fig. 4.39(*b*).

4.13.9   Circle tangent internally to one given circle and tangent externally to another given circle. To draw an arc or circle tangent internally to one circle and tangent externally to another, the construction shown in Fig. 4.40 is used. The tangent circle has a radius of r, is tangent externally to the circle with radius R_1, and tangent internally to the circle with radius R.

a. Draw arc *1* with the radius $r - R$, using the center of the circle with radius R.

b. Draw arc *2* with the radius $r + R_1$, using the center of the circle with radius R_1. The intersection of arc *1* and arc *2* determines the center of the tangent circle.

c. Through the point of intersection of arcs *1* and *2* draw the tangent circle using the radius r.

4.13.10   Connecting parallel lines with reverse curves using equal arcs. The problems in this paragraph and in the two that follow arise in the location of highways and railroads. In Fig. 4.41 lines AF and BE are to be connected at A and B with reverse curves.

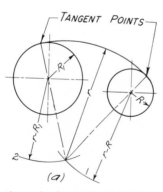
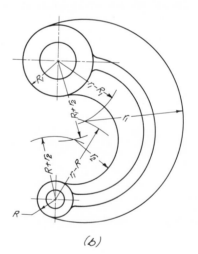

Fig. 4.39   Constructing a circular arc tangent to two other circles.

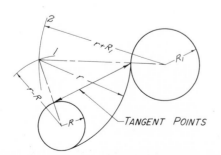

Fig. 4.40   Constructing a circular arc tangent to two circles.

a. Draw a straight line between *A* and *B*.

b. Draw perpendicular lines to the given lines at *A* and *B* as shown Fig. 4.41.

c. Divide line *AB* into two equal parts at *G*.

d. Bisect *AG* and *GB*.

e. The intersection of the bisectors with the perpendiculars from *A* and *B* locates the required centers at *C* and *D*. Draw the arcs with radii *CA* and *BD*. These arcs are tangent to each other at *G*.

4.13.11   Connecting parallel lines with reverse curves by unequal arcs. In Fig. 4.42 lines *AF* and *BG* are to be connected at *A* and *B* by a reverse curve made up of unequal arcs.

a. Draw a straight line between *A* and *B*.

b. Construct a perpendicular to *AF* at *A* and another to *BG* at *B*.

c. Locate point *D* on the perpendicular to *AF* so that *AD* is equal to the given radius *r* of one of the arcs.

d. Using the center *D* and the radius *r*, draw the arc from *A* till it intersects line *AB* at point *C*.

e. Extend line *DC* until it intersects the perpendicular to *BG* from *B* to locate point *E*. Point *E* is the center for the second arc.

f. Draw the second arc using *E* as the center and *EB* as the radius from point *B* to *C*.

4.13.12   Connecting two nonparallel lines by a reverse curve. In Fig. 4.43 lines *AL* and *BM* are to be connected by a reverse curve.

a. On a perpendicular to *BM* at *B* step off the chosen radius *BC*.

b. With *C* as a center, draw an arc tangent to the line at *B* as shown in Fig. 4.43.

c. On a perpendicular from *A* draw *AD* equal to *BC* and on the same side of the two lines as *BC*.

d. Join *D* and *C* with a straight line.

e. Bisect line *CD*.

f. Extend the bisector until it intersects the perpendicular from *A* at *F*. This is the center of an arc that is tangent to the line at *A* and to the other arc. Note that in all cases the tangent points are on the line joining the centers.

4.13.13   Rectifying an arc. To obtain the length of an arc of a circle, two common geometrical construction procedures can be used. The first method, shown in Fig. 4.44, uses the following steps:

a. Draw a line *BD* tangent to arc *BC* at *B* as in Fig. 4.44.

b. Divide arc *BC* into an equal number of chord lengths with a set of dividers.

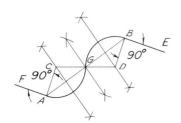

Fig. 4.41   Connecting parallel lines by equal arcs.

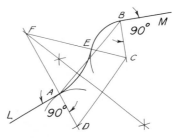

Fig. 4.43   Connecting nonparallel lines by a reverse curve.

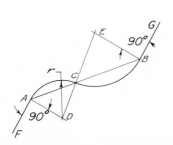

Fig. 4.42   Connecting parallel lines by unequal arcs.

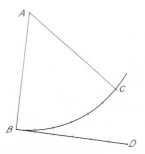

Fig. 4.44   Rectifying an arc.

c. Lay the same number of chord lengths along line *BD*. The greater the number of chords used, the greater will be the accuracy.

An alternate method to rectify arc *AB* is illustrated in Fig. 4.45.

a₁. Draw the chord *AB* and extend it beyond *A* to point *E* so that *AE* equals ½*AB* as shown in Fig. 4.45.

b₁. Draw a tangent line to the arc *AB* at *A* by making line *AD* perpendicular to *AC*.

c₁. Draw an arc with *E* as the center and *EB* as the radius until it intersects the tangent line to determine point *D*. *AD* is approximately equal in length to arc *AB*. For angles up to 60° the error is less than 1 in 1000.

This method of rectifying an arc is used to show the path of travel of the end of a spring for clearances. See Fig. 4.46.

4.13.14   To make a circular arc equal in length to a given straight line. In Fig. 4.47 it is required to lay off the length of line *AB* along the given arc. One method is to take the dividers to divide the line seg-

ment *AB* into a number of equal parts and then lay the same number of equal lengths along the arc as chord lengths.

Another method is illustrated in Fig. 4.47 and consists of the following steps:

a. Lay off the given length of line *AB* on a line tangent to the arc.

b. Divide this length into four equal parts.

c. With the first point *D* adjacent to the tangent point as a center draw an arc *DB* cutting the circle at *C*.

d. Arc *AC* is equal in length to line *AB* with an error of less than 6 parts in 1000 for angles less than 90°. This principle is used to determine the rebound limits of a spring as shown in Fig. 4.48.

4.14   CONIC SECTIONS. The ellipse, parabola, and hyperbola are curves that may be cut from a right circular cone by a plane. Since they are cut from a cone, they are called conic sections. See Figs. 4.49(*c*), (*d*), and (*e*). Straight lines and circles may also be cut from a cone. See Figs. 4.49(*a*) and (*b*). They are not commonly referred to as conic sections.

a. The ellipse. The ellipse may be defined as a section

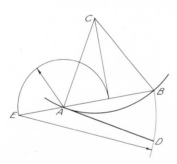

Fig. 4.45   Alternate method of rectifying an arc.

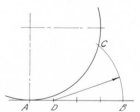

Fig. 4.47   Constructing an arc equal to a straight line.

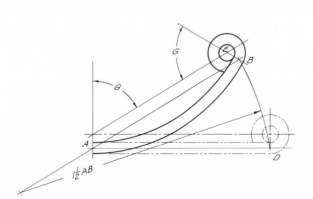

Fig. 4.46   Application of rectifying an arc. (Courtesy C. S. Mobley, Automotive Industries.)

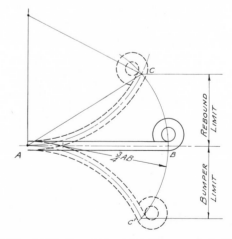

Fig. 4.48   Application of Fig. 4.47. (Courtesy C. S. Mobley, Automotive Industries.)

cut from a right circular cone by a plane making an angle with the axis greater than that made by the elements of the cone. See Fig. 4.49(c). The angle must be less than a right angle.

The ellipse may also be defined in mathematical form by the equation

$$\frac{x^2}{a^2} + \frac{y^2}{b^2} = 1.$$

This standard form of the equation places the major axis of the ellipse on the x-axis and the center of the ellipse at the origin of the coordinates. In the above equation the sum of the distances from the foci to any point P on the curve is $2a$.

b. *Parabola.* The parabola may be defined as a section cut from a cone by a plane making an angle with the axis, equal to the angle made by the elements with the axis. The cutting plane is therefore parallel to one of the elements. The parabola may be defined mathematically by the equation $y^2 = 2px$, where the x-axis is also the axis of the curve

and the vertex of the curve is on the y-axis and $p/2$ is the distance from the vertex to the focus and also to the directrix.

c. *Hyperbola.* The hyperbola may be defined as a section cut from a cone by a plane inclined to the axis at an angle less than the angle made by the elements. See Fig. 4.49(e). The section is usually taken parallel to the axis. This produces an hyperbola with two symmetric branches.

The standard form of the equation for the hyperbola is

$$\frac{x^2}{a^2} - \frac{y^2}{b^2} = 1.$$

The axis of this hyperbola is on the x-axis and it is symmetrical about the y-axis.

4.14.1 Ellipse as a section of a cone. The construction of an ellipse as a section of a cone is shown in Fig. 4.50. The steps are as follows:

Fig. 4.49 The conic sections.

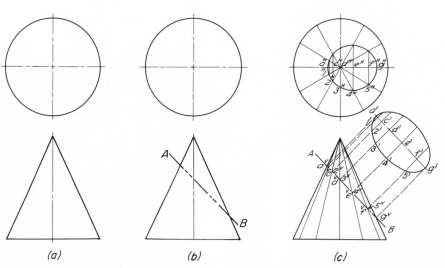

Fig. 4.50 The ellipse as a section of a cone.

a. Pass a cutting plane *AB* showing as an edge view in the front view as shown in Fig. 4.50(*b*).

b. Draw 12 equally spaced elements of the cone as shown in Fig. 4.50(*c*). Space them equally in the top view and then project them to the front view.

c. The points at which the respective elements pierce the plane can be seen by inspection at 1^V, 2^V, 3^V, etc.

d. Project these to the top view and draw the curve. This is an ellipse, but it is not the true shape of the one cut by plane *AB*.

e. To obtain the true shape of this ellipse, draw a center line $a^1 g^1$ parallel to *AB* at a convenient place. See Fig. 4.50(*c*).

f. Draw lines from 1^V, 2^V, 3^V, etc., in the front view, perpendicular to this center line.

g. Set off on these lines the distances f^H5^H, e^H4^H, etc., in the top view as f^15^1, e^14^1, etc., in the auxiliary view. Draw a smooth curve through these points to obtain the true shape of the curve.

4.14.2 Draw an ellipse by using the foci. Assume that the major and minor axes of an ellipse are given as in Fig. 4.51(*a*).

a. To locate the foci, set the compass to a length *AC*, equal to one-half the major axis.

b. With point *D*, one end of the minor axis, as a center draw an arc cutting the major axis *AB* at *F* and F_1, thus locating the foci.

c. Divide the space from *F* to the center into any convenient number of parts.

d. As an example, set the compass to the distance *A-4* and, with *F* and F_1 as centers, describe four arcs as in Fig. 4.51(*c*).

e. Then set the compass to the distance *B-4* and with the same centers describe four arcs intersecting the first four. These intersections are points on the ellipse.

f. Repeat the process, using the other points on the axis giving distances *A-1*, *B-1*, *A-2*, *B-2*, and so on. Draw a smooth curve through the points.

4.14.3 Draw an ellipse by the two-circle method. Assume the major and minor axes given as in Fig. 4.52(*a*).

a. Draw two concentric circles, one with the major axis as a diameter and the other with the minor

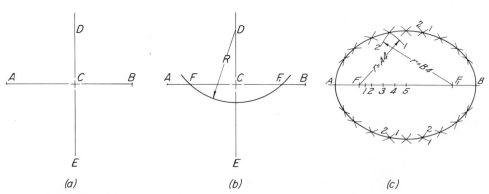

Fig. 4.51 The ellipse constructed from foci.

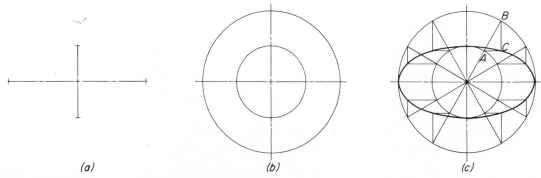

Fig. 4.52 Two-circle method for constructing an ellipse.

axis as a diameter, as shown in Fig. 4.52(*b*).

b. Draw radial lines through the center intersecting both circles as in Fig. 4.52(*c*).

c. From the points on the inner circle draw horizontal lines like *AC*.

d. From the points on the outer circle draw vertical lines like *BC*. *C* is a point on the ellipse.

e. Repeat the process for all points on the two circles and then draw the curve.

4.14.4 Construct an ellipse by the intersection method, having the major and minor axes given. This construction depends on the construction of a circle as shown in Fig. 4.33(*b*). This construction is geometrically correct.

a. Draw the rectangle that will enclose the ellipse, using the major and minor axes as center lines.

b. Divide the short center line into any number of equal parts as shown in Fig. 4.53.

c. Divide the long side of the rectangle into the same number of equal parts.

d. Draw *B-1* to intersect *A-a*, *B-2* to intersect *A-b*, and so on. These intersections are points on the ellipse.

e. The other half of the ellipse may be done in the same manner.

4.14.5 Draw an ellipse having the conjugate axes given. One of the simplest methods of making this construction is shown in Fig. 4.54. This is the same method as explained in Art. 4.14.4.

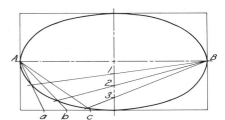

Fig. 4.53   Ellipse by intersection of lines.

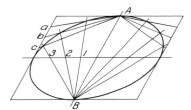

Fig. 4.54   Ellipse constructed on conjugate axes.

4.14.6 Ellipse by the four-center approximate method with major and minor axes given. To construct an ellipse by this method, follow the steps given below and shown in Fig. 4.55.

a. Draw a rectangle on the major and minor axes and construct arc AE with the radius equal to the semi-major axis, as shown in Fig. 4.55(a).

b. Draw the diagonal BC and swing the arc with radius CE, thus locating point F in Fig. 4.55(b).

c. Bisect line FB in the usual manner and extend the bisector to cross both axes at M and N as in Fig. 4.55(c).

d. Locate P and S with a compass on the basis of symmetry with M and N.

e. Draw arcs with the four centers at M, N, P, and S tangent to side of rectangle and to each other. These arcs will be tangent to each other at r, t, u, and v, as in Fig. 4.55(d).

4.14.7 Ellipse by the trammel method. The trammel method is a very convenient method for plotting any number of points on an ellipse, since it leaves the drawing free of all construction lines.

a. *First method.* On the edge of a strip of paper, lay off the distance cd equal to the semiminor axis of the ellipse as shown in Fig. 4.56(a). Also lay off ca on the same side of c as the point d, equal to the semimajor axis. By moving the strip of paper so that

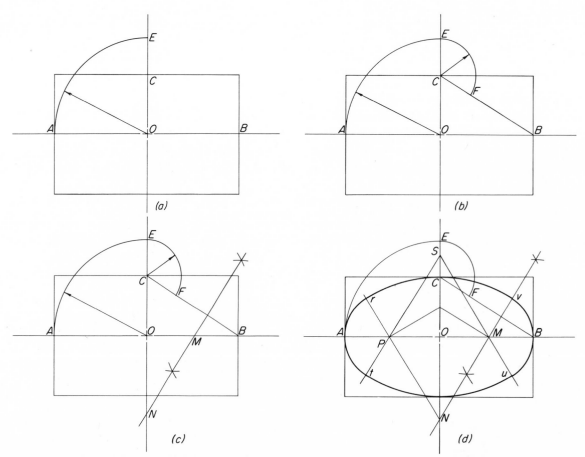

Fig. 4.55   Four-center approximate ellipse.

d is on the major axis and *a* on the minor axis, *c* will always be on the ellipse. Any number of positions for *c* may be located, and a smooth curve through them will give the ellipse.

b. Second method. This is similar to the preceding method except that *a* and *d* are laid off on opposite sides of *c*, as shown in Fig. 4.56(*b*). In all other respects the procedure is the same. This scheme is a little more accurate when the difference between the major and minor axes is small.

4.14.8   Ellipse by the diagonal method. An ellipse based on the oblique or perspective view of a circle can be drawn in a variety of positions by the diagonal method. See Fig. 4.57.

a. Ellipse in a rectangle. An ellipse can be constructed in a rectangle by the following steps:

1. On one side of the rectangle draw a semicircle and divide it into six equal parts with a 30–60° triangle as shown in Fig. 4.57(*a*).

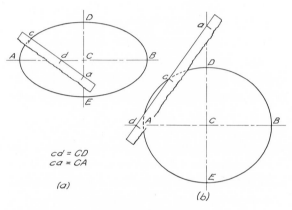

cd = *CD*
ca = *CA*

(*a*)

(*b*)

Fig. 4.56   Ellipse by the trammel method.

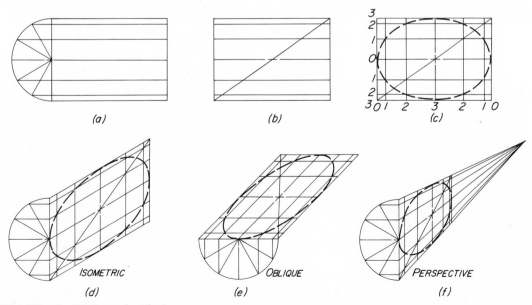

(*a*)   (*b*)   (*c*)

ISOMETRIC   *OBLIQUE*   *PERSPECTIVE*

(*d*)   (*e*)   (*f*)

Fig. 4.57   Ellipse by the diagonal method.

2. Draw horizontal lines across the rectangle at the division points.

3. Draw a diagonal across the rectangle as shown in Fig. 4.57(*b*).

4. Number the horizontal lines from the center outward in both directions as shown in Fig. 4.57(*c*).

5. Number the vertical lines inward from both ends.

6. Make a dot where lines having the same number cross. These are points in the ellipse.

7. Draw a smooth curve through the points.

b. Ellipse in isometric. This is the same problem as drawing an ellipse with the conjugate axes given. See Fig. 4.57(*d*). This ellipse can be constructed with the same steps as in (*a*) above.

c. Ellipse in oblique. For the oblique parallelogram the same principle using the diagonal can again be applied as in (*a*). See Fig. 4.57(*e*).

d. Ellipse in perspective. Having the perspective rectangle (actually a trapezoid) laid out, proceed in the same manner as in (*a*). See Fig. 4.57(*f*).

4.14.9   **Four-center approximate ellipse in a rhombus.** When a circle is tangent to two intersecting straight lines as AB and AC in Fig. 4.58(*a*), the distance Ae must be equal to Ad. Therefore, in the case of the rhombus the arcs must be tangent at the midpoint of the sides. Hence the center of each arc must lie on a perpendicular to the side at its midpoint.

a. In both Figs. 4.58(*b*) and (*c*), erect perpendiculars to the midpoints of the sides and extend these perpendiculars until they intersect.

b. With these intersection points as centers, draw four arcs tangent to the sides of the rhombus and, of course, to each other.

These ellipses are not quite accurate, but they are satisfactory and very useful in pictorial drawing.

4.14.10   **The parabola.** The parabola is one of the most useful curves not only in engineering computations but also in actual construction. Reflectors for light and sound are made in parabolic form, as are vertical curves on highways and railroads, just to mention two common applications.

4.14.11   **Draw a parabola as a section of a cone.** To draw a parabola as a section of a cone, the following steps are necessary, as shown in Fig. 4.59.

a. Draw the cutting plane A-A parallel to the outside element a^Vb^V in the front view. The cutting plane appears edgewise. See Fig. 4.59(*a*).

b. Draw a convenient number of equally spaced elements in the top view of the cone and project through to the front view as in Fig. 4.59(*b*)

c. The piercing points of these elements with plane A-A can be seen by inspection in the front view at 1^V, 2^V, 3^V, etc.

d. Project these points to the top view to obtain a view of the parabola. This does not show the true shape.

e. To obtain the true shape, draw a center line parallel to plane A-A at any convenient place.

f. Project the points 1^V, 2^V, etc., to it as in Fig. 4.59(*b*).

g. Measure from this center line the corresponding distances in the top view as indicated for distances a and b. A smooth curve through these points will show the true shape of the parabola.

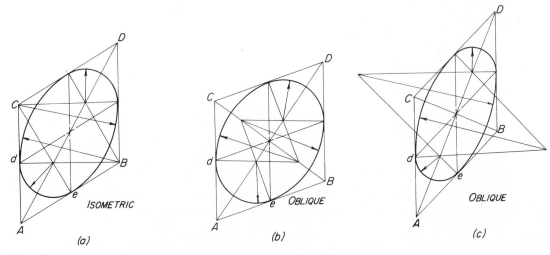

Fig. 4.58   **Four-center approximate ellipse in a rhombus.**

4.14.12 Draw a parabola with the focus and directrix given. The parabola may be described as the locus of a point, the distance of which from the focus is always equal to the perpendicular distance from the directrix. With AB the directrix and F the focus given as in Fig. 4.60, a series of points may be located by fulfilling the condition specified above. Thus, for any given distance r, draw an arc with center at F and radius r. Likewise draw a line parallel to AB at r distance from it. The intersections of the arc and line locate two points on the curve. Locate a sufficient number of points to determine accurately the curve.

4.14.13 Draw a parabola with one point A at the vertex, and two symmetrically placed points B and C given. The construction is as follows:

a. Divide BC in Fig. 4.61 into any even number of parts and the sides perpendicular to it into half as many parts.

b. Through the points on BC, draw lines parallel to the axis.

c. From A the vertex, draw lines to the points on the sides.

d. The intersections of the lines in pairs locate points on the parabola.

4.14.14 Draw a parabola as an element of a hyperbolic paraboloid. The hyperbolic paraboloid is a warped surface composed of straight line elements as shown in the top, front, and side views of Fig. 4.62.

The curve tangent to the elements in the front view

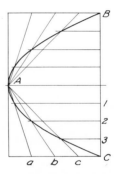

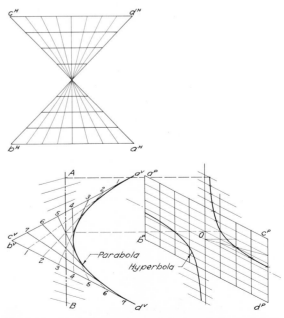

Fig. 4.61 Parabola by intersection method.

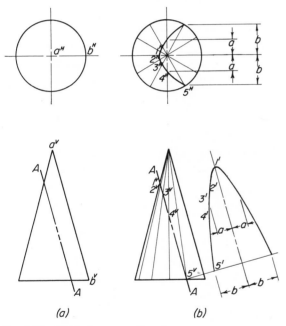

Fig. 4.59 Parabola as a section of a cone.

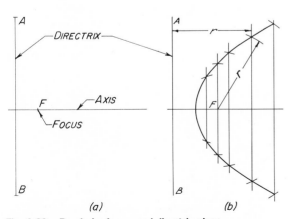

Fig. 4.60 Parabola, focus, and directrix given.

Fig. 4.62 Parabola as an element of a hyperbolic paraboloid.

is a parabola. A section cut perpendicular to the axis, like plane *A-B*, gives a hyperbola as shown in the side view.

4.14.15   Draw a parabola by offsets from a line. In Fig. 4.63 the construction of a parabola with its vertex at *B* and passing through *C* and *D* is shown. The steps are as follows:

a. Divide *BE* and *BF* each into a number of equal spaces. In this case five, as shown in Fig. 4.63. Erect perpendicular lines to *EF* at each point.

b. The offset from a straight line tangent to a parabolic curve is proportional to the square of the distance above the line from the tangent point. Therefore, divide the distance *AB* into 25 equal parts—proportional to the square of numbers from *1* to *5*.

c. Mark the points *1, 4, 9, 16,* and *25* on *AB* and draw horizontal lines through them.

d. The proper intersection of horizontal and vertical lines as shown in Fig. 4.63 locates points on the parabola.

4.14.16   Draw a parabola by offsets from two intersecting lines. This is the situation as it occurs in highway and railroad construction. See Fig. 4.64.

The two intersecting lines *EB* and *BD* in Fig. 4.64 may represent the grade lines on a highway. Each line

makes the same angle with the horizontal. Assume that the curve is to be tangent to the grade line 250 feet from *B* on each line at *E* and *D*. This is the usual practice in engineering. To draw the curve proceed as follows:

a. Connect *E* and *D* and draw a line perpendicular to it from *B*. This line bisects *DE* at *A*.

b. Find the midpoint of *AB* at *C*. Point *C* is the vertex of the parabola.

c. Divide the tangent *BE* and *BD* into five equal parts as shown in Fig. 4.64.

d. Divide *BC* into 25 equal parts.

e. From points *1, 4, 9,* and *16* on this scale, draw lines parallel to the tangents until they intersect lines drawn through the one-fifth division points parallel to the axis *BA*.

These points lie on the parabola.

4.14.17   The hyperbola. The hyperbola can be plotted by a number of methods. Three of the more useful methods are discussed in the following paragraphs.

4.14.18   Draw a hyperbola as a section of a cone. In Fig. 4.65 the construction of a hyperbola as a section of a cone is shown. Proceed as follows:

a. Draw three views of a right circular cone as shown in Fig. 4.65.

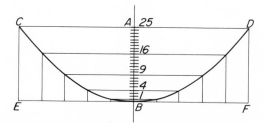

Fig. 4.63   Parabola by offsets from a tangent line.

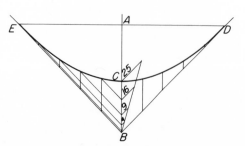

Fig. 4.64   Parabola tangent to two intersecting lines by offsets.

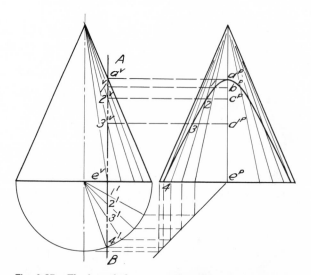

Fig. 4.65   The hyperbola on a section of a cone.

b. Draw a cutting plane *A-B* parallel to the axis of the cone so that it shows edgewise in the front view.

c. Draw twelve or more elements of the cone and find their piercing points with the plane *A-B* by inspection at a^V, 1^V, 2^V, 3^V, etc.

d. Project these points to the corresponding elements of the cone in the side view.

e. Draw a smooth curve through the points.

4.14.19 Draw a hyperbola with the foci and vertices given. With the axis and the foci F and F_1 given, locate the vertices a and b as in Fig. 4.66. The construction is as follows:

a. Mark off a series of points *1, 2, 3, 4,* etc., to the right of F_1.

b. With F and F_1 as centers and a radius *a-3*, draw four arcs. Only one is shown in the figure.

c. With F and F_1 again as centers and a radius *b-3*, draw four more arcs intersecting the first four.

d. The intersections are points on the curve.

e. Repeat the process with the other points *1, 2, 4,* etc., as far as needed.

f. Draw a smooth curve through the points.

Note that the constant difference between the radii is the distance *ab*. The asymptotes of the curve can be located by drawing a circle having FF_1 the distance between foci as its diameter. Lines drawn through the vertices *a* and *b* perpendicular to the axis intersect the circle at points on the asymptotes.

4.14.20 Draw a hyperbola with the asymptotes and one point on the curve given. The construction that can be made with the following steps is illustrated in Fig. 4.67.

a. Through the given point P draw two lines PM and PN respectively parallel to the asymptotes.

b. From the origin O draw a series of radial lines intersecting PN in points *1, 2, 3,* etc., and PM in the corresponding points *1', 2', 3',* etc.

c. The radial lines should be distributed on both sides of point P.

d. Draw line through *1* and 1^1 parallel to the corresponding asymptotes. The intersections of these lines are points on the hyperbola.

When the asymptotes are at right angles to each other, the hyperbola is called a rectangular or equilateral hyperbola. This curve occurs in thermodynamics in the study of the expansion of gases.

4.14.21 Draw a conic through five given points. The solution of this problem, which occurs in joining surfaces as in aircraft work, is an application of Pascal's theorem which states, "Opposite pairs of sides of a hexagonal figure inscribed in a conic intersect

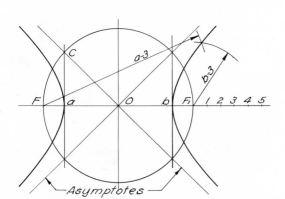

Fig. 4.66   To draw a hyperbola with the foci given.

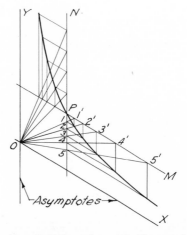

Fig. 4.67   Hyperbola through a point with asymptotes given.

in three points which lie in a straight line." Thus in Fig. 4.68 the sides *1-6* and *3-4* intersect at *A*, *1-2* and *4-5* intersect at *B*, and *2-3* and *5-6* intersect at *C*, and line *ABC* is referred to as Pascal's line.

If only points *1* to *5* are known, any sixth point *X* may be found on the conic as follows:

a. Extend the opposite sides *1-2* and *4-5* until they intersect at *B*. This point must be on every Pascal line of the conic.

b. Draw another Pascal line through *B*, intersecting the lines *2-3* and *3-4* as at *C'* and *A'*.

c. Draw the remaining sides of the hexagon from *1* to *A'* and from *5* to *C'*, thus locating point *X*, the sixth corner, at their intersection.

As many points as desired may be located on the conic by drawing successive Pascal lines through *B* and proceeding as outlined above.

4.15 TANGENT PROBLEMS. It is a common problem for a draftsman to locate a tangent to some geometric curve with considerable accuracy. The following situations are among those usually encountered.

4.15.1 Tangent to a circle through a point on the circle. This problem is usually solved in the drafting room by the method shown in Fig. 4.69.

a. Bring a triangle resting on another straight edge up to the figure so that one of the edges of the right angle of the triangle coincides with line *BC* joining the center and the point of tangency. See dotted line triangle.

b. Then slide the triangle along the straight edge until the other leg of the right angle passes through *B*. This edge is tangent to the circle at *B*.

Another way, using geometric methods, to construct such a tangent is shown in Fig. 4.70.

a_1. With *P* as a center, draw an arc through *C* until it cuts the circle at *A*. See Fig. 4.70(*a*).

b_1. With *A* as a center and radius *CA* draw a semi-

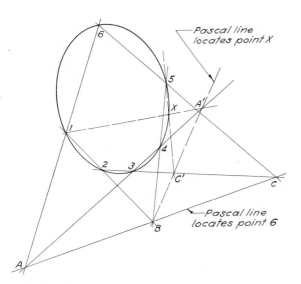

Fig. 4.68 Conic through five points.

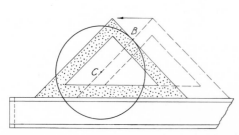

Fig. 4.69 Draftsman's method of drawing a tangent to a circle.

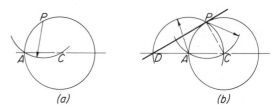

(a)   *(b)*

Fig. 4.70 Line tangent to a circle at a point on the circle.

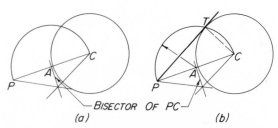

BISECTOR OF *PC*

(a)   *(b)*

Fig. 4.71 Line tangent to a circle through a point outside.

circle that will pass through P. See Fig. 4.70(b).

c_1. Extend line CA until it crosses the semicircle at D.

d_1. Line DP is the required tangent since it is perpendicular to the radius CP.

4.15.2   Draw a line tangent to a circle through a point outside. A tangent of this type may be constructed as shown in Fig. 4.71. The steps are as follows:

a. Draw a line from P to C, the center of the circle as in Fig. 4.71(a).

b. Bisect line PC at A.

c. With A as a center and radius AP, draw a semicircle cutting the original circle at T. See Fig. 4.71(b).

d. T is the tangent point. Draw PT.

4.15.3   Draw a line tangent to two circles on the same side. To draw a line tangent to two given circles with radii R and r as in Fig. 4.72, take the following steps:

a. At the center B of the larger circle, draw one concentric with it, having a radius R-r.

b. From the center A of the smaller circle, draw a tangent AC to the inner circle whose center is at B.

c. Draw the tangent to the original two circles PT parallel to AC.

4.15.4   Draw a line tangent to two circles crossing between them. The construction for a tangent in this position is shown in Fig. 4.73. The procedure is as follows:

a. With B the center of the larger circle, draw another circle concentric with it having a radius $R + r$ as in Fig. 4.73.

b. Draw a line AP from A, the center of the smaller circle tangent to the outer circle, whose center is at B.

c. The tangent, to both circles, MN is parallel to AP.

4.15.5   Draw a tangent to an ellipse from a point P on it. *Method A.* One method for making this construction is shown in Fig. 4.74. Proceed as follows:

a. From P draw lines to both foci F and F_1 as in Fig. 4.74. If the foci are not given, the construction for finding them is shown in Fig. 4.51.

b. Extend FP to any convenient point A.

c. Bisect the angle F_1PA. The bisector is tangent to the ellipse at P.

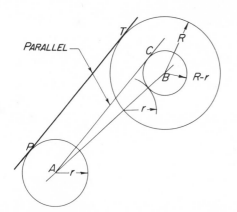

Fig. 4.72   Line tangent to two circles on same side.

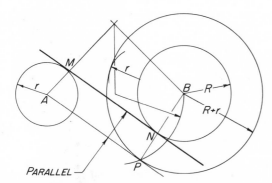

Fig. 4.73   Tangent to two circles on opposite sides.

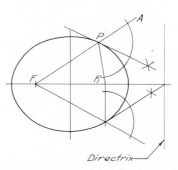

Fig. 4.74   Use of foci in drawing tangents to an ellipse.

Method B. Another method for drawing a tangent is based on the fact that an ellipse may be constructed as an oblique view of a circle, as shown in Fig. 4.75.

a_1. Having the ellipse given, describe a circle about it having the major axis as a diameter.

b_1. Project point A from the ellipse to the circle parallel to the minor axis.

c_1. Draw a tangent to the circle at A_1 and extend it until it cuts the major axis at X.

d_1. A line from X to point A on the ellipse is the required tangent.

4.15.6 Draw a line tangent to an ellipse from a point Y outside. The construction in Fig. 4.75 for drawing a line tangent to an ellipse from an external point is as follows:

a. Project Y to G on the revolved position of the circle.

b. Rotate G to G_1 on the edgewise view of the circle.

c. From G_1 project horizontally across to Y_1 directly under Y.

d. Draw the tangent to the circle from Y_1 at F_1.

e. From F_1 project perpendicular to the axis to F, which will be the tangent point on the ellipse.

f. Draw the tangent FY.

4.15.7 Find the axis of a parabolic curve. This axis may be found in the following manner, as shown in Fig. 4.76:

a. Draw any two parallel chords across the curve as in Fig. 4.76.

b. Bisect the chords at E and F. The line EF is parallel to the axis.

c. Draw a third chord GH perpendicular to EF.

d. Bisect this chord at M. A line through M parallel to EF is the axis of the parabola.

4.15.8 Draw a line tangent to a parabola from a point P on the curve with the axis given. Such a tangent may be found in the following manner, as shown in Fig. 4.77:

a. From P draw a perpendicular to the axis to locate

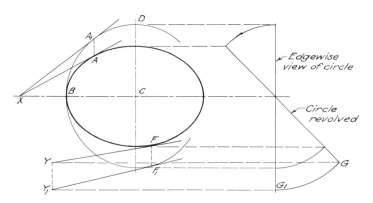

Fig. 4.75 Alternate method: line tangent to an ellipse.

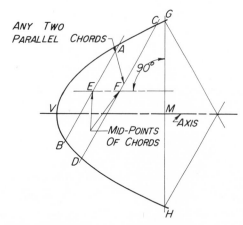

Fig. 4.76 Finding axis of given parabola.

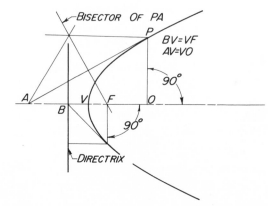

Fig. 4.77 Finding focus and directrix with parabola and axis given.

point *O* as in Fig. 4.77. With a divider step off *VA* equal to *VO*.

b. Line *AP* is the tangent.

4.15.9   Find the focus of a parabola having the axis given. The focus of a parabola may be found by the following steps, as shown in Fig. 4.77:

a. Find a tangent at some point on the curve as in Art. 4.15.8, Fig. 4.77.

b. Bisect the tangent.

c. Extend the bisector to cut the axis at *F* which is the focus.

4.15.10   Find the directrix of a parabola having the axis, focus and vertex given. With these given conditions, the directrix may be found as follows and as shown in Fig. 4.77:

a. Set the divider to the distance *FV*. See Fig. 4.77.

b. Step off the distance *VB* equal to *FV*. Point *B* is on the directrix.

c. Draw a line perpendicular to the axis through point *B*. This is the directrix.

4.15.11   Draw a line tangent to a parabola at a point *P* on it. *Method A.* With the focus and directrix given as in Fig. 4.78, proceed as follows:

a. From point *P* draw a line perpendicular to the directrix.

b. Draw a line from *P* to the focus *F*.

c. The bisector of the angle *APF* between these lines is the tangent to the curve.

Method B. Another method for drawing a tangent to a parabola at a point *P* on it when only the curve and axis are given is as follows. See Fig. 4.79.

$a_1.$ Through point *P* draw a line *PQ* parallel to the axis as in Fig. 4.79.

$b_1.$ Draw two lines parallel to *PQ* and at any equal distances from it.

$c_1.$ Extend these lines to cut the parabola at *A* and *C* and draw the line *AC*.

$d_1.$ A line through *P* parallel to *AC* is tangent to the parabola.

4.15.12   Draw a line tangent to a hyperbola at a point *P* on the curve. Axis and foci given. Under the conditions given in Fig. 4.80 the construction for the tangent is as follows:

a. From point *P* draw lines to the foci *F* and F_1 as in Fig. 4.80.

b. The bisector of the angle FPF_1 between these lines is the tangent at *P*.

4.15.13   Find the directrix and asymptotes of a hyperbola with axis and foci given. Under the condi-

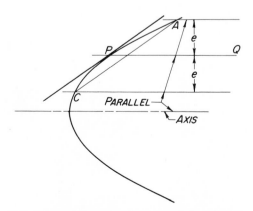

Fig. 4.78   Tangent to a parabola, focus and directrix given.

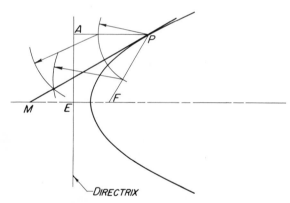

Fig. 4.79   Tangent through point on parabola, axis given.

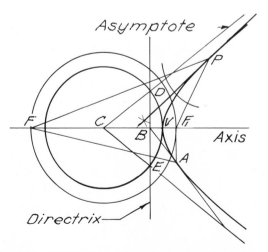

Fig. 4.80   Line tangent to a hyperbola, axis and foci given.

tions specified and shown in Fig. 4.80 the construction is as follows:

a. From one focus F_1 draw a perpendicular to the axis until it crosses the curve at A as in Fig. 4.80.

b. From A draw a line to the other focus F.

c. Bisect the angle F_1AF.

d. Where the bisector crosses the axis at B is a point on one directrix.

e. Through B draw a line perpendicular to the axis. This line is the directrix.

f. With the midpoint between F and F_1 labeled C as a center, draw a circle with radius CV. Point V is the vertex of the given hyperbola.

g. Where this circle crosses the directrix, locate two points D and E on the asymptotes.

h. Lines from C through D and E locate the asymptotes.

4.16 CONSTRUCTION OF OTHER CURVES COMMON IN PRACTICAL WORK.

Although the conic sections have a prominent place in engineering work, a number of other mathematical curves are widely used. Among these are the involute, the helix, the cycloids, and the spiral of Archimedes.

4.16.1 The involute. The involute may be defined as a curve that would be described if a string were unwound from some geometrical surface with the string kept taut and the end point describing the curve. Three involutes are shown in Fig. 4.81, one each for a triangle, a square, and a circle. The involute need not begin on the surface, although it may as in the triangle and the circle.

a. In the equilateral triangle, the curve consists of a series of 120° arcs with the radius increasing each time by the length of a side of the triangle. The corners of the triangle are the centers. This is also true for the square or any other figure with straight sides.

b. In the square, Fig. 4.81(b), the beginning point of the involute has been made at point E, which is three times the length AB from A. Arc BF is four times the length AB. CG is five times AB, and so on.

c. In the circle the circumference is divided into any convenient number of equal parts. Beginning at point 1 a tangent is drawn, and on it the length of the arc 0-1 is stepped off to locate A. At point 2 another tangent is drawn and a length equal to arc 0-1-2 is stepped off, and so on for as many points as may be desired. A smooth curve is then drawn

through these plotted points.

The involute is the basic curve for gear teeth and for the impeller of centrifugal pumps.

4.16.2 The cycloid. The cycloids form a group of curves generated by the path of a fixed point on the circumference of a rolling circle. When the circle rolls on a straight line, the path of the point is called simply a cycloid as in Fig. 4.82. If the circle rolls on the outside of another circle, the path of the point is called an epicycloid, whereas if the circle rolls on the inside of another circle, the path of the point is called a hypocycloid. These curves have a practical application in the design of gear teeth. To draw the cycloid, in Fig. 4.82, divide the rolling circle into 12 or more equal parts and lay out on the straight line 12 divisions equal to the arcs of the circle. As the circle rolls along, the center will occupy successively the positions 1, 2, 3, etc., while the point on the circumference will rise to the elevation on the horizontal lines A, B, C, D, etc. The intersections of the circle in its successive positions with the horizontal lines will give the required points.

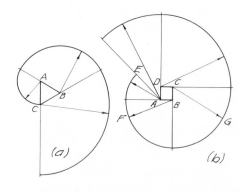

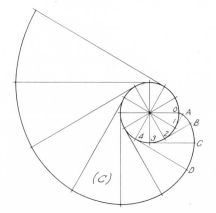

Fig. 4.81 Involutes.

4.16.3 The epicycloid and the hypocycloid. See Fig. 4.83. The constructions of the epicycloid and hypocycloid are quite similar to each other and can be readily grasped from the figure. Note that in both cases there is a separate line of centers for the rolling circles and, in place of the horizontal lines *A*, *B*, *C*, etc., we have the arcs *A*, *B*, *C*, etc.

4.16.4 The spiral of Archimedes. In the spiral of Archimedes, the radius of curvature increases directly as the angle through which it rotates. We may assume an arbitrary amount by which the radius shall increase in passing through a certain angle. See Fig. 4.84. With any convenient point as a center, draw a circle and divide it into 12 equal parts. Divide the radius into the same number of equal parts. One of the divisions of the radius is then the increment by which the radius of curvature increases in passing through an angle of 30°. Then beginning at the center and intersecting radius *1'* by arc *1*, radius *2'* by arc *2*, and so on, 12 points on the curve can be found. The curve thus generated is commonly used in cam design.

4.16.5 The helix. The helix is a space or three-dimensional curve. It is described by the path of a point that moves around a cylinder at a uniform angular rate while also moving parallel to the axis at a uniform linear rate. To represent the helix, draw the circle and divide it into 12 equal parts as shown in Fig. 4.85. On the front view of the cylinder draw 12 equal divisions of the desired length. Project the points on the circumference to the corresponding horizontal line as shown in the figure. Draw a smooth curve through the points.

A conical helix may be drawn as shown in 4.85(*b*). The curve is drawn first in the top view. Beginning at *1*, one-twelfth of the distance between the two circles is stepped off from the outer circle at point *2*. Additional twelfths are stepped off at each succeeding radial line. The curve is then projected to the front view.

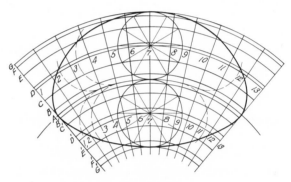

Fig. 4.83   Epicycloid and hypocycloid.

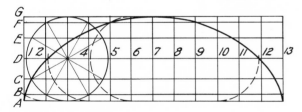

Fig. 4.82   The cycloid.

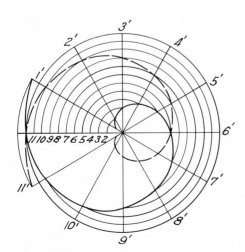

Fig. 4.84   Spiral of Archimedes.

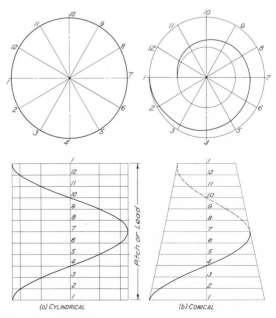

Fig. 4.85   The helix.

SELF-STUDY QUESTIONS

Before trying to answer these questions, read the chapter carefully. Then, without reference to the text, answer as many questions as possible. For those that cannot be answered, the number, in parentheses following the question number, gives the article in which the answer can be found. Look it up and write down the answer. Check the answers that you did give to see that they are correct.

4.1 **(4.2.1)** The bisector of a line or an angle is a line that divides a line into _____ parts.

4.2 **(4.2.3)** Parallel lines are the _____ distance apart throughout their length.

4.3 **(4.2.3)** Parallel lines are said to _____ when they are extended to infinity.

4.4 **(4.2.6; 4.3.4)** If two lines are perpendicular to each other, the angle between them is _____ degrees.

4.5 **(4.3.4)** Sketch the layout of a right triangle whose sides have the ratio of $3:4:5$.

4.6 **(4.4)** An equilateral triangle has three _____ sides.

4.7 **(4.5)** An isosceles triangle has only _____ equal sides.

4.8 **(4.5)** A scalene triangle has three _____ sides.

4.9 **(4.3)** To find the complement of an acute angle, subtract the angle from _____ degrees. Make a sketch and label the angles.

4.10 **(4.3)** To find the supplement of an obtuse angle, subtract the angle from _____ degrees. Make a sketch and label the angles.

4.11 **(4.4)** A pentagon has _____ sides.

4.12 **(4.5)** A parallelogram having four equal sides is called a _____.

4.13 **(4.5)** A trapezoid is a four-sided figure having two sides _____.

4.14 **(4.7.2)** If a circle is inscribed in a square, the circle is _____ to the sides of the square.

4.15 **(4.13)** A circle is the locus of points _____ from the center.

4.16 **(4.14)** Name the three principal conic sections. _____

4.17 **(4.14)** If a plane cuts a right circular cone parallel to its base, the shape of the section is _____.

4.18 **(4.14)** To cut straight lines from a cone, the cutting plane must pass through the _____.

4.19 **(4.14)** Which conic section is a single closed curve? _____

4.20 **(4.14)** Which conic section is a single open-ended curve? _____

4.21 **(4.14.10)** Name one common use of a parabola. _____

4.22 **(4.16.1)** What is a practical use of the involute curve? _____

4.23 **(4.14.2)** An ellipse has _____ foci.

4.24 **(4.14.2)** The sum of the distances from the foci to a point on an ellipse is equal to the _____ axis.

4.25 **(4.13.7)** If two circles are tangent to each other, the point of tangency lies on a line connecting _____.

4.26 **(4.13.3)** If a straight line is tangent to a circle, the radius to the point of tangency is _____ to the straight line.

4.27 **(4.16.4)** The spiral of Archimedes is sometimes used in the design of _____.

PROBLEMS

Problems introduced here and others that follow in this chapter are to be drawn on an 8½ × 11″ sheet. Draw one or more problems from the following group. Use good pencil technique, making the construction lines as light lines and the finished figure in contrasting dark lines. Make drawings full-size unless otherwise directed.

4.1 Draw a line 5″ long and divide it into six equal parts, using the construction in Fig. 4.7.

4.2 Draw a triangle having sides 1¼, 1½, and 2″ long.

4.3 Draw a triangle having a base 3″ long, with angles of 60° at its ends.

4.4 Inscribe a square inside a 3″ diameter circle.

4.5 Circumscribe a hexagon about a 2½″ diameter circle.

4.6 Inscribe a hexagon inside a 3″ diameter circle.

4.7 Draw a pentagon inscribed in a 2″ diameter circle. See Fig. 4.26.

4.8 Draw a pentagon 1″ on a side. See Fig. 4.29.

4.9 Draw a heptagon inscribed in a 2½″ diameter circle. See Fig. 4.28.

4.10 Draw a heptagon 1″ on a side. See Fig. 4.29.

4.11 Draw an octagon inside a 2″ square.

4.12 Circumscribe an octagon about a 2″ diameter circle.

4.13 Draw a circle through the three corners of the triangle in Problem 4-2. See Fig. 4.33.

4.14 Draw a right triangle with one side 2″ and the other 3″ long. Construct an arc with a radius of ½″ tangent to each of the interior angles.

4.15 Draw a 3″ diameter circle. Draw a horizontal line tangent to the circle. Draw a ½″ radius arc tangent to the circle and horizontal line.

4.16 Draw two circles with their center on a horizontal line 3″ apart. One circle is to be 1″ in diameter and the other 1¼″. Draw a circle of 2″ radius tangent to the two circles externally. See Fig. 4.38.

4.17 Same as Problem 4.16. Circle 3″ in diameter tangent internally to the small circle and externally to the large one. See Fig. 4.40.

4.18 Same as Problem 4.16. Circle of 6″ radius tangent internally to both circles. See Fig. 4.39.

4.19 Draw two horizontal parallel lines 1½″ apart. Two points, 3″ apart horizontally, one on each line, are to be connected by a reverse curve both parts of which have the same radius. See Fig. 4.41.

4.20 Draw two horizontal parallel lines 2″ apart and connect two points, one on each line, 3″ apart on the shortest distance, by two arcs, one of which has a radius of 2½″. See Fig. 4.42.

4.21 Draw an ellipse with a major axis of 3″ and a minor axis of 2″ by the two-circle method. See Fig. 4.52.

4.22 Draw an ellipse with a major axis of 3½″ and a minor axis of 2″ by the trammel method. See Fig. 4.56.

4.23 Draw a rectangle 4 × 2″ and draw a parabola through the corners and the midpoint of a long side. See Fig. 4.61.

4.24 The foci of an hyperbola are 2″ apart and the vertices 1¼″ apart. Draw one branch of the hyperbola. See Fig. 4.66.

4.25 Draw one turn of an involute based on a circle 1½″ in diameter. See Fig. 4.81.

4.26 Draw one turn of an involute based on a square ¾″ on a side. See Fig. 4.81.

4.27 Draw two projections of a helix of 2″ diameter and 3″ pitch. See Fig. 4.85.

4.28 Draw a cycloid having a rolling circle 2″ in diameter. See Fig. 4.82.

4.29 Draw a spiral of Archimedes. Begin curve 1″ from center and use a radial increment of ¼″ for each 30°. Make a half-turn and draw also the symmetrical portion on the opposite side of the center line. See Fig. 4.84.

CHAPTER 5
Sketching

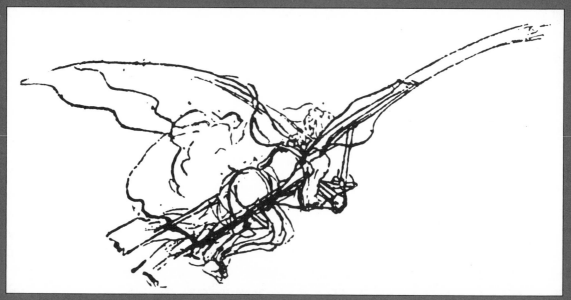

OLD: Drawing of a flying machine by Leonardo da Vinci in 1490. (The Bettmann Archive.)

NEW: Drawing of supersonic airliner. (The Boeing Company.)

Chapter 5   Sketching

5.1   INTRODUCTION. Many times the scientist or engineer finds himself in a position in which he cannot express his ideas mathematically or by words alone. In situations of this nature, the ideas may be expressed quite adequately by sketches. These sketches can then be used as a basis for further analysis and design.

It is sometimes assumed that skill in sketching can be acquired more rapidly than proficiency with instruments. This is not true. The same knowledge of the principles of projection is required in both cases, but it takes much more practice and effort to draw two parallel lines freehand than with instruments. It is simple to draw a circle with a compass but quite another matter to do it successfully freehand. This chapter is concerned chiefly with acquiring these sketching skills. How to make particular types of sketches is discussed in the latter part of this chapter where the basic arrangement of views is explained. The theory of various types of projection is explained in later chapters.

5.2   USES OF FREEHAND SKETCHES. Technical sketches are used for a wide variety of purposes, among which the following are the most important:

a. To transmit information, obtained in the field or shop, to the engineering office. This occurs when repairs have to be made or when changes in an existing structure are being considered.
b. To convey the ideas of the designer to the draftsman.
c. To make studies of the layout of the views required in an instrumental drawing. See Fig. 5.1.
d. As a means of making preliminary studies of a design to show how it functions.
e. To compute stresses in a design. See Fig. 5.2.
f. To provide a basis for communicating between engineers, technicians, and craftsmen.
g. To furnish a three-dimensional picture of an object, which will help to interpret the orthographic views.
h. To be used as shop drawings for manufacturing.

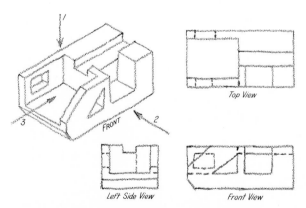

Fig. 5.1   Three-view sketch study for drawing layout.

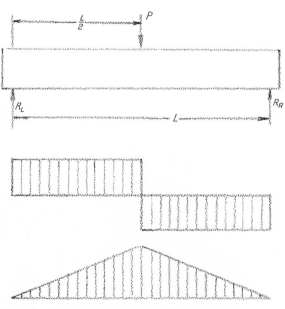

Fig. 5.2   Sketch for stress computation.

These are usually made on coordinate tracing paper with grid lines which will not show on a blueprint. See Fig. 5.3.

i. To serve as a teaching aid when discussing problems in the classroom.

5.3 MATERIALS FOR SKETCHING. One of the advantages of sketching is that only a minimum of equipment is required. This normally includes pencil, paper, and eraser.

5.3.1 Pencils and erasers. Most draftsmen prefer a soft pencil for sketching in the range from F to 2H. The H grade pencil is a good all-round tool. It should have a conical point and be frequently resharpened. A good eraser that will not smudge is essential.

5.3.2 Papers. Sketches have become so extensively used in industry that several different types of commercial paper are available. These are of great assistance to the engineer and technician in making industrial sketches.

a. Blank paper. For the experienced man blank paper of bond or ledger quality is satisfactory.

b. Rectangular coordinate paper. For multiview drawing, rectangular coordinate paper is an aid to the beginner. In many offices it is regularly used to produce dimensioned working drawings for the shop. Such coordinate papers can be obtained in a wide variety of divisions, both decimal and fractional. For ordinary purposes, subdivisions of ⅛ or ¼ inch are satisfactory, as shown in Fig. 5.3.

Rectangular ruled paper is also useful in making oblique pictorial sketches, since the front face of an object will be the same as in multiview drawings. See Fig. 5.4.

c. Isometric ruled paper. For pictorial sketches, isometric paper provides a guide to the correct position of the axes. See Fig. 5.5. It also provides units of measurement in proportioning.

d. Perspective grids. Perspective grids can be obtained in several sizes and with varying coordinate rulings. These are used most frequently for architectural projects. See Fig. 5.6.

5.4 TOOLS FOR MEASUREMENT. Although freehand sketches are not made to scale, it is often necessary to make measurements of the object to be sketched. In an emergency, measurements must be made when a broken part is to be replaced or when work is to be done in the field on large projects.

a. Field work. For measuring large projects, for ex-

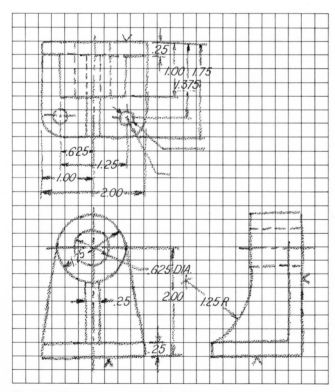

Fig. 5.3 Shop sketch for manufacturing.

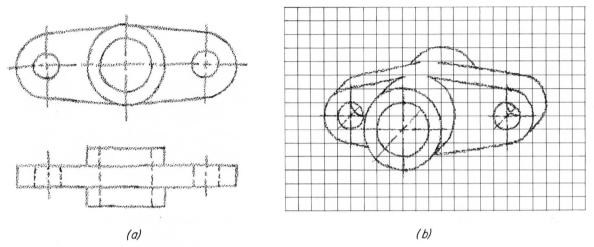

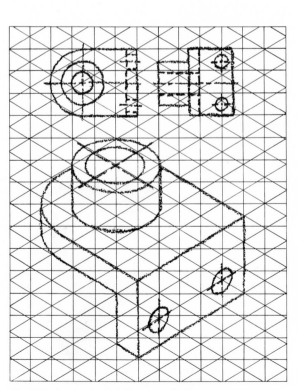

(a)

(b)

Fig. 5.4   Oblique sketch on coordinate paper.

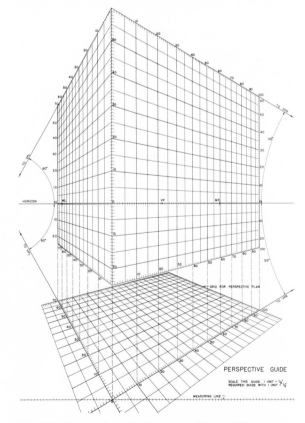

Fig. 5.5   Isometric sketch on coordinate paper.

Fig. 5.6   Perspective grid. (Courtesy of Grace Wilson.)

ample, a change in the layout and location of equipment in a shop, a 6-foot rule or even a 50-foot steel tape may be needed. For a plot plan, surveying instruments may be used.

b. Shop work. Sketches may be made of manufactured parts that are machined to close tolerances. Measurements of such objects may require the use of steel scales with divisions of one hundredth of an inch. Ordinary calipers or micrometer calipers may be needed. It may be necessary to use surface gages, depth gages, and thread gages.

c. Use of measuring tools. For either type of work the person making the sketches must know how to use the tool he needs to obtain the dimensions required. Some of these tools are shown in Fig. 5.7.

5.5 SKETCHING STRAIGHT LINES. It is important to be able to sketch lines rapidly whether they are horizontal, vertical, or inclined. The same general principles apply in all cases:

a. Determine and mark the end points of the line to be sketched.

b. Hold the pencil in a normal writing position as in Figs. 5.8 and 5.9.

c. Place the pencil point at one of the end points.

d. Sketch a light line with one stroke, or short overlapping strokes, by keeping the eye fixed on the point toward which the line is being drawn.

e. Go over the line to remove waviness or roughness and make it of the required weight and character. The final sketch stroke has a freedom and character

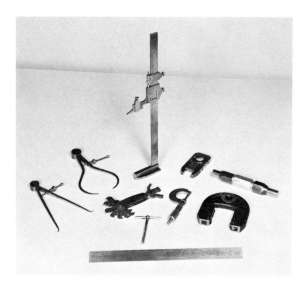

Fig. 5.7   Measuring tools.

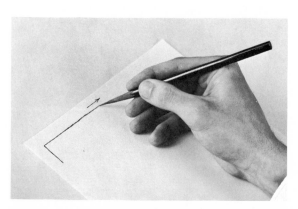

Fig. 5.8   Sketching a horizontal line.

Fig. 5.9   Sketching a vertical line.

that are entirely different from the clean-cut precision of the mechanically ruled line. The difference between ruled lines and the sketch line is illustrated in Fig. 5.10.

5.5.1 Sketching horizontal lines. For drawing horizontal lines, the forearm should be approximately at right angles to the line being sketched, as shown in Fig. 5.8. The strokes should be made from left to right according to the principles outlined in Art. 5.5.

5.5.2 Vertical lines. The same type of stroke should be used for vertical lines as described above. When using the finger and wrist movement, the forearm should be approximately parallel to the line or at an angle of not more than 45°. Draw the stroke from top to bottom as shown in Fig. 5.9.

5.5.3 Inclined lines. Inclined lines, whether on plain paper or on coordinate paper, are usually drawn between two given points or at some specified angle. On coordinate paper angles of 15, 30, 45, 60, and 75° can be estimated with sufficient accuracy as shown in Fig. 5.11. If difficulty is experienced in drawing inclined lines, the paper may be rotated until the lines are about horizontal. See Fig. 5.12.

5.5.4 Parallel lines. It is frequently necessary to draw lines parallel to each other quite accurately. Figure 5.13 shows one method that can be used. This consists of holding the pencil with the fingers as far from the point as convenient and then moving the hand so that the little finger slides along the original line.

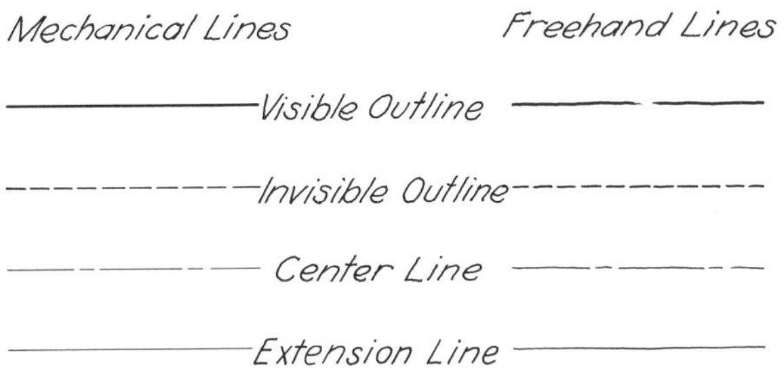

Mechanical Lines   *Freehand Lines*

———————— *Visible Outline* —— — —

— — — — — — — *Invisible Outline* — — — — — —

— — · — — · — — *Center Line* — — · — — ·

———————— *Extension Line* ————————

Fig. 5.10 Comparison between ruled lines and sketched lines.

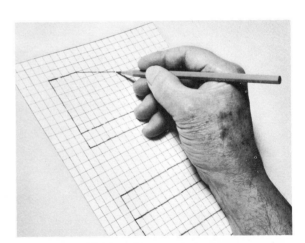

Fig. 5.12 Drawing inclined lines by turning paper.

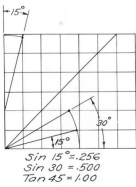

Sin 15°=.256
Sin 30 = .500
Tan 45 = 1.00

Fig. 5.11 Plotting angles.

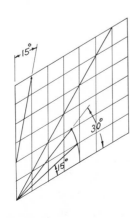

Fig. 5.13 Drawing parallel lines.

If this is not possible, the method shown in Fig. 5.14 will produce good results. The pencil is held as shown, directly above the line, and then moved to a parallel position. The pencil is moved lengthwise to draw the line, always keeping the pencil parallel to the original line.

5.5.5 Border lines. Border lines and some horizontal and vertical lines may be made easily by holding the edge of the paper parallel to the edge of the board. Then draw the line with the third and fourth fingers of the hand sliding along the edge of the board as a guide. See Fig. 5.15.

5.6 SKETCHING CIRCLES. Circles occur frequently in engineering drawings. It is therefore necessary for the engineering designer to sketch them easily.

5.6.1 Trammel method. On the edge of a piece of paper mark two points at a distance equal to the radius of the circle. With one point at the center, mark off as many points on the circumference as desired, as shown in Fig. 5.16. Sketch the circle through these points.

5.6.2 Enclosing-square method. On coordinate paper, a circle may be sketched in its enclosing square as shown in Fig. 5.17. On plain paper, the square can be sketched very lightly, the center lines drawn, and then the circle sketched, making the arcs tangent to the sides of the square at the midpoints.

5.6.3 Semimechanical method. A semimechanical method for drawing circles is to hold two pencils intersecting each other and having the distance between the points equal to the desired radius. By holding one pencil perpendicular to the paper with its point at the

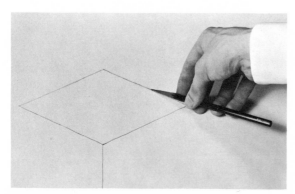

Fig. 5.14   Drawing parallel lines.

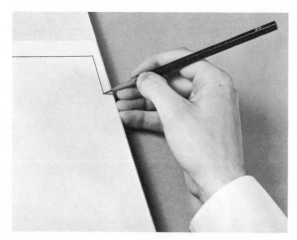

Fig. 5.15   Sketching border line along edge of drawing board.

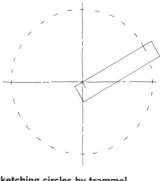

Fig. 5.16   Sketching circles by trammel.

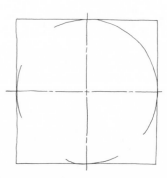

Fig. 5.17   Sketching a circle in a square.

center of the circle, the paper may be revolved about the point while the other pencil describes the circle. This method is illustrated in Fig. 5.18.

5.7   SKETCHING AN ELLIPSE. There are several methods in common use for sketching an ellipse. Four methods are described below.

5.7.1   Trammel method. For the ellipse, mark off three points, *a*, *b*, and *c*, as shown in Fig. 5.19, with *bc* equal to the semiminor axis and *ac* equal to the semimajor axis. Keeping points *a* and *b* always on the center lines of the ellipse, plot as many positions of point *c* as desired and sketch the ellipse.

5.7.2   Rectangle method. An ellipse may be sketched in a rectangle by drawing the center lines in the rectangle and making the arcs tangent at the midpoints of the sides in the same manner as for a circle in a square. Additional points may also be obtained as shown in Fig. 5.20.

5.7.3   Circles in pictorial sketches. Except for circles in the front face of an oblique sketch, all circles show as ellipses in pictorial drawings. These may be drawn by the enclosing pictorial square or parallelogram method as shown in Fig. 5.21. Arcs are always tangent at the midpoint of the sides of the parallelogram.

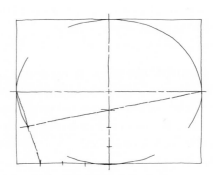

Fig. 5.18   Method of drawing circle with two pencils.

Fig. 5.19   Ellipse by the trammel method.

Fig. 5.20   Sketching an ellipse in a rectangle.

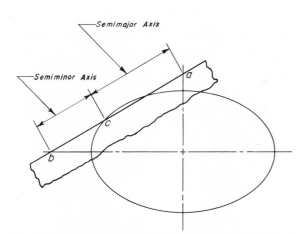

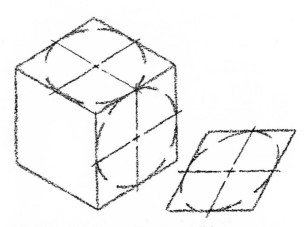

Fig. 5.21   Sketching an ellipse in a parallelogram.

5.7.4   Free arm movement. Another method of drawing ellipses is with a free arm movement as shown in Fig. 5.22. This method may be used to sketch a circle or ellipse so that it will go through certain points or be tangent to one or more straight lines or circles. For ellipses the forearm should be held approximately perpendicular to the major axis of the ellipse with the fourth and fifth fingers riding lightly on the paper. The procedure is as follows:

a. Move the arm freely so that the point of the pencil describes an ellipse just above the desired position on the paper.

b. After two or three complete circuits, allow the pencil to touch the paper lightly and draw several ellipses. Some of these will be inside the desired position and some outside.

c. With these trial lines as a basis, a sketch stroke ellipse may be drawn to satisfy the desired conditions of position or tangency.

d. Erase the trial lines and sketch stroke to the point where the ellipse is faintly visible.

e. Draw a smooth curve as shown in Fig. 5.22.

5.8   PROPORTIONING. It is important to maintain the relative proportions between the overall length, width, and height while making a sketch of an object. With practice, one can develop the ability to divide a line in half by eye and then these halves can be again divided to get fourths. To aid the beginner, several methods can be used to develop an eye for proportioning.

5.8.1   Counting squares. When coordinate paper is used, the proportioning can be done by "counting squares." This amounts to selecting a scale whereby the sketcher assumes a given number of squares to equal a unit of measure such as an inch or a foot or a fraction of either.

5.8.2   Scrap paper. Scales are assumed not to be available in sketching; however, a piece of scrap paper with a straight edge can be marked off to represent a given unit of measure. To get halves and fourths, the paper can be folded.

5.8.3   Geometric constructions. Figure 5.23(a) shows the steps in sketching a rectangle three times as long as it is wide. With AB given in a vertical position, erect perpendiculars to AB at A and B. Bisect the right angles at A and B with lines AC and BD to form the square $ABCD$. Through the intersection of AC and BD, sketch a line MN parallel to AD and BC. Sketch

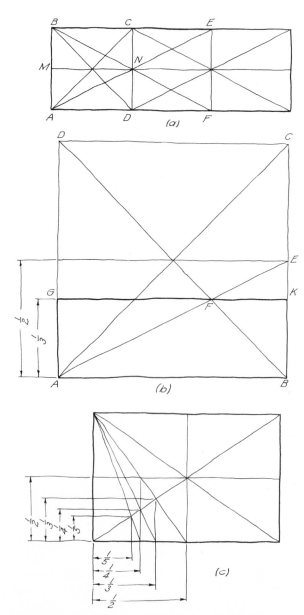

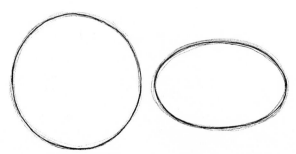

Fig. 5.22   Sketching circle or ellipse by use of the finding line.

Fig. 5.23   Method of proportioning or subdividing a rectangle.

BF through *N* and *AE* through *N* to locate points *E* and *F* on *BC* and *AD* extended. *CDFE* forms a square equal to *ABCD*. Repeat the process to obtain the third square.

A more accurate method is shown in Fig. 5.23(*b*). Here the long axis is assumed as *AB*. A square *ABCD* is sketched and the diagonals drawn to locate point *E*, the midpoint of *BC*. *AE* is sketched in to locate point *F* on diagonal *BD*. Line *GK* is drawn parallel to *AB* through *F*, thus making *AG* and *KB* equal to one-third the length of *AB*. Figure 5.23(*c*) shows how this method can be used to obtain various other subdivisions of a line segment such as ½, ⅓, ¼, and ⅕.

5.8.4 Proportioning large objects.
One convenient method for obtaining relative proportions when drawing large objects is illustrated in Fig. 5.24. The sketch board is held almost perpendicular to the line of sight. The arm is extended full length with the pencil held in the fingers. By holding the pencil between the eye and the object, one end of the pencil can be made to coincide with one end of a line and the thumb moved along the pencil until it coincides with the other end of the line. This length may then be used to obtain the relative proportions of the object. It is also possible to get the position of a line by holding the pencil parallel to any line of the object and then moving it to a paral-lel position on the drawing. Sketching in this manner results in a perspective drawing.

5.9 TYPES OF SKETCHES.
The engineer makes several kinds of sketches. He uses multiview ortho-graphic sketches when discussing a problem with his staff. The theory of multiview sketching is presented in Chapter 6.

For less experienced persons he may use a three dimensional sketch that looks like a picture. There are three types of three dimensional sketches; namely, axonometric, oblique, and perspective.

The theory of axonometric sketching with its three subdivisions—isometric, dimetric, and trimetric—is explained in Chapter 15.

Oblique projection theory, with two subdivisions—Cavalier and Cabinet drawing—is explained in Chapter 16.

Perspective sketching is explained in Chapter 17.

5.10 MULTIVIEW SKETCHES.
Multiview sketches may consist of one-view illustrations as in Fig. 5.25. These can be used only for very simple objects where the third dimension is a thickness given by a note. Gaskets, shims, and washers are in this class. For two- and three-view sketches a standard arrangement of views has been established, which has been adopted in the United States, Great Britain, and Canada, as

Fig. 5.24 Method of obtaining proportions by means of a pencil.

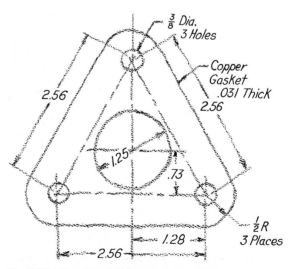

Fig. 5.25 One-view sketch.

shown in Fig. 5.26. While all six views of an object have been shown in this illustration, no more views should be made than are necessary to describe the shape of the object.

5.11 SKETCHING PRACTICE. Good technique in sketching can only be developed by practice. Problems have been provided at the end of this chapter for acquiring skill in sketching straight lines in various positions. These may be sketched right in this book or on separate sheets of paper.

5.12 SKETCHING MULTIVIEW DRAWINGS. In developing the theory and practice of multiview drawing, it is convenient to employ pictorial drawings that are used as a reference for sketching top, front, and side views of an object. In engineering design it is also convenient to sketch the various views from pictorial representations. This process is illustrated in Fig. 5.27. As a basis for proportioning, the object is assumed to be enclosed in a box to determine the relative dimensions. In Fig. 5.27(a) the bracket is in the proportion 2 × 2 × 3. The steps in sketching the three views are presented in the following articles.

5.12.1 Sketching the top view. To sketch the top view the enclosing box of the bracket is viewed from the top as indicated by arrow number 1 in Fig. 5.27(a). The proportions of the box are to be 2 × 3. The method of Fig. 5.23(a) is used to obtain these proportions.

a. Make line *AB*, representing two units, any length desired to make a sketch of suitable size.
b. Sketch the square *ABCD* and draw the diagonals.
c. Draw center lines through *O*.
d. Draw line *EF* to *G* on the upper line.
e. Complete the rectangle which is now in the proportion 2 × 3.

5.12.2 Sketching the front view. To sketch the front view of the enclosing box the bracket is viewed from the front as indicated by arrow number 2 in Fig. 5.27(a). The box will be the same size as the top view in this case.

a. The length can be sketched downward from the ends of the top view as in Fig. 5.27(b).
b. The height can be transferred from the top view with a piece of scratch paper. This makes the front view also in the proportion 2 × 3, as it should be.

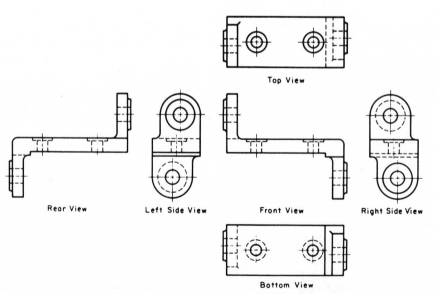

Top View

Rear View   Left Side View   Front View   Right Side View

Bottom View

THE SIX POSSIBLE PRINCIPAL VIEWS OF AN OBJECT

Fig. 5.26   Standard arrangement of six views of an object. (Courtesy United States of America Standards Institute.)

5.12.3 Sketching the side view. The side view is obtained by viewing the bracket from the side as indicated by arrow number *3* in Fig. 5.27(*a*). The enclosing box has a proportion of 2 × 2. This can be obtained as follows:

a. The height can be obtained by sketching across from the front view as in Figs. 5.27(*b*) and (*c*).
b. The depth can be transferred by a piece of paper from the top view. The proportion for the end view is therefore 2 × 2.

5.12.4 Sketching in the details. To sketch in the details for each of the views, the proportion of the parts can be obtained by subdividing the views with diagonals or by eye.

a. In the top view note that the thickness of the vertical back is one-sixth the length of the whole object. This thickness can be obtained by dividing the existing left-hand one third in two parts as in Fig. 5.27(*c*).
b. The thickness of the base is one-fourth the total height. This proportion can be obtained by diago-

nals in the front view as in Fig. 5.27(*c*).

c. From the dimensioned pictorial it can be seen that the sloping web has a thickness equal to one-fourth of the total depth.
d. This can be done by a series of diagonals in the side view as in Fig. 5.27(*d*).
e. The thickness of the base can be sketched across from the front view to the end view.
f. Mark tangent points in front view and sketch arcs. See Figs. 5.27(*e*) and (*f*).
g. Locate center of small holes by eye and the concentric arcs. Mark tangent points and sketch arcs.
h. Erase construction lines and make outlines firm.

5.13 PICTORIAL SKETCHING. The pictorial sketch is used for the following purposes:

a. To clarify or explain two or three views on the orthographic drawings.
b. To explain ideas to other persons.
c. As an aid in computation and design. Pictorial sketches may be made in isometric, oblique, or perspective. Of these three, isometric and oblique are the easiest to make. See Figs. 5.4 and 5.5.

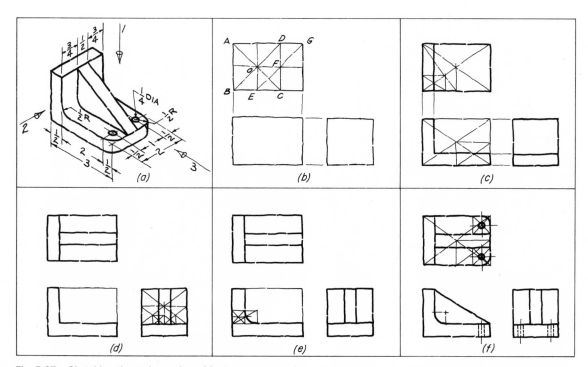

Fig. 5.27 Sketching three views of an object.

5.14 ISOMETRIC SKETCHING. The first step in making an isometric sketch is to draw a box that will just enclose the object. In Fig. 5.28 assume that the ratio of the three edges of the box are $2 \times 3 \times 4$. The steps are as follows:

a. Draw a vertical line AB two units long as in Fig. 5.28(a).
b. On this line construct a square and bisect the sides with the aid of the diagonals as in Fig. 5.28(b).
c. Using point O as the center, sketch an arc with a radius of one unit as shown in Fig. 5.28(b). Through point B sketch a line tangent to the arc. This line will therefore recede at an angle of 30° with the horizontal. Repeat on the right side to obtain the other 30° receding line. This makes the three axes at 120° with each other. See Fig. 5.28(e).
d. Through point A sketch a line parallel to line BD as in Fig. 5.28(c).

e. Locate point E on the receding line from A by extending line BC until it intersects the line at E. Line BE becomes one of the diagonals of the square in isometric (actually a rhombus). See Fig. 5.28(c).
f. Draw a line EH parallel to AB and draw the diagonal AH. Locate the horizontal center line and points F and G as in Fig. 5.28(c).
g. From A draw a line through F to D on the upper line, thus doubling the square.
h. Divide the second square in half by diagonals and the vertical line MN, thus making BM three units long.
i. In Fig. 5.28(d)—repeat the construction by laying out two equal squares, thus making this side four units long. The box is then completed by drawing the two remaining sides of the top as in Fig. 5.28(e).

5.14.1 Object with isometric lines only. The object shown in Fig. 5.29(a) is composed entirely of isometric

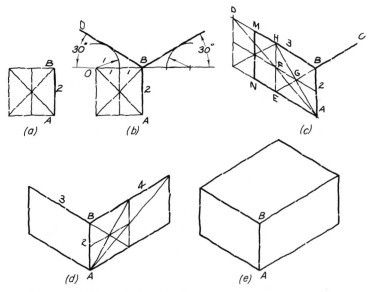

Fig. 5.28 Laying out an isometric box.

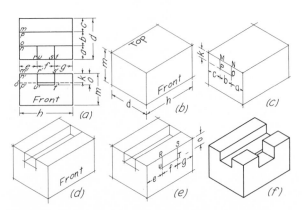

Fig. 5.29 Construction of an isometric drawing having isometric lines only.

lines that are parallel to the three axes. To sketch such an object, proceed as follows:

a. Construct an isometric box using the proper proportions for the object in Fig. 5.29(*a*). See Fig. 5.29(*b*)

b. Lay out the principal details, for example, the groove running across the top as shown in Figs. 5.29(*c*) and (*d*).

c. Next sketch in the remainder of the details in proper proportion as shown in Figs. 5.29(*e*) and (*f*).

d. Remove construction lines and finish the sketch as in Fig. 5.29(*f*).

5.14.2 Object with nonisometric lines. The general procedure for sketching an object with noniso-

metric lines is the same as that explained in the preceding paragraph, with the following exceptions. All nonisometric lines must be determined by locating their end points by means of isometric lines as shown for the top of the object in Fig. 5.30(*c*).

Next sketch in the lower step by estimating the upward distance equal to distance *n,* then along the width for the front and back-edge distances *h* and *m,* and then the depth *f* and *g* as shown in Fig. 5.30 (*d*). Having these eight points located, draw the sloping or nonisometric lines as in Fig. 5.30(*e*). Finish the sketch in the usual manner as in Fig. 5.30(*f*).

5.14.3 Cylindrical objects. Assume an object given as in Fig. 5.31(*a*). Instead of one large enclosing box draw several boxes in proper proportion and loca-

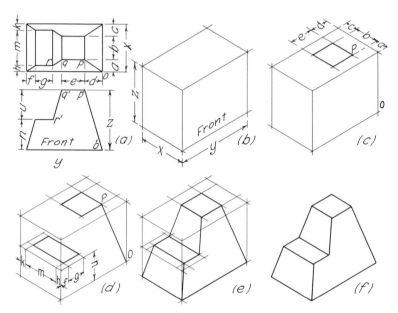

Fig. 5.30 Construction of an isometric drawing having nonisometric lines.

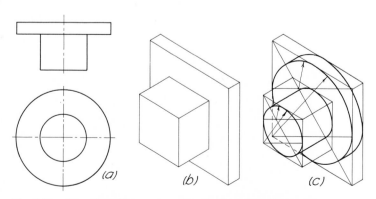

Fig. 5.31 Steps in making an isometric drawing of a cylindrical object.

tion which will just enclose the separate parts as in Figs. 5.31(*b*) and (*c*). These boxes must have their geometric centers lying on a common isometric axis, which slopes 30° up to the right in this case. Sketch the ellipses in the proper parallelograms. Draw the isometric tangent lines between them. Finish the sketch by erasing all construction and making the outlines firm. Hidden lines are not shown in pictorial drawings unless absolutely necessary for an understanding of the sketch.

5.15   OBLIQUE SKETCHING. Oblique sketching differs from isometric mainly in the position of the three principal axes. In isometric, the axes were at 120° with each other. In oblique, two axes are at right angles to each other; the third one may be at any desired angle with the horizontal. It is usually between 30 and 45°. See Fig. 5.32.

The sketch is again based on an enclosing box. This time, however, the front of the box is either a square or a rectangle, as the case may be. The front face, therefore, is just like an orthographic view and circles show as true circles. The ellipses in the top and side may be constructed by the four-center approximate method as shown in Fig. 5.32.

5.15.1   Box method. By proper selection of the

inclined axis either the side or top face may be emphasized. The steps in construction are similar to those for isometric, as shown in Fig. 5.33.

5.15.2   Center-line construction. For objects that are largely cylindrical in shape, as the object in Fig. 5.34(*a*), a center-line method of construction can be used advantageously.

a. The center lines are laid out first in their proper proportion and position as in Figs. 5.34(*b*) and (*c*).
b. Draw the circles and partial circles by the trammel method, using a scrap of paper.
c. Draw the tangent lines between parallel circles as in Fig. 5.34(*d*).

5.16   PERSPECTIVE SKETCHING. A perspective of an object is approximately the view as seen by the observer if he were to look at it with one eye. The most important difference between perspective and other forms of pictorial is that receding lines converge instead of remaining parallel. In perspective, lines that are parallel to the picture plane will show parallel on the drawing, but all parallel receding lines are drawn to converge at a point. For large objects proportioning may be done with a pencil as shown in Fig. 5.24. The complete theory of perspective is given in Chapter 17.

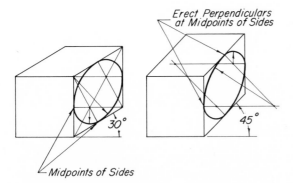

Fig. 5.32   Four-center method of constructing a circle in cavalier projection.

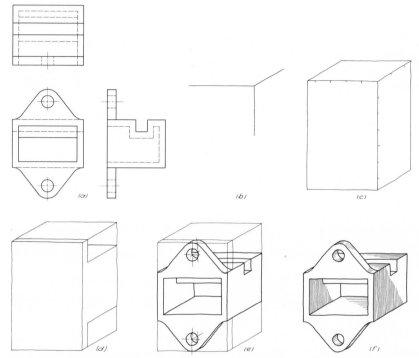

Fig. 5.33   Steps in making an oblique sketch.

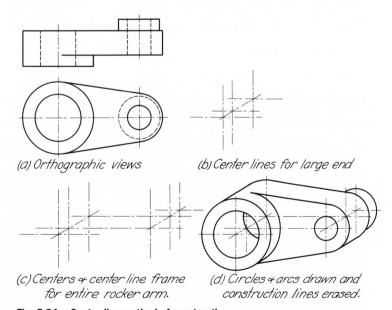

(a) Orthographic views

(b) Center lines for large end

(c) Centers & center line frame
for entire rocker arm.

(d) Circles & arcs drawn and
construction lines erased.

Fig. 5.34   Center-line method of construction.

SELF-STUDY QUESTIONS

In the questions that follow fill in the blank spaces or underline the correct word where a choice is given. If you cannot answer, look up the paragraph number immediately following the question number.

5.1 **(5.2)** Name three uses of freehand sketches. _____ _____ _____

5.2 **(5.3.1)** What equipment, besides paper and measuring instruments, is needed for sketching? _____

_____

5.3 **(5.3.2)** Name three kinds of commercially available coordinate papers. _____ _____ _____

_____

5.4 **(5.5.3)** Show by a sketch how to approximate angles of 30 and 45° on rectangular coordinate paper.

5.5 **(5.6.1)** Show by a well-labeled and noted sketch how to draw a circle, using a piece of paper that has

a straight edge.

5.6 **(5.8.2)** How may a given space be divided accurately into halves and quarters using only a strip of

paper? _____

5.7 **(5.9)** Name four different types of sketches used by engineers. _____ _____ _____

_____

5.8 **(5.10)** What type of objects can be shown by one (nonpictorial) view? _____ _____

5.9 **(5.12.1)** In making a top view, how does the engineer imagine himself to be looking at the object? _____

_____

5.10 **(5.12.2)** For making a front view the draftsman imagines himself to be looking from the _____.

5.11 **(5.12.1)** For the standard arrangement of views the draftsman places the top view _____ _____

_____ view.

5.12 **(5.12.3)** The side view is placed to the _____ _____ _____ of the front view.

5.13 **(5.13)** Name two purposes for which pictorial sketches may be used. _____ _____

5.14 **(513c)** Name three types of pictorial sketches. _____ _____ _____

5.15 **(5.14)** The first step in making an isometric sketch is to lay out a _____ which will just enclose

the _____.

5.16 **(5.14.1)** Isometric lines are those that are _____ to the three _____ axes.

5.17 **(5.14.2)** In sketching nonisometric lines, the _____ _____ must be located first.

5.18 **(5.15)** In oblique sketching two of the axes are at _____ _____ to each other and the third

may be _____ _____ _____ with the first two.

5.19 **(5.15.2)** In oblique sketching, the layout may be made around _____ _____ instead of using

the _____ method.

PROBLEMS

These problems are to be done freehand, without the use of any instruments other than a pencil and eraser.

If so specified by the instructor, any six of the problems may be arranged on an A-size sheet (8½ × 11″). Where lengths are specified, these are to be estimated.

5.1 Draw a vertical line *AB* about 1½″ long and then by the method of Fig. 5.23 draw a rectangle twice as long as it is high.

5.2 Draw a vertical line *AB* about 1″ long and then make a rectangle with *AB* as one side three times as long as it is high, by the method of Fig. 5.23.

5.3 Draw two center lines at right angles to each other and then, with the aid of a scrap of paper as a trammel, sketch a circle about 3″ in diameter. See Fig. 5.16.

5.4 Draw two center lines at right angles to each other and then, with the aid of a paper trammel, sketch an ellipse

with a major axis about 3″ long and a minor axis of 1½″. See Fig. 5.19.

5.5 Sketch a 2″ diameter circle by the finding-line method. See Fig. 5.22. Draw the center lines afterward.

5.6 Sketch an ellipse approximately the same size as in Problem 5.4 by the finding-line method. See Fig. 5.22. Draw center lines afterward.

The remainder of the problems in this group may be sketched in the book by using the figures referred to.

5.7 Reproduce the rectangle shown in Fig. 5.35 and then sketch a series of horizontal parallel lines.

5.8 Same as Problem 5.7; use Fig. 5.36 and sketch vertical lines.

5.9 Same as Problem 5.7; use Fig. 5.37 and sketch parallel 45° lines.

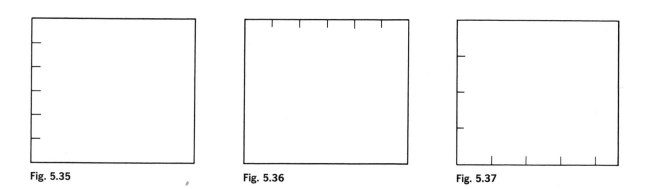

Fig. 5.35   Fig. 5.36   Fig. 5.37

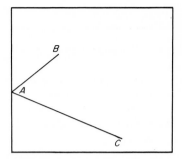

Fig. 5.38

Fig. 5.39

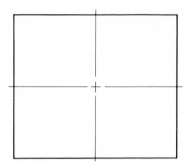

Fig. 5.40

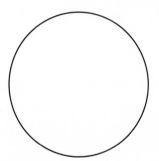

Fig. 5.41

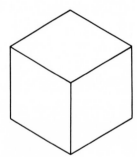

Fig. 5.42

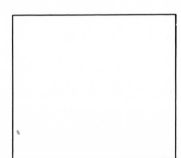

Fig. 5.43

5.10 Reproduce Fig. 5.38 and then sketch a line perpendicular to *AB* up to the left from point *B* and a second line perpendicular to *AC* up to the right from point *C*. Continue both lines to the edge of the rectangle.

5.11 Reproduce the square of Fig. 5.39. Draw the center lines and then sketch in an inscribed tangent circle.

5.12 Sketch a rectangle as in Fig. 5.40. Draw the center lines and then by the method of Fig. 5.20 sketch an ellipse in the rectangle.

5.13 Sketch a circle as in Fig. 5.41 about 3″ in diameter. Draw the center lines of the circle and then sketch an isometric of a cube with five corners on the circle and one at the center of the circle. See proportions in Fig. 5.42.

5.14 Sketch an isometric of a cube as in Fig. 5.42 and then draw an ellipse in each face tangent at the midpoints of the sides.

5.15 By the method of Fig. 5.23, divide a rectangle like that in Fig. 5.43 into three equal horizontal strips.

5.16 Reproduce the rectangle of Fig. 5.44 and then by the method of Fig. 5.23 divide it into five vertical strips.

5.17 By the method of Fig. 5.23, divide a parallelogram like Fig. 5.45 into five vertical strips.

5.18 Construct an oblique parallelogram as in Fig. 5.46 and then erect perpendiculars at the midpoint of each side. Carry the perpendiculars to their points of intersection. These intersections are the centers for drawing the arcs for a four-center approximate ellipse.

Two- and Three-View Sketches and Isometric Sketches

In each of the following problems, reproduce the existing views, at a suitable size. Using the problem assigned proceed to solve the problem.

5.19 Sketch three side views that will be consistent with the front and top views in Fig. 5.47. Use straight lines only.

5.20 Make an isometric sketch of each of your three solutions to Problem 5.19.

5.21 Sketch three side views consistent with the front and top views in Fig. 5.48. Use straight lines only.

5.22 Make an isometric sketch of each of your three solutions to Problem 5.21.

5.23 Sketch three front and side views that will be consistent with the top view given in Fig. 5.49.

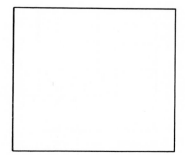

Fig. 5.44

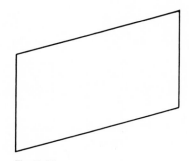

Fig. 5.45

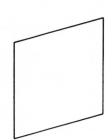

Fig. 5.46

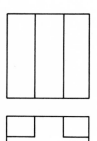

Fig. 5.47

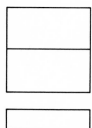

Fig. 5.48

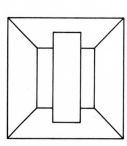

Fig. 5.49

5.24 Make an isometric sketch of each of your three solutions of Problem 5.23.

5.25 Sketch three front and side views consistent with the top view given in Fig. 5.50.

5.26 Make isometric sketches of each of your three solutions of Problem 5.25.

5.27 Sketch three top and side views consistent with the front view given in Fig. 5.51.

5.28 Make an isometric or oblique sketch of each of your three solutions of Problem 5.27.

5.29 Sketch three front and side views consistent with the top view given in Fig. 5.52.

5.30 Make an isometric or oblique sketch of each of your three solutions of Problem 5.29.

Pictorial Sketches

The making of pictorial sketches from orthographic drawings provides excellent practice in reading drawings. In all cases the object should be drawn to show its shape to best advantage.

5.31 Make an isometric sketch of the object shown in Fig. 5.53.

5.32 Sketch the object shown in Fig. 5.54 in isometric form as assigned by the instructor.

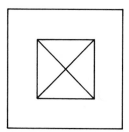

Fig. 5.50

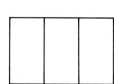

Fig. 5.51

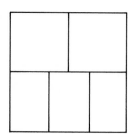

Fig. 5.52

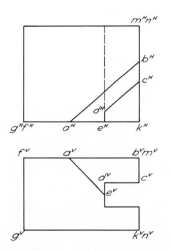

Fig. 5.53   Cut block.

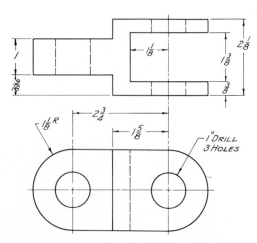

Fig. 5.54   Link.

5.33 Make an isometric sketch of the abutment shown in Fig. 5.55.

5.34 Make an oblique sketch of the bearing cap shown in Fig. 5.56.

5.35 Make an oblique sketch of the link shown in Fig. 5.54.

5.36 Make an oblique sketch of the face-plate blank shown in Fig. 5.57.

5.37 Make an isometric sketch of the lever shown in Fig. 5.58.

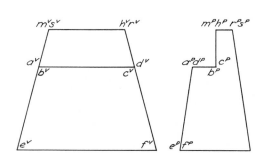

Fig. 5.55   Abutment.

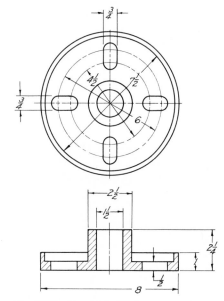

Fig. 5.57   Face-plate blank.

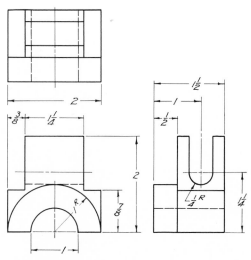

Fig. 5.56   Bearing cap.

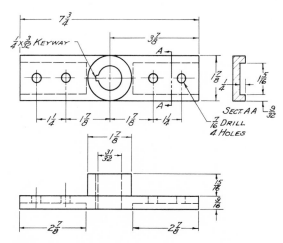

Fig. 5.58   Lever arm.

5.38 Make an isometric sketch of the bracket shown in Fig. 5.59.

5.39 Make an oblique sketch of the bevel washer shown in Fig. 5.60.

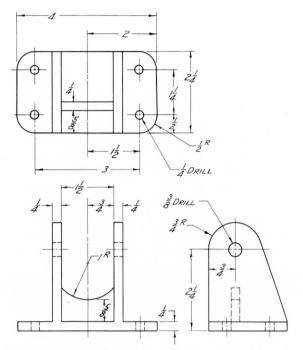

Fig. 5.59   Hinge bracket.

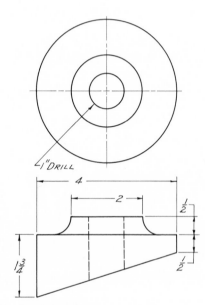

Fig. 5.60   Beveled washer.

5.40 Make a two- or three-view freehand sketch, as needed, to describe the shape of an object assigned from Fig.

5.61. Make your sketch about twice the size shown in the pictorial drawing.

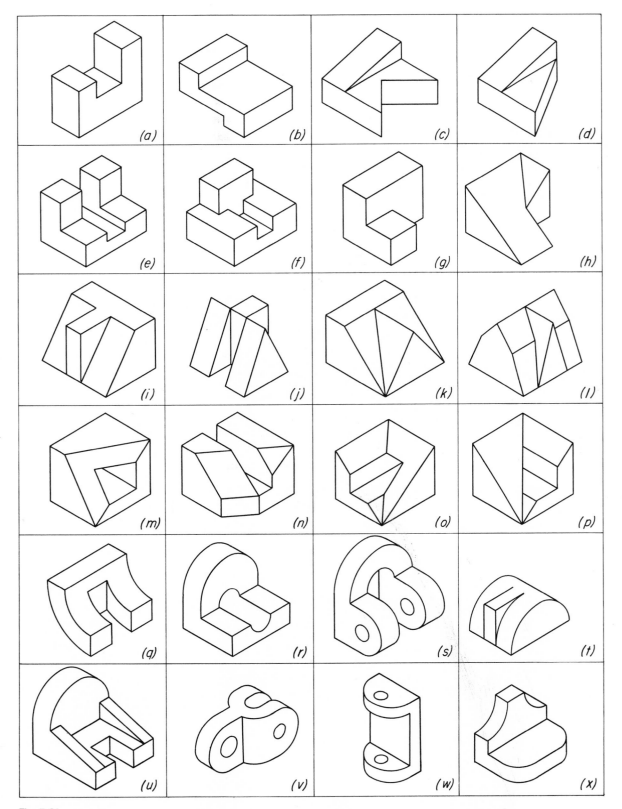

Fig. 5.61

CHAPTER 6
Orthographic Projection

NEW: Road grader. (The Caterpillar Tractor Company.)

OLD: Road building with primitive leveller. (The Bettmann Archive.)

Chapter 6   Orthographic Projection

6.1   DEFINITION. A projection is a drawing that represents or outlines a three-dimensional object on a two-dimensional surface. It is drawn on a plane or other surface as it would be seen by looking through the surface from a certain point of sight. See Fig. 6.1. In engineering the most commonly used type of projection is called orthographic projection.

Orthographic projection is the representation of an object on a plane of projection when the lines of sight from the eye to the object are perpendicular to the plane of projection. See Fig. 6.2.

6.2   ELEMENTS OF PROJECTION. In making any projection, there are four factors to be considered. These factors are called the elements of projection. They are:

a. The point of sight.
b. The lines of sight.
c. The plane of projection.
d. The object.

They are all illustrated in Fig. 6.1.

6.3   AXIOMS OF ORTHOGRAPHIC PROJECTION. In orthographic projection, the relationships among the four elements are definite and remain constant. These relationships identify orthographic projection and are listed in the following paragraphs.

6.3.1   Point of sight. The point of sight is the real or imaginary position of the eye of the observer when viewing the object. The eye of the observer may be placed at any position desired for this purpose.

For orthographic projection the point of sight is considered to be at an infinite distance from the object.

6.3.2   Lines of sight. All lines joining the eye or point of sight with points on the object are called lines of sight. *In orthographic projection, the lines of sight for any view are parallel to one another and perpendicular to the plane of projection.* See Fig. 6.2.

6.3.3   Plane of projection. The plane upon which the object is projected is called the plane of projection. Since the lines of sight must be perpendicular to the planes in orthographic projection, it is necessary to have a different plane for each point of sight. Thus for a one-view drawing there would be one plane and one point of sight and for a three-view drawing there would be three planes of projection and three points of sight.

The planes most commonly used are a *horizontal plane,* a *vertical plane* which is perpendicular to the horizontal plane, and a *profile plane* which is perpen-

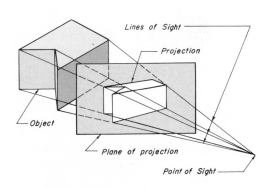

Fig. 6.1   Projection of an object.

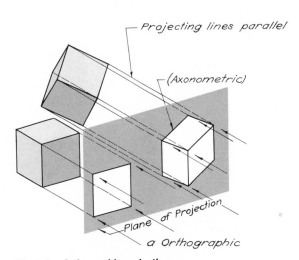

Fig. 6.2   Orthographic projection.

123

dicular to both the horizontal plane and the vertical plane. These are illustrated in Fig. 6.3. As a group they are called the *principal planes of projection*.

6.3.4   Object. Any object, either real or imaginary, may be drawn in orthographic projection. Theoretically, it can have any relation to the plane of projection. However, the usual purpose of making an orthographic projection is to give a complete and accurate description of the shape of the object. To accomplish this, certain rules for setting up the object have been established:

a. Place the object in its natural position or in the position in which it is to be used.
b. Place the object so that its faces will be parallel to the principal planes of projection.
c. Turn the object so that its most important or most descriptive face is parallel to the vertical plane.
d. Select the views that will show the most visible lines.

6.4   THE PROJECTION. The projection is obtained by finding the points at which the lines of sight pierce the plane of projection and connecting them in the proper order. *Every line on the object must show as a point or a line on the projection.* If the line can be seen from the point of sight, it is represented by a solid line known as a visible outline. See Fig. 6.4. If the line is

hidden behind some other part of the object, it is represented by a dashed line known as an invisible outline. See Fig. 6.4. All of the various kinds of lines that may be found on a drawing or projection are shown in Fig. 6.4.

6.5   QUADRANTS OR ANGLES. When the vertical plane, or *V*-plane, has been set up perpendicular to the horizontal plane, or *H*-plane, these two planes divide all space into four quadrants or angles, as shown in Fig. 6.3. In discussing these quadrants, the observer is considered to be in front of the *V*-plane and facing it. Thus the part of an object closest to the observer is said to be the front and the part farthest from the observer, the rear. Right and left are also taken from this position of the observer.

As indicated in Fig. 6.3, that portion of space in front of the *V*-plane and above the *H*-plane is called *first quadrant*. That portion of space behind the *V*-plane and above the *H*-plane is called the *second quadrant*. The *third quadrant* is behind the *V*-plane and below the *H*-plane, and the *fourth quadrant* is in front of the *V*-plane and below the *H*-plane.

It is possible to place an object in any of the quadrants for purposes of orthographic projection but *in the United States almost all drawings are made with the object in the third quadrant.* This has come to be known as third-angle projection. In Europe most of

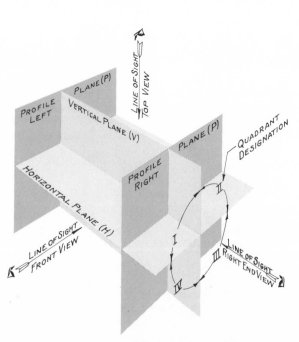

Fig. 6.3   The principal coordinate planes and quadrants.

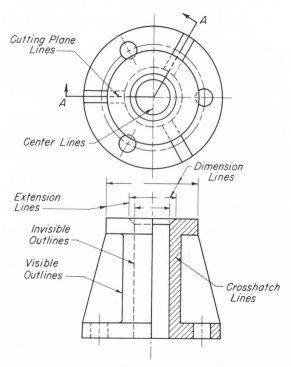

Fig. 6.4   Use of types of lines.

the drawings are made in first-angle projection. Figure 6.5 shows an object in each quadrant together with its projections.

The position of the profile plane, or P-plane, has no effect on the quadrant. It may be placed either to the right or to the left as desired. *In third-quadrant projection the plane of projection always lies between the* *point of sight and the object.*

6.6   ROTATION OF COORDINATE PLANES. When projections, such as those shown in Fig. 6.5, have been made on the various planes, they are still of little use until they can be brought together on a single sheet of paper. To do this, the planes of projection are considered to be the sides of a transparent box surrounding

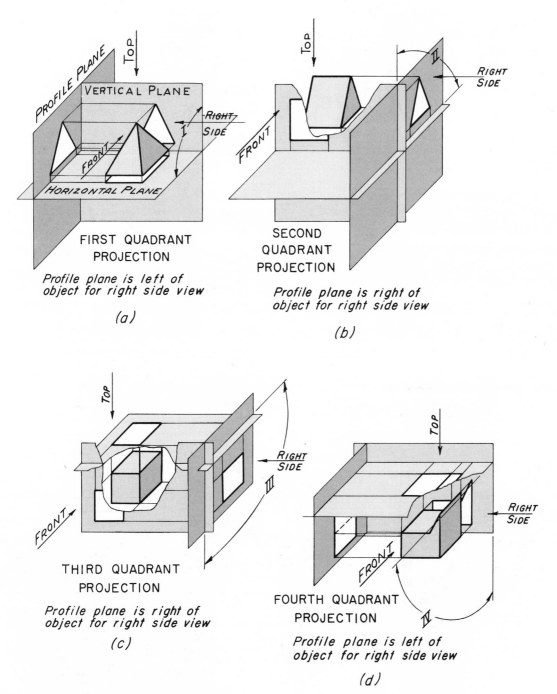

Fig. 6.5   Space location of objects in the four quadrants.

the object, as shown in Fig. 6.6. The sides of the box are then unfolded as shown in Fig. 6.6(*a*) until they lie in the vertical plane. The direction of rotation of the planes must be such that the lines of sight, if rotated with the planes, would point to the front of the sheet of paper as shown in Fig. 6.6(*b*). *In third and first quad-*

rant this means that the plane of projection always revolves away from the object. This is indicated by the curved arrows in Fig. 6.6(*a*).

There are six principal views that may be drawn, as shown in Fig. 6.7(*b*). The front, top, right-side, and left-side views are the views most used. The rear view

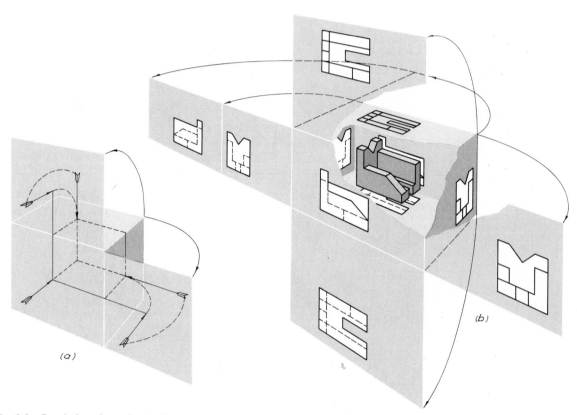

Fig. 6.6 Revolution of coordinate planes.

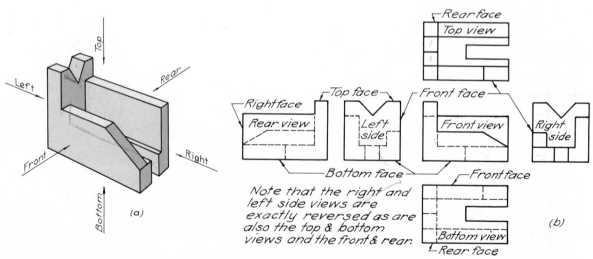

Fig. 6.7 Arrangements of views.

and the bottom view are used occasionally. The direction from which the object is viewed in each of these views is shown in Fig. 6.7(*a*).

There is a definite arrangement in which these views must be placed in third-angle projection as shown in Fig. 6.7(*b*).

a. The top view must be directly above the front view in vertical alignment so that points may be projected vertically from one view to the other.

b. The right-side view is directly to the right of the front view in horizontal alignment so that points may be projected horizontally from one view to the other.

c. The left-side view is directly to the left of the front view.

d. The rear view may be placed to the left of the left-side view or to the right of the right-side view.

e. The bottom view must be directly below the front view in vertical alignment so that points may be projected vertically from one view to the other.

These relationships are referred to as having the views in *projection*.

6.7 PROJECTION LINES. In constructing the views of any point, line, plane, or solid, it is frequently necessary to draw lines from one view to another to keep the projections in their proper alignment and to transfer distances from the front and top views to the side or profile views. This is shown in Fig. 6.8. The method shown at the right, using the 45° mitering line, is the best since it is easier to maintain accuracy when a single angle must be made. These distances can also be transferred very accurately by using dividers, as indicated in Fig. 6.9.

6.8 PROJECTION OF POINTS. Every corner of an object can be considered as an abstract point and can be projected accordingly. Theoretically a point has no dimensions, but does have a location. It can be located in space by measuring in three directions from the established planes of projection or from any other planes that appear edgewise in any view. A point also may be located in space by measuring from an established point in three directions, each perpendicular to one of the three principal planes of projection.

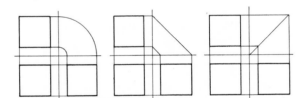

Fig. 6.8   Methods of transferring distances from top to side views.

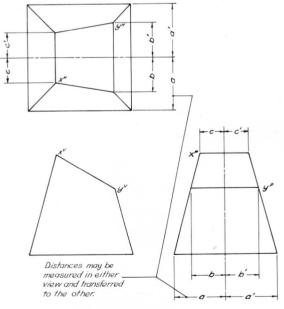

Distances may be measured in either view and transferred to the other.

Fig. 6.9   Transferring distances by measurement.

A point in space is located on a drawing by two or more projections, which are identified by an accepted system of lettering. See Fig. 6.10.

6.9 NOMENCLATURE. Each point in space is identified by a capital letter such as A. See Fig. 6.10. The capital letter will refer only to the point in space and will not appear on the drawing except for occasional use on a pictorial view. Projections of point A are designated by the small letter a. To differentiate the projections of the point, the horizontal projection or top view of point A will be marked a^H. The vertical projection or front view will be marked a^V, and the profile projection or side view will be marked a^P. In each case the superscript refers to the plane on which the point has been projected. Thus the projection of point A on an auxiliary plane 1 will be marked a^1, and on a second auxiliary plane 2 it will be marked a^2.

6.10 LOCATION OF A POINT. The principal views or projections of a point may be located when its dis-

tances from the three coordinate planes are known. These distances must be measured in the view in which the plane shows edgewise. Thus in Fig. 6.11(a) the line marked H-V represents the edgewise view of the H-plane when looking at the vertical and the profile planes of projection. The same line, H-V, becomes the edgewise view of the V-plane when seen from the top. The vertical line marked V-P is the edgewise view of the P-plane when seen from the top or front. It also represents the edgewise view of the V-plane when viewed from the profile point of sight. *Any two views that lie on the same perpendicular to a reference line are called adjacent views.*

In Fig. 6.11(a), the vertical projection or front view, a^V, of the point A has been located by measuring P distance to the left of the P-plane and h distance below the H-plane. The horizontal projection, a^H, of the point A has been located by measuring the same P distance left of the P-plane and v distance behind the V-plane. The profile projection, a^P, may be located by

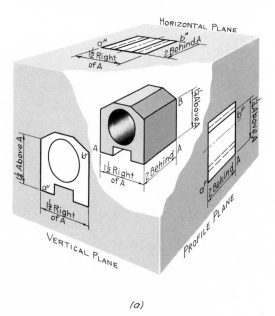

(a)

Fig. 6.10 Space relationship of points.

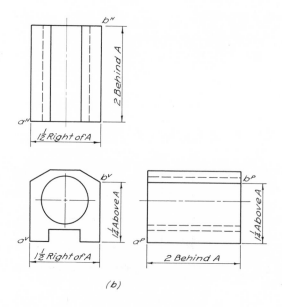

(b)

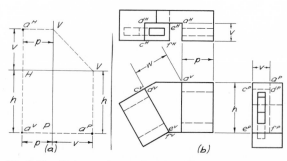

Fig. 6.11 Distances from points to planes.

projection, as in Fig. 6.8, or by measuring the h distance below the H-plane and the v distance behind the V-plane. In every such problem the projection, a^H, must be in vertical alignment above a^V, and a^P must be in horizontal alignment with a^V. The projection a^P must be to the right of a^V if a right-side is taken and to the left if a left-side view is taken.

The distance from a point to any plane may be measured in the view in which the plane shows edgewise. Thus in Fig. 6.11(b) the distance w from point A to the plane $CDEF$ will show in the front view.

A point may also be located from some other point as in Fig. 6.10. It can be seen that distances right or left and above or below may be measured in the front view. In the top view, distances right or left and front or back can be measured. The profile view will show distances above or below and front or back as indicated in Fig. 6.10.

EXERCISES

Use full scale on all problems. When the letters H, V, and P are used alone, they refer to the H-, V-, and P-planes.

6.1 On an $8\frac{1}{2} \times 11$ sheet assume two reference lines perpendicular to each other near the center of the sheet to represent the coordinate planes. Plot the H-, V-, and P-projections of the points specified below and letter them properly.

Locate point A $4''$ left of P, $3''$ below H, and $1\frac{1}{2}''$ behind V.

Locate point B $3''$ right of A, $1''$ above A, and $2''$ behind V.

Locate point C $1\frac{1}{2}''$ left of B, $1''$ below H, and $\frac{1}{2}''$ in front of A.

Locate point D $\frac{1}{2}''$ right of A, $\frac{1}{2}''$ below C, and $1\frac{1}{2}''$ in front of B.

6.2 In Fig. 6.10 there are two high points on the rear face. Locate the right one of these with respect to point A.

6.3 In Fig. 6.11(b) there is a point on the rear face, on the top face, and farthest to the left. How far is this point from the left inclined face and from the right vertical face? Letter this point O.

6.11   LINES. A line may be defined as the path of a moving point. Lines therefore have location, direction, and length. They may be either straight or curved.

On the drawing board or in the field, a straight line may be determined by the following:

a. Two points.
b. One point and a direction.

6.11.1   Position of lines. Lines may be grouped into three distinct classifications with respect to their relationship to the coordinate or reference planes. These classifications are:

a. Perpendicular to one of the coordinate planes and parallel to the other two.
b. Parallel to one of the coordinate planes and inclined to the other two.
c. Oblique to all three coordinate planes.

The angle that a line or plane makes with the H-plane is called θ, with the V-plane φ, and with the P-plane π.

It is easy to remember these notations if we think of the angle θ, which is the angle that a line or plane makes with the H-plane, as a circle with a horizontal line through it. Likewise, the angle ϕ, which is the angle that a line or plane makes with the V-plane, is a circle with a vertical line through it. The angle π, which a line or plane makes with the P-plane, is easy to remember.

6.12   LINES PERPENDICULAR TO ONE OF THE COORDINATE PLANES. When a line is perpendicular to a coordinate plane, it projects on that plane as a point. This is illustrated in the following paragraphs.

6.12.1   Line perpendicular to the horizontal plane. Figure 6.12(a) shows the line AB, which is perpendic-

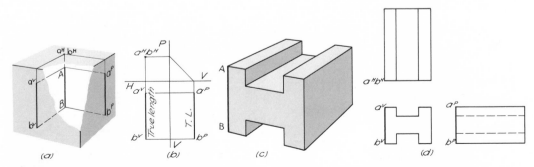

Fig. 6.12   Line perpendicular to the horizontal plane.

ular to the *H*-plane. The horizontal projection of the line, $a^H b^H$, projects as a point. This proves that the line is perpendicular to the *H*-plane. In that position the line must be parallel to the *V*- and *P*-planes. Therefore the vertical projection of the line, $a^V b^V$, and the profile projection of the line, $a^P b^P$, both show the true length of the line. The three orthographic views of this line are shown in Fig. 6.12(*b*). Figure 6.12(*c*) shows a pictorial view of an object having 12 such lines. One of these is lettered *AB* and shown in the orthographic projections in Fig. 6.12(*d*). When reading the orthographic drawing in Fig. 6.12(*d*), the student should be able to recognize and visualize the three projections of all 12 of these lines and letter them if desired.

6.12.2   Line perpendicular to the vertical plane.
Figure 6.13 shows the pictorial positions and projections of a line that is perpendicular to the *V*-plane. As in the previous figure, one projection, $a^V b^V$, is a point and the other two projections are true-length views of the line. As a reading exercise the student should be able to recognize and letter the three projections of all such lines on the object. There are 12 of these lines in Fig. 6.13(*c*).

6.12.3   Line perpendicular to the profile plane.
Figure 6.14 shows the pictorial view and projections of a line that is perpendicular to the *P*-plane. Here the profile projection is a point and the horizontal and vertical projections are in true length. There are 12 similar lines on the object. The student should be able to recognize all of these lines and letter them if necessary.

EXERCISES

Use full scale on all problems.

6.4   In Fig. 6.12(*d*), letter two other lines on the figure that are perpendicular to the *H*-plane. Choose one the same length as *AB* and one shorter. What is the length of each line? _____   _____

6.5   In Fig. 6.13(*d*), letter two other lines on the object that are perpendicular to the *V*-plane. Choose one of them on the top of the object and the other on the bottom. What is the length of each line? _____   _____

6.6   In Fig. 6.14(*d*), letter two other lines on the object that are perpendicular to the profile plane. Select a long one on the rear of the object and a short one on the front of the object. What is the length of each line? _____ _____

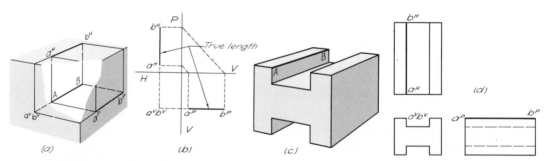

Fig. 6.13   Line perpendicular to the vertical plane.

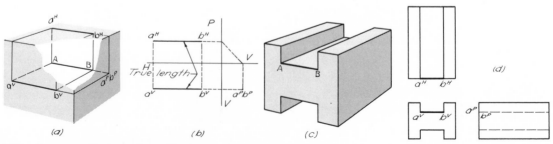

Fig. 6.14   Line perpendicular to the profile plane.

6.13 LINES PARALLEL TO ONE COORDINATE PLANE AND INCLINED TO THE OTHER TWO. When a line is parallel to a coordinate plane, the projection on that plane will be true-length. In the true-length view the angle that the line makes with two of the coordinate planes can be measured. The angle with the *H*-plane is called θ, with the *V*-plane ϕ, and with the *P*-plane π.

If a line is parallel to the horizontal plane, it is called an *H*-parallel. If it is parallel to the *V*-plane, it is called a *V*-parallel, and if it is parallel to the *P*-plane, it is called a *P*-parallel.

6.13.1 Line parallel to the horizontal plane. In Figs. 6.15(*a*) and (*b*), line *AB* is parallel to the horizontal plane and inclined to the vertical and profile planes. Therefore, both the vertical and profile projections appear parallel to the horizontal reference line which represents the edgewise view of the horizontal plane in those projections.

In this position the horizontal projection shows the true length of the line. It also shows the true size of the angles ϕ and π.

When measuring the angle between a line and a plane, it is necessary to have the true length of the line and the edgewise view of the plane in the same view.

Figures 6.15(*c*) and (*d*) show a line of this type on an object. In learning to read the drawing, the student should recognize and locate four such lines on the object.

6.13.2 Line parallel to the vertical plane. In like manner a line parallel to the *V*-plane and inclined to the *H*-plane and the *P*-plane is shown in Figs. 6.16(*a*) and (*b*). In this case the horizontal and profile projections are parallel to the reference line which represents the edgewise view of the *V*-plane. The vertical projection, a^Vb^V, is the true length of the line and the angles θ and π also are true-size. Such a line is shown on an object in Figs. 6.16(*c*) and (*d*). There are four such lines on the object, which should be identified by the student.

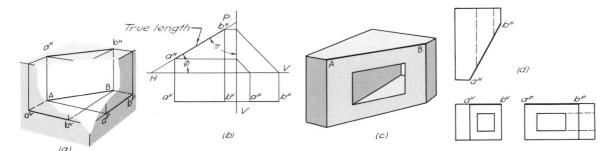

Fig. 6.15 **Line parallel to the horizontal plane.**

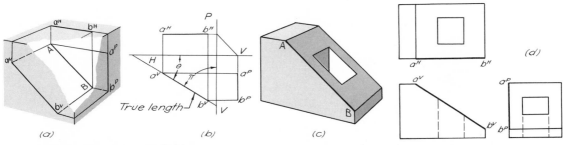

Fig. 6.16 **Line parallel to the vertical plane.**

6.13.3   Line parallel to the profile plane. Figure 6.17 shows a line parallel to the P-plane and inclined to the H-plane and V-plane. In this figure the profile projection, $a^P b^P$, shows the true length of the line and the true size of the angles θ and ϕ. The other two projections are parallel to the vertical reference line which represents the edgewise view of the P-plane. There are four such lines on this object. See Figs. 6.17(c) and (d).

EXERCISES

Use full scale on all problems.

6.7 In Fig. 6.15(d), letter the lower of the two short lines that are parallel to the horizontal and inclined to the vertical and profile planes. Indicate the correct values of ϕ and π. What is the length of this line? _____

6.8 In Fig. 6.16(d), letter the front one of the two short lines that are parallel to the vertical plane and inclined to the horizontal and profile planes. Indicate the true values of θ and π. What is the true length of the line? _____

6.9 In Fig. 6.17(d), letter the left one of the two short lines that are parallel to the P-plane and inclined to the H-plane and V-plane. Indicate the true values of θ and ϕ. What is the true length of the line? _____

6.14   LINES OBLIQUE TO ALL THREE COORDINATE PLANES. A line that is oblique to all three coordinate planes has all of its projections inclined to the reference lines. *Its true length does not show in any of these views nor do the true angles that the line forms with the coordinate planes.* Such a line is shown in Fig. 6.18.

EXERCISES

Use full scale in all problems. When the letters H, V, and P are used alone, they refer to the principal coordinate planes.

6.10 On an 8½ × 11 sheet near its center, assume two reference lines perpendicular to each other to represent the coordinate planes. Plot the H, V, and P projections of the following lines and letter them properly.

Point A is 2″ right of P, 2″ below H, and 1″ behind V. Draw line AB perpendicular to H, 1″ long; B is lower than A.
Draw line BC perpendicular to P, ½″ long; C is left of B.
Draw line CD perpendicular to H, 1½″ long; D is above C.

6.11 On an 8½ × 11 sheet, near its center assume two reference lines perpendicular to each other to represent the coordinate planes. Draw the projections of the following points and lines and letter them properly.

Point E is 1″ left of P, 2″ below H, and ½″ behind V.
EF is parallel to H, 45° to V, and 1½″ long. F is left of E and behind E.
FG is parallel to V, 30° to H, and 1″ long. G is right of F and above F.

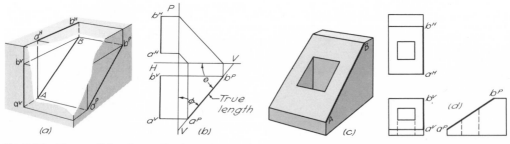

Fig. 6.17   Line parallel to the profile plane.

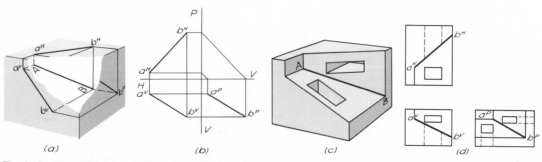

Fig. 6.18   Line oblique to all principal coordinate planes.

GK is parallel to *P*, 30° to *V*, and ¾″ long. *K* is in front of *G* and above *G*.

6.12 On an 8½ × 11 sheet, assume two reference lines perpendicular to each other to represent the coordinate planes. Plot the projections of *AB* and letter them properly.

Point *A* is 3″ right of *P*, 2″ below *H*, and 2″ behind *V*. Line *AB* is inclined to *H*, *V*, and *P*. *B* is left of *A*, above *A*, and in front of *A*.

6.13 In Fig. 6.18(*d*), construct and letter a line in space, *CD*, that joins two corners of the object and is inclined to all three coordinate planes. This will not be a line on the object.

6.14 In Fig. 6.18(*d*), letter a line, *EF*, on the object that is parallel to the vertical plane and inclined to the horizontal and profile planes.

6.15 In Fig. 6.18(*d*), letter a line, *GK*, on the object, that is parallel to the horizontal plane and inclined to the vertical plane.

6.16 In Fig. 6.18(*d*), construct and letter a line *MN*, in space that joins two corners of the object and is parallel to the profile and inclined to the horizontal and vertical planes. This will not be a line on the object.

6.15 PLANES. A plane is a flat surface which may be located or determined by the following:

a. A point and a line.
b. Three points.
c. Two intersecting lines.
d. Two parallel lines.
e. A line and an angle with some reference plane.

A plane surface has length and breadth but no thickness. A plane may be extended as far as desired in any direction, but cannot be bent or broken. All planes may be divided into three groups.

a. Parallel to one of the coordinate planes and perpendicular to the other two. These are sometimes called normal planes.
b. Perpendicular to one of the coordinate planes and

inclined to the other two. These are referred to as inclined planes.

c. Oblique to all three coordinate planes. These are called simply oblique planes.

For the purpose of reading and understanding orthographic projections, the ability to recognize and visualize planes in their various positions is very important. Recognizing the general shape of a plane is valuable. A plane will retain the same general shape in every view. If a plane is shaped like the letter U, as in Figs. 6.20(*c*) and (*d*), it will retain that same general shape whenever it appears as an area. In Figs. 6.24(*c*) and (*d*), the shaded plane is a trapezoid and therefore whenever it appears as an area it will still be a trapezoid.

6.16 PLANES PARALLEL TO ONE OF THE PRINCIPAL COORDINATE PLANES AND PERPENDICULAR TO THE OTHER TWO. These planes have two principal views which show edgewise. These views are always parallel to the reference lines which represent the edgewise view of the adjacent plane. This adjacent view in each case shows the true shape of the plane surface.

6.16.1 Parallel to the horizontal. In Fig. 6.19(*a*), the plane *ABCD* is parallel to the *H*-plane. In Fig. 6.19(*b*), the plane shows edgewise in the vertical and profile views, and these views are parallel to the horizontal reference line. The horizontal reference line in these views represents the edgewise view of the *H*-plane. Planes parallel to the *H*-plane are called *H*-parallels. The horizontal projection, $a^H b^H c^H d^H$, gives the true shape of the plane figure.

Figures 6.19(*c*) and (*d*) show an object on which such a plane surface has been shaded. The vertical and profile views are indicated by a heavy line.

There are three other *H*-parallel planes on the object. The student should identify all of them and label the projections.

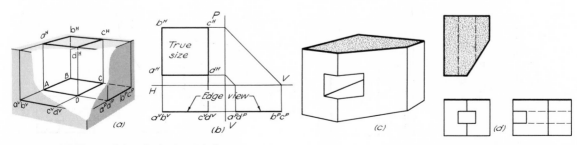

Fig. 6.19 **Plane parallel to the horizontal plane.**

6.16.2   Parallel to the vertical. In Fig. 6.20(*a*), the plane *ABCD* is parallel to the vertical plane. In Fig. 6.20(*b*), the plane shows edgewise in the horizontal and profile views. These views are parallel to the reference line that represents the edgewise view of the vertical plane in each case. The vertical projection $a^V b^V c^V d^V$ gives the true shape of the plane figure. Such a plane on an object is shown as a shaded area in Figs. 6.20(*c*) and (*d*). In Fig. 6.20(*d*) the horizontal and profile views of the plane are shown as heavy lines. Planes parallel to the *V*-plane are called *V*-parallels. There is one other *V*-parallel plane on the object. The student should recognize and identify it and label the projections.

6.16.3   Parallel to the profile. In Fig. 6.21(*a*) the plane *ABCD* is parallel to the profile plane. In Fig. 6.21(*b*) the plane projects edgewise in both the horizontal and vertical projections. These views in each case are parallel to the reference line that represents the edgewise view of the profile plane. The profile projection $a^P b^P c^P d^P$ gives the true shape of the plane

figure. Planes parallel to the *P*-plane are called *P*-parallels.

In Fig. 6.21(*c*) the shaded area identifies a plane on an object in this position. In Fig. 6.21(*d*) the horizontal and vertical projections are shown as heavy lines and the profile projection of the area is shaded.

There are three other *P*-parallel planes on the object. The student should identify each and label the projections.

6.17   PLANES PERPENDICULAR TO ONE OF THE PRINCIPAL COORDINATE PLANES AND INCLINED TO THE OTHER TWO. These planes have one principal view which shows edgewise. This view is inclined to both of the principal reference lines. The other two views show as areas, but they are not of true size.

The angle between two planes can be measured when both planes show edgewise in the same view. Therefore it is possible to measure the angles between one of these planes and two of the coordinate planes in the view that shows the given plane edgewise.

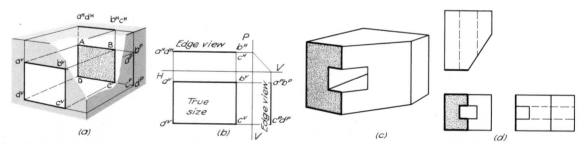

Fig. 6.20   Plane parallel to the vertical plane.

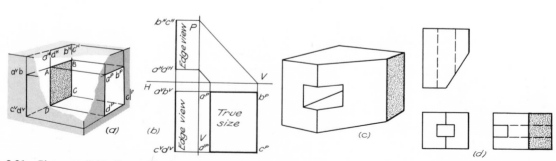

Fig. 6.21   Plane parallel to the profile plane.

6.17.1   Planes perpendicular to the horizontal plane. Figure 6.22(*a*) shows a pictorial view of a plane that is perpendicular to the horizontal plane and inclined to the *V*- and *P*-planes. In this case, as illustrated in Fig. 6.22(*b*), the horizontal projection or top view of the plane must be edgewise and inclined to the reference lines that represent the edgewise views of the *V*-plane and *P*-plane. The angle ϕ between the edgewise view of the plane ($a^H b^H c^H d^H$) and the horizontal reference line that represents the edgewise view of the *V*-plane is the angle that the plane makes with the *V*-plane. The angle π between the edgewise view of the plane ($a^H b^H c^H d^H$) and the vertical reference line that represents the edgewise view of the *P*-plane is the angle between the plane *ABCD* and the *P*-plane.

The other two views of the plane show as areas that are not of true shape. This plane is frequently called an *H*-projecting plane.

Figure 6.22(*c*) shows a picture of this plane on an object, and Fig. 6.22(*d*) shows the projections of the object with the edgewise view made heavy and the other two shaded. Examine Fig. 6.22(*d*) to see if any other similar planes can be found.

6.17.2   Planes perpendicular to the vertical plane. Figure 6.23(*a*) shows a plane in the pictorial form which is perpendicular to the *V*-plane and inclined to the *H*-plane and *P*-plane. Figure 6.23(*b*) shows the three principal projections of the plane with the edgewise view of the plane *ABCD* and the angle θ and π indicated in the vertical projection. The horizontal and profile projections of plane *ABCD* show as areas which are not true in shape. This plane is commonly called a *V*-projecting plane.

Figures 6.23(*c*) and (*d*) show a plane perpendicular to the *V*-plane and inclined to the *H*-plane and *P*-plane, in a pictorial and in a two-view drawing. Identify any other planes on the object which are also perpendicular to the *V*-plane and inclined to the *H*-plane and *P*-plane.

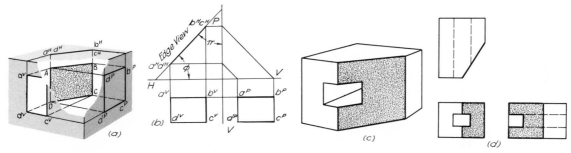

Fig. 6.22   Plane perpendicular to the horizontal plane.

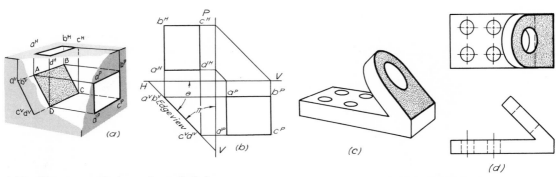

Fig. 6.23   Plane perpendicular to the vertical plane.

6.17.3 Planes perpendicular to the profile plane.
A plane perpendicular to the profile and inclined to the
H-plane and *V*-plane is shown pictorially in Fig.
6.24(*a*). The three views of this plane are shown in Fig.
6.24(*b*), with the edgewise view and the angles θ and ϕ
indicated in the profile projection. The two views of
the plane *ABCD* which show as areas are not of true
shape. Figures 6.24(*c*) and (*d*) show such a plane on an
object with the areas shaded and the edgewise view
made heavy.

Examine Fig. 6.24(*d*) to see if any other planes of
this kind can be found on the object.

**6.18 PLANES OBLIQUE TO ALL THREE PRINCI-
PAL COORDINATE PLANES.** A plane of this kind does
not have an edgewise view in any of the three principal views and consequently none of the angles with
the coordinate planes can be measured. All three
principal projections will show as areas which are not
of true shape. Figures 6.25(*a*) and (*b*) show a plane of
this kind in pictorial form and in orthographic projection. Figures 6.25(*c*) and (*d*) show an object in pictorial
form and in projection with a plane oblique to all three
principal coordinate planes.

At the present time it is possible to describe these

planes only as oblique to *H*, *V*, and *P*. In the following
chapters methods will be shown to determine the true
shape of the plane and the true size of the angles θ, ϕ,
and π. Examine Fig. 6.25(*d*) to see if any similar planes
can be found.

EXERCISES

Use full scale in all problems.

6.17 On an 8½ × 11 sheet, near its center, assume two reference lines perpendicular to each other to represent
the coordinate planes. Draw the projections of the
point and planes.

Point *A* is 3″ left of *P*, 2″ below *H*, and 2″ behind *V*.
Plane *ABCD* is a 1″ square parallel to *H*. *A* is the left
   rear corner, the sides are all parallel or perpendic-
   ular to the coordinate planes, and *B* is right of *A*. *C*
   is in front of *B*.
Plane *CDEF* is a 1″ square parallel to *V*, and *E* is below
   D.
Plane *BCFG* is a 1″ square parallel to *P*.

6.18 On an 8½ × 11 sheet, near its center, assume two reference lines perpendicular to each other to represent
the coordinate planes. Draw the projections of the
point and planes.
Point *A* is 3″ left of *P*, 2″ below *H*, and 2″ behind *V*.
Plane *ABCD* is a 1″ square perpendicular to *H*, ϕ is

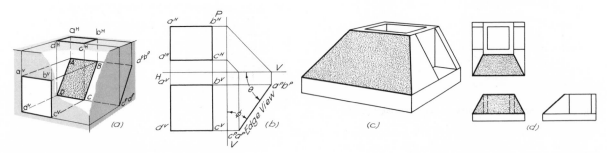

Fig. 6.24   Plane perpendicular to the profile plane.

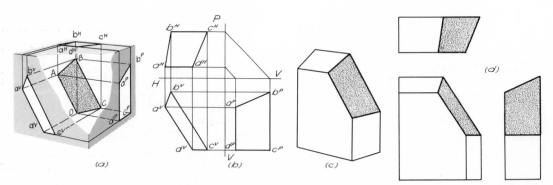

Fig. 6.25   Plane oblique to the *H*-, *V*-, and *P*-planes.

30°, and *D* is directly below *A*. *B* and *C* are closer to the *V*-plane than *A* and *D*. *B* is at the same height as *A* and to the right of *A*.

Plane *BEFG* is a 1″ square perpendicular to *V*, θ is 45°, and *G* is directly behind *B*. *E* is the same distance from the *V*-plane as *B*. *E* is above and to the right of *B*.

Plane *EHKN* is a 1″ square perpendicular to *P*, θ is 60°, and *H* is directly to the right of *E*. *K* and *N* are nearer the *H*-plane and farther from the *V*-plane than *E* and *H*. *K* is the same distance from the *P*-plane as *H*.

6.19 On an 8½ × 11 sheet, near its center, assume two reference lines at right angles to each other to represent the coordinate planes. Plot the *H*, *V*, and *P* projections of each plane and letter them properly.

Point *A* is 2″ right of *P*, 2″ below *H*, and 2″ behind *V*. Plane *ABCD* is a rhomboid inclined to *H*, *V*, and *P*. Make the lines and angles of any desired size.

6.20 How can you tell by the projections when a line is perpendicular to the horizontal? _____ ____ ____
_____

6.21 In Fig. 6.25(*d*), letter all three projections of a line, *AB*, that is perpendicular to the *H*-plane.

6.22 In Fig. 6.24(*d*), letter the shortest line, *BC*, that you can find that is perpendicular to the *V*-plane.

6.23 In Fig. 6.23(*d*), letter a line, *CD*, that is perpendicular to the profile.

6.24 How do you know from the projections when a line is parallel to one of the coordinate planes? ____ _____
____ _____ ____ _____ ____ ____ _____ ____ _____
____ _____ ____ _____ ____ _____ ____ _____
_____ ____ _____ ____ _____ ____ _____

6.25 In Fig. 6.24(*d*), letter a line, *DE*, on the object that is parallel to the *V*-plane and inclined to the *H*- and *P*-planes. Indicate the angle that the line makes with the horizontal.

6.26 In Fig. 6.15(*d*), letter the corners of a plane that is perpendicular to the *H*-plane and inclined to the *V*-plane. Label the angle π.

6.27 In Fig. 6.24(*d*), indicate, by shading, a plane that is perpendicular to the *V*-plane and inclined to the *P*-plane. Indicate the angle θ.

6.28 In Fig. 6.17(*d*), indicate, by shading, a plane that is perpendicular to the *P*-plane and inclined to the *V*-plane. Indicate the angle φ.

6.29 For a plane that is oblique to all three principal coordinate planes, the horizontal projection shows as an _____ .

6.19 SOLIDS. Points, lines, and planes are the building blocks from which three dimensional objects, known as solids, are constructed. The purpose of orthographic projection is to enable one person to make an engineering drawing of a solid which will so completely describe the shape of an object that another person can visualize it without further information.

6.19.1 Solids bounded by plane surfaces. There are many solids bounded by plane surfaces, but the most common ones are illustrated in Fig. 6.26. The cube and the rectangular solid are used more than any others in engineering work. The prism and pyramid also appear frequently. For complete description three views are almost always necessary. However, common usage has come to accept two views by assuming that

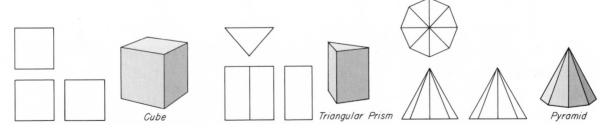

Fig. 6.26 Solids bounded by plane surfaces.

the simplest form is the one meant. Thus in Fig. 6.27, if only the top and the front views were given, the object would be accepted as a cube. The additional side views show possible shapes having the same top and front views. If any of these were desired, the side view would have to be shown.

6.19.2 Solids bounded by plane and single-curved surfaces. Objects such as the cylinder, cone, and frustum are shown in Fig. 6.28. These solids are bounded by plane surfaces on the ends and single-curved surfaces on the sides. For these objects, two views are sufficient even though three views are shown.

Cylindrical holes in a part form a good illustration of this shape. They are shown by two dotted lines that form the boundary of the surface in one view and by a circle in the other view. See Fig. 6.10.

6.19.3 Solids bounded by double-curved surfaces. The sphere, spheroid, and torus are examples of objects bounded by double-curved surfaces. They are illustrated in Fig. 6.29. Two views are sufficient.

6.19.4 Surfaces involving warped surfaces. There is a wide variety of warped surfaces that may become a bounding surface of solid objects. A few common objects involving helicoids are shown in Fig. 6.30.

6.20 READING A DRAWING. The interpretation or reading of a drawing requires an analysis of the various views of the object. It is necessary to find the various projections of each individual point and the relation of each point to the others. The location, length, and direction of each line must be visualized. The planes formed by these points and lines as well as their position and shape must be evident. And, finally, the simple solids of which the part is composed must be separated mentally or pictorially before the object as a whole can be completely understood.

6.20.1 Interpretation of lines. A line may represent one or more of three things in any sketch or drawing.

a. The intersection of two plane faces.
b. The edgewise view of a plane surface.
c. The outside line of a curved or cylindrical object.

The engineer or technician must always have these interpretations in mind when reading or making a drawing.

In Fig. 6.31, lines *AB*, *BC*, and *AC* represent the intersection of two plane surfaces. The *H*- and *V*-projections of *BC* also represent the edgewise views of plane *CBE*. The *H*-projection of *AC* represents the edgewise view of plane *ACF*. Similar meanings can be pointed out for many lines on this figure.

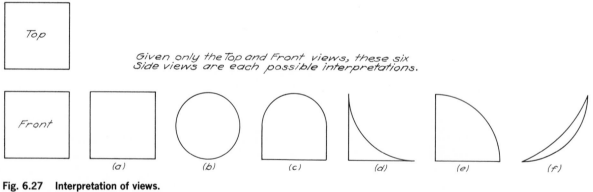

Fig. 6.27   Interpretation of views.

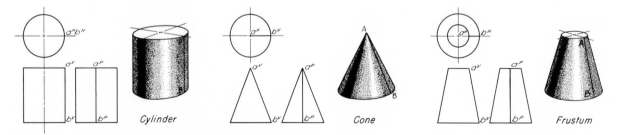

Fig. 6.28   Solids bounded by plane and single-curved surfaces.

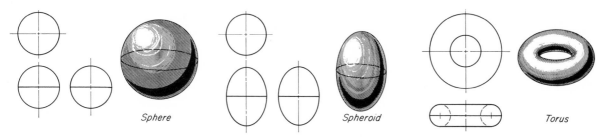

Fig. 6.29   Solids bounded by double-curved surfaces.

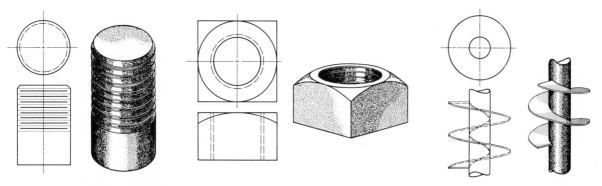

Fig. 6.30   Solids involving warped surfaces.

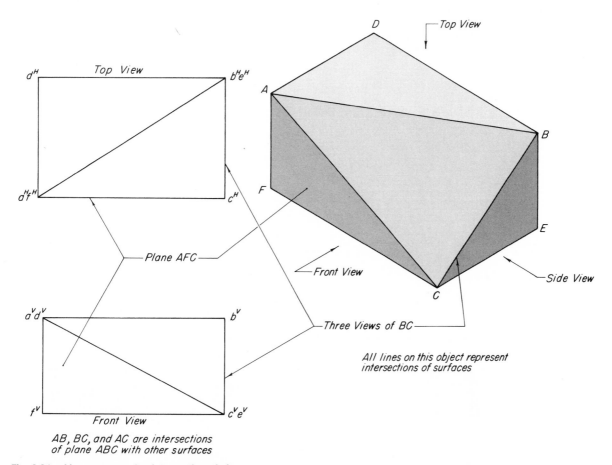

Fig. 6.31   Lines representing intersection of planes.

In Fig. 6.32 the long line, AB, in the top view of the cylinder or the inclined line AB in the front view of the cone represents the outside line or edge of a curved surface.

6.20.2   Interpretation of planes or areas. Areas in any view of a drawing may have a number of possible meanings. The adjacent view must always be examined and sometimes all views must be considered. An area may represent one of the following things in a drawing:

a. An area in one view that shows as a straight line in another view is a plane surface. See AFC in Fig. 6.31.

b. A surface that shows as an area in two views and as a straight line in the third view is a plane surface. See the shaded area in Fig. 6.24(*d*).

c. A surface that shows as an area in three views bounded by straight lines is a plane surface or a warped surface. For a plane surface see the shaded area in Fig. 6.25(*d*). For a warped surface see Figs. 13.74 through 13.79.

d. A surface that is curved in one direction only is called a single-curved surface. See Figs. 6.32(*a*) and (*b*). They usually show as an area in one view and as a curved line in an adjacent view if the simplest views are shown.

e. A surface that is curved in two directions is called a double-curved surface. It is illustrated in Fig. 6.29 and Fig. 6.32(*c*).

6.20.3   Interpretation of solids. One method of interpreting solids is to break the object into its basic elementary solids such as prisms, pyramids, and cylinders. In Fig. 6.33 the rectangular solids, the prisms,

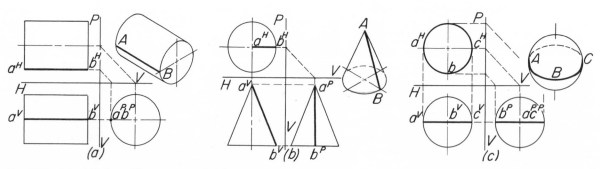

Fig. 6.32   Interpretation of lines on curved surfaces.

and the cylinders have been separated and drawn as individual units. The holes have even been drawn as cylinders. Sketching the small units is a good method of interpreting a drawing, but if these parts can be visualized in the mind, much time can be saved. Separating these units is an essential process when the volume or weight is to be computed, as is often the case for a new product.

For the sake of clarity, this breakdown was made from the pictorial view, but the same thing can be done from the orthographic projections.

Figures 6.13 to 6.25 show the pictorial view of an object from which to visualize the position of the line or plane. In learning to read a drawing this process is reversed, and it is frequently worthwhile to sketch the pictorial form of all or part of the object from the orthographic projections.

There are three approaches to the problem of reading a drawing:

a. Analyze the location, position, length, and shape of the various points, lines, planes, and solids.
b. Make a pictorial sketch of all or part of the object.
c. Break the object down into its individual units, from which the shape can be visualized and the weight computed. Some even suggest carving these parts out of soap or modeling clay.

Various exercises have been developed to give experience in reading drawings. In making the third view of an object, it is sometimes found that more than one solution is possible. This emphasizes the necessity for a third view in such a case.

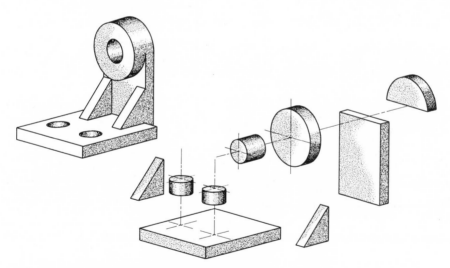

Fig. 6.33   Breakdown of object into component parts.

EXERCISES

6.30 One line may have been omitted in some view of each object in Figs. 6.34 and 6.35. Sketch this line in its proper place.

6.31 Sketch the missing view for each of the objects in Figs. 6.34 and 6.35.

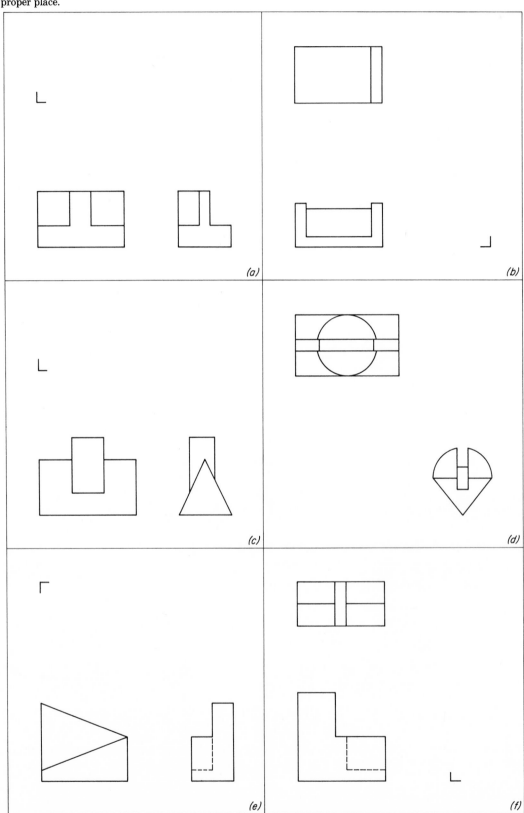

Fig. 6.34   Missing-view problems.

6.32 Make a pictorial sketch of each object shown in Figs. 6.34 and 6.35.

6.33 Make a sketch showing the individual parts of the objects shown in Figs. 6.34 and 6.35. This should be similar to Fig. 6.33.

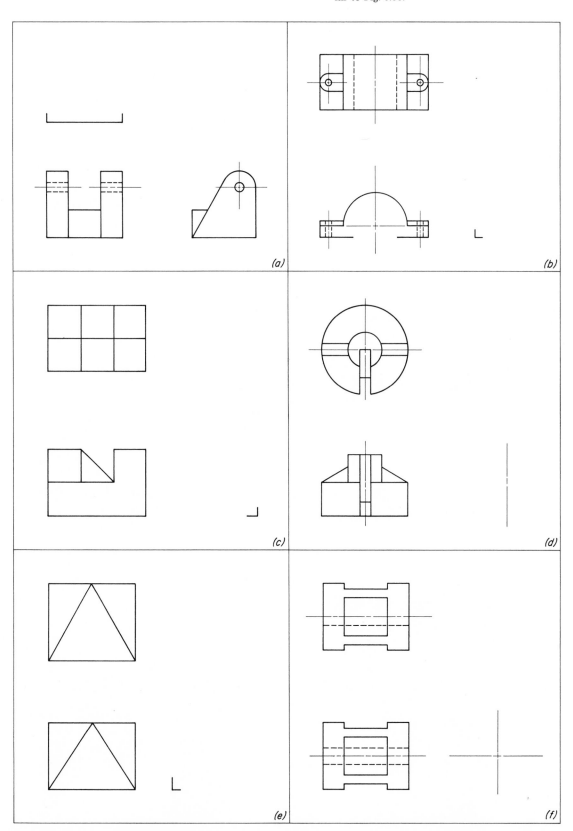

(a)

(b)

(c)

(d)

(e)

(f)

Fig. 6.35 Missing-view problems.

6.21 SELECTION OF VIEWS IN MULTIVIEW DRAWINGS. The three rules previously stated governing the placement of the object will automatically control the views to be drawn.

a. The views should be drawn with the object in its natural position. Thus, in Fig. 6.36(a), the two views shown can be easily recognized as a chair. However, the same views inverted, as in Fig. 6.36(b), have little resemblance to a chair.

b. The front view should show the most distinctive outline or contour. Figure 6.37 shows the pictorial drawings of several objects and the proper selection of front view in each case.

c. Having the object in its natural position and the front view having been selected, the top view is automatically chosen.

d. In selecting the proper side view, when the two are similar, the one having the fewest invisible lines should be chosen. Figure 6.38 illustrates this point. The right- and left-side views have the same lines, but the right-side view is preferable because more of the lines are visible from the right side.

6.22 NUMBER OF VIEWS TO BE DRAWN. After the object is placed in the proper position and the desired front view is selected, the next step is to decide on the number of views to be drawn. This requires a careful study of the object because *it is essential that all of the necessary information be given.* However,

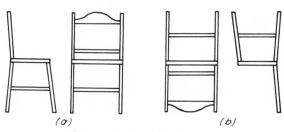

(a)   (b)

Fig. 6.36   Natural position of object.

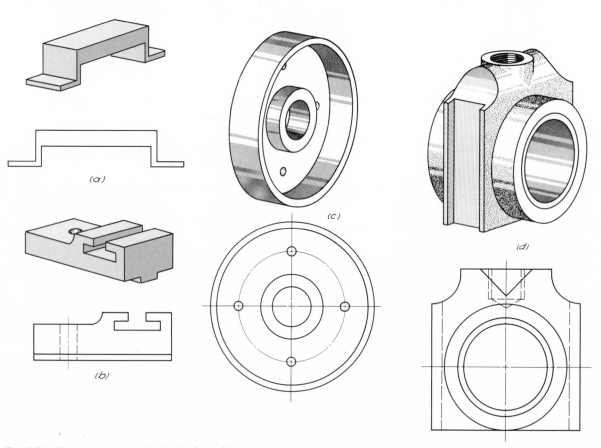

(a)

(b)

(c)

(d)

Fig. 6.37   Principal contour of object in front view.

for the sake of economy, *it is very important that no more views be drawn than the minimum number required for clear understanding.*

In selecting the proper views to be shown, the final dimensioning or specifying sizes must be considered. The views chosen must be such that as many dimensions as possible can be shown in true length and in a convenient position.

6.23   ONE-VIEW DRAWINGS. A single orthographic view is often adequate to represent thin flat objects having uniform thickness if the thickness is specified by a note. Simple cylindrical parts may require only one view, provided that the diameter is given. Such objects as shims, gaskets, steel springs, and many parts cut from thin plate may be represented in a single view, as in Fig. 6.39. The top view of the shim in Fig. 6.39 shows its true length and width together with the cuttings that must be made. The thickness and material are shown in the note. No additional information is necessary for its manufacture. Such a one-

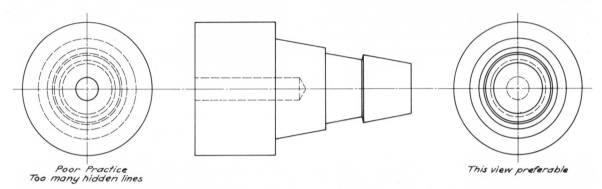

Fig. 6.38   **Selection of views to avoid hidden lines.**

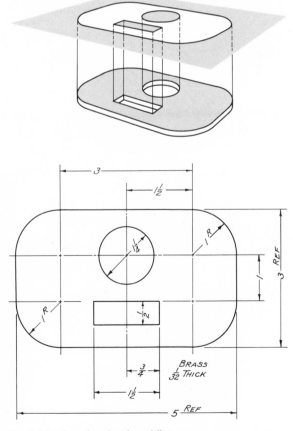

Fig. 6.39   **One-view drawing of flat part.**

view drawing, when executed to full scale, is sometimes called a pattern or template. Similarly, the one-view drawing of the cylindrical part shown in Fig. 6.40 is sufficient for all purposes of manufacture. The fact that the part is cylindrical is shown by the two dimensions with the notation Dia added to indicate diameter measurements. Except for extremely simple objects of the kind just mentioned, one-view orthographic drawings are rarely used.

6.24   TWO-VIEW DRAWINGS. The most common two-view drawing is obtained by projecting the object on the V- and H-planes. The method of obtaining the projection of an object on these two planes, the rotation of the horizontal plane, and the resultant arrange-

ment of views are shown in Fig. 6.41. The two views are called the vertical and horizontal projections or, more commonly, the *front* and *top* views. From the pictorial view in Fig. 6.41(b) it can be seen that the vertical distances and those right or left are shown in the front view. Distances right or left and front or back are shown in the top view. These two views enable all three major dimensions to be specified.

Another common arrangement of a two-view drawing is shown in Fig. 6.42. In this drawing, projecting the object on the vertical and profile planes shows the front and side views respectively. The front view shows the vertical distances and those right or left. The side view shows the vertical distances and those front or

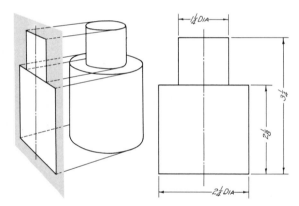

Fig. 6.40   One-view drawing of cylindrical part.

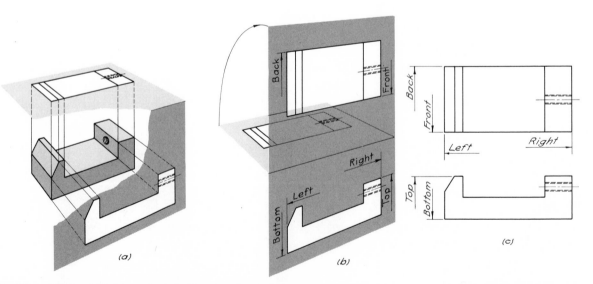

Fig. 6.41   Third quadrant arrangement of two-view drawing.

back as indicated in Fig. 6.42.

When top and front views are used, the top view must be above the front view in exact vertical alignment. When the front and right-side views are used, the right-side view is to the right of the front view in exact horizontal alignment. This relationship is often referred to as the views being "in projection."

6.25 THREE-VIEW DRAWING. Many objects cannot be satisfactorily described with two-view drawings, even with the addition of notes and symbols. In such cases three principal views—horizontal, vertical, and profile—are used, as shown in Fig. 6.43(a). The method of revolving the planes is shown in Fig. 6.43(b). The subsequent arrangement of views is shown in Fig. 6.43(c).

If the right- and left-side views are equally effective in showing the shape of the object, the right-side view is usually drawn.

In a three-view drawing, each of the major distances is shown in two places. The vertical distances (heights) are shown in the front and side views. The right or left distances (widths) are shown in the front and top views. The front or back distances (depths) are shown in the top and side views. See Fig. 6.43(c).

6.26 ALTERNATE ARRANGEMENT OF VIEWS. Occasionally the standard arrangement of views as shown in Fig. 6.43 is not satisfactory because of the necessity to clear a certain portion of the sheet for a title, bill of materials, or some other purpose. In that event, the planes may be revolved and the views

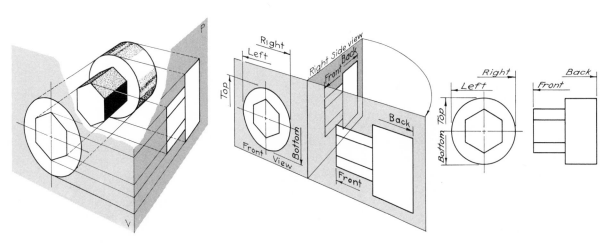

Fig. 6.42 Arrangement of front and side views.

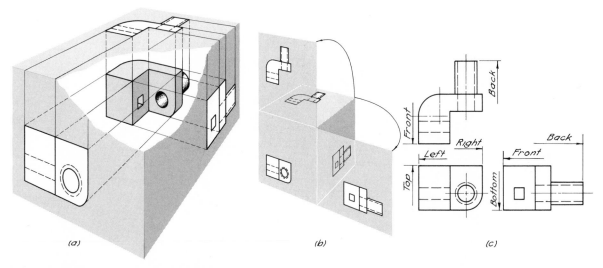

Fig. 6.43 Third quadrant arrangement of three views.

arranged as shown in Fig. 6.44. This is not considered a desirable arrangement and should not be used unless absolutely necessary.

In this arrangement the front view is always below the top view and in exact vertical alignment with the top view. The right-side view is to the right of the top view and in exact horizontal alignment with the top view.

6.27 DETERMINATION OF VISIBILITY. When drawing a projection of an object, it is important to remember that *every line on the object, such as corners and intersections, must be shown in some manner in every view*. Since some lines on an object are invisible from a particular point of sight, there must be some method of distinguishing the visible line from the in-

visible. Dashed lines are used to represent the invisible line. See Figs. 6.4 and 6.44. These lines must be very carefully made, with the dashes approximately 3/16 of an inch long and not more than 1/16 of an inch apart.

Figure 6.45 shows the pictorial sketch of an object with the correct projections. In the top view, face *ABCD* will be edgewise, so that only *AB* will be visible. Lines *CD*, *KN*, and *LM*, which are invisible from the top, will not show in dashed form because they are below *AB*. *The visible lines take precedence over the invisible lines.* The edges of the holes and the edge of the face *EFGH* will show as dashed lines in the top view. In the side view, the top edge of the large hole, although invisible, will not show as dashed because it is behind the visible line of the notch. The lower edge

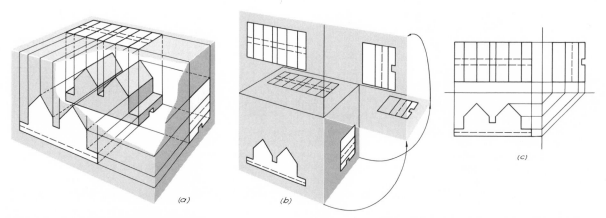

Fig. 6.44 Alternate arrangement of views.

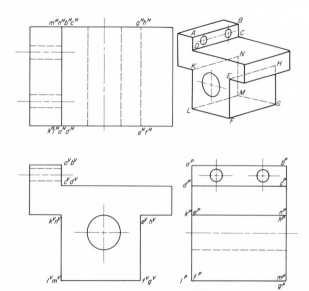

Fig. 6.45 Three-view drawing with visibility of lines.

of the hole will show as dashed because there is no other line between it and the profile point of sight.

A dashed line takes precedence over a center line when they happen to coincide.

The rules governing visibility in any view are the following:

a. In the top view, the highest parts will be visible. These are determined from the front view.
b. In the front view, the parts nearest the observer (front parts) will be visible. These are determined from the top or side view.
c. In the right-side view, the parts on the right will be visible. They are determined from the front or top views.

EXERCISES

Figure 6.46 shows another object with the correct views given.

6.34 Is point *S* visible or invisible in the front view? _____

_____

6.35 Is line *EF* visible or invisible in the top view? _____

_____

6.36 Why is the line *NK* invisible in the front view? _____

6.37 Is the plane *WFS* visible or invisible in the front view?

_____

6.38 What is the visibility of plane *RSTW* in the top view?

_____

Why? _____

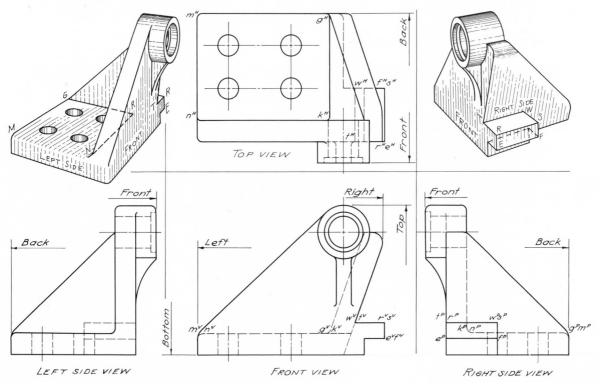

Fig. 6.46 Determining visibility of lines.

6.28 ELIMINATION OF INVISIBLE LINES. Sometimes there is an advantage in choosing a combination of views such as shown in Fig. 6.47 to reduce the number of invisible lines to be represented. This figure shows a front and two partial end views. Each end view contains only the features on one side of the central flange. This simplifies both the making and the reading of the drawing.

6.29 TECHNIQUE OF DRAWING INVISIBLE OUTLINES. Various conditions arise in the representation of invisible outlines, and all nationally recognized standards have agreed on the proper method of showing them.

These conditions are illustrated on the drawing in Fig. 6.48 and are lettered to correspond to the list shown in the figure.

6.30 PROJECTION OF CURVED LINES. Curved lines on a drawing may consist of circles, arcs of circles, parts of ellipses, hyperbolas, parabolas, other geometric curves, or just irregular curves. For noncircular curves a sufficient number of points on the curve must be located so that a smooth curve can be drawn

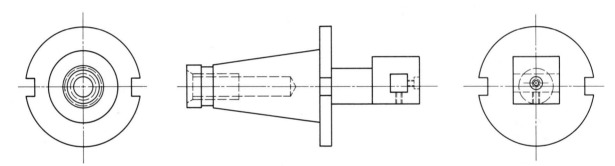

Fig. 6.47   Use of two end views to avoid hidden lines.

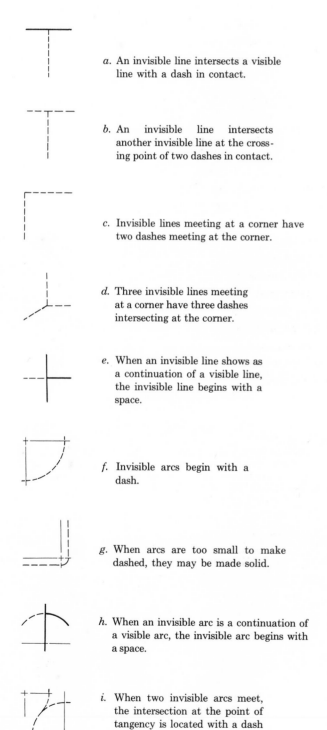

a. An invisible line intersects a visible line with a dash in contact.

b. An invisible line intersects another invisible line at the crossing point of two dashes in contact.

c. Invisible lines meeting at a corner have two dashes meeting at the corner.

d. Three invisible lines meeting at a corner have three dashes intersecting at the corner.

e. When an invisible line shows as a continuation of a visible line, the invisible line begins with a space.

f. Invisible arcs begin with a dash.

g. When arcs are too small to make dashed, they may be made solid.

h. When an invisible arc is a continuation of a visible arc, the invisible arc begins with a space.

i. When two invisible arcs meet, the intersection at the point of tangency is located with a dash on each arc.

Fig. 6.48   Invisible-line technique.

through them. These points must be close together when the curvature is sharp, but may be spread out when the curvature is flat. Figure 6.49 shows an object with a curved line in the top view. This curve, which is a portion of an ellipse, has been determined by projecting points from the other two views. The proper way to use an irregular curve to connect the points is discussed in Art. 3.26.

6.31   PROJECTION OF CURVED SURFACES. Such surfaces as cones, cylinders, and spheres often form the exterior or interior surfaces of objects to be drawn. A curved surface is usually represented by drawing the outlines of the object as seen from the appropriate point of sight. Thus a cylinder would be a circle in one view and a rectangle in the adjacent view. A sphere would be a circle in every view.

When curved surfaces occur in combination with each other or with plane surfaces, it is frequently necessary to decide whether to show the intersections or the tangencies. In Fig. 6.50(a) the tangency should be

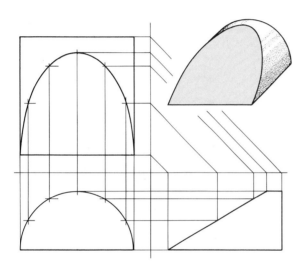

Fig. 6.49   Projection of a curved line.

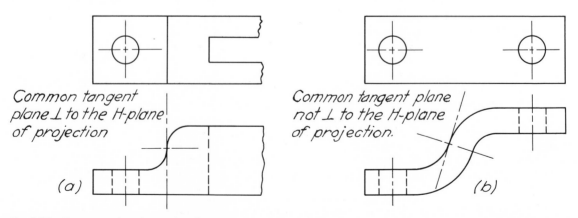

Fig. 6.50   Representation of curved contours.

shown in the top view because both curved surfaces are tangent to a vertical plane. This is not true in Fig. 6.50(*b*) where the line may be omitted in the top view.

Frequently the theoretical intersections are projected as lines when it is necessary to give meaning to the drawing. This is shown in Figs. 6.51 and 6.52.

The intersections of two unfinished surfaces on a casting will always have the corners rounded or the angles filleted as in Fig. 6.53. These rounds and fillets are always shown with a line in the adjacent view just as though the intersection were sharp. This is seen in Fig. 6.54(*a*). When surfaces are streamlined, as in Fig. 6.54(*c*), all intersections are shown to make it possible to interpret the drawing.

6.32 PARTIAL VIEWS. If space is limited on the drawing sheet and the object is symmetrical about a

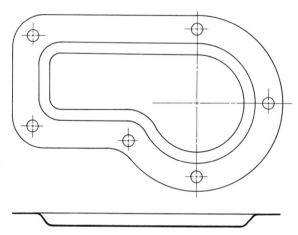

Fig. 6.51   Representation of curved contours.

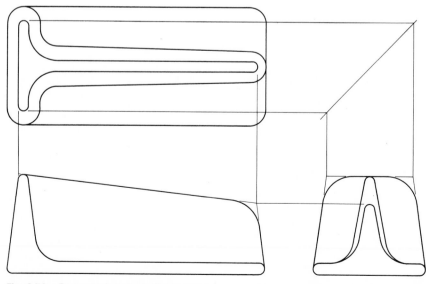

Fig. 6.52   Representing streamlined object.

central cutting plane, one half of a view may be omitted, as has been done in Fig. 6.55. If the front view is a full or a half section, it is customary to draw the rear half of the top view, as in Figs. 6.55(a) and (b). If the front view is not sectioned and only half of the top view is shown, it should be the front half of the object, as in Fig. 6.55(c). If the partial view is drawn exactly to the center line, it should be marked "symmetrical about the center line."

6.33 RUNOUT LINES. When the intersection between two surfaces is filleted, standard practice is to use a conventional representation, as illustrated in Fig. 6.56. These curved extensions of true projections are commonly referred to as runout lines for rounded or filleted corners. They have no specified radius of curvature but are done to suggest the general shape of the theoretical line of intersection.

6.34 CONVENTIONAL PRACTICES. Certain violations of the true projections are sometimes desirable. Some of these violations are discussed below. This

Fig. 6.53 Rounded and filleted corners.

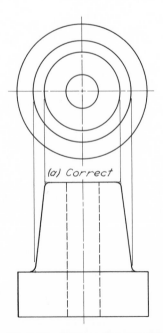 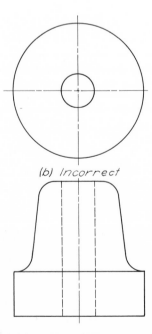 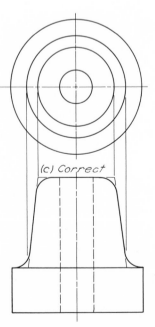

Fig. 6.54 Representing rounded corners.

may be done for any one of a number of reasons.

a. Clarity.

b. Ease of making or reading a drawing.

c. To provide information needed in the shop.

6.34.1   Odd number of axes. When an object has three or any other odd number of axes, the projections may become confused by the excess lines needed to show the correct projections. In such a case the part that does not show on the center line may be shown in the front view in a revolved position. This is illustrated in Fig. 6.57 where the lug on the right side has been

shown in the front view as though it were actually on the center line. The top view shows the true position of the lug. This can be done only with cylindrical objects where the revolution does not change the true relation with the center line.

6.34.2   Alternate positions. When a part is designed to operate in two positions, it is frequently drawn in one position and the other position is indicated by phantom lines. See Fig. 6.58.

6.34.3   Right- and left-hand parts. In actual practice, parts frequently work in pairs, one of which is called right-handed and the other left-handed. It is

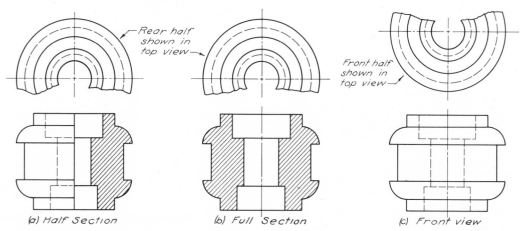

Fig. 6.55   **Arrangement of partial top views.**

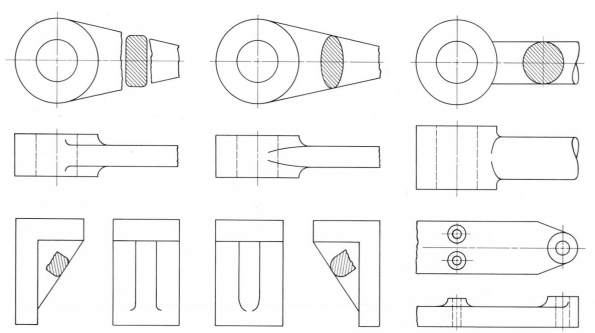

Fig. 6.56   **Standard runouts. (Courtesy United States of America Standards Institute.)**

not necessary to draw both parts. They may be listed in the bill of materials as one right-handed and one left-handed of the same drawing. The left-hand part is the mirror image of the right-hand part. Figure 6.59 shows a drawing of both parts.

6.35   LAYOUT OF A THREE-VIEW DRAWING. In making a three-view drawing, it is necessary to develop a method of procedure that will enable the draftsman to proceed rapidly. The following paragraphs suggest a method of procedure for the beginner, which he may vary to suit his convenience and desires as he gains experience.

The complete layout of a three-view drawing may be subdivided into steps that are illustrated in Fig. 6.60.

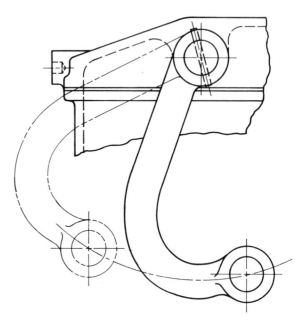

Fig. 6.58   Alternate position shown by phantom lines.

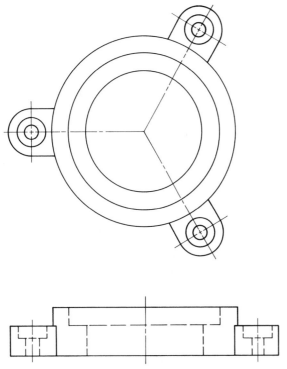

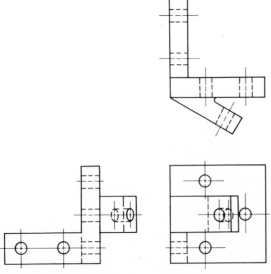

Fig. 6.57   Rotation for odd number of axes.

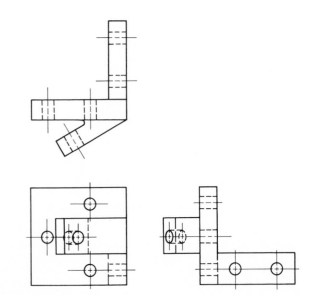

Fig. 6.59   Right- and left-hand parts—only one to be drawn.

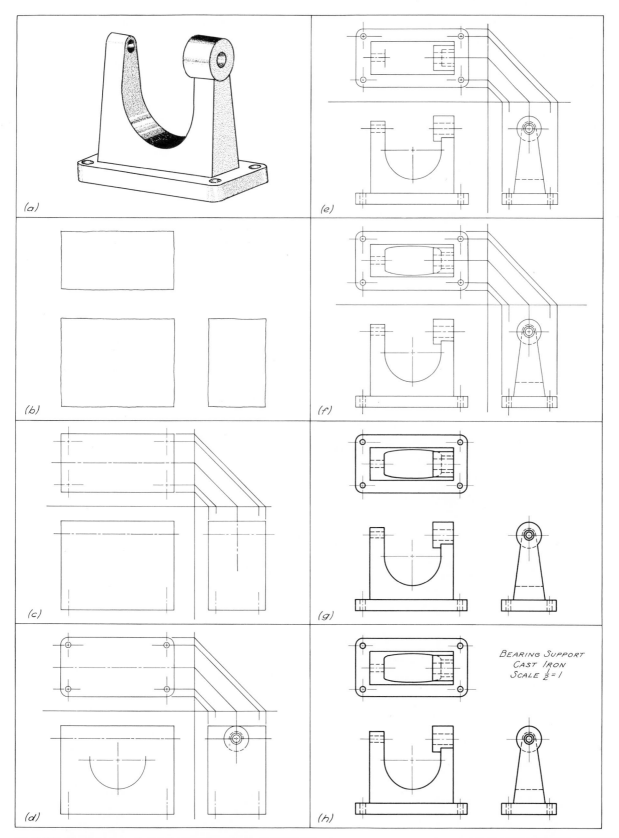

(a)

(b)

(c)

(d)

(e)

(f)

(g)

BEARING SUPPORT
CAST IRON
SCALE ½ = 1

(h)

Fig. 6.60   Development of an orthographic projection.

a. Choose the number and arrangement of views.

b. Make a freehand layout of the areas for each view. From this determine the scale of the drawing or the size of the paper and the spacing of the views. See Fig. 6.60(*b*).

c. Make an accurate mechanical layout of the outlines of the views, using reference lines. Then add the main center lines and the center lines of the details. Figure 6.60(*c*).

d. Draw the circular parts. Figure 6.60(*d*).

e. Draw the straight lines. Figure 6.60(*e*).

f. Locate intersections and irregular curves. Figure 6.60(*f*).

g. Clean up the drawing with art gum or a soft eraser. Take out excess lines, construction lines, and reference lines. Figure 6.60(*g*).

h. Go over all lines to make them heavier and to improve the technique. Figure 6.60(*h*).

i. Put in title and scale. *Every drawing, whether dimensioned or not, must have a title and must have the scale specified.*

6.36   FIRST-QUADRANT DRAWING. In Europe and frequently in Great Britian, an object to be drawn is placed in the first quadrant instead of the third, as in the United States and Canada.

The rules of projection are the same, except that in the first quadrant the object is between the plane and the point of sight. As in third quadrant, the plane must be revolved away from the object, to bring the point of sight to the front of the paper. This is shown in Fig. 6.61.

The actual difference between third- and first-quadrant drawings lies in the arrangement of the views. In first-quadrant drawings the top view is below the front view, the right-side view is to the left of the front view, and the left-side view is to the right of the front view. This gives a rather awkward arrangement, but with a little practice it soon becomes possible to read the first-quadrant drawings.

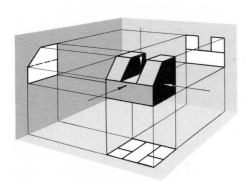
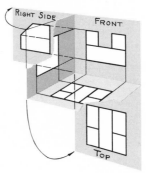
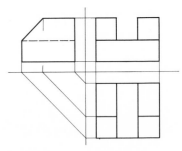

Fig. 6.61   First-angle projection.

SELF-STUDY QUESTIONS

Before trying to answer these questions, read the chapter carefully. Then, without reference to the text, answer as many questions as possible. For those that cannot be answered, the number, in parentheses following the question number, gives the article in which the answer can be found. Look it up and write down the answer. Check the answers that you did give to see that they are correct.

6.1 **(6.1)** In orthographic projection, the lines of sight are _____ to the plane of projection.

6.2 **(6.5)** In orthographic projection in the United States, the plane of projection is between the object and the _____.

6.3 **(6.3.1)** In orthographic projection, the point of sight is at an _____ distance from the object.

6.4 **(6.3.3)** In orthographic projection there is _____ plane for each view.

6.5 **(6.3.3)** The three principal planes of projection are _____, _____, and _____.

6.6 **(6.3.4)** To make the most useful orthographic projection there are four rules for placing the object:

1. Place the object in its _____ position.

2. Place the object so that its faces will be _____ to the principal planes of projection.

3. Place the object so that its most descriptive contour will become the _____ view.

4. Select the views that will show the fewest _____ lines.

6.7 **(6.4)** Every line on an object must show as a _____ or a _____ on the projection.

6.8 **(6.5)** The planes of projection divide all space into _____ quadrants.

6.9 **(6.5)** In the United States, the _____ quadrant is used for almost all drawings.

6.10 **(6.5)** The space described by the third quadrant is _____ the horizontal plane and _____ the vertical plane.

6.11 **(6.6)** In multiview drawing, the _____ view is always above the _____ view.

6.12 **(6.6)** In multiview drawing, the right-side view is to the _____ of the _____ view.

6.13 **(6.8)** A point in space may be definitely located by _____ projections.

6.14 **(6.9)** The projection of point A on the horizontal plane is lettered _____.

6.15 **(6.9)** The projection of point A on the third auxiliary plane is lettered _____.

6.16 **(6.10)** If point B is behind point A, the distance may be measured in the _____ or _____ projections.

6.17 **(6.10)** Vertical distances can be measured in the _____ or _____ views.

6.18 **(6.10)** Right and left distances can be measured in the _____ or _____ views.

6.19 **(6.13.1)** If the vertical projection of a line is parallel to the horizontal reference line, the true length of the line will show in the _____ projection.

6.20 **(6.13.3)** If the horizontal projection of a line is parallel to the vertical reference line, the true length of the line will show in the _____ projection.

6.21 **(6.13.1)** In measuring the angle between a line and a plane, it is necessary to have the _____ _____ of the line and the _____ _____ of the plane in the same view.

6.22 **(6.13.2)** If a line is parallel to the vertical plane, the angle π between the line and the profile plane will show in the _____ projection.

6.23 **(6.13.1)** If a line is parallel to the horizontal plane, the angle ϕ between the line and the vertical plane will show in the _____ projection.

6.24 **(6.14)** If a line is oblique to all three coordinate planes, its true length will show in _____ principal views.

6.25 **(6.16.2)** A plane that is parallel to the vertical plane will show edgewise in the _____ and _____ _____ projections.

6.26 **(6.17.3)** When a plane is perpendicular to the profile plane and inclined to the vertical, the angle θ will show as the angle between the _____ projection of the plane and the horizontal reference line.

6.27 **(6.17)** To measure the angle between two planes, it is necessary to have both planes showing _____ _____ in the same view.

6.28 **(6.18)** When a plane is oblique to all three principal coordinate planes, all principal projections will show as areas that _____ _____ true size.

6.29 **(6.23)** To make a one-view drawing complete, a _____ must be added.

6.30 **(6.20.3)** A _____ drawing is often useful in reading a drawing.

6.31 **(6.25)** If two side views give the same information, the _____ side view is usually drawn.

6.32 **(6.27)** The proper visibility of lines in the top view may be determined by a careful study of the _____ _____ view.

6.33 **(6.27)** The proper visibility of lines in the front view may be determined by a careful study of the ____ _____ view.

6.34 **(6.27)** When a visible and an invisible line coincide, the _____ line takes preference.

6.35 **(6.27)** When a center line and an invisible line coincide, the _____ line takes preference.

6.36 **(6.29)** When an invisible line is a continuation of a visible line, the invisible line begins with a _____ _____ .

6.37 Sketch the missing line in one of the views shown below.

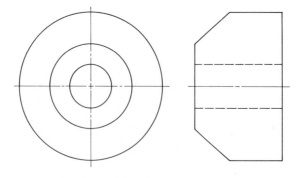

6.38 Sketch the right-side view of the object shown.

6.39 Make a three-view sketch of the object shown.

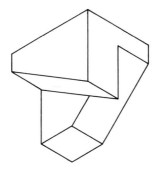

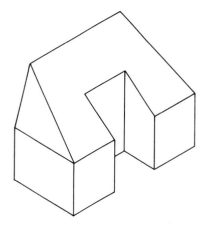

PROBLEMS

In the following group of problems the student is to select and draw the minimum number of views that will unmistakably describe the shape of the object. The scale given is for an 8½ × 11″ sheet. It is recommended that the student make a freehand sketch showing the views he proposes to make before beginning the instrumental layout.

The views should be well balanced on the sheet with ample space between and around them for dimensions. The drawings, however, are not to be dimensioned unless the instructor so specifies.

For fillets and rounded corners not dimensioned on the figures or for other missing dimensions, the student is to use

his own judgment. The objects in Figs. 6.80 to 6.87 are assumed to be finished all over. On a shop drawing this is shown by the abbreviation F.A.O. In all cases the material is assumed to be cast iron.

In a space below the views, or elsewhere if necessary, to balance the sheet place a well-balanced title giving the name of the object, the material of which it is made, and the scale.

6.1 Make the missing third view of the object shown in any one of the illustrations in Figs. 6.62 to 6.79 and in Fig. 6.102. Using a soft pencil these problems may be solved freehand on the figures in the text or they can be traced if desired.

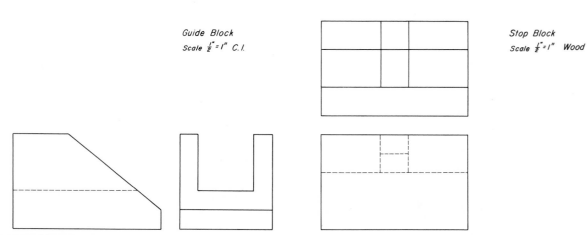

Fig. 6.62   Guide block.

Fig. 6.63   Stop block.

6.2 Make the necessary views needed to completely describe the object shown in any of the Figs. 6.80 to 6.101 and 6.103.

6.3 Make a freehand pictorial of any object assigned by your instructor from Figs. 6.62 to 6.79.

Creative Design Problems

6.4 Make the necessary drawings to completely describe a simple implement to be fastened to a door, which will hold the door in any desired position.

6.5 Make the necessary drawings to completely describe a simple implement to be fastened to a box, which will keep the lid open in any desired position.

6.6 Make the necessary drawings to design a simple implement to hold up a large drawing before a class. It must be possible to change the drawing quickly.

6.7 Make the necessary drawings to completely describe a simple implement to hold a water glass on a boat so that it will not spill when the boat pitches or rolls.

6.8 Make the necessary drawings to completely describe a simple implement to hold the cards of a bridge hand so that a one-armed man can play. It must be so built that the other players cannot see the hand.

6.9 Make the necessary drawings to completely describe a simple implement to hold a book open on the table. It must be possible to turn pages easily.

6.10 Make the necessary drawings to completely describe a simple implement to hold a picnic tablecloth or a beach

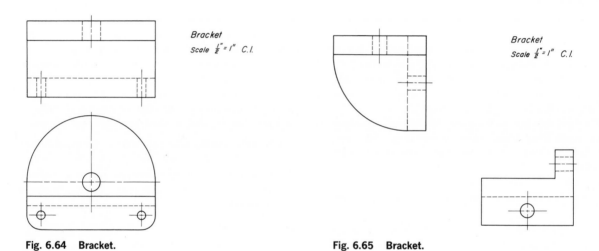

Fig. 6.64   Bracket.

Fig. 6.65   Bracket.

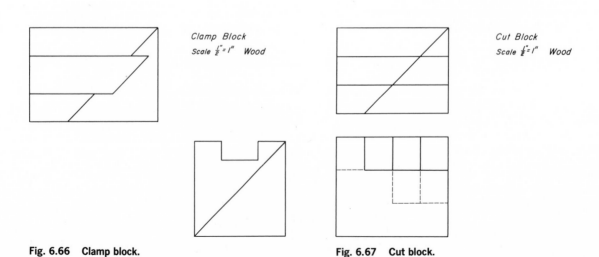

Fig. 6.66   Clamp block.

Fig. 6.67   Cut block.

towel firmly to the ground so that it will not blow in the wind. It must not injure the cloth or interfere in any way with any object or person resting on the cloth or towel.

6.11 Make the necessary drawings to completely describe a simple implement to hold a pencil, eraser, and a small 6″ scale and fasten it to a clipboard. The equipment must be easily available, but must be fastened so that it will not fall out when the clipboard is held in any position.

6.12 Make the necessary drawings to completely describe a simple bird feeder. The feeder must allow cardinals

and smaller birds to feed but must keep out all larger birds and squirrels.

6.13 Make the necessary drawings to completely describe a simple pillbox. The box must keep four kinds of pills separate and must allow removal of any kind without losing the others. The box is so small that it is impossible to pick the pills up with the fingers.

6.14 Make the necessary drawings to completely describe a two-piece bracket that will attach a folding shower seat to the wall. It must hold the seat in normal sitting position and in the folded position against the wall. Stiffness and strength are essential.

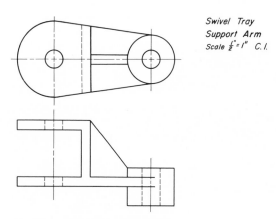

Swivel Tray
Support Arm
Scale ½″=1″ C. I.

Fig. 6.68   Swivel tray support arm.

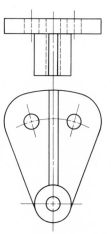
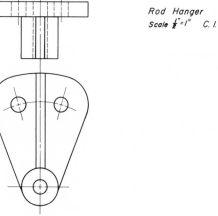

Rod Hanger
Scale ½″=1″ C. I.

Fig. 6.69   Rod hanger.

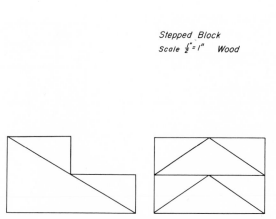

Stepped Block
Scale ½″=1″ Wood

Fig. 6.70   Stepped block.

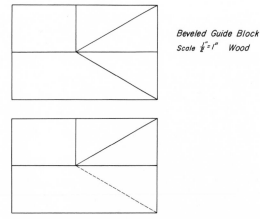

Beveled Guide Block
Scale ½″=1″ Wood

Fig. 6.71   Beveled guide block.

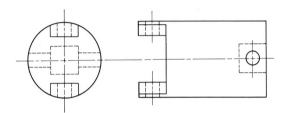

Swivel Rod
Scale ½"=1" Steel

Fig. 6.72 Swivel rod.

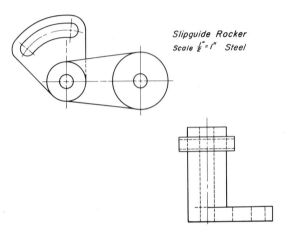

Slipguide Rocker
Scale ½"=1" Steel

Fig. 6.73 Slipguide rocker.

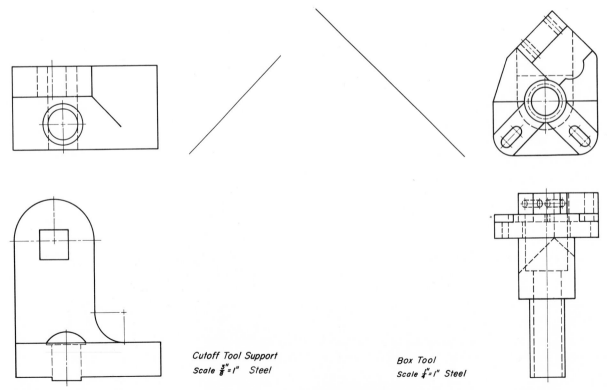

Cutoff Tool Support
Scale ⅜"=1" Steel

Fig. 6.74 Cutoff-tool support.

Box Tool
Scale ¼"=1" Steel

Fig. 6.75 Box tool.

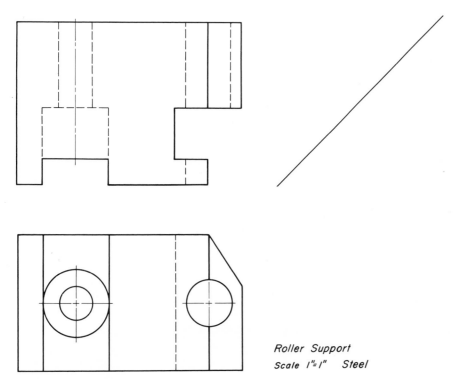

Roller Support
Scale 1"= 1"   Steel

Fig. 6.76   Roller support.

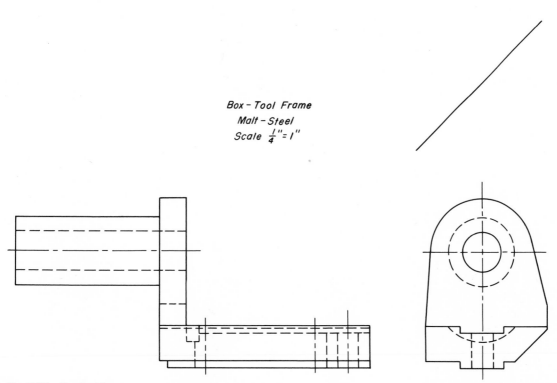

Box - Tool Frame
Malt - Steel
Scale ¼"= 1"

Fig. 6.77   Box-tool frame.

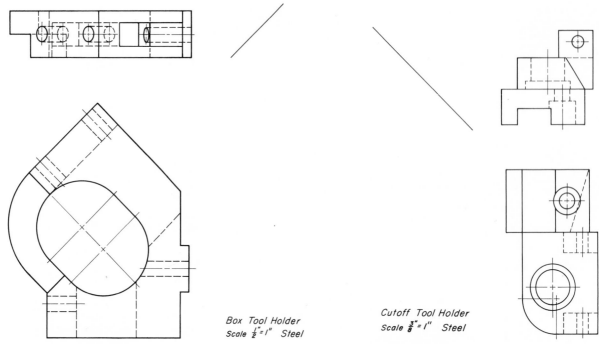

Box Tool Holder
Scale ½" = 1" Steel

Fig. 6.78 Box-tool holder.

Cutoff Tool Holder
Scale ⅜" = 1" Steel

Fig. 6.79 Cutoff-tool holder.

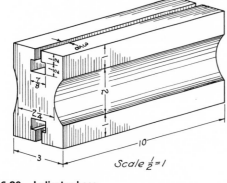

Scale ½ = 1

Fig. 6.80 Indicator base.

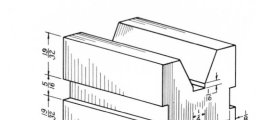

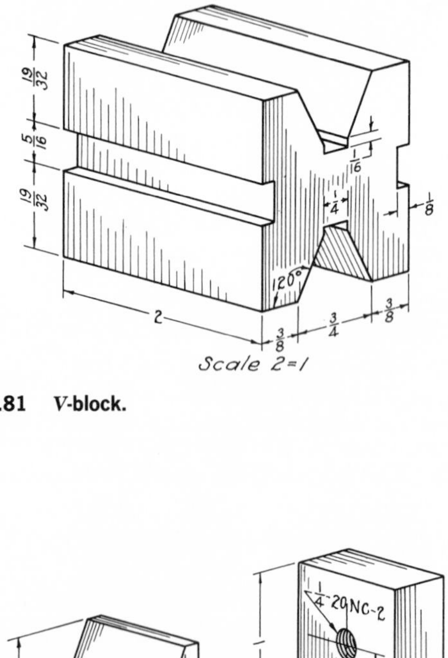

Scale 2 = 1

Fig. 6.81 V-block.

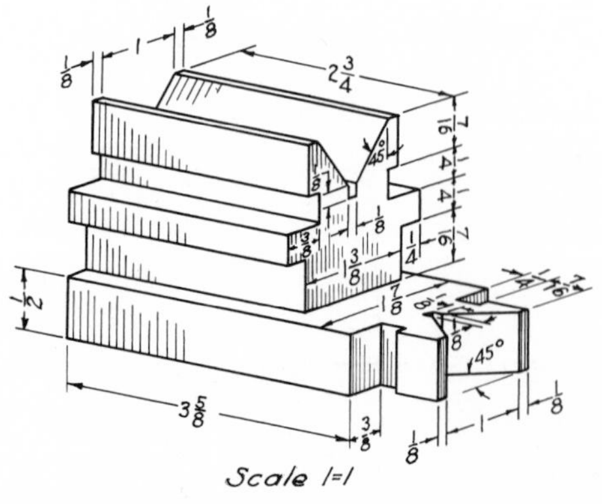

Scale 1 = 1

Fig. 6.82 V-block.

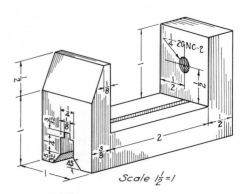

Scale 1½ = 1

Fig. 6.83 Vise base.

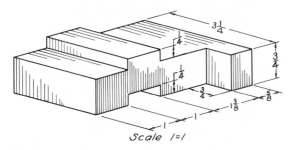

Fig. 6.84   Guide block.

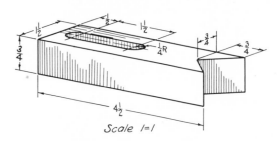

Fig. 6.85   V-slide.

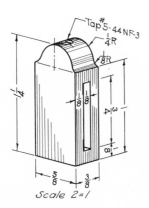

Fig. 6.86   Gage clamp.

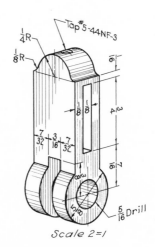

Fig. 6.87   Vernier clamp.

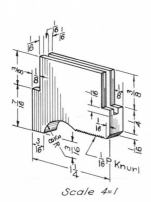

Fig. 6.88   Caliper slide.

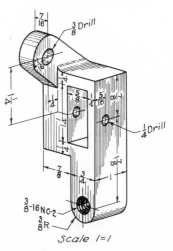

Fig. 6.89   Swing tool.

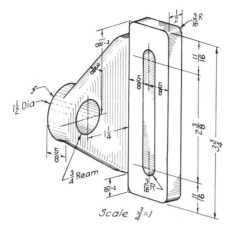

Fig. 6.90   Adjustable bearing.

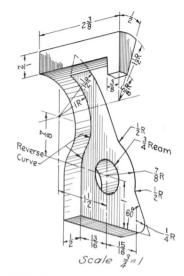

Fig. 6.91   Clutch finger.

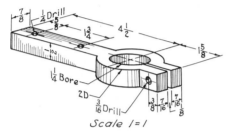

Fig. 6.92   Collar clamp.

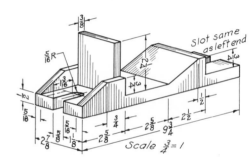

Fig. 6.93   Fixture.

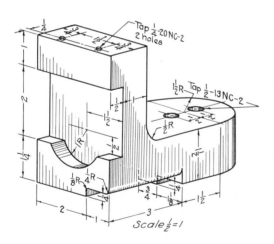

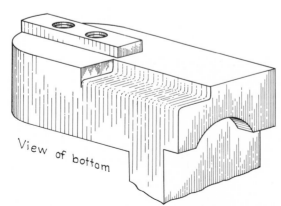

Fig. 6.94   Turret tool post.

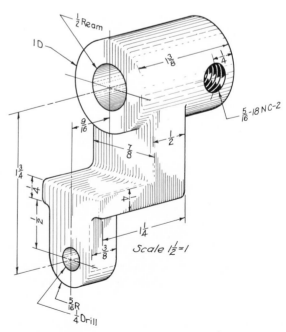

Fig. 6.95   Adjustable bearing.

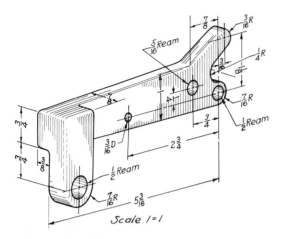

Fig. 6.96 Roller release.

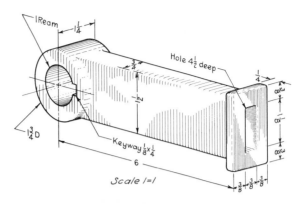

Fig. 6.97 Lever handle socket.

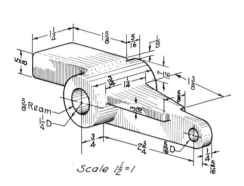

Fig. 6.98 Stripper bracket.

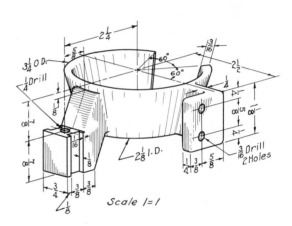

Fig. 6.99 Developer tank support.

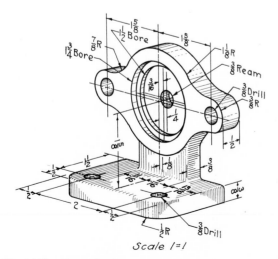

Fig. 6.100 Pump stand.

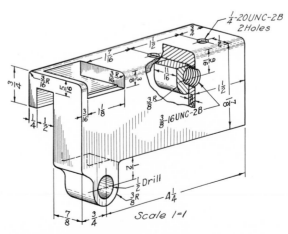

Fig. 6.101 Fence clamp.

170 BASIC DRAWING

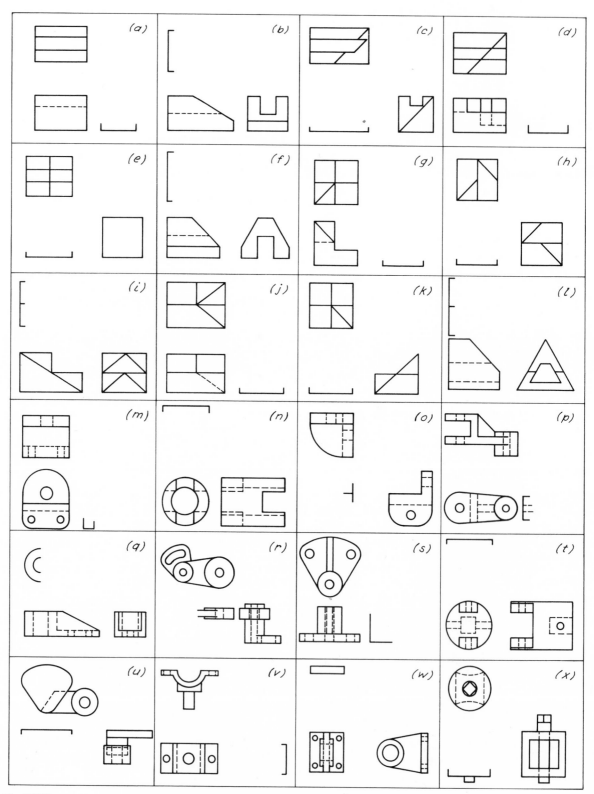

Fig. 6.102

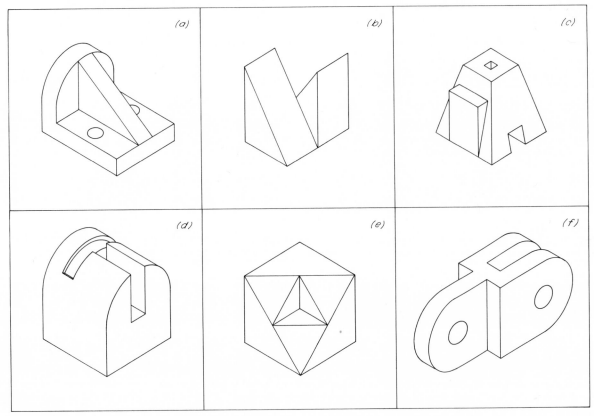

Fig. 6.103

CHAPTER 7
Auxiliary Views

OLD: Venetian galley used in 14th and 15th centuries. (Philip Gendreau.)

NEW: Prow of U.S.S. Missouri. (Philip Gendreau.)

Chapter 7   Auxiliary Views

7.1   NEED FOR AUXILIARY VIEWS. On many objects there are lines that do not show in true length and faces that do not show in true size in any of the three principal views. In manufacturing and construction it is also necessary in many cases to know the true value of the angle between lines and between plane faces. When these values do not appear in the three principal views it is necessary to set up additional planes of projection and make views that will give the necessary information. These additional planes are called auxiliary planes.

7.2   PLACING THE AUXILIARY PLANE OF PROJECTION. To serve the purposes described above, the auxiliary plane must be placed to satisfy the following conditions:

a. It must be perpendicular to one of the planes of projection already in use.

b. It must be parallel or perpendicular to some line or plane face of the object.

c. For the first auxiliary plane, the choice of which of the three principal planes to use is determined by the shape and position of the object and the problem to be solved.

7.3   NOTATION OF AUXILIARY PLANES AND VIEWS. A method of marking the *H*-, *V*-, and *P*-planes and their projections was established in Art. 6.9. A similar system is used for the auxiliary views. The first auxiliary plane is numbered *1*, the second *2*, and so on.

When the first auxiliary plane is perpendicular to the *H*-plane, the line of intersection of the two planes, called a reference line, is labeled *H-1* as in Fig. 7.1(*a*). This means that the auxiliary plane will be revolved about this line until it coincides with the *H*-plane. When the auxiliary plane is perpendicular to the *V*-plane, the reference line is marked *V-1* as in Fig. 7.1(*b*). When it is perpendicular to the *P*-plane, it is called *P-1* as in Fig. 7.1(*c*).

In Fig. 7.2 the projections of point *A* on the *H*- and *V*-planes are shown as well as its projections on auxiliary planes *1* and *2*. The auxiliary projections of the point are labeled with the lower-case *a* with an appropriate superscript. Thus a^1 is the projection on auxiliary plane *1*, and a^2 is the projection on plane *2*. The reference line between the *V*-projection and the *1*-projection is labeled *V-1*. The reference line between the *1*-projection and the *2*-projection is labeled *1-2. The adjacent projections in every case lie on a perpendicular to the reference line between them.*

The distance from the point in space to any plane is marked with the letter or number of the plane. Thus the distance from the point to the *H*-plane is marked *h*, from the *V*-plane *v*, from the *P*-plane *p*, from the *1*-plane *1*, and from the *2*-plane *2*. These distances in each case are indicated in Fig. 7.2.

7.4   RELATIONSHIP OF THE AUXILIARY PLANE TO THE OBJECT. It is possible to place auxiliary planes in any relation to the object, as shown in Fig. 7.3. The

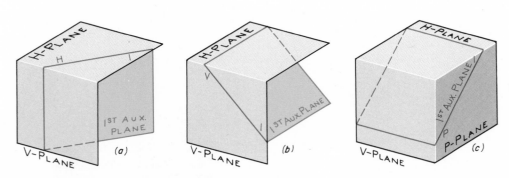

Fig. 7.1   Method of placing auxiliary planes.

object can be projected on any one of these planes, thus giving a view in any desired direction. In Fig. 7.3 the projections marked a, b, and c are correct projections and each could possibly be useful for some purpose. However, projection d is the one that is most useful because it gives the true size and shape of the inclined face. Another feature of this view is that only the inclined face is shown. This is customary in most auxiliary projections.

It is also noticeable that point A has been projected to each view and in each case it has been labeled a^1. From this it can be seen that it is possible to have several first auxiliary projections in a single problem. Every first auxiliary projection is labeled a^1, although there is no relation between them.

7.5   THEORY OF MAKING AUXILIARY PROJECTIONS.

The orthographic theory of projection, as discussed in Chapter 6, is used when making auxiliary projections. In Fig. 7.2(b) point A has been projected upon all three principal planes of projection, as well as into the first and second auxiliary planes.

The principle of the projections of a point on two adjacent planes being "in projection" is used to obtain the auxiliary views. Therefore, a^1 and a^H lie on a line perpendicular to the H-1 reference line; and a^1 and a^2 lie on a line perpendicular to the 1-2 reference line. The distance from the respective planes is indicated on Fig. 7.2(b).

7.6   USES OF AUXILIARY VIEWS.

There are four fundamental operations for which auxiliary planes are used. The ability to solve these four problems is the basis for the successful solution of many problems in drawing and engineering geometry. They are:

a. Find the true length of an oblique line.

b. Find the point projection of a line.

c. Find the edgewise view of a plane.

d. Find the true shape of a plane surface.

7.7   TRUE LENGTH OF AN OBLIQUE LINE.

When a line is parallel to one of the principal planes of projection, its projection upon that plane will be the true length of the line. Its projection on the adjacent planes will be parallel to the reference line.

When a line is oblique to all three principal planes of projection, as line AB in Fig. 7.4, none of its principal projections show in true length and none are parallel to any of the reference lines. To obtain the true length of the line, an auxiliary plane is used that is passed parallel to line AB. The line projected upon this plane will show the true length of the line.

In Fig. 7.4 the position of the auxiliary plane is shown by the reference line V-1. When viewed in the vertical projection, the V-1 line represents the edge view of the first auxiliary plane. The steps in projecting line AB onto the auxiliary plane are as follows:

a. At any convenient place draw the V-1 reference line parallel to the vertical projection $a^V b^V$ of the line.

b. Through points a^V and b^V draw perpendiculars to reference line V-1. These lines determine one locus of projection a^1 and b^1.

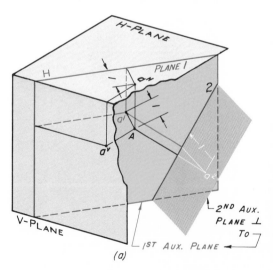

(a)

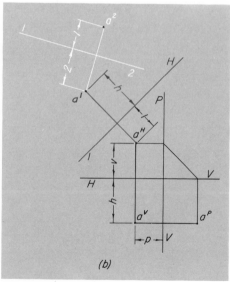

(b)

Fig. 7.2   Nomenclature and theory of auxiliary projection.

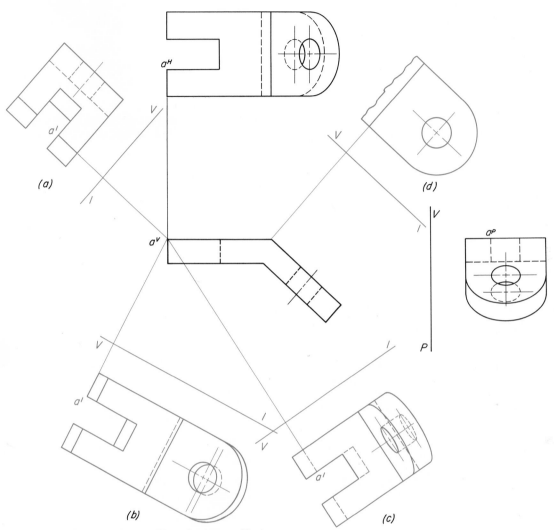

Fig. 7.3   Relationship of the auxiliary plane to an object.

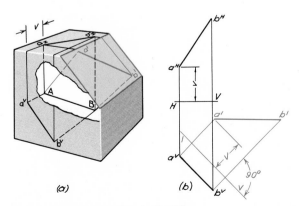

Fig. 7.4   True length of an inclined line.

c. To locate a^1 and b^1, the distance they each lie from the *V*-plane is required. This distance *v* is obtained in the horizontal projection and is measured from the *H-V* reference line.

d. To locate a^1 lay off the distance *v* from the horizontal projection along the perpendicular to *V-1* through a^V. Locate b^1 in the same manner.

e. Draw a line connecting a^1 and b^1, thus obtaining the true length of line *AB*.

7.8   POINT PROJECTION OF A LINE.

There are many problems that require the point projection of a line to determine the solution. These include the clearance between two members, the angle between two planes, the distance between parallel lines, the right section of a cylinder or prism, and many others.

To find the point projection of a line, the auxiliary plane must be set up perpendicular to the true-length projection of the line.

7.8.1   Line parallel to one coordinate plane and inclined to the others.

When a line is parallel to the vertical plane as shown for line *AB* in Fig. 7.5(*a*), any plane that is perpendicular to line *AB* must be perpendicular to the *V*-plane since the true length of the line appears in the front view. For this reason only one auxiliary plane is needed. This plane is shown in Fig. 7.5(*a*) with the reference line marked *V-1*. In Fig. 7.5(*b*) the orthographic solution is shown. The following steps were necessary.

a. Set up the *V-1* reference line perpendicular to a^Vb^V.

b. Construct a projection line through a^V and b^V perpendicular to *V-1*.

c. Measure the distance *v* from each point to the vertical plane in the *H*-projection.

d. Lay out this distance on the perpendicular through a^V and b^V from the *V-1* reference line to obtain a^1b^1. This is the point projection of line *AB*.

Figure 7.5(*c*) shows an object with a *T*-slot in which all lines are parallel to line *AB* in Figs. 7.5(*a*) and (*b*). If the size of the *T*-slot is known, it may be necessary to have an end view in order to complete the other projections or to design the cutting tool. Figure 7.5(*c*) shows a pictorial of the object with the *H*-, *V*-, and auxiliary planes. Figure 7.5(*d*) shows the orthographic projections giving the top, front, and auxiliary views. The steps necessary in making these views are as follows:

e. Construct the outlines of the top and front views.

f. Construct the *V-1* reference line perpendicular to the *V*-projection of the inclined line.

g. Draw lines from the *V*-projection perpendicular to the *V-1* reference line.

h. Measure distances *v* and v^1 in the *H*-projection.

i. Lay out the distances *v* and v^1 on the perpendicular drawn in step *g*, by measuring from the *V-1* reference line.

j. Construct the cross-section of the *T*-slot from the known dimensions.

k. Project the lines back to the *H*- and *V*-projections.

7.8.2   Line oblique to all of the principal coordinate planes.

To obtain the point projection of a line inclined to the three principal planes of projection, the true-length projection of the line must first be obtained.

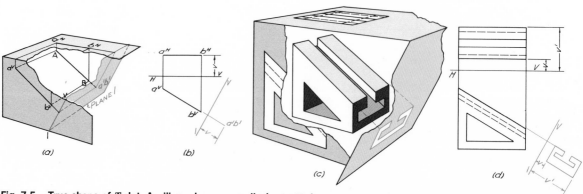

Fig. 7.5   True shape of *T*-slot. Auxiliary plane perpendicular to *V*-plane.

The steps for the solution of this problem are illustrated in Fig. 7.6(a) and are as follows:

a. Set up the first auxiliary plane parallel to line AB by making reference line H-1 parallel to $a^H b^H$.

b. Construct lines through a^H and b^H perpendicular to the H-1 reference line.

c. Measure the distance h from each point to the H-plane as shown for point A in the V-projection.

d. Lay off these distances on the perpendiculars through a^H and b^H by measuring from the H-1 reference line. The true length of AB is shown at $a^1 b^1$, and it is now possible to set up a plane perpendicular to line AB and to the first auxiliary plane.

e. Set plane 2 perpendicular to plane 1 and the line

AB by making the 1-2 reference line perpendicular to $a^1 b^1$.

f. Through a^1 and b^1 construct a line perpendicular to the 1-2 reference line.

g. Measure the distance from a^H and b^H to the H-1 reference. This gives the distance from the points to the first auxiliary plane.

h. Lay out this distance on the perpendicular through a^1 and b^1. The distance is laid out from the 1-2 reference line to locate $a^2 b^2$ as shown. This is the point projection of the line.

In Fig. 7.6(b) line AB is the line of intersection between planes ABC and ABD and is identical to line AB in Fig. 7.6(a). To obtain its point projection, the construction in Fig. 7.6(b) is exactly the same as described in Fig. 7.6(a). By following these steps carefully and projecting points C and D also, the second auxiliary view is obtained. It can be seen in the second auxiliary view that both planes show edgewise so that the angle between them must show in true size.

7.9 LINE IN A PLANE. Before proceeding to the next step in auxiliary plane projection it is necessary to explain the method of constructing a line in a plane. *A straight line will lie in a plane when any two points on the line lie in the plane.* In each of the illustrations of Fig. 7.7 the plane surface is represented as a triangle. In this case each of the bounding lines is a line in the plane. In Fig. 7.7(a) point M was chosen as a point on AB and N was taken as a point on BC. Line MN must therefore lie in the plane because it connects two points that lie in the plane.

A horizontal line, called an H-parallel, may be con-

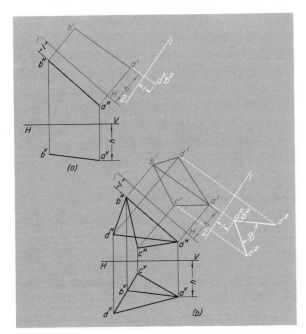

Fig. 7.6 Endwise view of a line and angle between planes. Double auxiliary.

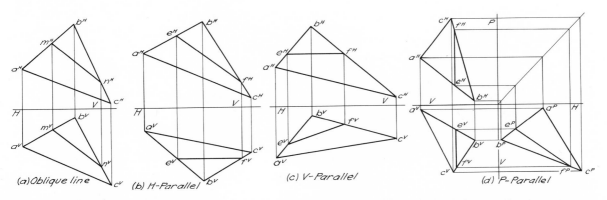

Fig. 7.7 Line in a plane.

structed in the plane by making the V-projection, e^Vf^V, parallel to the H-V reference line as in Fig. 7.7(b). Point E is made to lie on line AB by placing e^H on a^Hb^H. Point F is made to lie on line BC by placing f^H on b^Hc^H. Then since E and F lie in the plane, the line joining them must lie in the plane.

The same reasoning will prove that line EF in Fig. 7.7(c) may be made a V-parallel in the plane ABC by making e^Hf^H parallel to H-V. It also follows that the line EF in Fig. 7.7(d) is a P-parallel in plane ABC because the H- and V-projections were made parallel to the V-P reference line and points E and F were made to lie in the plane.

7.10   EDGEWISE VIEW OF A PLANE. A plane figure shows edgewise when projected on an auxiliary plane that is perpendicular to any line in the plane. If the line chosen is an oblique line, it will be necessary to use two auxiliary planes as illustrated for line AB in Fig. 7.6. However, if an H- or V-parallel is chosen lying in the plane as shown in Fig. 7.8, only one auxiliary plane is required to obtain the edge view. The edgewise view of the plane is obtained in the following steps:

a. Construct a V-parallel in the plane as AD in Fig. 7.8.

b. Set up an auxiliary plane perpendicular to AD by drawing V-1 perpendicular to a^Vd^V since a^Vd^V is the true length of AD.

c. Project points A, B, and C on the first auxiliary plane.

d. The projection $a^1b^1c^1$ will be a straight line, which proves that this is the edgewise view.

7.11   TRUE SIZE OF A PLANE FIGURE. *To find the true size and shape of a plane figure it is necessary to set up an auxiliary plane parallel to the given plane.* In actual practice the views of an object are frequently so arranged that one of the principal views of a face is an edgewise view. In such a situation only one auxiliary plane is needed. When an edgewise view is not given, two auxiliary views are necessary.

7.11.1   Edgewise view given. In the pyramid shown in Fig. 7.9 each of the inclined planes shows edgewise in either the front view or the side view. In this problem it is desired to find the true size and shape of the face ACD. Figure 7.9(a) shows the pictorial of the object and the planes of projection. Since the face ACD shows edgewise in the front view, it is necessary to set up an auxiliary plane perpendicular to the vertical plane and parallel to the face.

This is done in Fig. 7.9(b) by making the V-1 reference line parallel to the edgewise view of the plane. The auxiliary plane has been revolved about the V-1 reference line until it coincides with the vertical plane. In these two views it can be seen that the distance v from point C to the vertical plane shows in the top view as the distance from c^H to the H-V reference line, and in the auxiliary view as the distance from c^1

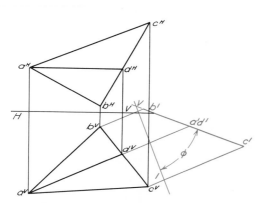

Fig. 7.8   Edgewise view of a plane.

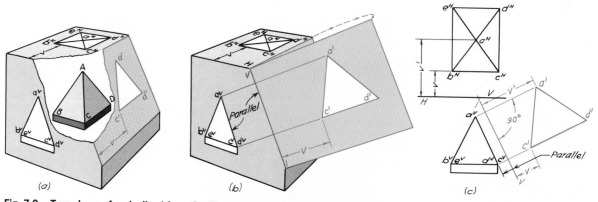

Fig. 7.9   True shape of an inclined face. Auxiliary plane perpendicular to V-plane.

to the *V-1* reference line. The orthographic projections of this problem are shown in Fig. 7.9(*c*). The steps to be followed to obtain the true size are:

a. Place the *V-1* reference line parallel to the edge-wise view $a^v d^v c^v$.

b. Construct lines through a^v, d^v, and c^v perpendicular to the *V-1* reference line.

c. Measure the distance from each of these points to the vertical plane in the horizontal projection. They are marked v and v^1.

d. Lay out these distances on the perpendiculars through a^v, d^v, and c^v. Measurements are laid out from the *V-1* reference line to locate a^1, b^1, and c^1. The area $a^1 b^1 c^1$ is the true size and shape of the given triangle.

Another example is shown in Fig. 7.10. In this case the edgewise view is in the profile projection. The aux-

iliary plane is therefore set up perpendicular to the profile plane and the distances measured are the distances from the points to the profile plane.

7.11.2   Oblique plane. *When a plane does not show edgewise in any of the principal views it is necessary to set up the first auxiliary plane so that an edgewise view will be obtained.* The second auxiliary plane will then be made parallel to the plane, as explained in the previous article.

Figure 7.11 shows the method of finding the true size of an oblique plane. The following steps are necessary:

a. Construct an *H*- or *V*-parallel in the plane. In Fig. 7.11(*a*) a *V*-parallel *CD* is used.

b. Set up an auxiliary plane perpendicular to the plane *ABC* by making the *V-1* reference line perpendicular to $c^v d^v$.

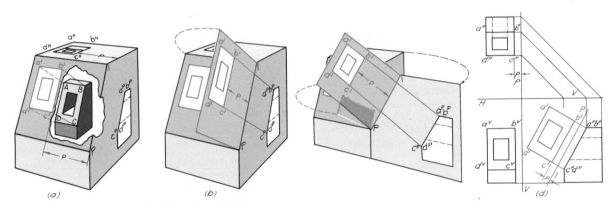

Fig. 7.10   True shape of inclined face. Auxiliary plane perpendicular to *P*-plane.

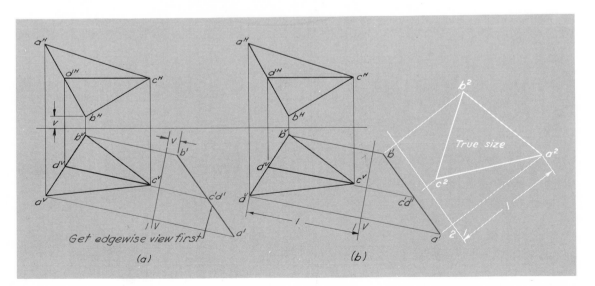

Fig. 7.11   True size of a plane figure by auxiliary projection.

c. Project the plane *ABC* onto plane *1* to obtain the edgewise view $a^1b^1c^1$.

d. Set up the second auxiliary plane *2* parallel to plane *ABC*. This is done by making the *1-2* reference line parallel to $a^1b^1c^1$. See Fig. 7.11(*b*).

e. Construct lines through a^1, b^1, and c^1 perpendicular to the *1-2* reference line.

f. Measure the distance that each point is from the first auxiliary plane in the *V*-projection. This is illustrated for point *A* in Fig. 7.11(*b*).

g. Lay out these distances on the perpendiculars from a^1, b^1, and c^1. Measurements are made from the *1-2* reference line to determine the projections a^2, b^2, and c^2. This determines the true size of the triangle *ABC*.

7.12 ELIMINATION OF REFERENCE LINES BETWEEN VIEWS.

In all of the foregoing discussion, the planes of projection, represented by reference lines, were used as the reference planes. All measurements were made from these reference planes when constructing the various views. The necessity of having a reference line between adjacent views sometimes causes the views to be spaced too far apart for efficient use of the drawing paper.

In order to avoid this difficulty, a plane of symmetry on the object or some face of the object may be used as a reference. The only condition to be met is that these surfaces be parallel to the plane of projection

that would have been used if reference lines had been drawn. These reference planes may be indicated on the drawing if necessary, but frequently it is not considered necessary.

Figure 7.12(*a*) shows a drawing having an auxiliary view laid out in the usual manner by the use of reference lines. Projecting lines are perpendicular to the reference lines and the proper distances have been laid out on these projecting lines.

7.12.1 Face of object used as a reference plane.

In Fig. 7.12(*b*) one face of the object has been used as a reference plane. The procedure given below is then followed:

a. Select a face of the object that is parallel to the coordinate plane on which the inclined face shows edgewise. Use this face as the reference plane. Thus, if the inclined face shows edgewise in the vertical projection, the face used as a reference plane must be parallel to the vertical plane.

b. Construct projecting lines perpendicular to the edgewise view of the inclined face which appears in the front view in this case.

c. Place the line that represents the edgewise view of the reference plane at a convenient distance from the edgewise view. See Fig. 7.12(*b*).

d. Measure distances such as *m* from the reference plane in the top view.

e. Lay out these distances from the reference plane

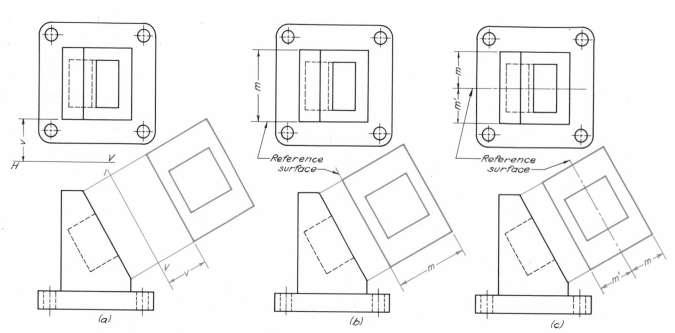

Fig. 7.12   Use of reference planes on an object.

in the auxiliary view, as shown for the distance m in Fig. 7.12(b).

7.12.2 Center line used as a reference plane.
It is frequently more convenient to use a plane through the center line of a symmetrical object as the reference plane. This has been done in Fig. 7.12(c). The auxiliary projection lines are perpendicular to the edgewise view of the inclined face, and all distances are measured and laid out from that center line as indicated for the m distances. The use of the center line is particularly helpful when circles are to be projected, because several points can be laid out with one setting of the dividers.

7.13 USE OF AUXILIARY VIEWS FOR THE CONSTRUCTION OF PRINCIPAL VIEWS.
The auxiliary view may be used to advantage when the shape of the face is known and when it may be drawn in true shape in the auxiliary view. This is illustrated in Fig. 7.13. The true shape of the flange may be drawn in the auxiliary view from known dimensions. From the auxiliary view and the adjacent side view, the front view can be constructed. To do this a series of points, similar to A and B can be assumed on the side and auxiliary views, from which they can be projected back to the front view. The following procedures may be used:

a. Choose any points, one on the upper and one on the lower circles in the auxiliary view, whose projections are a^1 and b^1.

b. From a^1b^1 draw projecting lines perpendicular to the edgewise view of the inclined face in the side view.

c. Mark the positions of a^P and b^P at the place where the perpendiculars cross the edgewise views of the top and bottom faces of the lug.

d. From the positions of a^P and b^P draw horizontal projecting lines to the front view.

e. Measure the distance x from the center line to a^1b^1 in the auxiliary projection.

f. Lay off the distance x on each of the horizontal projecting lines (drawn in step d) on both sides of the center line in the front view. This locates the various positions of a^V and b^V.

g. Repeat the process for as many points on the circle as desired.

h. Connect the points in the front view to form the ellipses.

7.14 ELIMINATION OF MEASUREMENTS IN AUXILIARY PROJECTION.
When reference lines are used, it is sometimes convenient to project the points back from the auxiliary view to the principal views without the necessity of measuring any distances. This method is illustrated in Fig. 7.14. The construction may be completed in the following steps:

a. From the point of intersection of the H-V reference line and V-1 reference line, erect a new line to bisect the angle between the two reference lines.

b. Select projections of points on the auxiliary view, such as a^1 and b^1. Construct through them a line parallel to the V-1 reference line.

c. From the point where this line intersects the bisector, construct a line parallel to the H-V reference line.

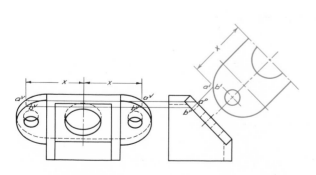

Fig. 7.13 Front view constructed from known auxiliary view.

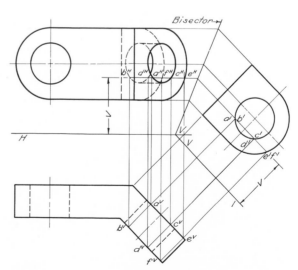

Fig. 7.14 Top view constructed from known shape of auxiliary view.

d. From the auxiliary projections a^1 and b^1, construct projection lines perpendicular to the *V-1* reference line. The projections a^V and b^V will be found at the place where this projection line crosses the edgewise views of the top and bottom faces of the angle.

e. From projections a^V and b^V, construct vertical projection lines to locate projections a^H and b^H on the horizontal lines drawn in step *c*.

f. Repeat the process to obtain as many points as desired. Connect them with a smooth curve to complete the horizontal projection.

7.15   PARTIAL VIEWS. Objects such as that shown in Fig. 7.15 would be rather difficult to draw if the complete projections were to be made. For this reason it is common practice to show one complete view and two partial views. One of these views may be an auxiliary. This simplifies the drawing and makes it easier to read. Since this object is symmetrical, only one half of the

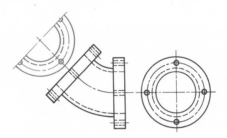

Fig. 7.15   Partial auxiliary view.

auxiliary view is drawn. If space is limited, the side view could have been made as a half view also.

7.16   PROCEDURE IN LAYING OUT A DRAWING HAVING ONE AUXILIARY VIEW. For speed and efficiency in his work, the draftsman should develop a regular procedure for laying out a drawing. Figure 7.16 gives a step-by-step layout that may be varied to suit conditions. The object to be drawn is shown pictorially in Fig. 7.16(*a*). The various steps and the order in which they should be taken are listed below.

7.16.1   Draw front view and locate top view. In Fig. 7.16(*b*) the following steps are taken.

a. Draw the front view.

b. Draw the auxiliary projection lines perpendicular to the edgewise view of the inclined plane.

c. Locate and outline the top view so that the desired clearance between the top and auxiliary views will be maintained.

7.16.2   Locate center line. Figure 7.16(*c*) reveals the next two steps.

a. Draw the horizontal center line in the top view.

b. Locate the same center line in the auxiliary view so that the desired spacing between front and auxiliary views will be maintained.

7.16.3   Outline auxiliary view. Figure 7.16(*d*) shows additional construction as follows:

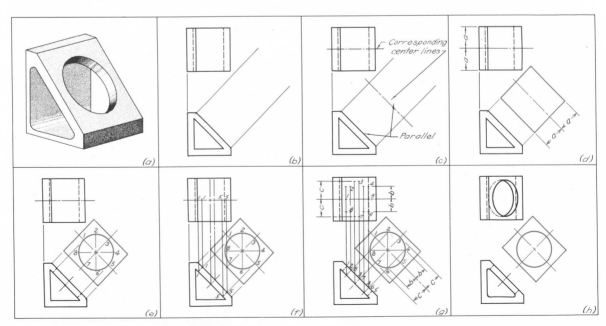

Fig. 7.16   Constructing the views of an object with the aid of an auxiliary view.

a. Transfer distance *a* with dividers from the top view to the auxiliary view.

b. Outline the auxiliary view of the inclined face.

7.16.4   Complete details of auxiliary view. Figure 7.16(*e*) shows the auxiliary view complete in three steps.

a. Locate the center of the circle in the auxiliary view.

b. Draw the circle.

c. Divide the circle into eight (or more) equal parts.

7.16.5   Construct projection lines. In Fig. 7.16(*f*) the first steps for the completion of front and top views are made.

a. Project the *3-7* center line back to the front view and from there to the top view.

b. Project points *1* and *5*, which are on the original center line, back to the front view and from there to the top view.

7.16.6   Complete all projections. In Fig. 7.16(*g*) the work of projection is completed.

a. Project all points from the circle to the edgewise view of the inclined faces in the front view.

b. Project these points from the front view to the top view.

c. Transfer distances *b* and *c* from the auxiliary view to the top view on the proper projection line.

7.16.7   Finish drawing. Figure 7.16(*h*) shows the necessary steps for finishing the drawing.

a. Connect the points with a smooth curve, showing the proper visibility.

b. Clean up the drawing.

c. Work over the lines to give them the proper weight and character.

7.17   PROCEDURE IN LAYING OUT A DRAWING HAVING TWO AUXILIARY VIEWS. In theory the procedure is an extension of that used for a single auxiliary plane. In practice a few difficulties may be encountered that can be cleared up with a step-by-step analysis. The object chosen for this illustration is shown pictorially in Fig. 7.17. Note that the first auxiliary plane, numbered *1*, is perpendicular to the horizontal plane and parallel to the cylinder. The second auxiliary plane, numbered *2*, is perpendicular to plane *1* and to the axis of the cylinder.

The following step-by-step analysis, illustrated in Fig. 7.18, gives a procedure that may be followed in laying out a drawing of this kind. The steps taken in each part of the figure have been listed in proper order following the figure number.

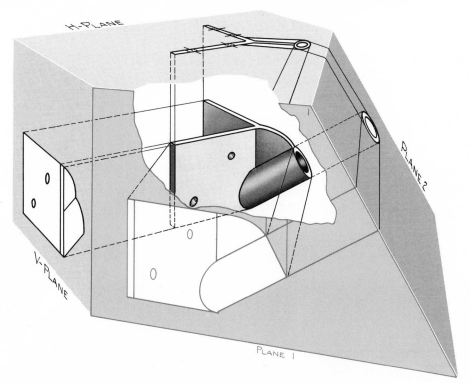

Fig. 7.17   Pictorial drawing of auxiliary planes.

7.17.1 Locate the layout of the front and top views. In Fig. 7.18(a) the following steps are taken.

a. Make top and front views of the main body of the casting.

b. Lay out the center line and edge lines of the supporting web in the top view at the proper angle.

7.17.2 Lay out first auxiliary view. Figure 7.18(b) reveals the next four steps.

a. Place auxiliary reference line $H\text{-}1$ parallel to the top view of the web.

b. Draw auxiliary projection of the nearest face of the bracket.

c. Draw center line of the cylinder at the proper angle and at the proper height according to design specifications.

d. Complete the first auxiliary projection of the web by drawing the arc tangent to the surface of the bracket and to the end face of the cylinder.

7.17.3 Draw second auxiliary view. Figure 7.18(c) shows further auxiliary view construction.

a. Locate the center line marked x^2 parallel to the edgewise view of the end of the cylinder. This is perpendicular to the axis of the cylinder. Place this line at a convenient distance from the cylinder. (Note that this is the same center line as the one marked x^H in the top view.)

b. Extend the center line of the cylinder to form the other center line for the second auxiliary projection.

c. Draw the circles representing the end view of the cylinder.

7.17.4 Begin completion of top view. Figure 7.18(d) illustrates the transfer of points from the second auxiliary view to the top view.

a. Divide the circles into eight (or more) equal parts.

b. Project these points to the edge view of the end of the cylinder in the first auxiliary projection.

c. Project the points from the first auxiliary view perpendicular to the $H\text{-}1$ reference line.

d. Measure, with dividers, the distances marked a and b in the second auxiliary view and lay them out as indicated in the top view.

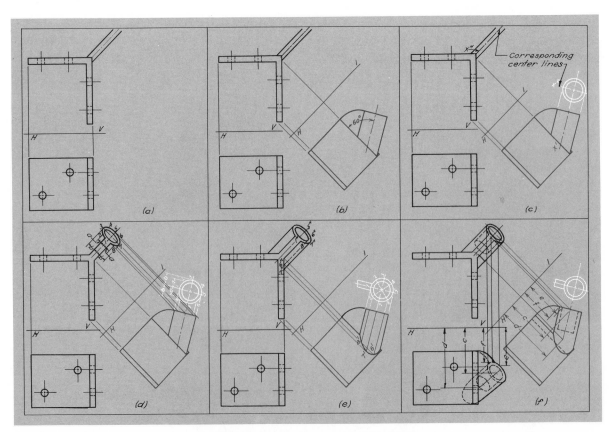

Fig. 7-18   Steps in making complete views of object with the aid of two auxiliary views.

e. Connect the points with a smooth curve.

7.17.5   Complete first auxiliary view. Figure 7.18(*e*) completes the intersection of the cylindrical part in the first auxiliary view.

a. Lay out a portion of the web in the second auxiliary projection.
b. Project the intersection of the web and cylinder from the second auxiliary view to the first auxiliary projection.
c. Draw elements of the cylinder such as *6, 7,* and *8* in the top view.
d. Find the points 6^H, 7^H, and 8^H where these elements cut the face of the bracket in the top view.
e. Project these points back to the first auxiliary projection to obtain 6^1, 7^1, 8^1, etc.
f. Connect these points to form the intersection of the cylinder with the side face of the bracket.

7.17.6   Finish front view. Figure 7.18(*f*) shows steps for completing the cylindrical part of the front view.

a. Project points from the top view of the end of the cylinder vertically to the front view.
b. Measure distances such as *e* and *f* in the auxiliary view and lay them out as indicated in the front view.
c. Connect these points to form the ellipses representing the end of the cylinder.
d. Locate points on the front view of the web in a similar manner.
e. Locate the intersection of the cylinder with the back face of the bracket and any other necessary lines.
f. Determine the visibility of all lines. Finally, clear up the drawing and erase all construction lines. Work over all lines, giving them the proper weight and character.

SELF-STUDY QUESTIONS

Before trying to answer these questions, read the chapter carefully. Then, without reference to the text, answer as many questions as possible. For those that cannot be answered, the number, in parentheses following the question number, gives the article in which the answer can be found. Look it up and write down the answer. Check the answers that you did give to see that they are correct.

7.1 **(7.7)** To find the true length of an oblique line, an auxiliary plane must be set up _____ to the line.

7.2 **(7.2)** The first auxiliary plane is always set up _____ to one of the principal planes of projection.

7.3 **(7.3)** The projection of point A on auxiliary plane 3 is labeled _____ .

7.4 **(7.8.2)** The distance from a^H to the H-1 reference line is the distance from point A to the _____ plane.

7.5 **(7.4)** It is possible to have _____ projections marked a^1 in a single problem.

7.6 **(7.2)** To be useful, an auxiliary plane should be set up _____ or perpendicular to a face or line of an object.

7.7 **(7.8.2)** The second auxiliary plane is set up _____ to the first auxiliary plane.

7.8 **(7.6)** The four fundamental operations for which auxiliary planes are used are:

1.

2.

3.

4.

7.9 **(7.5)** The distance from a^1 to the 1-2 reference line is the distance from A to the _____ plane.

7.10 **(7.7)** In the first auxiliary view, the V-1 reference line represents the edge view of the _____ plane.

7.11 **(7.8)** To find the point projection of a line, the auxiliary plane must be set up _____ to the line.

7.12 **(7.8.2)** To find the point projection of a line, it is necessary to have the _____ of the line first.

7.13 **(7.8.1)** When the true length of the line shows in the vertical projection, the auxiliary plane must be set up _____ to the vertical plane and to the line, to find the point projection.

7.14 **(7.7)** When a line is oblique to all the principal planes, it requires _____ plane(s) to find the true length.

7.15 **(7.8.2)** When a line is oblique to all the principal planes, it requires _____ auxiliary planes to find the point projection.

7.16 **(7.10)** To find the edgewise view of a plane, the auxiliary plane should be set up _____ to some line in the plane.

7.17 **(7.10)** To find the edgewise view of a plane, it is best to work with a line _____ to a principal plane of projection.

7.18 **(7.11)** To find the true shape of a plane, an auxiliary plane should be set up _____ to the plane.

7.19 **(7.11.2)** To find the true shape of a plane, the first step is to find the _____ of the plane.

7.20 **(7.11.1)** To find the true shape of a plane, the reference line should be set up _____ to the edge view of the plane.

7.21 **(7.8)** To find the true size of the right section of a cylinder, the auxiliary plane should be set up _____ _____ to the elements of the cylinder.

7.22 **(7.12)** In place of a reference plane, some _____ of the object or some axis of symmetry of the object may be used.

7.23 **(7.15)** To save space on a drawing, it is possible to show _____ views of symmetrical parts.

7.24 **(7.8.2)** Show by a sketch how to find the point projection of an oblique line.

7.25 **(7.11.2)** Show by a sketch how to find the true size of a triangular inclined plane figure.

PROBLEMS

The following problems may be solved on the standard A-size sheet (8½ × 11). They are designed to familiarize the student with the theory of orthographic projection as it relates to auxiliary projection.

Theory Problems

7.1 Figure 7.19 shows a front and partial top view of an extrusion. The extrusion is to be cut at an angle of 60° with the axis as indicated in Fig. 7.19. The maximum length is to be 2″. Find the true size of the cut face. The

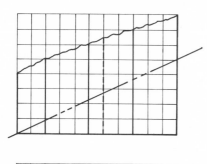

Fig. 7.19

small squares in the grid may be made any size specified by the instructor. If no size is specified, use ¼″ for each square. The grid need not be drawn by the student.

7.2 Figure 7.20 gives the front view of an extrusion. The top view can be drawn as indicated in Fig. 7.19. The cutting plane is 60° with the axis. The maximum length is 2″. Find the true size of the cut face. Scale will be as prescribed in Problem 7.1.

7.3 Same as Problem 7.2, using Fig. 7.21.

7.4 Same as Problem 7.2, using Fig. 7.22.

7.5 Same as Problem 7.2, using Fig. 7.23.

7.6 Same as Problem 7.2, using Fig. 7.24.

7.7 Same as Problem 7.2, using Fig. 7.25.

7.8 Find the true length of the line assigned from Figs. 7.26 to 7.31. The scale can be specified as desired. If not specified, each square of the grid will be ¼″. The grid need not be copied by the student.

7.9 Find the point projection of the line assigned from Figs. 7.26 to 7.31. The scale can be specified as desired. If not specified, each square of the grid will be ¼″. The grid need not be copied by the student.

Applied Problems

The following problems may be solved on the standard A-size sheet (8½ × 11). The point p shown in the problem layout, if used as the center of the drawing area, will make a well-balanced sheet at the scale specified in the layout for each problem.

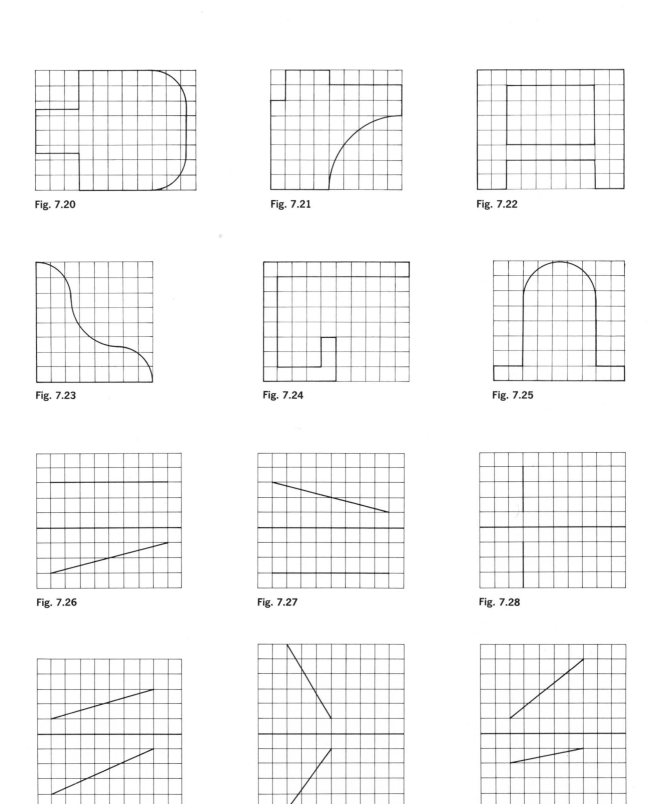

Fig. 7.20

Fig. 7.21

Fig. 7.22

Fig. 7.23

Fig. 7.24

Fig. 7.25

Fig. 7.26

Fig. 7.27

Fig. 7.28

Fig. 7.29

Fig. 7.30

Fig. 7.31

One-Auxiliary-View Problems

7.10 Lay out the pyramid shown in Fig. 7.32 and then find the true length of line *AC* and the angle it makes with the *H*-plane.

7.11–7.15 Same as Problem 7.10, using Figs. 7.33, 7.34, 7.35, 7.36, or 7.37, as assigned.

7.16 Find the true length of line *AC* and the angle it makes with the *V*-plane, using the layout of Fig. 7.32.

7.17–7.21 Same as Problem 7.16, using layout of Figs. 7.33, 7.34, 7.35, 7.36, or 7.37, as assigned.

7.22 Lay out the pyramid shown in Fig. 7.32 and then find the true shape of face *ABC*.

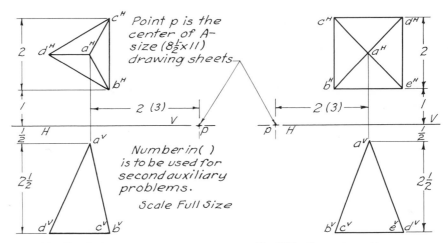

Fig. 7.32   Tetrahedron.   Fig. 7.33   Square pyramid.

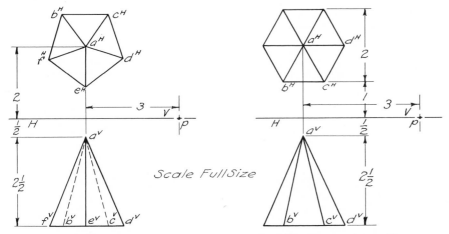

Fig. 7.34   Pentagonal pyramid.   Fig. 7.35   Hexagonal pyramid.

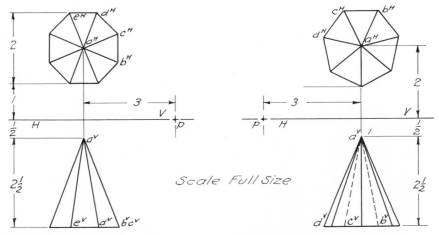

Fig. 7.36   Heptagonal pyramid.   Fig. 7.37   Octagonal pyramid.

7.23 Same as Problem 7.22, using the layout of Fig. 7.33.

7.24–7.27 Same as Problem 7.22, using the layout of Figs. 7.34, 7.35, 7.36, or 7.37, as assigned.

7.28 Find the edgewise view of the plane assigned from Figs. 7.38, 7.39, or 7.40. The scale can be specified as desired. If not specified, each square of the grid will be ¼″. The grid need not be copied by the student.

7.29 Find the true size of the plane assigned from Figs. 7.38, 7.39, or 7.40. The scale can be specified as desired. If not specified, each square of the grid will be ¼″. The grid need not be copied by the student.

7.30 Project the cube in Fig. 7.41 on an auxiliary plane perpendicular to line *AC*. Draw full-size. This picture will be an isometric projection of the cube.

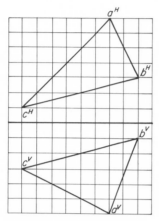

Fig. 7.38

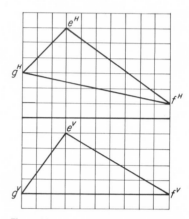

Fig. 7.39

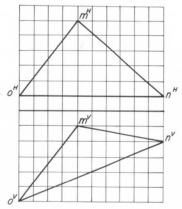

Fig. 7.40

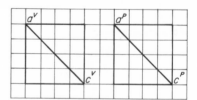

Fig. 7.41

Layout for Working Drawing Problems

In the remaining problems of this chapter, it is recommended that the student make a freehand sketch of the views he plans to use in order that the solution may fall within the limits of his drawing paper. The sketch should be planned so that the views make a well-balanced working drawing.

In the interest of drawing for simplification and clarity, rounded corners have been omitted.

In each drawing, use the scale specified if the drawing is to be made on an 8½ × 11″ sheet. Room must be allowed for dimensioning between views and around them. Problems are to be dimensioned, however, only if so specified.

7.31–7.42 Make the orthographic projections, including necessary auxiliary views, to describe fully the shape of the object assigned from Figs. 7.42, 7.43, 7.44, 7.45, 7.46, 7.47, 7.48, 7.49, 7.50, 7.51, 7.52, and 7.53. All views must be planned and drawn so that they may be adequately

dimensioned as shop drawings. Dimension the object if so assigned by the instructor.

7.43 Make the top and front views of the bin shown in Fig. 7.44 and then find the true shape of the sloping faces assigned by the instructor. Find the true size of the faces of the bin in Fig. 7.44 mathematically. Compare results with those obtained graphically.

7.44 Make the front and top views of the bin shown in Fig. 7.44 and then find the true value of the angles between the four sloping faces.

7.45 Make two orthographic views of the roof-rafter layout shown in Fig. 7.51. Make a separate layout of the cuts required to frame the hip rafter. Note: on a ½ pitch roof the height is ½ the span.

7.46 Make two orthographic views of the roof framing shown in Fig. 7.56. Make a separate detail showing the cuts required to form the jack rafter.

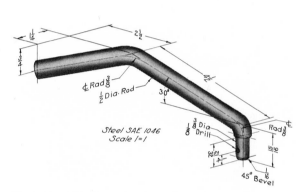

Fig. 7.42   Adjusting rod.

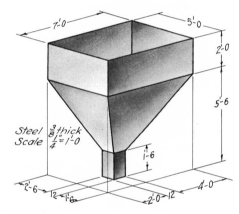

Fig. 7.44   Steel bin.

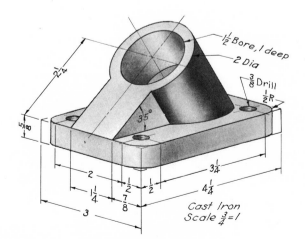

Fig. 7.43   Angle step bearing.

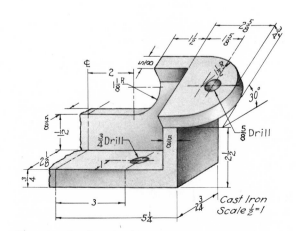

Fig. 7.45   Sandbox step base.

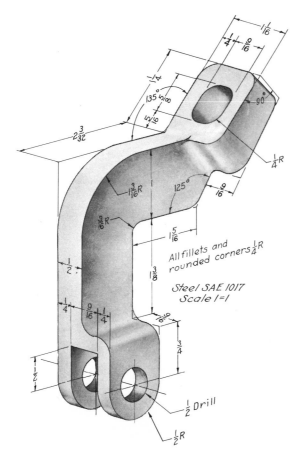

Fig. 7.46   Valve-stem clamp.

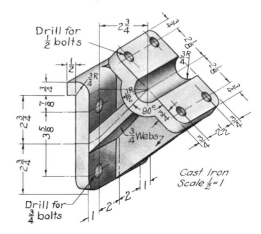

Fig. 7.47   Angle-bearing bracket.

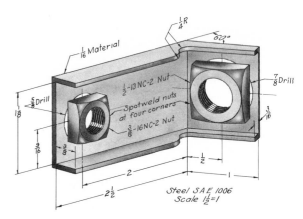

Fig. 7.48   Radiator bracket.

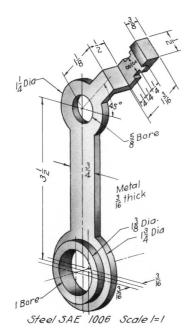

Fig. 7.49   Lever arm.

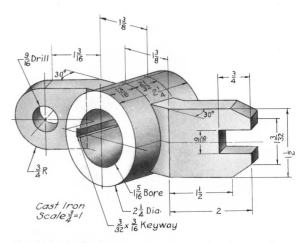

Fig. 7.50   Inclined stop.

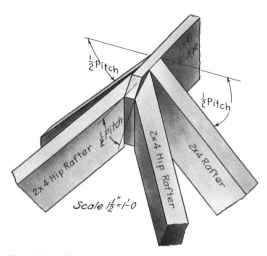

Fig. 7.51   Roof framing.

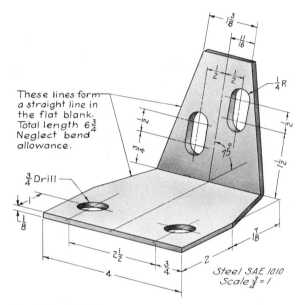

Fig. 7.52   Bracket.

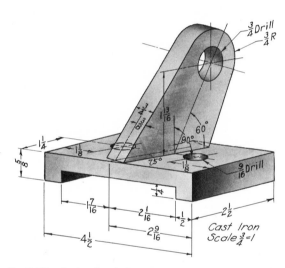

Fig. 7.53   Anchor bracket.

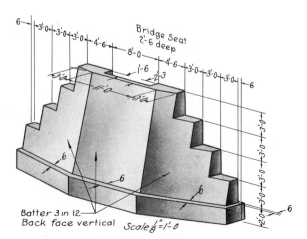

Fig. 7.54   Stepped abutment wall.

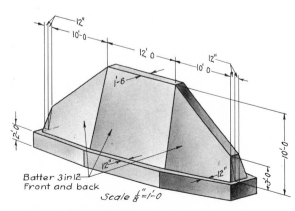

Fig. 7.55   Abutment wall.

7.47 Draw the necessary orthographic views to describe the shape of the abutment shown in Fig. 7.54. Find the true shape of the sloping wing wall face.

7.48 Same as Problem 7.47, using the abutment shown in Fig. 7.55.

7.49 Find the true shape of the developed pattern for the gusset plate connecting the purlin to the hip rafter in Fig. 7.57. Find also the angle of the bend. Ignore thickness of metal.

7.50 Same as Problem 7.31, using Fig. 7.58.

Creative Design Problems

Make the drawings necessary to give the complete shape description of an object designed by you to satisfy the given specifications.

7.51 Design a bracket to hold a music rack at an angle of 60° with the horizontal. The bracket is to fit over a ½″ vertical rod. Two screws will hold the bracket to the music rack. Show the true size of the inclined face.

7.52 Make the necessary views to describe a 30° pipe bend. The center line radius of bend is 4″. The pipe has an internal diameter of 1.61″ and an external diameter of 1.96″. There shall be a 4″ flange on each end ¼″ thick. Each flange shall have holes for four ⅜″ bolts.

7.53 A ceiling light fixture is 8″ square at the top, 6″ square at the bottom, and 4″ high. It is made of bent iron strips ¹⁄₃₂ × 1″ welded together. The fixture screws to the ceiling. Design the fixture and specify the sizes of glass for sides and bottom. Use ¹⁄₁₆″ glass.

7.54 The ceiling of a room is gabled with each side having a pitch of 5 on 12. A bracket is to be placed in the peak to support a light fixture. The bracket has two 6 × 6″ faces fastened to the faces of the ceiling by 4 screws each. A 2″ ring will be supported from the center so that the bottom of the ring will be 8″ below the peak. Show the projections and true size of the inclined face.

7.55 A coffee table is 2 × 4′ and is 18″ high. A socket must be designed to fasten the legs to the top. The legs are 2″ in diameter at the top. The legs have a batter of 2″ in 12″ on the diagonal of the top. The socket has a 4″ plate which is held to the top with 3 screws. Draw the projections of the socket.

7.56 The windshield of a boat is composed of two pieces of glass. The angle between the two pieces is 150°. They are held together at the center by means of an *H*-shaped aluminum extrusion. The opening for the glass is 16″ vertically with horizontal surfaces at top and bottom. The *H*-shaped extrusion slopes backward at an angle of 75° with the horizontal and fastens to the horizontal surfaces both top and bottom with two screws each. Make a detail drawing of the extrusion.

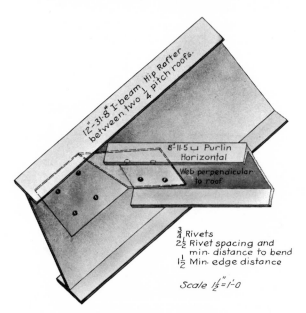

Fig. 7.57   Purlin connection to hip rafter.

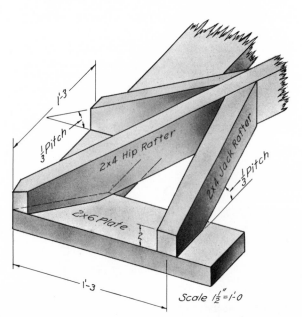

Fig. 7.56   Roof framing.

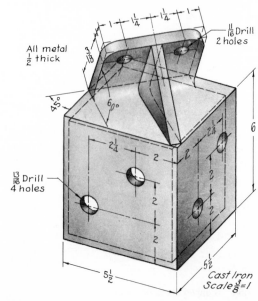

Fig. 7.58   Corner bracket.

Sectional Views

NEW: Shasta dam and power plant (Philip Gendreau)

OLD: Early sectional drawing of a waterwheel (New York Public Library Picture Collection)

Chapter 8   Sectional Views

8.1   PURPOSE OF SECTIONAL VIEWS. With the principles of projection thus far discussed, the interior parts of an object that are hidden from view can only be represented by dash lines. When these dash lines become numerous, the drawing is difficult to interpret. To overcome this difficulty the sectional view is used.

A sectional view is any view seen when a portion of the object nearest the observer has been imagined removed by cutting planes, thus revealing the interior construction. See Fig. 8.1.

A sectional view, or section as it is called, is also used to show the exact shape of exterior parts that are so rounded or curved or change shape so rapidly that the usual two- or three-view drawings do not reveal their true form. The fenders on cars, housings for revolving parts, ship propellers, and airplane wings are of this type.

8.2   CUTTING PLANE SYMBOLS. Since the location of cutting planes must frequently be shown, a standard type of line is used for this purpose. See Fig. 8.2. This distinguishes it from other lines used on the drawing. It should also be noted that for certain types of sections a center line is sometimes used to show the location of the cutting plane.

8.3   LOCATION OF CUTTING OR SECTION PLANES. To show the interior construction of an object, the main cutting plane is passed through an axis of symmetry parallel to one of the principal planes of projec-

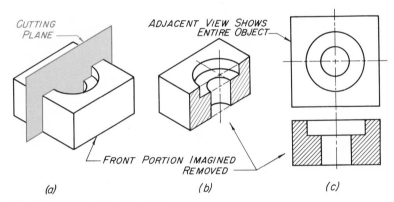

Fig. 8.1   Theory of sectional views.

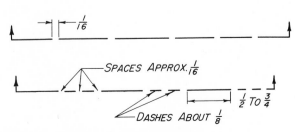

Fig. 8.2   Symbol for cutting plane line.

tion, as shown in Fig. 8.3. Other cutting planes, if necessary, are passed parallel or perpendicular to the main cutting plane, as shown in Fig. 8.4.

The cutting plane need not be continuous but may be offset as shown in Fig. 8.5. It may also be turned through an angle, as shown in Fig. 8.16. This gives rise to various types of sectional views, as discussed later.

To show the true shape of a part such as a spoke of a wheel or a connecting arm, the plane may be passed perpendicular to the axis, as shown in Fig. 8.6(*a*) and then revolved about its central axis, in place, as in Fig. 8.6(*b*).

When a cutting plane is passed on an axis of symmetry, as shown in Figs. 8.13 and 8.14, it is not necessary to indicate the location of the plane. When, however, the cutting plane is offset, as in Figs. 8.5 and 8.15, its location must be shown in the view where it appears edgewise.

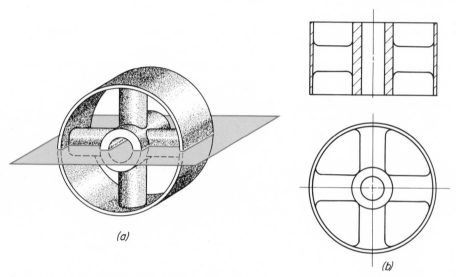

(a)

(b)

Fig. 8.3   Cutting plane parallel to horizontal plane.

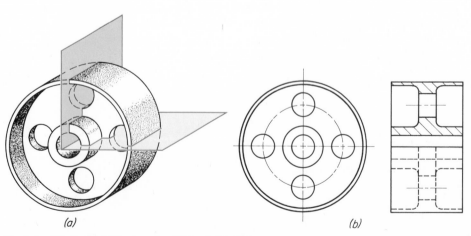

(a)   (b)

Fig. 8.4   Principal cutting plane parallel to profile plane.

8.4 DRAWING THE SECTIONED VIEWS. The view that is to be made in section is represented as though the portion of the object nearest the observer were actually cut away by the section planes and removed. It should be noted that the other views are not affected in any way and always represent the entire object. See Figs. 8.13, 8.14, and 8.15.

8.5 SECTION LINING. In order that those parts of an object that have been cut by the section plane may stand out on the drawing, a conventional scheme called crosshatching, or section lining, is employed. This is done by drawing light, inclined lines on those parts of the view of the object where the plane actually cuts the material of which the object is made.

8.5.1 Direction of section lines. The section lines may be drawn at any angle to the horizontal, but 45° lines are usually employed. The direction should be chosen so that the crosshatch lines will not be parallel

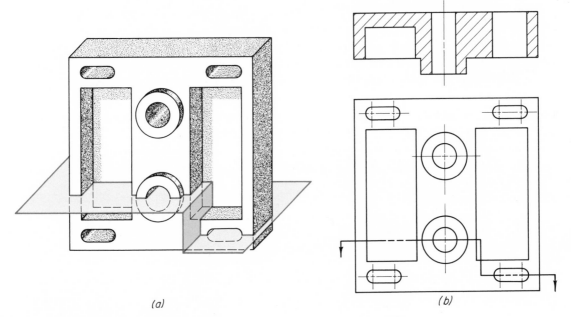

(a)

(b)

Fig. 8.5 Cutting plane parallel to horizontal but offset.

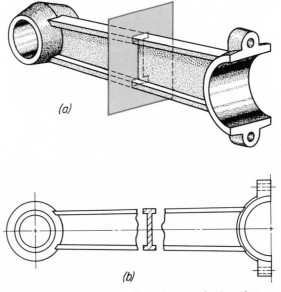

(a)

(b)

Fig. 8.6 Position of cutting plane for a revolved section.

or perpendicular to any of the bounding lines of the area being shaded. See Fig. 8.7.

8.5.2   Spacing of section lines. Section lines should be spaced uniformly and approximately ³⁄₃₂ to ⅛ inch apart. See Fig. 8.8(*d*). For very large areas the spacing may be ³⁄₁₆ inch.

8.5.3   Weight of section lines. The weight and thickness of section lines should be the same as those for dimension lines. In all cases they should come completely up to the outlines of the object. Figure 8.8 shows examples of good and faulty section lining.

8.5.4   Crosshatching adjacent parts. When several adjacent parts of a machine are of the same material and are cut by a section plane, each part should be distinguished from its neighbor by a change in slope of the section lining. The more nearly the crosshatch lines approximate 90° to each other, the better the effect will be. See Fig. 8.9.

If the section plane cuts the same part at different places in the object, the section lining should be given the same slope in the corresponding places on the drawing, as shown in Figs. 8.12 and 8.29.

When three adjacent parts of an assembly are cut, two of the parts can usually be crosshatched at 45°, but a different angle such as 30° or 60° must be used for the third part. See Fig. 8.9.

8.5.5   Partial or outline section lining. In some instances, the appearance of large areas that must be sectioned can be improved by carrying the crosshatching only a short distance from the outlines and leaving the central portions blank, as in Fig. 8.10. Not only is time saved by this practice, but the appearance of the drawing is improved by eliminating large shaded areas.

8.6   HIDDEN LINES IN SECTIONED VIEWS. It is standard practice to omit all hidden lines in the sectioned portion of a view. In making a detail of a single part, the invisible lines may be shown on the unsectioned half of the view if they are needed for dimensioning.

In making a half-sectioned assembly, the invisible outlines are usually omitted from the unsectioned half

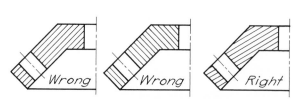

Fig. 8.7   Correct and incorrect section lining.

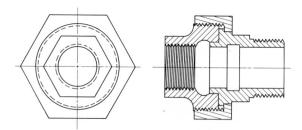

Fig. 8.9   Sectioning adjacent parts of the same material.

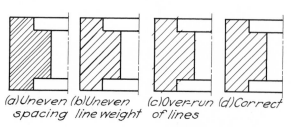

Fig. 8.8   Common errors in section lining.

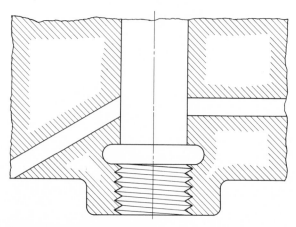

Fig. 8.10   Partial section lining.

as well as from the sectioned half so that one side shows internal construction and the other half the external appearance. See Fig. 8.11.

8.7 VISIBLE LINES BEHIND THE SECTION PLANE.

Visible outlines appearing behind the cutting plane must always be shown in the sectioned view. Beginners frequently omit them. Correct and incorrect practice is shown in Fig. 8.12.

8.8 FULL SECTIONS.

When the section plane passes completely through the object on the plane of

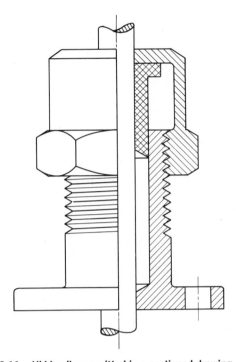

Fig. 8.11   Hidden lines omitted in a sectioned drawing.

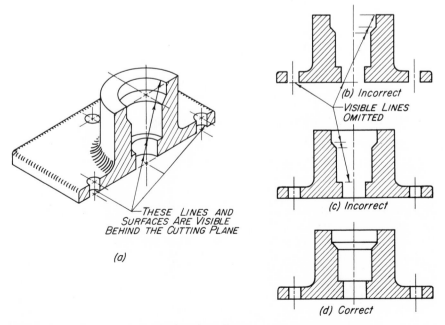

THESE LINES AND SURFACES ARE VISIBLE BEHIND THE CUTTING PLANE

(a)

(b) Incorrect

VISIBLE LINES OMITTED

(c) Incorrect

(d) Correct

Fig. 8.12   Visible lines behind cutting plane shown.

symmetry, as shown in Fig. 8.13(*a*), one half of the object is imagined to be removed in drawing the section view. Figure 8.13(*b*) shows the object as it is imagined to appear in making the section view. From this it can be seen that the entire front view will be in section, which gives it the name "full section." The correct orthographic projections of the object with a full section in the front view are shown in Fig. 8.13(*c*). The following points should be observed in making a drawing with one view in full section:

a. In making the sectioned view, one half of the object is imagined removed.

b. The adjacent view shows the entire object, unless a part is shown broken away beyond the center line to save space as in Fig. 6.55.

c. Invisible lines behind the section are omitted.

d. Visible lines behind the section are shown.

e. Only the parts actually cut by the section plane are crosshatched.

f. The position of the cutting plane is not shown on the final drawings, for full sections.

8.9   HALF SECTIONS. When two perpendicular cutting planes are passed partway through the object on planes of symmetry, as shown in Fig. 8.14(*a*), one quarter of the object is imagined to be removed in drawing the sectioned view. Figure 8.14(*b*) shows the casting as it would appear in making the sectioned view. From this it can be seen that only one half of the front view will show in section and the other half will be an external view. From this the name "half section" is derived for such a view.

The following rules should be observed in making a half section:

a. One half of the sectioned view will be in section, while the other half is an external view.

b. Hidden lines will normally be omitted from both sides of the view unless necessary for clearness of interpretation.

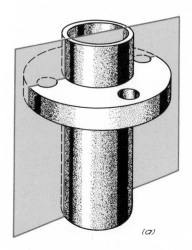
(a)

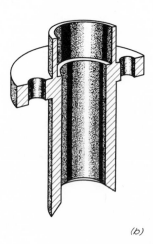
(b)

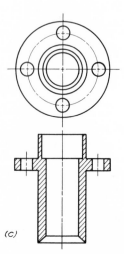
(c)

Fig. 8.13   A full-sectioned view.

c. Hidden lines may be shown on the external half, if needed for dimensioning.

d. The line separating the sectioned half from the external half should preferably be a solid line but the use of a center line is also approved by the USASI. See Figs. 8.14(*c*) and (*d*).

e. The location of the cutting plane is not shown in the view adjacent to the sectioned view. See top view in Figs. 8.14(*c*) and (*d*).

8.10 OFFSET SECTIONS. The section cutting planes are almost always passed through axes of symmetry of the object. If several such axes of symmetry

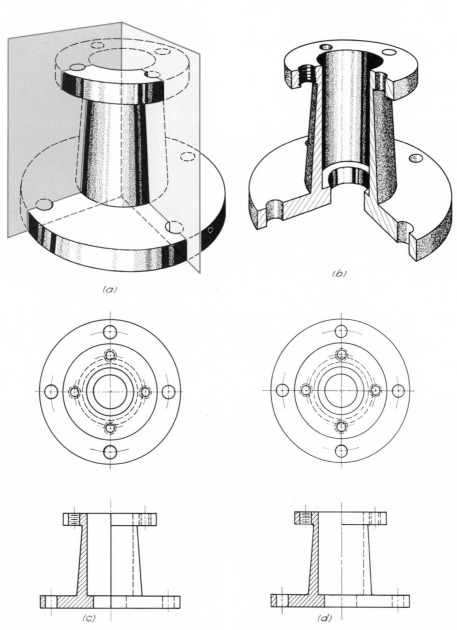

(a)

(b)

(c)

(d)

Fig. 8.14   A half-sectioned view.

occur, not coinciding with a single central axis of the object, the cutting plane is offset, as in Fig. 8.15, to include two or more of these axes of symmetry. No particular difficulty is experienced in reading a drawing when this is done.

The following rules should be observed for offset sections:

a. The location of the cutting plane must be shown by the proper symbolic line in the adjacent view. See Figs. 8.5 and 8.15.

b. Arrows should be placed on the ends of the cutting-plane line, always pointing away from the sectioned view. This shows the direction in which the view is made.

c. No indication of the offset, or break in the cutting plane is shown in the sectioned view.

8.11   ALIGNED SECTIONS. In sectioning certain objects, more information can be given if the section plane is bent or turned at an angle, as shown in Fig. 8.16. The various segments of the cutting plane are imagined to be revolved until they are parallel to the principal plane of projection. This shows all cut portions of the object in true size in the sectioned view. This is known as an "aligned section."

In this type of sectional view the following rules should be observed:

a. No indication of the bends in the cutting plane is shown in the sectioned view.

b. The exact location of the cutting plane must be shown in the adjacent view by the proper symbolic line. See Figs. 8.16 and 8.17.

c. Arrows must be placed at the ends of the cutting plane line, showing the direction in which the object is viewed in the sectioned view.

d. The arrows always point away from the section.

e. The sectioned view is made as though the parts at an angle were rotated to be parallel to the plane of projection.

f. The sectioned view, therefore, shows the true shape of the entire section.

8.12   REVOLVED SECTIONS. In many cases the cross section of some part of a structure or machine is necessary for the purpose of giving the shape or size description. Frequently the easiest way to obtain this without drawing an extra view is by means of a revolved section. The revolved section is obtained by passing a cutting plane through the member perpendicular to one of the principal planes of projection and then revolving the cross section thus obtained about its own axis of symmetry until it is parallel to the plane of projection. In this position the section will show the true shape directly on that view. This method is particularly useful for structural shapes, spokes of wheels,

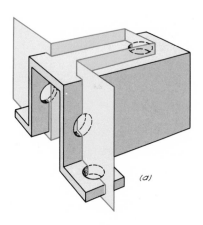
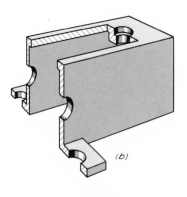
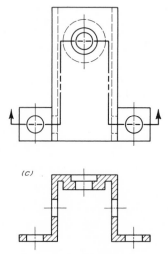

(*a*)   (*b*)   (*c*)

Fig. 8.15   An offset section.

arms, handles, and the like. Several examples of re-volved sections are shown in Figs. 8.18 and 8.19.

The advantages of these cross sections are very great, inasmuch as they convey instantly to the mind the shapes of pieces used in the design of any structure, simply from an examination of one view of the object. Dimensions are frequently placed on such sections,

thereby adding to their effectiveness. Many draftsmen make a break in the piece and place the revolved section in the opening between the broken ends. This convention may be used for any revolved section but is almost a necessity for sections such as the one in the front view of Fig. 8.19. It should be observed in this connection that the revolved section always shows the

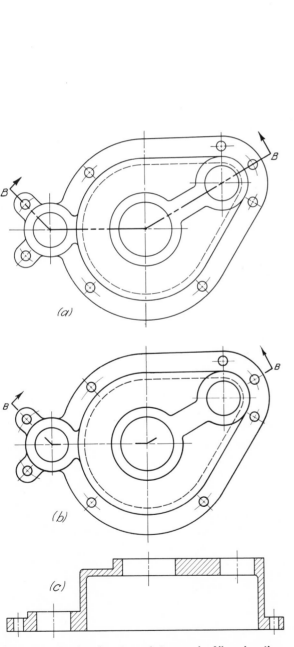

Fig. 8.16   Section plane turned at an angle. Aligned section.

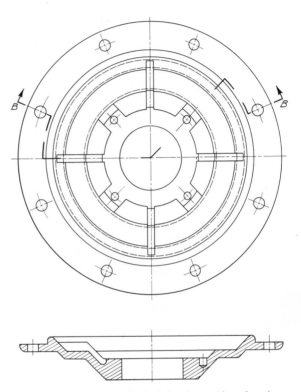

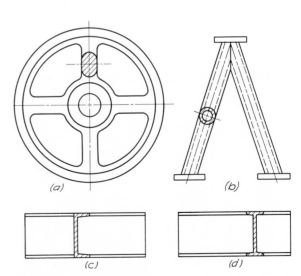

Fig. 8.17   Alternate method of showing cutting plane in an aligned section.

Fig. 8.18   Revolved sections.

true shape of the cross section of the piece regardless of the direction of the axis or boundary lines of the part sectioned. Streamlined objects, such as car fenders and propeller blades, are sometimes shown by taking sections at regular intervals.

8.13   REMOVED SECTIONS. In complicated drawings it frequently happens that it is necessary to clarify the construction of certain parts of a machine when it is not desirable to take a full or half section. This may be done by drawing what is known as a "removed" or "detail" section. The removed section is similar to the revolved section except that it is not revolved in place but removed to another area on the drawing. The location and extent of the cutting plane are indicated on the principal views by means of the usual symbol, with arrows indicating the direction of viewing the section.

The cutting-plane line is marked with a capital letter at each end of the cutting plane. See Fig. 8.20.

8.13.1   Drawing the removed section. The following points should be observed for removed sections:

a. The removed section is drawn at some clear place on the drawing sheet to give it a well-balanced appearance.

b. It should be drawn in the same position that it would have in the original view of the object; that is, it should not be upside down, nor at an angle.

c. The location of the cutting plane must be clearly labeled, as in Fig. 8.21.

d. If a scale larger than that of the original view is used, it must be specified under the title, as in Fig. 8.21.

e. Removed sections may also be placed on a center line extended, when the center line serves as a cutting-plane line, as in Fig. 8.22.

8.13.2   The removed section on a separate sheet. In some cases the sheet on which a removed section would normally be drawn is so full that there is no room for the removed section. When this occurs, observe the following rules:

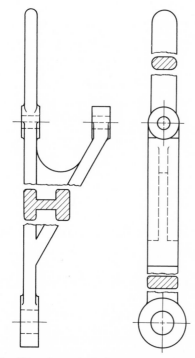

Fig. 8.19   Alternate method of showing a revolved section.

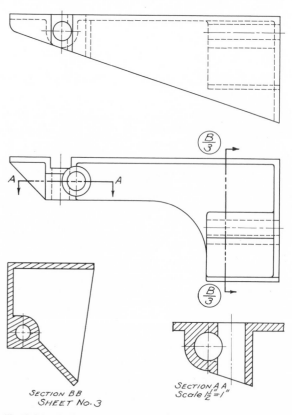

Fig. 8.21   Removed sections.

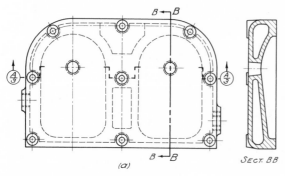

Fig. 8.20   Marking removed sections.

a. The removed section may be drawn on another sheet. This sheet may have other details on it.

b. The location of the cutting plane must be marked by letters and the number of the drawing sheet on which it occurs, as in Fig. 8.20(*a*). The letter *A* above the line in the circle is the name of the section and the number *3* below the line is the sheet on which the removed section will be found.

c. The removed section must be labeled, the scale given, and the sheet number given which shows the location of the section on the principal views. In other words, the section and its location must be cross-referenced.

8.13.3 Removed section on zoned drawings. For ease of reference, very large drawings are frequently zoned by marking off equal spaces horizontally and vertically along the border lines. The horizontal spaces are lettered *A, B, C,* etc., and the vertical spaces are numbered as shown in Fig. 8.23. For example, the area in vertical band *C* and horizontal row *3* is designated zone *C-3*. Thus any removed section can easily be located when the zone is specified.

If the removed section is not on the same zoned sheet with its cutting-plane location on a principal view, both drawings must be cross-referenced by sheet and zone numbers, as well as by letters such as Section *A-A*. The cutting-plane location would likewise have to be indicated in a similar manner.

8.13.4 Advantages of removed sections. The removed section gives considerable freedom of choice.

a. The first advantage of the removed section lies in the fact that the sectioned views may be drawn to a much larger scale than the main or principal views, thus showing the details more clearly. The scale must always be indicated with each section, as shown in Fig. 8.21.

b. A second advantage is that the main views showing the general outlines of the object are not confused by a large number of broken lines or cross-section lines.

c. A third advantage may be found in the better balanced drawing sheets, since the removed section may be placed in any open space on the sheet.

8.14 AUXILIARY SECTIONS. Another type of removed section is the auxiliary section. The section is easily understood since it is made in projection with

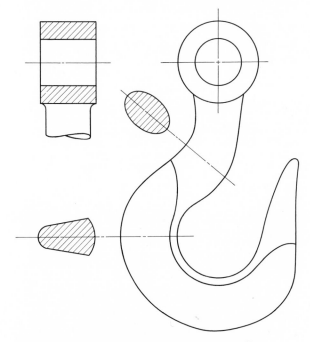

Fig. 8.22 Removed section on extended center line.

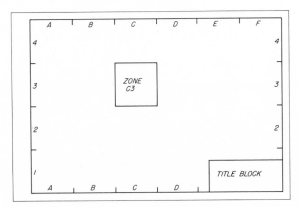

Fig. 8.23 Zoned drawing sheet.

one of the principal views, as shown in Fig. 8.24. The auxiliary plane is set parallel to the cutting plane and the auxiliary section drawn as though the object had been actually cut on the section plane. When the position of the section plane is shown, the arrows should point away from the sectional view.

8.15 BROKEN-OUT SECTIONS. In some instances a single interior detail needs to be made clearer than any of the principal views are able to make it and yet it does not justify a full or half section. Or it may be possible that a full or half section would eliminate some exterior detail that must be preserved. In a situation of this kind it is possible to break out a small portion of the outer part covering just the area desired. The broken part is outlined with an irregular freehand line to mark the break. See Fig. 8.25. This is called a broken-out section.

Another type of section that may be classified as a broken-out section is coming into use. This type of section, shown in Fig. 8.26, functions as a half section and serves its purpose better. Drawings that have been sectioned exactly to the center line have sometimes been manufactured exactly as shown, even though noted "symmetrical about $\mathcal{L}$." Thus three fourths of a part may be made and shipped. This error is not likely to occur with the type of section shown in Fig. 8.26.

8.16 PHANTOM SECTION. One type of section that is seldom used is the invisible or phantom section

illustrated in Fig. 8.27. This section is marked by dotted crosshatching and is used to emphasize some inner part while at the same time retaining all the exterior construction. It is also used occasionally to show the method of attaching or the manner in which an adjacent part joins the part being drawn.

8.17 THIN SECTIONS. When thin members such as gaskets, plates, channels, and angles are shown in section, they may be made solid black if the scale of the drawing is small. Adjacent pieces should then be separated by a space, as shown in Fig. 8.28.

8.18 CONVENTIONAL PRACTICE IN SECTIONING. In ordinary two- and three-view drawings the rules and principles of orthographic projection are strictly followed. When sectional views are introduced, however, situations arise in which the drawing can be more readily understood and more easily made if some principles of projection are violated. Some of these situations are discussed in the following paragraphs.

8.18.1 Solid shafts and bars, bolts, pins, keys, and screws in sections. When the cutting plane passes through the longitudinal axes of solid cylinders such as shafts, bolts, and screws, it is the custom to consider that these parts are not cut by the section plane. Nothing would be gained by showing the solid interior of such parts. A great deal of time is saved by eliminating large areas of crosshatching. Figure 8.29 illustrates a safety valve, the stem, weight bar, and two bolts of which come under this rule.

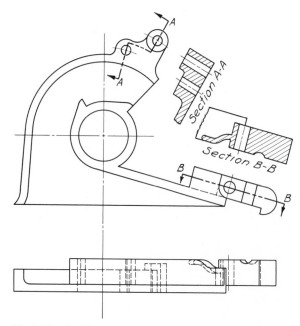

Fig. 8.24 Auxiliary sections.

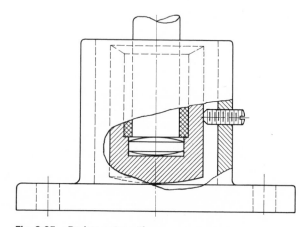

Fig. 8.25 Broken-out section.

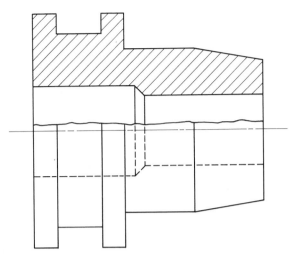

Fig. 8.26   Half-sectioned view.

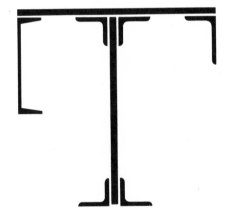

Fig. 8.28   Showing thin members in section.

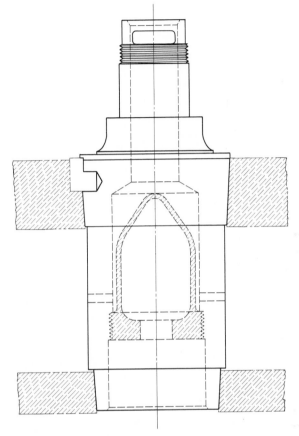

Fig. 8.27   A phantom section.

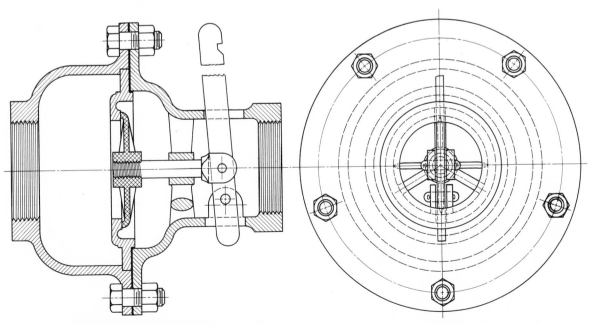

Fig. 8.29   Solid shafts, bolts, bars, and screws in section.

8.18.2   Spokes of wheels and thin webs. Spokes of wheels are not sectioned, even though the cutting plane passes through them. This not only saves time, but also gives a method of distinguishing, in the sectioned view, between a wheel with spokes and a wheel with a web. Figure 8.30 illustrates the general practice in the arms of a sheave.

When the section plane passes through a thin web parallel to its larger dimensions, as in Fig. 8.31, the most commonly accepted practice is to omit the section lining on the web and show a visible outline at the intersection of the web with the body of the piece. This

is the preferred method and is illustrated in Fig. 8.31(*a*). Sometimes the line of intersection between the web and the body is drawn as an invisible outline and every other crosshatch line is extended through the web. This method is illustrated in Fig. 8.31(*b*). When a section plane cuts through a web perpendicular to its larger dimensions, the web is crosshatched.

8.19   OTHER CONVENTIONAL PRACTICES FOR ODD-NUMBERED AXES OF SYMMETRY. In passing a section plane through such objects as a cover plate with three webs, as in Fig. 8.32, or webs of couplings with an odd number of drilled holes, only one of the

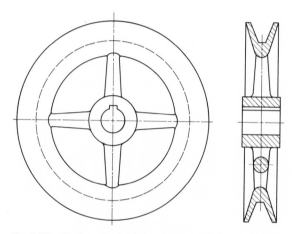

Fig. 8.30   Spokes of wheels in sectional views.

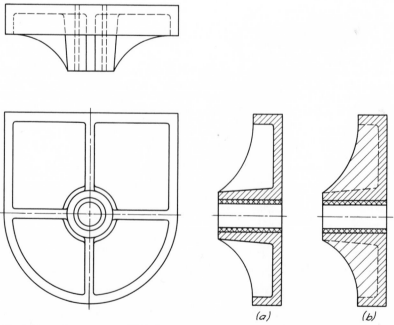

Fig. 8.31   Thin webs in sectioned views.

webs or holes will fall in the plane. To show the other webs or holes in their true positions by projecting them in the section view would usually require the use of a large number of hidden lines and difficult projections. This would make the object appear unsymmetrical. To avoid this confusion and to make the drawing easier to read it is customary, in representing the areas not on the section plane, to consider them rotated into the section plane, as shown in Fig. 8.32(*b*). Certain features contiguous to these areas must also be considered revolved at the same time.

This rotation of parts, though not in strict accord with the theory of orthographic projection, is so commonly used that it has come to be recognized and accepted as standard practice. It is used on both sectioned and unsectioned drawings. See Figs. 8.32(*c*) and 8.33. A part should not be revolved if its true relation to the rest of the object will be changed by the revolution; that is, only those areas that are on objects that fall in the class of cylindrical shapes can be treated in this manner.

8.20 CONVENTIONAL BREAKS. Long members of uniform cross section are usually not drawn to scale lengthwise. This fact is brought out by showing a con-

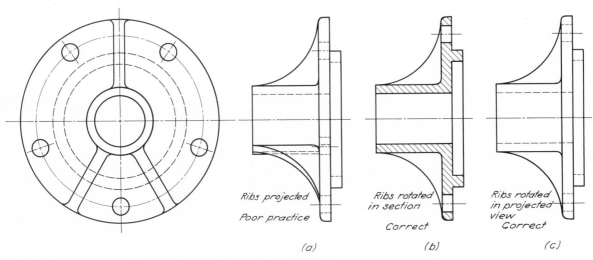

Fig. 8.32 Section of object with odd-numbered axes of symmetry.

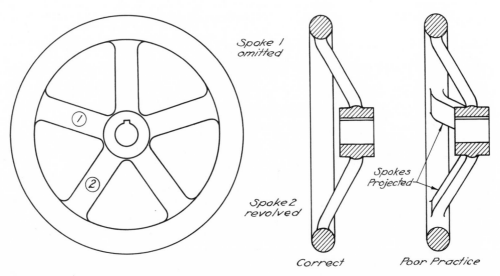

Fig. 8.33 Spokes of wheel in sectional view.

ventional break in the member, as illustrated in Fig. 8.34. The correct length of the member is shown by a dimension. A revolved section may or may not be interpolated in the break. However, the appearance of the break usually gives some indication of the shape of the cross section. Structural members when not to scale are not broken.

8.21   THREADS   AND   BOLTS   IN   SECTION. Threaded holes and bolts in section are represented by conventional symbols. A complete discussion of the methods of representing threads is given in Chapter 9. Typical sections involving threads, bolts, and screws are shown in Figs. 9.13 and 9.39 to aid the student in interpreting some of the drawings in this chapter.

Notice that the bolts and screws are drawn as though the section plane did not pass through them.

8.22   MATERIAL SYMBOLS IN SECTIONS. Many industries indicate the kind of material by using a different type of section lining. The USASI Drafting Standards Manual recommends the symbolic sections shown in Fig. 8.35. Their use is particularly valuable in assemblies where the drawing is complicated and several kinds of material are to be shown. For detail drawings it is usually preferable to use the standard symbol of parallel, uniformly spaced lines for all materials and specify the material with a note. An assembly is shown in Fig. 8.36, in which various materials are indicated by characteristic section lining.

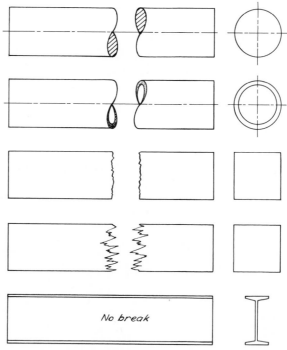

No break

Fig. 8.34   Conventional breaks.

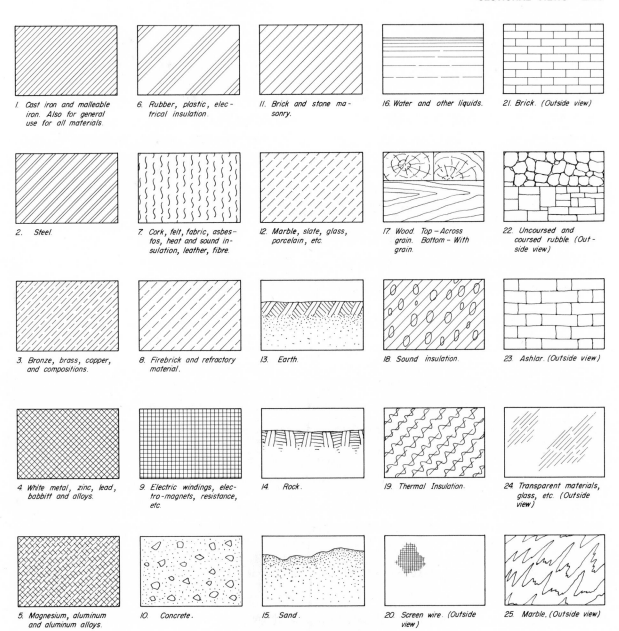

1. Cast iron and malleable iron. Also for general use for all materials.

6. Rubber, plastic, electrical insulation.

11. Brick and stone masonry.

16. Water and other liquids.

21. Brick. (Outside view)

2. Steel.

7. Cork, felt, fabric, asbestos, heat and sound insulation, leather, fibre.

12. Marble, slate, glass, porcelain, etc.

17. Wood. Top – Across grain. Bottom – With grain.

22. Uncoursed and coursed rubble. (Outside view)

3. Bronze, brass, copper, and compositions.

8. Firebrick and refractory material.

13. Earth.

18. Sound insulation.

23. Ashlar. (Outside view)

4. White metal, zinc, lead, babbitt and alloys.

9. Electric windings, electro-magnets, resistance, etc.

14. Rock.

19. Thermal Insulation.

24. Transparent materials, glass, etc. (Outside view)

5. Magnesium, aluminum and aluminum alloys.

10. Concrete.

15. Sand.

20. Screen wire. (Outside view)

25. Marble. (Outside view)

Fig. 8.35 Standard symbols for sections and outside views. (Courtesy USASI.)

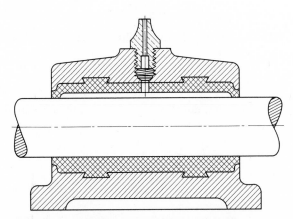

Fig. 8.36 Symbolic crosshatching in an assembly.

SELF-STUDY QUESTIONS

Before trying to answer these questions, read the chapter carefully. Then, without reference to the text, answer as many questions as possible. For those that cannot be answered, the number, in parentheses following the question number, gives the article in which the answer can be found. Look it up and write down the answer. Check the answers that you did give to see that they are correct.

8.1 **(8.1)** The purpose of sectional views is to show the _____ shape of the part.

8.2 **(8.3)** When the cutting plane goes entirely across an object along an axis of symmetry, the _____ _____ of the cutting plane is not shown.

8.3 **(8.5)** The areas where material is cut by the section planes are _____.

8.4 **(8.5.1)** Crosshatch lines are usually drawn at an angle of _____ with the horizontal.

8.5 **(8.5.2)** Crosshatch lines are drawn about _____ to _____ apart.

8.6 **(8.5.4)** Crosshatch lines for adjacent parts should be approximately at _____ to each other.

8.7 **(8.7)** Visible lines behind a section plane $\left(\begin{array}{c}\text{should}\\\text{should not}\end{array}\right)$ be shown.

8.8 **(8.6)** Hidden lines on a sectioned view usually $\left(\begin{array}{c}\text{are}\\\text{are not}\end{array}\right)$ shown.

8.9 **(8.8)** A sectional view that cuts entirely across an object is called a _____ section.

8.10 **(8.8)** In making a full section, _____ of the object is imagined removed.

8.11 **(8.9)** When one fourth of a symmetrical part is imagined removed, the section is called a _____ section.

8.12 **(8.9d)** The line on the drawing separating the external half from the sectioned half may be either a _____ line or a _____ line.

8.13 **(8.10b)** The arrows at the ends of the cutting plane showing an offset section always point _____ from the sectioned view.

8.14 **(8.11)** When the cutting-plane line is turned at an angle one or more times, the section is known as an _____ section.

8.15 **(8.12)** A _____ section has the section rotated to show the true shape in the sectioned view.

8.16 **(8.13)** A removed section should be drawn in the _____ it would have been in the original view as a revolved section.

8.17 **(8.18.1)** When the cutting plane passes through the axis of solid shafts, bolts, pins, and screws, they are _____ _____.

8.18 **(8.18.2)** Spokes of wheels and thin webs are not crosshatched when the cutting plane passes through them in a direction _____ to their larger dimension.

8.19 **(8.19)** A part should not be revolved if its _____ to the rest of the object is changed by the revolution.

8.20 Convert the front view of the object shown below into a full section.

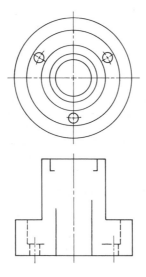

PROBLEMS

The following problems are designed for 8½ × 11″ or 11 × 17″ paper. The student should select his scale to suit the size of paper. Ample space should be allowed between views to place dimensions in later assignments.

Drawings are not to be dimensioned unless specified by the instructor.

It should be noted that the dimensions given on the pictorial drawings are not necessarily those that would be used on a working drawing, nor are they always placed where they should be on a working drawing.

Half Sections

8.1 Make the necessary views to describe the shape of the packing gland in Fig. 8.37. One view to be in half section.

8.2 Same as Problem 8.1; Fig. 8.38.

8.3 Same as Problem 8.1; Fig. 8.39.

8.4 Same as Problem 8.1; Fig. 8.40.

8.5 Same as Problem 8.1; Fig. 8.41.

8.6 Same as Problem 8.1; Fig. 8.43.

Full Sections

8.7 Make the necessary views to describe the shape of the object shown in Fig. 8.39. Make one view in full section.

8.8 Same as Problem 8.7; Fig. 8.38.

8.9 Same as Problem 8.7; Fig. 8.41.

8.10 Same as Problem 8.7; Fig. 8.42.

8.11 Same as Problem 8.7; Fig. 8.43.

8.12 Same as Problem 8.7; Fig. 8.44.

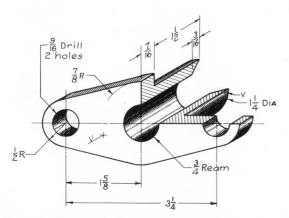

Fig. 8.37   Packing gland.

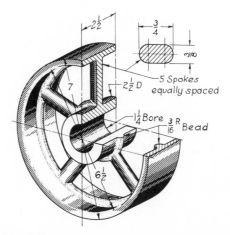

Fig 8.38   Pulley.

Removed Sectional Views

8.13 Make the necessary views to describe the shape of the object shown in Fig. 8.45. Show a removed section.

8.14 Same as Problem 8.13; Fig. 8.46.

8.15 Same as Problem 8.13; Fig. 8.47.

8.16 Same as Problem 8.13; Fig. 8.48.

8.17 Make the necessary two or three views to adequately describe the object in Fig. 8.49. Include a removed section.

8.18 Same as Problem 8.17; use Fig. 8.50.

8.19 Make the necessary two-view drawing to describe the object in Fig. 8.51. Side view in half section. Revolved section of spoke in front view.

8.20 Draw the necessary views to describe the object in Fig. 8.52. Side view in full section. Show shape of three spokes in a removed section.

8.21 Make the necessary views to describe the shape of the object in Fig. 8.53. Side view in full section.

8.22 Draw the necessary views to describe the shape of the object in Fig. 8.54. Side view in half section.

8.23–8.29 Make the necessary views including sectioned ones to adequately describe the shape of the object shown in Figs. 8.55 through 8.61 as assigned. Make full-size except Fig. 8.59, which should be one-half size.

8.30–8.34 Reproduce the views for the problem assigned from Figs. 8.62 to 8.73. Make them at least 3 times the size shown to the nearest one sixteenth of an inch. Change any view that should be in section and add other views and sections as needed. Dimensions may be transferred with dividers.

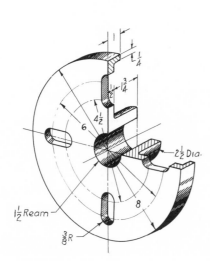

Fig. 8.39   Face plate.

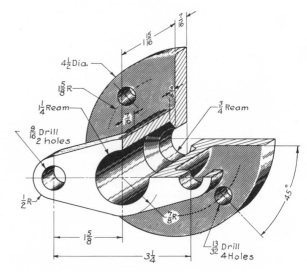

Fig. 8.40   Stuffing box body.

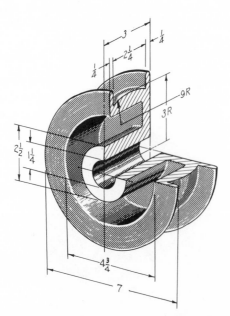

Fig. 8.41   Flanged pulley.

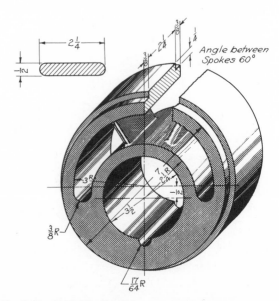

Fig. 8.42   Eccentric sheave.

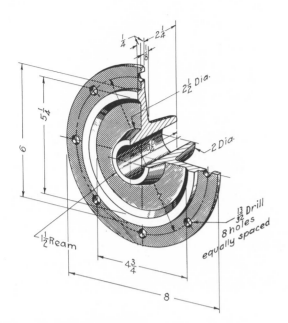

Fig. 8.43 Motor end bearing.

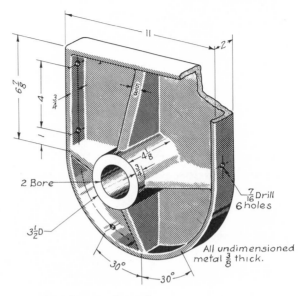

Fig. 8.44 Conveyor box end.

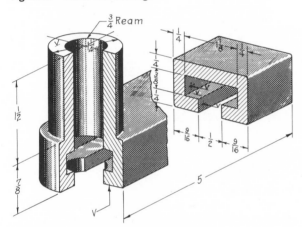

Fig. 8.45 Tool rest holder.

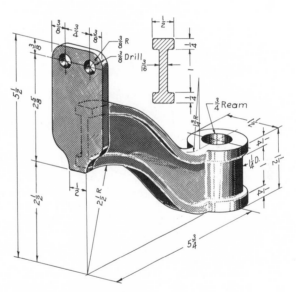

Fig. 8.46 Tool box holder.

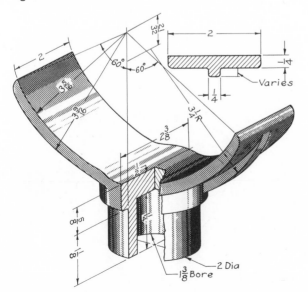

Fig. 8.47 Pipe support.

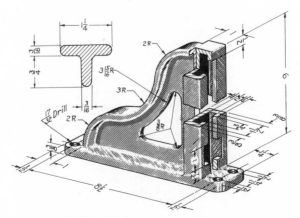

Fig. 8.48 Wall bracket.

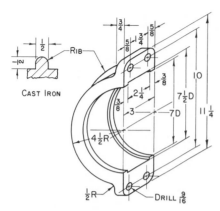

Fig. 8.49 Eccentric cap.

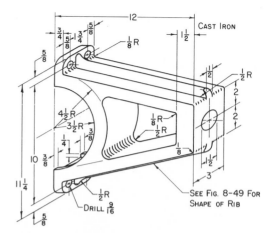

Fig. 8.50 Eccentric body.

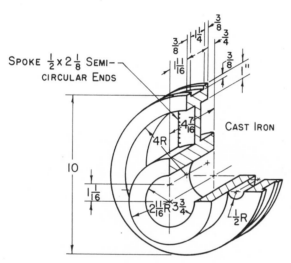

Fig. 8.51 Eccentric sheave.

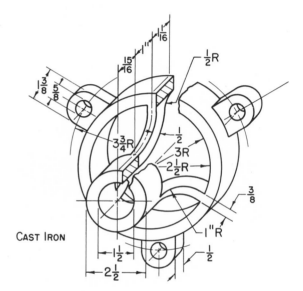

Fig 8.52 Offset bearing.

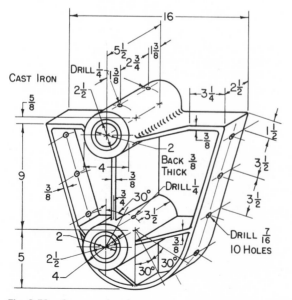

Fig. 8.53 Conveyor bearing.

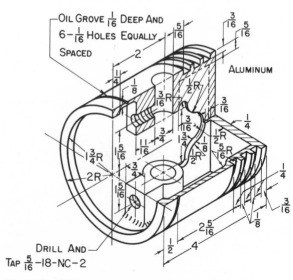

Fig. 8.54 Piston.

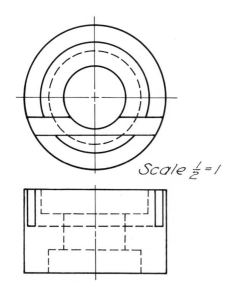

Scale $\frac{1}{2}$ = 1

Fig. 8.55   Cutter holder.

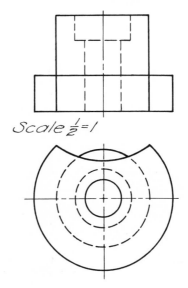

Scale $\frac{1}{2}$ = 1

Fig. 8.56   Cam guide.

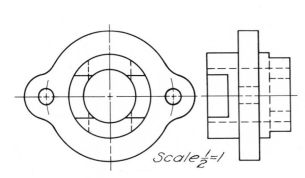

Scale $\frac{1}{2}$ = 1

Fig. 8.57   Coupler.

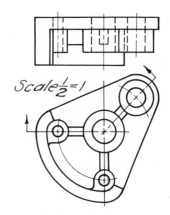

Scale $\frac{1}{2}$ = 1

Fig. 8.58   Rocker.

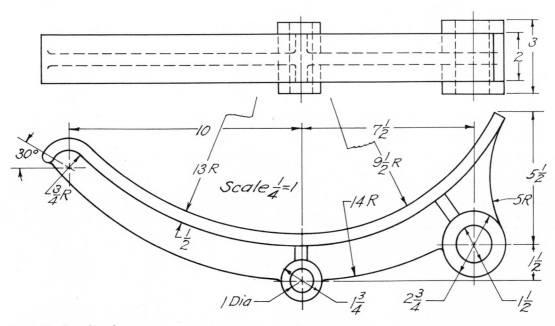

3

2

10

$7\frac{1}{2}$

$13R$

$9\frac{1}{2}R$

$5\frac{1}{2}$

Scale $\frac{1}{4}$ = 1

30°

$\frac{3}{4}R$

$14R$

$5R$

$1\frac{1}{2}$

$\frac{1}{2}$

1 Dia

$1\frac{3}{4}$

$2\frac{3}{4}$

$1\frac{1}{2}$

Fig. 8.59   Barrel carrier.

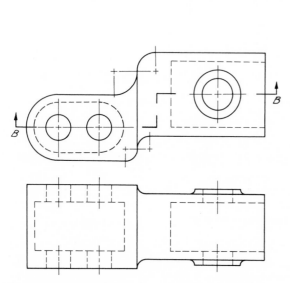

Fig. 8.60   Offset rocker arm.

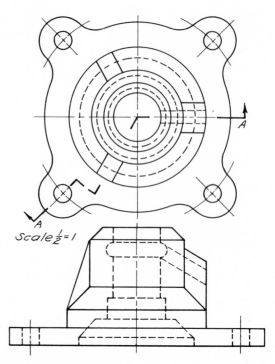

Scale ½ = 1

Fig. 8.61   Cover plate.

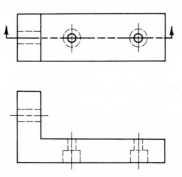

Fig. 8.62   Guide block.

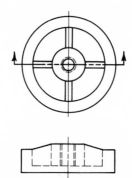

Fig. 8.63   Press plate.

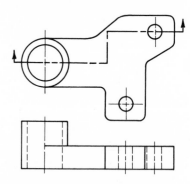

Fig. 8.64   Offset bearing.

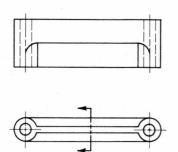

Fig. 8.65   Rocker arm.

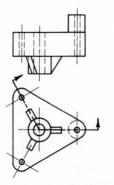

Fig. 8.66   Bearing bracket.

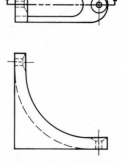

Fig. 8.67   Corner brace.

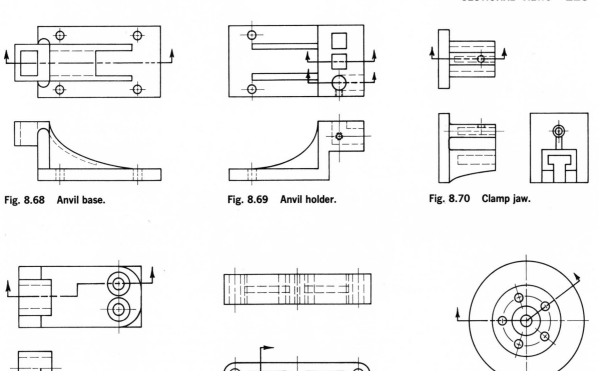

Fig. 8.68   Anvil base.

Fig. 8.69   Anvil holder.

Fig. 8.70   Clamp jaw.

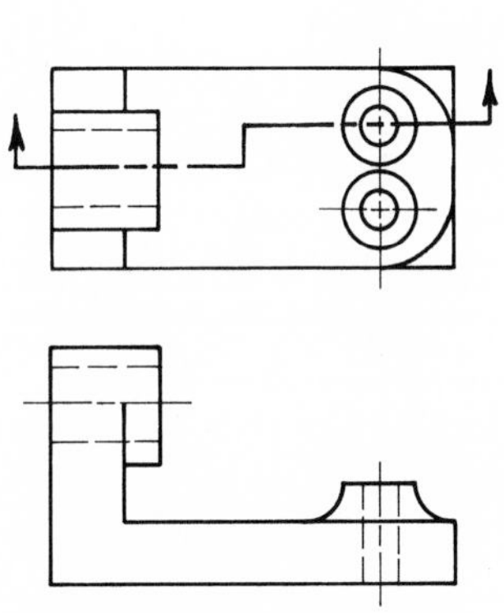

Fig. 8.71   Bearing bracket.

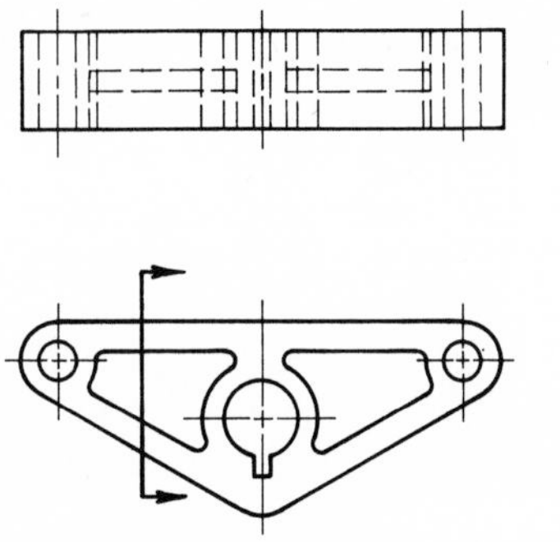

Fig. 8.72   Gate lever arm.

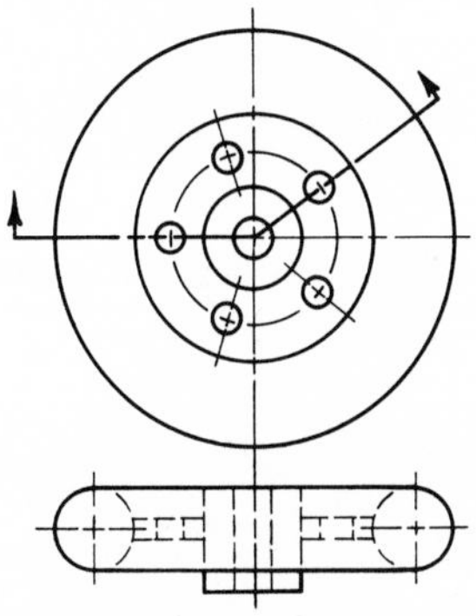

Fig. 8.73   Handwheel.

CHAPTER 9
Fasteners

NEW: Bolting structural steel members of Verrazano Narrows Bridge (Courtesy of Bethlehem Steel Corporation)

OLD: Construction of pyramids in ancient Egypt with blocks of stone. (New York Public Library Picture Collection)

Chapter 9   Fasteners

9.1   INTRODUCTION. In all kinds of structures and machines designed by engineers, the various parts are held together by devices known as fasteners. These fasteners vary in kind and use, from ordinary nails and glue for wood structures to bolts, machine screws, keys, splines, and rivets for machines varying in size from locomotives to watches.

On working drawings the engineer may specify some fasteners by means of notes, without actually showing the fasteners themselves. Other fasteners may be shown in actual projected outline or in some common conventionalized form.

9.1.1   Fasteners not commonly shown on drawings. Such fasteners as brads, nails, spikes, cotterpins, dowel pins, and spring clips are specified as to size, kind, and use rather than being represented on a drawing. A few of the many kinds are illustrated in Fig. 9.1.

9.1.2   Fasteners usually shown by symbols only. On certain types of drawings some fasteners such as rivets, weldments, standard bolts, and screws are shown by symbols. These are conventionalized so that they are easily recognizable. See Fig. 9.2.

9.1.3   Fasteners usually detailed on drawings. Special fasteners, which are designed for one particular usage, must be detailed. They may have standard parts such as a hexagon head or screw threads. A fastener of this type is shown in Fig. 9.3. Some stud bolts come under this class.

9.2   STANDARD FASTENERS. It is estimated that there are approximately 500,000 standard fastener items which can be identified by name, type, size, and material.* These can be found listed and shown in one or more published standards or specifications.

9.2.1   National standards. A number of fastener standards are identified as bona fide national standards. Among them are those issued by the following:

a. United States of America Standards Institute. A list of these is provided in the appendix to this book.

b. National Bureau of Standards.

* Machine Design, "The Fastener Book Issue," March 21, 1963, page 10.

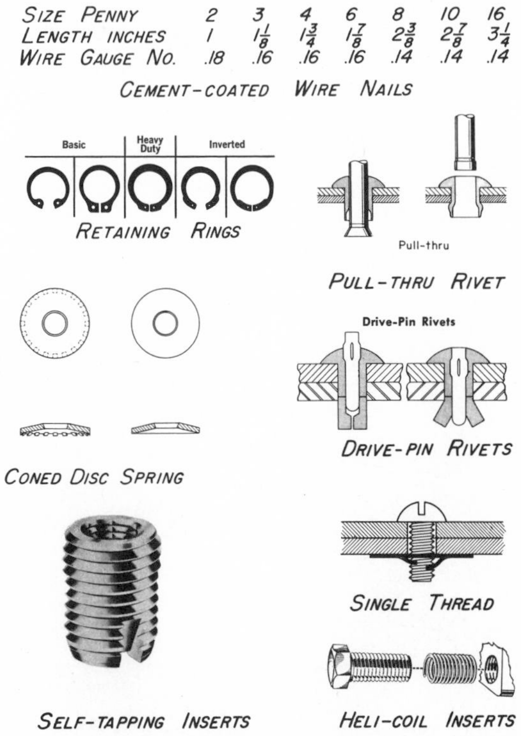

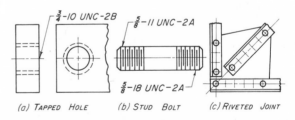

Fig. 9.2   Fasteners shown by symbols.

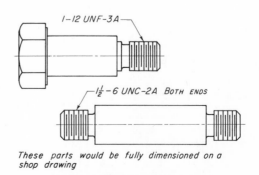

These parts would be fully dimensioned on a shop drawing

Fig. 9.3   Fasteners detailed on drawings.

Fig. 9.1   Fasteners not commonly shown detailed on drawing. (Courtesy Machine Design Fastener Book.)

c. Index of Federal Specifications Standards and Handbooks—A complete listing of all Federal documents—is issued annually (Business Service Center, General Services Administration, Washington 25, D.C.).

Other fastener standards that have national recognition are issued by various technical and engineering societies such as the SAE, ASME, and ASTM.

9.2.2   Industry standards. Many large companies also have standards of their own. These usually conform to national standards where these exist but they also apply to company products and widely used components.

9.3   FASTENERS USING SCREW THREADS. Fasteners such as those described in Arts. 9.1.2 and 9.1.3 need careful study from the standpoint of the drafting room methods and conventions employed in representing and specifying them on drawings. It is essential therefore to understand the generation and projec-

tions of the helix, which is the basic curve of all threaded fasteners.

9.3.1   The helix. This curve is generated by a point moving on the surface of a cylinder or cone in a circumferential direction, at a constant angular speed, and with a simultaneous uniform rate of advance in an axial direction. A helix may be obtained by wrapping a string around a cylinder or cone in such a manner that the string advances parallel to the axis at a constant rate or, in other words, by the same amount for each revolution. The amount of this advance for one revolution is called the pitch, or lead, of the helix. See Fig. 9.4. If the cylinder were to be developed, the helix would become the hypotenuse of a right triangle whose base is the circumference of the cylinder and whose altitude is the lead of the helix. The angle between the hypotenuse and the base of the triangle is known as the helix angle. The geometrical construction of a helix is shown in Chapter 4.

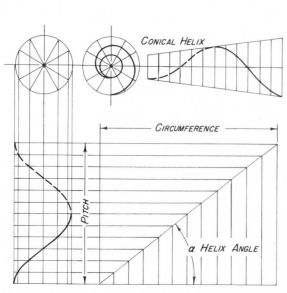

Fig. 9.4   Cylindrical and conical helix.

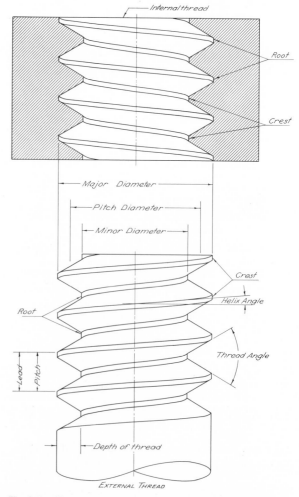

Fig. 9.5   Illustration of thread terms. (Courtesy USASI.)

9.4   THREAD TERMS. In a study of threads and the representation of them on a drawing, it is advisible to define a few terms. These definitions (abbreviated from USASI B1.2—1951 Screw Thread Gages and Gaging Standard) are illustrated in Figs. 9.5 and 9.6.

Screw thread. A ridge of uniform cross section in the form of a helix on the surface of a cylinder; Fig. 9.5.

External thread. A thread on the outside of a member, such as a bolt; Fig. 9.5.

Internal thread. A thread on the inside of a member, such as a threaded hole or nut; Fig. 9.5.

Major diameter. The largest diameter of a screw thread; Fig. 9.5.

Minor diameter. The smallest diameter of a screw thread; Fig. 9.5.

Pitch diameter. On a cylindrical screw thread, the diameter of an imaginary cylinder, the surface of which would pass through the threads at such points as to make equal the width of the threads and the width of the spaces between the threads. See Figs. 9.5 and 9.6.

Pitch. The distance from a point on a screw thread to a corresponding point on the next thread measured parallel to the axis; Fig. 9.5.

Lead. The distance a screw thread advances axially in one turn; Figs. 9.5 and 9.7.

Angle of thread. The angle between the sides of a thread measured in an axial plane; Fig. 9.5.

Crest. The top surface joining the two sides of a thread; Fig. 9.5.

Root. The bottom surface joining the sides of two adjacent threads; Fig. 9.5.

Base. Bottom section of thread. Greatest section between two adjacent roots; Fig. 9.6.

Depth of thread. The distance between the crest and root of a thread measured perpendicular to the axis; Fig. 9.5.

Single thread. All the threads on a member are built on a single helix. On a single thread the pitch is equal to the lead; Fig. 9.7.

Double thread. Two threads are wrapped around the cylinder on two parallel helices. The lead is twice the pitch; Fig. 9.7.

Multiple thread. Two or more separate threads on as many parallel helices are wrapped around the cylinder; Fig. 9.7.

Helix angle. Angle that the helix makes at any point with a plane perpendicular to the axis. The tangent of this angle is equal to the lead divided by the circumference of the helix cylinder. See Fig. 9.4.

Fit. The relative size of the pitch diameter of external and internal mating threads.

Clearance. An intentional difference between the major and minor diameters of the external and internal mating threads. Clearance is provided on the major and minor diameters of the nut as shown in Figs. 9.6 and 9.17.

Thread profile. The shape of the thread on a section plane containing the axis of the thread; Figs. 9.9 and 9.10.

Right-hand thread. A thread that advances into engagement in a direction away from the observer when turned in a clockwise direction; Fig. 9.8.

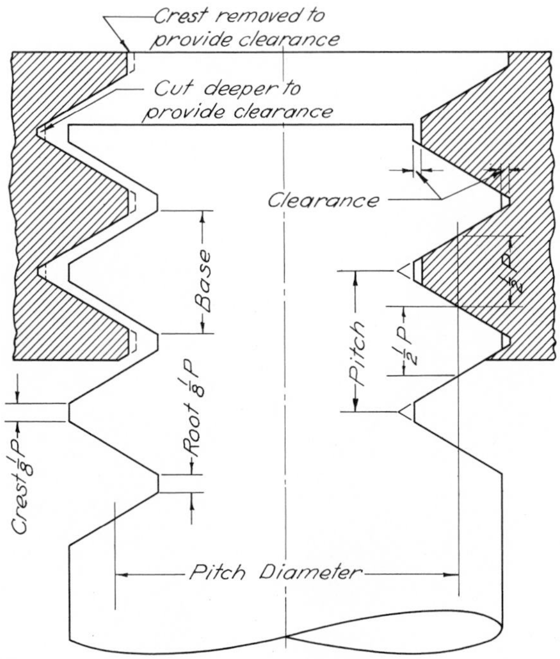

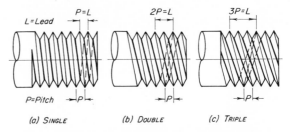

(a) SINGLE   (b) DOUBLE   (c) TRIPLE

Fig. 9.7   Pitch and lead on single and multiple threads.

Fig. 9.6   Clearance on threads.

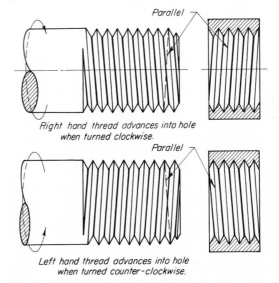

Right hand thread advances into hole when turned clockwise.

Left hand thread advances into hole when turned counter-clockwise.

Fig. 9.8   Right-hand and left-hand threads.

Left-hand thread. A thread that advances into engagement in a direction away from the observer when turned in a counterclockwise direction; Fig. 9.8.

9.5 THREAD TYPES AND PROFILES. The purpose for which the screw is to be used determines the profile of the thread. In the United States, general-purpose threads usually are of the Unified or American National thread form. The profile of the Unified thread is shown in Fig. 9.9. This thread form has been agreed upon as a standard for general-purpose threads by the United States, Great Britain, and Canada. It is therefore referred to as the Unified thread. Various other forms are shown in Fig. 9.10.

Among the thread profiles shown in Fig. 9.10, the Sharp-V is rarely used but it is the basic form from which others were developed. The Unified National Thread has practically replaced the American National form. The Whitworth thread is the general-

purpose thread used in England. The knuckle thread has a rounded profile, which is convenient because it can be easily cast or rolled. The thread on the base of light bulbs is a form of the knuckle thread.

9.5.1 Power and translating threads. The Unified thread form is not suitable for transmitting power because it develops too great a radial force. The Square, Acme, Buttress, and Worm threads shown in Fig. 9.10 are used to transmit motion and power. The shape of these threads is shown in the figure. The Stub Acme and the Modified Square thread profiles are not shown. The Stub Acme has a depth of 0.3P. In other respects it is like the Acme. The Modified Square thread has flanks at a 10° included angle between them.

Translating threads, which must move freely for such things as steering gears, sometimes have ball bearings between the internal and external thread. Thus the entire load is transmitted through the ball

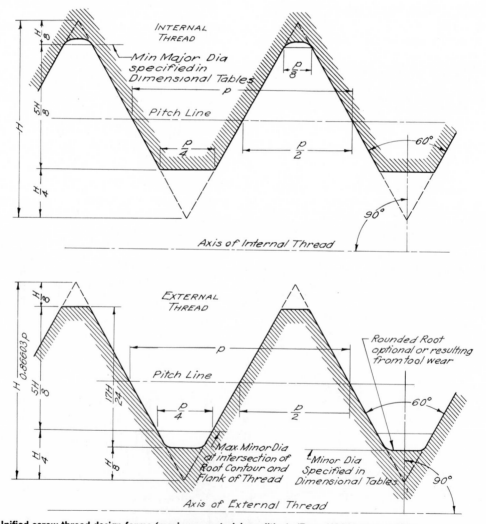

Fig. 9.9   **Unified screw thread design forms (maximum material condition). (From USASI B1.1–1960.)**

bearings which roll in the threads as one part moves in relation to the other. A tube is provided to carry the balls from one end to the other, thus keeping the same balls in continual motion.

9.6 DRAWING SHARP-V, UNIFIED AND AMERICAN NATIONAL THREADS, LARGE SIZE. Since the crest and root lines of a thread are always helices, it is a slow and difficult job to show a thread in its true projection. For this reason, the thread is seldom drawn in exact projection. Occasionally very large threads on display drawings may be drawn accurately, in which case one thread would be drawn carefully and the other threads reproduced by means of templates cut from the first thread.

On most working drawings the large threads would be drawn as shown in Fig. 9.11. This is a conventionalized form in which the profile for the Unified and American National thread is made the same as for the Sharp-V thread. The crest and root lines are drawn as straight lines instead of helices. The slope of

these lines indicates the lead of the thread and shows the difference between right-hand and left-hand threads. For a right-hand single thread these lines on the bolt slant down to the right, in the position shown in Fig. 9.11, and advance parallel to the axis one half of the lead in going across the width of the bolt.

In a section view of a nut or internal thread the lines slope up to the right because these threads must fit the threads on the back of the bolt. The end view of the bolt or threaded hole is represented by two circles of the proper visibility, as shown in Fig. 9.11. The nominal size of the thread is always the size of the larger circle regardless of its visibility. This convention is preferred when the diameter of the bolt projects on the drawing as 1 inch or larger.

9.6.1 Construction of conventional threads, large size. The steps to be followed in laying out this conventional thread are illustrated in Fig. 9.12.

a. Draw two light parallel lines so that the distance

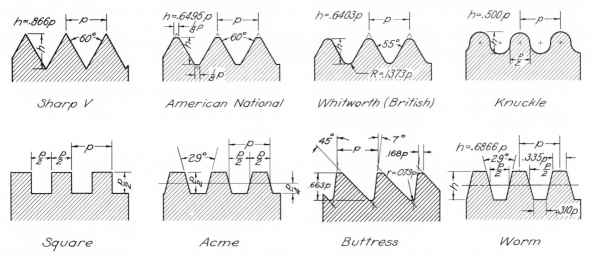

Fig. 9.10 **Types of threads.**

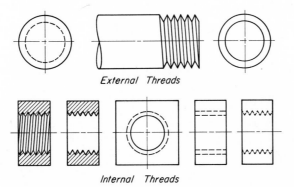

Fig. 9.11 **V-thread symbols.**

between them is equal to the diameter of the bolt.

b. On one of these lines mark off distances equal to the pitch of the thread. If convenient, the pitch should be laid out accurately, but if not convenient the nearest even number can be used, but the crest lines should not be closer than 1/16 inch.

c. At the first point erect a perpendicular to the lines, and on the other line mark off from this perpendicular a distance equal to one-half the lead. See Fig. 9.12(a). In a single thread this distance will be one-half the pitch since pitch and lead are equal.

d. Draw a line joining the two end points m and n on the parallel lines. Draw lines parallel to this first line through the points previously marked off on the lower lines. These lines represent the crest lines of the thread; Fig. 9.12(b).

e. With the 60° triangle, draw the V in the first space on each side of the bolt. Through the point of the V thus formed, draw light guidelines parallel to the sides of the bolt; Fig. 9.12(c).

f. For the sake of speed, draw one side of each V from the ends of the crest lines to the guidelines on both sides as in Fig. 9.12(d).

g. Complete the other side of the 60° V's and then draw the lines joining the bottoms of the V notches. These lines form the root lines of the thread; Fig. 9.12(e).

h. Erase all construction lines; work over all lines to give good clean lines. Make the root lines and out-

lines heavier than the crest lines; Fig. 9.12(f).

9.6.2 Representation and construction of Unified and American National threads, small size. For threads that project smaller than 1 inch diameter the convention is still further simplified. The thread profile along the edge is replaced by a straight line at the edge of the bolt. The root and crest lines are drawn *perpendicular* to the edges instead of at a slant. The lines should be spaced at approximately the correct pitch. However, for convenience the pitch may be changed slightly. A minimum distance between crests should be set at approximately 1/16 inch, even though the threads may be actually much finer. An invisible threaded hole is represented by two sets of parallel lines, one representing the major diameter and the other the minor diameter. Figure 9.13 shows the conventional representation of threads under various conditions. When the thread does not go completely through a member, the drill point is always shown. The drilled hole should be deeper than the desired depth of thread because it takes an extra operation to thread a hole to the bottom. The internal angle for the point of the drill is 118°, but it is always drawn 120°. This conventional representation must always be accompanied by a thread specification.

The steps to be followed in laying out this conventional symbol are listed below and illustrated in Fig. 9.14.

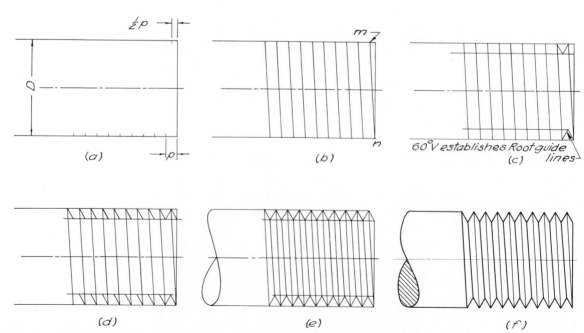

Fig. 9.12   Construction of V-thread symbols.

a. Draw two parallel lines at a distance apart equal to the diameter of the thread. Using the pitch of the thread (actual or assumed) as a base, draw a 60° triangle to determine the depth of thread on each side. Project the vertices of the triangles to the end of the bolt and from these points draw the 45° chamfer. This locates the first crest line. From this line mark off distances equal to the pitch of the thread. This spacing does not have to be exactly equal to the pitch, and the minimum spacing should be not less than ¹⁄₁₆ inch; Fig. 9.14(*a*).

b. Through each of these points, draw lines perpendicular to the axis of the thread. These represent the crest lines of the thread. Through the points of the V's previously constructed, draw light guidelines parallel to the axis; Fig. 9.14(*b*).

c. Draw the root lines midway between the crest lines and ending on the guidelines, Fig. 9.14(*c*).

d. Clean up the drawing and go over all lines, making light lines for crest lines and heavy lines for outline and root lines; Fig. 9.14(*d*).

9.6.3 Thread specifications. Since the thread symbol tells so little about the thread, it is necessary to give complete specifications in note form as shown in Fig. 9.15 and on other thread drawings. The meaning of each term is shown in the illustration. The terms should always appear in the order given. The last term indicating the class of fit is explained in detail in Arts. 9.10.1 through 9.10.3.

9.6.4 Simplified thread symbols. In order to save time and money, another simplified set of thread symbols is coming into ever wider use. The symbols are

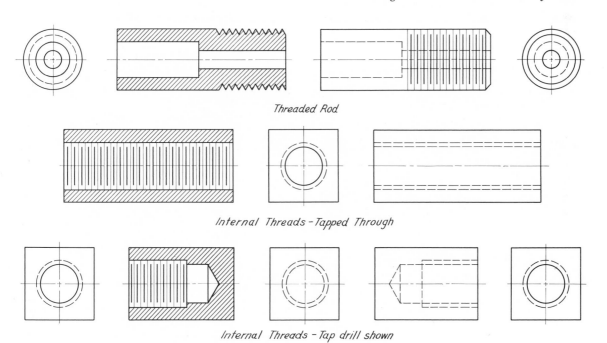

Fig. 9.13 Conventional thread symbols.

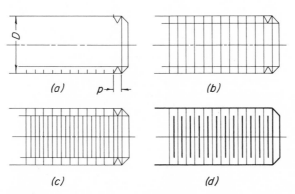

Fig. 9.14 Construction of conventional symbols.

shown in Fig. 9.16. They are much faster to draw because they avoid the necessity of showing the root and crest lines. These symbols should be used with discretion on drawings involving a large number of hidden outlines.

9.7   MULTIPLE THREADS. Multiple Unified threads are shown in Fig. 9.7. They are used to secure faster movement in threads used for translation as on

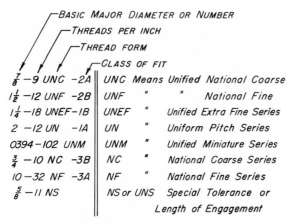

$\frac{7}{8}$ –9 UNC –2A	UNC Means Unified National Coarse
$1\frac{1}{2}$ –12 UNF –2B	UNF " " National Fine
$1\frac{1}{4}$ –18 UNEF –1B	UNEF " Unified Extra Fine Series
2 –12 UN –1A	UN " Uniform Pitch Series
0394 –102 UNM	UNM " Unified Miniature Series
$\frac{3}{4}$ –10 NC –3B	NC " National Coarse Series
10 –32 NF –3A	NF " National Fine Series
$\frac{5}{8}$ –11 NS	NS or UNS Special Tolerance or
	Length of Engagement

Fig. 9.15   Thread specification of threads and meaning.

lathes and valves. Thus with a double thread a valve will move twice as far in one revolution of the screw as it would for a single screw of the same pitch. An examination of Fig. 9.7 will show that on single and odd-numbered multiple threads the crest is directly across from the root on opposite sides of the symbol. On double and other even-numbered threads crest is opposite crest. These facts are of assistance in drawing multiple threads. Square and Acme threads are used for translation of machine parts and power transmission. These threads are stronger than the Unified thread, of either single or multiple types. They are discussed in Art. 9.11 through 9.13.

9.8   RIGHT- AND LEFT-HAND THREAD. All threads are assumed to be single and right-hand unless they are specifically indicated to be otherwise. See Art. 9.4 and Fig. 9.8. A right-hand thread advances into a hole when turned clockwise. The left-hand thread advances when turned counterclockwise.

9.9   THREAD SERIES. Before the standardization of the American National thread, there were two main groups of threads in use in the United States. For most work the United States Standard or Sellers thread was

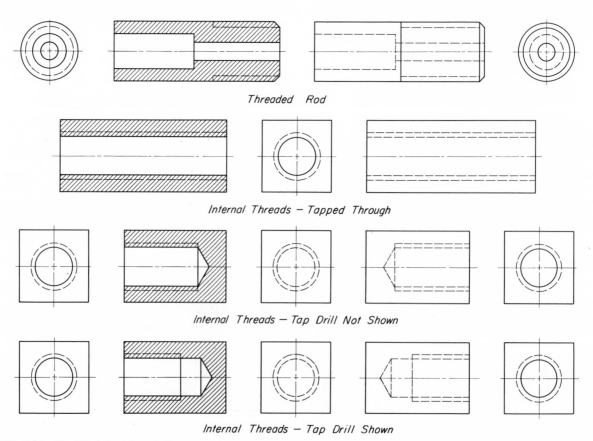

Threaded   Rod

Internal Threads – Tapped Through

Internal Threads — Tap Drill Not Shown

Internal Threads — Tap Drill Shown

Fig. 9.16   Simplified thread symbols.

specified, but for automotive work a special thread was devised by the Society of Automotive Engineers. This thread had a smaller pitch than the United States Standard to give better resistance to vibration. These two groups were taken over almost entirely as the American National Coarse and American National Fine series. The SAE extra fine series and eight uniform series were added later. All of these are now included in the Unified National Standard. This means that this standard is used in the United States, Canada, and the United Kingdom. Since almost 99 per cent of all threads manufactured in the United States conform to the Unified Standards, only these forms will be discussed. Dimensional specification for all thread series are given in the appendix.

9.9.1   Unified National Coarse Series. These are used for bolts, screws, and nuts in general engineering application in materials such as malleable iron, soft metals, and plastics. This series is preferred where rapid assembly or disassembly is required. These threads are specified as ⅝-11 UNC-2A. See Fig. 9.15 for the meaning of this note and those that follow.

9.9.2   Unified National Fine series. This series is the same as the old SAE series with the addition of numbered sizes 0 to 12 below ¼-inch diameter. These threads are recommended for bolts, screws, and nuts where the engagement of the thread is limited. Not used in soft metals and plastics. These threads are specified as ⅝-18 UNF-2A or 10-32 UNF-2A.

9.9.3   Unified National Extra Fine series. This series has more threads per inch than the other two series. It is used primarily in thin sections such as aircraft, missiles, and other aeronautical equipment where a maximum number of threads is desired. This thread is noted as ⅜-32 UNEF-2A.

9.9.4   Unified National Miniature threads. Specifications can be found in USASI. B1.10—1958. This thread is used for general-purpose screws in instruments and miniature devices. The diameters are usually specified in millimeters. The thread note is shown as 0.70-145 UNM.

9.9.5   Uniform pitch thread series. These threads have the same profile as other unified threads but the pitch is constant for all sizes. There are eight different pitches: 4, 6, 8, 12, 16, 20, 28, and 32 threads per inch. They are designated as 1½-8 UN-2A.

a. *4 UN—4 threads per inch.* This series begins at 2½-inches diameter and is the same as the coarse series up to 4 inches. It continues above that for all sizes

up to 6 inches. Basically it is an extension of the coarse thread series.

b. *6 UN—6 threads per inch.* Similar to others beginning at 1⅜-inch diameter but it is not a preferred series. Note that the beginning number after the diameter specification in these uniform pitch series means the number of threads per inch.

c. *8 UN—8 threads per inch.* It is used primarily for bolts on high-pressure pipe flanges, cylinder head studs, and the like. This series begins at 1-inch diameter.

d. *12 UN—12 thread, per inch.* The 12 UN and the 16 UN series are used for large diameter fasteners that require a medium pitch such as thin nuts on shafts. Sizes from ⁹⁄₁₆ inch to 1¾ inches are used in boiler practice which requires that more holes be retapped with a tap of the next larger size but having the same number of threads per inch.

e. *20 UN, 28 UN and 32 UN.* These uniform pitch threads are used where very fine pitch threads are needed. They are not recommended for regular fasteners. They are used in highly special situations.

9.10   CLASSES OF THREAD FITS. In a study of thread fit it is necessary to understand the meaning of a few terms. Fit is the relation between the size of two mating parts with reference to ease of assembly. In a thread the fit determines the pitch diameter of the screw. The quality of the fit is dependent on relative size, and quality of the finish, of mating parts.

Basic diameter is the theoretical or nominal standard size from which all variations are made. See Fig. 9.17.

Tolerance is the amount of variation allowed in manufacture.

Allowance is the intentional difference in size between mating parts.

Crest clearance is the space between the crest of a thread and the root of its mating thread.

The Unified National thread series provide for three principal classes of fits. These meet the requirements for most usage.

These classes are distinguished by numbers and letters. Classes 1A, 2A, and 3A apply to external threads only. Classes 1B, 2B, and 3B apply to internal threads only. The fits are obtained by the application of specific tolerances, or tolerances together with allowances to the basic pitch diameter of the thread. This basic pitch diameter is the same for both internal and external threads of like size and pitch. The tolerances throughout are applied plus to the hole and minus to the screw, as shown in Fig. 9.17. The allowances when used are applied to the bolt only. For this reason the external threads have been designated as A and the internal as B so that pitch diameters can be more easily specified.

An additional Class 5 fit, which is an interference fit, is used mostly for tap end stud bolts. In assembling a Class 5 fit the material of the thread is plastically deformed and makes a very tight fit.

9.10.1 Classes 1A and 1B, loose fit. The maximum pitch diameter of the screw is always smaller by a definite allowance than the minimum pitch diameter of the hole. Tolerances will tend to increase this difference so that there will always be a play or looseness between the mating parts when this fit is used. It is recommended only for work where clearance between mating threads is essential for rapid assembly and when shake or play is not objectionable.

9.10.2 Classes 2A and 2B, free fit. Maximum dimensions of Class 2A are reduced from the basic size by an allowance for clearance. This is 30 per cent of the Class 2A pitch-diameter tolerance. This provides for plating or coating if desired. This class is the one most generally used for interchangeable works.

9.10.3 Classes 3A and 3B, medium to close fit. There is no allowance in this class of fit. There is a variation from the tightest fit when both pitch diameters are at basic value to the loosest fit when Class 3A tolerance has been applied to both parts. The maximum play will be about 70 per cent of that found in Class 2A fit.

This class of fit is used for an exceptionally high grade of commercial product and is recommended only where the high cost of precision tools and continual checking of tools and product are warranted.

9.10.4 Classes 2 and 3, free and medium fits. Classes 2 and 3 are American National only. They are quite similar to 2A and 3A.

9.11 REPRESENTATION OF SQUARE THREADS. The true Square thread profile shown in Fig. 9.10 is rarely used because of machining difficulties. The Modified Square thread is more generally used, but no attempt is made in representing Square threads on drawings to show these refinements in detail. The thread is drawn as a square.

The representation of Square threads has been conventionalized as shown in Figs. 9.18(*e*) and 9.19(*d*). When the diameter of the threads shows 1 inch or over, the form shown in Figs. 9.18 and 9.19 is preferred. When the diameter is less than 1 inch the simplified form shown in Fig. 9.20 may be used. On a long screw ditto marks or phantom lines may be used to avoid the necessity of drawing all the threads. This is shown in Fig. 9.20(*d*). The method of showing internal Square threads is shown in Figs. 9.19 and 9.20(*e*), (*f*), (*g*), and (*h*).

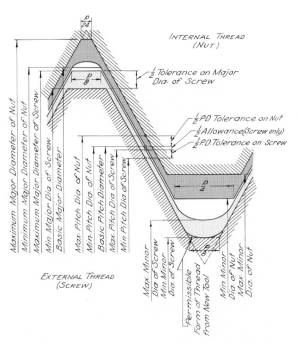

Fig. 9.17 Tolerance on Unified form screw threads. (USASI B1–1960.)

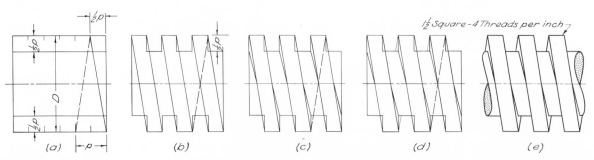

Fig. 9.18 Construction of external Square-thread symbol.

9.11.1 Construction of the external Square thread symbol. The steps for making a right-hand, single, external thread are listed as follows and as shown in Fig. 9.18:

a. Lay out four parallel lines spaced as shown in Fig. 9.18(a).

b. Mark off from a right section distances equal to one-half the pitch on the two outside lines.

c. Draw the indicated inclined lines to follow one edge of a thread for one complete revolution.

d. Lay out the squares shown in Fig. 9.18(b) lightly, for the sides will be erased later.

e. For a single or triple thread, the opposite squares

will be laid out in the same direction. See Figs. 9.18(b) and 9.21(b).

f. For double or quadruple threads, the opposite squares will be laid out in opposite directions. See Fig. 9.21(a).

g. From the external corners of the squares, draw lines parallel to the visible inclined line in Fig. 9.18(a). These are the crest lines of the threads.

h. The root lines will be drawn to join the interior corners of the squares. Only the half of this line that lies outside the crest lines should be drawn, since the other half will be invisible, as in Fig. 9.18(c).

i. From the external corners of the squares, draw

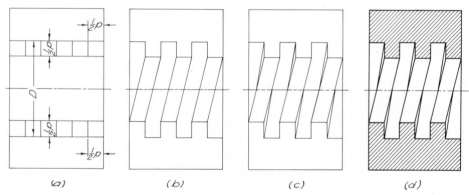

(a)   (b)   (c)   (d)

Fig. 9.19 Construction of internal Square-thread symbol.

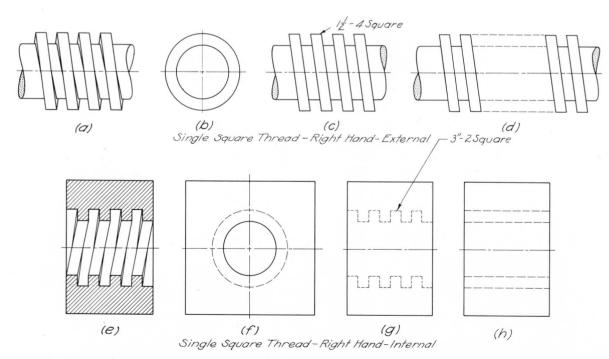

Fig. 9.20 Simplified Square-thread symbols.

lines as indicated in Fig. 9.18(*d*), which are parallel to the dotted line shown in Fig. 9.18(*a*).

j. Erase all unnecessary lines and go over the remaining lines to make them heavier. The drawing will now be complete, as shown in Fig. 9.18(*e*).

9.11.2 Construction of internal Square thread symbol. To make the internal Square thread symbol, the steps will be slightly different, as illustrated in Fig. 9.19.

a. Draw lightly the four lines representing the major and minor diameter of the thread as in Fig. 9.19(*a*). Note that these lines are one-half the pitch apart in pairs.

b. Measure off distances equal to one-half the pitch on both outer lines and draw the squares as shown in Fig. 9.19(*b*).

c. Connect the inside corners of the squares to represent the root lines of the threads. Note that the slope is just the opposite of the external thread shown in Fig. 9.18.

d. Connect the outer corners of the squares but draw them only to the center line since the remaining part will be invisible and is not shown.

e. Make all visible outlines heavy and crosshatch the proper areas.

9.11.3 Multiple Square threads. Double and triple Square threads are shown in Fig. 9.21. The construction is similar to that in Fig. 9.18 except that for double threads crest is opposite crest. For triple threads crest is opposite root.

9.12 REPRESENTATION AND CONSTRUCTION OF ACME THREAD SYMBOLS. Although the Acme thread is used for the same purpose as the Square thread, the layout of this thread on the drawing is somewhat different. The following paragraphs give a description of the steps shown in Fig. 9.22.

a. Lay out two sets of three parallel lines with the spacing shown in Fig. 9.22(*a*). The two outside lines represent the major diameter of the thread, the two inside lines represent the minor diameter, and the intermediate lines represent the pitch diameter.

b. Starting from a right section, measure off distances equal to $\frac{1}{2}p$ on the two pitch lines.

c. From these points on the pitch lines, draw lines making 15° with a perpendicular to the axis, as shown in Fig. 9.22(*b*).

d. Draw lines joining the root lines on the profile. See Fig. 9.22(*c*).

e. Draw that part of the crest line on the back of the

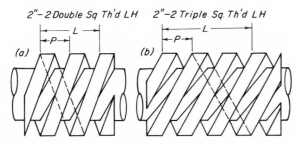

Fig. 9.21 Multiple Square-thread symbols. Double and triple left-hand.

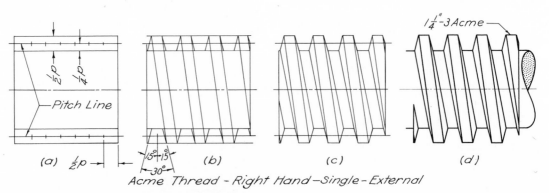

Fig. 9.22 Construction of external Acme thread symbol.

thread which is visible. As none of the crest line on a single thread is visible, the single thread is actually finished in (*d*).

If a single thread is being drawn, a ridge on one side is opposite a groove on the other side.

9.12.1 Internal Acme thread. The steps in making the construction are clearly shown in Figs. 9.23(*a*), (*b*), (*c*), and (*d*).

9.12.2 Drawing the stub Acme thread. The stub Acme thread may be represented in the same manner as the Acme, except that the depth of the thread is only 0.3*p* instead of 0.5*p*. This makes the crest width and root width 0.422*p* as against 0.371*p* for the regular Acme. The steps in construction are the same as in Figs. 9.22 and 9.23.

9.12.3 Multiple Acme threads. Multiple Acme threads are shown in Fig. 9.24. These threads are used to transmit power and for more rapid motion.

9.13 REPRESENTATION AND CONSTRUCTION OF THE BUTTRESS THREAD. The construction of the

Buttress thread symbol is shown step by step in Fig. 9.25. To simplify construction the pressure face is drawn perpendicular to the axis of the thread instead of the 7° angle. This thread is used to transmit power in one direction only. The construction is as follows:

a. Draw four parallel lines as in Fig. 9.25(*a*). The outer pair are at the major diameter from each other. The inner pair are ⅔*P* from the outer ones.

b. On the top outer line mark off distances equal to the pitch.

c. On the lower line mark off first a distance equal to ½*P* from the end and then the other distances equal to the pitch.

d. On both outer lines mark off 0.163*p* or ⅙*p* from the previous marks to represent the crest of the thread.

e. Draw very lightly vertical lines between the upper and lower pairs of lines to represent the face of the thread.

f. Outline lightly the profile of each thread at the top and bottom.

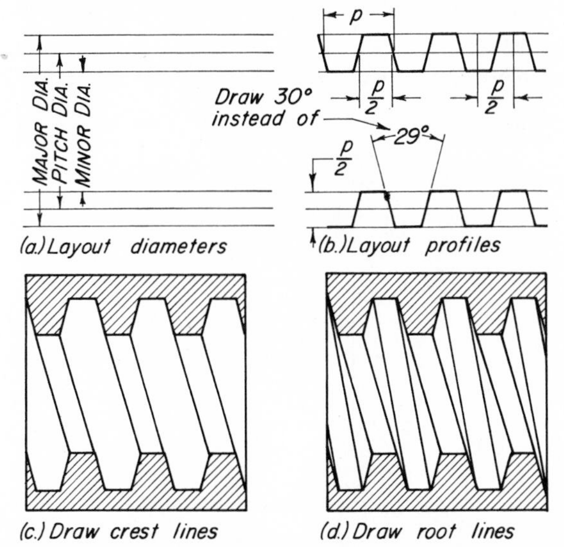

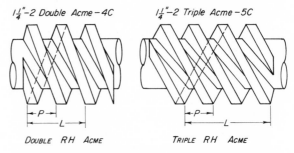

Fig. 9.24 Double and triple Acme thread symbol. Right-hand.

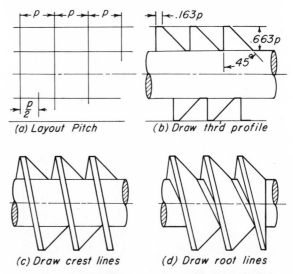

Fig. 9.23 Construction of internal left-hand Acme thread symbol.

Fig. 9.25 Construction of single right-hand external Buttress thread symbol. *(Size of thread exaggerated in relation to diameter to show construction.)*

g. Draw the crest lines all the way across.

h. Draw the root lines as far as they are visible.

i. Draw the short visible portion of the crest line on the rear.

For the internal thread follow the same general procedure as shown in Fig. 9.26.

9.14   AMERICAN PIPE THREADS. The pipe thread used in this country is known as the American, formerly the Briggs, standard. It differs from the British pipe thread in that the sides of the thread form an angle of 60°, whereas the British thread, which is built on the Whitworth system, shows an angle of 55°. The crest and root of the Standard American thread are slightly flattened, as shown in Fig. 9.27.

Pipe threads are cut on a taper of 1 in 16 measured on the diameter. Both internal and external threads are tapered. This taper allows the first few turns to be made by hand and insures a tight joint when the threads are well engaged. A few of the threads on the pipe are slightly imperfect owing to the taper on the dies and taps used in making the threads. Figure 9.28 shows the American Standard pipe thread.

The pitch of pipe threads has been standardized for the various sizes of pipes, as shown in Table 43 in the Appendix. They are specified on drawings by the letters NPT, National Pipe Tapered.

For certain purposes, for example, when a pipe must pass through the walls of a tank, for hose couplings, and free-fitting couplings, straight pipe threads are used. These threads have the same form as the standard pipe thread, but do not have any taper. The straight pipe threads are designated by the letters NPS, National Pipe Straight. American Standard pipe threads are described in "USASI B2.1 Regular Pipe Threads." This is the standard used by the plumbing trade.

9.14.1   Representing pipe threads on drawings—regular, tapered, and straight. Pipe threads are shown and specified on drawings by either the conventional system shown in Fig. 9.29 or by the simplified system shown in Fig. 9.30.

9.15   THREADED COMPONENTS. The foregoing paragraphs have shown methods of representing screw threads of various kinds. These threads are always a part of some component of a machine part or structure. These components include threaded holes as the simplest application, together with bolts and screws

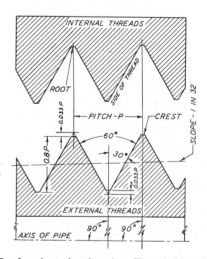

Fig. 9.27   American pipe thread profile and dimensions.

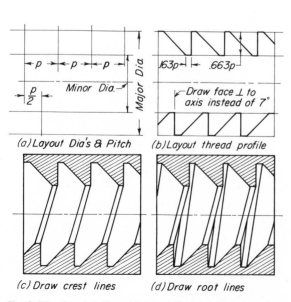

Fig. 9.26   Construction of internal Buttress thread symbol.
(Size of thread exaggerated in relation to diameter.)

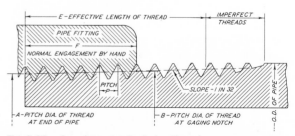

Fig. 9.28   American standard pipe thread.

of many kinds and sizes. The methods of drawing and specifying these components are discussed in the following paragraphs.

9.16 THREADED HOLES. In many machines the parts are held together by machine screws, cap screws, or stud bolts. Where such fasteners are used the machine part usually has threaded holes to receive these bolts and screws. If a regular bolt is used the nut, of standard form, has a threaded hole clear through.

9.16.1 Holes clear through. Unless the part through which a tapped hole is to go is very much thicker than needed by design requirements, the hole should be shown as threaded clear through. Tap drill sizes are given in Tables 2 and 3 in the Appendix. A complete thread note with pitch diameter tolerances is shown in Fig. 11.54. Regular thread notes are shown in Figs. 9.15, 9.21, and 9.24. Holes are usually countersunk on the side where the tap enters, unless the tap has a long taper of seven or eight threads.

9.16.2 Blind holes. Blind holes should be avoided if possible. When possible blind holes should be drilled considerably deeper than the full thread engagement required. This allows for chips and makes tapping simpler.

Unless a bottoming tap is to be used, the drilled hole should be shown beyond the thread and dimensioned as shown in Fig. 11.54. The SAE Drawing Standard recommends drawing the run-out on threads as well as the countersink. Depth of drill and depth of thread may be dimensioned instead of being noted.

9.16.3 Internal thread relief. If internal thread

relief is required to develop full engagement for the length of thread, this may be shown as in Fig. 11.59. The diameter of the relief must be greater than the major diameter of the internal thread. The depth of the relief must be not less than three times the thread pitch.

9.16.4 External thread relief. When external threads must be brought close to a shoulder as in Fig. 11.59, relief for the cutting tool must be provided as shown. Note that the diameter must be less than the minor diameter of the screw.

9.17 STANDARD BOLTS. Square head and hexagon head bolts with correspondingly shaped nuts are used to hold two or more parts of some assembly together.

The following types of bolts are produced by manufacturers in conformity with the American Standard USASI B18.2—1960.

Regular square
Regular hexagon
Heavy hexagon
Regular semifinished hexagon
Heavy semifinished hexagon
Finished hexagon
Heavy finished hexagon

All dimensions for these bolts are given in the above standard. See Tables 7, 9, 11, and 13 in the Appendix

9.17.1 Regular bolts. Regular bolts are not finished on any surface. The square bolts are supplied only in this form. The threads are coarse thread series Class 2A. See Fig. 9.31(a).

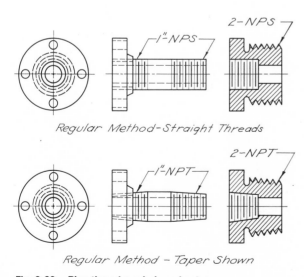

Regular Method—Straight Threads

Regular Method — Taper Shown

Fig. 9.29 Pipe thread symbols and notes.

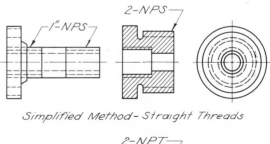

Simplified Method—Straight Threads

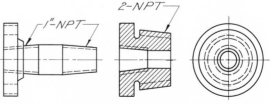

Simplified Method—Taper Shown

Fig. 9.30 Simplified pipe thread symbols.

9.17.2   Semifinished bolts. Semifinished bolts are manufactured to produce a flat bearing surface under the head only. This is usually a circular washer-type face approximately ⅟₆₄ inch thick with a diameter equal to the distance across flats. Coarse thread series Class 2A are used. See Fig. 9.31(*b*).

9.17.3   Finished bolts. Finished bolts are not necessarily completely machined. The term finish refers to the quality of manufacture and the closeness of the tolerance. The circular bearing face may be made as a washer-type face or by chamfering the corners to produce a circular bearing area. See Fig. 9.31(*b*).

These bolts may be obtained with coarse, fine, or the 8 uniform pitch threads Class 2A. Figures 9.31 through 9.34 show drafting methods for constructing standard bolt heads.

9.18   STANDARD NUTS. The standard nut which is used on various types of bolts is a direct application of the threaded hole. The outside shape of the nut is standardized as well as the threads. Typical standard nuts are shown in Fig. 9.35. Dimensions of these nuts are specified in USASI B18.2—1960.

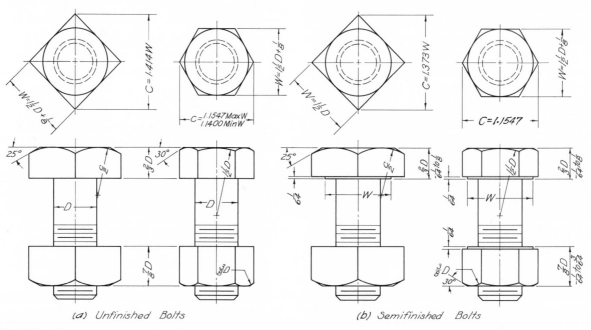

(a) Unfinished Bolts   (b) Semifinished Bolts

Fig. 9.31   Hexagon- and square-head bolts with dimensions for drawing.

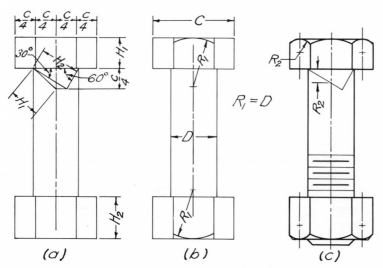

(a)   (b)   (c)

Fig. 9.32   Conventional construction of hexagon bolt head and nut.

Methods of drawing the regular and semifinished nuts are shown in Figs. 9.31 through 9.34. These are simplified methods but they are sufficiently accurate for all drawing purposes.

9.19 LOCKING DEVICES. It is frequently necessary to provide some method of preventing the nut from unscrewing and thus leaving a loose connection. This is particularly true when the fastening is subject to vibration.

9.19.1 Jam nuts. There are many different devices that have been designed for this purpose, the most common of which is the lock nut or jam nut. The American National jam nut has the same dimensions as the regular nut except for thickness, which is smaller because it is not designed to develop the full strength of the bolt but merely to hold the regular nut in place; Table 10 in the Appendix gives dimensions of regular jam nuts such as that illustrated in Fig. 9.36(a). Jam nuts may be obtained in the regular, heavy, and light series and also in unfinished, semifinished, and finished design.

9.19.2 Palnut. A patented lock nut known as Palnut, shown in Fig. 9.36(i), is used principally in electrical work and holds by tightening sufficiently to deform the rounded web of the nut.

9.19.3 Lock washers. Various kinds of lock washers are in use, some of which hold the nut by exerting a spring pressure on one side of the nut and others by a positive action that prevents the nut from turning. These are illustrated in Figs. 9.36(b) and 9.36(c).

9.19.4 Cotter pins. The bolt may be drilled and a cotter pin or wire may be placed through the bolt and above the nut, as in Fig. 9.36(d). This will prevent the nut from coming off, but does not avoid a certain amount of loosening. A more definite lock is obtained by using a slotted nut so that the cotter pin may be placed in the slot and through the bolt, as shown in Fig. 9.36(e).

9.19.5 Split nuts. The nut may be split and deformed in various ways before it is in place. The deformation exerts a pressure on the threads that holds the nut in place by its friction. One method of doing this is shown in Fig. 9.36(f).

9.19.6 Elastic stop nut. This is a patented fastener that has an elastic collar built into the nut, which grips the threads of the bolt when screwed on.

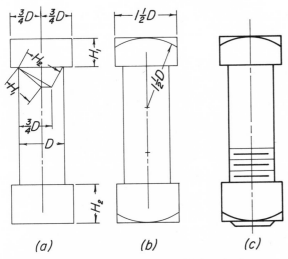

Fig. 9.33 Construction of square-head bolt and nut.

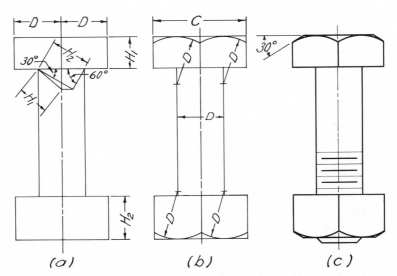

Fig. 9.34 Alternate construction of square-head bolt and nut.

This gripping action prevents the nut from backing off even when subjected to vibration. It has been used frequently in the airplane industry. Figure 9.36(g) shows a section of an elastic stop nut. Another form in which the elastic stop nut is used is shown in Fig. 9.36(h). In aircraft work it is frequently used to fasten a bolt to a thin web, in which case a flanged nut is riveted to the web to provide a suitable length of penetration.

Various other methods of locking a nut are in use, some of which are as simple as the use of a set screw in a nut and others as complicated as the use of a specially designed thread which is cut on a taper so that the friction is increased when the load is applied.

9.20 STUD BOLTS. The stud bolt has threads on both ends so that one of the pieces being held together must be threaded to replace the head. See Fig. 9.37. The stud bolt is turned into the threaded hole by

means of a pipe wrench or a special lock-nut device until the threads jam. The bolts then become an assembly guide by means of which the other part, which is drilled but not threaded, is properly placed. A nut screwed on the other end of the bolt holds the two parts together. The Industrial Fastener Institute has established four basic classes of studs. These can be described only briefly.

9.20.1 Class 1—tap end studs. This stud has a Class 5 interference fit on the tap end. The tap end is the part that screws into a threaded hole in a machine part. This hole has a Class 3 thread. During assembly the threads compress and flow elastically and plastically. This gives a very tight grip on the stud. The other end may have any type of relatively free-running thread.

9.20.2 Class 2—double end studs. This stud is similar to the Class 1 stud, except that it has free-run-

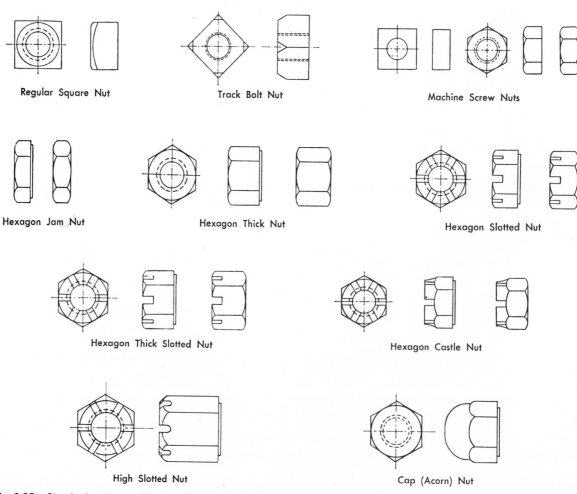

Regular Square Nut

Track Bolt Nut

Machine Screw Nuts

Hexagon Jam Nut

Hexagon Thick Nut

Hexagon Slotted Nut

Hexagon Thick Slotted Nut

Hexagon Castle Nut

High Slotted Nut

Cap (Acorn) Nut

Fig. 9.35 Standard nut types. (Courtesy Machine Design Fastener Book.)

ning threads on both ends. These may be obtained in any one of four types. See Fig. 9.37 for a stud bolt of this type.

9.20.3 Class 3—bolt studs for pressure-temperature piping. These are threaded for their full length and are used in high-temperature, high-pressure conditions.

9.20.4 Class 4—continuous threaded studs. These are general-purpose studs ranging from large-diameter studs for heavy work to threaded wire.

9.21 OTHER TYPES OF BOLTS. Many other types of bolts for special purposes can be obtained from the trade. See Fig. 9.38. The Industrial Fastener Institute has standardized quite a number of these bolts.

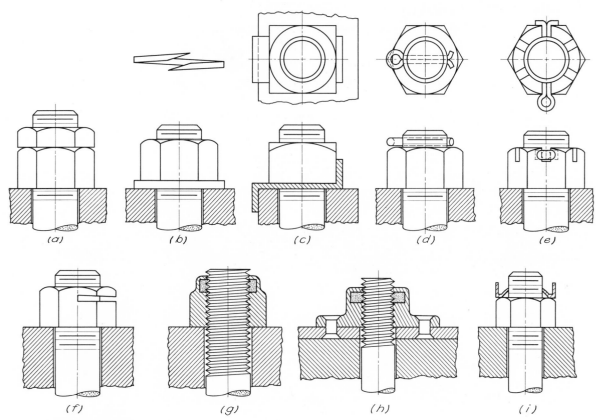

(a)   (b)   (c)   (d)   (e)

(f)   (g)   (h)   (i)

Fig. 9.36 Locking devices.

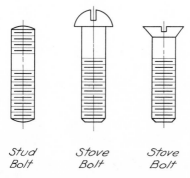

Stud   Stove   Stove
Bolt   Bolt   Bolt

Fig. 9.37 Stud and stove bolts.

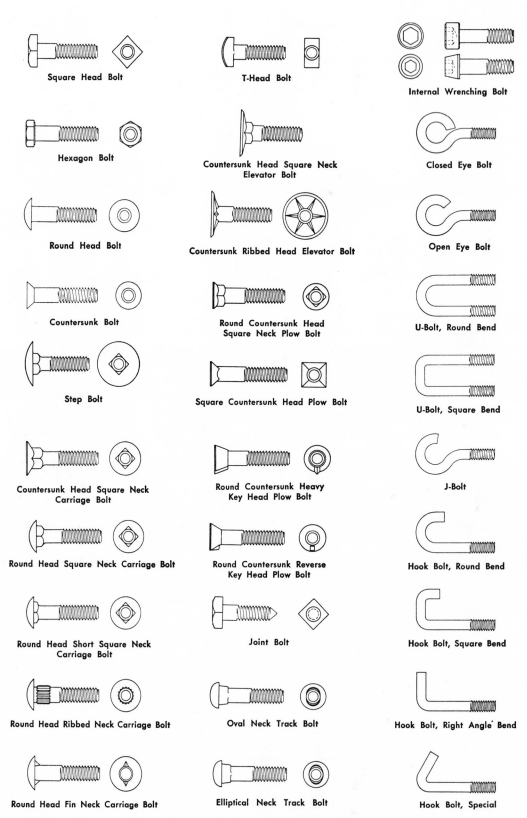

Fig. 9.38   Standard bolt forms. (Courtesy Machine Design Fastener Book.)

9.21.1 Carriage bolts. The carriage bolt is used principally for woodwork. It has a smooth oval head for a finished appearance and a square shank that prevents the bolt from turning as the nut is tightened. Four other types of heads, in addition to that shown in Fig. 9.38, are regularly manufactured.

9.21.2 Stove bolts. The standard stove bolt (see Fig. 9.37) is peculiar in that is has a round flat head which is beveled on the underside to fit a countersunk hole. It is provided with a screwdriver slot for turning the threaded end into the nut. This bolt is used where it is desirable to have the head of the bolt flush with the surface of the metal held in place. A second kind of stove bolt has a button-shaped head with a slot for a screwdriver but is not beveled on the underside.

9.21.3 Plow bolts. The plow bolt is similar to the stove bolt except that it does not have the screwdriver slot. The head has a projecting lug or square shank to keep the bolt from turning as the nut is being tightened. See Fig. 9.38. Three other types of plow bolts are regularly supplied by the trade.

9.22 DRAWING SQUARE AND HEXAGONAL HEAD BOLTS AND NUTS. Dimensions for regular square- and hexagonal-head unfinished and semifinished bolt heads and nuts are given in Tables 7 to 14 in the Appendix.

On regular unfinished and semifinished bolt heads the distance across flats (W) as indicated in Fig. 9.31 is one and one-half times the diameter, with adjustments to sixteenths to eliminate $\frac{1}{32}$-inch wrench openings. Regular nuts follow the same rule except that $\frac{1}{16}$ inch is added in sizes from $\frac{1}{4}$ to $\frac{5}{8}$ inch.

The nominal height of the regular unfinished head is $\frac{2}{3}D$ and that of the semifinished head $\frac{2}{3}D$ minus $\frac{1}{64}$ to $\frac{1}{8}$, depending on the size. The height of the semifinished and finished bolt head includes the height of the washer face, which is usually $\frac{1}{64}$ inch.

The nominal thickness of the regular unfinished nut is $\frac{7}{8}D$ and that of the unfinished nut $\frac{7}{8}D$ minus $\frac{1}{64}$ to $\frac{3}{64}$, depending on the size.

Bolt heads and nuts may be laid out on the drawing by means of dimensions taken from the tables, but for speed and convenience the method illustrated in Figs. 9.31 through 9.34, known as the Jorgensen method, is preferred. Although the dimensions obtained by this method are not exactly accurate, they are as close as would be required, except when clearances are involved. To lay out a hexagonal bolt head by this method, the following steps are necessary.

a. Draw the outline of the bolt and the base of the head and nut. With a 30–60 triangle, draw the sides of the triangle with the hypotenuse equal to the diameter of the bolt. See Fig. 9.32.

b. The altitude of the triangle is equal to $C/4$ as indicated in Fig. 9.32(a). This distance should be laid off twice on each side of the center line of the bolt to give the vertical lines of the bolt head and nut.

c. The long leg of the triangle marked H_2 gives the thickness of the nut, which may be laid off as shown in Fig. 9.32(a).

d. By projecting the apex of the triangle horizontally to the center line, the distance H_1 is obtained, which is the height of the head, and is laid off as shown in Fig. 9.32(a).

e. By using a radius $R_1 = D$, the curve on the front face of head and nut may be drawn as in Fig. 9.32(b).

f. The distance R_2 is taken from the point where the long leg of the triangle crosses the center line of the bolt and is used as a radius for the curves on the side faces of head and nut. The center point is on the center line of the face as shown in Fig. 9.32(c). The corners may be chamfered to finish the drawing if desired.

Similar steps for the square head and nut are illustrated in Figs. 9.33 and 9.34.

9.22.1 Standard length of threads on bolts and screws. For all standard bolts the minimum length of thread for bolts up to and including 6-inch lengths shall be

$$L = 2D + \frac{1}{4}''$$

For lengths over 6 inches the threaded length shall be

$$L = 2D + \frac{1}{2}''$$

The tolerance on thread lengths shall be plus $\frac{3}{16}$ of an inch or $2\frac{1}{2}$ threads, whichever is greater. For bolts too short to meet the above requirements the distance from the bearing surface of the bolt to the first full thread shall not exceed $2\frac{1}{2}$ threads for diameters up to 1 inch and $3\frac{1}{2}$ threads for sizes greater than 1-inch diameter.

9.22.2 Bolt specifications. In many instances the fasteners are not drawn in projection but are listed in the bill of material. All the information necessary for ordering the bolt must therefore be included. This will require specifying the following items:

Diameter is the diameter of the rod from which the bolt is made and is usually the same as the thread diameter. It is always in the specification.

Length is the distance from the underside of the head to the tip of the bolt. When a countersunk head is used, the length is to the top of the head. This dimension must be given in the specification.

Material is assumed to be steel unless otherwise specified.

Finish should be specified as semifinished or finished. If finished, the special kind of finish must be specified. If type of finish is not specified, the bolt is assumed to be unfinished.

Kind of head should be specified as hexagonal or square. If head and nut are different, this should be noted.

Series is assumed to be regular unless heavy or light is specified.

Length of thread is assumed to be normal unless otherwise noted.

Thread specification consists of the four items previously mentioned. A typical specification would be ¾-10 UNC-2A.

Typical bolt and screw specifications are given below. Abbreviations are usually used to save time and space.

⅝-11 UNC-2A × 3 Brass Fin Hex Hd Bolt.
½-13 UNC-2A × 2½ Semifin Hex Nut.
⅜-16 UNC-2A × 1⅝ Sq Hd Bolt.
⅜-16 UNC-2A × 2 Sq Hd Cup Point Set Scr.
¾-10 UNC-2A × 3 Heavy Hex Hd Bolt.

9.22.3 Length of engagement of steel bolts and screws in various materials. This is the item of first consideration in determining the full thread length of mating components. For steel bolts or screws the following lengths of engagement with other materials is recommended by the SAE Aerospace-Automotive Drawing Standard:

L = length of thread engagement
D = nominal diameter of thread
For steel $L = D$
For cast iron, brass, bronze, or zinc $L = 1.5D$
For forged aluminum $L = 2D$
For cast aluminum or forged magnesium $L = 2.5D$
For cast magnesium or plastic $L = 3D$

9.23 CAP SCREWS. Cap screws are similar to bolts in that they have a head on one end and threads on the other. But, in the method of holding two pieces together, they differ widely. The bolt clamps two pieces between the head and the nut, and the cap screw is threaded into one of the pieces, thus clamping one piece between the head and the other piece. The bolt requires a smooth hole in both pieces slightly larger than the bolt, whereas the cap screw requires a smooth hole in one piece and a threaded hole in the other. Cap screws are manufactured with several styles of heads, as shown in Fig. 9.39, and in diameters varying from ¼ to 1¼ inches. The point of all cap screws is flat and chamfered 35° (drawn 30°) to the flat surface and to a depth equal to the depth of the thread.

9.23.1 Length of cap screws. Cap screws may be obtained in lengths varying from ¼ to 6 inches.

Lengths from ¼ to 1 inch change by ⅛-inch increments.

Lengths from 1 to 4 inches change by ¼-inch increments.

Lengths from 4 to 6 inches change by ½-inch increments.

The length of a cap screw is measured from the largest diameter of the bearing surface of the head to the entrance point parallel to the axis of the screw. Dimensions of cap screws are given in Tables 5 and 6 in the Appendix.

9.23.2 Cap screw threads. Slotted-head cap screws are regularly threaded with American National coarse threads with a usable length of thread equal to $2D + ¼$ inch. Screws that are too short for this length of thread will be threaded as close to the head as practicable. Cap screws may also be obtained with threads of the fine-thread series. All dimensions for laying out cap screws are given in Tables 5 and 6 in

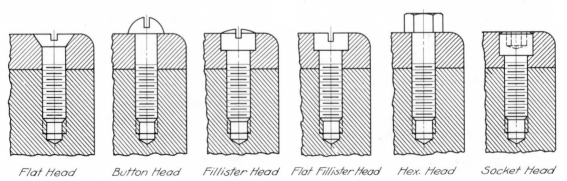

Flat Head   Button Head   Fillister Head   Flat Fillister Head   Hex. Head   Socket Head

Fig. 9.39 Cap screws.

the Appendix. The standard specification for a cap screw would be

⅝-11 UNC-2A × 1⅝ Brass Fillister Hd Cap Screw

If made of steel, the material term is omitted.

9.24 MACHINE SCREWS. Machine screws are similar in function and operation to cap screws, but are usually smaller in diameter. Machine screws are specified by numbers from 2 to 12 below the ¼-inch size and then by diameter up to ⅜ inch. The lengths of machine screws vary from ⅛ to 3 inches, changing by 1⁄16 increments up to ½ inch, then by ⅛-inch up to 1 inch, and finally by ¼-inch up to 3 inches. They are threaded not less than 1¾ inches for all screws over 2 inches in length, and within two threads of the bearing surface or closer if practicable for shorter screws. Machine screws may be obtained with either fine or coarse threads and with four types of heads, all slotted, as shown in Fig. 9.40. Square and hexagonal nuts may be obtained for all sizes of machine screws. The usual

method of specifying machine screws is

No. 10-24 NC-3 × 1 Flat Hd Mach Scr.

The material should also be specified if other than steel. Dimensions for drawing machine screws are given in Table 4 in the Appendix.

9.25 SET SCREWS. The purpose of a set screw is to prevent rotation or sliding between two parts. It is screwed into one part so that its point presses against the other, thus resisting relative motion between the two parts by means of the friction between the point of the set screw and one of the parts. The standard square-head set screw and several kinds of headless set screws are shown in Fig. 9.41. Information necessary for drawing set screws is given in Tables 15 and 16 in the Appendix. They are specified on the drawing by giving the diameter, length, type of head, type of point, and thread specification. Thus the specification should read

¼-20 NC-2 × ¾ Socket Hd, Cone Pt, Set Scr.

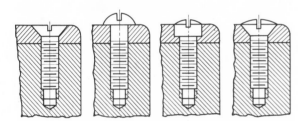

Fig. 9.40 Machine screws.

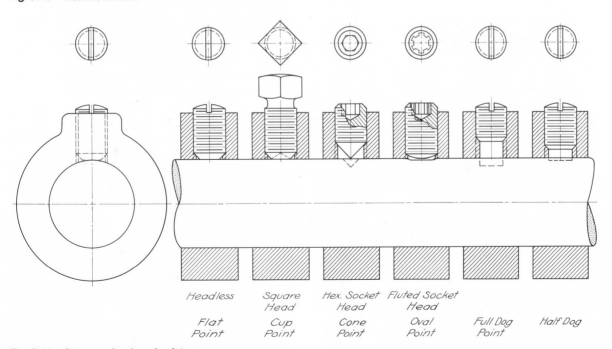

Fig. 9.41 Set screw heads and points.

9.26   OTHER TYPES OF STANDARD AND SPECIAL BOLTS AND SCREWS. Screw threads have been used on many kinds of screws and bolts which cannot be discussed in detail because of lack of space. Some of these are shown in Fig. 9.38 and discussed briefly in the following paragraphs.

9.26.1   Unslotted-head bolts. Unslotted-head bolts such as carriage bolts, step bolts, tire bolts, plow bolts, and track bolts are used frequently in woodwork as well as metalwork where the square shank keeps the bolt from turning. They may have round, oval, or countersunk heads, as shown in Fig. 9.38.

9.26.2   Slotted-head bolts. Slotted-head bolts such as stove bolts are used chiefly for metalwork. They may have round or countersunk heads as shown in Fig. 9.37. The slot allows them to be tightened with a screwdriver.

9.26.3   Special-purpose bolts. Special-purpose bolts having threads on one end only, such as eye bolts, U bolts, hook bolts, and thumb screws, are also illustrated in Fig. 9.38. They are used in many places where ordinary bolts would not be satisfactory.

9.26.4   Wood screws. Wood screws are usually designed with the thread forming a conical helix although they sometimes continue long threads on a cylindrical helix, as on the lag screw. They are designed in this manner so that they will cut their own threads in the wood as they are driven. The heads are usually slotted for a screwdriver and may be either round, elliptical, or countersunk. Wood screws are

specified by number as shown in Table 9.1, which is abstracted from USASI B18.6.1—1961.

Wood screws are threaded for approximately two thirds their length. The length of screw is measured from the diameter of the widest bearing surface of the head to the point. Various types of screws are illustrated in Fig. 9.42. A special type head known as the Phillips recessed head is used frequently for production work.

9.26.5   Tapping screws. These screws, sometimes called self-tapping screws, are made to either cut or form a mating thread, in metal, plastics, or other material, without having the holes previously tapped. This makes a very tight fit which prevents the screw from backing out even under vibrating conditions.

The dimensions of these standard screws are given in USASI B18.6.4.—1958. Two general types are listed:

a. Thread-forming USASI Types A, B, BP, C, and U.
b. Thread-cutting USASI Types D, F, G, T, BF, BG, and BT.

9.26.6   Rivnut. Rivnut is the patented name of a fastener that may be used to fasten two plates together and at the same time provide a nut plate to which other parts may be fastened. One of the important features of this fastener is that the entire operation can be completed from one side of the plate. Figure 9.43 shows the Rivnut being used as a rivet to hold two plates together and also as a nut plate by means of which the clip is fastened to the plate.

TABLE 9.1   WOOD SCREW DIMENSIONS

Nominal size	0	1	2	3	4	5	6	7	8	9	10	12	14	16	18	20	24
Threads per inch	32	28	26	24	22	20	18	16	15	14	13	11	10	9	8	8	7
Basic diameter	0.060	0.073	0.086	0.099	0.112	0.125	0.138	0.151	0.164	0.177	0.190	0.216	0.242	0.268	0.294	0.320	0.372

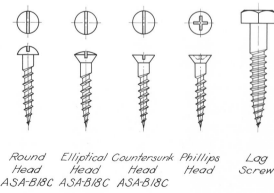

Round Head ASA-B18C   Elliptical Head ASA-B18C   Countersunk Head ASA-B18C   Phillips Head   Lag Screw

Fig. 9.42   Wood screws.

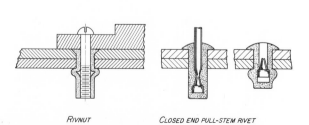

RIVNUT   CLOSED END PULL-STEM RIVET

Fig. 9.43   Self-locking screws.

9.27 RIVETS. The chief purpose of rivets is to make a permanent fastening between plates or rolled sections. Rivets are made with various shapes of heads, but all function alike in their method of holding the parts together. They are manufactured with a head on one end only, the other head being formed in the driving. Holes for the rivets are punched slightly larger than the rivet so that they may be put in place easily. They are first heated and then inserted in the hole, after which the other head is formed by hammering with a pneumatic hammer or by pressure. The length of a rivet is figured from the area of greatest bearing on the head to the point. This length is specified so as to allow only enough material to form the head and fill the hole around the rivet.

The various shapes of rivet heads are shown in Fig. 9.44. Rivets are sometimes shown on the drawing and sometimes omitted entirely. When shown they are represented by a circle as indicated in Fig. 9.45 or simply by center lines.

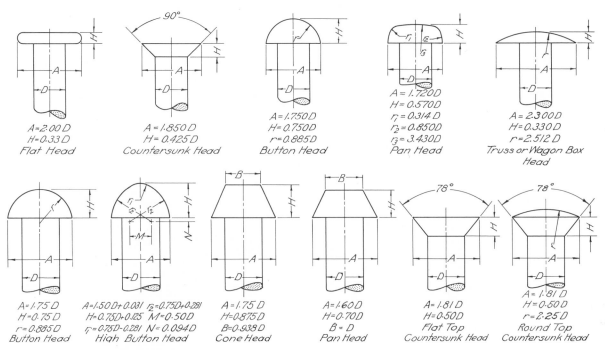

A=2.00 D
H=0.33 D
Flat Head

A = 1.850 D
H = 0.425 D
Countersunk Head

A = 1.750 D
H = 0.750 D
r = 0.885 D
Button Head

A = 1.720 D
H = 0.570 D
r_1 = 0.314 D
r_2 = 0.850 D
r_3 = 3.430 D
Pan Head

A = 2.300 D
H = 0.330 D
r = 2.512 D
Truss or Wagon Box Head

A = 1.75 D
H = 0.75 D
r = 0.885 D
Button Head

A = 1.50 D + 0.031 r_3 = 0.75D + 0.281
H = 0.75D + 0.125   M = 0.50D
r_2 = 0.75D - 0.281   N = 0.094D
High Button Head

A = 1.75 D
H = 0.875 D
B = 0.938 D
Cone Head

A = 1.60 D
H = 0.70 D
B = D
Pan Head

A = 1.81 D
H = 0.50 D
B = D
Flat Top Countersunk Head

A = 1.81 D
H = 0.50 D
r = 2.25 D
Round Top Countersunk Head

Fig. 9.44   Rivet heads. (Courtesy USASI.)

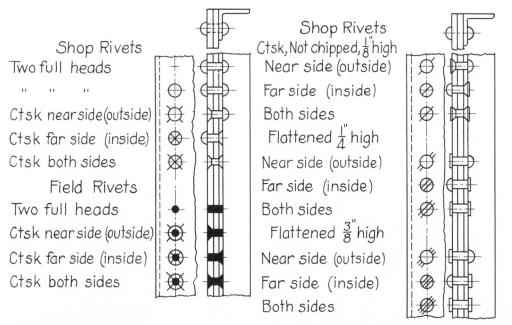

Shop Rivets
Two full heads
   "   "   "
Ctsk near side (outside)
Ctsk far side (inside)
Ctsk both sides
      Field Rivets
Two full heads
Ctsk near side (outside)
Ctsk far side (inside)
Ctsk both sides

Shop Rivets
Ctsk, Not chipped, $\frac{1}{8}$" high
Near side (outside)
Far side (inside)
Both sides
Flattened $\frac{1}{4}$" high
Near side (outside)
Far side (inside)
Both sides
Flattened $\frac{3}{8}$" high
Near side (outside)
Far side (inside)
Both sides

Fig. 9.45   Rivet symbols.

Since the pieces held together by rivets may be joined in the field or in the shop, it is necessary to have other symbols to indicate which way the riveting is to be done. Also rivet heads may be countersunk and/or chipped to provide clearances, and symbols have been devised to show these things. These symbols are shown in Fig. 9.45.

In boiler and tank work, considerable pains may be taken to show the actual shape of the rivet head. See Fig. 9.44. A drawing for several types of joints is shown in Fig. 9.46. In structural work the shape of the rivet head is seldom shown.

Explosive rivets are used in aircraft work where it is not convenient to work on both sides of the plate. These are aluminum rivets that have been hollowed out at the end to allow space for the explosive charge. When exploded the rivet is expanded to grip the plates as shown in Fig. 9.47.

9.28   KEYS. These fasteners called keys are chiefly used to hold pulleys, gears, and rocker arms on rotating shafts. There are several standard types.

Figure 9.48 shows five common types. Square, flat, taper, and gib-head taper keys are dimensioned by notes giving the width, height, and length. Whenever possible, sizes should conform to standards. The keys need not be drawn except for special keys or when limits other than those of the standard are necessary. Patented keys such as the Woodruff and, Pratt and Whitney, shown in Fig. 9.48, are specified by number.

Keyways on shafts or internal members may be dimensioned as shown in Fig. 9.49(*a*). On the hub or external member the keyway may be dimensioned as shown in Fig. 9.49(*b*). The key seat for patented varietes may be specified by the key number.

Tables 17, 18 and 19 in the Appendix give dimensions for several standard keys. More complete infor-

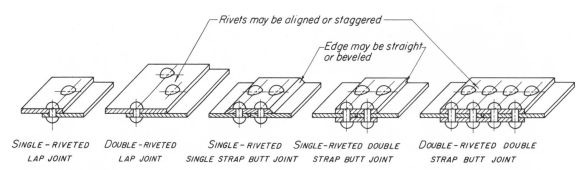

Fig. 9.46   Riveted joints.

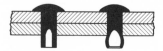

Fig. 9.47   Explosive rivet.

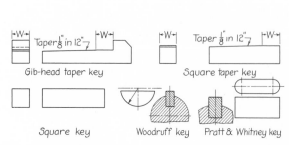

Fig. 9.48   Types of keys.

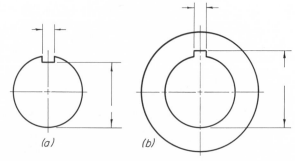

Fig. 9.49   Dimensioning keyways.

mation may be found in any mechanical engineer's handbook.

When heavy loads are to be transmitted from the shaft to the pulley or vice versa, two or more keys may be used or the Kennedy or Lewis systems may be practicable. See Fig. 9.50.

9.29   INVOLUTE SPLINES. In many cases where heavy loads are to be transmitted, keys have been eliminated by the use of multiple spline shafts as illustrated in Figs. 9.51 and 9.52. Involute splines and serrations are commonly used.

9.30   TAPER PINS. In light work taper pins are sometimes used as fasteners in place of keys or as dowels. They taper ¼ inch in diameter per foot of length. Dimensions of standard taper pins may be obtained from Table 20 in the Appendix.

9.31   SPRINGS. Although springs are not considered fasteners, the method of representing them is closely related to the drawing of screw threads.

Springs are formed by winding the wire in the form of a cylindrical or conical helix. In actual practice, the projections of the spring are conventionalized in a manner similar to threads by using straight lines instead of helices. Figure 9.53 shows by steps the method of drawing a spring. Compression springs are usually ground on the ends to provide a flat bearing. Tension springs must have a loop of some kind on each end. In long springs a few turns may be shown on each end with ditto marks between, rather than drawing the entire spring. These things are illustrated in Figs. 9.53, 9.54, 9.55 and 9.56. For further information on springs see Mil. Std. 29-1958.

In specifying a spring, the following information should be given: diameter and kind of wire, free length of spring, number of turns, and controlling diameter.

Springs are frequently represented by single lines as in Fig. 9.57 instead of the more complicated double line.

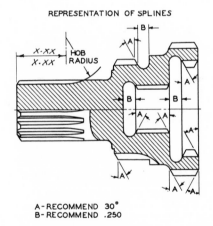

REPRESENTATION OF SPLINES

A - RECOMMEND 30°
B - RECOMMEND .250

Fig. 9.52   Representation of splines. (Courtesy USASI.)

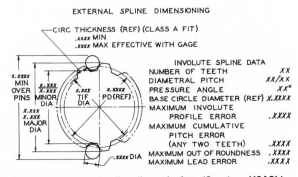

Two-Key   Kennedy   Lewis

Fig. 9.50   Heavy-duty keys.

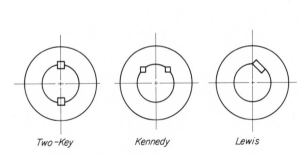

Fig. 9.51   External spline dimensioning. (Courtesy USASI.)

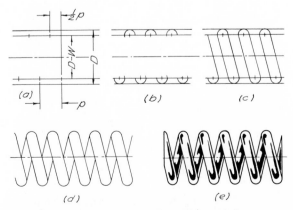

Fig. 9.53   Construction of a coiled spring symbol.

9.31.1   Flat springs. The coned disk or Belleville Spring is shown together with dimensions and other specifications in Fig. 9.58. The method of drawing and dimensioning an underslung leaf spring is shown in Fig. 9.59.

9.32   WELDING. Welding is a very valuable method of making permanent connections. Because of its increasing importance in both mechanical and structural design, an entire system of nomenclature and symbols has been developed to transmit the desired information. So many methods and techniques have been developed that welding is discussed separately in Chapter 27.

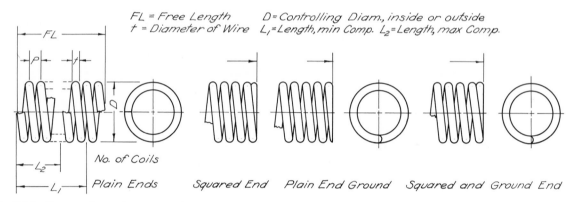

Fig. 9.54   **Compression springs.**

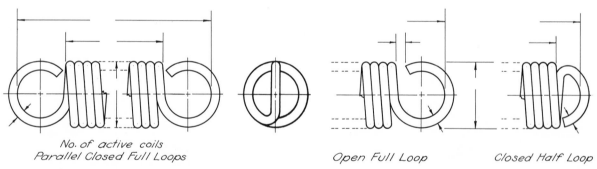

Fig. 9.55   **Tension springs.**

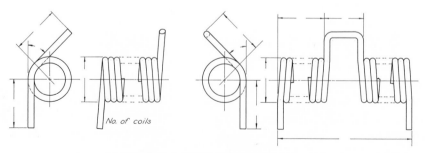

Fig. 9.56   **Representing and dimensioning torsion springs.**

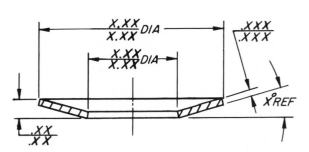

NOTE:-BREAK SHARP CORNERS .XX-.XX
(10-20% OF STOCK THICKNESS)

TEST LOAD XX LB FOR .XX-.XX DEFLECTION

Fig. 9.58 Coned disk or Belleville spring. (Courtesy SAE.)

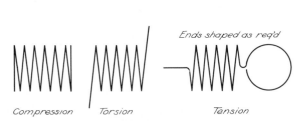

Fig. 9.57 Single line spring symbols.

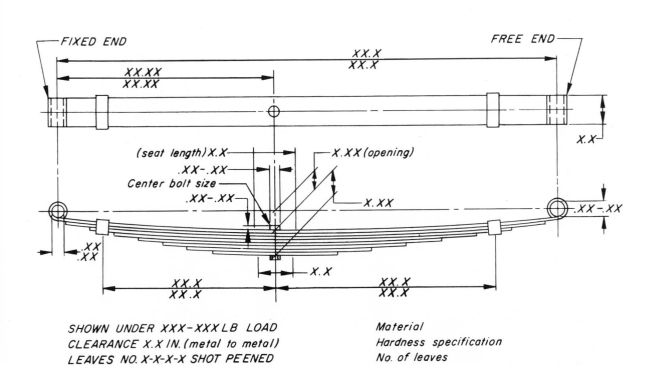

SHOWN UNDER XXX-XXX LB LOAD
CLEARANCE X.X IN. (metal to metal)
LEAVES NO. X-X-X-X SHOT PEENED
RATE XXX-XXX LB/IN

Material
Hardness specification
No. of leaves
Thickness of leaves

Fig. 9.59 Underslung leaf spring. (Courtesy SAE.)

SELF-STUDY QUESTIONS

Before trying to answer these questions, read the chapter carefully. Then, without reference to the text, answer as many questions as possible. For those that cannot be answered, the number, in parentheses following the question number, gives the article in which the answer can be found. Look it up and write down the answer. Check the answers that you did give to see that they are correct.

9.1 **(9.2.1)** Name one important source of national standards. _____ .

9.2 **(9.4)** The top edge or surface joining the two sides of a thread is called _____ .

9.3 **(9.4)** The pitch of a sharp V-thread is the distance from crest to _____ .

9.4 **(9.4)** The lead of a thread is the distance it advances in _____ turn.

9.5 **(9.4; 9.8)** A _____ hand thread advances into a hole when turned clockwise.

9.6 **(9.4)** The largest diameter of a thread is called the _____ diameter.

9.7 **(9.5.1)** Two thread types used for transmitting power are _____ and _____ .

9.8 **(9.6.3; 9.9.1)** The letters UNC in a thread specification mean _____ _____ _____ .

9.9 **(9.6.3; 9.9.2)** The letters UNF in a thread specification mean _____ .

9.10 **(9.10)** The three classes of fits for an external thread are _____ _____ _____ .

9.11 **(9.10)** The three classes of fit for an internal thread are _____ _____ _____ .

9.12 **(9.10.1)** Classes 1A and 1B are described as a _____ fit.

9.13 **(9.10.2)** Classes 2A and 2B are commonly used for _____ .

9.14 **(9.11)** Show by a small sketch the profile shape of a square thread.

9.15 **(9.5; 9.12)** Show by a small sketch the profile shape of an Acme thread.

9.16 **(9.12)** The angle between the sides of an Acme thread is _____ _____ .

9.17 **(9.16.2)** Holes that do not go clear through a part are called _____ .

9.18 **(9.17.1)** Regular bolts are not _____ on any surface.

9.19 **(9.17.2)** Semifinished bolts have a circular _____ face under the head only.

9.20 **(9.19)** Two common locking devices for nuts are _____ and _____ .

9.21 **(9.20)** Stud bolts are threaded on _____ _____ .

9.22 **(9.21)** Name three other types of bolts besides the regular, semifinished, and finished hexagon-head bolts. _____ _____ _____ .

9.23 **(9.22.1)** The standard length of threads on bolts up to 6 inches in length is _____ $D +$ _____ inch.

9.24 **(9.23)** The cap screw requires a _____ hole in one part and a threaded hole in the other of two parts to be held together.

9.25 **(9.24)** Machine screws differ from cap screws in that they are _____ than cap screws.

9.26 **(9.25)** _____ screws are used to prevent rotation and sliding between parts.

9.27 **(9.27)** When permanent fastenings are to be made between two parts _____ may be used.

9.28 **(9.28)** Gears and pulleys are secured to shafts by means of _____ .

9.29 **(9.28)** Show by a small sketch the shape of a Woodruff key.

9.30 **(9.28)** Show by a small sketch the shape of a Pratt and Whitney key.

9.31 **(9.32)** Welding is one method of making _____ fastening between two parts.

PROBLEMS

Standard bolts and screws are not ordinarily shown on working drawings, except in assemblies, but it is necessary to make drawings of all bolts and screws that depart from the standard forms. This is a common occurrence.

The problems below, however, have been confined to standard forms since they provide the necessary practice and are completely specified as to form and dimensions without the use of text figures. The student is referred to tables of standard dimensions in the Appendix. The bolts and screws should be shown holding two parts together as they would function in an assembly drawing.

The problems are to be made in ink or pencil as directed by the instructor. In either case show the necessary construction lines for bolt heads and nuts in light pencil lines. The scale is full-size unless otherwise specified. Specify the threads by means of a note of standard form, but in other respects leave the drawings undimensioned.

When the bolt or screw is under 1″ actual diameter on the paper, use the straight-line convention for threads; when 1″ or more in diameter, use the V symbol for threads.

9.1 Make a two-view drawing of an American Standard bolt as described: Square head unfinished bolt and nut 2″ in diameter and 4″ long. Show the nut on the bolt.

9.2 Same as Problem 9.1: square-head semifinished bolt and nut, 1¾ × 5″.

9.3 Same as Problem 9.1: hex-head unfinished bolt and nut, 2¼ × 4½″.

9.4 Same as Problem 9.1: hex-head semifinished bolt and nut, 1½ × 5″.

9.5 Make a two-view drawing of an American Standard machine, cap, or set screw as described: flat-head machine screw, ¼ × 1½″. Scale 2″ = 1″. Use the straight-line symbol for threads.

9.6 Same as Problem 9.5: flat-head machine screw, ³⁄₁₆ × 2″. Show in a blind tapped hole.

9.7 Same as Problem 9.5: round-head machine screw, ⁵⁄₁₆ × 1¾″.

9.8 Same as Problem 9.5: fillister-head machine screw, ⁵⁄₁₆ × 1¾″. Show in a blind tapped hole.

9.9 Same as Problem 9.5: oval-head machine screw, ⅜ × 2¼″.

9.10 Same as Problem 9.5: flat-head cap screw, ⁵⁄₁₆ × 2″. Show in a blind tapped hole.

9.11 Same as Problem 9.5: button-head cap screw, ⅜ × 2½″.

9.12 Same as Problem 9.5: fillister-head cap screw, ⁹⁄₁₆ × 2¼″.

9.13 Same as Problem 9.5: hex-head cap screw, ⅝ × 2½″.

9.14 Same as Problem 9.5: square-head set screw, ¾ × 2″. Point as assigned: (*a*) cup, (*b*) flat, (*c*) cone, (*d*) dog, (*e*) round.

9.15 Make a one-view drawing of the thread specified. Use straight lines to represent the helix curve. Show one turn of the invisible part of the thread. Make the thread 3″ long, and show ½″ of shaft beyond the thread on each end, equal to the minor diameter of the thread. Show the conventional break on each end. The thread to be: single, right-hand, square thread, 2½″ diameter, ½″ pitch.

9.16 Same as Problem 9.15: double, left-hand, Square thread, 3″ in diameter, and ¾″ pitch.

9.17 Same as Problem 9.15: double, right-hand, Square thread, 2¾″ diameter, ⅝″ pitch.

9.18 Same as Problem 9.15: triple, right-hand, Square thread, 3″ diameter, ¾″ pitch.

9.19 Same as Problem 9.15: single, right-hand, Acme thread, 2″ diameter, ½″ pitch.

9.20 Same as Problem 9.15: single, left-hand, Acme thread, 2½″ diameter, ⅝″ pitch.

9.21 Same as Problem 9.15: double, right-hand, Acme thread, 3″ diameter, ¾″ pitch.

9.22 Same as Problem 9.15: double, left-hand, Acme thread, 3″ diameter, ¾″ pitch.

The following problems are of a type that engineers meet in practice. Screw thread fasteners are not designed by the engineer but rather the proper kind and size are selected from the many varieties available that will best do the job. Several cases are shown in Figs. 9.60 to 9.63. In each case, represent all parts and completely specify the fasteners.

9.23 In this case the lower part of Fig. 9.60 which is quite heavy had to be lowered into place by means of a crane, hence the heavy lug. When in place the lug is not accessible from below. Select and draw an economic fastener which shall be ½″ in diameter and which can be tightened from the top only. Since the top part is rather large and not easily moved, it is desirable to have some guidance system when it is lowered into place.

9.24 In another case, let it be assumed that the cover or upper part of Fig. 9.60 is light enough to be moved by hand once it has been lowered into place, but that there is not room enough to tighten the fastener with a wrench. Select and draw the fastener which is to be ½″ in diameter.

9.25 In the case of Fig. 9.61 clearance problems require that the fastener not protrude above the upper surface of the top part. Select and draw a fastener to hold the two parts together. The fastener needs to be more than ⅜″ in diameter.

9.26 In the case of Fig. 9.61 assume that a fastener of not less than ¾″ diameter is necessary. Redesign the top and bottom parts so that a hexagon head bolt of this size could be used.

9.27 In the case of the pulley and shaft of Fig. 9.62 considerable torque (rotating force) is to be transmitted to the shaft. The pulley is not near the end of the shaft. The pulley can be moved along the shaft for a distance somewhat greater than the width of the hub. Select and represent a fastener that can be used in this situation, assuming that all machining is done prior to assembly. Sliding along the shaft is not a problem.

9.28 In the case of the preceding problem (Fig. 9.62) let it be assumed that the fastener selected will not be tight enough to prevent motion of the pulley along the shaft. If the outside diameter of the rim of the pulley does not exceed 6″, select and draw a fastener that will prevent sliding and which can be conveniently tightened. Assume that the pulley and its hub are easily accessible.

9.29 In the case of the handwheel and shaft in Fig. 9.63 assume that neither the fit of the wheel on the shaft nor the key and keyway are tight enough to prevent sliding. There must be no projection above the top level of the handwheel. Select and draw a fastener that will prevent sliding.

9.30 In the case of the handwheel in Fig. 9.63 assume that it is uneconomical to make a tight fit of the wheel and shaft. Select and draw a fastener that will prevent both sliding downward and rotation. Redesign the parts if necessary. The wheel must be removable.

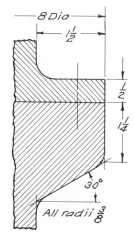

Fig. 9.60

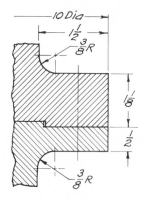

Fig. 9.61

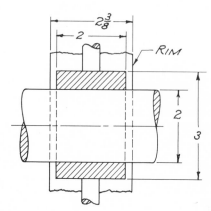

Fig. 9.62

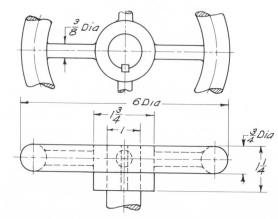

Fig. 9.63

Shop Terms and Processes

NEW: Modern Airplane factory. (K. W. Gullers, Rapho Guillumette)

OLD: 19th century glass works. (The Bettmann Archive)

Chapter 10   Shop Terms and Processes

10.1   INTRODUCTION. The relation of the drafting room to the various shops is often underestimated in teaching the draftsman the techniques of his profession. No design has commercial value unless the thing designed can be made in the shops, and at a cost that will allow it to compete with similar products in the markets. Odd-size tools, impractical methods, and even impossible operations are often specified on drawings of the uninformed. The draftsman must know the capabilities and limitations of the shops. His drawings must "talk" in the shopman's language.

10.2   CASTINGS. The genesis of all cast metal work is found in the pattern shop. All drawings specifying castings must *first go to the patternmaker who constructs a wood or plaster model of the object to be cast. This model, called a pattern,* is then sent to the foundry where the actual casting is made. Castings are made from various kinds of iron and steel and also from nonferrous metals, such as aluminum, magnesium, zinc, copper, bronze, and brass. To understand the processes that are carried on in the pattern shop and foundry, it is necessary to have a general knowledge of the terms employed there.

10.3   PATTERN DRAWING OR LAYOUT. The source from which the patternmaker obtains his information is the working drawing made in the drafting room. Since this working drawing contains information to be used in other shops but not needed by the patternmaker, he sometimes makes a new drawing called a pattern drawing or layout. This omits all unnecessary information and adds such items as parting plane, finish allowance, draft, and core prints. This drawing is made full-scale with the shrink rule. On the drawings many curves and intersections must be carefully constructed, since dimensions are taken directly from the pattern drawing. Sections may also be taken at different places on the pattern drawing for the purpose of cutting sheet metal templates with which to check the pattern. Figure 10.1 shows the working drawing of a simple object and also the pat-

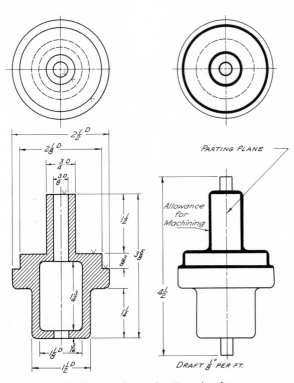

Fig. 10.1   Machine drawing and pattern drawing.

261

tern drawing for the same object.

10.4 PATTERNMAKER'S SHRINK RULE. When the metal in a casting is cooling, it continues to get smaller until room temperature is reached. The amount of this shrinkage varies with different metals, but in any case the patternmaker must allow for it by making the layout and the pattern oversize. This is done by using a shrink rule on which the divisions are all slightly larger than a normal rule. The amount of allowance made for the shrinkage of various metals is given below in inches per foot.

Cast iron	$\frac{1}{8}$
Cast steel	$\frac{1}{4}$
Aluminum alloys	$\frac{5}{32}$
Magnesium alloys	$\frac{11}{16}$

Thus a 12-inch shrink rule for cast iron would actually measure $12\frac{1}{8}$ inches.

10.5 FINISH ALLOWANCES. Before the pattern drawing is complete, the patternmaker must add the "finish," which may be indicated by means of a heavy line. *The term "finish" as applied to pattern drawings means the amount of material added to the pattern to provide metal on the casting that is to be cut away in the finishing process.* The amount of this allowance varies from $\frac{1}{8}$ to $\frac{3}{4}$ of an inch, depending on the size of the casting and the metal from which it is made. The finish allowance on the drawing in Fig. 10.2 has been indicated by dotted lines which show the outline of the finished piece. On the engineer's working drawing the finished surfaces must always be indicated by one of the standard methods explained in Chapter 12.

10.6 PARTING PLANE. Before the pattern drawing can be carried any further, the location of the parting line or plane must be determined. This is not indicated on the engineer's working drawing, but the designer must have considered the matter to avoid a design that is unusually hard to cast and therefore expensive. *The purpose of the parting plane is to enable the pattern to be removed from the mold without breaking the walls of the sand.* The parting plane should be at the largest part of the object and so arranged that there are no undercut faces or projections. In casting the object, the parting plane is made to coincide with the plane between the two parts of the mold or flask. In simple objects such as that shown in Fig. 10.3(*a*), it is sometimes possible to use one face of the object as the parting plane, thus making the work of casting easier and less expensive. Usually one parting plane is necessary, as in Fig. 10.3(*b*). Occasionally more than one plane is necessary, but this should be avoided if possible. The line on the drawing that shows the position of the parting plane is called the parting line. This line is marked on the patternmaker's layout.

10.7 CORE PRINTS. As soon as the position of the parting plane has been determined, the core prints should be added to the full-size drawing. *Core prints are projections from the pattern whose purpose is to make an impression in the sand mold into which the core will be placed.* Since the core will completely fill the impression made by the core print, the function of the core print is merely to hold the core in the proper position until the metal has cooled. Figure 10.2 shows the core prints added to the pattern layout and to the

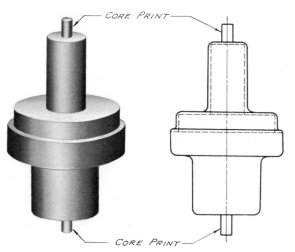

Fig. 10.2 **Core prints on pattern.**

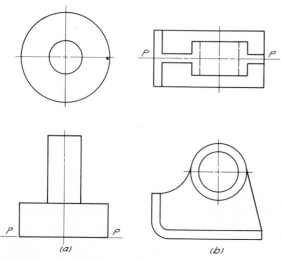

Fig. 10.3 **Parting plane.**

pattern. Core prints are not shown on the working drawing.

10.8   DRAFT. *To make the removal of the pattern from the mold easier, the pattern is tapered away from the parting plane. This taper is called "draft" or "draw."* The draft can be added to the pattern by increasing the size at the parting plane, thus making the piece stronger and heavier, or by allowing the material to remain the same at the parting plane and decreasing it at the top or bottom. The latter method decreases the strength and weight. When a wood pattern is used, a draft of ⅛ inch per foot is used, but with a metal pattern ¹⁄₁₆ inch per foot is sufficient. Draft may be specified by degrees and will usually be from ½ to 3°. The draft is shown on the full-size patternmaker's layout. It is not indicated in any way on the engineer's working drawing.

10.9   DESIGN DETAILS. In making a working drawing for a casting there are many design details with which the engineer should be familiar. These have been well standardized within the industry or by individual companies. Such things as fillets and rounded corners, bosses, pads, ribs, and rib intersections must be provided for by the draftsman to facilitate production and insure good quality.

10.9.1   Fillets and rounds. When the metal in a casting cools, the crystals tend to arrange themselves so that their lines of strength are perpendicular to the cooling surface, as indicated in Fig. 10.4. Therefore sharp angles tend to become planes of weakness where holes or cracks may occur during cooling. *For this reason the sharp internal angles on a pattern are filled with wood, leather, or wax, as illustrated in Fig. 10.5. This process is called filleting. Sharp external corners on a casting should also be rounded.* Careful attention to these details makes it easier to remove the pattern from the mold, allows the metal to flow more freely through the casting, and helps to avoid cracks and planes of weakness.

Each company usually has its own rules concerning size of fillets. Some require the fillets to have a radius equal to the thickness of the section, as shown in Fig. 10.6; others give the radii for fillets in tabular form. The following design data for minimum webs and fillet radii on aluminum alloy castings are used by a large industrial company.

Material No.	43	356	195	220	AM 265
t Min. web thickness	⁵⁄₃₂	⁵⁄₃₂	⁵⁄₃₂	⁵⁄₁₆	⁵⁄₃₂
r Min. fillet radii	⁵⁄₃₂	³⁄₁₆	³⁄₁₆	⅜	³⁄₁₆

Although it is essential that all angles be filleted and corners rounded, it is also important to avoid using too large a radius for fillets with thin web sections. Too large fillets may cause cooling stresses in thin webs, owing to the heavy concentration of material at the intersections and consequent unequal cooling.

The engineer's working drawing should always show all fillets and carry a note such as "All fillets are (*x*) radius and rounds (*x*) radius unless otherwise specified."

10.9.2   Section thickness in castings. As the casting is being poured, the metal flows in various directions into the parts of the mold and gradually cools as it flows. *If sections are too thin, the metal may cool so much that it will not be hot enough to join properly when metal flowing in two directions comes together. This forms a plane of weakness called a "cold shut."*

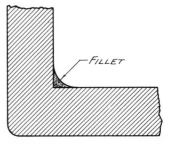

Fig. 10.5   Filleted corner.

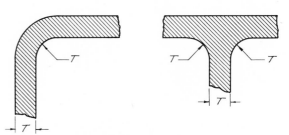

Fig. 10.4   Corners rounded and filleted to relieve stress.   **Fig. 10.6   Relation of fillet radii to thickness.**

The minimum thickness of webs varies with the kind of material and with company practice. For instance, one company recommends the following minimum thickness in inches: iron, $\frac{5}{32}$; brass and bronze, $\frac{3}{32}$; aluminum, $\frac{1}{8}$ to $\frac{3}{16}$.

A thin web intersecting a heavier member may develop cracks, owing to unequal cooling of the two parts. For this reason it is well to avoid too abrupt a change in cross section of the members. When such a change cannot be avoided, the thin member should be tapered to reduce the shrinkage stresses. It is recommended that the heavy section be not more than twice the thickness of the thin section, as shown in Fig. 10.7(*a*). When the minimum 2 to 1 ratio cannot be maintained, the thin section shall be tapered as shown in Figs. 10.7(*b*) and (*c*), according to the dimensions given in Table. 10.1.

Intersecting webs may tend to cause cooling cracks because of the heavy concentration of material at the intersection. See Fig. 10.7(*d*). This may be avoided or improved by alternating the webs as in Fig. 10.8, whenever possible.

10.9.3 Bosses. *Projections on a casting to allow for drilling holes or to provide bearing for a bolt head are called bosses.* When bosses occur they must be filleted to provide as gradual a change in cross section as possible, as shown in Fig. 10.9(*a*). When bosses must be placed in webs, the web must be tapered, as in Fig. 10.9(*b*), to provide the proper thickness.

10.9.4 Pads. Pads as illustrated in Fig. 10.10 will

TABLE 10.1   LENGTH OF TAPER *L*-WALL THICKNESS *W*

| T | *t*-Aluminum and Magnesium Alloys | | | | | | | | | | Max. R |
| | $\frac{5}{32}$ | | $\frac{3}{16}$ | | $\frac{7}{32}$ | | $\frac{1}{4}$ | | $\frac{5}{16}$ | | |
	L	W	L	W	L	W	L	W	L	W	
$\frac{5}{32}$											$\frac{3}{16}$
$\frac{3}{16}$											$\frac{3}{16}$
$\frac{7}{32}$			Values in this area								$\frac{7}{32}$
$\frac{1}{4}$			under critical								$\frac{1}{4}$
$\frac{5}{16}$			2 to 1 ratio								$\frac{5}{16}$
$\frac{3}{8}$	$1\frac{1}{8}$	$\frac{3}{8}$									$\frac{3}{8}$
$\frac{7}{16}$	$1\frac{1}{4}$	$\frac{3}{8}$	$1\frac{1}{4}$	$1\frac{3}{32}$							$\frac{3}{8}$
$\frac{1}{2}$	$1\frac{1}{4}$	$\frac{3}{8}$	$1\frac{1}{4}$	$1\frac{3}{32}$	$1\frac{1}{4}$	$\frac{7}{16}$					$\frac{7}{16}$
$\frac{3}{4}$	$1\frac{1}{4}$	$\frac{3}{8}$	$1\frac{1}{4}$	$1\frac{3}{32}$	$1\frac{1}{4}$	$\frac{7}{16}$	$1\frac{1}{4}$	$\frac{1}{2}$	$1\frac{1}{4}$	$1\frac{7}{32}$	

Courtesy Douglas Aircraft Co.

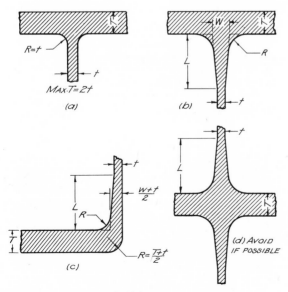

Fig. 10.7   Web and wall thickness.

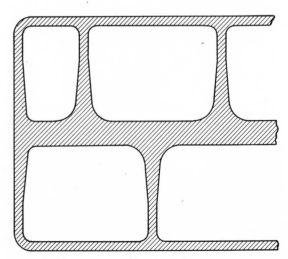

Fig. 10.8   Arrangement of interior webs.

save in the cost of the part by eliminating large areas that must be machined.

10.9.5   Ribs. On a casting, ribs perform two functions: to strengthen and stiffen the part and to prevent cooling cracks by acting as heat conductors, thus promoting the cooling of a section.

10.10   DEFINITION OF PATTERN AND FOUNDRY TERMS. The following terms are used in the pattern shop, core shop, and foundry.

Boss. A projection on an object whose height is usually less than its diameter. It is placed there for the purpose of providing a bearing surface or to enable the shop to drill a hole to better advantage. See Fig. 10.9.

Core. A sand model of the hollow interior of a casting. See Fig. 10.11.

Core box. A wooden box whose internal shape is such that, when it is packed with sand, the desired core is formed. See Fig. 10.11.

Core print. A projecting part of the pattern that makes an impression in the sand mold into which the core is placed. See Fig. 10.2. This supports the core in the mold.

Cupola. A furnace in which the metal is melted in the foundry.

Draw or draft. The taper on a pattern that makes it easier to withdraw the pattern from the mold.

Fillet. The concave surface that fills in the sharp angles between two faces on a pattern. See Fig. 10.5.

Finish allowance. Extra material allowed on a pattern to provide additional metal for finishing a face on the casting. See Fig. 10.1.

Flask. Two or more boxlike parts having the same

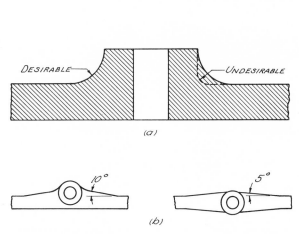

Fig. 10.9   Filleted bosses.

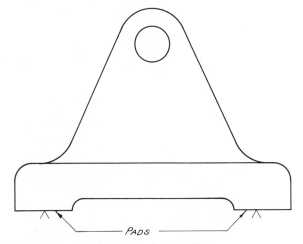

Fig. 10.10   Use of pads to reduce machining.

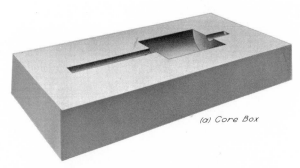

Fig. 10.11   Core box and core.

cross section into which the sand is packed to form the mold. See Fig. 10.12.

Cope. The upper part of the flask. See Fig. 10.12(*b*).

Drag. The lower part of the flask. See Fig. 10.12(*a*).

Gate. The opening in the sand through which the metal flows to the casting. See Fig. 10.13.

Parting plane. A plane on which the pattern can be divided so that both parts can be removed from the sand. See Fig. 10.3.

Pattern. A slightly oversize model of the object to be cast, usually made of wood. See Fig. 10.2.

Shrinkage allowance. The oversized measurement of the pattern to allow for the shrinkage of the metal when cooling.

Shrink rule. A rule used by the patternmaker which is made sufficiently oversize to allow for the shrinkage of the metal being used.

10.11   COLOR. For ease of interpretation, the complete pattern is stained in various colors. The parts that are to be unfinished are made black, those that are to be finished are red, and the core prints are yellow. Other color symbols are in use, but these are the most important.

10.12   CORE BOX. Since the pattern forms only the outer surface of a casting, it is necessary to have some method of forming the interior surfaces. The shape of these interior surfaces is determined by the shape of the core that is molded in the core box. It is

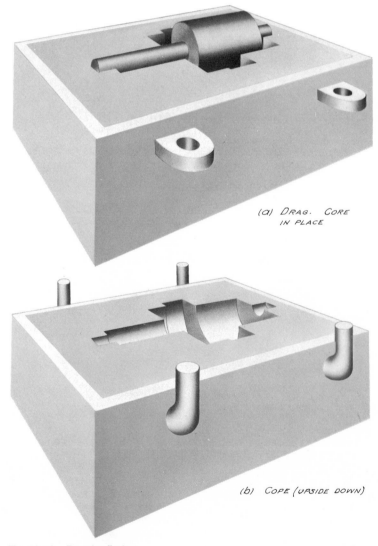

(a) DRAG. CORE IN PLACE

(b) COPE (UPSIDE DOWN)

Fig. 10.12   Foundry flask.

part of the patternmaker's job to build up the core box, which is merely a hollow box whose interior shape conforms to the shape of the interior surfaces of the object to be cast. Since the core is usually made in two parts, which are later glued together, the construction of the core box will involve consideration of parting plane, shrinkage, draft, and finish, just as was done in the construction of the pattern itself. Figure 10.11(a) shows a core box.

10.13 CORES. After the patternmaker has completed the core box, it is sent to the core shop where the core itself is made. *The purpose of the core is to occupy the space in the mold where an opening is desired.* The engineer must design interior spaces so that it is possible to remove the core after the metal has been cast.

10.14 FLASK. The sand in which the imprint of the casting is made must have a strong boxlike container which is called a flask. See Fig. 10.12. The flask is made in two parts which can be separated to remove the pattern and then be accurately put together again. See Fig. 10.13. The lower part is called the drag. The upper portion is referred to as the cope. See Fig. 10.12.

10.15 FOUNDRY. The draftsman has little immediate connection with the foundry, since the patternmaker acts as an intermediary between him and the molder.

Shop drawings do not, as a rule, include any reference to foundry operation. However, there probably is no place where the item of cost is of more vital importance than in the foundry. Excessive metal and difficult shapes to cast make the manufactured product costly. The designer must always be on guard against these expensive items.

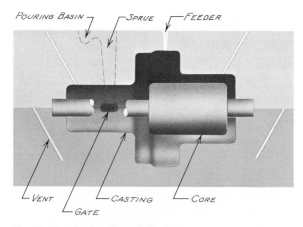

Fig. 10.13 Section through flask.

10.16 PERMANENT MOLDS. When a large number of castings are to be made, a metal or permanent mold will decrease the cost and improve the quality of the casting. The metal mold must be thick and heavy enough to have a large heat-absorbing capacity and have enough cooling capacity so that the temperature of the mold does not get too high.

10.17 CENTRIFUGAL CASTINGS. In this type of casting the mold is rotated while the metal is being poured. There are three types of centrifugal castings: (1) die molds; (2) semicentrifugal or center-pour; and (3) true centrifugal for cylindrical shapes where the inner diameter is controlled by the volume of metal poured.

Centrifugal casting is occasionally used as a substitute for forging, since it seems to give a product that has characteristics somewhat similar to a forging. It requires a rigid control of temperature and speed, but when it can be used it is sometimes cheaper than sand casting, because it is possible to hold the casting closer to finished specifications, thus saving in machining.

10.18 DIE CASTING. When a large number of castings of the softer metals are desired on which considerable machining would be necessary if sand castings were used, the cheapest and best method is die casting. This requires the construction of very accurate dies from high-grade steel. *The molten metal is forced into the dies under pressure, forming a casting that is as accurate as would be obtained by ordinary machine work and harder than a sand casting made from the same metal.* Much machine work can thus be eliminated. Die castings are made from various alloys of zinc, aluminum, magnesium, and copper. This process is used for any small object that does not have undercut parts.

10.19 POWDER METALLURGY. A process that is being used extensively at the present time and that shows promise of still further usefulness is that of forming objects from metal powder. *The powder is placed in accurately cut dies and formed under heavy pressure varying from 5 tons to 100 tons per square inch.* The object is then turned out of the die and heated or sintered at temperatures below the melting point until the grains of powder unite to form a solid piece.

10.20 FORGING. Many parts of a machine or structure must be designed to withstand shock or sudden stress, a characteristic for which castings are not recommended.

Hand forging is forming a piece to specified size by hammering or pressing with flat surfaces. *The hot metal is moved around on the anvil as desired and pounded into the desired shape either by hand or machine.* Considerable machining may be necessary to produce a finished piece from a hand forging, and the waste is apt to be large. This method is not used in mass production.

Drop forging is a process in which the hot metal is forced into dies by means of drop hammers. The dies are similar in principle to those used in die casting or powder metallurgy; the metal, very hot but not in a molten condition, is forced into the die by pounding.

Because of the hammering that the metal receives in the forging process, it is much less porous than a casting and the consistency is more uniform. Another important characteristic of a forging that affects its physical properties is the fiber direction or grain of the metal.

10.21 DESIGN DETAILS FOR FORGING. For this type of work a special forging drawing is made, which differs from the engineer's working drawing in that it shows the piece as it will be forged rather than the finished part after the machining has been completed. Figure 10.14 shows a forging drawing. Some of the practical considerations that must be kept in mind when making a forging drawing are given below.

10.21.1 Scale. All forging drawings should be made full-scale.

10.21.2 Draft. The draft angle is usually shown in degrees on the forging drawing. The slope begins at the parting line but must be measured from the direction of stroke of the forging press. For exterior surfaces the draft varies from 5 to 7°, depending on the shape of the piece, but for internal surfaces it should be about 10°, as shown in Figs. 10.15(*a*) and (*b*). Bathtub-type fittings such as that in Fig. 10.15(*d*) should have approximately 5° draft for both interior and exterior surfaces.

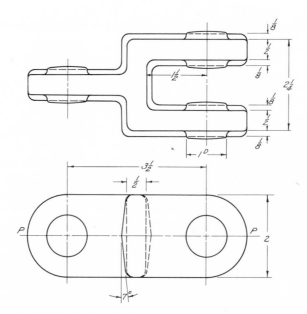

Fig. 10.14 Forging drawing.

10.21.3 Parting plane. The parting plane should be indicated on the forging drawing and when possible it should be located so that one die half contains all the impression. When both die halves contain part of the impression, the parting line will usually be placed on the center of a web, if there is a web in the object, but it need not be one continuous plane surface. See Fig. 10.16.

10.21.4 Forging plane. The forging plane that is perpendicular to the direction of stroke, on which the dies come together, must be arranged to avoid unbalanced die load. Care should be exercised to avoid interference between die and piece and to take advantage of natural draft. Notice that the forging plane in Fig. 10.16(g) has been located to give a better balanced die load than would have occurred if the forging plane had been made to coincide with the main parting line. Figure 10.16(d) shows a forging plane located to take advantage of the natural draft angle of the piece.

10.21.5 Minimum fillets. To facilitate the flow of metal through the die, the angles should be filleted. No fillet should be less than ⅛-inch radius. The chart

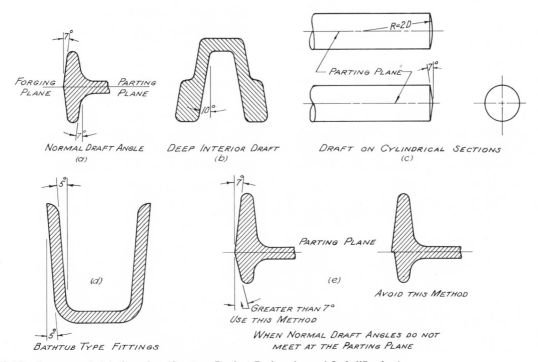

Fig. 10.15 Recommended draft angles. (Courtesy Product Engineering and O. A. Wheelon.)

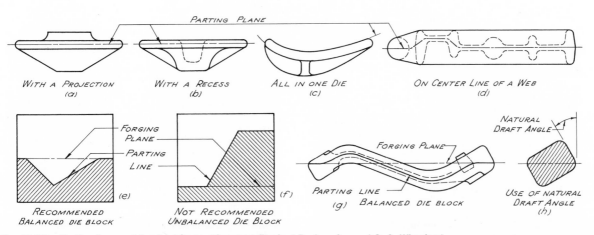

Fig. 10.16 Parting lines and forging planes. (Courtesy Product Engineering and O. A. Wheelon.)

shown in Fig. 10.17 gives recommended fillet radii.

10.21.6   Rounded corners. To avoid excessive hammering and consequent breakage of dies, the corners should be rounded to allow the metal to fill the die more easily. Figure 10.18 gives recommended edge radii.

10.21.7   Thin webs on I-beam sections. In I-beam sections the web has a tendency to cool rapidly, owing to the large area of contact with the die, thus making it hard to forge. At the same time the flange tends to fill first, leaving no place for the metal to flow as the web is brought down to size. This sometimes causes the shearing of the flange, as indicated in Fig. 10.19(*a*). The design suggestions given in Figs. 10.19(*b*) and (*c*) are recommended.

10.21.8   Tolerances. Dimensional tolerances should be as large as possible on all forgings to avoid excessive cost. The variations that must be allowed for are (1) shrinkage and warping as forging cools, (2) mismatching of dies, (3) failure to bring finish dies together, and (4) die wear. The following minimum dimensional tolerances, in inches, illustrated in Fig. 10.20, may be held without excessive cost:

a. Width for small forgings, $\pm\frac{1}{32}$.

b. Length for large forgings, $\pm\frac{1}{32}$ per foot of length.

c. Thickness across parting plane, $+\frac{1}{32}$, -0 for small forgings.

d. Thickness across parting plane, $+\frac{1}{16}$, $-\frac{1}{32}$ for large forgings.

e. Location of punched holes, at least $\pm\frac{1}{32}$, preferably $\pm\frac{1}{16}$.

f. When bosses that are to be bored out are located far apart, one should be made circular and the other elongated by an amount equal to twice the tolerance on the dimension between bosses, as shown in Fig. 10.21.

g. Tolerances for warping and mismatching of dies, shown in Figs. 10.20(*b*) and (*c*), must be added to the above tolerance.

h. Allowance for machining. The amount of material to be allowed for finishing operations should include the dimensional tolerances plus an allowance for warping and mismatching of dies, which may vary from 0 to $\frac{1}{8}$ inch, depending on the size of the piece. If the corner radius is to be cut away, that radius or a portion of it must also be added to the allowance for machining. See Fig. 10.22.

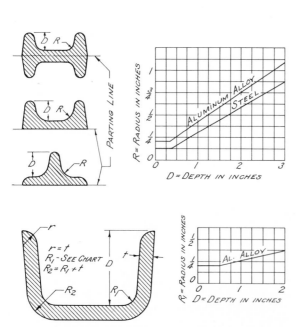

Fig. 10.17   Recommended fillet radii for forgings. (Courtesy Product Engineering and O. A. Wheelon.)

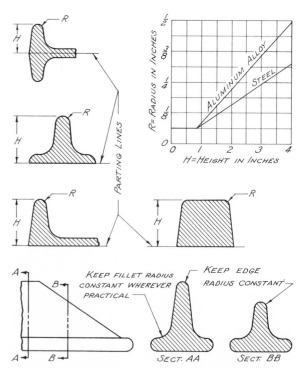

Fig. 10.18   Recommended edge radii for forgings. (Courtesy Product Engineering and O. A. Wheelon.)

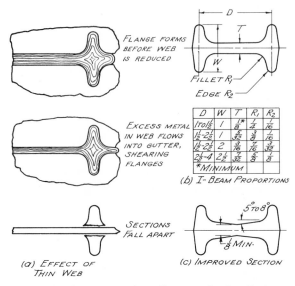

FLANGE FORMS
BEFORE WEB
IS REDUCED

FILLET R_1
EDGE R_2

EXCESS METAL
IN WEB FLOWS
INTO GUTTER,
SHEARING
FLANGES

D	W	T	R_1	R_2
1 TO $\frac{1}{2}$	1	$\frac{1}{8}$*	$\frac{1}{4}$	$\frac{1}{16}$
$\frac{1}{2}$-2$\frac{1}{2}$	1	$\frac{5}{32}$	$\frac{3}{8}$	$\frac{1}{16}$
1$\frac{1}{2}$-2$\frac{1}{2}$	2	$\frac{3}{16}$	$\frac{7}{16}$	$\frac{3}{32}$
2$\frac{1}{2}$-4	2$\frac{1}{2}$	$\frac{7}{32}$	$\frac{5}{8}$	$\frac{1}{8}$

*MINIMUM

(b) I-BEAM PROPORTIONS

SECTIONS
FALL APART

5° to 8°

$\frac{1}{8}$ MIN.

(a) EFFECT OF
THIN WEB

(c) IMPROVED SECTION

Fig. 10.19 Beam proportions. (Courtesy Product Engineering and O. A. Wheelon.)

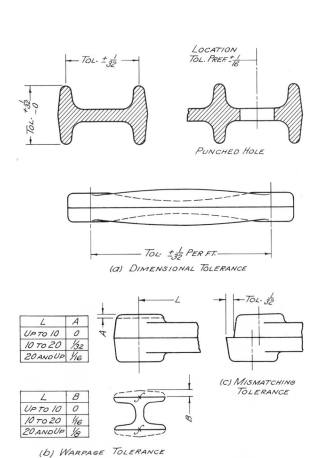

TOL. ±$\frac{1}{32}$

LOCATION
TOL. PREF.$^{+\frac{1}{16}}_{-}$

TOL. $^{+\frac{1}{32}}_{-0}$

PUNCHED HOLE

TOL. ±$\frac{1}{32}$ PER FT.

(a) DIMENSIONAL TOLERANCE

L	A
UP TO 10	0
10 TO 20	$\frac{1}{32}$
20 AND UP	$\frac{1}{16}$

L	B
UP TO 10	0
10 TO 20	$\frac{1}{16}$
20 AND UP	$\frac{1}{8}$

TOL. $\frac{1}{32}$

(c) MISMATCHING
TOLERANCE

(b) WARPAGE TOLERANCE

Fig. 10.20 Forging tolerances. (Courtesy Product Engineering and O. A. Wheelon.)

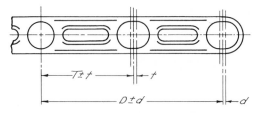

$T±t$ t

$D±d$ d

Fig. 10.21 Tolerance on location of bosses. (Courtesy Product Engineering and O. A. Wheelon.)

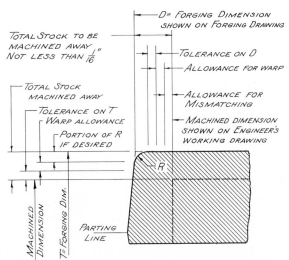

TOTAL STOCK TO BE
MACHINED AWAY
NOT LESS THAN $\frac{1}{16}$"

TOTAL STOCK
MACHINED AWAY

TOLERANCE ON T
WARP ALLOWANCE

PORTION OF R
IF DESIRED

MACHINED
DIMENSION

T= FORGING DIM.

PARTING
LINE

D= FORGING DIMENSION
SHOWN ON FORGING DRAWING

TOLERANCE ON D

ALLOWANCE FOR WARP

ALLOWANCE FOR
MISMATCHING

MACHINED DIMENSION
SHOWN ON ENGINEER'S
WORKING DRAWING

R

Fig. 10.22 Summary of tolerances and allowances needed on a forging. (Courtesy Product Engineering and O. A. Wheelon.)

10.22   STAMPING. *The term "stamping" is applied to a variety of processes used in the forming of thin metal parts.* It often includes cutting of the metal as well as shaping. A series of definitions with appropriate illustrations will give the best idea of some of the processes.

a. *Blanking* means cutting of the metal to the desired shape with one stroke of the press. See Fig. 10.23.
b. *Nesting* of blanks means that they should be designed so that they can be cut from the metal sheet with as little waste as possible. See Fig. 10.24.
c. *Punching* is a method of producing a hole in a part by one stroke of the press. A cylindrical punch produces a hole with practically smooth sides, as in Fig. 10.25(a). A conical punch produces a flanged hole with ragged edges, as in Fig. 10.25(b). A com-

bination of the two punches having a cylindrical shape with a shoulder, as in Fig. 10.25(c), produces a flanged hole with a fairly smooth edge.
d. *Trimming* is the process of removing excess metal from a stamping. Sometimes trimming is recommended rather than developing a blank.
e. *Shaving or burnishing* is a process that removes a very small amount of metal to produce a surface with a very close tolerance.
f. *Cutting off* is a process of cutting a blank to length from a strip of metal that has been slit or sheared to correct width.
g. *Notching* is done for the purpose of providing clearance, for attachment, or for locating elements, or to facilitate forming.
h. *Bending, forming, and embossing* are names applied to shaping a blank without materially changing the thickness of the metal.
i. *Drawing* is a process of forcing a metal blank to assume the shape of a die by stretching the metal. The depth of draw should be as shallow as practicable to keep down the number of operations.
j. *Coining* is a process by which great pressure forces the metal to flow in the die, thus making it thicker in some places and thinner in others.
k. *Swaging* is a cold forging operation in which the metal is squeezed to reduce the thickness in certain places. The metal flows outward and must be trimmed off.
l. *Extrusion* is a process whereby the metal is made to flow in a die either by pressure or impact.

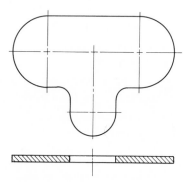

Fig. 10.23   Stamped blank.

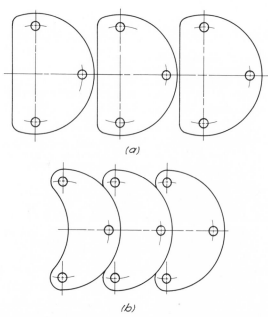

(a)

(b)

Fig. 10.24   Redesign for economy of material.

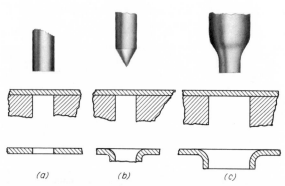

(a)   *(b)*   *(c)*

Fig. 10.25   Effect of type of punch.

m. Necking, bulging, and curling are processes for reducing, enlarging, or forming a rounded edge on drawn shells. Curling may be done on flat blanks for such purposes as hinge manufacture.

10.22.1 Design limitations for stamping. Certain limitations on the design of blanked parts must be considered for economical and efficient operation. A few of these will be mentioned.

a. Grain. Sometimes the functioning of a part requires that the grain of the metal run in a certain direction. This direction may be marked on the blank, but, as it can usually be allowed to vary by as much as 45° in either direction, it is usually specified by an arrow with a tolerance of ±45°.

b. Radii of blanked parts. To facilitate tool construction the radii should be as large as possible. The ends are usually made as semicircles, as shown in Fig. 10.23.

c. Hole spacing. To avoid distortion of the metal when holes are to be punched, the distance between centers of the holes should be a minimum of two times the thickness of the metal plus the sum of the two radii, but never less than ⅓₂ inch plus the sum of the radii.

d. Edge distance. The clear distance between the edge of the metal and the center of a punched hole should be a minimum of two times the thickness of the metal plus the radius of the hole, but not less than ⅓₂ inch plus the radius of the hole.

e. Spacing for drawn holes. To avoid distortion, the distance between drawn holes or between a drawn hole and an edge, or between a drawn hole and another bend should be not less than that shown in Fig. 10.26.

f. Clearance at bends. Formed parts should be so designed that there is a clearance of at least half the thickness of the metal, in order that there is no metal interference and the tools can make a satisfactory bend. This is illustrated in Fig. 10.27.

g. Radius for right-angle bends. The radius varies with the kind and temper of the material, direction of the grain, and type of die used. In general it is well to allow a radius not less than the thickness of the material. As large a tolerance as possible should be allowed in the size of the angle of bend.

h. Dimensions for drawing. The depth of draw should be as small as possible. Figure 10.28 shows acceptable dimensions for single-operation draws.

i. Size of punched holes. Punched holes of a diameter less than the thickness of the material are not practical unless the punch is supported.

10.23 MACHINE SHOP. The draftsman must be most familiar with the machine-shop processes. Dimensions on the drawing must be arranged so that they can be conveniently used in the shop. Machine-shop processes such as drill, ream, bore, and mill are sometimes indicated on the drawing. The degree and method of finish, and sometimes even the direction of the cutting strokes, are specified on the drawing. The draftsman must therefore be familiar with the tools, the machines in which they are used, and the limita-

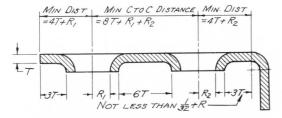

Fig. 10.26   Minimum material between drawn holes.

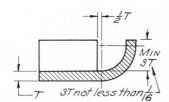

Fig. 10.27   Clearance for bending.

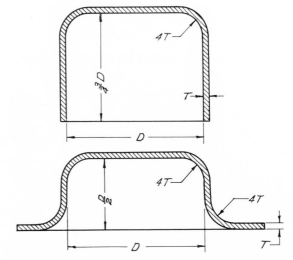

Fig. 10.28   Depth of draw.

tions and possibilities of each. Some companies do not specify shop operations on their drawings. In the following paragraphs a brief explanation of the important machines and tools are given, as well as the method of indicating on the drawing what processes are to be used.

10.23.1 Tooling points. All location dimensions on a casting are measured from three datum planes that are usually mutually perpendicular. These planes are located by tooling points on the casting jig or fix-

ture. These points form a contact between the jig or fixture and the object used to locate a casting for measuring or machining. The symbols suggested by the American Society for Metals to mark the tooling points are shown in Fig. 10.29.

a. The first datum plane is located by three points (actually minute areas) which are not on a straight line. These three points are made to come in actual contact with a surface to determine the plane, as shown in Fig. 10.30(*a*).

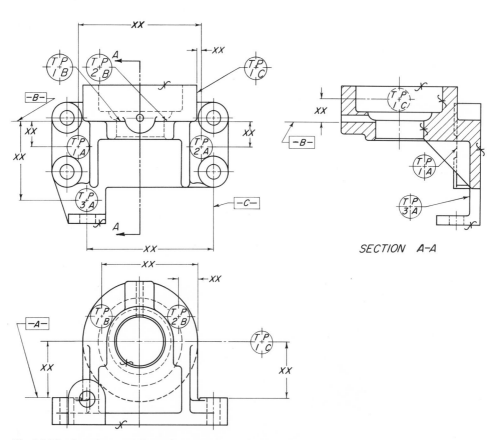

Fig. 10.29 Locating or tooling points. (Courtesy USASI Y14.8.)

b. The second datum plane is defined by two other tooling points and its relation to the first plane. See Fig. 10.30(*b*).

c. The third datum plane is located by one additional tooling point and its relation to the other two planes. See Fig. 10.30(*c*).

10.24   MACHINE TOOLS. Many of the tools in common use in the machine shop may be used in more than one machine. The following tools may be used on either the drill press or the lathe.

10.24.1   Twist drill. When a hole is to be drilled in a piece, it may be marked on the drawing by giving the diameter followed by the word "drill," thus ⅝ Drill. Usually the diameter of the hole is specified with the required finish. This makes it possible for the machine shop to use any method desired as long as the result is satisfactory. Metal drills, such as that shown in Fig. 10.31 are obtainable in sizes varying from ¹⁄₆₄ to 3 inches in diameter and in length up to 14 inches. The smaller drills are not rigid enough to prevent a slight deflection; consequently the tolerances indicated in Table 1 in the Appendix will have to be allowed. When used to precede a threading operation the tool is called a *tap drill.* Sizes of tap drills are given by numbers, letters, and fractional dimensions as listed in Table

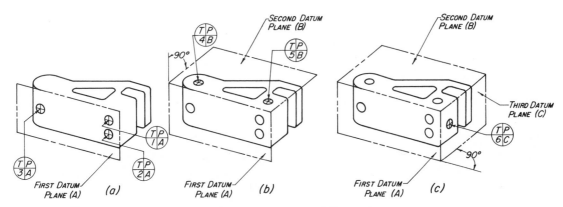

Fig. 10.30   Locating points on successive datum surfaces. (Courtesy USASI Y14.8.)

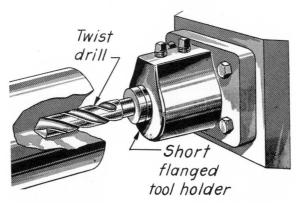

Fig. 10.31   Drilling on a lathe.   (Courtesy Warner and Swasey Co.)

2 in the Appendix. Figure 10.32 gives some suggestions concerning design details for drilling operations.

10.24.2   Reamer. A hole that has been drilled is left with a rough and slightly scarred surface, which is not suitable for close fits or for tapping if fine thread crests are desired. A reamer similar to the one illustrated in Fig. 10.33 is used to finish this rough surface. Reamers may be either straight or tapered for cylindrical or conical holes. See Fig. 10.34. The drawing usually indicates the diameter with the tolerance re-

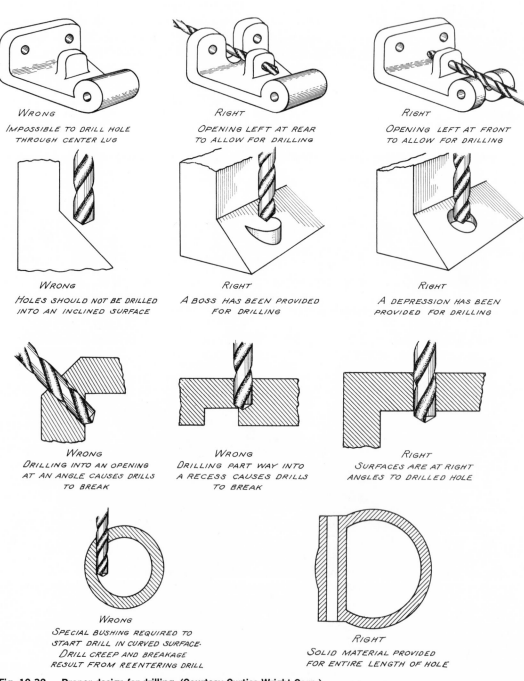

Wrong
IMPOSSIBLE TO DRILL HOLE
THROUGH CENTER LUG

Right
OPENING LEFT AT REAR
TO ALLOW FOR DRILLING

Right
OPENING LEFT AT FRONT
TO ALLOW FOR DRILLING

Wrong
HOLES SHOULD NOT BE DRILLED
INTO AN INCLINED SURFACE

Right
A BOSS HAS BEEN PROVIDED
FOR DRILLING

Right
A DEPRESSION HAS BEEN
PROVIDED FOR DRILLING

Wrong
DRILLING INTO AN OPENING
AT AN ANGLE CAUSES DRILLS
TO BREAK

Wrong
DRILLING PART WAY INTO
A RECESS CAUSES DRILLS
TO BREAK

Right
SURFACES ARE AT RIGHT
ANGLES TO DRILLED HOLE

Wrong
SPECIAL BUSHING REQUIRED TO
START DRILL IN CURVED SURFACE.
DRILL CREEP AND BREAKAGE
RESULT FROM REENTERING DRILL

Right
SOLID MATERIAL PROVIDED
FOR ENTIRE LENGTH OF HOLE

Fig. 10.32.   Proper design for drilling. (Courtesy Curtiss-Wright Corp.)

quired. Occasionally it may be desirable to specify the operation in full as "³⁹⁄₆₄ Drill, ⅝ Ream."

Reamers up to 3 inches in diameter and 17 inches in length can be secured. For holes up to ¾ inch in diam-

eter, ¹⁄₆₄ inch should be left for reaming; for holes over ¾ inch in diameter, ¹⁄₃₂ inch may be left.

A few suggestions about the proper use of a reamer are given in Fig. 10.35.

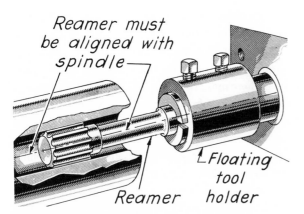
Fig. 10.33   Reaming. (Courtesy Warner and Swazey Co.)

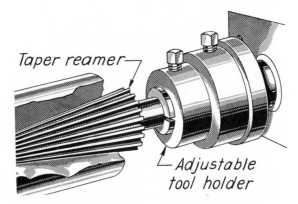
Fig. 10.34   Taper Reaming. (Courtesy Warner and Swazey Co.)

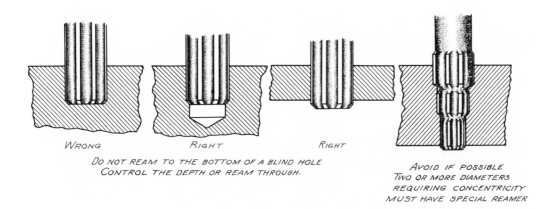

WRONG

RIGHT

RIGHT

DO NOT REAM TO THE BOTTOM OF A BLIND HOLE
CONTROL THE DEPTH OR REAM THROUGH.

AVOID IF POSSIBLE
TWO OR MORE DIAMETERS
REQUIRING CONCENTRICITY
MUST HAVE SPECIAL REAMER

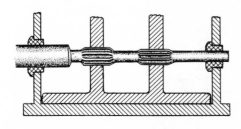

LINE REAM FOR CONCENTRICITY AND
ALIGNMENT OF HOLES. HOLES MUST BE
THE SAME SIZE OR PROGRESSIVELY
SMALLER FOR LINE REAMING.

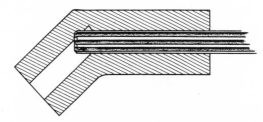

HOLES REAMED AT AN ANGLE SLOW DOWN
PRODUCTION. ALL TEETH SHOULD ENGAGE FOR
A GOOD START.
DEPTH CONTROL IS DIFFICULT. THERE IS
DANGER OF HAVING SHOULDERS AT THE
CORNERS AND OF LEAVING THIN WALLS.

Fig. 10.35   Proper design for reaming. (Courtesy Curtiss-Wright Corp.)

10.24.3 Countersink. When a flat-headed screw is used, the hole must be enlarged in a conical manner to allow the top of the head to come flush with the surface of the piece. This enlarging is called *countersinking*. The note on the drawing should be similar to the following: "Countersink 82° to ⅞″ Diameter." For details of dimensioning a countersink, see Chapter 11.

10.24.4 Counterbore. Heads of bolts and screws may be brought level with the surface of the part by enlarging the hole to a depth equal to the height of the head. This operation is called *counterboring* and is done with a tool similar to the one illustrated in Fig. 10.36(*c*). The pilot on the tool fits into a drilled hole and insures concentricity. The specifications on the drawing are usually given by dimensions and tolerances, but occasionally the following note may be found: "⅜ Drill, ¾ Counterbore, ½ Deep."

10.24.5 Spotface. Sometimes it is desired to make a smooth-bearing surface for the head of a bolt or a nut. This situation frequently occurs on a projection, called a boss. *Spotfacing* is accomplished by using a counterboring tool, as illustrated in Fig. 10.36. The note on the drawing should read "Spotface ¾″ Diameter." Figure 10.36 gives a few design suggestions for pieces on which spotfacing is specified.

10.24.6 Taps and dies. These tools are used for cutting internal and external threads. For more detailed information, see Chapter 11. The use of a tap is shown in Fig. 10.37 and a die in Fig. 10.38.

10.25 THE DRILL PRESS. The single-spindle drill press shown in Fig. 10.39 is found in practically every machine shop. It may be used for drilling, reaming, countersinking, and counterboring. For special purposes where more than one hole is to be drilled at one time, multiple-spindle drill presses are used. Several design suggestions for efficient use of multiple-spindle drills are shown in Fig. 10.40. The radial drill press shown in Fig. 10.41 is a very useful type of machine because holes can be drilled in almost any part of a rather large piece without reclamping or moving it. This is accomplished by having the chuck mounted on an arm that can be revolved around and moved up and down on a vertical axis of the machine while at the same time the chuck may be given a horizontal motion

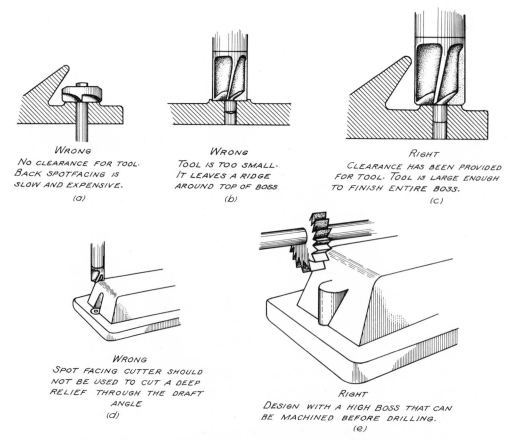

Fig. 10.36 Proper design for spot facing. (Courtesy Curtiss-Wright Corp.)

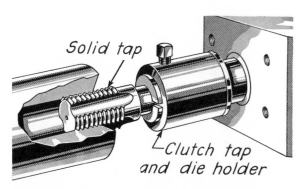

Fig. 10.37 Tapping internal threads. (Courtesy Warner and Swazey Co.)

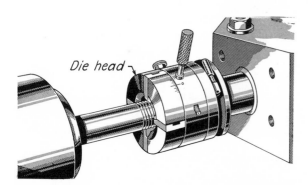

Fig. 10.38 Cutting external threads. (Courtesy Warner and Swazey Co.)

Fig. 10.39 Single-spindle drill press. (Courtesy Barnes Drill Co.)

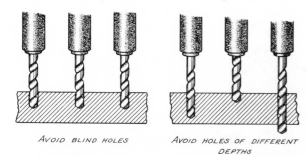

AVOID BLIND HOLES

AVOID HOLES OF DIFFERENT DEPTHS

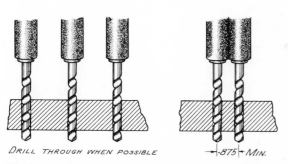

DRILL THROUGH WHEN POSSIBLE

.875 MIN.

Fig. 10.40 Design suggested for multiple drilling. (Courtesy Curtiss-Wright Corp.)

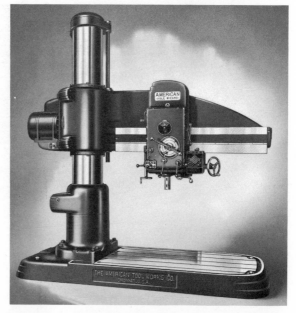

Fig. 10.41 Radial drill. (Courtesy The American Tool Works Co.)

along the arm by means of a screw and gear arrangement. The radial drill is a very versatile machine and can be used for such purposes as tapping and hollow milling. For practical purposes, the depth of the hole should not exceed five diameters.

10.26   THE LATHE. The lathe is one of the most useful machines in the shop because of the many different operations that may be performed on it. The piece to be machined is supported between two centers, one in the tail stock and the other in the head stock, and then revolved by power supplied through the head stock. A tool post, which may be moved longitudinally along the lathe, carries the cutting tool. This tool removes a thin layer of metal each time it traverses the length of the surface being machined. This process is called turning and is used for machining practically all cylindrical surfaces. Figure 10.42 shows a lathe and Fig. 10.43 shows a close-up of an operation being performed on the lathe. In addition to turning, the lathe is used for drilling, reaming, boring, counterboring, facing, threading, knurling, and polishing. For rough turning, normal tolerances vary from 0.005 to 0.015 inch, depending on the diameter. For the finish cut the tolerance may vary from 0.002 inch for a ¼-inch diameter to 0.007 inch for a 4-inch or larger diameter. Parts may also be clamped to the head stock alone by means of a chuck, and turning operations may be performed on the end face.

10.27   THE BORING MILL. The boring machine does practically the same work as the lathe but is used for larger pieces. In the vertical boring machine, the table holding the work revolves while the cutting tool moves horizontally or vertically on the crossrail. A horizontal boring machine is also available on which an almost unlimited number of operations may be performed. Production tolerances of 0.003 inch for a 1-inch diameter to 0.01 inch for 54-inch diameter may be used.

10.28   THE MILLING MACHINE. A machine, in which circular-type revolving cutters remove the metal as a worktable to which the piece is clamped moves under the cutter, is called a milling machine. The machine is designed so that the worktable can be moved in three directions at right angles to each other,

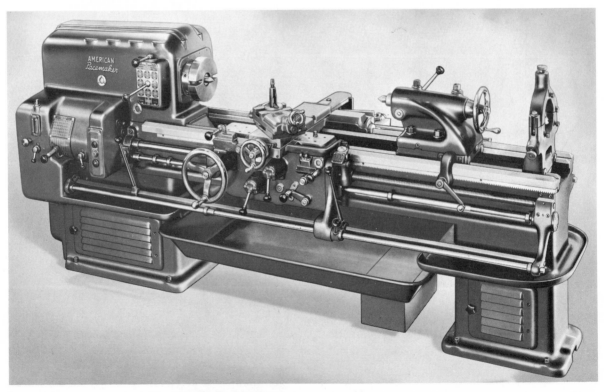

Fig. 10.42   A lathe. (Courtesy The American Tool Works Co.)

either manually or automatically. The rate of feed of the table and the speed of the cutter must be adjustable for various kinds of material and depth of cuts. Figure 10.44 shows a close-up of a milling machine cutting flutes on a drill, and Fig. 10.45 shows multiple operations being performed.

Many different kinds of cuts may be made on the milling machine, depending on the design of the cutting tool. These tools may have straight teeth or helical teeth, and the cutting edge may be ground on the tool itself or a cutting tooth may be inserted. Either the cylindrical surface of the tool or the end face may be used as the cutting surface. The milling machine may be used for cutting plane or irregular surfaces,

slots, keyways, gears, and similar surfaces. Production tolerances of about 0.005 inch may be specified for work to be done on a milling machine. Figure 10.46 gives a few suggestions for the design of parts that are to be finished on the milling machine.

10.29 THE GRINDING MACHINE. The wheel on a grinding machine may vary from the ordinary fine and coarse emery wheels to high-speed carborundum wheels. The purpose of grinding is to leave a finely finished surface on the metal and at the same time to remove economically the small amount of stock left after the previous finishing operation has brought the piece almost to size. In grinding a cylindrical surface the piece may be revolved between two centers during

Fig. 10.43   Turning operation on a lathe. (Courtesy Warner and Swazey Co.)

Fig. 10.44   Milling flutes on a drill. (Courtesy Cincinnati Milling Machine Co.)

Fig. 10.45   Multiple operations on a milling machine. (Courtesy Kearney-Trecker Co.)

the grinding, as shown in Fig. 10.47, or it may be allowed to roll between the grinding wheel and a regulating wheel, as shown in Fig. 10.48. A work rest is used to help hold the work in place. The latter method is known as centerless grinding. Both external and internal grinders are used for cylindrical surfaces where fine finish and close tolerances are desired. For surface grinding, the piece is usually clamped to a movable table, which is traversed to bring the work under the grinding wheel. A surface grinder is shown in Fig. 10.49. The grinding machine is also used for grinding threads when close fits are desired and for making and sharpening tools for other machines. The draftsman indicates the grinding operation on his drawing by means of a note when the limits and finish require its use. A tolerance of 0.0005 inch may be obtained by grinding.

10.30 POLISHING. Polishing must not be confused with grinding. Although a ground surface is very smooth, it is not said to be a polished surface until it has been gone over carefully with a rapidly revolving disk of material like muslin or leather, containing a fine abrasive, which gives it a luster impossible to attain with the finest grinders. The draftsman indicates such an operation by the note "grind and polish."

10.31 THE PLANER. When large flat surfaces are

to be finished, a machine called a planer is used. The piece to be planed is mounted on a long horizontal bed which moves forward and backward under the cutting tool. The tool advances a small amount across the surface with each run of the bed, the width of each cut being determined by the distance that the tool advances. Numerous pieces of the same kind may be clamped to the bed and planed at the same time. The draftsman makes no reference to this machine on his drawing, but simply marks the surface to be finished by one of the standard symbols. Tolerances of 0.005 inch are obtained with this machine.

10.32 THE SHAPER. The shaper is used for finished surfaces on pieces that are smaller than those for which a planer is required or for surfaces that are curved. For pieces within the capacity, the shaper is preferred to the planer because it is less cumbersome and faster. In the shaper, the piece to be finished is fastened to a table while the cutting tool moves backward and forward. The table advances the piece a small amount with each stroke of the cutting tool until the entire surface has been machined. Figure 10.50 shows a standard shaper. The shaper is particularly useful for cutting slots, keyways, and small flat or curved surfaces. Tolerances of 0.004 inch may be obtained with this machine. However, the draftsman

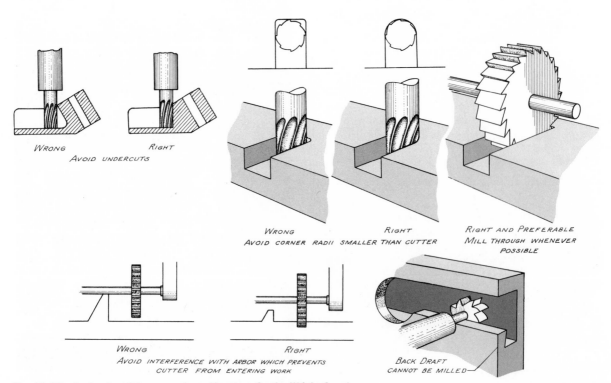

Fig. 10.46 Design for milling operations. (Courtesy Curtiss-Wright Corp.)

does not refer to this machine on the drawing.

10.33   THE BROACHING MACHINE. Originally the broach was used for cutting keyways and internal work such as forming square and hexagonal holes or holes of other shapes from a drilled hole, but now many external surfaces are machined by this method. The broach is a tool having a series of teeth or cutting edges which progressively increase in size so that each tooth removes a small amount of material, thus giving the desired surface quickly and accurately. Figure 10.51 illustrates the action of the broach. The broaching machine provides a method of holding the work and of supplying the power to force the broach through the work. This power is usually supplied hydraulically or by means of a screw. In cutting keyways, a guide bushing is inserted in the hole to hold the tool in the desired position. The broaching tool is rather expensive, but because it is especially useful for interchangeable work, it is extensively used in automotive work.

10.34   NUMERICALLY CONTROLLED MACHINES. With the proper selection of parts to be processed,

Fig. 10.49   Surface grinding. (Courtesy The Carborundum Co.)

Fig. 10.47   Cylindrical grinding. Center type. (Courtesy The Carborundum Co.)

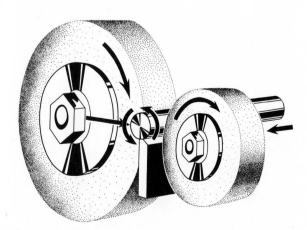

Fig. 10.48   Cylindrical grinding. Centerless type. (Courtesy The Carborundum Co.)

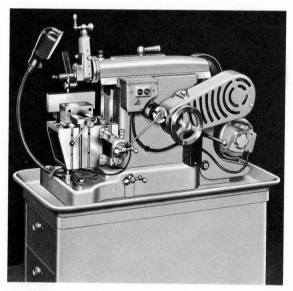

Fig. 10.50   A shaper. (Courtesy South Bend Lathe Works.)

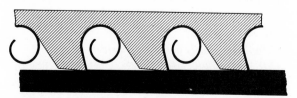

Fig. 10.51   Action of a broaching tool.

numerically controlled or tape-controlled machines offer productivity increases of from two to ten times that obtainable with conventional equipment. To justify their cost, the more expensive tape-controlled machines must have a productive capacity three times as high as regular equipment. For successful use of these machines, all cutting tools must be precision-ground and accurately preset in order that approximately 90 per cent of the required setup can be accomplished beforehand. A clean, air-conditioned temperature-controlled room for the machines is important. The work should be brought into this room and allowed to stabilize dimensionally for increased accuracy in machining. For cost economy it is important that the machine be kept operating as much as possible.

10.34.1 Kinds of work accomplished. A completely tape-controlled machine will position the various machine elements, select spindle speeds and feed rates, select and change tools, turn the coolant on and off, and start or stop the machine. The machines are controlled by a tape into which the necessary instructions have been punched.

10.34.2 Maintenance. With such a highly mechanized system, the necessary planned and preventive maintenance can be accurately scheduled. This is very important in keeping the machines in the best condition and preventing a gradual deterioration of the product. Careful production scheduling and planned maintenance make it possible to keep the machines operating 75 to 90 per cent of the time.

10.34.3 Benefits. The high cost of these machines is counteracted by many advantages.

a. *Increased flexibility.* Numerical control permits greater freedom in design with a minimum of delay and tool cost.

b. *Reduction in setup time.* Lead time is drastically reduced.

c. *Fewer fixtures are necessary.* Savings are made in the cost of making, handling, storing, and maintaining these items.

d. *Increased productivity.* Numerically controlled machines offer productivity increases of two to ten times over manually controlled epuipment.

e. *Less scrap loss.*

f. *Tapes are easily and inexpensively stored.*

g. *Higher quality parts.* Accuracy is increased by the repetitive precision assured by numerical controls.

h. *Inspection costs are reduced.*

10.34.4 Controls. There are various makes of numerically controlled machines, each with their own characteristics. Figure 10.52 shows one such machine which has five axes of motion. Machining can be done at almost any compound angle and contouring can be done by combining any or all of the five axes.

The part shown being machined in Fig. 10.53 is completed in three operations in 14 hours. With conventional equipment, 17 individual operations would be needed, each requiring a new setup. The time for the operation would be 56 hours.

The operations performed include face milling, contour milling, drilling, tapping, boring, and counterboring. Approximately 350 positionings, slide movements, tool changes, and other functions are completely tape-controlled.

10.35 HEAT TREATMENT OF STEEL. The properties of steel, such as tensile strength, ductility, and hardness, depend on two items, namely, the chemical composition of the metal and the heat treatment to which it has been subjected. The principal heat treatments used in the production of steel products are annealing, normalizing, hardening, tempering, and

Fig. 10.52 Machine with five axes of motion. (Courtesy Machinery.)

case hardening. These processes involve the heating and cooling of the metal for the purpose of altering the grain structure and the amount of carbon or other substances dissolved in the steel.

10.36 ANNEALING. The steel is heated to a temperature close to the lower limit of the critical range, as shown in Fig. 10.54, and then cooled very slowly. Of the many purposes for annealing, the principal ones

Fig. 10.53 Turbojet engine frame. (Courtesy Machinery.)

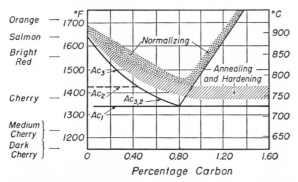

Fig. 10.54 Temperature ranges for heat treatment. (Courtesy *ASM Handbook*, 1948.)

are probably to remove stresses and induce softness or increase ductility.

10.37 NORMALIZING. This involves heating the steel to the temperature indicated in Fig. 10.54 and cooling in air. This gives faster cooling than annealing. The treatment increases the tensile and yield strength over annealed steel while still retaining sufficient ductility for many purposes.

10.38 HARDENING. When steel is heated and cooled quickly, by quenching in water, oil, or some other cooling substance, the metal becomes hard and brittle. The temperature range for hardening is shown in Fig. 10.54.

10.39 TEMPERING. As hardened steels are too brittle for most uses, they must be tempered. This is done by heating the hardened steel to some point below the lower critical temperature, holding for a sufficient period of time and cooling as desired. Quenching is sometimes used.

10.40 CASE HARDENING. For high surface hardness and resistance to abrasion, case hardening is used. This is done by raising the temperature to 1700 or 1800° Fahrenheit and packing the steel in some carburizing compound. Carbon is absorbed to a certain depth, forming a hard case on the outside of the metal.

10.41 HEAT TREATMENT OF NONFERROUS ALLOYS. When the percentage of one metal dissolved in the other metal can be changed by varying the temperature, the properties of the alloy can usually be changed by heat treatment. For further information on this subject, see any good book on metallography.

10.42 MATERIAL SPECIFICATION. It is very important for the engineer to be able to specify the exact material that is to be used by the manufacturer in producing a certain product. Several societies have developed standards for this purpose. One of these which is frequently used is that of the Society of Automotive Engineers. They have a numbering system consisting of four digits. In its original conception the first digit represented the type to which the steel belonged. Thus 1 indicated carbon steel, 2 indicated nickel steel, and 3 was nickel chromium steel. In the case of simple alloy steels, the second digit generally indicated the approximate percentage of the predominant alloying element. Usually the last two digits indicated the approximate average carbon content in hundredths of one percent. Thus 2317 represented a nickel steel of approximately 3 per cent nickel and 0.17 per cent carbon.

Tables 10.2 and 10.3 give a few of the important steel numbers with their characteristics and uses. Table 10.4 gives the numbers and suggested uses for various kinds of grey iron. Table 10.5 lists some of the numbers, uses, and general properties of aluminum. (The tables are taken from the SAE Manual.)

TABLE 10.2*

SAE	Characteristics and Uses of Plain Carbon Steels
1006 1008 1009 1010 1012 1015	These steels are the lowest carbon steels of the plain carbon type and are selected where cold formability is the primary requisite. They have relatively low tensile values, but may have excellent surface finish and good drawing qualities. These steels are nearly pure iron or ferritic in structure and do not machine freely; rimmed steel is used for cold-heading wire for tacks and rivets, for body and fender stock, hoods, lamps, oil pans, and other deep-drawn products.
1016 through 1027	Steels in this group, because of the carbon range covered, have increased strength and hardness and reduced cold formability. These steels are used for numerous forged parts. SAE 1020 is used for fan blades and some frame members. SAE 1024 may be used for such parts as transmission and rear axle gears.
1030 1033 1035 through 1043 1045 1046 1049 1050 1052	These steels, of the medium carbon type, are selected where their higher mechanical properties are needed. All steels in this class are used for forgings. As a class they are considered good for normal machining operations. SAE 1030 and 1035 are used for shifter forks and many small forgings. SAE 1038 is used for bolts and studs.
1055 1060 1064 1065 1070 1074 1078 1080 1084 1086 1090 1095	Steels in this group are of the high carbon type. They are used principally for applications where the higher carbon is needed to improve wear characteristics for cutting edges, to make springs of various types, and for special purposes, such as valve-spring wire and music wire. These steels find wide usage in the farm implement industry.

* Tables No. 2 through No. 5 are abstracted from the SAE Handbook of the latest years. This courtesy of the SAE is hereby acknowledged.

TABLE 10.3

SAE	Characteristics and Uses of Free-Cutting Carbon Steels
1111 1112 1113	These steels have excellent machining characteristics and are used for a wide variety of machined parts. They are not commonly used for vital parts owing to an unfavorable property of cold shortness.
1108 1109 1115 1117 through 1120 1126	Steels in this group are used where a combination of good machinability and uniform response to heat treatment is needed. These steels are used for small parts that are to be case-hardened.
1132 1137 1138 1140 1141 1144 1145 1146 1151	These steels are widely used for parts where a large amount of machining is necessary, or where threads, splines, or other operations offer special tooling problems. SAE 1137 is widely used for nuts, bolts, and studs with machined threads.

TABLE 10.4

SAE	Suggested Uses for Automotive Gray Iron Castings
110	Miscellaneous soft iron castings in which strength is not of primary importance. Exhaust manifolds.
111	Small cylinder blocks, cylinder heads, air-cooled cylinders, pistons, clutch plates, oil-pump bodies, transmission cases, gear boxes, clutch housings, and lightweight brake drums.
120	Automobile cylinder blocks, cylinder heads, flywheels, cylinder liners, and pistons.
121	Truck and tractor cylinder blocks and heads, heavy flywheels, tractor transmission cases, differential carrier castings, and heavy gear boxes.
122	Diesel-engine castings, liners, cylinders, pistons, and heavy parts in general.

TABLE 10.5   PROPERTIES OF ALUMINUM

SAE	ASTM Designation	Usual Form	General Data
300	CS66A	Permanent mold castings	Pistons primarily
304 305 306 308 309	S5C S12A SC84A SC84B SG100A	Die castings	Good to excellent casting characteristics and good to high corrosion resistance. Suited for use in thin-walled or intricate castings.
310	ZG61A	Sand castings	General-purpose structural castings.
320	G4A	Sand castings	Moderate strength, high corrosion resistance.
321	SN122A	Permanent-mold castings	Pistons, low expansion.
322	SC51A	Sand and permanent mold castings	High strength and pressure for general use, such as pump bodies and liquid-cooled cylinder heads.
324	G10A	Sand castings	High strength and ductility, requires special foundry practice.
326	SC64B	Sand and permanent mold castings	General-purpose alloy.
328	SC122A	Permanent-mold castings	Pistons.
330	SC64A	Permanent-mold castings	Moderate strength, general-purpose alloy.
332		Permanent-mold castings	Automotive pistons.
34	CG100A	Sand and permanent mold castings	Pistons, air-cooled cylinder heads, and valve tappet guides.
35	S5B	Sand and permanent mold castings	Intricate castings having thin section.
38	C4A	Sand castings	General structural castings. High strength and shock resistance.
39	CN42A	Sand and permanent mold castings	Air-cooled cylinder heads, and high strength pistons.

SELF-STUDY QUESTIONS

Before trying to answer these questions, read the chapter carefully. Then, without reference to the text, answer as many questions as possible. For those that cannot be answered, the number, in parentheses following the question number, gives the article in which the answer can be found. Look it up and write down the answer. Check the answers that you did give to see that they are correct.

10.1 **(10.2)** An object made by pouring molten metal into a mold is called a _____.

10.2 **(10.2)** A wooden mold of the object is called a _____.

10.3 **(10.10)** A sand model of the hollow interior of a casting is called a _____.

10.4 **(10.10)** Draft on a pattern is to make it easier to draw from the _____.

10.5 **(10.4)** A pattern is made slightly _____ to allow for _____ of the metal.

10.6 **(10.4)** A pattern is made oversize by using a _____ _____ in constructing it.

10.7 **(10.4)** The shrinkage allowed for cast iron is _____ _____ inch per _____.

10.8 **(10.7)** A _____ _____ is a projection on a pattern that makes an impression in the sand to support the core.

10.9 **(10.9.1)** Sharp angles on a casting are eliminated by using _____ and _____.

10.10 **(10.9.2)** A _____ "shut" is when metal flowing into a casting in opposite directions fails to _____.

10.11 **(10.13)** A hole is made in a casting by using a _____.

10.12 **(10.16)** When a large number of castings are to be made a _____ mold may be used.

10.13 **(10.17)** A hollow pipe might be formed by _____ casting.

10.14 **(10.20)** When hot metal is forced into shape it is called a _____.

10.15 **(10.20)** When hot metal is forced into dies by drop hammer it is called a _____ _____.

10.16 **(10.21.4)** The forging plane should be _____ to the direction of the stroke.

10.17 **(10.22)** Making a hole in a part by one stroke of the press is called _____.

10.18 **(10.22)** Forcing metal to flow through a die by pressure is called _____.

10.19 **(10.24.2)** To finish the surface of a hole, a _____ should be used.

10.20 **(10.24.3)** A hole should be _____ to fit the head of a flat-headed screw.

10.21 **(10.24.4)** A hole should be _____ to fit the head of a fillister-headed screw.

10.22 **(10.24.5)** A spot face makes a _____ _____ for the head of a bolt.

10.23 **(10.24.6)** A _____ is used to cut a thread in a hole.

10.24 **(10.24.6)** A _____ is used to cut a thread on a rod.

10.25 **(10.27)** The machine most commonly used to cut a large cylindrical hole in a piece of metal is called a _____ _____.

10.26 **(10.27)** The _____ _____ can be used for almost the same work as the lathe.

10.27 **(10.28)** The _____ _____ has circular-type revolving cutters.

10.28 **(10.29)** For very fine finish the _____ _____ may be used.

10.29 **(10.31)** The planer is used for milling large _____ _____.

10.30 **(10.31)** On the planer the work moves backward and forward under the _____ .

10.31 **(10.32)** On the shaper the _____ _____ moves backward and forward.

10.32 **(10.33)** To cut a square hole, the _____ _____ is used.

10.33 **(10.36)** The process of relieving temperature stresses is called _____ .

10.34 **(10.39)** Reducing the brittleness of hardened steel is called _____ .

10.35 **(10.34)** A numerically controlled machine must have a productivity of _____ to _____ times that of conventional equipment.

PROBLEMS

The problems that follow are designed so that the student must apply the principles that have been explained in this chapter. The figures are intended to represent a preliminary drawing of the part to be built. In each case only the major dimensions have been given, thus making it necessary for the student to scale or proportion other parts. *In many cases corners should be rounded to save excess metal.* It is always assumed that necessary changes can be made in adjacent parts. *Each problem also has some features that would be difficult or impossible to manufacture in the shop.* These points should be apparent to anyone who has studied the chapter carefully, and *it is expected that the student will use his ingenuity to correct these errors.* It is quite probable that there will be several answers equally correct for these problems.

To illustrate the purpose and use of these problems, consider the crank support in Fig. 10.55.

The size of the base is given as ¾ × 3 × 5⅛, the center line of the bearing is 3″ above the base, and the right bearing is ¾ Dia. The whole part is to be fastened down by means of four ¾″ cap screws. Other dimensions must be scaled or estimated on the basis of the information given. In this particular problem, the student should make several corrections and adjustments. First, the center supporting web is too thin; second, the larger bearing in the center cannot be reamed; third, the corners of the base should be rounded to make casting easier and to save metal; fourth, to save time in machining there should be pads on each end of the base; fifth, *all unfinished corners and angles should be rounded or filleted;* sixth, *the surfaces where finish and limits are necessary must be recognized.* When the student has recognized these problems, he can begin the drawing and make all necessary corrections.

All problems in this group contain situations similar to this one, and in each case the errors must be recognized before drawing is begun.

The scale given under each problem is the scale at which the student's drawing is to be made and not the scale of the pictorial drawing.

Read general instructions before solving any problems.

10.1–10.13 Make a complete working drawing of an object assigned from Figs. 10.55 to 10.67. In each case change the design of the part so that it can be made economically.

10.14 Make a freehand sketch showing one view of any object assigned by your instructor from Figs. 6.62 to 6.101. Assuming the object is formed by casting, show the location of the parting plane. The view drawn should show the parting plane edgewise.

10.15 Same as Problem 10.14, using Figs. 7.42 to 7.57.

10.16 Same as Problem 10.14, using Figs. 10.55 to 10.67.

10.17 In the view drawn in Problem 10.14 indicate any finish allowance that shows in that view.

10.18 Same as Problem 10.17, using the view drawn in Problem 10.15.

10.19 Same as Problem 10.17, using the view drawn in Problem 10.16.

10.20 Assume that you are the production superintendant of a large plant that manufactures all of the objects shown in Figs. 6.62 to 6.101. Make a list of all of the shops, processes, machines, and tools necessary to manufacture the object assigned by your instructor.

10.21 Same as Problem 10.20, using Figs. 7.42 to 7.57.

10.22 Same as Problem 10.20, using Figs. 10.55 to 10.67.

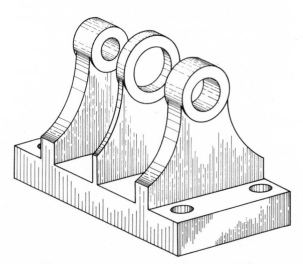

Fig. 10.55 Crank support. Size of base 3″ × 5½″ × ¾″; center line of bearing 3″ above bottom of base; bearing on the right ¾″ diameter; base to be fastened down by four ⅜″ hex-head cap screws; scale ¾″ = 1″.

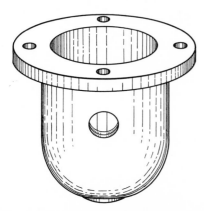

Fig. 10.56   Cover. Problem (a). Interior diameter 2⅜″ × 3″ high; material ³⁄₁₆″ thick, base ⁵⁄₁₆″ thick; flange drilled for four ¼″ cap screws; ¼″ pipe tap through side ¾″ from center line and 1¼″ from base; scale 1″ = 1″.

Problem (b). Change the cover to a pressed-steel part, and show holes as punched. Use same general dimensions. Include proper data for pressed-steel part. Use SAE 1010 Sheet Metal–16 gage. Inside radius of bends must be equal to the thickness of the stock. Extrude the pipe center hole for pipe tap before threading. The four cap-screw holes must allow head clearance for the screw.

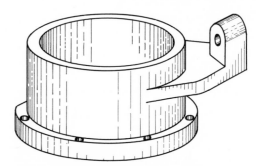

Fig. 10.59   Gear housing. The internal diameter is 3″. The total depth of the hole and housing is 1⅞″; flat side on the left is tangent to outside of housing; center line of the hole in the bracket is parallel to the flat side of base, is 1¹⁵⁄₁₆″ from the main center line and level with the top of the housing; it must clear the main hub by ¾″; the housing is held down by seven #12 fillister-head machine screws; scale 1″ = 1″.

Fig. 10.57   Bearing bracket. Center line of a ¾″ shaft to be supported 2″ ± .005 above bottom of base; bracket to be held down by two ½″ bolts or the equivalent; bosses are to be spot faced; oil hole to be threaded for standard oil cup; base is 3⅜″ × 2″ × ¼″; scale 1″ = 1″.

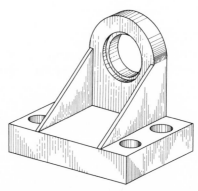

Fig. 10.60   Bearing bracket. Center line of 1½″ bronze bushing is 3″ above base; counterbore is 1¾″ diameter, ³⁄₁₆″ deep; the back of bracket is ¾″ thick; base is 5¼″ × 3″ × 1″; counterbore base for four ¾″ fillister-head cap screws; bracket rests on steel plates; scale ½″ = 1″.

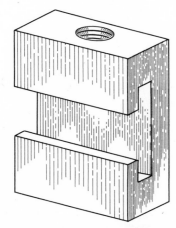

Fig. 10.58   Clamp. The clamp is to slide on a ¼″ × 1¼″ rod; the threaded hole is tapped for a ⅜″ cap screw which locks the clamp in place; scale 1″ = 1″.

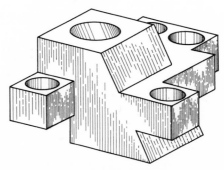

Fig. 10.61   Angle bearing bracket. Bearing is 2½″ long and 1″ bore; support lugs are ¾″ thick; center line of bearing makes an angle of 60° with the plane of the supports. Held down by four ½″ fillister-head cap screws with heads flush; scale 1″ = 1″.

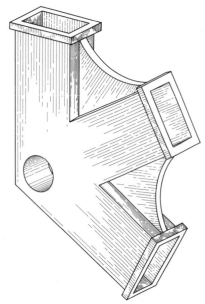

Fig. 10.62   Lever fulcrum. Cross section of lever is ¾″ × 1½″; it must slide in easily to a depth of 3 inches. Purpose of lever is to turn the shaft; lever positions are 60° apart; shaft is 1″ diameter; length of bearing 1½″; scale ¾″ = 1″.

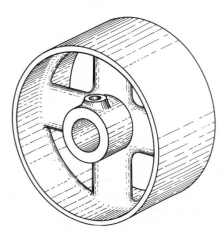

Fig. 10.63   Pulley. The 4″ pulley has a 2″ face; the hole is to be tapped for standard ⅜″ set screw; scale 1″ = 1″.

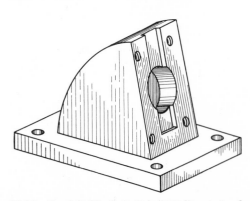

Fig. 10.64   Bracket. The large hole is 1″ diameter and goes through ½″ material; the slot is ⅛″ × ⅝″. The inclined face is 75° to the horizontal; four holes in inclined face for #10 machine screws; drill four holes in base for 5⁄16″ cap screws; center line of large hole at front face is 1 9⁄16″ above base; scale 1″ = 1″.

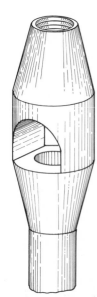

Fig. 10.65   Handle. Total length 14″; length of enlarged tip 2⅝″; drilled hole in handle ¼″ diameter, 1″ deep; it is desired to make ¼″ threads in threaded hole; scale 2″ = 1″.

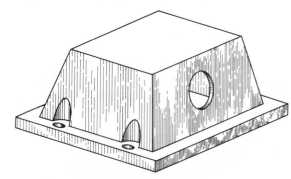

Fig. 10.66   Cover. This cover must clear a small machine 2″ × 3″ × 1⅝″ high; thickness of box ⅛″, base ¼″; fastened down by four ¼″ hex-head bolts; ¾″-diameter horizontal hole to be drilled in the center of long side, one side only; scale ¾″ = 1″.

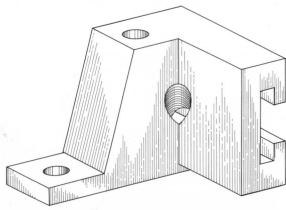

Fig. 10.67   Saw fence clamp. This clamp slides on a bar ¼″ × 1 1⁄16″; distance from base to center of slot, 1 5⁄32″; the two drilled holes are for 5⁄16″ cap screws; the threaded hole is for a ⅜″ cap screw which should bear against the center of the bar; this threaded hole makes 45° angle with the horizontal and equal angles with the two faces of the clamp; if desired this hole can be placed in a plane perpendicular to the slide and 45° with the horizontal; scale 1″ = 1″.

CHAPTER 11
Basic Dimensioning

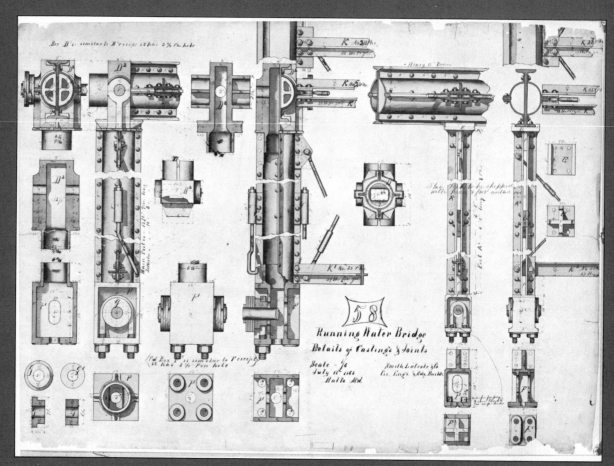

OLD: Basic drawing for castings and joints of a running water bridge, 1868. (The Smithsonian Institution, Division of Mechanical and Civil Engineering)

NEW: Cutaway drawing of a large steam turbine generator unit. (Courtesy of the General Electric Company)

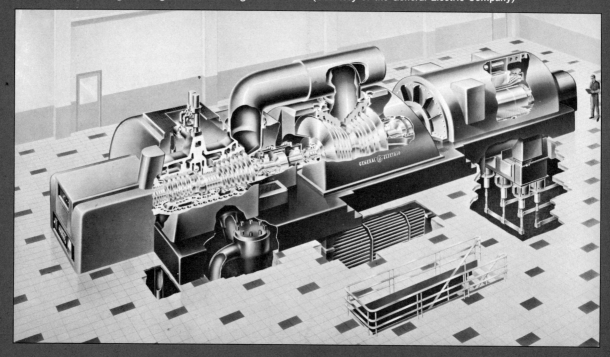

Chapter 11 Basic Dimensioning

11.1 INTRODUCTION. The preceding chapters discussed methods for describing the shape of an object by means of projection drawings. However, no structure or part can be made unless the drawing has on it all of the dimensions and allied data, such as material, heat treatment, or finish.

In dimensioning a drawing it must be remembered that it is impossible for the workman to measure and reproduce dimensions exactly. Some variation in size, known as tolerance, must be permitted in the manufacture of mechanical parts. For parts that must fit closely this tolerance must be specified on the drawing. For architectural and civil engineering projects, the tolerances are usually larger and are frequently covered by a good-workmanship clause in the specifications.

This chapter gives the fundamentals of dimensioning that apply to all branches of engineering. Later chapters will discuss the special problems involved in the various applications.

11.2 GENERAL PRINCIPLES. Since mechanical parts usually require the most refined dimensioning, this chapter will deal mostly with such parts. However, the following general principles may be applied to almost any kind of drawing.

a. There is a tolerance for every dimension.
b. Dimensions should be measured from some datum or reference plane that can be readily located on the part.
c. Dimensions should not be repeated.
d. On mechanical parts, tolerances should not be allowed to accumulate by giving a long, continuous series of dimensions.
e. Every feature on the object must be dimensioned for size and location.
f. Where practical, the finished part should be defined without specifying manufacturing methods.
g. No surface, line, or point should be located by more than one dimension in any given direction.
h. Dimensions for size, form, and location should be so complete that no scaling of a drawing is required.

11.3 DIMENSIONING A DRAWING. There are three factors that must be considered when placing dimensions on a drawing.

a. Technique of dimensioning.
b. The rules for placing the dimensions on a drawing.
c. The methods of deciding what dimensions are appropriate and necessary.

These techniques are discussed in the following paragraphs.

11.4 TECHNIQUE OF DIMENSIONING. The technique of dimensioning includes the mechanics of constructing dimension lines, leaders, arrowheads, and lettering. To facilitate the interpretation of a drawing, it is necessary for the draftsman to follow certain standard procedures. These procedures are listed below.

11.4.1 Dimension lines. Dimension lines are the lines with arrowheads on each end that show the length of the dimension. See Fig. 11.1. They should be made according to the following instructions, which are illustrated in Fig. 11.1.

a. Draw them as thin, black lines, much thinner than

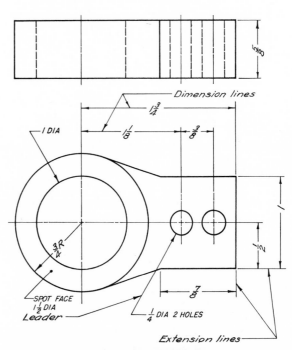

Fig. 11.1 Definition of dimensioning terms.

the visible or invisible outlines, for contrast purposes.

b. Make them parallel to the line or length being dimensioned.

c. Construct an arrowhead at each end. See Fig. 11.8.

d. Do not allow them to coincide with a center line or an extension of a center line.

e. Do not place them on a line of the view or on an extension of such a line.

f. Break the dimension line to allow space for the numeral when dimensioning a mechanical part. See Fig. 11.1.

11.4.2 Extension lines. Extension lines, sometimes called witness lines, are the lines that extend from the object to show the limits of a dimension. See Fig. 11.1.

The following rules concerning extension lines are illustrated in Fig. 11.2.

a. Make the extension lines the same weight as dimension lines.

b. Construct the extension lines perpendicular to the line being dimensioned. See Fig. 11.3.

c. Allow a gap of $\frac{1}{16}$ inch between the view and the extension line. See Fig. 11.2.

d. Carry the extension line $\frac{1}{8}$ inch beyond the dimension line, as shown in Fig. 11.1.

e. Do not cross extension lines unless necessary. If they must cross, they should do so without a break, as shown in Fig. 11.2.

f. Break the extension line when it crosses an arrowhead, as illustrated in Fig. 11.23.

g. Do not break the extension line when it crosses a line of the figure. See Fig. 11.2.

h. In special cases, such as flat curves, where there is not enough room for perpendicular extension lines, they are occasionally placed at an angle, as shown in Fig. 11.4. The dimension line is still parallel to the line being dimensioned.

11.4.3 Leaders. A leader is a line that runs from some part of a drawing, indicated by an arrow, to a note which concerns that part of the drawing. See Figs. 11.1 and 11.5. They are drawn in accordance with the rules stated below.

a. Make leaders the same weight as dimension lines.

b. Construct leaders with a straight edge, as indicated in Figs. 11.1 and 11.5.

c. When leaders point to a line, end them with an arrow. See Figs. 11.1 and 11.5.

d. When leaders point to an area, end them with a dot, as shown in Figs. 11.1 and 11.5.

e. Always draw a short horizontal line on the end of the leader, as illustrated in Fig. 11.5.

f. Make the leaders parallel when two or more are close together. If possible, they should be 60° with the horizontal. See Fig. 11.5(a).

g. Construct the leaders so that they do not make an angle of less than 30° with the line to which they point. See Fig. 11.5(b).

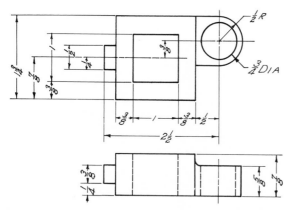

Fig. 11.2   Extension lines cross outlines and each other.

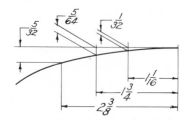

Fig. 11.4   Dimension lines.

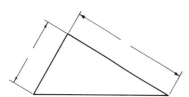

Fig. 11.3   Dimensioning inclined lines.

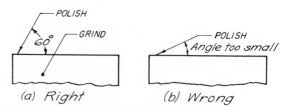

Fig. 11.5   Leaders steeply inclined to surface.

h. When a leader points to a circle or an arc, construct the leader so that the arrow touches the circle or arc, not the center. *Always make the leader point toward the center.* This rule is illustrated in Fig. 11.6.

i. When there are two circles, as for a threaded hole, countersink, or counterbore, the leader points to the circle indicated in the first line of the note. See Fig. 11.6.

j. When the same note applies to a group of elements, the leader should point to one of the group, as shown in Fig. 11.7.

k. The following should be avoided:
  Crossing leaders.
  Long leaders.
  Leaders in horizontal or vertical position.
  Leaders parallel to adjacent dimension lines.

11.4.4 Arrowheads. An arrowhead is placed on both ends of a dimension line and on one end of a leader. They should be made according to the following rules.

a. The arrowhead must be at least three times as long as it is wide. See Fig. 11.8.

b. In most drawings, the arrowheads should be about ³⁄₁₆ inch long. The size may vary with the amount of space available, as in Fig. 11.8.

c. Arrowheads may be made open or solid according to the practice of the company. See Fig. 11.8.

d. Both barbs should be the same length and should be balanced about the dimension line as in Fig. 11.8.

e. The point of the arrow should just touch the ex-

tension line or the line to which the leader points. They should not overrun or stop short.

11.4.5 Lettering notes. Letters must be large enough to be easily read and so carefully made that they cannot be misinterpreted. The following rules apply.

a. Notes always read horizontally. See Fig. 11.5. This means that they read in the same direction as the title block.

b. Capital letters are preferred, as indicated in Fig. 11.5(*a*).

c. All lettering should be at least ⅛ inch high. It should be larger if the drawing is to be microfilmed with a large reduction.

d. Guidelines should be always used for all lettering.

e. Numerals should be placed in a break in the dimension line, as shown in Fig. 11.9.

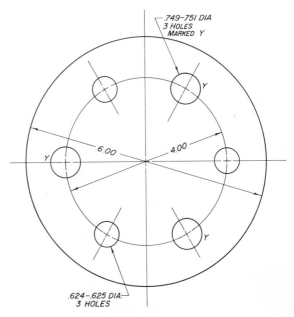

Fig. 11.7 Dimensioning diameters.

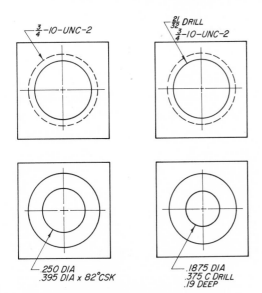

Fig. 11.6 Leaders to circular holes.

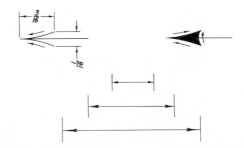

Fig. 11.8 Arrowheads.

f. In fractions, the bar is placed in line with the dimension line, but is not a part of it. See Fig. 11.9.

g. The numerator and denominator of a fraction are made at least two thirds of the height of the whole number integers. They should not touch the bar. The total height of the fraction must be at least 1½ times the height of the integer. This rule is illustrated in Fig. 11.9.

h. Notes with leaders should begin with the midpoint of the first line of lettering at the level of the horizontal line that ends the leader. See Fig. 11.6.

i. When a dimension is not to scale, a wavy line is placed under the dimension or it is marked NTS (not to scale). See Fig. 11.10.

j. Abbreviations should be avoided. Only those recommended as American Standards should be used. See Appendix.

11.4.6 Units of measurement in dimensioning.
The units of measurement specified by dimensions should be clearly stated. This may be accomplished as follows.

a. A general note in the title block may specify that "all dimensions are in inches." If this is done, no inch marks are necessary.

b. When dimensions include both feet and inches, a single accent mark is used to designate feet and the inches are unmarked. The various situations that may arise are shown correctly in Fig. 11.10.

c. The double accent mark should be used to indicate inches if there is any danger of misinterpretation. Thus 1 Valve should read 1″ Valve.

d. If other units such as millimeters are used on a drawing, they should be clearly marked MM. When millimeters are used on a drawing that has been dimensioned in inches, the millimeter dimension shall be enclosed in parenthesis as well as being marked MM, thus (12.4 MM).

e. In dimensioning angles, the following symbols should be used: degrees, °; minutes, ′; seconds, ″. Thus an angle could be dimensioned 134° 29′ 30″. If only degrees are used, the abbreviation DEG. may be used, as 30 DEG. If minutes alone are to be specified, they should be preceded by 0°, thus 0° 17′. An angle also can be specified by degrees and decimals of a degree. See Fig. 11.11.

11.4.7 Fractions. It is very seldom that a dimension will be of a size that can be expressed completely in full inches. There must be some system for expressing parts of inches. At the present time there are two such systems.

Common fractions have been most frequently used in the past and are still used in many companies. When fractions are used they should be expressed in units of ⅛, 1/16, 1/32, and 1/64. Figure 11.12(*a*) shows an object dimensioned with fractions. Other fractions such as ⅓, ⅙, or 1/7 are never used. Fractions are difficult to add or subtract, and their use leads to many mistakes. When the distances become very small, as in modern industrial practice, fractions become very cumbersome and slow. For this reason decimals are frequently used.

11.4.8 Decimals. In a complete decimal system the fundamental base is a two-place decimal. Whenever possible, the dimension should be an even two-place number, as in Fig. 11.12(*b*). It can be divided easily by two, for such purposes as converting diameters to radii, and still maintain a two-place decimal. In decimal dimensioning the decimal points must be sufficiently large so that they cannot be misread. The following rules apply to the use of decimals.

a. Decimal point. The decimal point shall be in line with the bottom of the lettering and shall be given sufficient space.

b. Rounding off decimals. When it becomes necessary to convert a fraction into a two-place decimal, the third place is dropped if it is less than five. The next

Fig. 11.9 Method of lettering fractions.

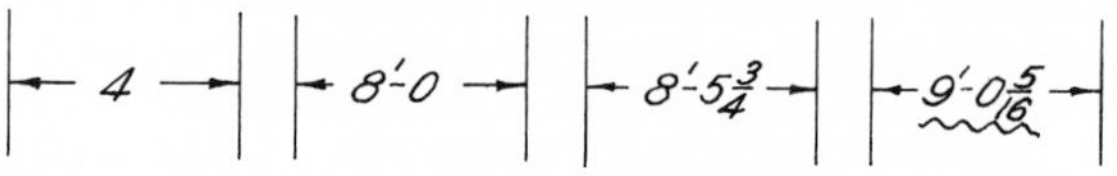

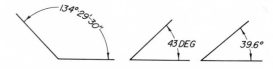

Fig. 11.10 Dimensioning in feet and inches.

Fig. 11.11 Dimensioning angles.

higher number in the second place is used if the third place is more than five. Thus 1.5625 becomes 1.56, and 1.627 becomes 1.63. If the third place is exactly five, the nearest even number in the second place is used. Thus 1.625 becomes 1.62, and 1.615 also becomes 1.62.

The same rules for rounding off can be used for three-place decimals. Three- or four-place decimals may be needed when converting fractions to decimals or when requirements make greater accuracy necessary.

c. *Advantages of the decimal system.* There are many advantages to the use of the decimal system for dimensioning. Some of them are listed below.

1. It simplifies arithmetical computations.
2. It greatly reduces mistakes.
3. It decreases the time required for calculations.
4. It is easier to read and understand.

5. It simplifies conversion to the metric system.
6. Decimals are used in data processing and in numerically controlled equipment.

11.5 WHERE TO PLACE DIMENSIONS ON A DRAWING. It is important to place dimensions on a drawing in such a manner that the drawing will be clear and easy to read. Because of long practice, workmen have become accustomed to looking for dimensions in certain places. These customs should be followed unless there is a good reason for changing. However, almost all rules may be broken for the sake of clearness. The most important of these rules are given here.

a. Dimension lines are spaced so that the first line is at least ⅜ inch from the outline of the view. Approximately ⅜ inch is allowed between dimension lines. This is shown in Fig. 11.13.

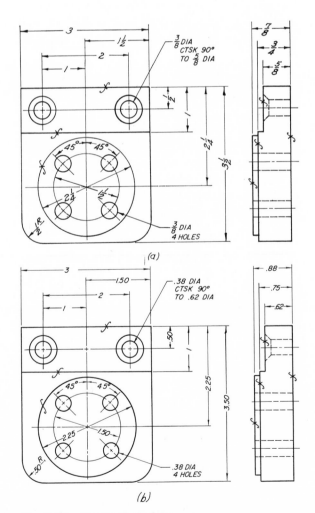

Fig. 11.12 Spacing dimensions.

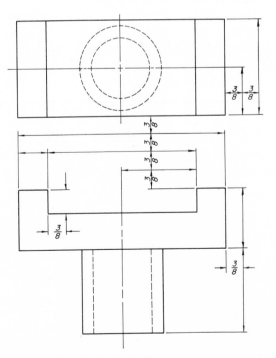

Fig. 11.13 Spacing dimension lines.

b. The numerals in adjacent dimensions should be staggered to avoid crowding, as in Fig. 11.14.

c. Dimensions should be placed outside the views whenever possible. To avoid long extension lines or crossing extension lines it is sometimes best to put a dimension line inside the view. See Fig. 11.15.

d. Dimensions should be placed between views, but closest to the appropriate view. See Fig. 11.16.

e. Extension lines or center lines should not be carried through from one view to another.

f. When several dimensions are to be placed on the same side of a view, the smallest is placed closest to the view. This will avoid crossing of extension or dimension lines. See Fig. 11.16.

g. Related dimensions that are to be used in the same shop operation should be placed on a single line of dimensions. See Fig. 11.17. The series of dimensions placed below the front view in this drawing will be used in the machine shop.

h. Unrelated dimensions that refer to different operations or that are to be used by different men should be placed on separate lines. See Fig. 11.17. The series of dimensions placed above the front view in this drawing will be used in the pattern and core shops.

i. Avoid duplicate dimensioning. No feature should be located in two different ways or places. This is illustrated in Fig. 11.17. When an overall dimension is given in conjunction with a series, one number in the series is always omitted or marked reference (REF).

j. Avoid cumulative tolerances. Tolerance is the variation in size allowable in the manufacture of a part. A series of dimensions in one long line is known as chain dimensioning. Such an arrangement allows a cumulation of tolerances. See Fig. 11.18. This should be avoided.

k. Select three reference or datum planes before beginning the dimensioning. These should be finished surfaces or center planes. Center planes frequently make good datum planes, particularly if there are other features on them, such as holes, that enable the plane to be located in the shop. In dimensioning mating parts, the adjoining or functional surface should be used as a datum for both parts. Three possible reference planes are indicated in Figs. 11.19 and 11.42.

l. Individual features can be located from datum planes to save tolerance accumulation. This is illustrated in Fig. 11.20.

m. Dimensions should be placed on the view that is most descriptive or that shows the contour of the feature being dimensioned. Fig. 11.20 shows the dimensions properly placed according to this rule.

n. Do not dimension to invisible lines. Hole patterns should be located on the view where the circles show. See Fig. 11.21, right-side view.

o. In a half section it is proper to dimension to an in-

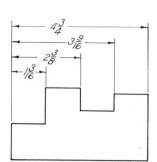

Fig. 11.14 Staggering dimensions.

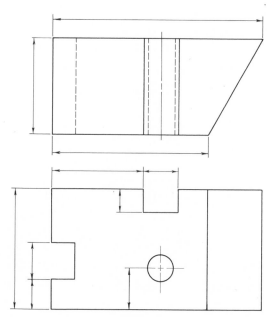

Fig. 11.15 Dimensioning inside a view.

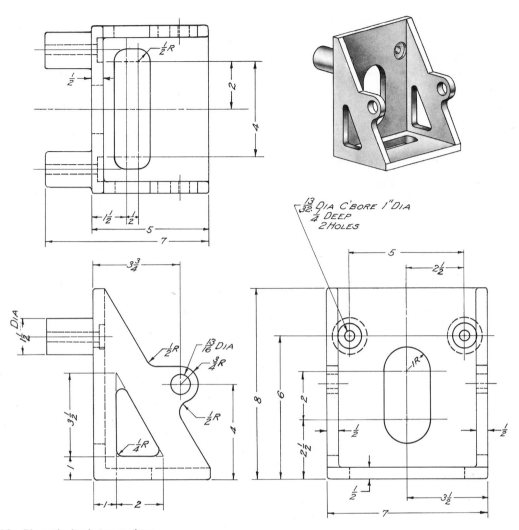

Fig. 11.16   Dimensioning between views.

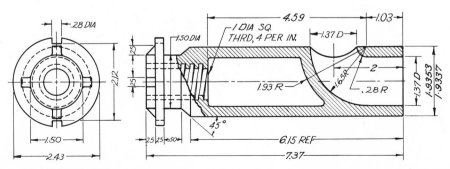

Fig. 11.17   Related dimensions in line.

visible line in the unsectioned part, if the dimension line is carried to a visible line in the sectioned half. This is also shown in Fig. 11.21, front view.

p. The diameter of a cylinder should be dimensioned on the view that shows as a rectangle, rather than the circular view. See Fig. 11.22. If only one view is given, it should be marked DIA.

q. For dimensioning very narrow spaces, several methods are available, as shown in Fig. 11.23.

11.6 DIMENSIONING SYSTEMS. There are two systems in use for placing the numerals in the dimension line. They are called the aligned system and the unidirectional system.

11.6.1 Aligned system. The aligned system has

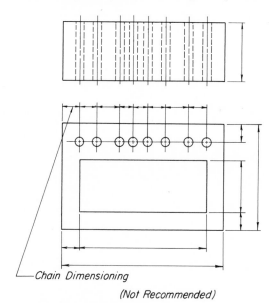

Chain Dimensioning

(Not Recommended)

Fig. 11.18 Chain dimensioning.

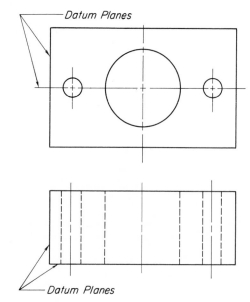

Datum Planes

Datum Planes

Fig. 11.19 Datum planes.

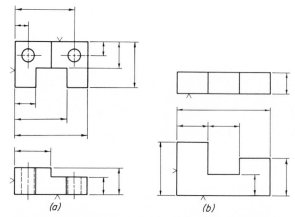

(a)   (b)

Fig. 11.20 Contour dimensioning. Features dimensioned from datum planes.

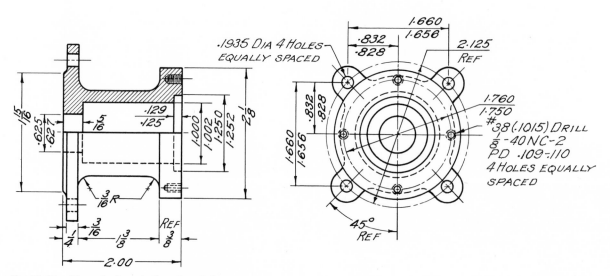

Fig. 11.21 Dimensioning a half-sectioned view.

the dimensions reading from the bottom when the
dimension line is horizontal and from the right when
the dimension line is vertical. For inclined dimension
lines, the numerals are parallel to the dimension line,
but the preference is given to having them read from
the bottom of the drawing. This method is illustrated
in Fig. 11.24(*a*).

11.6.2 Unidirectional system. When all of the
numerals are placed so that they read from the bottom
of the sheet regardless of the direction of the dimension line, the system is called unidirectional. This
means that everything reads in the same direction as
the title. Figure 11.24(*b*) illustrates the use of this
method.

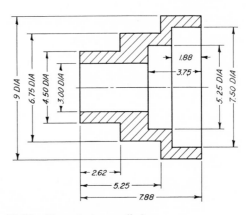

Fig. 11.22 Dimensioning a cylinder.

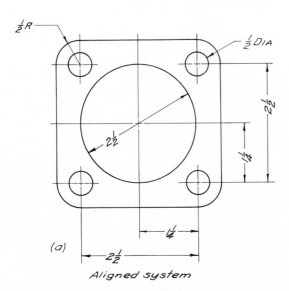

Fig. 11.23 Dimensioning narrow spaces.

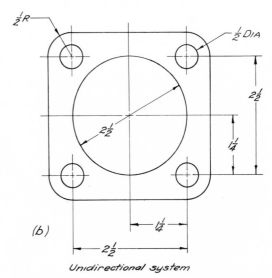

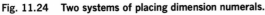

Fig. 11.24 Two systems of placing dimension numerals.

11.7 SELECTION OF APPROPRIATE DIMENSIONS.
A part must be dimensioned with four things in mind.

a. The part must operate properly.
b. The manufacturing process must be as economical as possible.
c. The inspection and gaging must be as simple as possible.
d. The number to be produced must be known.

When these things have been considered, the draftsman must make sure that the size of the entire part and of every feature has been specified. Also the location of every feature must be completely specified.

11.7.1 Size dimensioning. Giving the size dimensions of any object requires that these dimensions be placed on the proper views of the object. Since a view is a projection on a plane, it is first necessary to learn to dimension a plane figure, such as a triangle, rectangle, circle, or any combination of them. The proper method of dimensioning some basic plane figures is shown in Fig. 11.25. This involves careful following of the rules already given:

a. Dimension everything from a datum surface if possible.
b. Do not dimension anything twice.
c. Avoid cumulative tolerances.
d. The size of all features must be given.
e. The location of all features must be given.

11.7.2 Dimensioning simple objects. Every object must be dimensioned in three directions. This means that at least two views must be dimensioned unless a note can be used to replace one view. The dimensions must be so complete that it will not be necessary to add or substract dimensions or scale the drawing.

a. Prism and wedge. For a prism, it is only necessary to dimension two rectangles. See Fig. 11.25. A wedge, a triangle, and a rectangle must be dimensioned, as in Figs. 11.25 and 11.26.
b. Torus. A torus can be dimensioned in three ways. The proper one to choose is determined by the method of manufacture. If the torus is to be formed by bending a rod around a mandrel, the method of Fig. 11.27(*a*) should be used. If the torus is to be formed by bending a rod to fit inside a cylinder, the method of Fig. 11.27(*c*) would be used. However, if the torus is to be turned on a lathe, the method of Fig. 11.27(*d*) might be preferable.
c. Sphere. Only one view of a sphere is necessary if the dimension is marked "spherical." See Fig. 11.27(*b*).
d. Cylinders and cones. For a complete circle, the diameter should always be given. Methods for dimensioning cones and cylinders are shown in Fig. 11.28.
e. Tubing details. The minimum dimensions for describing a bent tube are shown in Fig. 11.29. Note that the center lines of straight portions of the tube, between curves, are carried to their points of intersection and that these points are dimensioned. In addition, this information may be supplemented by specifying the straight lengths, angles of bend, bend radii, and angles of twist or rotation for all

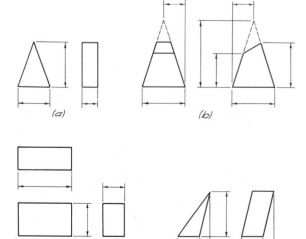

Fig. 11.25 Dimensioning solids.

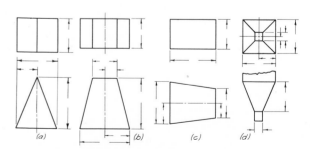

Fig. 11.26 Dimensioning wedges and pyramids.

portions of the tube. This is commonly done by means of auxiliary views.

11.7.3   Dimensioning other features. In addition to the simple solids dimensioned in the preceding article, there are many features that form only a part of a more complicated object that must be clearly dimensioned.

a. *Circular arcs.* For a circular arc, the radius rather than the diameter is given. The center may be marked with a small cross, if desired. The size of the

radius is placed on a leader. The dimension must always be marked *R*. See Fig. 11.30. When the center is inaccessible or off the paper, Fig. 11.31 shows the method of dimensioning.

b. *Concentric circles.* Whenever possible, circular cylinders should be dimensioned as in Fig. 11.22. When it is necessary to dimension circles on the circular view, Fig. 11.32 shows the approved methods. When using aligned dimensioning, the shaded area of Fig. 11.32(a) should be avoided.

c. *Compound curves.* A series of tangent circular arcs

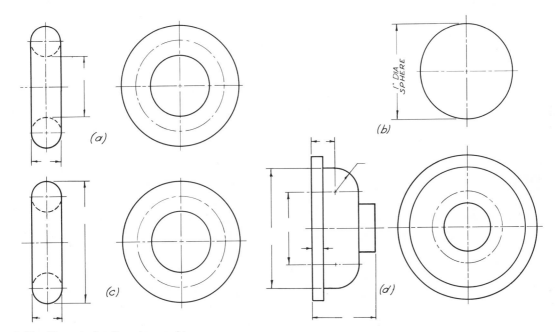

Fig. 11.27   Dimensioning the sphere and torus.

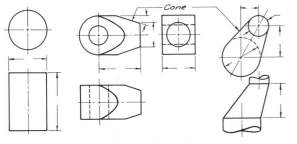

Fig. 11.28   Dimensioning cylinders and cones.

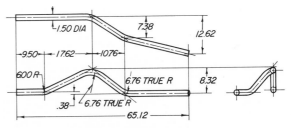

Fig. 11.29   Tubing layout. (Courtesy SAE.)

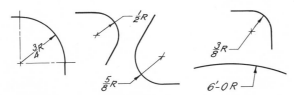

Fig. 11.30   Dimensioning arcs.

may be dimensioned by giving the radii and locating the centers. The centers may be located by giving two rectangular coordinates as in Fig. 11.31(*a*), by an angle and a distance as in Fig. 11.31(*b*), or by two arcs as in Fig. 11.33.

d. Noncircular curves. Points on noncircular curves should be located by coordinates as in Fig. 11.34. This figure also shows a rather unusual use of dimension lines as extension lines.

e. Progressive dimensioning. When space is limited, a system known as progressive dimensioning may be used. This method places all of the numerals on one dimension line, but each one refers back to the datum plane. To indicate that this is the method used, only one arrowhead is drawn for each dimension. These arrows all point away from the datum. The only arrow pointing in the opposite direction is placed at the datum plane. See Fig. 11.35. This

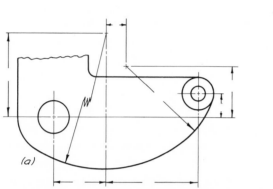
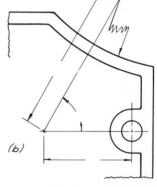

Fig. 11.31   Dimensioning long-radius arcs.

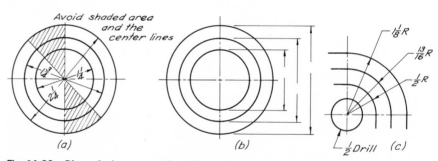

Fig. 11.32   Dimensioning concentric circles and arcs.

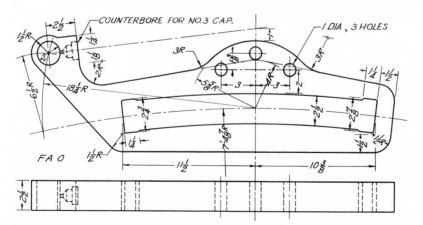

Fig. 11.33   Location dimensioning with arcs and radii.

method is seldom used on machine drawings because of the danger of its being misread.

f. *Angles.* In dimensioning angles, as shown in Fig. 11.36, the number should read from the bottom of the drawing as in unidirectional dimensioning. For large angles, the number is sometimes placed in the dimension line as in aligned dimensioning.

An angle may also be expressed by giving the two legs of a right triangle, known as the run and rise.

One of the legs is always made 12 inches. Slopes may be expressed as the ratio of the horizontal distance to the vertical distance, as a batter of 1:4, or a slope of 1½:1. See Fig. 11.37. In architecture, the pitch or slope of a roof may be given as the ratio of the rise to the total span, such as ⅓ pitch. It may also be expressed as the number of inches of rise to one foot of horizontal distance.

g. *Tapers.* A taper is a conical surface on a machine part. It is specified as the change in diameter in inches per foot of length. In dimensioning a taper, there are four dimensions that can be given: the diameters at two different points, the taper in inches per foot, and the length. Any three of these will completely describe the part. All four should never be given, since that would be double dimensioning. The three that are given will be determined by the purpose of the part or by the method of manufacture. The various methods of dimensioning a taper are shown in Fig. 11.38. In this drawing the tolerances allowed in manufacture have been specified on the drawing. This is done by giving a top and bottom limit of size or by giving a plus or minus distance that will be allowed in the size.

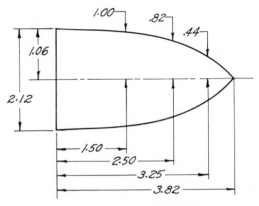

Fig. 11.34   Dimensioning non-circular curves.

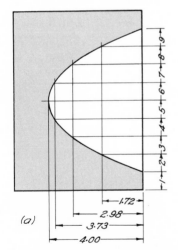

(a)

(b)

Fig. 11.35   Progressive dimensioning.

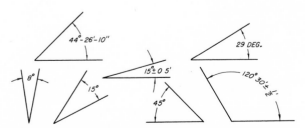

Fig. 11.36   Dimensioning angles.

h. Machining centers. Shaft centers may be required on shafts, spindles and other cylindrical parts to receive machine centers on which the work pieces are supported during manufacture and inspection.

There are two types of center drilling: the regular type shown in Figs. 11.39(a) and (b) and the Bell type, which is countersunk to provide protection to the working surface as shown in Fig. 11.39(c). The method of dimensioning or specifying is shown in the figure.

11.7.4   Location dimensioning. As previously stated, every feature of a part must be completely located by giving dimensions in three directions. These dimensions must be measured from properly selected datum planes and must be so chosen that the part will operate properly, may be made economically, and may be easily laid out and inspected.

a. Location of holes. One very common problem in dimensioning is to locate a pattern of holes in a part. Locating dimensions to circles or holes should always be given to the centers on the view where they show as circles. If the holes are in a circular pattern, they may be dimensioned by giving the diameter of the center-line circle and distances or angles from a datum plane as shown in Fig. 11.40. They are also frequently located by giving the number of holes and specifying that they must be equally spaced. This method is illustrated in Fig. 11.41. When the holes are not in a circular pattern, they are usually located by dimensioning each hole from two datum planes. See Fig. 11.42.

If it should be necessary to keep the distance between the holes within specifications, it is possible to dimension one hole from the datum plane and the second from the first as shown in Figs. 11.43 and 11.44. This is the usual procedure for dimensioning parts that must fit together.

If still more accuracy is desired, it is best to use true-position dimensioning as explained in Chapter 12.

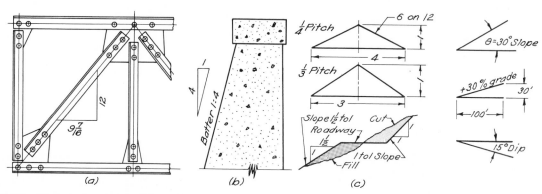

Fig. 11.37   Dimensioning slopes, pitch, and batter.

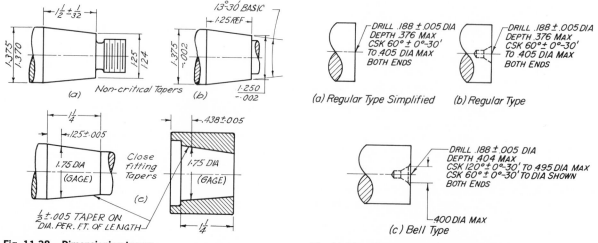

Fig. 11.38   Dimensioning tapers.

Fig. 11.39   Dimensioning machining centers.

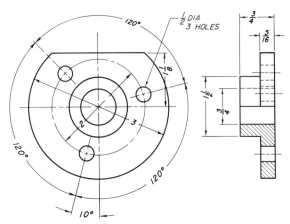

Fig. 11.40 Dimensioning holes in circular pattern—three holes, half section.

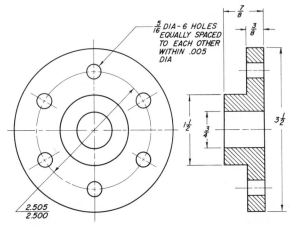

Fig. 11.41 Dimensioning holes in circular pattern—six holes, full section.

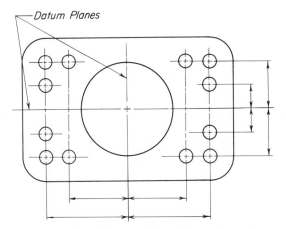

Fig. 11.42 Dimensioning pattern of holes that must be held within one tolerance from center lines.

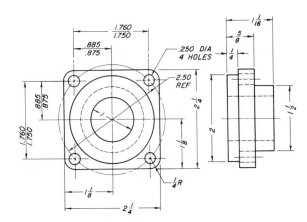

Fig. 11.43 Dimensioning a four-hole symmetrical flange.

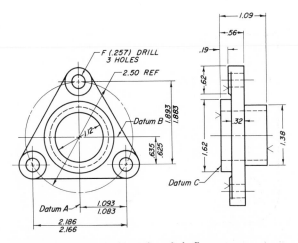

Fig. 11.44 Dimensioning a three-hole flange.

b. Symmetrical parts. When the features of a part are symmetrical about a center line, the preferred method is to dimension one side from the center line and the other side from the first, as shown in Fig. 11.45(*a*). The method of Fig. 11.45(*b*) is frequently used, but this requires the assumption that the center line indicates symmetry and that therefore the features would be made that way. The chain dimensioning shown in Fig. 11.45(*c*) should never be used.

c. Partial circular parts. Objects such as that shown in Fig. 11.46 may be dimensioned by giving the radius and the length or range of it by an angle. In other cases, such as that shown in Fig. 11.47, the radius may be given and the distances along the surface may be dimensioned. In such a case it is understood that the distances are to be measured on the part, even though the dimension line is outside the given surface.

d. Coordinate dimensioning. When there are many holes or features to be located in a small area, this may be done by establishing two datum or reference lines and giving dimensions from them. They may be specified on the drawing or in a table.

When a table is used, each feature must be numbered or lettered as in Fig. 11.48. When the information is given on the drawing, the coordinate axes or datum lines are marked zero and distances are all shown from the zero points without putting in dimension lines. See Fig. 11.49.

e. Slotted holes. Slots of regular shape are dimensioned for size, by length and width, and shape of

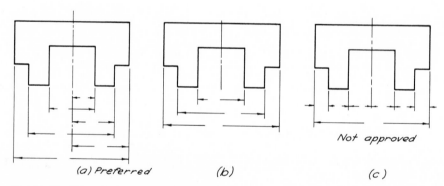

(a) Preferred   (b)   (c)

Not approved

Fig. 11.45   Dimensioning symmetrical parts.

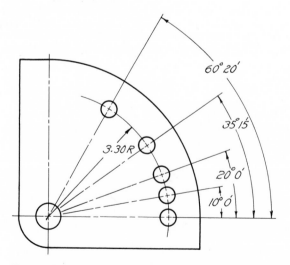

60°20'

35°15'

3.30 R

20°0'

10°0'

Fig. 11.46   Polar-coordinate dimensioning.

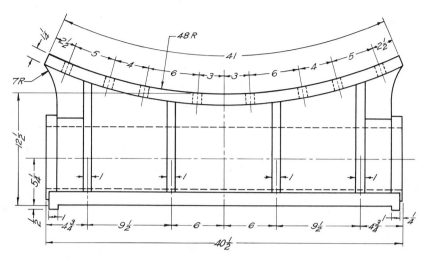

Fig. 11.47 Circumferential dimensioning.

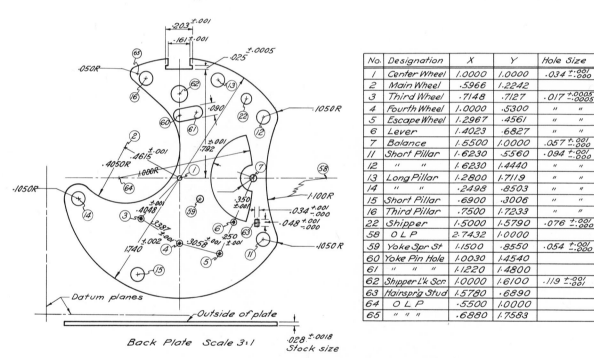

No.	Designation	X	Y	Hole Size
1	Center Wheel	1.0000	1.0000	.034 $^{+.001}_{-.000}$
2	Main Wheel	.5966	1.2242	
3	Third Wheel	.7148	.7127	.017 $^{+.0005}_{-.0005}$
4	Fourth Wheel	1.0000	.5300	" "
5	Escape Wheel	1.2967	.4561	" "
6	Lever	1.4023	.6827	" "
7	Balance	1.5500	1.0000	.057 $^{+.001}_{-.000}$
11	Short Pillar	1.6230	.5560	.094 $^{+.001}_{-.000}$
12	" "	1.6230	1.4440	" "
13	Long Pillar	1.2800	1.7119	" "
14	" "	.2498	.8503	" "
15	Short Pillar	.6900	.3006	" "
16	Third Pillar	.7500	1.7233	" "
22	Shipper	1.5000	1.5790	.076 $^{+.001}_{-.000}$
58	O L P	2.7432	1.0000	
59	Yoke Spr St	1.1500	.8550	.054 $^{+.001}_{-.000}$
60	Yoke Pin Hole	1.0030	1.4540	
61	" "	1.1220	1.4800	
62	Shipper L'k Scr.	1.0000	1.6100	.119 $^{+.001}_{-.001}$
63	Hairspr'g Stud	1.5780	.6890	
64	O L P	.5500	1.0000	
65	" " "	.6880	1.7583	

Fig. 11.48 Location dimensions by coordinates. (Courtesy Westclox Watch and Clock Company.)

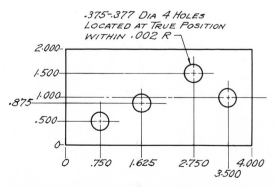

Fig. 11.49 Coordinate dimensioning without dimension lines.

end by *R* for radius if this applies, as in Fig. 11.50.

For location, when there are several identical slots they are dimensioned along their longitudinal center lines to their near ends as shown in Fig. 11.50(*c*).

f. Parts with curved ends. Parts of this type may be dimensioned as in Fig. 11.51. Three situations are shown.

1. When the holes near the ends have the same centers as the semicircular ends, the dimensioning should be as shown in Fig. 11.51(*a*).

2. When the centers of the semicircular ends are not the same as the centers of the holes, the dimensioning of Fig. 11.51(*b*) should be used.

3. When the ends are short circular arcs not concentric with the end holes, the dimensioning should be as shown in Fig. 11.51(*c*) In all cases duplicate dimensioning should be avoided.

g. Toleranced dimensions. When specific manufacturing tolerances are given on the dimensions, the method shown in Fig. 11.52 is used. This is discussed in Chapter 12.

11.8 DIMENSIONING FOR NUMERICALLY CONTROLLED MACHINES. Most of the basic dimensioning

practices apply when the information is to be put into tapes used as manufacturing machine controls. However, to make the best use of this type of manufacturing, certain rules should be observed.

a. It is well to consult with manufacturing representatives before release of the final drawings.

b. Maximum use of standard tools, such as drills, reamers, and taps should be part of the planning.

c. It is desirable to have all dimensions in decimals.

d. Angles may be specified but it is usually desirable to dimension by coordinates.

e. Tolerances should be based on design requirements and should not be made smaller than required just because the machine can handle them.

f. Coordinate dimensioning should be used from three main axes.

g. The reference planes may be common with the datum plane or they may be located outside of the object. They must be clearly marked on the drawing.

h. If possible, is is well to locate the reference planes so that all measurements will be positive.

i. True position and geometrical tolerances may also apply to parts manufactured by tape-controlled machines.

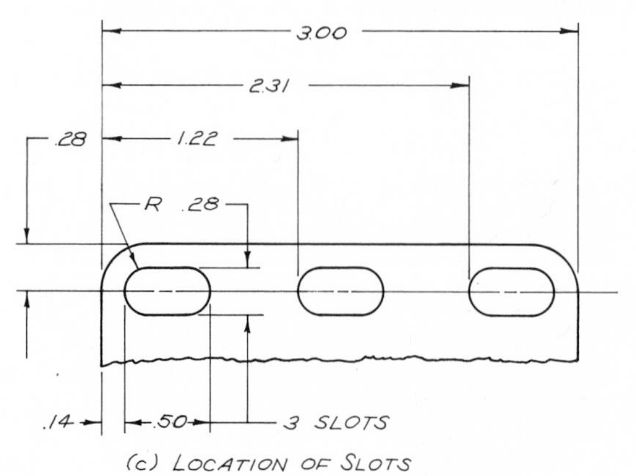

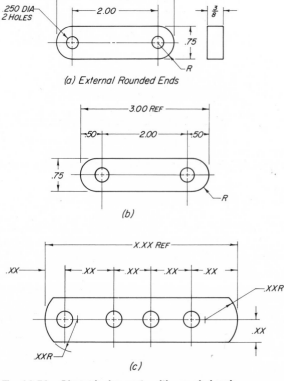

Fig. 11.50 Dimensioning slots with rounded ends.

Fig. 11.51 Dimensioning parts with rounded ends.

11.9 DIMENSIONING STANDARD FEATURES. Many features of mechanical parts are produced by standard shop operations. The methods of specifying these procedures are given in the following paragraphs.

11.9.1 Blind holes. When a hole does not go all the way through a part, it is referred to as a blind hole. It is specified by giving the diameter and the depth. The depth is given to the shoulder and not to the drill point. See Fig. 11.53.

11.9.2 Tapped or threaded holes. The method of specifying threads is given in Art. 9.6.3. The accuracy and purpose of the work as well as the method of manufacture will determine the amount of information to be given about the thread. In case of doubt complete

data should be given. Two methods are illustrated in Fig. 11.54.

For blind holes, the depth of the hole must be greater than the depth of the thread to allow for economical manufacture. See Fig. 11.54.

11.9.3 Countersinking. A conical hole cut so as to allow a beveled screw head to fit flush with the surface is called a countersink. Two methods of showing a countersink are given in Fig. 11.55. Although the actual angle is 82°, it is always drawn at 90° for simplicity.

11.9.4 Counterbore. A cylindrical hole made to allow a fillister-head screw to fit flush with the surface of the part is called a counterbore. Two methods of specifying a counterbore are shown in Figs. 11.56(a)

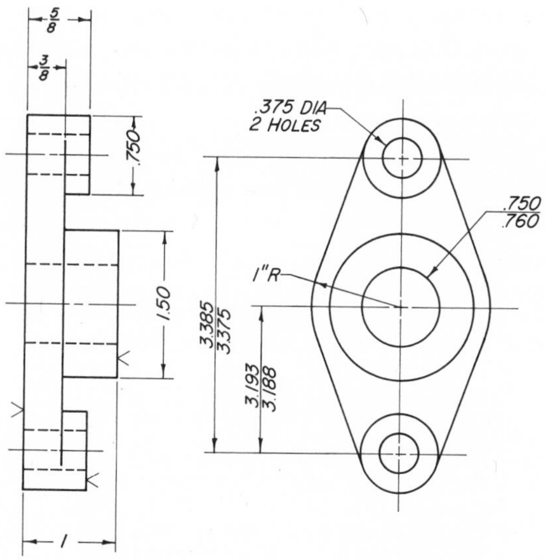

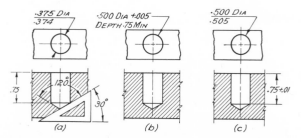

Fig. 11.53   Dimensioning blind holes.

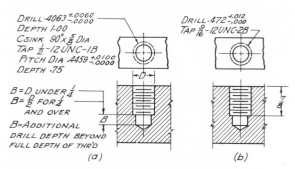

Fig. 11.54   Dimensioning threaded holes.

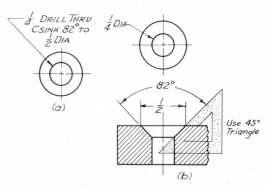

Fig. 11.52   Location of holes with limit dimensions.

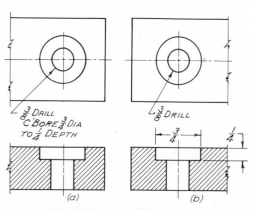

Fig. 11.55   Dimensioning a countersink.

Fig. 11.56   Dimensioning a counterbore.

and (*b*). Clearance for screws or bolts must be allowed in both the drill and the counterbore. The amount of clearance varies with the size.

11.9.5 Spotface. To provide a smooth bearing for a bolt head or nut, an operation called spotfacing is done. The diameter of the spotface is given as shown in Fig. 11.57. The depth is seldom given since it is intended only to smooth off the surface.

11.9.6 Chamfer. The ends of rods and bolts are usually beveled as shown in Fig. 11.58. When the bevel is at 45°, it may be shown as in Fig. 11.58(*a*). *When the bevel is at any other angle, it must be shown as in Fig. 11.58(b).* Chamfering may be applied to a hole, as shown in Fig. 11.58(*c*).

11.9.7 Threading against a shoulder. In this case it is necessary to cut a groove to provide clearance for the thread-cutting tool. This is known as thread relief. The method of dimensioning is shown in Fig. 11.59.

11.9.8 Keyways. The proper method for dimensioning keyways is shown in Fig. 11.60.

11.9.9 Dovetail tongue and slot. The method of dimensioning a dovetail tongue and slot is shown in Fig. 11.61. The 60° angle marked "basic" means that the angle must fall within the tolerance zones established by the other dimensions with their tolerances. The datum surface must be carefully selected for proper functioning. In this case it was assumed that

the bearing was to be maintained on the shoulder.

11.9.10 Knurls. Knurling is used to give a better grip on a part or for joining two parts together with a press fit. It is done by producing a series of ridges on the part. It may be dimensioned as shown in Fig. 11.62.

11.9.11 Parts dimensioned with true radius. Rods with spherical ends are dimensioned as shown in Fig. 11.63(*a*), even though only one view of the spherical end is shown.

A bent bar which has a circular curve at the end that does not show in true shape in the end or side view may be dimensioned as shown in Fig. 11.63(*b*). This eliminates an auxiliary view which would be required to show the true shape of the curve.

11.10 NOTES. There are two kinds of notes that may be placed on a drawing: special notes and general notes.

11.10.1 Special notes. Special notes refer to a specific part of the drawing. If the same note applies to several places, individual leaders may be carried to the same note. It is usually better to repeat the note if the leaders become long.

11.10.2 General notes. General notes are placed in or near the title block. They are used to cover many items. Some of those most frequently used are as follows:

a. All dimensions in inches.

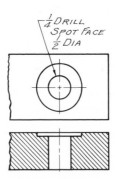

Fig. 11.57 Dimensioning a spotface.

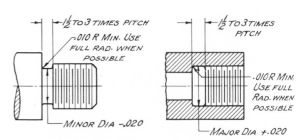

Fig. 11.59 Threading against a shoulder.

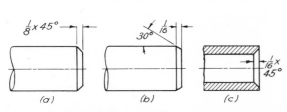

Fig. 11.58 Dimensioning a chamfer.

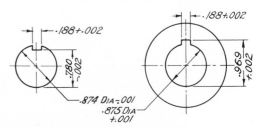

Fig. 11.60 Dimensioning a keyway.

b. Finish all over or *FAO*.

c. Break sharp edges 0.01 to 0.03 *R* unless otherwise specified.

d. All small fillets ⅛-inch radius.

e. All dimensions to be met after plating.

f. Remove burrs.

g. All draft angles 7° unless otherwise specified.

h. Paint one coat red lead.

i. Rivets ¾ DIA unless otherwise noted.

11.11   LIMIT DIMENSIONS. Dimensioning for interchangeable assembly is covered in Chapter 12. This includes such things as limits and fits, true-positioning dimensioning, and geometric form or form tolerancing.

11.12   USE OF STANDARD PARTS. The draftsman and engineer must always make use of standard parts, tools, and gages when designing a product. Such standard parts include:

a. Standard sizes of material such as bar stock, sheet metal, and wire.

b. Standard bolts, nuts, keys, washers, springs, ball bearings, and the like.

c. Part sizes that can be produced with standard tools, and equipment.

11.13   FINISHED SURFACES. Certain surfaces of a part are made smooth or finished. This may be necessary for the proper functioning of the part, for appearance, or for ease of handling. The surfaces where mating parts come together must always be finished. In the machine shop this is done by cutting away a small amount of metal. It is very important that these finished surfaces be marked on the drawing so that the patternmaker will allow the extra material to be cut away and so that the machinist will know where to cut. The surfaces to be finished are marked with a 60° *V*, with the point resting on the edgewise view of the specified surface. See Fig. 11.64. For complete information about finish marks, see Art. 12.38 in Chapter 12.

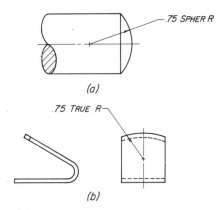

(a)

(b)

Fig. 11.63   Dimensioning special parts.

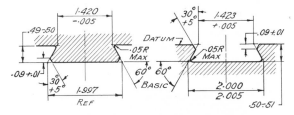

Fig. 11.61   Dimensioning a dovetail tongue and slot.

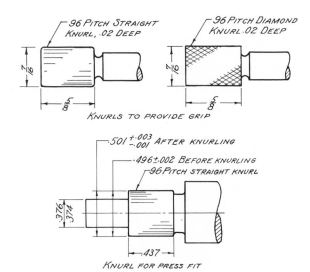

Fig. 11.62   Dimensioning a knurled part.

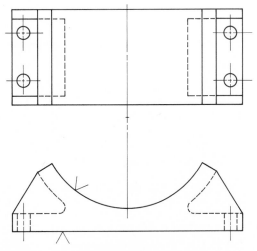

Fig. 11.64   Use of finish marks.

SELF-STUDY QUESTIONS

In the questions that follow fill in the blank spaces or underline the correct word where a choice is given. If you cannot answer, look up the paragraph number immediately following the question number.

11.1 **(11.2)** Dimensions should be measured from some _____ _____ .

11.2 **(11.2)** Tolerances should not be allowed to _____ .

11.3 **(11.2)** Every feature must be dimensioned for _____ and _____ .

11.4 **(11.4.1)** The weight of a dimension line should be _____ than visible outlines.

11.5 **(11.4.1)** Dimension lines should not coincide or be an extension of a _____ _____ or a line on the object.

11.6 **(11.4.1)** An arrow should be placed on _____ end of a _____ line.

11.7 **(11.4.1)** The numeral should be placed in a _____ in the dimension line.

11.8 **(11.4.2)** A line that extends from the object to show the _____ of a dimension is called an

_____ _____ .

11.9 **(11.4.3)** A line connecting a view to a note is called a _____ .

11.10 **(11.4.3)** A line connecting a note to an area of a drawing should have a _____ on the end.

11.11 **(11.4.3)** A line connecting a note to a circle should end at the circle and point toward _____ .

11.12 **(11.4.4)** An arrowhead should be _____ times as long as it is wide.

11.13 **(11.4.4)** On most drawings, the arrows should be about _____ _____ of an inch long.

11.14 **(11.4.4)** The point of the arrow ends exactly at the _____ _____ .

11.15 **(11.4.5)** Notes should always read _____ .

11.16 **(11.4.5)** No letter on a drawing should be smaller than _____ _____ inch.

11.17 **(11.4.5)** For all lettering, _____ lines should be used.

11.18 **(11.4.6)** Feet and inch marks should always be used on a drawing.   True   False

11.19 **(11.4.8)** The number 4.3175 should be rounded off to two places as _____ .

11.20 **(11.4.8)** The number 2.9125 should be rounded off to two places as _____ .

11.21 **(11.4.8)** The number 3.265 should be rounded off to two places as _____ .

11.22 **(11.5)** The first dimension line should be _____ _____ of an inch from the object line of a view.

11.23 **(11.5)** Dimensions should be placed outside and _____ views when possible.

11.24 **(11.5)** Unrelated dimensions should be placed on _____ _____ of dimensioning.

11.25 **(11.5)** Dimensions should be measured from _____ _____ when possible.

11.26 **(11.5)** Dimensions should be placed on the view that shows the _____ of the object.

11.27 **(11.6.2)** When the numerals all face the bottom of the drawing in dimensioning, the system is called the _____ system.

11.28 **(11.7.4)** A pattern of holes should be dimensioned in the view that shows the holes as _____ .

11.29 **(11.7.3)** In dimensioning a taper only _____ of the possible _____ dimensions should be given.

11.30 **(11.7.4)** When a graph of dimensions is given in a table, this is called _____ dimensioning.

11.31 **(11.8)** For numerically controlled machines:

    1. It is best to use _____ dimensions.

    2. _____ dimensioning should be used.

    3. _____ tools should be specified.

    4. Reference planes should be located so that all dimensions will be _____ if possible.

11.32 **(11.9.1)** The depth of a blind hole should be measured to the _____ rather than the _____.

11.33 **(11.9.2)** For blind threaded holes, the depth of the thread should be _____ than the depth of the hole.

11.34 **(11.9.3)** Cutting a conical hole to fit a beveled screwhead is called _____.

11.35 **(11.9.4)** A cylindrical hole to fit a fillister-head screw is called a _____.

11.36 **(11.9.5)** Smoothing a surface to allow for the bearing of a bolt head or nut is called _____.

11.37 **(11.9.10)** A rough surface provided to give a better grip is called a _____.

PROBLEMS

The following problems are designed for 8½ × 11 or 11 × 17 inch paper. The student should select his scale to suit the size of paper. Ample space should be allowed between views in which to place dimensions in later assignments.

Drawings are not to be dimensioned unless specified by the instructor.

It should be noted that the dimensions given on the pictorial drawings are not necessarily those that would be used on a working drawing nor are they always placed where they should be on a working drawing.

11.1 Construct the necessary extension lines, dimension lines, and leaders to dimension properly the plane figures given in Fig. 11.65. Indicate the chosen reference or datum planes by short leaders marked datum with a letter as datum _A_. This work may be done freehand on the figures in the text.

11.2 Construct the necessary extension lines, dimension lines, and leaders needed to dimension properly the object assigned in Fig. 11.66. Indicate the datum planes used, by a short leader marked datum _A_, datum _B_, etc. This work may be done freehand on the figures in the text.

11.3 Construct the necessary dimension lines, extension lines, and leaders to properly dimension the objects shown in Figs. 6.102 and 6.103. Before beginning the dimensioning, it will be necessary to supply the line

that is missing in one of the views and sketch the third view. This work may be done freehand on the figures in the text.

The following problems have most of their dimensions given in the form of verbal size specifications. A few dimensions, principally radii, are shown on the figures. The student should read the specifications under each problem very carefully while referring to the pictorial figure. Some dimensions must be worked out from others: a radius may give the diameter of a part and the width of a straight part tangent to the circular part. Corners should be rounded and filleted when necessary, even though not so shown in the illustrations.

In all problems, draw the views necessary to describe adequately the shape of the object. Allow ample space between and around views for dimensions.

11.4–11.15 Make the necessary views of the object assigned from Figs. 11.67 to 11.78, dimension the drawing, indicate finished surfaces, and add any necessary notes so that no further information is needed to manufacture the object. Place name of object, material specification, and scale under the views or in a title block if one is provided on the sheet.

11.16–11.32 Copy any of the drawings in Figs. 6.62 to 6.78 and dimension them completely. Construct the third view whenever necessary.

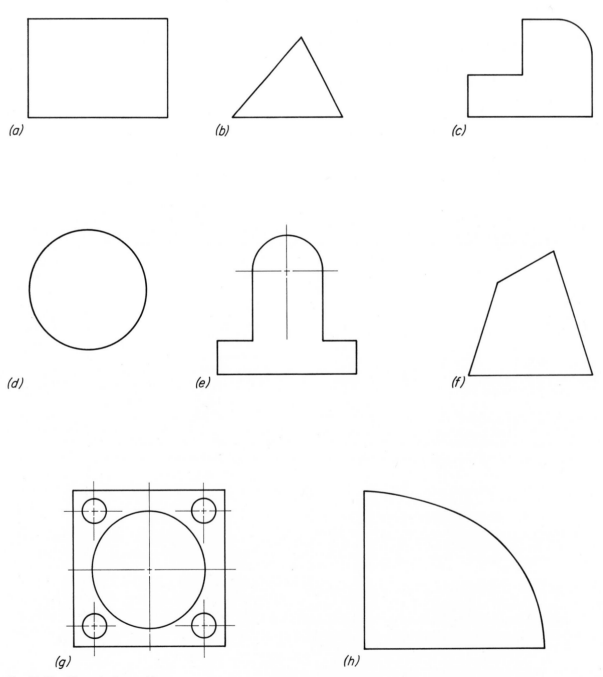

(a) *(b)* *(c)*

(d) *(e)* *(f)*

(g) *(h)*

Fig. 11.65   Dimensioning problems.

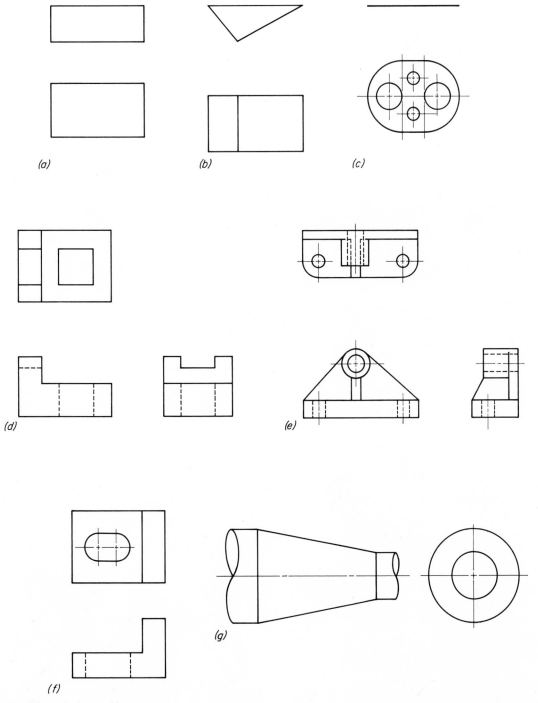

Fig. 11.66 Dimensioning problems.

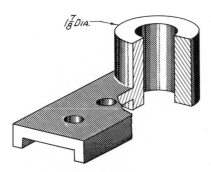

Fig. 11.67   Connecting-rod end.
Rectangular groove ¼″ × 1⅜″ sliding fit; surrounding material ¼″ thick; nominal size of shaft ¹⁵⁄₁₆″, class-2 fit; overall length 5″; height 1½″; ⁷⁄₁₆″ holes spread 1½″ center-to-center, ³⁄₃₂″ × ¼″ keyway; cast steel; finish as needed; scale 1″ = 1″.

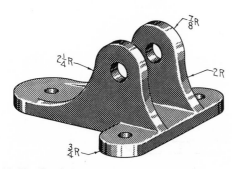

Fig. 11.68   Bracket.
All material ⅜″ thick, three ⁷⁄₁₆″ holes in base, located on corners of an isosceles triangle having a base of 3¾″ and an altitude of 3⅞″; center line of ⁹⁄₁₆″ holes in uprights is 1½″ above top of base and ¾″ left of base of the hole triangle; clear distance between uprights is 1½″; cast iron; unfinished; scale ½″ = 1″.

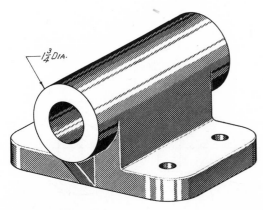

Fig. 11.69   Pillow block.
Shaft ¹⁵⁄₁₆″ nominal diameter, class-2 fit; center of shaft 1⅝″ above base plane; bearing 5″ long; base 3½″ × 4¾″; four ¹³⁄₃₂″ holes in base, ¾″ from each edge; brace on each end ⅜″ thick; base ½″ thick; cast iron; finish as needed; scale ½″ = 1″.

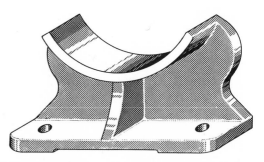

Fig. 11.70   Saddle.
Supports 9″ pipe so that center line is 7⅞″ above support under base surface; saddle has 120° bearing 2″ long; all material ½″ thick; base 2¾″ × 12″; holes in base ¹³⁄₁₆″ diameter, 1½″ from ends and 1¼″ from front of base; ⅛″ pads on base, 3″ on each end; design back and center brace to suit; cast iron; finish as needed; scale ⅜″ = 1″.

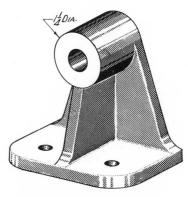

Fig. 11.71   Bearing bracket.
Supports shaft ½″ diameter so that center line is 2⅜″ above base plane; use class-2 fit; bearing 1½″ long; base 2¼″ × 3¼″; two ⁵⁄₁₆″ holes in base with their center lines ¾″ from ends and front of base; base and supports ¼″ thick; design shape of back and center brace to suit; cast iron, finish as necessary; scale ¾″ = 1″.

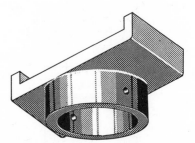

Fig. 11.72   Post cap.
Beam seat 6″ × 12″; all material ¾″ thick; post collar 2″ deep; designed for 4½″ OD post; drill two ½″ holes in collar; cast iron; unfinished; scale ½″ = 1″.

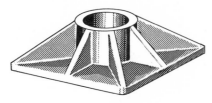

Fig. 11.73   Column base.
Size of base 12″ × 12″; designed for 4″ OD column; all material ⅝″ thick; height of collar 3″; cast iron; unfinished; scale ¼″ = 1″.

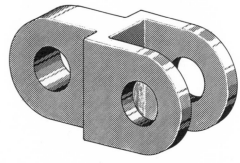

Fig. 11.76   Link.
Holes 1″ diameter, 2¾″ center to center; external radius of ends 1⅛″; material in clevis end ⅜″ thick; clear opening of clevis 1⅜″; clearance center line of holes to back of clevis 1⅛″; single end 1″ thick; steel; finish as needed; scale 1″ = 1″.

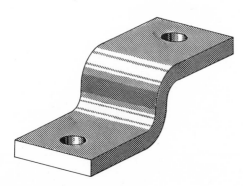

Fig. 11.74   Offset strap.
Blank ⅜″ × 2″ × ?; offset 1³⁄₁₆″; two ⁹⁄₁₆″ holes 3¾″ center to center; interior radius of bend ⅜″; wrought iron; unfinished; scale 1″ = 1″.

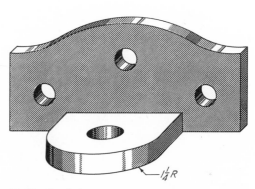

Fig. 11.77   Bracket.
Overall dimensions of back 2¼″ × 5″; overall dimensions of base 1¼″ × 2½″; all material ⅜″ thick; three ⁷⁄₁₆″ holes in back located on corners of isosceles triangle; base of triangle 3½″; height ¾″; base of triangle ¾″ from bottom of bracket; hole in base 1³⁄₁₆″; center line of hole 1¼″ from back of bracket; design shape of back and base to suit; cast iron; unfinished; scale ¾″ = 1″.

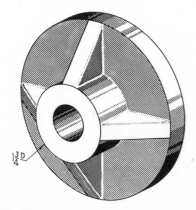

Fig. 11.75   Washer.
Maximum diameter 4″; hole 1³⁄₁₆″; total height 1½″; height of base ½″; thickness of braces ⅜″; cast iron; finish as necessary; scale ¾″ = 1″.

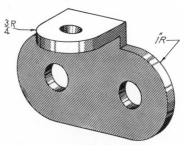

Fig. 11.78   Chain-link attachment.
All material ¼″ thick; drill 2 holes in back ⅝″ diameter, 2″ center to center; drill one hole in top ½″ diameter; clearance between center line of holes in back and the top of bracket 1¼″; clearance between center line of hole in top and the back of bracket ¾″; wrought iron; unfinished; scale 1″ = 1″.

Production Dimensioning

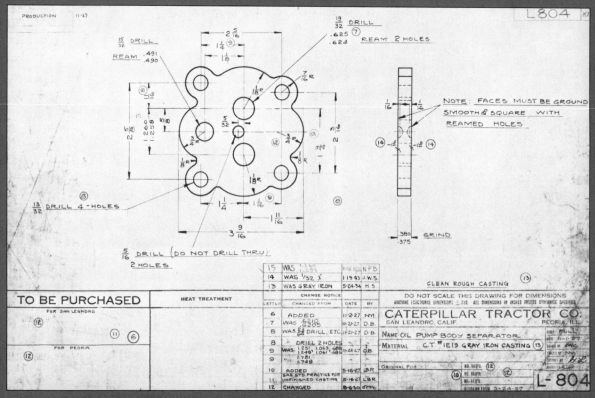

OLD: Drawing of Oil Pump Body Separator of 1927 illustrates old method of dimensioning. (The Caterpillar Tractor Company)

NEW: Drawing of fan drive adapter illustrates modern day practice of geometrical positional form tolerancing. (The Caterpillar Tractor Company)

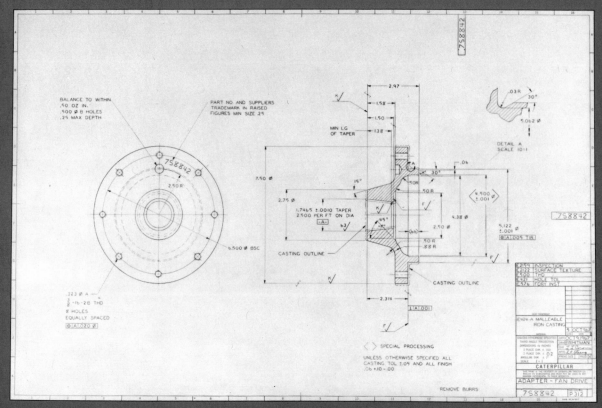

Chapter 12   Production Dimensioning

12.1   INTRODUCTION. Production dimensioning is the dimensioning of parts that are to be manufactured in large quantities. This involves first of all an understanding of what the finished product is to do and how its various parts fit together. Moreover, in today's manufacturing operations, the various parts of a machine may be produced at widely separated places by different companies. It is therefore necessary that the drawing be so clearly dimensioned that only one interpretation of it can be made. How this can be accomplished is the major subject of this chapter. The process, obviously, begins with an assembly drawing or sketch.

12.2   ASSEMBLY DRAWINGS. Even the simplest machines have several parts. It is necessary, for purposes of both design and production, to know how the various parts fit together. Drawings made to show these relationships are called assembly drawings. As the name clearly implies, an assembly drawing shows the parts of a machine put together in their proper working position relative to each other. Drawings of this kind may serve a number of purposes as indicated in the following paragraphs. These purposes determine the character of the drawing and the dimensions placed upon it.

12.3   LAYOUT DRAWINGS. Most of the machines that an engineer is called upon to design have their beginning as an idea in someone's imagination. This idea is first explained by a sketch. The draftsman then makes a mechanical drawing showing the complete machine and how its parts are to function. See Fig. 12.1. In this first design assembly or layout, the size and shape of parts are determined by judgement based on past experience. Many times these drawings are schematic in character.

From these layout drawings two basic items must

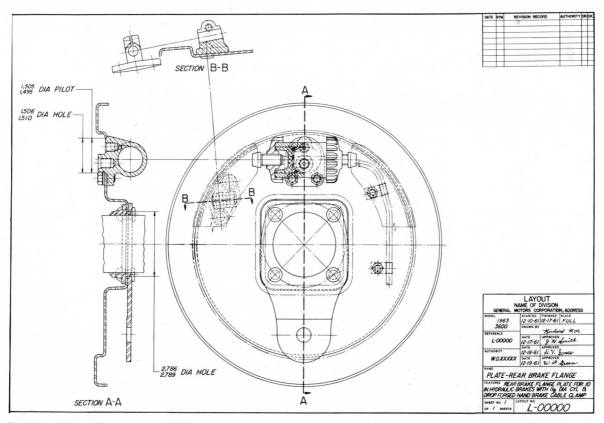

Fig. 12.1   Automotive part assembly layout.

be considered in the design of the various parts: (*a*) the movement and speed of the parts, which will insure the performance of the machine; (*b*) design for strength and rigidity with minimum weight; and (*c*) dimensions and limits of size and location, which will permit economical production and satisfactory operation. The details of parts made from the layout of Fig. 12.1 are shown later in this chapter.

12.4 FINAL OR CHECK ASSEMBLIES. In some cases the original layout is sufficiently accurate so that no further work need be done. In other cases the actual design of parts will change their shape and dimensions from those shown in the original assembly. It then becomes necessary to redraw the assembly to make certain that the following things have been accomplished:

a. All the designed parts fit together.

b. There is ample clearance for all moving parts.

c. Bolts and screws can actually be reached and tightened in the position indicated. An assembly of this type is shown in Fig. 12.2.

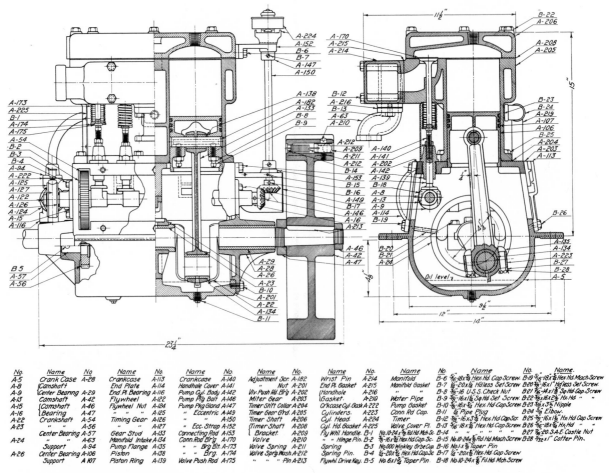

Fig. 12.2 Machine assembly drawing.

12.5 SHOP AND FIELD ASSEMBLIES. Assembly drawings may be used in the shop as a guide for the workmen who are putting the machine together. They are even more useful where a machine is shipped "knocked down" and assembled elsewhere. These drawings show each part numbered, and this number is placed on the part. The part can therefore be identified on the job, or the drawing of it can be located in the files. Such an assembly is shown in Fig. 12.2. In some cases exploded pictorial views are made, as in Fig. 12.3, which represents the same assembly as Fig. 12.7.

WATER PUMP

NO.	REQ.	DESCRIPTION	NO.	REQ.	DESCRIPTION
1	4	$\frac{15}{16}" \times 1"$ HEX-HEAD BOLTS	9	1	PLUNGER BOLT
2	1	OUTLET FLANGE	10	1	ECCENTRIC STRAP
3	2	STEEL BALLS	11	1	ECCENTRIC (INSIDE)
4	1	PUMP BODY	12	1	ECCENTRIC (OUTSIDE)
5	1	PACKING RING	13	1	FLAT HEAD SCREW
6	1	PUMP PACKING GLAND	14	1	CAM SHAFT REAR BEARING
7	1	PUMP PLUNGER	15	2	NO. 9 WOODRUFF KEYS
8	1	COTTER PIN	16	1	INTAKE FLANGE

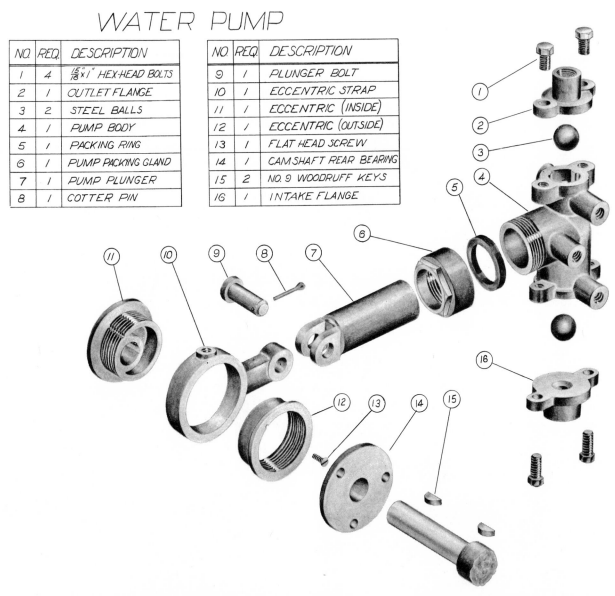

Fig. 12.3 Pictorial exploded assembly drawing. (Courtesy E. R. Blackwell.)

12.6 ERECTION DIAGRAMS. Large structures such as bridges and steel buildings also require a type of drawing that will enable the workmen to assemble the parts properly. Such drawings are commonly referred to as erection diagrams. See Figs. 12.4.

12.7 INSTALLATION DRAWINGS. Frequently machine units are fitted into larger machines, and large machines require foundations or footings designed to support them. Assemblies are made showing principally the fastenings, anchor bolts, and clearances required and all necessary dimensions to show these things. Figures 12.5 and 12.6 are illustrations of this type of drawing.

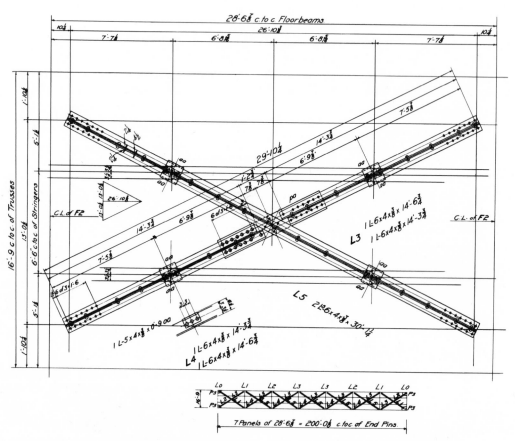

Fig. 12.4 Erection diagram of wind bracing.

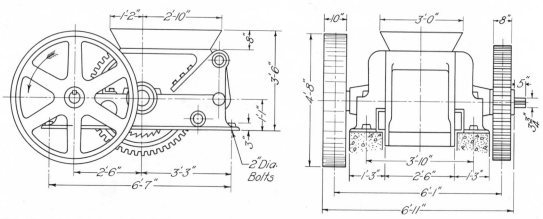

Fig. 12.5 Assembly drawing for installation.

12.8 DIMENSIONING ASSEMBLIES. The dimensioning of assembly drawings depends on the use for which they are intended. In general, it may be said that only the controlling dimensions, distance of travel of moving parts, and the like are shown on assemblies, as illustrated in Figs. 12.5 and 12.7.

12.9 CROSSHATCHING IN ASSEMBLIES. The system of using only one type of crosshatching is a common one on detail drawings. The use of different types of crosshatching to represent different materials is the more common practice on assembly drawings. This calls attention in an unmistakable way to the difference in materials. Figure 12.7 illustrates the use of symbolic crosshatching as aproved by the United States of America Standards Institute and illustrated in Figs. 8.35 and 8.36 in Chapter 8.

12.10 HIDDEN LINES IN ASSEMBLIES. It is the usual practice to omit hidden lines entirely in assembly drawings unless it is necessary to show them for clarity. Then it is customary to show only the principal outlines of the object that may be needed.

12.11 REFERENCE OR PART NUMBERS. On assembly drawings for the shop, or for sales and service organizations, all parts are identified by numbers or letters. Each manufacturer has his own system of identification. In some shops the drawing number of the part is commonly used as a part number. See Figs. 12.2 and 12.7.

12.12 STANDARD DETAILS. Standard parts such as bolts, springs, and threaded parts are shown in conventional form. Hexagonal heads of bolts show three faces in both front and side views rather than as true projections. This identifies the bolt in either view. For economy in manufacturing, standard commercial parts should be used in design whenever possible.

Features produced by certain tools should also be specified and dimensioned in such size that standard drills, countersinks, counterbores, spot faces, milled slots, and the like can be produced by the tools carried in stock.

12.13 SUBASSEMBLIES. In larger and more complicated machines, it is impossible to show all parts in one assembly. The usual practice in such cases is to take groups of related parts that form a unit and make what is called a subassembly. See Fig. 12.7.

12.14 SELECTIVE ASSEMBLY. To make parts completely interchangeable there must be clearance between the parts at their maximum material condition (MMC). That is, when the allowance is positive, the largest shaft must be smaller than the smallest hole. When not at MMC, the hole is larger and the shaft smaller, so that there is more clearance, which is equal to the allowance plus both measured tolerances on the actual parts. For further discussion of the MMC principle, see Art. 12.16.11. There are two methods of reducing this clearance to get a closer fit. One method is by reducing the tolerance. The other is by selective assembling.

When selective assembly has been chosen, the parts are gaged and placed in various bins, depending on their actual size. In this manner the larger internal parts can be fitted to the external parts having the larger hole. The smaller internal parts can be fitted to the mating parts with the smaller holes. In this manner the excess clearance owing to parts not being at maximum material condition can be made smaller because the actual measured allowance on the parts is reduced.

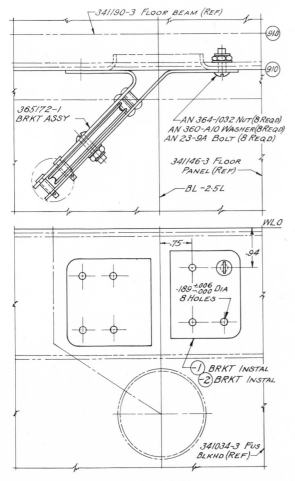

Fig. 12.6 Aircraft installation assembly.

12.15 INTERCHANGEABLE ASSEMBLY. The assembly drawings as discussed in the preceding paragraphs show how the parts of an object fit together. Before any part can be manufactured it must be detailed in a separate drawing. Usually each part is drawn on a sheet by itself, but occasionally the several parts of small assemblies may be detailed on one sheet.

Experience has shown that parts cannot be manufactured economically to exact dimensions. Hence when two or more parts must fit together some latitude in the size of each part must be allowed the workman producing the parts. It is therefore necessary to dimension parts in such a manner that the workman knows exactly how much leeway he has in producing them. This leads to the use of some new terms in production dimensioning that must be thoroughly understood.

12.16 DEFINITION OF TERMS. In order to comprehend a discussion of methods of tolerancing dimensions, it is necessary to have a clear understanding of the following terms that are used in the discussion.

12.16.1 Feature. Features are specific parts of an object such as holes, bosses, lugs, and faces of a part.

12.16.2 Reference dimension. This is a dimension, without tolerance, used for information only. It is not used in manufacturing or inspection. On the drawing it is marked REF.

12.16.3 Nominal size.* The nominal size is the designation used for the purpose of general identification. It is most often used to designate a commercial product and is not in any sense the numerical size of the part. An example of a nominal size is ⅜-inch pipe, which actually has an outside diameter of 0.675 inch

---

* All definitions of terms, classes of fits, some sentences or phrases in this chapter, and drawings, when so indicated, have been taken from USASI Y14.5 and USASI B4.1—1955 with the permission of the publisher, The American Society of Mechanical Engineers.

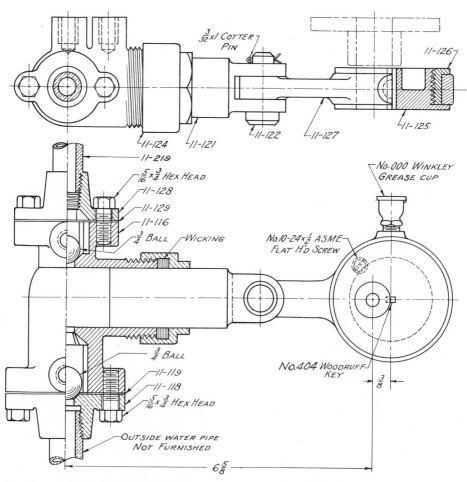

Fig. 12.7   Subassembly of parts from Fig. 12.3.

and an inside diameter of 0.493 inch. Another is a piece of lumber called a 2 × 4, which is actually 1⅝ × 3⅝.

12.16.4   Basic size. This is the size of a part determined by design computations, from which the limits of size are determined by the application of allowances and tolerances. Thus the requirements of strength and stiffness may demand a 2-inch diameter shaft. This is the basic size. On the drawing, a dimension marked "Basic" is an untoleranced dimension giving

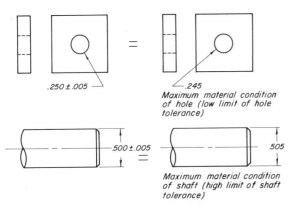

.250±.005

.245
Maximum material condition of hole (low limit of hole tolerance)

.500±.005

.505
Maximum material condition of shaft (high limit of shaft tolerance)

Fig. 12.8   Meaning of maximum material condition. MMC.

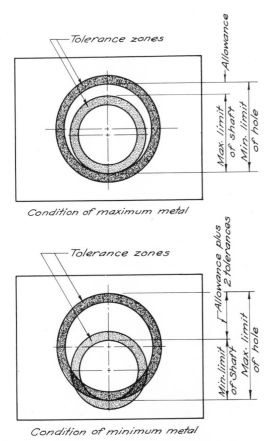

Tolerance zones

Allowance

Max. limit of shaft

Min. limit of hole

Condition of maximum metal

Tolerance zones

Allowance plus 2 tolerances

Min. limit of shaft

Max. limit of hole

Condition of minimum metal

Fig. 12.9   Relation of tolerance and allowance to limits.

the theoretically exact size or location. It may also be the basic size of the hole into which the shaft must fit, since the allowance is usually applied to the shaft. When it is necessary for special reasons the allowance may be applied to the hole.

12.16.5   Design size. Design size is the size from which limits of size are derived by the application of tolerances. When there is no allowance, the design size is the same as the basic size. *Thus the application of an allowance to the basic size is considered a part of the design process.* In the previous illustration, if 2 inches is the basic size of the hole, then this is also the design size for the hole. If an allowance of 0.003 for clearance is applied to the shaft, then the design size of the shaft is 1.997 inches. A tolerance is then applied to this dimension.

12.16.6   Actual size. The actual size is a measured size.

12.16.7   Fit. Fit is the general term used to specify the closeness (tightness or looseness) with which two mating parts are assembled. This results from a combination of allowances and tolerances. For types of fits see Art. 12.18.

12.16.8   Limits. The term *"limits" may be defined as the extreme permissible dimensions of a part.* Two limit dimensions are always involved, a larger and a smaller or a maximum size and a minimum size.

12.16.9   Tolerance. *Tolerance is defined as the total amount of variation permitted in the size of a part.* It is the difference between the two limits of the same dimension. The variation permitted in the dimensions for locating holes or other parts is also called a tolerance. Again, it should be emphasized that *the tolerance on a dimension is the total variation permitted.* See Art. 12.19 for method of tolerancing.

12.16.10   Allowance. Another important term used in production dimensioning is allowance, which is defined as the *intentional difference in the dimensions of mating parts* to provide the minimum clearance or the maximum interference that is intended between the parts. If allowance only exists between two parts, it represents the condition of the tightest permissible fit, or the largest internal member mated with the smallest external member. This is sometimes referred to as the maximum material condition, since both parts contain the maximum material. Allowance may be neutral or negative, thus providing interference fits for permanent assembly.

The student should note that the term *"allowance" refers to the difference in size between two different parts*. Thus the distinction between the three terms, limits, tolerance, and allowance, should be quite clear and unequivocal. They are illustrated in exaggerated form in Fig. 12.9. The purpose of an allowance is to provide for different classes of fits.

12.16.11   Maximum material condition (MMC). On the drawing this is designated MMC. This condition exists when external dimensions are at their maximum size and internal dimensions are at their minimum size, as in Fig. 12.8.

12.16.12   Datum. A datum is a surface or line from which dimensions are indicated on the drawing and measured in the shop. The surface may be a plane or cylinder. If it is a line this is usually a center line. See Art. 12.25 for further discussion.

12.17   SELECTING TOLERANCES. Great care and good judgement must be exercised in deciding upon tolerances that may be permitted on a part. The greater the demand for accuracy, the higher will be the cost of production. Since the specified tolerances will govern the method of manufacture, it is very important that tolerances be made as large as possible. When tolerances are reduced, the cost of manufacture rises very rapidly. The chart in Fig. 12.10 shows the accuracy that may be obtained economically in various common machine-shop operations, assuming the machines to be in good condition.

In working out limit dimensions the draftsman makes use of tables. Many companies have their own tables; others use the USASI Standards. In either case the method of computation is the same. Two systems are in use: the basic hole method and the basic shaft method. The choice of which to use depends upon the method of manufacture. In most cases the basic hole method is preferred, because standard tools can be used to produce the hole, whereas it is comparatively easy to turn or grind a shaft to any desired size. The methods of making computations for both systems are illustrated in Art. 12.20.

12.18   CLASSES OF FITS. DESIGNATION OF STANDARD FITS. Standard fits are designated by means of the following symbols, which are used in the tables in the Appendix. They are for educational purposes, to facilitate reference to various classes of fits. *They are not to be shown on manufacturing drawings.* Actual dimensions, as worked out from the tables, are used on drawings. The letter symbols have the following meanings:

RC   Running or sliding fit
LC   Location clearance fit
LT   Location transition fit
LN   Location interference fit
FN   Force or shrink fit

12.18.1   Running and sliding fits. Running and sliding fits, for which limits of clearance are given in Table 21 in the Appendix, are intended to provide an equivalent running performance, with suitable lubrication allowance, throughout the range of sizes.

RANGE OF SIZES		TOLERANCES								
FROM	TO & INCL									
.000	.599	.00015	.0002	.0003	.0005	.0008	.0012	.002	.003	.005
.600	.999	.00015	.00025	.0004	.0006	.001	.0015	.0025	.004	.006
1.000	1.499	.0002	.0003	.0005	.0008	.0012	.002	.003	.005	.008
1.500	2.799	.00025	.0004	.0006	.001	.0015	.0025	.004	.006	.010
2.800	4.499	.0003	.0005	.0008	.0012	.002	.003	.005	.008	.012

TOLERANCE RANGE OF MACHINING PROCESSES										
LAPPING & HONING										
GRINDING, DIAMOND TURNING & BORING										
BROACHING										
REAMING										
TURNING, BORING, SLOTTING PLANING & SHAPING										
MILLING										
DRILLING										

Fig. 12.10   Tolerance range for machining processes. (Courtesy Mil. Std. No. 8C–1962.)

RC 1.   *Close-sliding fits* are intended for the accurate location of parts that must assemble without perceptible play.

RC 2.   *Sliding fits* are intended for accurate location, but with greater maximum clearance than RC 1. Parts made to this fit move and turn easily, but are not intended to run freely, and in the larger sizes may seize with small temperature changes.

RC 3.   *Precision-running fits* are the closest fits that can be expected to run freely and are intended for precision work at slow speeds and light journal pressures, but are not suitable where appreciable temperature differences are likely to be encountered.

RC 4.   *Close-running fits* are intended chiefly for running fits on accurate machinery with moderate surface speeds and journal pressures, where accurate location and minimum play is desired.

RC 5-RC 6.   *Medium-running fits* are intended for higher running speeds, or heavy journal pressures, or both.

RC 7.   *Free-running fits* are intended for use where accuracy is not essential, or where large temperature variations are likely to be encountered, or under both of these conditions.

RC 8-RC 9.   *Loose-running fits* are intended for use where materials such as cold-rolled shafting and tubing, made to commercial tolerances, are involved.

12.18.2 Locational Fits. Locational fits are intended to determine only the location of the mating parts; they may provide rigid or accurate location, as with interference fits, or some freedom of location, as with clearance fits. Accordingly they are divided into three groups: clearance fits, transition fits, and interference fits. These are more fully described as follows:

LC.   *Locational clearance fits* are intended for parts that are normally stationary, but which can be freely assembled or disassembled. They run from snug fits for parts requiring accuracy of location, through the medium clearance fits for parts such as spigots, to the looser fastener fits where freedom of assembly is of prime importance.

LT.   *Transition fits* are a compromise between clearance and interference fits, for application where accuracy of location is important, but a small amount of either clearance or interference is permissible.

LN.   *Locational interference fits* are used where accuracy of location is of prime importance and for parts requiring rigidity and alignment with no special requirements for bore pressure. Such fits are not intended for parts designed to transmit frictional loads from one part to another by virtue of the tightness of fit. These conditions are covered by force fits.

12.18.3 Force fits. Force or shrink fits constitute a special type of interference fit, normally characterized by maintenance of constant bore pressures throughout the range of sizes. The interference therefore varies almost directly with diameter, and the difference between its minimum and maximum value is small in order to maintain the resulting pressures within reasonable limits. These fits may be described briefly as follows:

FN 1.   *Light-drive fits* are those requiring light assembly pressures, and they produce more or less permanent assemblies. They are suitable for thin sections or long fits, or in cast-iron external members.

FN 2.   *Medium-drive fits* are suitable for ordinary steel parts or for shrink fits on light sections. They are about the tightest fits that can be used with high-grade, cast-iron external members.

FN 3.   *Heavy-drive fits* are suitable for heavier steel parts or for shrink fits in medium sections.

FN 4-FN 5. *Force fits* are suitable for parts that can be highly stressed or for shrink fits where the heavy pressing forces required are impractical.

12.19 TOLERANCING SYSTEMS FOR SIZE. There are three systems of expressing tolerances on drawings in addition to the specification of general tolerances by note. The note form usually applies to all dimensions not specifically toleranced and is placed in or near the title block. The three systems are known as the unilateral, bilateral, and limit systems.

12.19.1 Unilateral system. In the unilateral system the tolerance is shown in one direction only, either plus or minus as illustrated in Fig. 12.11(a). It may also be expressed by giving the basic dimension and either a plus or a minus tolerance without indicating that the other is zero. This is shown in Fig. 12.11(b).

12.19.2 Bilateral system. In the bilateral system the tolerance is divided into two parts, thus permitting a variation on either side of the basic dimension. The tolerance is usually divided equally, as shown in Fig. 12.12(a), but it is not required that it should be. The tolerance of Fig. 12.12(b) is expressed in this manner. These deviations from the basic or design dimension are sometimes loosely called bilateral tolerances, but it should be noted that the tolerance is the total variation. Thus in Fig. 12.12(a) the tolerance is 0.002 and not 0.001. In no case may the two deviations be in the same direction, that is, both plus or both minus. The bilateral system is most useful for parts that are to be produced on machines with numerical control systems. Inspection or quality-control departments also find this method very convenient.

12.19.3 Limit system. In the limit system the extreme permissible dimensions are given on the drawing, as shown in Fig. 12.13. Note that in this case the tolerance is the difference between the limits. Two methods for placing limit dimensions on a drawing are approved in the United States of America Standard.

a. Maximum material method. In this method the number giving the maximum material size is placed above the line, that is, the largest dimension for a shaft and the smallest for a hole. This system lends itself well to situations where individual parts, perhaps only one, are produced and measured by the machinist. This method is shown in Fig. 12.14(a).

b. Maximum number method. This second method is more commonly used on mass-production drawings, and in this scheme the largest number is always placed above the line as shown in Fig. 12.14(b). This is simpler for the draftsman and is preferred by quality-control departments. Both methods should not be used on the same drawing.

12.19.4 Note form. For dimensions that need not be held to close tolerances, the variation permitted is frequently specified by a general note in the form illustrated by the following examples.

Unless otherwise specified, tolerances are as follows:

> Fractional dimensions $\pm$ $\frac{1}{32}$
> Decimal dimensions $\pm$ 0.01
> Angular dimensions $\pm$ 0°30′
> All diameters concentric within 0.001 FIR.

FIR means full indicator reading. The letters TIR are sometimes used for the same purpose and mean total indicator reading.

12.20 COMPUTING SIZE TOLERANCE DIMENSIONS FOR CYLINDRICAL MATING PARTS FROM TABLES. The computation of tolerances for mating parts may be determined in the following ways:

a. From USASI B4.1—1955 preferred limits and fits for cylindrical parts or from company standards.
b. By selecting standard parts such as bolts and then standard drills for holes of a somewhat larger size and computing tolerances from these dimensions.

12.20.1 Basic hole method. In this method the computed size of the hole is considered as the basic size, and the size of the shaft is determined by subtracting the allowance from the hole size, thus giving the design size for the shaft. Tolerances are then applied to each part. For example, if the basic diameter of a hole is to be 3.0000 inches and a class RC 7 fit is desired, the table below shows the following data (limits are in thousandths of an inch):

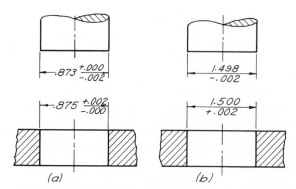

(a)   (b)

Fig. 12.11 Unilateral tolerance system.

Nominal Size Range, Inches	Limits of Clearance	Standard Limits	
		Hole	Shaft
1.97–3.15	4.0	+3.0	−4.0
	8.8	0.0	−5.8

For the hole the limits are:

$$3.0000 + 0.0000 \quad \text{and}$$
$$3.0000 + 0.0030 = 3.0030$$

For the shaft the limits are:

$$3.0000 - 0.0040 = 2.9960 \quad \text{and}$$
$$3.0000 - 0.0058 = 2.9942$$

The tightest fit therefore is $3.0000 - 2.9960 = 0.004$, which is the allowance, and the loosest fit is $3.0030 - 2.9942 = 0.0088$, which equals the allowance plus both tolerances. See second column in the table; also Fig. 12.15(a).

As a second illustration, let us consider a force fit FN3 for a 3-inch diameter hole. The data below are from Table 5, USASI B4.1–1955. Limits are in thousandths of an inch.

Nominal Size Range, Inches	Limits of Interference	Standard Limits	
		Hole	Shaft
2.56–3.15	1.8	+1.2	+3.7
	3.7	0.0	+3.0

For the hole the limits are:

$$3.0000 + 0.0012 = 3.0012 \quad \text{and}$$
$$3.0000 + 0.0000 = 3.0000$$

For the shaft the limits are:

$$3.0000 + 0.0037 = 3.0037 \quad \text{and}$$
$$3.0000 + 0.0030 = 3.0030$$

The tightest fit occurs when the largest shaft, 3.0037, is placed in the smallest hole, 3.0000, giving an interference of 0.0037. In a similar manner the loosest fit occurs with the smallest shaft and the largest hole, giving an interference of 0.0018.

Other types of fits are handled in the same manner. Although the tables in USASI B4.1–1955 do not show allowance and tolerances as such, it may be noted that the upper figure in the shaft column for each size is the

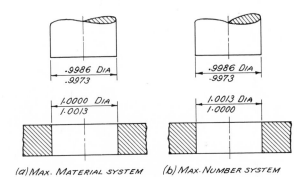

(a) MAX. MATERIAL SYSTEM   (b) MAX. NUMBER SYSTEM

Fig. 12.14   Two methods of placing limit dimensions.

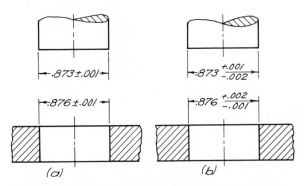

(a)   (b)

Fig. 12.12   Bilateral tolerance system.

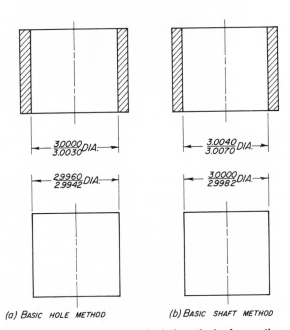

(a) BASIC HOLE METHOD   (b) BASIC SHAFT METHOD

Fig. 12.15   Basic hole and basic shaft methods of computing limits.

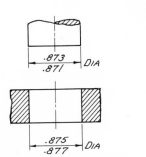

Fig. 12.13   Limit tolerancing system.

allowance and the difference between this figure and the lower one is the shaft tolerance.

12.20.2 Basic shaft method. The tables in USASI B4.1—1955 are designed specifically for tolerances by the basic hole method, which is usually preferred. The basic shaft is the system used when purchased finished parts, such as assembled ball bearings, must be fitted into machined housings.

The simplest way for computing the limits for the basic shaft method in the case of clearance fits is to add the allowance (upper figure in the shaft column of the table) to each of the limits obtained by the basic hole method. Using the same illustration as given for the basic hole method, add 0.0040 to each dimension, thus finding the values shown in the column marked Basic Shaft Method. See Table in Art. 12.20.1 at bottom of page 334.

Basic Hole Method		Basic Shaft Method	
Hole	Shaft	Hole	Shaft
3.0000	2.9960	3.0040	3.0000
3.0030	2.9942	3.0070	2.9982

The limits of clearance will be the same in both cases. See Fig. 12.15(*b*).

For interference fits the allowance (upper number in the shaft column) is subtracted from the basic hole limits. Using the same illustration as before for an FN3 fit, subtract 0.0037 from each value listed under Basic Hole Method.

Basic Hole Method		Basic Shaft Method	
Hole	Shaft	Hole	Shaft
3.0000	3.0037	2.9963	3.0000
3.0012	3.0030	2.9975	2.9993

The loosest fit is −0.0018 and the tightest fit is −0.0037, which agrees with the data in the table under limits of interference.

12.21 ANALYSIS OF DIMENSIONING. A technical drawing, as discussed previously, involves three elements:

a. Shape description by means of two or more orthographic views, which completely define the geometric shape of an object and all of its related features or elements.

b. Description of size of features and location of features relative to each other. This is done by means of dimensions, symbols, and notes, which clearly and unmistakably define the size and relationships of all features of an object.

c. The specification of the kind and quality of materials to be used and of the finish, as to both surface quality and protective coatings such as plating or painting.

12.21.1 Methods of inspection. In this chapter we are concerned primarily with dimensioning. If we consider only size dimensioning, this seems to be a simple matter, since the part is relatively easy to inspect. It should be noted, however, that the method of inspection may make a difference in the acceptance or rejection of parts.

In Fig. 12.16 a single hole is shown with limits (0.375–0.390) specified by note, but the part has been produced to the actual measurements shown. With a "Go/No-Go" gage, as illustrated in the sectioned front view, this part will be accepted, since the "Go" part enters the hole, but the "No-Go" part does not,

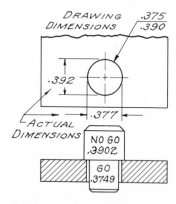

Fig. 12.16 Acceptance of part by plug gage not to specifications by reason of out of roundness.

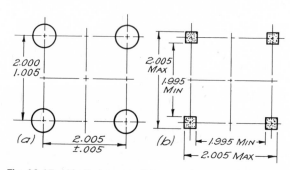

Fig. 12.17 Limited center distances give rectangular tolerance zones. (Courtesy USASI.)

even though it is oversize and out of round. But if it were inspected with a micrometer caliper, the reading would show 0.392, which indicates departure from specified dimensions, and the part would be rejected.

To achieve the design intent, engineering, manufacturing, and inspection departments must be consulted if economical production is to result. Dimensioning with respect to size and location relationships must be so specified that manufacturing and inspection will use the same datum surfaces, points, or axes. It should be further emphasized that the method of verification must be agreed upon, whether it is to be "open set-up" inspections with standard gages, calipers, surface plates, and the like or with functional, fixed-pin acceptance gages. The method to be used will depend on the intent and function of the design and the number of parts to be made.

When location is involved, in addition to size, the problem becomes more complicated and the need for coordination of manufacturing and inspection becomes more important.

12.22 COORDINATE SYSTEMS OF DIMENSIONING. Two systems of coordinate dimensioning are in common use. Their application depends on the form and function of the part. These methods are discussed in the following paragraphs.

12.22.1 Rectangular coordinates. Holes, for example, may be located by giving limit dimensions to their centers from each of two planes at right angles to each other as shown in Fig. 12.17(a). This method results in a square tolerance zone for the location of centers, as shown in Fig. 12.17(b). It will be noted in Fig. 12.18 that the tolerance along the diagonal of the square is 1.4 times the tolerance specified. This is not a desirable feature.

Methods of coordinate dimensioning are discussed in Art. 11.7.4 and are illustrated in Figs. 11.48 and 11.49 of Chapter 11.

12.22.2 Polar coordinates. Location tolerances may also be specified in polar-coordinate form by giving limits on the radial and angular dimensions as shown in Fig. 12.19(a). This results in a sector tolerance zone, as shown in Fig. 12.19(b).

12.23 ACCUMULATION OF TOLERANCES IN THE COORDINATE SYSTEM. In coordinate dimensioning tolerances may accumulate and interfere with assembly or function of the parts or feature. This may occur in several ways.

12.23.1 Accumulation by chain dimensioning. If chain dimensioning is used, an undesirable accumulation of tolerances results, as shown in Fig. 12.20. The tolerance between any two holes is not that specified on the drawing. Thus between A and B in Fig. 12.20 the variation in position could be from 1.95 to 2.05 inches.

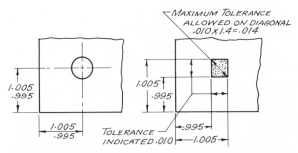

Fig. 12.18 Greater tolerance on diagonal then specified. Courtesy (USASI.)

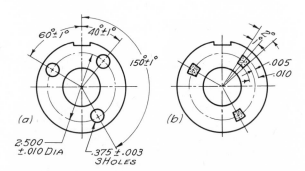

Fig. 12.19 Polar coordinates give sector tolerance zones. (Courtesy USASI.)

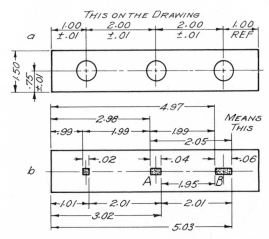

Fig. 12.20 Chain dimensioning produces cumulative Tolerances.

12.23.2 Accumulation by a stack-up of toleranced parts. Tolerances may also accumulate simply as a result of the assembly of a group of toleranced pieces. Thus, in Fig. 12.21, several pieces, each with a tolerance of its own, are assembled with a bolt as shown. The toleranced dimensions are shown in Fig. 12.21(a).

When all of the parts are at maximum size and the length of the bolt to the shoulder is at minimum size, as in Fig. 12.21(b), the plates are firmly clamped together. When the parts are at minimum size and the length of the bolt to the shoulder is at maximum size, as shown in Fig. 12.21(c), the plates are not clamped and there will be some play between the parts. If it is intended that the parts be clamped together, the second situation will not be acceptable.

The stack-up of parts in Fig. 12.21 could have been reduced by a choice of smaller tolerances. This method, of course, can be more expensive. In this

tween successive holes remains constant at 2.00 plus or minus 0.02 inch.

12.25 SELECTION OF DATUM SURFACES OR LINES. In dimensioning mating parts, the surfaces that will function or fit together must be used as datum surfaces for both parts. Thus in Fig. 12.23 if the dimension a in Fig. 12.23(a) is to be controlled and no bearing at surface B can be permitted, then surface C must be the datum for both parts, as shown in Figs. 12.23(b) and (c).

12.25.1 Identification of datum by dimensioning. On some drawings the datum surface or surfaces can be readily implied by the position in which dimensions are placed. Thus in Fig. 12.22 the left end is clearly the datum surface for the holes.

In Fig. 12.24(a), the left and bottom sides are indicated as the datum surfaces by the method of dimensioning that is used to locate the hole and the other

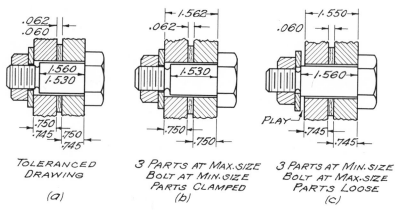

TOLERANCED DRAWING

(a)

3 PARTS AT MAX. SIZE BOLT AT MIN. SIZE PARTS CLAMPED

(b)

3 PARTS AT MIN. SIZE BOLT AT MAX. SIZE PARTS LOOSE

(c)

Fig. 12.21   Tolerance accumulation of three parts.

case, however, a gasket having a thickness of 0.082–0.084 would have solved the problem. With the plates at minimum dimensions, the gasket between them also at minimum thickness, and the bolt at maximum length, the nut could be tightened enough to take up the 0.012 inch oversize and clamp the plates. With all parts at maximum size, there is an 0.024 take up for clamping and no problem.

12.24 CONTROL OF CUMULATIVE TOLERANCES BY DATUM DIMENSIONING. Some control of cumulative tolerances can be attained by referring all dimensions in a given direction to the same datum surface. Thus in Fig. 12.22 the left end of the part has been used as a datum and each hole has been located from this datum individually. Note that the distance be-

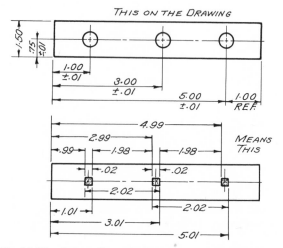

Fig. 12.22   Datum dimensioning reduces cumulative tolerances.

two sides. While the roughness of the surface of the part is exaggerated in Fig. 12.24(*b*), it does indicate that the real datum at inspection is on the gage and is identified on the part by the bearing points. This fact should not be overlooked, even though surfaces on the object must be used or marked as datums.

Features that are selected to serve as datum surfaces must be clearly identified and easily recognizable on the part. To be useful for measurement, a datum indicated on an actual piece must be accessible during manufacture so that measurement can be made readily. Sometimes a single pilot hole may not be adequate. Two aligned holes or a hole and a slot are pref-

erable, since this provides both location and orientation. See Fig. 12.25.

12.25.2 Datum indicated by note. In more complicated parts the datum should be indicated by note, as in Fig. 12.25. The center line through the large pilot hole and the slot is thus specified for both location and orientation. Other methods of identifying datum surface and lines are discussed in Art. 12.34.2.

12.25.3 Accuracy of datum surfaces. Even though the theoretical datum is on the gage, the datum surface indicated on an actual piece must nevertheless be more accurate than any location established from it. Thus if measurements are made from a datum surface

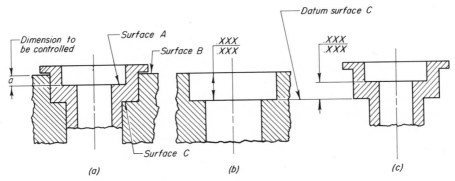

Fig. 12.23 Controlling part tolerances by selection of datum. (Courtesy SAE.)

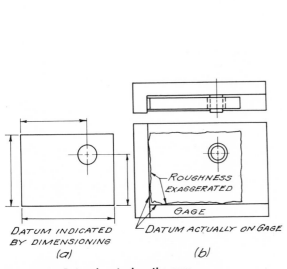

Fig. 12.24 Datum is actual on the gage.

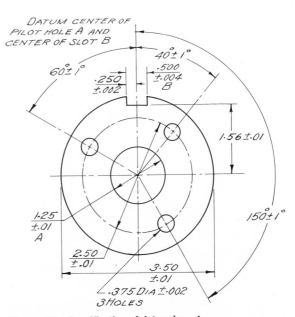

Fig. 12.25 Specification of datum by note.

to establish hole locations with a tolerance of 0.010, the total effect of surface inaccuracies on the measurements must be considerably less than 0.010, or the locations will not have the specified accuracy. It may be necessary to specify the accuracy of a datum surface by giving tolerances on features such as straightness, flatness, and roundness to assure that locations can be established with the specified accuracy.

12.25.4   Location of surface finished first on a casting. Since most machined parts begin with a casting or a forging, it is necessary for the machinist to locate the first surface to be finished from some relatively rough surface on the original casting. This surface should therefore be located only once from one suitable, unfinished surface. The finished surface thus established may be the datum for the location of other finished features. See Fig. 12.26.

12.26*   GEOMETRIC FORM, TRUE-POSITION DIMENSIONING, AND TOLERANCING. This form of dimensioning does not supersede or displace coordinate dimensioning discussed in preceding paragraphs. Rather, it supplements this system and produces greater efficiency in drafting and manufacturing since it frequently provides extra tolerances.

American, British, and Canadian industries, as well as the military services and governments, are essentially agreed upon this system. Subcontracting of

---

* Some of the material in the following articles has been abstracted from *A Treatise on Geometric and Positional Dimensioning and Tolerancing,* by Lowell W. Foster, Senior Standardization Engineer, Honeywell, Inc., Minneapolis, Minn.

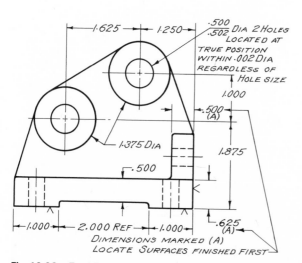

Fig. 12.26   Establishing first finished surface from one rough surface only.

work and the transfer of personnel between plants and industries make a uniform and clear drawing and dimensioning system essential.

12.27   WHEN TO USE GEOMETRIC FORM AND POSITIONAL TOLERANCING. In many cases where fit and function of parts is not critical the coordinate system of dimensioning and tolerancing is satisfactory and may be used.

Geometric form and true position dimensioning and tolerancing are very useful and are recommended in the following situations.

a. Where the size, form, and location of part features are critical with respect to function or interchangeability.

b. When functional gaging or inspection techniques are desirable. See Art. 12.28(*b*).

c. When datum references are desirable to insure compatability between manufacturing and inspection methods.

d. When interpretation of tolerances is not clearly evident or implied.

12.28   TRUE-POSITION DIMENSIONING. In this system the location of features is given by basic or untoleranced dimensions. These dimensions give the true position of the features, and the tolerance around these centers is given by a note along with the size of the feature, as shown in Fig. 12.27(*b*). True-position dimensions, that is those without tolerances, are enclosed in a rectangle in the symbolic system, as shown in Fig. 12.27(*b*). When notes are used, the word Basic or the abbreviation BSC is placed under the dimension. This method results in a circular tolerance zone, as shown in Fig. 12.28(*b*) as distinguished from the rectangular zone shown in Fig. 12.28(*a*). The true-position method has the following advantages over the coordinate method with limited center distances.

a. It corresponds to the distribution of errors that normally arise in production.

b. It corresponds to the control established by fixed-position gages.

c. It permits the use of chain dimensioning without the accumulation of tolerances.

d. It makes possible the specification of different tolerances for each of a number of features lying on a common center line.

e. It makes it simpler to determine the clearance between mating components because equal deviation is permitted in all directions.

12.28.1   Dimensioning methods compared. In Fig. 12.27 a simple plate with four holes has been dimensioned. In Fig. 12.27(*a*) the coordinate method has been used, while in Fig. 12.27(*b*) the true position has been used. Note the difference in the methods.

a. In the coordinate method the positional tolerance is given with the location dimension as 0.625 ± 0.005 and 2.000 ± 0.005.

b. In the true-position method the positional tolerance is given with the hole specification; see Fig. 12.27(*b*). True-position dimensions are enclosed in a rectangle. The word Basic or abbreviation BSC may be used in the note form.

c. This results in a difference in the shape and size of the tolerance zones, as shown in Figs. 12.28(*a*) and (*b*).

12.28.2   Tolerance zones compared. In Fig. 12.28(*a*) the tolerance zone is a square 0.01 inch on a side. The center of the holes could be anywhere within this square, even at the end of a diagonal. If it were at this point, it would be at 0.007 from the true position and would be acceptable, even though this is more than the 0.005 specified.

In the true-position method, the tolerance zone will be a circle, since the diameter is specified. To give the same extreme tolerance as the square, this zone diameter can be 0.014 inch. This provides greater leeway in manufacturing, yet controls functioning as well as the square zone. With this larger tolerance more acceptable parts are produced and fewer parts must be scrapped.

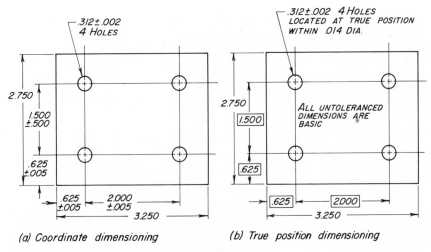

(a) Coordinate dimensioning   (b) True position dimensioning

Fig. 12.27   **Dimensioning methods compared.**

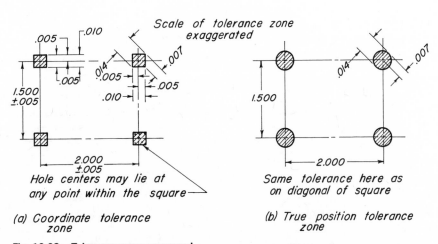

(a) Coordinate tolerance zone   (b) True position tolerance zone

Fig. 12.28   **Tolerance zones compared.**

12.28.3   Additional tolerance available when feature is not at MMC. When true-position dimensioning is used, the tolerance is assumed to be with the features at MMC even though not specified. The maximum material condition may be specified, if desired, by adding "at MMC" to the tolerance note.

When the holes shown in two parts in Fig. 12.29 are away from MMC toward the largest permissible size, more positional tolerance is available, as shown in Fig. 12.29(b).

If the design function of the part will prohibit this additional locational tolerance, the tolerance *must be marked* RFS, which means "Regardless of Feature Size." This holds the tolerance to the specified size.

12.28.4   Size of fixed-position functional gage pins. With the true-position dimensioning shown in Fig.

12.27, the size of the functional gage pin is shown in Fig. 12.29(a). From this fixture it can be seen that the *size of gage pins for circular holes is equal to the minimum size of the hole minus the diameter of the positional tolerance zone.*

Thus if two circles representing the minimum size of the holes (MMC) are drawn with centers at the opposite ends of the tolerance zone diameter, it can be seen that the diameter of the gage pin must be

$$0.310 = \text{smallest hole size}$$
$$\frac{0.014}{0.296} = \frac{\text{diameter of tolerance zone}}{\text{diameter of gage pin}}$$

On the other hand, if the diameter of the holes at their largest size (minimum material) is used, as in Fig. 12.29(b), and the same gage pin is used for check-

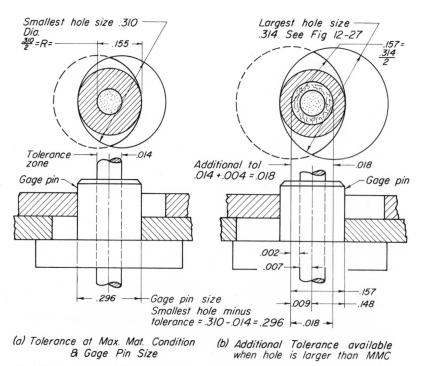

(a) Tolerance at Max. Mat. Condition & Gage Pin Size

(b) Additional Tolerance available when hole is larger than MMC

Fig. 12.29   Additional tolerance available when position tolerance is noted at MMC.

ing, then the locational tolerance is

0.314 = hole size
0.296 = gage pin size

0.018 = diameter of tolerance zone
0.014 = specified tolerance

0.004 = increase of tolerance, which is equal
to the hole size tolerance

12.28.5 Computation of positional tolerance from bolt and hole sizes. Where positional tolerances do not need to be as close as those given in the USASI Standard for cylindrical fits, as discussed in Art. 12.20, a satisfactory tolerance can be chosen by using standard parts such as bolts and standard tool sizes such as drills for making the holes.

a. The bolt size can be determined by computation for strength and rigidity. Thus computations might call for a bolt 0.367 inch in diameter. The next larger standard size would be chosen, namely 0.375 inch. The actual body diameter is 0.388.

b. The hole could then be chosen to give approximately $\frac{1}{32}$ inch clearance

$$0.388 + 0.031 = 0.419$$

A $^{27}\!\!/_{64}$-inch drill could be chosen. The diameter in decimals is 0.422.

The actual clearance would then be 0.422 − 0.388 = 0.034.

Due to vibration and wear of the tools the holes could be 0.422 ± 0.002.

If the bolts also were permitted to vary between

0.388 + 0.002 and 0.388 − 0.002, the locational tolerance at MMC would then be 0.420 − 0.390 = 0.03 or ±0.015.

In many cases a much more generous clearance or allowance could be provided.

12.29 METHODS OF SPECIFYING TRUE-POSITION TOLERANCES. As already mentioned, a tolerance is the total variation permitted; hence, for location, the diameter of the tolerance zone is the total tolerance. The note, or other specification, should be unmistakable in this respect.

12.29.1 By note specifying the diameter. One method of specifying the true-position tolerance is to give the diameter of the tolerance zone, as shown in Fig. 12.30.

12.29.2 By note specifying the radius. Because of long practice in some industries, the specification of the radius of the tolerance zone is also approved, as shown in Fig. 12.31. The modifier MMC in Fig. 12.31 indicates the possibility of a more liberal tolerance, as discussed in Art. 12.28.3. The radius, however, must be recognized as a *deviation* from true position and the tolerance is twice the radius. The modifier, "Regardless of Feature or Hole Size," in Fig. 12.31, sometimes abbreviated to RFS, indicates restriction to the specified tolerance, no matter what the hole size.

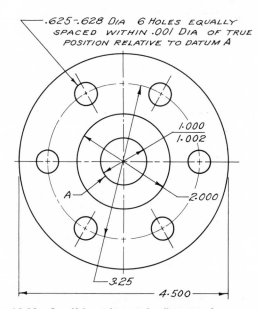

Fig. 12.30 Specifying tolerance by diameter of zone.

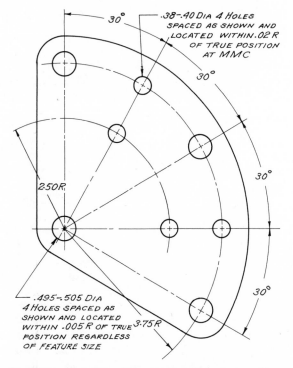

Fig. 12.31 Specifying tolerance by radius of zone. (Courtesy USASI.)

12.30 APPLICATION OF TRUE-POSITION DIMENSIONING AND DATUM SELECTION. As a practical illustration of true-position dimensioning and of proper selection of datum surfaces, Figs. 12.32, 12.33, and 12.34 are presented. These figures are detailed drawings needed to implement the design layout shown in Fig. 12.1.

In the subassembly layout shown in Fig. 12.1, the flange plate functions as the mounting base for the two other parts. It should therefore be detailed first, as shown in Fig. 12.32.

12.30.1 Primary datum. The center of the large pilot hole *A* (Dia. 2.786-2.789) and the square plate mounting face are chosen as the primary datum for dimensioning, since they establish the position of the flange plate relative to the wheel hub and position the entire assembly.

The general shape of the plate is defined by dimensioning the square-shaped depression surrounding the pilot hole. Then the step to the next level (0.98) is given and finally the step to the outer rim (9.68 and 12.00), as shown in Fig. 12.32. While the latter dimensions are not specifically tied into the center of the pilot hole by half-diameter dimensions, the symmetry of the piece indicates that this is the datum. It should be noted that all form dimensions are given to the same side of the metal. This is done to assist the die designer and to avoid unnecessary tolerance accumulation due to variation in stock thickness.

The four mounting holes (3.91-0.406 Dia.) are located from the primary datum with basic dimensions, since their tolerance is given in relation to the pilot hole by the true-position tolerance (0.005R), given in the note for the diameters of the mounting holes. See Fig. 12.32.

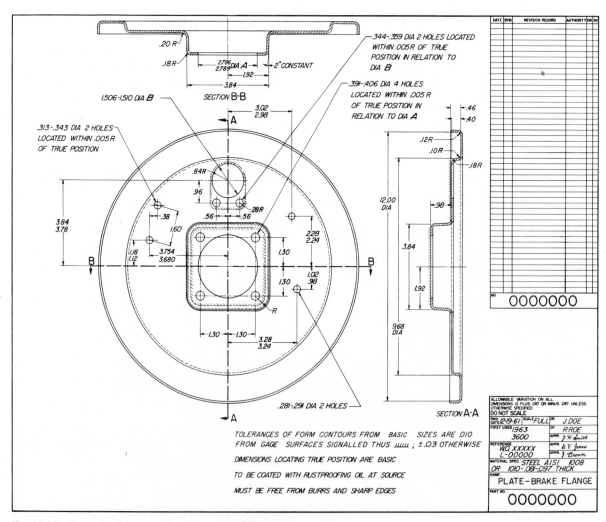

Fig. 12.32 Example of true-position tolerancing. (Courtesy General Motors Corp.)

12.30.2 Secondary datum. The smaller wheel-cylinder pilot hole (1.506-1.510 Dia. *B*) and the two bolt holes are located as a group by the toleranced dimension (3.84-3.78 at the left) from the primary datum to the center of the wheel-cylinder pilot hole. See Fig. 12.33 for fitting spigot (1.495-1.505 Dia. *Y*). The center of the wheel-cylinder pilot hole is the datum for the group, and the two bolt holes are dimensioned in relation to the group datum *B* with basic dimensions. The true-position tolerance for these holes is given with the note for these holes and with the note for the diameter (0.344-0.359) of the two bolt holes.

The two holes at the left on the flange-plate detail, Fig. 12.32, which are used for mounting the brake-cable clamp, are located as a group by toleranced dimensions from the primary datum. In this case the lower left hole becomes the group datum, and the other hole is located from the first by basic dimensions with a true-position tolerance.

The two holes at the right in Fig. 12.32 are clip holes used independently of each other and of other features. Therefore, they are located with liberally toleranced dimensions from the primary datum.

12.30.3 Form-contour tolerances. Since the position and form-contour variations (flatness and parallelism) must be limited on both flange-plate mounting surface and the wheel-cylinder mounting surface, these tolerances are expressed with the contour-tolerance note, with the affected areas signaled _∕∕∕∕∕∕∕_ as shown in Fig. 12.32.

12.30.4 Wheel-cylinder body. The second part of the subassembly shown in Fig. 12.33 mounts on the flange plate. The same fundamental method or pattern of dimensioning must be used. Note that the

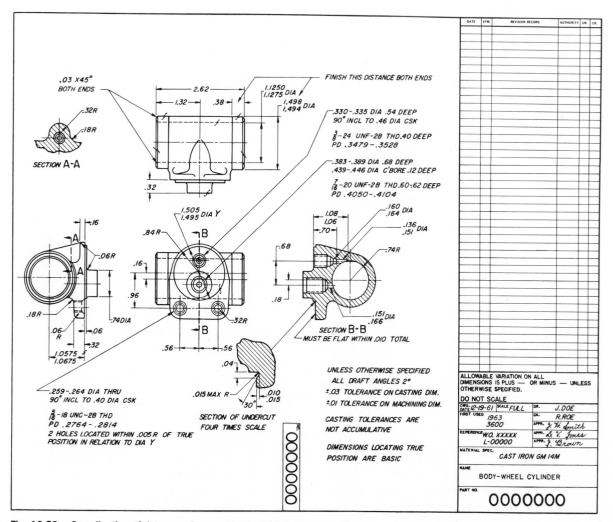

Fig. 12.33 Coordination of datum surfaces with Fig. 12.32. (Courtesy GMC.)

spigot (1.495-1.505 Dia. *Y*) in Fig. 12.33 is toleranced to mate with pilot hole *B* (1.506-1.510) in Fig. 12.32. The two threaded holes are located by true-position dimensioning from the center of the spigot, insuring assembly with the hole pattern on the flange plate. Note that the untoleranced basic dimensions from spigot and pilot hole are the same on both drawings and the true-position tolerance is also the same. The two threaded holes that enter the cylinder, in section *B-B*, are located by basic or untoleranced dimensions so that the general tolerance of 0.01 given in the general notes applies.

The surface of the mounting flange of the wheel-cylinder body and the center of the spigot Dia. *Y* are chosen as primary datums for dimensions of this part, since it is located by these features at assembly to the flange plate. The cylinder bore (1.1250-1.1257 Dia.) in turn becomes the datum for the location of the threaded holes that enter the bore.

12.30.5   Brake-cable clamp. Although this part is in an angular position on the layout, Fig. 12.1, it is drawn in relation to its own logical bases in Fig. 12.34.

This is done to provide practical datums for dimensioning and to simplify manufacture and inspection of the detail part. The surface of the mounting flange and the center of one mounting hole are chosen as primary datum surfaces for dimensioning the part, since it is located by these features at assembly to the flange plate. The position of the plan view is determined by the center of the clamp hole. The flange thickness and the center of the clamp hole are located from the primary datum.

The clamp hole is located at one end by a height dimension (0.704-0.734), by the dimension 0.30 from the datum hole, and by an angle. See front view in Fig. 12.34. The use of an angle instead of a height dimension at the other end is justified in this case, since forging variations on the boss would not be compatible with the tolerances that would have to be applied to the second height dimension to control the finished hole properly.

Secondary datum. The center of the clamp hole in turn becomes the datum for the boss, slot, and clamp-bolt hole.

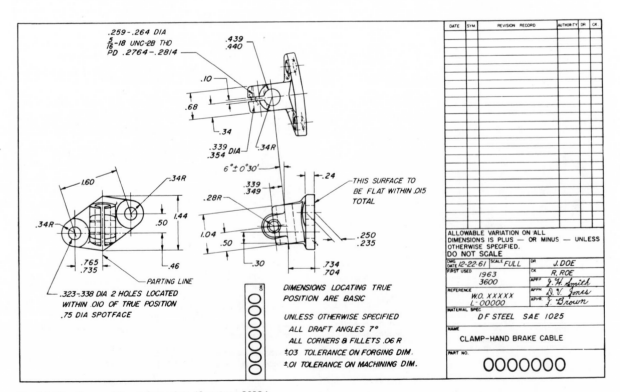

Fig. 12.34   True-position tolerancing. (Courtesy GMC.)

12.30.6 Gaging control. To make the drawing more effective for the control of inspection, the following note could be added to Fig. 12.32 with a leader to one of the four wheel-mounting holes:

0.391 Dia. 4 holes must freely admit basically located
0.406

gage pins 0.010 under minimum hole size when gage is piloted in Dia. *A* with 2.776 Dia. pilot.

Other holes, such as the wheel-cylinder mounting and the cable-clamp mounting, would be controlled in the same way.

12.31 TRUE-POSITION DIMENSIONING WITH SYMBOLS. In the foregoing articles true-position dimensioning has been accomplished by the use of notes. This can be simplified by the use of symbols, which are shown in Fig. 12.35. The application of the true-position symbol and the datum symbol are shown in Fig. 12.36.

		CHARACTERISTICS	APPLICABILITY OF MODIFIERS TO FEATURE
FORM TOLERANCE SYMBOLS	FOR SINGLE FEATURES	FLATNESS (Applied to a plane surface)	NOT APPLICABLE
		STRAIGHTNESS (Other than planes)	MMC APPLICABLE
		ROUNDNESS	NOT APPLICABLE
		CYLINDRICITY (Not in Mil Std 8c)	NOT APPLICABLE
		SURFACE PROFILE	NOT APPLICABLE
		LINE PROFILE	NOT APPLICABLE
	FOR RELATED FEATURES	SQUARENESS OR PERPENDICULARITY	MMC & RFS MODIFIER APPLICABLE IF TOLERANCE APPLIES TO AXIS OR CENTER PLANE OF A FEATURE WITH SIZE; NOT APPLICABLE IF CONSIDERED FEATURE IS A PLANE
		PARALLELISM	
		ANGULARITY	
		RUNOUT	NOT APPLICABLE
POSITIONAL TOLERANCES		TRUE POSITION & SYMMETRY	SEE NOTE ABOVE
		CONCENTRICITY	SEE NOTE ABOVE
		SYMMETRY (Old symbol)	SEE NOTE ABOVE
		DATUM (Any letters except I,O,Q & RMS)	MODIFIER MAY BE APPLIED WHEN DATUM IS NOT A PLANE
MODIFIERS	Ⓜ Ⓢ	Ⓜ = MMC = MAXIMUM MATERIAL CONDITION Ⓢ = RFS = REGARDLESS OF FEATURE SIZE	

Fig. 12.35 Form tolerancing symbols.

12.32 FORM TOLERANCES CONTROLLED BY SIZE AND LOCATION TOLERANCE. In the past the geometric form of parts was assumed to be as shown by the drawing; that is, when two faces of a part are shown at right angles to each other on a drawing, these faces were assumed to be made at right angles to each other in the shop.

12.32.1 Control by size tolerance. When there is doubt that ordinary shop practice will produce this form, it should be controlled in some way by a form tolerance. In many instances, the size tolerance given a part is sufficient to control the form. Thus in Fig. 12.37 the form implied by the drawing is a true hexagon, and the size tolerance given will control the shape within the limits shown in (b). In Fig. 12.38, straightness of a pin and hole is controlled by size tolerance only, and illustrations of permissible departure from straightness are shown in (b), (c), (e), and (f). Where greater accuracy of form is required, form tolerances must be specified. Such tolerances must naturally al-

ways be smaller than the size tolerances.

12.32.2 Form control by location tolerance. True-position tolerancing establishes a tolerance zone for the location of the axis of a feature such as a hole. The axis must lie within this tolerance zone throughout its length. Thus location tolerance automatically controls squareness of the axis of the hole with the surface to which the drawing shows it to be perpendicular, as shown in Fig. 12.39. It will also control the parallelism of one hole with another.

12.33 GEOMETRIC FORM TOLERANCING. When greater accuracy of form must be obtained than that given by size and location tolerances, specific form tolerancing must be used. Form tolerances are also necessary for some geometric shapes that cannot be controlled by size and location tolerancing. This may be done by (a) the use of notes and (b) the use of the symbols shown in Fig. 12.35.

In order to simplify the specification of form and also true-position tolerances, symbols have been de-

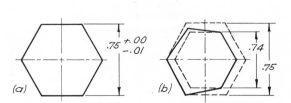

Fig. 12.36   True position with symbols.

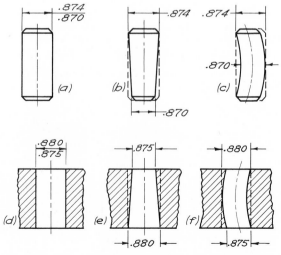

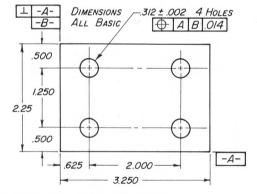

Fig. 12.37   Form controlled by size tolerance. (Courtesy USASI.)

Fig. 12.38   Straightness controlled by size tolerance. (Courtesy USASI.)

signed, used, and standardized as shown in Figs. 12.35 and 12.40.

12.33.1 Specifying form tolerance by notes. In the following paragraphs and illustrations form tolerance by the use of notes is shown. Their meaning or interpretation is also given.

12.33.2 Specifying form tolerance by symbols. The specification of form tolerancing and true-positional tolerancing are more rapidly done by the use of symbols. The following paragraphs show how to use the symbols and where to place them.

12.34 GENERAL RULES FOR USE OF SYMBOLS*. When using symbols for geometric form and true-position tolerancing, the following rules should be observed:

a. When no modifier is specified, true-position tolerances apply at maximum material condition. This condition also applies to datum references other than plane surfaces.

* From *A Treatise on Geometric and Positional Dimensioning and Tolerancing,* by Lowell W. Foster, Senior Standards Engineer, Honeywell, Inc., Minneapolis, Minn.

b. When no modifier is specified, all other positional or form tolerances apply regardless of feature size. See Fig. 12.40. "Regardless of feature size" also applies to datum surfaces.

c. All tolerances specified in connection with positional or form tolerancing are preferably totals, but radial deviations may be used if designated *R.* Military Standard 8C* also permits the use of "radius," "either side," or "on radius" if designated by *R,* "either side" or "on *R*" in the note or symbol. Total width, thickness, or diameter is preferred.

12.34.1 Placing symbols on drawings. All symbols are placed in enclosing rectangular boxes in order to call attention to them and to separate them clearly from other notes. In Figs. 12.40 and 12.41 the minimum size of the enclosing rectangles has been shown. Other symbols, abbreviations, and their meaning are also indicated in the figures.

* Mil. Std. 8C no longer available. See USASI Y–14.5.

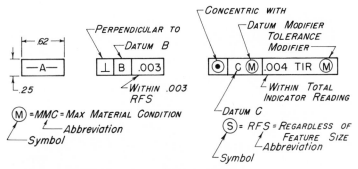

Fig. 12.40   Meaning and arrangement of symbols.

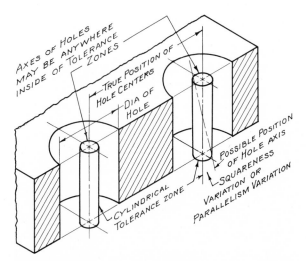

Fig. 12.39   Form tolerance controlled by location tolerance. (Courtesy USASI.)

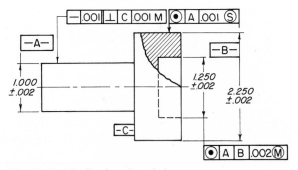

Fig. 12.41   Application of symbols.

As a further guide in the use of symbols and notes, the rules governing the use of the modifiers MMC and RFS and their symbols (M) and (S) should be noted. These rules are summarized in Fig. 12.42.

12.34.2 **Datum symbol.** (Symbol $\boxed{-A-}$.) The datum used for dimensioning is always marked when using the symbolic method. A part may have one, two, or more datum surfaces. These are indicated by capital letters enclosed in a box as shown in Figs. 12.40 and 12.41. There may be primary, secondary, and other datum surfaces. The alphabetical sequence of letters has no significance in this respect. The letters I, O, and Q should not be used, since they may be confused with other letters. The letters R, M, and S should not be used, since they are already reserved for other uses. The placing of the datum box will be indicated in the illustration that follows.

12.34.3 **Straightness.** (Symbol ——.) The straightness symbol is a single short (¼-inch) line placed in a box as shown in Fig. 12.43. Any element of the feature must be between two parallel lines spaced at the specified distance apart, as in Fig. 12.43(c). These lines lie in the same plane as the axis of the feature. If there is no modifier, straightness is implied to mean regardless of the size of the feature. The note form is shown in Fig. 12.43(b).

Type of Tolerance	Applicability of MMC and RFS	
	For the Feature	For the Datum Reference(s)
Flatness Straightness Roundness Cylindricity	Not applicable	No datum reference
Profile of any line Profile of any surface	Not applicable	If a datum reference is necessary, RFS applies.
Perpendicularity Parallelism Angularity True Position	MMC or RFS applicable if tolerance applies to axis or center plane of considered feature; not applicable if considered feature is one plane surface.	MMC or RFS applicable if datum feature has an axis or center plane; not applicable if datum feature is one plane surface.
Runout	Not applicable	Not applicable
Concentricity Symmetry	Only RFS applicable	Only RFS applicable

Fig. 12.42 **Application of tolerance modifiers. (Courtesy USASI.)**

In Fig. 12.43(c) the diametral dimensions could be 0.745 and 0.750 or any other pair differing by 0.005.

Straightness applies regardless of the length of the part. For long parts such as tubes or long shafts the tolerance could be specified as "straight within 0.001 per ft." In this case the note form would be used.

12.34.4   Flatness. (Symbol ▭.) The symbol form is shown in Fig. 12.44(a), the note form in Fig. 12.44(b), and the meaning in Fig. 12.44(c). The flatness tolerance of a plane surface is the zone between two parallel planes the specified distance apart. If applicable, a note such as "must not be convex" or "must not be concave" may be added to the note form.

12.34.5   Parallelism. (Symbol ‖.) This symbol specifies a tolerance zone prescribed by two planes parallel to a datum between which the surface or axis must lie. Parallelism could be specified for one plane parallel to a datum plane, as in Fig. 12.45, or as an axis parallel to a datum plane. It could also be an axis parallel to a datum axis, as in Fig. 12.46. Either the feature or the datum could be specified at RFS or MMC if datum is other than a plane. A plane has only location, and measurements are made from it. In the case of an axis, the hole around it must be used for gaging, hence it can be specified RFS or MMC.

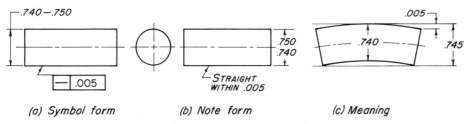

(a) Symbol form   (b) Note form   (c) Meaning

Fig. 12.43   Specifying straightness tolerance.

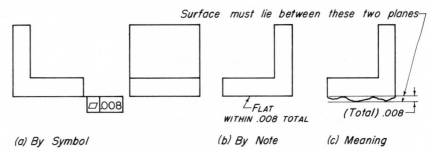

(a) By Symbol   (b) By Note   (c) Meaning

Fig. 12.44   Methods of specifying flatness.

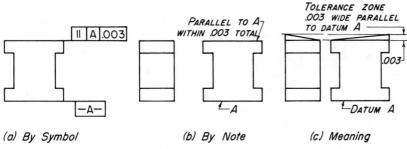

(a) By Symbol   (b) By Note   (c) Meaning

Fig. 12.45   Specifying parallelism between surfaces.

12.34.6 Squareness or perpendicularity. (Symbol ⊥.) The symbol form and note form for the squareness of one surface to a datum surface is shown in Fig. 12.47, as well as the interpretation.

For a slot the specification is shown in Fig. 12.48 and for a cylinder with reference to a datum plane in Figs. 12.49 and 12.50. Note that when the feature is specified at MMC there is always a greater tolerance available when the part is not at MMC.

12.34.7 Specifying dimensional tolerance and squareness. In some situations, when size is involved

as well as squareness, the squareness tolerance must lie within the size tolerance; otherwise it is meaningless. See Fig. 12.47.

12.34.8 Angularity. (Symbol ∠.) Angularity may be specified by note giving an angular tolerance as in Fig. 12.51. It may also be specified by giving a tolerance zone between two parallel planes either by symbols as in Fig. 12.52(*a*) or by note as in Fig. 12.52(*b*). Obviously the draftsman must be governed by the practice of his company.

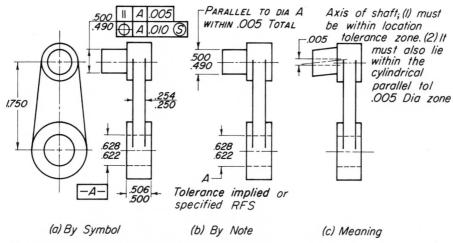

(a) By Symbol   (b) By Note   (c) Meaning

Fig. 12.46 Parallel form tolerance and location tolerance.

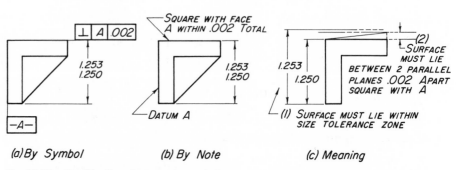

(a) By Symbol   (b) By Note   (c) Meaning

Fig. 12.47 Specification of squareness and size.

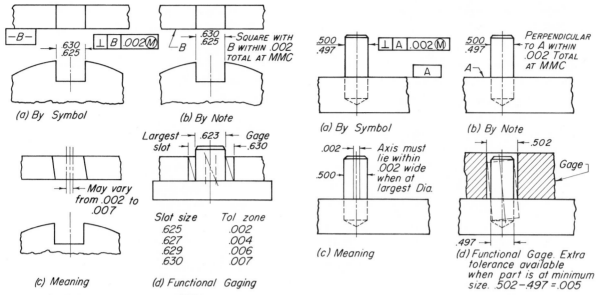

Fig. 12.48   Specifying squareness at MMC.

Fig. 12.49   Squareness tolerance for a pin at MMC.

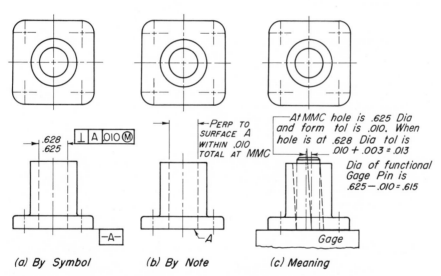

Fig. 12.50   Specifying perpendicularity of a cylindrical hole with plane datum.

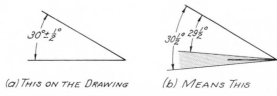

Fig. 12.51   Specifying angles.

12.34.9   Tapers. Applications of angularity tolerance are shown in Fig. 12.53. In Fig. 12.53 the gage diameter on the taper is not toleranced because doing so would give a cumulative tolerance. There are four possible dimensions that may be used to specify a taper. Any three may be employed, but the fourth may be given for reference only. Various combinations of the four dimensions are given in Figs. 12.53(*a*), (*b*), and (*c*). In Fig. 12.53(*d*) two dimensions are given for reference, and the location of the gaging point is toleranced.

12.34.10   Roundness. (Symbol ○.) Roundness may be specified as shown in Fig. 12.54, using either the radius or the diameter in describing the tolerance zone. The radius is preferred. Gaging, however, cannot be done with a micrometer caliper, since the lobed figures in Fig. 12.55 will measure the same as a true circle. Gaging should be done with three-point devices, as shown in Fig. 12.56. Roundness on a cone may be specified as shown in Fig. 12.57.

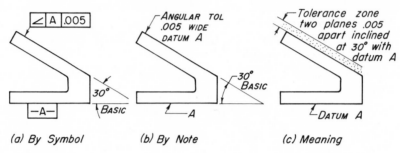

(a) By Symbol   (b) By Note   (c) Meaning

Fig. 12.52   Specifying angularity.

DRAWING CALLOUT

(a) DIMENSIONING OF CONICAL TAPERS BY SPECIFYING
A BASIC TAPER AND BASIC DIAMETER

DRAWING CALLOUT

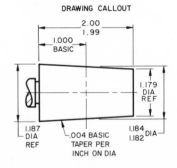

(c) DIMENSIONING OF CONICAL TAPERS BY
SPECIFYING A BASIC TAPER AND
BASIC DIAMETER

INTERPRETATION

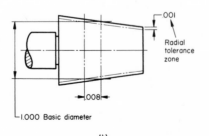

(b)

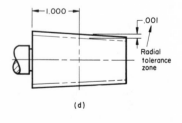

(d)

Fig. 12.53   Specification of taper tolerances. (Courtesy USASI.)

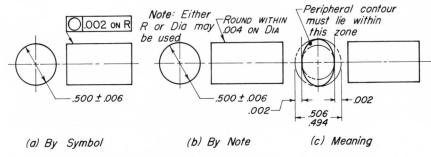

Fig. 12.54   Specifying roundness.

(a) By Symbol   (b) By Note   (c) Meaning

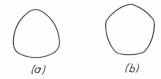

(a)   (b)

Fig. 12.55   Lobed shapes with constant diameters.

Fig. 12.56   Practical methods of checking roundness. (Courtesy British Standards Institution.)

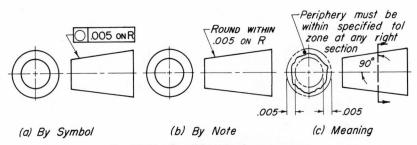

(a) By Symbol   (b) By Note   (c) Meaning

Fig. 12.57   Specifying roundness on a cone.

12.34.11   Concentricity. (Symbol ⊙.) The tolerance governing the concentricity of axes is the diameter of the tolerance zone within which the axis must lie, as shown in Fig. 12.58. The zone for the outside surface where gaging must be done is shown in Fig. 12.59(c). It should be noted that the actual eccentricity of the axis will be just one-half the diametral tolerance. The full indicator reading will be just twice the eccentricity.

Figure 12.60 gives an illustration of concentricity

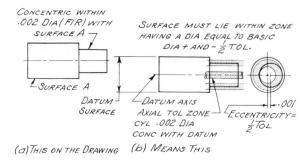

Fig. 12.58   Specifying concentricity.

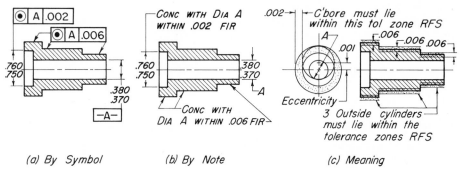

Fig. 12.59   Specifying concentricity.

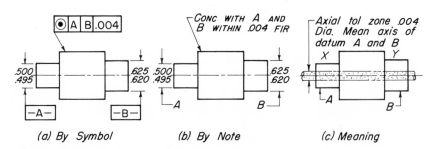

Fig. 12.60   Specifying concentricity with two datum references.

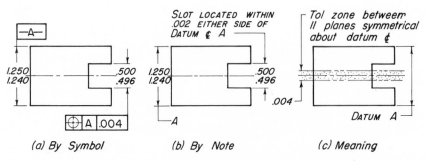

Fig. 12.61   Specifying symmetry (only RFS applicable).

specifications when two datum surfaces are involved. The datum axis is then the mean axis of the two parts.

When there are two datum surfaces, as in Fig. 12.60, the general procedure for checking is to mount the part on V blocks, one at X and one at Y. When the part is rotated on these V blocks, a gage on the surface under consideration will give a full indicator reading. However, this reading will include other items as well as concentricity, such as roundness and variation in angle between the center lines of surfaces X and Y. Because this fact is recognized, a composite tolerance is sometimes specified that will control all these variations. This is discussed in Arts. 12.34.12 and 12.34.13 and illustrated in Fig. 12.62.

12.34.12 Symmetry. (Symbol ⊕, old symbol ═.) Since symmetry is a form of true-position dimensioning, this symbol is now recommended. On older drawings the symbol previously used may be found. Both have the same connotation. See Fig. 12.61. The notes for symmetry, as well as all notes for other conditions, should state exactly what is meant. To say that the part is symmetrical within 0.001 would normally mean that it can vary by this amount on either side of the axis, making a tolerance zone 0.002 wide. The correct specification should read "symmetrical

with A within 0.002 total or within 0.002-wide zone."

12.34.13 Cylindricity. (Symbol ⌀.) This symbol for cylindricity is not included in Mil. Std. 8C. If used for military contracts, its meaning must be defined on the drawing. Cylindricity tolerance specifies a tolerance zone confined to the annular space between two concentric cylinders within which the entire surface must lie. See Fig. 12.62. It should be noted that cylindricity tolerance simultaneously controls roundness, straightness, and parallelism of the elements of the surface.

12.34.14 Profile of a surface. (Symbol ⌒.) This symbol for the control of the profile of a surface is taken from the USASI Y14.5—1966. A contour tolerance is used on shapes other than cylindrical. It may be unilateral or bilateral. The zone is shown by phantom lines, as in Fig. 12.63. This also indicates whether the zone is on one side or both sides of the specified surface. Measurements are made perpendicular to the contour at the point of measurement. An appropriate view or section showing the surface edgewise is drawn including the desired profile.

The profile is dimensioned by untoleranced dimensions referred to as basic. General tolerance notes do not apply and the drawing should be so noted.

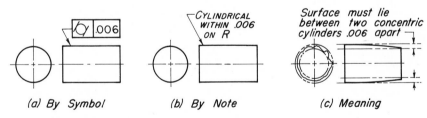

(a) By Symbol   (b) By Note   (c) Meaning

Fig. 12.62   Specifying cylindricity.

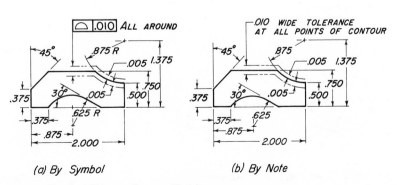

(a) By Symbol   (b) By Note

Fig. 12.63   Specifying surface profile tolerance.

12.34.15 Line profile. (Symbol ⌒.) The profile of a line is specified as in Fig. 12.64. This can be used when the line profile of a surface requires closer control than in the other direction.

12.34.16 Runout. (Symbol ↗.) This symbol is from USASI Y14.5—1966. The meaning of the runout tolerance is stated as in the following paragraphs:

a. Runout tolerance. A runout tolerance establishes a means of controlling the functional relationship of two or more features of a part within the allowable errors of concentricity, perpendicularity, and align-

ment of features. It also takes into account variations in roundness, straightness, flatness, and parallelism of individual surfaces. In essence, it establishes composite form control of those features of a part that have a common axis. Necessarily, then, measurements should be taken under a single setup and normal to the true, desired geometrical shape. In applying a runout tolerance, the accessibility of datums for single, setup measurements should be given consideration.

b. Basis of control. As a basis for the control of the relationship of features, it is necessary to establish a datum axis about which the features are related. This axis may be established by a diameter of considerable length, two diameters having considerable axial separation, or a diameter and a face that is at right angles to it. Insofar as possible, surfaces

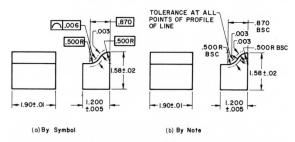

(a) By Symbol   (b) By Note

Fig. 12.64 Specifying line profile tolerance.

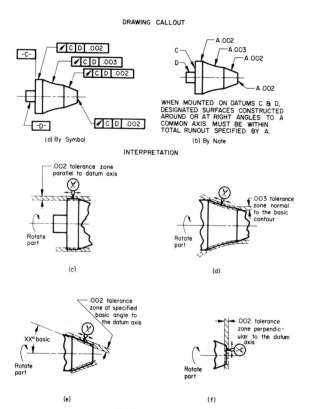

Fig. 12.65 Specifying runout tolerance zone. (Courtesy USASI.)

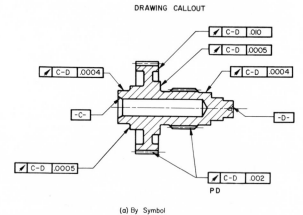

(a) By Symbol

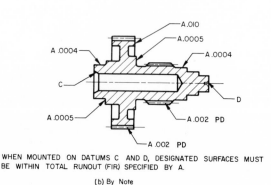

WHEN MOUNTED ON DATUMS C AND D, DESIGNATED SURFACES MUST BE WITHIN TOTAL RUNOUT (FIR) SPECIFIED BY A.

(b) By Note

Fig. 12.66 Runout tolerance for part with machine center datum. (Courtesy USASI.)

used as datums for establishing axes should be functional. Various phases of mount control are illustrated in Fig. 12.65 and Fig. 12.66 as further explained in the text.

c. *Basic control notes.* Where the functional requirements of surfaces are in reference to a common axis, one of the basic form control notes stated below can be specified. The form control is assigned a suitable designation letter, such as *A* in Fig. 12.65, and the letter is applied to each related surface. The notes or symbols control concentricity, parallelism, and perpendicularity of specified surfaces to the mounting surface or surfaces and roundness, flatness, parallelism, and straightness of each specified surface.

Where the basic form control is specified by a feature control symbol, the runout symbol ↗ is used to designate the required form and notes are not used.

1. Where the related surfaces to be controlled have a single common axis, the general note is: *When mounted on datums C and D, designated surfaces must be within total mount specified by A.* See Fig. 12.66.

2. *Where datums C and D must be cylindrical within .XXXX on R.* This note is used where it is necessary to control roundness, parallelism, and straightness of an individual diameter more accurately than the diametral tolerances. See Fig. 12.67.

d. *Applications.* Applications of the proper methods of using runout tolerances on drawings by notes or symbolically are shown in Figs. 12.66 through 12.68.

1. For a part mounted on machining centers, see Fig. 12.66.

2. For a part mounted on two bearing surfaces, see Fig. 12.67.

3. For a part mounted on a large flat surface with narrow finished diameters, see Fig. 12.68.

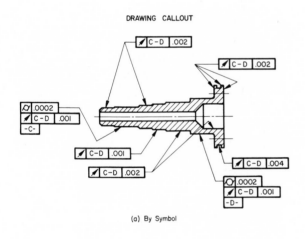

(a) By Symbol

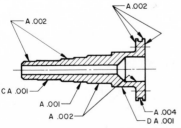

WHEN MOUNTED ON DATUMS C AND D, DESIGNATED SURFACES MUST BE WITHIN TOTAL RUNOUT (FIR) SPECIFIED BY A. DATUMS C AND D MUST BE CYLINDRICAL WITHIN .0002 FIR.

(b) By Note

Fig. 12.67 Runout tolerance for part with two bearing surface datums. (Courtesy USASI.)

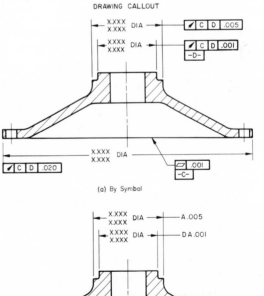

(a) By Symbol

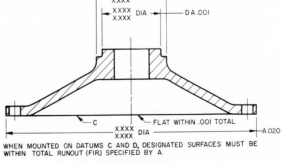

WHEN MOUNTED ON DATUMS C AND D, DESIGNATED SURFACES MUST BE WITHIN TOTAL RUNOUT (FIR) SPECIFIED BY A.

(b) By Note

Fig. 12.68 Runout tolerance for part with large flat surface datum having narrow finished diameters. (Courtesy USASI.)

12.35 EFFECTIVE HOLE DIAMETER. Because of departure from true perpendicularity, there are situations in which a hole might meet specifications as to size when measured with a micrometer, but still not accept a functional fixed position pin gage. When a hole is not square with a surface to which mating stud bolts or dowel pins are perpendicular, the effective hole diameter may be reduced as shown in Fig. 12.69.

engagement of the threaded screw through the upper mating part 2, the tolerance zone must be projected through the full thickness of the mating part.

12.36.3 Projected tolerance on stud bolt. Figure 12.70 shows that the tolerance zone must be projected or extended for the full length of the stud above the contact surface with part 1. Since the stud bolts must be assembled before part 2 can be put on, the bolt must

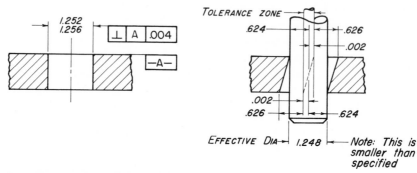

Fig. 12.69 Effective diameter of toleranced hole.

Thus if the hole is in its smallest size, namely 1.252, and the axis slopes across the full tolerance zone as shown in Fig. 12.69, the effective diameter of the hole for a perpendicular pin or stud has been reduced to 1.248. To insure assembly, the minimum diameter of a clearance hole must equal the maximum diameter of the stud bolt plus twice the positional tolerance.

12.36 PROJECTED TOLERANCE ZONE FOR THREADED PARTS. In this discussion the following points are assumed:

a. That both parts 1 and 2 in Fig. 12.70 have the same locational tolerance.

b. That perpendicularity is controlled only by locational tolerance.

When a hole is threaded to take a cap screw or stud bolt, any departure from perpendicularity is magnified, as shown in Fig. 12.70(c).

12.36.1 Minimum size of clearance hole. Figure 12.70(a) shows that with exact perpendicularity, the size of the clearance hole must be equal to the maximum diameter of the bolt plus twice the diameter of the tolerance zone. This is greater than the size required for two matching clearance holes.

12.36.2 Projected tolerance zone for cap screws. Figure 12.71 shows that the tolerance zone for a cap screw or stud bolt is based on the full height of the screw. Figures 12.71(b) and (c) show that to permit

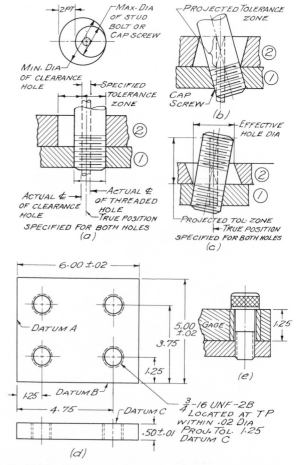

Fig 12.70 Tolerance zones for threaded parts.

pass through the effective diameter of the clearance hole.

Although the diameter of the clearance hole is as specified in Art. 12.35, the effective diameter may not be less than the maximum diameter of the bolt plus the tolerance zone of part 2. See Fig. 12.70(c).

12.36.4 Dimensioning and gaging. Figure 12.70(d) shows one method of dimensioning the part with threaded holes to take advantage of the projected tolerance zones. The gage for checking is shown in Fig. 12.70(e).

From the various parts of Fig. 12.70 the following facts may be noted.

a. In (b) and (c) the most adverse assembly conditions have been shown.

b. The center of the threaded hole on the contact surface between parts 1 and 2 must be on or within the periphery of the tolerance zone.

c. The axis of the threaded hole may lie outside the tolerance zone. This gives greater manufacturing tolerance than the drawing would show.

d. To insure assembly of either cap screws or stud bolts, the diameter of the gage-plate hole must be the effective diameter of the clearance hole rather than its true diameter. See Figs. 12.70 and 12.71.

The method of specifying the projected tolerance zone is shown in Fig. 12.71.

A complete drawing with the use of symbols for the specification of form tolerances and datum surfaces is shown in Fig. 12.72.

12.37 SURFACE FINISH. The engineer should understand clearly that the specification of surface finish is entirely distinct from specifying tolerances and limits. The finish of a surface determines its quality as to smoothness, surface marks, and the like, whereas tolerance refers to size and position only.

In certain applications the quality and degree of finish must be specified very clearly so that manufacturing processes may be determined and cost estimates prepared. Special operations must be employed to obtain very fine finishes, and consequently the cost increases rapidly as the finish is improved.

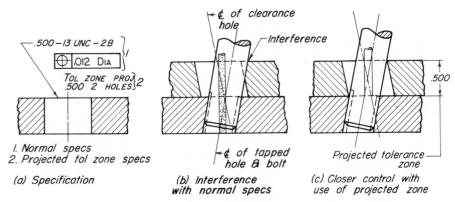

Fig. 12.71 Use of projected tolerance zone specifications.

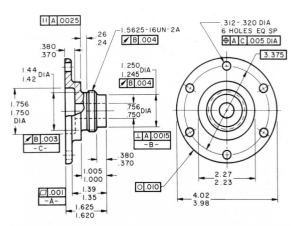

Fig. 12.72 Application of symbols for form- and position-tolerance specification. (Courtesy Mil. Std. 8C–1962.)

12.38 FINISH MARKS AND SPECIFICATIONS.
One of the oldest methods of indicating a finished surface on a drawing is by placing the letter f across the edgewise view of the surface to be finished. The f is made as shown in Fig. 12.73(a), and the correct method of placing it on the drawing, as well as several incorrect methods, is shown in Fig. 12.73(b). This symbol calls for an ordinary machine finish and makes no attempt to indicate the quality of the surface finish.

On some drawings this symbol is improved by adding a circle to the tail of the f, in which a number is placed, as shown in Fig. 12.73(c). A note indicating the meaning of the number is placed on the drawing. By this means more specific information may be given concerning the character of the finish desired for that surface.

For some years American Standards have recommended the V symbol for indicating finish. The simplest form of this symbol is constructed as shown in Fig. 12.73(d). Although it is not considered the best form, Fig. 12.73(e) shows one method of using the V symbol. The V is placed with its point touching the line that represents the edgewise view of the surface to be finished. The letters R and G mean "rough finish" and "grind." Other letters may be used to indicate certain operations or finishes.

The symbol for a finished surface should be placed wherever the surface shows edgewise as a visible or invisible line. This means that the symbol for finishing

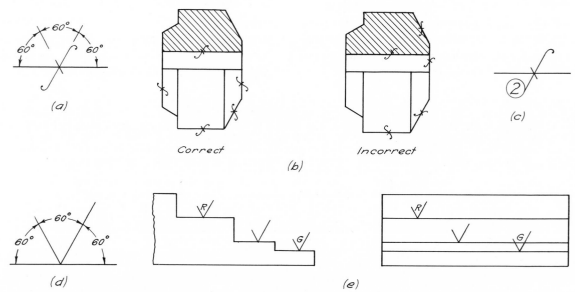

Fig. 12.73   General machining finish marks.

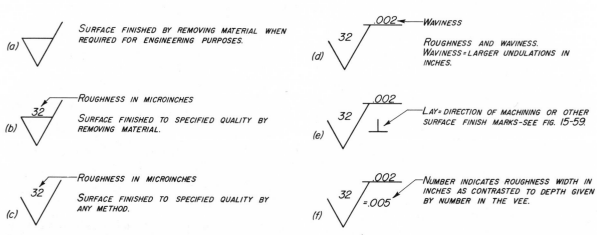

Fig. 12.74   Specific finish marks.

a single surface may be repeated in several views.

The more complete form of the V in which roughness, waviness, and lay are specified is shown in Figs. 12.74(a) through (f). The first two forms have recently been adopted.

a. *Roughness* may be defined as the closely spaced surface irregularities produced by machining or grinding operations.
b. *Waviness* refers to the more widely spaced irregularities which may be produced by vibration, deflection of the part in machining, warping, or in the release of strains in the material.
c. *Lay* refers to the direction of the surface pattern of irregularities produced in the finishing of the surface.

The roughness height may be specified as the peak-to-valley height or as the average arithmetic deviation from the mean surface. Measurements are taken across the lay pattern. Roughness is specified in microinches (millionths of an inch). The values given in Tables 12.1 and 12.2 (from USASI B46.1—1955) are commonly used in roughness and waviness specifications.

Waviness specifications are given in inches. Roughness width, as contrasted to depth, is also specified in inches, and this number appears after the lay symbol as shown in Fig. 12.74(f).

TABLE 12.1 WAVINESS HEIGHT VALUES (INCHES) TO BE USED WITH SYMBOL

0.00002	0.00008	0.0003	0.001	0.005
0.00003	0.0001	0.0005	0.002	0.008
0.00005	0.0002	0.0008	0.003	0.010

TABLE 12.2 PHYSICAL SPECIMENS OF SURFACE ROUGHNESS AND LAY*

Type of Surface	Roughness Height (Microinches)	Lay	Feed (Inches)	Minimum Roughness-Width Cutoff (Inches)
Honed, lapped, or polished	2	Parallel to long dimension of specimen	. . .	0.030
	4		. . .	0.030
	8		. . .	0.030
Ground with periphery of wheel	4	Parallel to long dimension of specimen	. . .	0.030
	8		. . .	0.030
	16		. . .	0.030
	32		. . .	0.030
	63		. . .	0.030
Ground with flat side of wheel	4	Angular in both directions	. . .	0.030
	8		. . .	0.030
	16		. . .	0.030
	32		. . .	0.030
	63		. . .	0.030
Shaped or turned	32	Parallel to long dimension of specimen	0.002	0.030
	63		0.005	0.030
	125		0.010	0.030
	250		0.020	0.100
	500		0.030	0.100
Side-milled, end-milled, or profiles	63	Circular	0.010	0.030
	125		0.020	0.100
	250	Angular in both directions	0.100	0.300
			0.100	0.300
Milled with periphery of cutter	63	Parallel to short dimension of specimen	0.050	0.300
	125		0.075	0.300
	250		0.125	1.000
	500		0.250	1.000

*Extracted from *American Standard Surface Roughness, Waviness and Lay,* USASI B46.1—1955, with permission of the publisher, The American Society of Mechanical Engineers.

In addition to roughness and waviness, it is sometimes necessary to specify the lay or the direction of the dominant lines of the surface. This is done by means of a set of symbols which may be placed to the right of the V as shown in Fig. 12.74(e). The meaning of these symbols is explained as follows:

$\sqrt{=}$ Lines to be parallel to the boundary line representing the surface on the drawing to which the symbol is attached.

$\sqrt{\perp}$ Perpendicular to the boundary line.

$\sqrt{x}$ Angular in both directions to the boundary line.

$\sqrt{M}$ Multidirectional.

$\sqrt{c}$ Approximately circular relative to the center of the surface indicated.

$\sqrt{R}$ Approximately radial relative to the center of the surface indicated.

The final addition to this symbol is the roughness width, placed to the right of the lay symbol as shown in Fig. 12.75. The meanings of all these terms and a complete specification thereof are also shown in this figure.

This symbol may be used completely or any part may be used separately as occasion demands. It should be clearly understood that the specification of surface quality is not the same as specifying limits. In other words, a surface may be given both limit dimensions and surface quality specifications, as indicated in Fig. 12.76.

12.39   CHECKING A DRAWING. Before a drawing is released for production or construction, it must be very carefully checked. Men selected to do this work

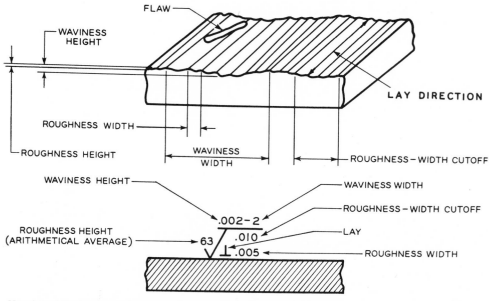

Fig. 12.75   Meaning of the terms roughness, waviness, and lay. (Courtesy USASI.)

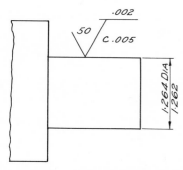

Fig. 12.76   Application of limit dimensions and finish marks.

must be thoroughly familiar with construction methods or shop processes as well as being absolute masters of the theory and practice of drafting.

It is good practice for the checker to have an established routine to follow in order that he may not overlook some phase of his work. The following checking routine, slightly modified, is used by a large manufacturing concern. Corrections are usually noted on a print of the drawing, which is returned to the person who made the original drawing. This also makes it simpler for the checker to ascertain that all corrections have been made.

1. Does the general appearance of the drawing conform to the standard drafting practice?
2. Is the part sufficiently strong and suitable for the function it has to perform?
3. Can the weight be reduced without sacrificing strength or function?
4. Does the drawing represent the most economical method of manufacture?
5. Are all necessary views and sections shown and are they in proper relation to one another?
6. Are all necessary dimensions shown?
7. Do the dimensions agree with the layout and related parts and are duplicate and unnecessary dimensions avoided?
8. Is the drawing to scale?
9. Is the drawing dimensioned to avoid unnecessary calculations in the shop?
10. Are stationary and operating clearances adequate?
11. Can the part or parts be assembled, disassembled, and serviced by the most economical methods?
12. Are proper limits or tolerances specified to produce the desired fits?
13. Have undesirable limit accumulations been avoided?
14. Are proper draft angles, fillets, and corner radii specified?
15. Are all necessary symbols for finishing, grinding, etc., shown?
16. Are locating points and proper finish allowances provided?
17. Are sufficient notes, including concentricity, parallelism, squareness, flatness, etc., shown?
18. Is the approximate developed length shown?
19. Is the stock size specified?
20. Are material and heat-treatment specifications given?
21. Are plating and painting specifications, either for protective or decorative purposes, given?
22. Are company trademark, part number, and manufacturer's identification shown according to divisional requirements?
23. Has the title block been filled in completely and is the information correct?
24. Are primary and secondary part numbers identical?
25. Are necessary part numbers of detail parts and subassemblies shown on assembly drawings?
26. Have original lines and drawing information damaged by erasures been properly restored?
27. Are revisions properly recorded?
28. Have all related drawings been revised to conform?

12.40 SIMPLIFIED DRAFTING. Because of high costs of drafting and their effect on total production costs, industrial drafting rooms are making efforts to reduce these costs by simplifying their drafting practice as much as possible without sacrificing clarity of meaning.

The first consideration in making any drawing should be the question, Who will use the drawing? With this question always in mind, the following list will suggest means of reducing drafting costs. Many of these are illustrated in this book.

1. Make freehand sketches of simple objects instead of instrumental drawings.
2. Take advantage of symmetry to reduce drawing time and drawing size.
3. Avoid the use of repetitive detail.
4. Omit unnecessary views and sections. Use partial views and sections where necessary for clarity.
5. Eliminate unnecessary use of letters and notes.
6. Use standard symbols wherever possible, for example, thread and welding symbols.
7. Eliminate inch marks; retain foot marks.
8. Omit drawing of standard bolts, nuts, and other hardware; list them.
9. Reduce hand lettering to a minimum.
10. Avoid ink drawings.
11. Use coordinate dimensioning where applicable.

SELF-STUDY QUESTIONS

Before trying to answer these questions, read the chapter carefully. Then, without reference to the text, answer as many questions as possible. For those that cannot be answered, the number, in parentheses following the question number, gives the article in which the answer can be found. Look it up and write down the answer. Check the answers that you did give to see that they are correct.

12.1 **(12.2)** Assembly drawings are used to show the parts of a machine in their _____ _____ position.

12.2 **(12.5)** Assembly drawings are used in the shop or field to show how parts are to be _____.

12.3 **(12.6)** Assembly drawings of such large structures as bridges are called _____ _____.

12.4 **(12.8)** Dimensioning of assembly drawings is based upon _____ for which they are intended.

12.5 **(12.10)** Hidden lines are _____ shown in assembly drawings.

12.6 **(12.12)** When selecting parts of a design such as bolts, screws, and springs, _____ sizes should be used.

12.7 **(12.12)** Holes, countersinks, counterbores, and other common features should be specified so that they can be produced by standard _____.

12.8 **(12.16.1)** The term "features" means parts of an object such as _____ and _____.

12.9 **(12.16.8)** The term "limits" is defined as the _____ permissible dimensions of a part.

12.10 **(12.16.9)** The term "tolerances" is defined as the _____ amount of variation permitted in the size of a part.

12.11 **(12.16.10)** The term "allowance" is the intentional _____ in the size of mating parts.

12.12 **(12.16.11)** A feature is said to be at maximum material condition when it contains the most _____.

12.13 **(12.16.12)** A line, plane, or surface from which other parts are dimensioned is called a _____.

12.14 **(12.19)** The three systems of tolerancing are known as _____, bilateral, or _____ systems.

12.15 **(12.20.1; 12.20.2)** The two systems for computing and tolerancing the fit between shafts and their associated bearing holes are known as the basic _____ method and the basic hole method.

12.16 **(12.22.1; 12.22.2)** Two systems of coordinate dimensioning are the _____ coordinate and the polar coordinate systems.

12.17 **(12.23.1)** If chain dimensioning is used in the coordinate systems, an _____ of tolerances may occur.

12.18 **(12.24)** An accumulation of tolerances may be prevented by using _____ surfaces.

12.19 **(12.27)** When the size, form, and location of a part are critical to function or interchangeable assembly, geometric form and _____ position dimensioning should be used.

12.20 **(12.28)** True-position dimensioning corresponds to the _____ of errors that normally arise in production.

12.21 **(12.28)** True-position dimensioning corresponds to the control established by _____ _____ gages.

12.22 **(12.28.2)** For rectangular coordinate dimensioning the shape of the tolerance zone is a _____.

12.23 **(12.28.2)** For true-position dimensioning the shape of the tolerance zone is a _____.

12.24 **(12.33)** When greater _____ is required than that given by size and location tolerances, geometric form _____ should be used.

In the following questions show your answer by a small sketch.

12.25 **(12.34.2)** The datum symbol is shown by

12.26 **(12.34.3; 12.34.4)** The straightness and flatness symbols are shown thus:

12.27 **(12.34.5)** Parallelism is shown by the symbol

12.28 **(12.34.6)** Squareness is shown by the symbol

PROBLEMS

The illustrations for the problems of this chapter show the complete details of several subassemblies. In each case, the student is to make the necessary correct and complete shop drawings. All required dimensions are shown on the pictorial drawings, but not necessarily in the place or form in which they should appear on a working drawing. The student must therefore exercise his judgment in applying the rules for dimensioning instead of copying the illustrations.

Where moving parts assemble together, a class RC 7 fit should be used. The basic sizes are given in the illustrations, and the tolerances may be obtained from tables in the Appendix. Finished surfaces must be indicated, and all other information necessary for manufacturing, including part numbers, should be incorporated in the drawings.

The exploded views or pictures indicate the order of assembling the parts, and if time permits an assembly drawing with the assignment of part numbers should be made.

Where the material of the part is not indicated in the pictorial drawing, the part should be made of steel or cast iron as the shape and function of the part would indicate. Dimensions of rounded corners and fillets are left to the discretion of the student.

If the instructor so desires, the parts of an assembly may be assigned to groups of students. They should then check each other's work for accuracy of fit and all other aspects of the drawing and dimensioning that may be in error. All true-position and geometric-form tolerancing should be shown in either note form or symbol form, as assigned by the instructor.

12.1 Make a complete set of details of all parts of the governor shown in Figs. 12.77 to 12.86.

12.2 Make an assembly drawing of the governor detailed in Problem 12.80.

12.3 Make a complete set of details of the pump shown in Fig. 12.3 and in Figs. 12.87 to 12.95.

12.4 Make an assembly drawing of the pump as detailed in Problem 12.3.

12.5 Make a complete set of details of the swivel pulley shown in Figs. 12.96 and 12.97.

12.6 Make an assembly drawing of the swivel pulley including sectional views where necessary and general overall dimensions.

12.7 Make a complete set of details of the bell ringer shown in Figs. 12.98 and 12.99.

12.8 Make a sectional assembly of the bell ringer detailed in Problem 12.7.

12.9 Make a complete set of details of the parts of the machinist's jack shown in Fig. 12.100.

12.10 Make an assembly drawing of the machinist's jack shown in Fig. 12.100.

12.11 Make a complete working drawing fully dimensioned and noted from any part assigned from Figs. 12.77 through 12.100.

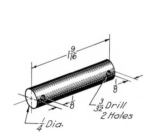

Fig. 12.77 Weight pin.

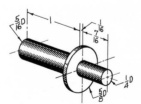

Fig. 12.78 Pin.

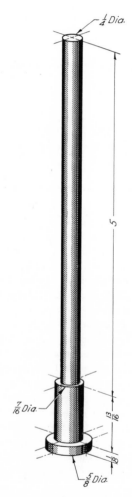

Fig. 12.79 Plunger.

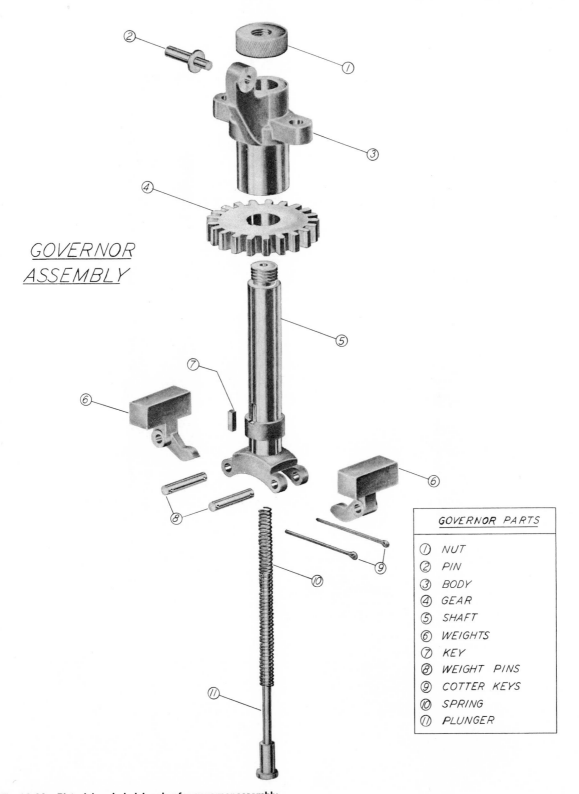

GOVERNOR
ASSEMBLY

GOVERNOR PARTS	
①	NUT
②	PIN
③	BODY
④	GEAR
⑤	SHAFT
⑥	WEIGHTS
⑦	KEY
⑧	WEIGHT PINS
⑨	COTTER KEYS
⑩	SPRING
⑪	PLUNGER

Fig. 12.80   Pictorial exploded drawing for governor assembly.

Free length $5\frac{1}{4}$
O.D. $\frac{3}{8}$
Pitch 0.1
No. 18 Hard drawn
spring steel wire

Fig. 12.81   Spring.

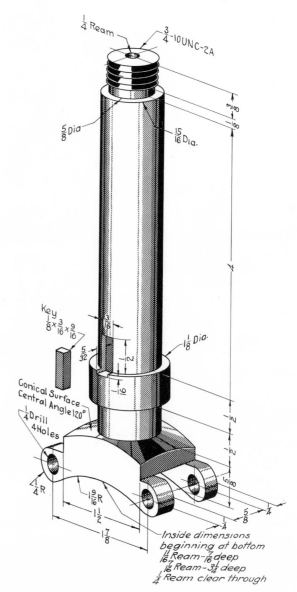

Fig. 12.82   Shaft.

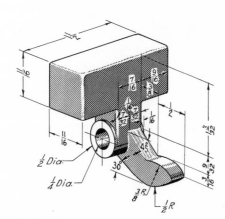

Fig. 12.83   Weight.

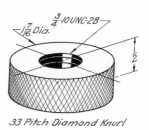

33 Pitch Diamond Knurl

Fig. 12.84   Nut.

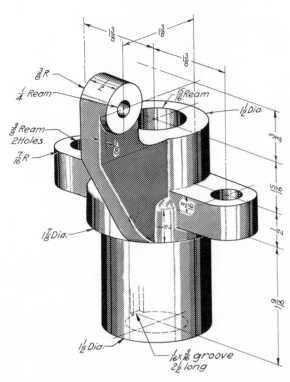

Fig. 12.85 Body.

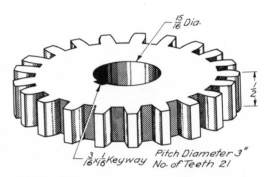

Fig. 12.86 Gear.

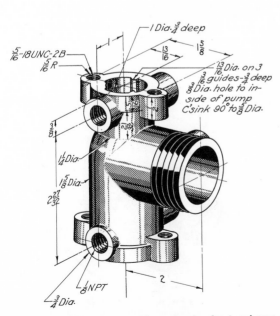

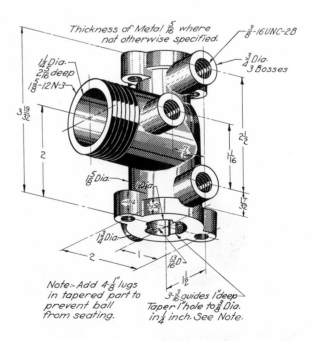

Fig. 12.87 Pump body, two views showing front and rear.

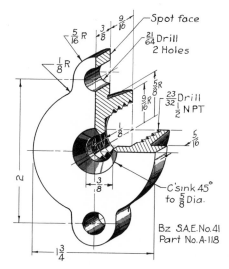

Fig. 12.88 Intake flange.

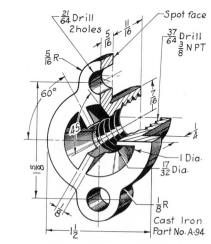

Fig. 12.89 Outlet flange.

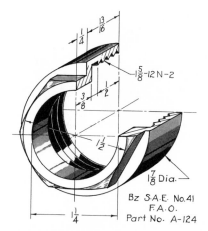

Fig. 12.90 Pump packing gland.

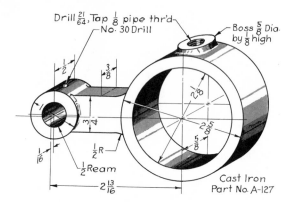

Fig. 12.91 Eccentric strap.

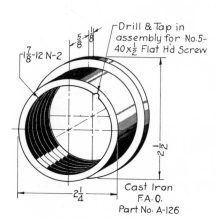

Fig. 12.92 Eccentric (outside).

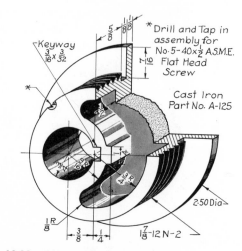

Fig. 12.93 Eccentric (inside).

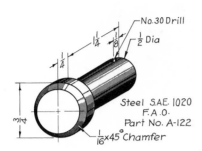

No. 30 Drill

$\frac{1}{4}$ $\frac{1}{8}$

$\frac{1}{2}$ Dia

$\frac{3}{4}$

Steel S.A.E. 1020
F.A.O.
Part No. A-122

$\frac{1}{16}$ x 45° Chamfer

Fig. 12.94   Plunger bolt.

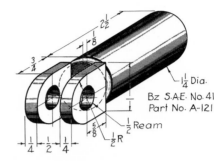

$2\frac{1}{2}$

$\frac{1}{8}$

$\frac{3}{4}$

$1\frac{1}{4}$ Dia.

Bz S.A.E. No. 41
Part No. A-121

$\frac{1}{2}$ Ream

$\frac{5}{8}$

$\frac{1}{2}$ R

$\frac{1}{4}$ $\frac{1}{2}$ $\frac{1}{4}$

Fig. 12.95   Pump plunger.

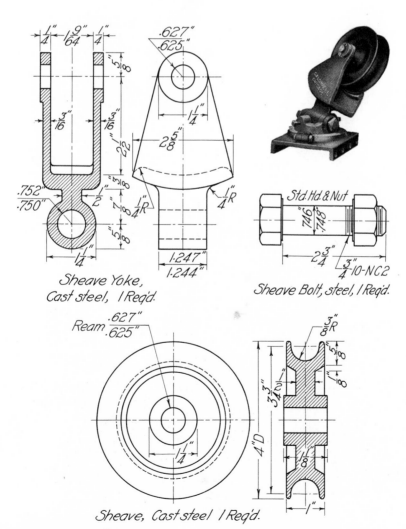

$\frac{1}{4}''$ $1\frac{9}{64}''$ $\frac{1}{4}''$

$.627''$
$.625''$

$\frac{5}{8}''$

$\frac{3}{16}''$ $\frac{3}{16}''$

$1\frac{1}{4}$

$2\frac{5}{8}''$

$2\frac{1}{2}''$

$\frac{3}{8}''$

$.752''$
$.750''$

$\frac{1}{2}''$

$\frac{1}{4}R$

$\frac{1}{4}''$

$\frac{5}{8}''$

$\frac{1}{4}$

$\frac{7}{8}''$

$1.247''$
$1.244''$

$\frac{1}{4}R$

**Sheave Yoke,
Cast steel, 1 Req'd.**

Std. Hd. & Nut

$.746''$
$.748''$

$2\frac{3}{4}''$

$\frac{3}{4}''$-10-NC2

Sheave Bolt, steel, 1 Req'd.

Ream $\frac{.627''}{.625''}$

$\frac{3}{8}R$

$\frac{5}{8}''$

$\frac{1}{8}''$

$3\frac{3}{4}''$

$4''D$

$\frac{1}{4}''$

$1\frac{1}{8}''$

$1''$

Sheave, Cast steel 1 Req'd.

Fig. 12.96   Details and photograph of universal sheave.

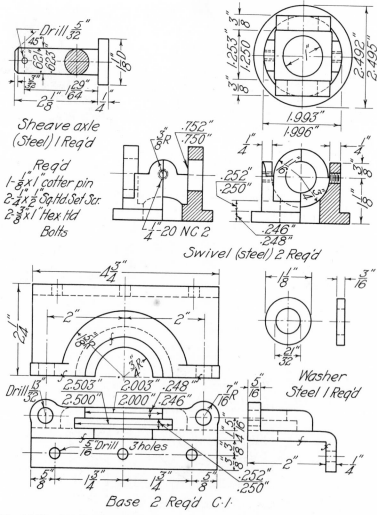

Fig. 12.97 Details of universal sheave.

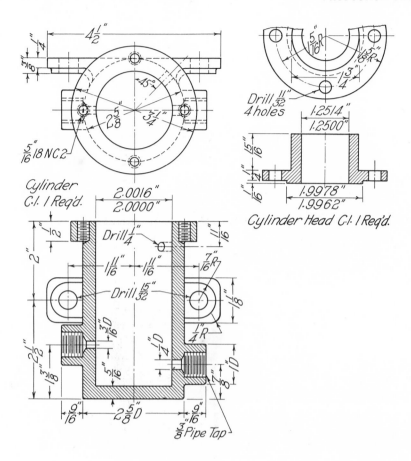

Cylinder C.I. 1 Req'd.

Cylinder Head C.I. 1 Req'd.

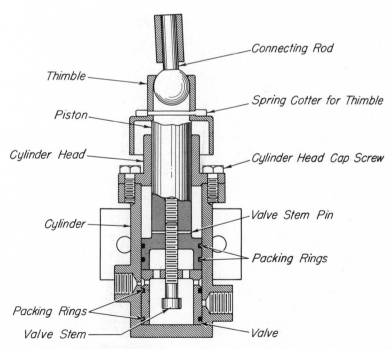

Fig. 12.98 Details of bell ringer.

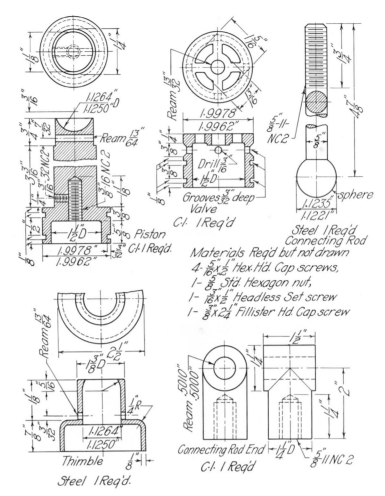

Fig. 12.99 Details of bell ringer.

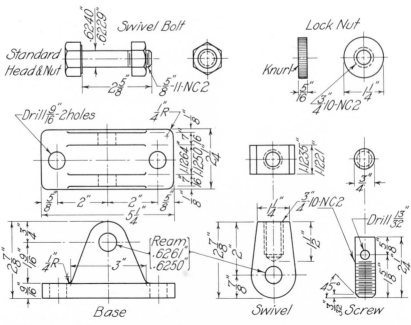

Fig. 12.100 Details of machinist's jack.

PART TWO

Advanced Projection Systems

Geometry of Engineering Drawing

OLD: Ancient Roman bridge in Nimes, France. (Philip Gendreau)

NEW: Concrete bridge in Venezuela (Hamilton Wright)

Chapter 13   Geometry of Engineering Drawing

13.1   INTRODUCTION. Many engineering problems dealing with space structures and positions may be solved graphically with sufficient accuracy and in much less time than is required for a mathematical solution. As a basis for these solutions, the engineer must have a thorough understanding of the space relations existing between the various geometrical magnitudes, such as points, lines, planes, surfaces, and solids. The preliminary and simpler relationships of points, lines, and planes have been presented in Chapters 6 and 7. In the same chapters the four fundamental operations for solving problems in engineering drawing and descriptive geometry have been thoroughly discussed. These operations are:

a. Finding the true length of a line.
b. Finding the point projection of a line.
c. Finding the edgewise view of a plane.
d. Finding the true size of a plane figure.

If the student is not thoroughly familiar with this material, it should be reviewed before proceeding with this chapter.

13.1.1   Meaning of a space analysis. In most of the paragraphs in this chapter there will be a statement printed in italics entitled Space analysis. This analysis sets forth the geometric principles involved in the solution of the problem. The material that follows in each paragraph is an explanation of the methods of showing these principles in orthographic projection.

Most problems can be solved by the use of one or more auxiliary planes. A few require special devices, which are introduced in both the space analysis and the discussion that follows where this is necessary.

13.2   STRAIGHT OR RIGHT LINES. This section deals with the position and true length of single straight lines.

13.2.1   Slope of a line. *The angle or slope of a line is defined as the angle that the line makes with the horizontal plane.* The slope of a line should always be given a plus or minus sign. It is plus when the line slopes upward from the beginning point and minus when it slopes downward from this point. In this book this angle will always be designated by the Greek letter θ.

a. *Line parallel to V-plane.* If a line is parallel to the V-plane, the slope is shown in the true-length view, in this case, in the front view. See Fig. 13.1(*a*).
b. *Line parallel to P-plane.* When the line is in this position the profile view shows the true length of the line and the slope angle θ. See Fig. 13.1(*b*).
c. *Oblique line.* If the line is oblique to the H-, V-, and P-planes, as in Fig. 13.1(*c*), an auxiliary view on a plane perpendicular to H and parallel to the line is required. Note again that the slope angle θ is shown in the true-length view of the line.

13.2.2   Other methods of expressing slope. As a result of varying practice in engineering areas, different methods of specifying the slope of a line have developed.

a. On *railroads and highways* the slope of the grade line (center line) is expressed in per cent as shown in Fig. 13.2(*a*).
b. In *structural work* the slope of a member is expressed in terms of run and rise as shown in Fig. 13.2(*b*). The larger dimension is always 12 inches whether it is horizontal or vertical.
c. In *roof construction* the slope of the roof is called the pitch. The pitch is the ratio of the rise to the span. See Fig. 13.2(*c*).
d. When *concrete or stone walls* have a very steep slope this is called the batter. The batter is specified as the ratio of the horizontal distance to the vertical distance, as shown in Fig. 13.2(*d*).

13.2.3   Bearing of a line. *Space analysis. The bearing of a line is defined as the smaller of the two angles*

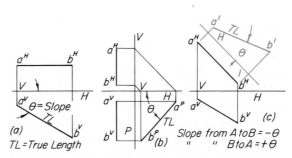

Fig. 13.1   Slope of a line.

that the horizontal projection of the line makes with a north and south line. It may be measured from the north or south.

On a map the north and south line is frequently a vertical line with north at the top. Thus east will be to the right and west to the left. The bearing should be taken from the horizontal projection and marked with the angle and direction as shown in Fig. 13.3.

It should be noted that the bearing of a line is simply a directed line segment. Thus the bearing of *BA* in Fig. 13.3(*b*) is just 180° from that of *AB* in Fig. 13.3(*a*).

13.2.4   Azimuth of a line. The term azimuth is sometimes used to define the direction of a line. *This means the angle that the horizontal projection of the line makes with a north and south line, measured clockwise from the north,* as illustrated in Fig. 13.4. For further discussion see Chapter 23, Fig. 23.18.

13.2.5   True length of an oblique line—construction cone or rotation method. *Space analysis. If the line is considered to be an element of a right circular cone whose axis is perpendicular to one of the coordinate planes, the cone may be revolved about its axis until the line becomes parallel to one of the coordinate planes.*

In Fig. 13.5, four different cones have been set up, any one of which may be used to determine the true length of the line *AB*. In actual practice only that portion of the cone between the projection and the revolved position need be constructed.

Each cone not only gives the true length of the line but also the angle that the line makes with the coordinate plane to which the axis of the cone is perpendicular. Thus, Figs. 13.5(*a*), (*b*), and (*c*) show the angles θ, ϕ, and π, respectively, and Fig. 13.5(*d*) shows the angle α that the line makes with the auxiliary plane *1*.

13.2.6   To determine the projections of a line of given length, bearing, and slope. This may best be illustrated with an example. Let it be required to draw a

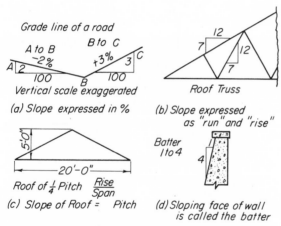

(a) Slope expressed in %

(b) Slope expressed as "run" and "rise"

(c) Slope of Roof = Pitch

(d) Sloping face of wall is called the batter

Fig. 13.2   Engineering methods of giving a slope.

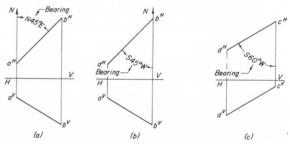

Fig. 13.3   Bearing of a line.

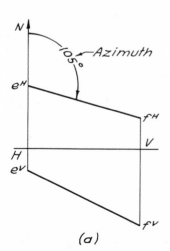

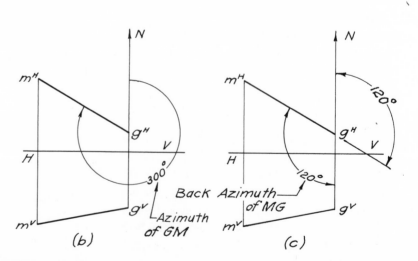

Fig. 13.4   Azimuth of a line.

line *AB* from a known point *A* in Fig. 13.6, 200 feet long, having a bearing North 45° East and a slope of 30° downward from *A* to *B* at a scale of 100 feet = 1 inch.

The student must analyze the three known facts about this line to determine the order in which he will use the facts to solve the problem.

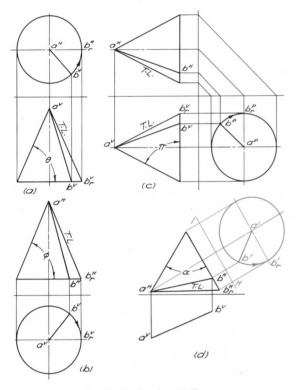

Fig. 13.5   **True length of a line by rotation.**

a. Clearly the *H*-projection of a line having the required bearing can be drawn, but since it is a sloping line, its true length cannot be shown immediately. The *H*-projection $a^H c^H$ of random length will therefore be drawn having the correct bearing as shown in Fig. 13.6(*a*).

b. An auxiliary reference line may be placed parallel to this projection and *A* projected to this plane. The slope can be drawn as shown in Fig. 13.6(*b*).

c. This auxiliary view also gives the true length of the line *AC*, hence a length of 2 inches (200 feet) can be scaled off from a^1 and the end marked b^1.

d. The projection of *B* can be returned from b^1 to b^H on the horizontal projection of *AC*, as in Fig. 13.6(*c*). From these two views the vertical projection can be constructed, thus completing the problem as in Fig. 13.6(*c*).

13.3   RELATIONSHIP BETWEEN LINES. If two lines in space intersect, they may be either inclined or perpendicular to each other. If they do not intersect, they may be parallel, nonparallel, or perpendicular to each other. Two nonintersecting lines are said to be perpendicular to each other when one of the lines lies in a plane that is perpendicular to the other line. These relationships are established by means of their projections.

13.3.1   Identifying parallel lines. *Space analysis. By definition, lines are said to be parallel when they meet at infinity. In projection drawing, two lines are parallel when their respective projections on any and all planes are parallel.*

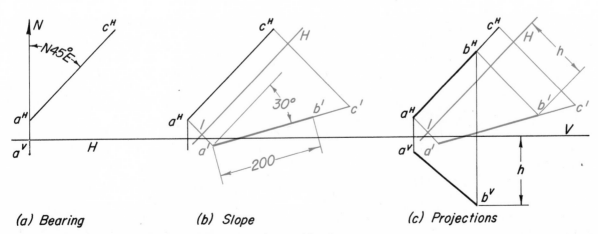

(a) Bearing   *(b) Slope*   *(c) Projections*

Fig. 13.6   **Constructing a line having a given bearing, slope, and length.**

In Fig. 13.7 this principle has been illustrated for four projections of the lines. By examining Figs. 13.8 and 13.9 it will be seen that when two projections of a set of lines are both parallel to the same reference line, the lines may, or may not, be parallel. In these cases a third view is necessary, as shown in Figs. 13.8(*b*) and 13.9(*b*). In both illustrations it can be seen that the line *EF* is not parallel to the other two lines.

13.3.2   Drawing a line through a point parallel to another line. This problem occurs regularly in solving stress problems by means of vectors. Thus to draw a line through *C* in Fig. 13.10(*a*) it is necessary to draw the *H*-projection c^Hd^H parallel to a^Hb^H and the *V*-projection c^Vd^V parallel to a^Vb^V.

As can be seen from Figs. 13.8 and 13.9, two projections will suffice except where the adjacent projections are both perpendicular to the reference line between them. In this situation three views will be necessary.

13.3.3   Intersecting lines. *Space analysis. If two lines intersect, there must be one point common to both lines.*

The various projections of this point must have the proper alignment with each other and must be on the corresponding projections of both lines, as in Fig. 13.11(*a*). In Fig. 13.11(*b*) the crossing point of the hori-

zontal projections represents two points, *E* and *F*, since their vertical projections do not coincide, and consequently these lines do not intersect.

13.3.4   Angle between two lines. *Space analysis. If two lines are parallel to the same plane of projection, the angle between them will show in its true size on the plane to which they are parallel.*

Thus in Fig. 13.24 the value of the angle between the vectors shows in true size in the front view since both are parallel to the *V*-plane as shown by the top view.

If the lines are oblique, it may be necessary to obtain their projections on a plane parallel to both lines by means of an auxiliary view as shown in Fig. 13.25. In some situations two auxiliary views may be needed.

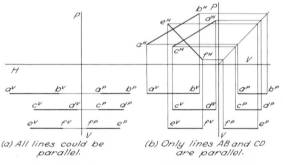

(a) All lines could be parallel.   (b) Only lines AB and CD are parallel.

Fig. 13.8   Identifying parallel lines when two views are inadequate.

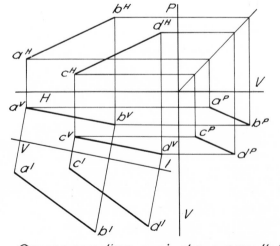

Corresponding projections parallel.

Fig. 13.7   Parallel lines.

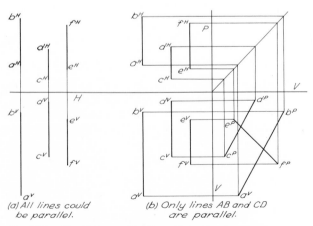

(a) All lines could be parallel.   (b) Only lines AB and CD are parallel.

Fig. 13.9   Identifying parallel lines. Two views inadequate.

13.3.5   Line through a point making a given angle with a given line. *Space analysis. The angle between two lines shows in its true value on any plane parallel to both lines.* The construction is as follows:

a. Draw a *V*-parallel from the point to the line *CD* and obtain an edgewise view of their plane as in Fig. 13.12(*a*).

b. On a second auxiliary view, find the true shape of the plane of the point and line and draw the line making the required angle with the given line. See Fig. 13.12(*b*).

c. Return the projection of this new line to the original views. See Fig. 13.12(*b*).

13.3.6   Distance between two parallel lines by the point projection method. *Space analysis. The distance* between the point projections of the two lines will be the shortest distance between the lines.

Project both lines on an auxiliary plane perpendicular to the lines and measure the distance between the point projections, as illustrated in Fig. 13.13. Proceed as follows:

a. Set up the first auxiliary plane with reference line *1-V* parallel to the front view of the lines.

b. Obtain the first auxiliary view of the two lines at a^1b^1 and c^1d^1 in Fig. 13.13(*a*). These are true-length views.

c. Set up the second auxiliary plane with reference line *1-2* perpendicular to the true-length projections of the lines as in Fig. 13.13(*b*) and project them onto the second auxiliary plane to obtain a^2b^2 and c^2d^2. The distance between these points is the distance between the lines.

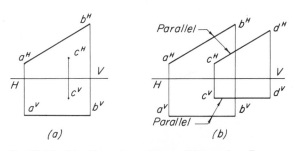

(a) **(b)**

Fig. 13.10   Line through a point parallel to a given line.

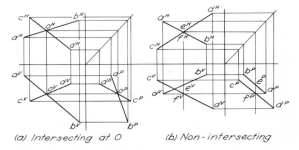

(a) Intersecting at O **(b) Non-intersecting**

Fig. 13.11   Intersecting lines.

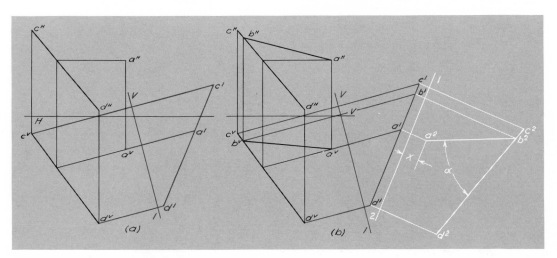

(a) **(b)**

Fig. 13.12   Line making specified angle with another line.

13.3.7   Distance between two parallel lines by the plane method. *Space analysis. The true distance between the lines will show in that projection which gives the true size of the plane of the two lines.* The procedure is as follows:

a. Draw a *V*-parallel *AE* between the two lines as in Fig. 13.14(*a*) and obtain the edge view of the plane of the lines.

b. Draw the second auxiliary plane with reference line *1-2* parallel to the first auxiliary view of the two lines and obtain the true shape of the plane.

c. The true distance can be measured anywhere between c^2d^2 and a^2b^2 perpendicular to them, as in Fig. 13.14(*b*).

13.3.8   Distance from a point to a line by the point projection method. *Space analysis. The shortest distance from a point to a line will show on a view that gives the point projection of the line.*

a. Line parallel to a plane of projection. For a line like *AB* in Fig. 13.15 parallel to *H*-plane, the true length appears in the top view and an auxiliary plane reference line *1-H* can be set up perpendicular to the line at once. The distance between c^1 and a^1b^1 is the true distance of the point from the line. Since c^1d^1 is perpendicular to a^1b^1 and shows in true length, the projection c^Hd^H must be parallel to the reference line *1-H*.

b. Oblique line. For an oblique line like *CD* in Fig. 13.16 the first step is to find a true-length view of the line. This is obtained on a first auxiliary plane parallel to c^Vd^V, represented by reference line *V-1*. Carry the point *A* along in the auxiliary view.

The second step is accomplished by obtaining a point projection of the line on the second auxiliary plane at c^2d^2 in Fig. 13.16. The distance from a^2 to c^2d^2 is the required distance.

Since the shortest distance is the perpendicular from *A* to *CD*, a^1b^1 must be at right angles to c^1d^1 or parallel to reference line *1-2*. The *H*- and *V*-projections of *B* are carried back by direct projection to b^V and b^H.

13.3.9   Distance from a point to a line by the plane method. *Space analysis. The true distance between the point and line will show on a view that gives the true size of the plane of the point and line.*

Project the point and line on an auxiliary plane parallel to the plane of the point and the line. The true length of the perpendicular may be measured on this view and projected back directly. See Fig. 13.17.

13.3.10   Revolve a point around an *H*- or *V*-parallel. *Space analysis. When a point is revolved about a line, it revolves in a circle that lies in a plane perpendicular to the line and the center of the circle is a point on the line.* It is sometimes very useful to revolve a

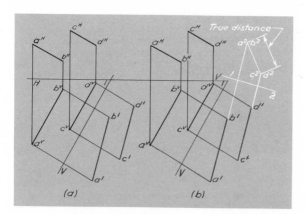

Fig. 13.13   Distance between two parallel lines. Point projection method.

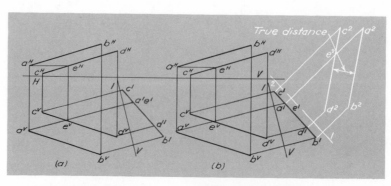

Fig. 13.14   Distance between two parallel lines. Plane method.

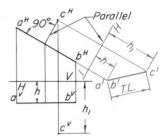

Fig. 13.15   Distance from a point to a line.

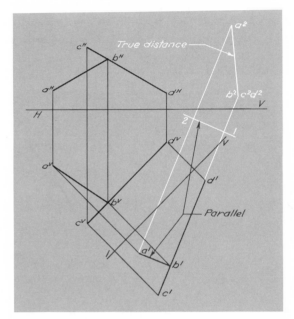

Fig. 13.16   Distance from a point to a line. Point projection method.

point around a line into some specified position. In Fig. 13.18 line AB is an H-parallel and point C is to be revolved about AB until AB and C are in a plane parallel to the H-plane. The following steps will solve the problem.

a. Set up an auxiliary plane perpendicular to AB, by making the reference line perpendicular to $a^H b^H$.

b. Find $a^1 b^1$ and c^1 in the auxiliary view.

c. With $a^1 b^1$ as a center revolve c^1 until it is in the plane through $a^1 b^1$ parallel to H at C_r^1. See Fig. 13.18(*a*).

d. In the top view draw the edge view of a plane through C^H perpendicular to $a^H b^H$, the axis of rotation.

e. Project C_r^1 back to C_r^H, and then to C_r^V as shown in Fig. 13.18(*a*).

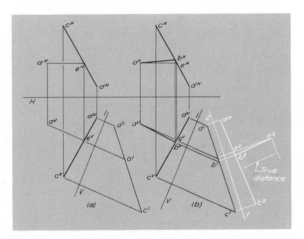

Fig. 13.17   Distance from a point to a line. Plane method.

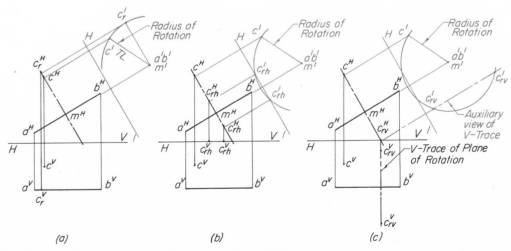

Fig. 13.18   Rotation of a point around a line into the H- and V-planes.

13.3.11 Revolve a point around a line into the H- and V-planes. In the situation shown in Fig. 13.18(a) the rotation of point C into the H- and V-planes can be accomplished by continuing the rotation into the edge view of the H-plane as shown in Fig. 13.18(b). The revolved point may fall at either of two places as shown.

In Fig. 13.18(c) the intersection of the plane of rotation with the V-plane, which is a vertical line, has been shown in the first auxiliary view, and the circle of rotation is simply continued until C^1 strikes this line in the V-plane at two places. Projection of the point can be returned to H- and V-projections in the usual manner.

13.3.12 Perpendicular lines. *Space analysis. One line is perpendicular to another line when it lies in a plane perpendicular to the other line.* A line constructed perpendicular to another line may have an infinite number of positions. Thus, in Fig. 13.19(a), each spoke of the wheels lies in a plane perpendicular to the axle

joining them. When the axle is horizontal, the wheels will project edgewise on the horizontal plane. This edgewise view is perpendicular to the horizontal projection of the axle. It follows therefore that, if one of two perpendicular lines is parallel to a coordinate plane, the projections of both lines on that plane will be at 90° to each other. Thus, in Fig. 13.19(b), the axle AB is parallel to the horizontal plane, and every spoke of the wheel projects in the line $c^H a^H d^H$. Since the wheel may be revolved into any position, the vertical projection of a spoke may have any direction, for example, $a^V e^V$ in Figs. 13.19(b) and (c). If the length of the perpendicular is to be determined or constructed, this may be done by a single auxiliary projection as shown in Fig. 13.20.

Although the preceding discussion has been limited to the horizontal plane, the same principles apply to any coordinate plane or any auxiliary plane. See Figs. 13.21 and 13.22.

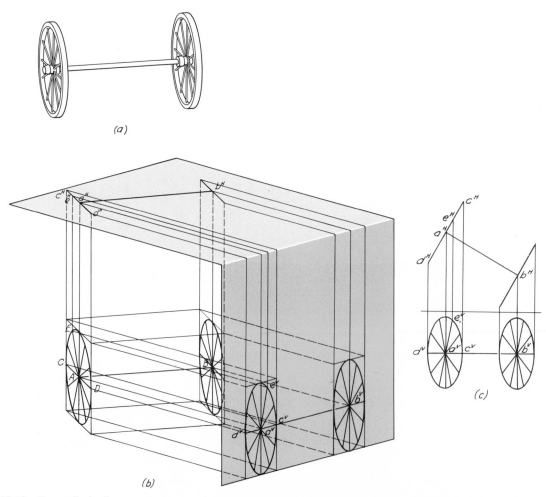

(a)

(b)

(c)

Fig. 13.19 Perpendicular lines.

If the given line *AB* in Fig. 13.22, to which another is to be made perpendicular, is not parallel to a principal plane, an auxiliary plane may be set up parallel to the line. The auxiliary view will then show the right angle in true size, as shown in Fig. 13.22. After the auxiliary projections have been drawn at right angles to each other, the vertical projection of the perpendicular may be drawn in any direction. The horizontal projection is then obtained in the usual manner.

There are three situations in which a line may be drawn at right angles to an oblique line directly. This construction is useful in many problems. Thus if we consider *AC* in Fig. 13.23(*a*) to be any spoke of the wheel in Fig. 13.19, the axle may be drawn by making

a^Hb^H perpendicular to a^Hc^H and a^Vb^V parallel to the reference line. Lines *BA* and *AC* are then at right angles to each other. Figure 13.23(*b*) shows another solution in which the axle *AB* is drawn parallel to the vertical plane, and Fig. 13.23(*c*) shows a third solution with the axle parallel to the profile plane.

13.4   VECTOR DIAGRAMS. *A vector is a line used to represent any quantity that has both magnitude and direction, for example, a force.* The direction of the line is the same as the direction of the force, and the length of the line is equal to the magnitude of the force to some convenient scale. Vector diagrams can be used to solve graphically problems involving vector quantities. The geometry involved is an application of the principal of parallel lines.

13.5   CONCURRENT COPLANAR FORCE SYSTEMS. If there are several forces acting on a body, the vector sum of these forces, a single force that would produce the same effect as the combined forces, is

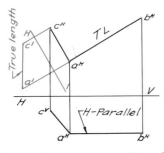

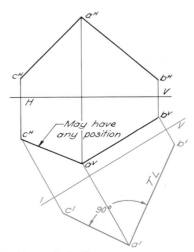

Fig. 13.20   Perpendicular lines, one an *H*-parallel.

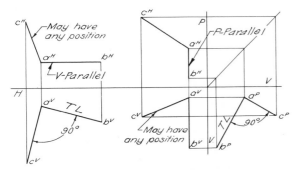

Fig. 13.21   Perpendicular lines. *V*- and *P*- parallels.

Fig. 13.22   Perpendicular lines.

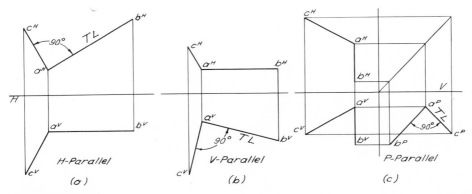

Fig. 13.23   Perpendicular lines.

called the *resultant* of the forces. A force of equal magnitude and in the opposite direction is called the *equilibrant;* in other words, it is the force that will hold the whole system in equilibrium.

13.5.1   Forces in a plane parallel to the *V*-plane.

In Fig. 13.24 let it be required to construct the vector diagram to determine the load in the two ropes supporting the 100-pound weight.

Since the ropes are parallel to the vertical plane, the vertical projection will show all lines in true length. Hence the horizontal projection that is parallel to the reference line need not be considered. In vector diagrams it is customary to letter the spaces between the forces as *D*, *E*, and *F*, shown in Fig. 13.24(*a*). The lines of the vector diagram are then designated by the two letters adjacent to them as *DE*, *EF*, and *FD*. This is known as Bow's notation.

To solve the problem proceed as follows:

a. In Fig. 13.24(*b*) draw a line *EF* parallel to the vertical rope and make the length equal to 100 pounds to some convenient scale, for example, 1 inch equals 50 pounds.

b. From end *E* draw a line parallel to $e^v d^v$ of indefinite length.

c. From *F* draw another line parallel to $d^v f^v$.

d. These two lines will intersect at *D*, and the true length of lines *ED* and *FD* will give the load in the inclined ropes at the same scale used in drawing the first line.

13.5.2   Forces in oblique positions.

When the ropes are not parallel to one of the principal planes, as in Fig. 13.25, the same construction may be used by setting up an auxiliary plane parallel to the two ropes, as shown in Fig. 13.25. The auxiliary view will show all lines and angles in the true size and length. Using the auxiliary view the steps are exactly the same as in the preceding problem.

13.5.3   Three concurrent noncoplanar forces.

Frequently it is necessary to find the resultant of several forces that act through one point but do not all lie in the same plane. These are called concurrent noncoplanar forces. The resultant is the single force that can be used to replace the entire system of forces. This problem can be solved by constructing a diagram similar to the vector diagram of the previous paragraph, with the exception that it will not form a closed polygon and that it *must be constructed simultaneously in two views.* The line necessary to close the polygon will be the resultant. The equilibrant is a force of the same magnitude but with the direction reversed. Thus, in Fig. 13.26(*a*), a group of three forces whose directions are indicated by lines *AB*, *AC*, and *AD* and whose magnitudes are specified in pounds are acting on point *A*. The solution of this problem is shown in Fig. 13.26. The spaces between the forces should first be lettered in one view as *O*, *M*, and *N* in Fig. 13.26(*a*) and (*b*). The forces are laid out in order by proceeding in a counterclockwise direction around point *A*.

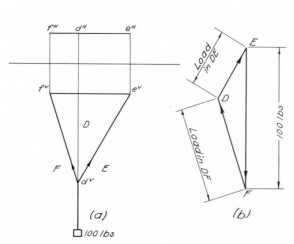

Fig. 13.24   Vector diagram.

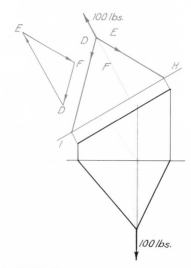

Fig. 13.25   Vector diagram.

a. *Find the true-length projections of the forces.* The simplest method of procedure is to lay out the forces in proper direction and then to obtain the true-length projections as in Fig. 13.26(*b*). Proceed as follows.

1. Lay out lines *AX*, *AY*, and *AZ* in the proper direction of random length, a little longer than the true lengths, as shown in Fig. 13.26(*b*).
2. Find the true length of each line by rotation at $a^H x_r{}^H$, $a^H y_r{}^H$, and $a^H z_r{}^H$.
3. Measure off the required true length for each force as shown in the top view of Fig. 13.26(*b*).
4. Return this true length to the original projections.
5. These projected true lengths may then be used directly in the vector diagram of Fig. 13.26(*c*).

b. *Draw the vector diagram.* The vector diagram may be drawn by taking the forces in consecutive order either clockwise or counterclockwise. In Fig. 13.26(*c*) they have been taken counterclockwise. The forces will be designated by the capital letters between which they lie. Proceed as follows [see top view in Fig. 13.26(*c*)].

1. Begin with force line *AD*, which will be marked *MN* since it lies between these letters. Select the projections of points m^H and m^V so that there will be ample room for the diagram. Then draw $m^H n^H$ and $m^V n^V$ of the same length as $a^H d^H$ and $a^V d^V$, the projected true length of this force, from Fig. 13.26(*b*).
2. Draw *NO* in the same manner.
3. Draw from *O* the force *AB* parallel and equal to the true-length projections in Fig. 13.26(*b*) and letter the end point *P*.
4. Line *MP* with the arrow as indicated is the resultant of this force system.
5. Find the true length of this line, which scales 87 pounds.

13.6 RELATIONSHIP OF PLANES. The relationship of inclined and oblique planes to the principle coordinate planes has been presented in Chapters 6 and 7. Further relationships of planes in space such as parallel, perpendicular, and those at specified angles with each other are presented in the following paragraphs.

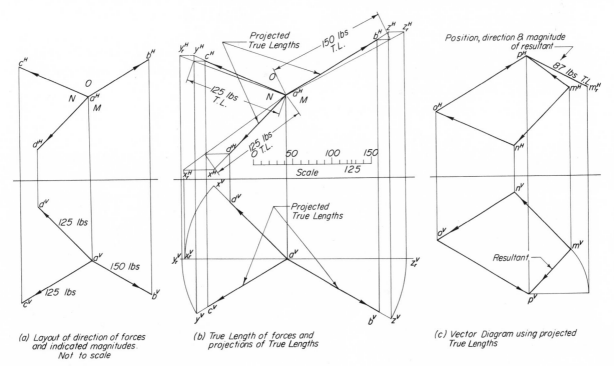

(a) Layout of direction of forces and indicated magnitudes. Not to scale

(b) True Length of forces and projections of True Lengths

(c) Vector Diagram using projected True Lengths

Fig. 13.26 Three-dimensional vector diagram.

13.6.1   True shape of a plane figure by rotation. *Space analysis. If a horizontal line is drawn in a plane, the plane may be revolved about this line as an axis until the plane is parallel to the H-plane. In this position it may be projected on the H-plane in true shape.*

The steps are as follows and as shown in Fig. 13.27.

a. In the plane *ABCDE* draw an *H*-parallel such as *AF*.

b. Place an auxiliary plane with reference line *H-1* perpendicular to $a^H f^H$ and get the edge view of the plane upon it at $b^1 c^1 a^1 d^1 e^1$.

c. In the auxiliary view revolve the corners of the plane until they are in a plane parallel to *H*, as at e_r^1 to b_r^1.

d. Project the revolved position back to the *H*-projection and connect the points e_r^H, d_r^H, etc., to form the true shape of the figure.

See Art. 13.3.10 for method of revolving a point about a line.

It should be noted that a *V*-parallel could also be used as the axis of rotation, thus bringing the true-shape figure in the vertical plane.

13.6.2   Construction of a plane figure in a specified plane. A plane is determined in a number of ways. The more common methods are those by two intersecting lines or two parallel lines, to which all the other methods such as that by three points can be reduced. In the plane determined by lines *AB* and *AC* in Fig. 13.28, let it be required to construct a square of a given size with one side parallel to *AC* and ½ inch from it. The first step is to find the true value of the angle between the lines *AB* and *AC* by means of two auxiliary views, as shown in Fig. 13.28(*b*). In the second auxiliary view the square may be drawn in its proper size and position. The projections are then carried back to the horizontal and vertical projections in the usual manner, as shown in Fig. 13.28(*c*).

This problem could also be solved by the rotation method.

13.6.3   Angle which a plane makes with the H-, V-, and P-planes. *Space analysis. If the edge view of both planes is obtained in any single view, the angle between the planes shows in true value in this view.*

Two situations arise for the problem. In the first situation the planes are inclined to two of the planes of projection and are perpendicular to the third and sec-

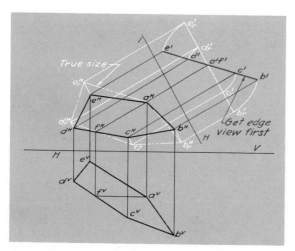

Fig. 13.27   True size of a plane figure by rotation.

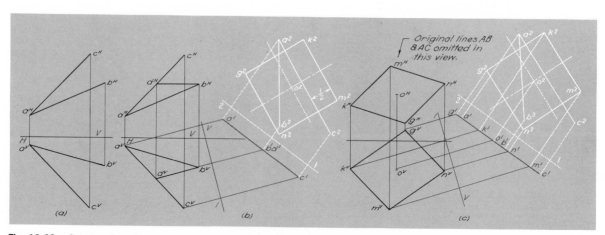

Fig. 13.28   Construction of a plane figure in a specified position.

ond, when the planes are oblique to all three planes of projection.

13.6.4   Inclined planes. This situation is discussed in Arts. 6.17.1, 6.17.2, and 6.17.3 of Chapter 6.

13.6.5   Oblique planes. The angles θ, ϕ, and π for oblique planes may be found as follows:

a. *Angle with the H-plane.* In Fig. 13.29 it is required to find the angle θ that the plane ABC makes with the H-plane. This can be done in the following manner.

   1. Draw an H-parallel BD in the plane.

   2. Obtain an end view of line BD and also the edge view of the plane on the auxiliary plane *1*.

   3. The true value of θ shows between the reference line *H-1* and the edge view of the plane.

b. *Angle with the V-plane.* For the angle ϕ between a given plane ABC and the V-plane proceed in the same manner as in (a) above, using a V-parallel as shown in Fig. 13.30.

c. *Angle with the P-plane.* For the angle π between a given plane ABC and the P-plane proceed in the same manner as in (a) above, using a P-parallel and as shown in Fig. 13.31.

13.6.6   Strike of a plane. *The strike of a plane is defined as the bearing of a horizontal line in the plane.* Hence to obtain the strike of any plane it is only necessary to draw an H-parallel in the plane and measure the angle that its H-projection makes with a north and south line. This is illustrated in Fig. 13.32. The strike of a plane together with the *dip* is used in geology and mining to describe the position of a vein of ore, coal, or rock that may occur in the form of planar beds.

13.6.7   Dip of a plane. *Space analysis. Since the slope of a plane is defined as the angle that the plane makes with the horizontal plane, the true value of this angle will show in a plane perpendicular to any horizontal line in the plane.*

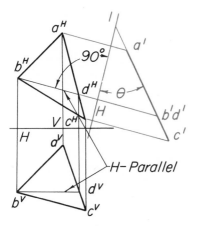

Fig. 13.29   Angle θ of an oblique plane with the H-plane.

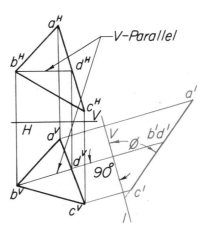

Fig. 13.30   Angle ϕ of an oblique plane with the V-plane.

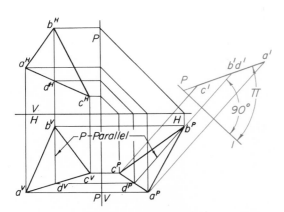

Fig. 13.31   Angle π of an oblique plane with the P-plane.

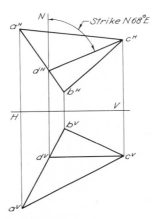

Fig. 13.32   Strike of a plane.

In geology and mining problems the slope, in a downward direction, is referred to as the dip. Dip is expressed as an angle and a general direction, such as 46° N.W. When the plane appears edgewise in either the front or side views, the slope or dip may be measured directly as the angle between the plane and the horizontal reference line, as shown in Figs. 13.33(a) and (b).

For an oblique plane, the dip may be obtained by drawing an *H*-parallel in the plane as in Fig. 13.33(c) and then finding the edge view on an auxiliary plane perpendicular to the *H*-parallel as in Fig. 13.33(c). The angle between the edge view and the auxiliary reference line is the dip. The method of showing the dip on a map is illustrated in Fig. 13.33(c) and consists of an arrow drawn in the horizontal projection perpendicular to the strike line, pointing down the slope. The angle of the dip is placed near the arrow. The complete symbol for strike and dip is shown in Fig. 13.34.

13.6.8 Plane through a point with specified strike and dip. Let it be required to represent a plane through point *A* in Fig. 13.34 having a strike of N. 60° W. and a dip of 30° NE.

a. Through point *A* draw a horizontal line having a strike of 60° N.W. as shown in Fig. 13.34(b).
b. Draw an auxiliary plane *1* perpendicular to $a^H b^H$ and find the point projection of *AB* at $a^1 b^1$ as shown in Fig. 13.34(c).
c. Through $a^1 b^1$ draw the edge view of the plane making an angle of 30° downward from the horizontal plane in a northeasterly direction. This determines the plane that is identified by the notes along the strike and dip lines in the top view.
d. To give greater usefulness to the top and front views, a point c^1 may be located in the edge view of the plane and then returned to the top and front views.
e. The plane could also be further identified by ex-

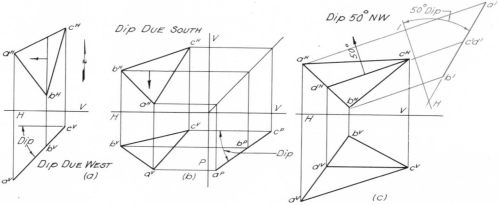

Fig. 13.33   Dip of a plane.

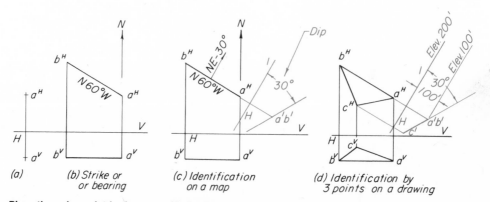

Fig. 13.34   Plane through a point having a specified strike and dip.

tending the edge view to the *H*-plane and drawing the outcrop line, that is, the line of intersection of the planes. This line has not been drawn.

13.6.9   Elevations of points in the plane.

Elevations in the plane *ABC* in Fig. 13.34(*d*) can be obtained by measuring perpendicular to the *1-H* reference line as shown in Fig. 13.34(*d*). These elevations will be relative to that of the *H*-plane.

13.6.10   Distance between two parallel planes.

Space analysis. The distance between two parallel planes can be measured directly between the edge view of the two planes.

The edge view of a plane can be obtained on an auxiliary plane placed perpendicular to any line in the plane. This could be cumbersome and may require two auxiliary views. If a *V*-parallel is chosen as the

line, one auxiliary view will solve the problem as in Fig. 13.35. An *H*-parallel would be equally good.

13.6.11   Draw a plane through a point parallel to a given plane.

Space analysis. One plane is parallel to a second plane when two intersecting lines in the first are respectively parallel to two lines in the second or when the edge view of one is made parallel to the other.

a. Thus, in Fig. 13.36(*a*), the hexagon *ABCDEF* is parallel to the triangle *MNO* because *AB* is parallel to *MN* and *CD* is parallel to *NO*. Thus by the simple principle of parallel lines it is possible to lay out one plane parallel to another.

b. When two planes are parallel, they will appear parallel in any principal or auxiliary view in which they appear edgewise. This method may therefore be used to determine the parallel relationship or to construct one plane parallel to another, as shown in Fig. 13.36(*b*). If the edgewise views are parallel, the other projections may have any shape as long as they remain in projection.

13.7   RELATIONSHIPS OF LINES AND PLANES.

Some problems concerning planes alone cannot all be solved without considering some aspects of the relationships between lines and planes given in the following articles.

13.7.1   Point in which a line pierces a plane. Edgewise view method.

Space analysis. Whenever a plane appears as an edgewise view, the piercing point of a line with that plane can be seen by inspection to be at the crossing point of the proper projection of the line with the edgewise view of the plane.

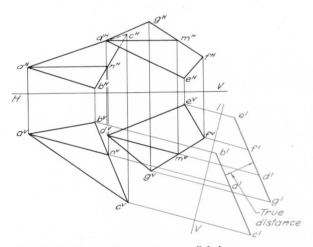

Fig. 13.35   Distance between two parallel planes.

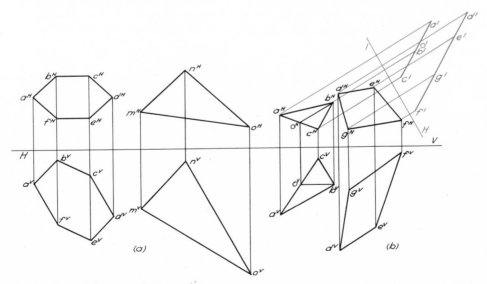

Fig. 13.36   Constructing one plane parallel to another.

a. Edge view of plane given. Figure 13.37(a) shows the edgewise view of plane *ABC* in the vertical projection and therefore the piercing point of the line *MN* with the plane can be located in that view at p^V by inspection. The remaining projections of the piercing point are carried to the other projections of the line in the usual manner.

b. Oblique plane. When the plane does not appear edgewise in any principal view, an auxiliary view can be made that will give an edgewise view of the plane by using an *H-* or *V*-parallel of the plane. The point where the auxiliary projection of the line crosses the edgewise view of the plane will be the auxiliary projection of the point where the line

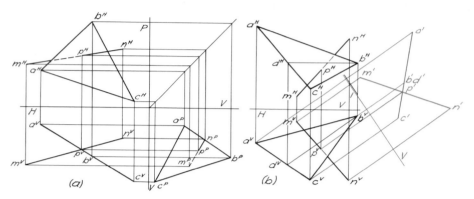

Fig. 13.37   Point in which a line pierces a plane. Edgewise view method.

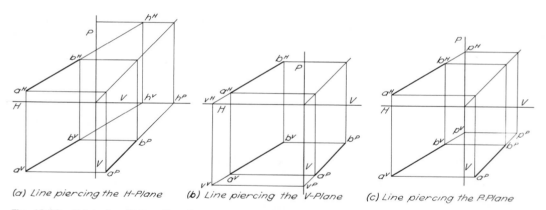

(a) *Line piercing the H-Plane*   (b) *Line piercing the V-Plane*   (c) *Line piercing the P-Plane*

Fig. 13.38   Points in which a line pierces the coordinate planes.

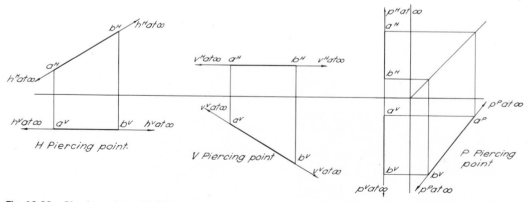

H Piercing point.   *V Piercing point*   *P Piercing point*

Fig. 13.39   Piercing points at infinity.

pierces the plane. See Fig. 13.37(b). The other views are found by projecting back from the auxiliary view.

13.7.2 Piercing point of a line with the coordinate planes.

a. *Oblique lines.* The piercing point of a line with the coordinate planes can be found in the same manner since the reference line is always an edgewise view of one of the coordinate planes. Thus, in Fig. 13.38(a), when one is looking at the vertical projection, $a^V b^V$, of a line, the horizontal reference line is the edgewise view of the H-plane. Hence extend $a^V b^V$ until it pierces the H-plane at h^V. The horizontal projection is then at h^H on $a^H b^H$ extended, and h^P on $a^P b^P$ extended.

In the same manner, when one is looking at $a^H b^H$, the top view of the line in Fig. 13.38(b), the horizontal reference line represents the edgewise view of the V-plane. Hence extend $a^H b^H$ until it pierces the V-plane at v^H. The vertical projection v^V is directly below v^H on $a^V b^V$ extended.

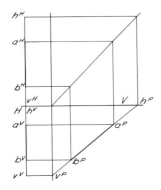

Fig. 13.40 Piercing points of a *P*-parallel.

The profile plane appears edgewise in both the front and top views, and the piercing point may be determined simply by extending both projections of AB until they cross the profile reference line at p^H and p^V. See Fig. 13.38(c). It will be noted in the above discussion that the piercing point with the coordinate planes is always given the letter of the plane. Thus h^H, h^V, and h^P for the H-plane and v^H, v^V, and v^P for the V-plane and so on.

b. *Lines parallel to one or two coordinate planes.* If a line is parallel to one of the coordinate planes, it is said to pierce it at infinity. Obviously, this cannot be shown on a drawing. It may, however, be indicated by an arrow with the symbol for infinity at the end of the line, as illustrated in Fig. 13.39.

When a line is parallel to the profile plane, its H- and V-piercing points are obtained by making the profile view. Since both H- and V-planes appear edgewise in this view, the piercing points can be obtained by inspection, as shown in Fig. 13.40. The other views can then be obtained by projection.

The piercing point of a line with the coordinate planes has many applications, for example, in oblique projection (Chapter 16) and perspective (Chapter 17).

In other problems such as outcrop problems in mining (see Fig. 23.30), highway or railroad cuts and fills (see Figs. 23.31 and 23.32), and intersection problems (Chapter 14), the principle of piercing points of lines with other surfaces must be used.

13.7.3 Point in which a line pierces a plane. Cutting plane method. *Space analysis. If any plane is passed through the line and the line of intersection of this plane with the given plane is found, the piercing point*

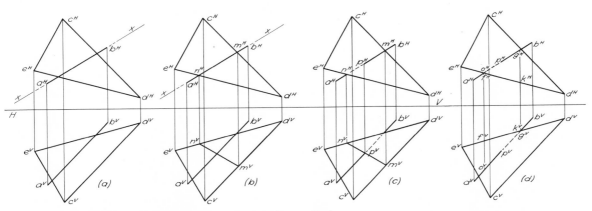

Fig. 13.41 Point in which a line pierces a plane. Cutting plane method.

will be the crossing of the given line with the line of intersection. This method, as illustrated in Fig. 13.41, is often more convenient than the auxiliary plane method. It is used extensively for finding the intersection of any two surfaces.

The procedure may be stated briefly as follows:

a. Pass a projecting plane through the line such as X-X in Fig. 13.41(a). A projecting plane always shows edgewise in the view in which it is used.

b. Find the intersection MN of the given plane with the projecting plane, Fig. 13.41(b).

c. Find the point of intersection P of the given line with this line of intersection MN, Fig. 13.41(c).

d. Since lines AB and MN both lie in the plane X-X, they must intersect or be parallel. In this case they intersect at point P, in Fig. 13.41(c), which is the piercing point of AB with plane CDE. If AB were parallel to MN, line AB would be parallel to the plane.

13.7.4 Visibility. In order to complete the drawing in Fig. 13.41, it is necessary to show which portion of line AB is visible. In the top view of Fig. 13.41(d), it

is necessary to determine which of lines AB and DE is above the other by examining the apparent crossing point $o^H f^H$ of their projections. By drawing a vertical projecting line from $o^H f^H$ it can be seen from the front view that f^V on line DE is above o^V on line AB. At this point, therefore, line AB goes below DE and the plane, and is therefore invisible in the top view from this point until it emerges above the plane at the piercing point.

The visibility in the front view can be determined in the same manner by observing the apparent crossing point of the vertical projection of lines AB and DE at $g^V k^V$. By erecting a vertical projecting line from $g^V k^V$ to the top view, it can be seen that k^H on DE is in front of g^H on AB. Hence AB goes behind DE and the plane, and, at this point, becomes invisible until it emerges at the piercing point.

13.7.5 Line parallel to a plane. *Space analysis. A line is parallel to a plane when it is parallel to any line in that plane.*

a. *Line method.* Thus, in Fig. 13.42, let it be required to construct a line through O parallel to plane CDE. One may draw any line AB in plane CDE and then

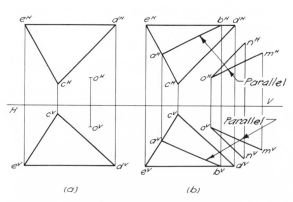

Fig. 13.42 Lines parallel to a plane.

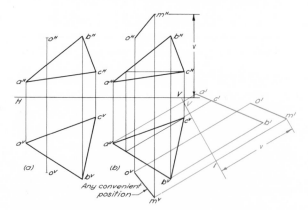

Fig. 13.43 Line parallel to a plane.

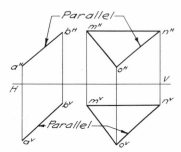

Fig. 13.44 Plane parallel to one line.

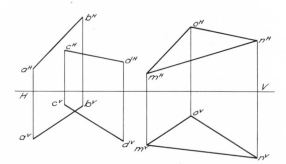

Fig. 13.45 Plane parallel to two lines.

draw through O the projections of OM parallel to the corresponding projections of AB. Any edge line of triangle CDE could also have been used; for example, ON is parallel to CD.

b. *Edge view method.* A line may also be drawn parallel to a plane by making one projection of the line parallel to the corresponding edgewise view of the plane, as shown in Fig. 13.43. The other projections may have any convenient position so long as they are in correct alignment with each other. For example, let it be required to draw a line through O in Fig. 13.43(a) parallel to plane ABC. The edgewise view of the plane with the corresponding projection of O may be obtained by auxiliary projection as shown in Fig. 13.43(b). Through o^1 draw o^1m^1 parallel to $a^1b^1c^1$. The adjacent projection of o^Vm^V may be made in any direction. The projection o^Hm^H is found in the usual way.

13.7.6 Plane parallel to one or two lines. *Space analysis. If any plane contains a line parallel to a second line, that plane is parallel to this second line.*

a. *Parallel to one line.* When only one line is involved, there are an infinite number of solutions, but if two nonparallel lines are involved, only one solution is possible.

To construct a plane through a point parallel to a given line it is only necessary to draw a line ON through the point parallel to the given line AB, as shown in Fig. 13.44. Any plane such as OMN containing this line satisfies the condition.

b. *Parallel to two lines.* If a plane is to be constructed through a point parallel to two given lines, two lines must be drawn through the point respectively parallel to the two given lines, as shown in Fig. 13.45. The plane of the two lines is the required plane. Line ON is parallel to CD, and OM is parallel to AB, thus satisfying the conditions.

13.7.7 Angle between a line and a plane. *Space analysis. The true angle between a line and a plane will show on an auxiliary plane which is simultaneously parallel to the line and perpendicular to the plane.* The solution of this problem may require three auxiliary views as illustrated in Fig. 13.46. First, secure an edge view of the plane. Second, make a true-shape view of the plane as in Fig. 13.46(a). Third, construct another edge view of the plane on an auxiliary plane parallel to the line. See Fig. 13.46(b). The view gives the required angle. The angle could also be obtained by revolving the line in the second auxiliary view until it is parallel to the reference line 1-2.

13.7.8 Line perpendicular to a plane. *Space analysis. A line is perpendicular to a plane when it is perpendicular to any two nonparallel lines in the plane.*

a. *Line method.* Theoretically any two intersecting lines may be used but to make the construction as easy as possible, it is best to use an H-parallel and a V-parallel. Figure 13.47(a) shows a plane ABC with the H-parallel AD and the V-parallel AE already constructed. To make AG perpendicular to ABC, a^Hg^H is drawn perpendicular to a^Hd^H and a^Vg^V is drawn perpendicular to a^Ve^V, as in Fig. 13.47(b), thus making AG at right angles to both lines AD and AE, as explained in Art. 13.3.12. Any line parallel to AG will also be perpendicular to the plane.

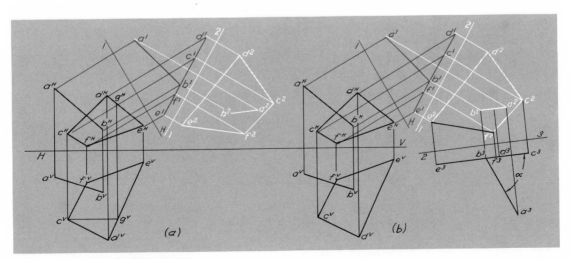

Fig. 13.46 Angle between a line and a plane.

b. Edge view method. The edgewise view of a plane may also be used to construct a perpendicular. In Fig. 13.48, the plane *ABC* shows edgewise in the front view. Any line perpendicular to this plane must also be parallel to the *V*-plane. Line *DE* is therefore drawn at right angles to plane *ABC* by making $d^V e^V$ perpendicular to $a^V b^V c^V$ and $d^H e^H$ parallel to the reference line.

This method may be used for any plane by obtaining first an edge view by auxiliary projection, as shown in Fig. 13.49. In the auxiliary view, draw $d^1 e^1$ perpendicular to $b^1 a^1 c^1$ and the adjacent view parallel to the auxiliary reference line. The remaining projection is obtained in the usual way.

13.7.9   Projection of a point on a plane. *Space analysis. The piercing point of a line through the point drawn perpendicular to the plane is the projection (orthographic) of the point on the plane.*

This is an application of the preceding paragraph. For this purpose the edge view method is best, as shown in Fig. 13.50.

Given point *O* and plane *ABCD*, proceed as follows:

a. Using an *H*-parallel of the plane obtain an edge view. Obtain also the auxiliary projection of the point at o^1.

b. From o^1 draw a line perpendicular to the plane and label the point where it pierces the plane p^1.

c. The horizontal projection of the line *OP* is drawn perpendicular to *BM* or parallel to the *1-H* reference line.

d. The vertical projection can be obtained from the preceding projections in the usual way.

13.7.10   Plane perpendicular to a line. This is simply the reverse of the preceding problem and may be solved by either procedure discussed in that paragraph.

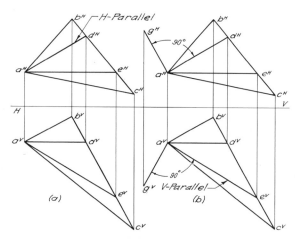

Fig. 13.47   Line perpendicular to a plane.

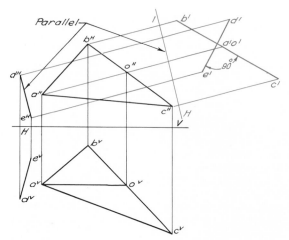

Fig. 13.49   Line perpendicular to an oblique plane. Edgewise view method.

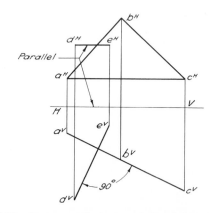

Fig. 13.48   Line perpendicular to an inclined plane. Edgewise view method.

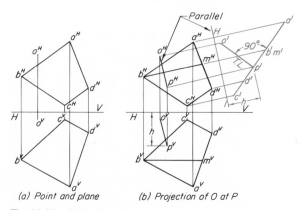

(a) Point and plane   (b) Projection of O at P

Fig. 13.50   Projection of a point on an oblique plane.

a. Line method. The first solution, shown in Fig. 13.51(*a*), consists of drawing two lines *BC* and *BD* each perpendicular to line *AB*, as explained in Art. 13.3.12 and illustrated in Fig. 13.23. The plane of these two lines is the required plane.

b. Edge view method. In the second method shown in Figs. 13.51(*b*) and (*c*), the edgewise view of the plane is drawn perpendicular to the true-length view of the line. The adjacent view may be drawn in any position so long as the points are in proper alignment. In Fig. 13.51(*b*), the true-length view of the line is the top view or horizontal projection, but the same principles would apply in any view.

For an oblique line as shown in Fig. 13.51(*c*), it is first necessary to obtain a true-length view of the line by auxiliary projection. Beginning in the auxiliary view the procedure is the same as outlined above.

13.7.11   Construction of a solid in a specified position. As an illustration, let it be required to construct a right pentagonal pyramid with line *AB* of Fig. 13.52(*a*) as an axis and point *C* as one corner of the base. To solve this problem, the following steps are necessary.

a. Project the point and line on an auxiliary plane perpendicular to the line. See Fig. 13.52(*a*).

b. Construct the true size of the base in the second auxiliary projection and letter the corners. See Fig. 13.52(*b*).

c. Construct the elevation of the pyramid in the first auxiliary projection. See Fig. 13.52(*b*).

d. Project the pyramid back to the vertical projection as shown in Fig. 13.52(*c*).

e. Project the pyramid back to the horizontal projection as shown in Fig. 13.52(*d*).

f. Determine the visibility in each view.

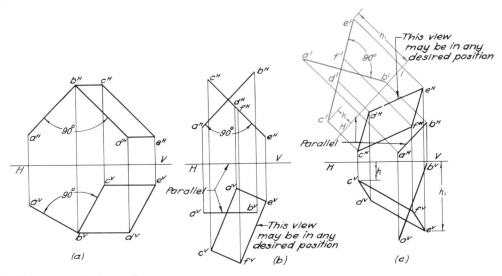

Fig. 13.51   Plane perpendicular to a line.

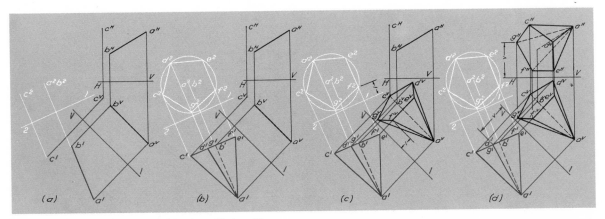

Fig. 13.52   Construction of a solid in a specified position.

13.7.12 Plane perpendicular to a plane. *Space analysis. If a line is perpendicular to a given plane, any plane containing the line is perpendicular to the given plane.*

a. *Line method.* Thus in Fig. 13.53(a) line AB has been constructed perpendicular to plane DEFG by the method discussed in Art. 13.7.8. Since plane ABC contains line AB, the plane is perpendicular to DEFG.

b. *Edge view method.* If an edge view of one plane is found as $a^1b^1c^1$ in Fig. 13.53(b), another plane such as DEFG may be set up perpendicular to ABC, or at any other angle, by making the edge view $d^1e^1f^1g^1$ at the prescribed angle with $a^1b^1c^1$. The adjacent projection of DEFG may be placed in any convenient position so long as it is in proper alignment with $d^1e^1f^1g^1$.

13.7.13 Intersection of two planes. *Space analysis. The intersection of two planes is a straight line which is determined by two points each common to both planes.*

a. *Cutting plane method.* The problem, therefore, resolves itself into finding two points common to both planes. Using the method described in Art. 13.7.3, the point O in Fig. 13.54(a), where line BC pierces plane DEFG, is found. Point P in Fig. 13.54(b) in which DG pierces plane ABC locates the second point of line OP. Line OP shown in Fig. 13.54(c) is the required line of intersection. Visibility may be determined as described in Art. 13.7.4 and shown in Figs. 13.54(c) and (d).

b. *Strike and dip method.* Another method for determining the line of intersection of two planes is useful for geologists when the planes are determined

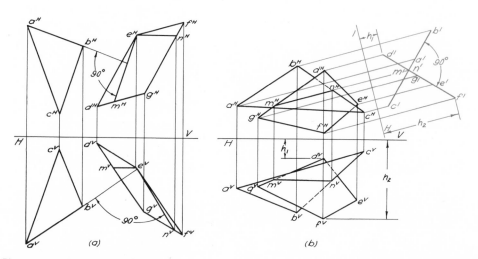

Fig. 13.53   Plane perpendicular to another plane.

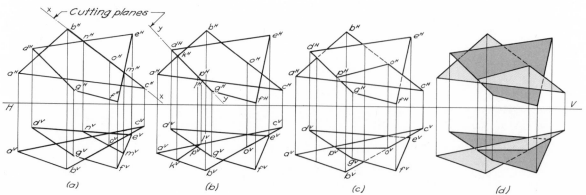

Fig. 13.54   Intersection of two planes.

by strike and dip. In Fig. 13.55, two planes through point A are determined by their strikes and dips as they would appear on a geologic map. By placing an auxiliary plane perpendicular to AB, the edgewise view of one of the planes can be obtained by laying off the dip as indicated in Fig. 13.55(b).

Another auxiliary plane perpendicular to AC will make it possible to construct the edgewise view of the second plane by laying off the dip as shown in Fig. 13.55(b). If a cutting plane T-T is passed parallel to the horizontal, as in Fig. 13.55(c) the edgewise views of this plane may be shown in both auxiliary views. The line of intersection of this cutting plane with the plane through AB is DE and with the plane through AC it is KG. Point F where these two lines intersect, is a point on both planes, and therefore one point on their line of intersection. Line AF is therefore the line of intersection of the two given planes.

13.7.14 Outcrop of a plane. *The line in which any plane such as a vein of coal or a bed of stone intersects*

the surface of the earth is called an outcrop. The outcrop on a horizontal surface is a strike line and may be found by obtaining the points in which any two lines in the plane of the vein pierce the horizontal surface. Joining these two points with a straight line, as shown in Fig. 13.56, gives the outcrop line. This outcrop can also be found by setting up an auxiliary plane perpendicular to any strike line in the plane to obtain the edgewise view of the plane.

The point where the auxiliary reference line and the edgewise view of the plane intersect is the point projection, e^1f^1, of a line that lies in the horizontal plane and in the plane of the vein. Line EF is the outcrop which can be located in the horizontal view at e^Hf^H by projecting from e^1f^1 perpendicular to the 1-H reference line. This line is indefinite in length, so the projections e^H and f^H may be placed anywhere along the outcrop as shown in Fig. 13.56. The outcrop on a vertical plane such as the side of an excavation can be found by obtaining the piercing points of any two lines in the vein with the given vertical plane and joining them together. Usually the surface of the earth is de-

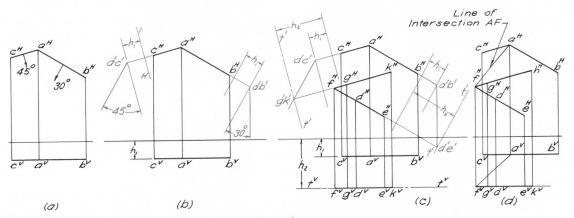

Fig. 13.55 Intersection of two planes when strike and dip are given.

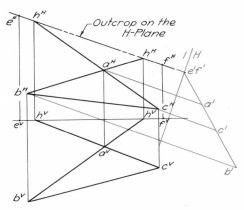

Fig. 13.56 Outcrop of a plane.

fined by contours; the method of finding the outcrop in such cases is explained in Art. 23.26.

13.7.15   Angle between two planes. *Space analysis. When two planes show edgewise on the same plane of projection, the true angle between the planes will show between the edge views.*

When the angle between two given planes is required, the edge views of both planes can be found on an auxiliary plane perpendicular to their line of intersection. In Fig. 13.57(a), it is therefore necessary to find the line of intersection *MN* of the two planes by the usual methods. In Fig. 13.57(b), the first auxiliary plane is set up parallel to *MN* and a second auxiliary plane perpendicular to *MN*, thus giving the edge view of both planes and the angle between them.

An application of this problem is found very frequently in structural engineering. Thus in Fig. 13.58 a bent gusset plate is shown attached to a steel channel. It is necessary for fabrication to find the angle between the two portions of this plate and also the developed flat pattern.

Angle *X* between the faces *ABCD* and *ABEF* is found as described in the preceding paragraph and illustration.

Having the true angle *X* between the faces in the second auxiliary view as shown in Fig. 13.58, find the true shape of one face on an auxiliary plane parallel to it. Then revolve the other face about the line of intersection, until it is also parallel to the same auxiliary plane, as explained in Art. 13.6.1. This layout will give the true size of the plate before bending.

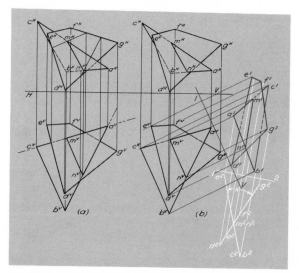

Fig. 13.57   Angle between two planes.

13.8   SKEW LINES. *Lines that are nonparallel and nonintersecting are called skew lines.* Skew lines can occur in various engineering situations such as in mining and piping.

13.8.1   Shortest distance between two skew lines. *Space analysis. The shortest distance between two nonparallel, nonintersecting lines is the true length of their common perpendicular.*

a. Point projection method. This problem can be solved by projecting both lines on a plane perpendicular to one of them as in Fig. 13.59(a) by means of auxiliary projection. Having this projection, draw a line from a^2b^2 perpendicular to c^2d^2 as in Fig. 13.59(b) and letter it m^2n^2. Point n^1 may be found on c^1d^1 by direct projection. Construct m^1n^1 parallel to reference line *1-2*, since *MN* is perpendicular to *AB*, hence parallel to plane *2*. Return the projections of *M* and *N* to the original views by the usual methods.

b. Parallel plane method. The shortest perpendicular between two skew lines will project as a point on a plane parallel to both skew lines.

1. In Fig. 13.60 determine a plane parallel to *AB* and *CD* by drawing a line *AE* through *A* parallel to *CD*. Any plane parallel to *AB* and *AE* is parallel to both lines. See Fig. 13.60.

2. By means of an *H*-parallel, *EF*, in plane *ABE* obtain an edge view of the plane. The two skew lines will show parallel in this auxiliary view.

3. On a second auxiliary plane obtain a true-shape view of the plane *ABE* as in Fig. 13.60(a). The two skew lines appear in true length in this view.

4. The crossing point m^2n^2 of the lines in the true-length view locates the end view of their common perpendicular. Return this line to the original views.

13.8.2   Shortest horizontal line between two skew lines. This problem is best solved by the parallel plane method. The first auxiliary plane must be set up perpendicular to the *H*-plane. See Art. 13.8.1(b) and Fig. 13.60(b).

a. In Fig. 13.60 follow steps 1 and 2 in Art. 13.8.1(b).

b. Set up the second auxiliary plane perpendicular to the first auxiliary reference line *H-1*, since this reference line represents the *H*-plane in the first auxiliary view. Project the two lines on this plane.

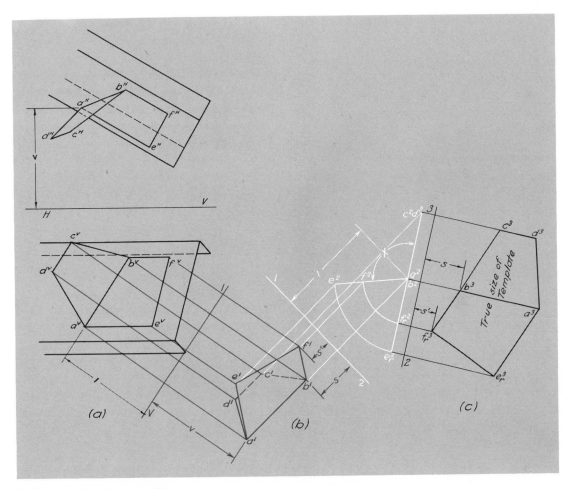

Fig. 13.58   True size of a gusset plate.

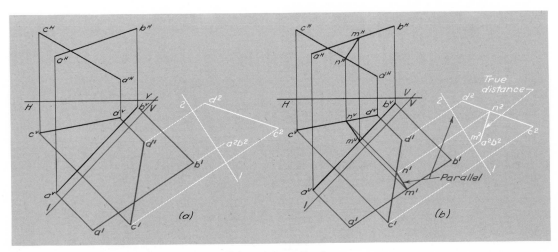

Fig. 13.59   Shortest distance between two nonparallel, nonintersecting lines.

c. The crossing point r^3s^3 of the two lines locates the shortest horizontal line between the two skew lines.

13.8.3 Shortest line of specified slope or grade between two skew lines.

This problem also is best solved by the parallel plane method. Again, the first auxiliary plane must be perpendicular to the H-plane. See Art. 13.8.1(*b*) and Fig. 13.60(*c*).

a. In Fig. 13.60(*c*) follow steps 1 and 2 of Art. 13.8.1(*b*).

b. With the first auxiliary reference line as a datum,

at some convenient place in the first auxiliary view draw a line of the specified slope or grade. In Fig. 13.60(*c*) the grade line is $+15$ per cent from W to T.

c. Set up a second auxiliary plane perpendicular to the grade line and project both skew lines on this plane. The crossing point x^4y^4 of the lines locates the shortest 15 per cent grade line between them. The projections of this line can be returned to the original views in the usual manner.

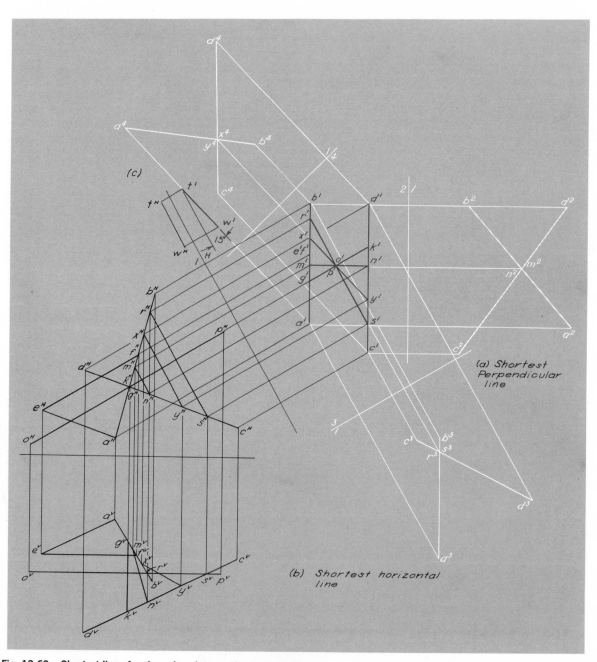

Fig. 13.60 Shortest line of a given slope intersecting two skew lines.

13.8.4   Grade line having a given bearing and slope between two skew lines. In the preceding problem (Art. 13.8.3) the grade line was assumed to be parallel to the first auxiliary plane represented by the reference line *H-1* in Fig. 13.60(*c*).

If the grade line is to have some other bearing and slope, the problem may be solved as follows:

a. Lay out the grade line with the proper bearing and slope.

b. Find its vertical projection.

c. Then proceed in a manner similar to that for line *EF* in the following article.

13.8.5   Line parallel to a given line and intersecting two nonparallel, nonintersecting lines. Let it be required to draw a line parallel to *EF* and intersecting *AB* and *CD* as shown in Fig. 13.61.

Space analysis. If the point projection of one of the lines is found, the required line can be drawn in that projection through the point and parallel to the given line until it intersects the other of the two skew lines.

The solution for this particular problem is found by projecting all three lines on a plane perpendicular to *AB*, as shown in Fig. 13.61(*b*). Since parallel lines always have their projections parallel, draw a line from a^2b^2 parallel to e^2f^2 until it intersects c^2d^2 at n^2, as in

Fig. 13.61(*c*). In the first auxiliary view, draw a line from n^1 parallel to e^1f^1 until it intersects a^1b^1 at m^1, thus determining a line between *AB* and *CD* parallel to *EF*. Return line *MN* to the original views in the usual manner.

The solution could also have been obtained by placing an auxiliary plane perpendicular to line *EF*, in which case the required line *MN* would have shown as a point in the second auxiliary view.

13.9   CONSTRUCTION CONES. The right circular cone provides a very useful tool in the solution of certain problems involving angles between lines and planes.

a. First, it should be noted that the elements of a cone all make the same angle with the plane of the base.

b. Second, these elements also make a constant angle with the axis of the cone. The problems in the following paragraphs illustrate the use of the cone. Review Art. 13.2.5. See Fig. 13.5.

13.9.1   Line through a point making a given angle with *H-*, *V-*, or *P-*plane. *Space analysis. A right circular cone having the specified base angle may be set up with its vertex at the given point and its axis perpendicular to the required plane. Any element of this cone will satisfy the conditions of the problem.*

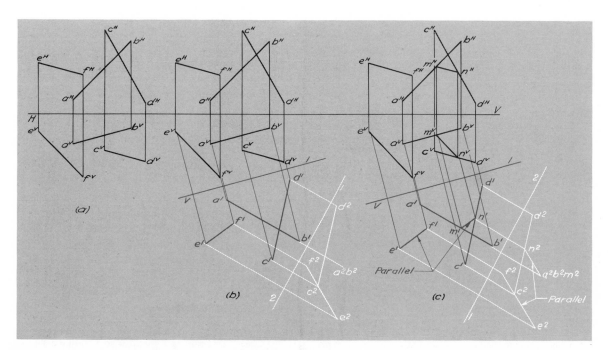

Fig. 13.61   Line parallel to a given line and intersecting two skew lines.

As an illustration, let it be required to draw a line through point A in Fig. 13.62, making an angle of 45° with the H-plane. The solution is as follows:

a. Through A draw a line AB of any convenient length perpendicular to the H-plane.
b. With AB as an axis, draw a right circular cone whose elements make 45° with the base.
c. Any element such as AC will satisfy the conditions of the problem.

A similar construction for the vertical and profile planes can be made by drawing the axis of the cone perpendicular to either of these planes, as shown in Figs. 13.63 and 13.64.

13.9.2   Line through a point making given angles with both H- and V-planes. *Space analysis. If two cones are drawn from the same point as a vertex with one having its axis perpendicular to the H-plane and the other perpendicular to the V-plane and each having the proper base angle and elements of the same length, the intersection of these cones will satisfy the conditions of the problem.*

For simplicity of solution the bases of both cones should be on the surface of a sphere whose center is at the given point through which the line is to be constructed. The outer circles in Fig. 13.65 represent the projections of the sphere. Every element of both cones is therefore a radius of the sphere and consequently the elements of both cones are of equal length. If the solution is possible, the cones will intersect, and since the elements are all the same length and the bases lie on the surface of the sphere, the bases will intersect each other at one or two points. These points, when connected with the apex of the cones, will be the required lines since they are elements of both cones.

Let it be required to construct a line through point A in Fig. 13.65, making an angle of 30° with the H-plane and 45° with the V-plane. The construction is as follows:

a. With point A as a center, draw the H- and V-projections of a sphere whose radius will be equal to the desired length of elements for the cones.
b. With A as the apex, construct a right circular cone with its axis perpendicular to the H-plane, its elements equal to the radius of the sphere, and making an angle of 30° with the H-plane.

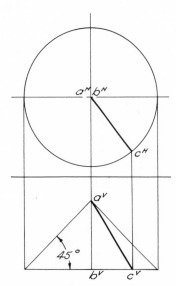

Fig. 13.62   Line making a specified angle with the H-plane. Cone method.

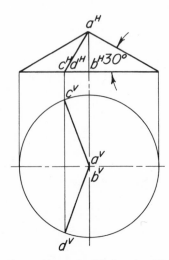

Fig. 13.63   Line making a specified angle with the V-plane.

c. With the same apex, construct another cone with its axis perpendicular to the *V*-plane, its elements making 45° with the *V*-plane, and equal in length to the radius of the sphere.

d. The bases will now intersect each other at points *B* and *C* in Fig. 13.65.

e. Joining these points to the apex gives lines *AB* and *AC*, which satisfy the conditions of the problem.

In this problem the profile view is useful since both axes are parallel to profile and consequently both cones show as triangles.

13.9.3   Line through a point making a given angle with any two planes. The solution of this problem illustrated in Fig. 13.66 is the same as the preceding one but represents a more general case. Here the line of intersection of the two planes has been made perpendicular to the *V*-plane. The solution involves the construction of two cones with axes perpendicular respectively to the two planes, as shown in Fig. 13.66.

If the line of intersection of the two planes is not perpendicular to one of the coordinate planes, the first step in the solution will be to find the edge view of both planes on a plane perpendicular to their line of intersection. This auxiliary plane will be parallel to the axes of both cones and therefore will show both cones as triangles. The remainder of the solution is similar to that shown in Fig. 13.66.

13.9.4   Line making specified angles with two intersecting lines. *Space analysis. If a right circular cone having the specified vertex angle is constructed around each line, with the vertex of both cones at the point of intersection of the two lines, the intersection of these cones will give the specified lines. Let it be required to draw lines making 75° with both AB and BC.*

The solution may be found in the following manner.

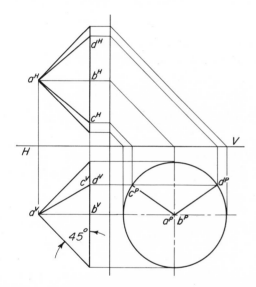

Fig. 13.64   Line making a specified angle with the *P*-plane.

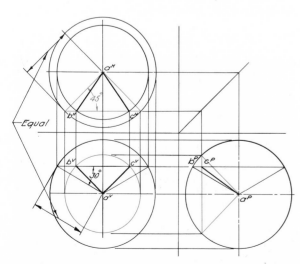

Fig. 13.65   Line making specified angles with both *H*- and *V*-planes.

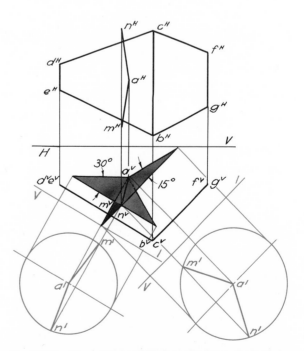

Fig. 13.66   Line making specified angles with any two planes.

a. Draw an *H*-parallel *BD* in the plane of the two lines as in Fig. 13.67.

b. Find the edge view $a^1b^1c^1$ of the plane of the lines in the first auxiliary view.

c. Find the true-shape view (angle between the lines $a^2b^2c^2$) in the second auxiliary view.

d. At the intersection of the two lines draw a sphere of convenient diameter and construct the cones around each line with their bases on the sphere. Note that the specified angle of 75° must be between the element and the axis of the cones.

e. The crossing points of the bases of the cones locates two lines which fulfill the requirement of the problem.

f. In order to return the projections of the lines to the original views make a third auxiliary view of the base of one of the cones and locate the two points on the base. This gives the necessary measurements for the return of the two required lines.

A second illustration of this problem is shown in Fig. 13.68. In this case the specified angles are 60° with *AB* and 45° with *BC*. It will be noted in this figure that the two cones are tangent to each other. Therefore, only one solution, namely line *BM* is possible. From the figure it can be seen that in this situation a third auxiliary view is not necessary.

13.9.5   Line intersecting two skew lines and making specified angles with them. *Space analysis. Since the elements of a right circular cone make a constant angle with the axis, construction cones may be used to draw a line making a given angle with another line or two separate lines. Lines parallel to these con-*

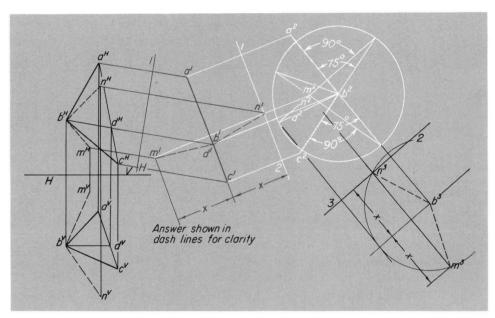

Fig. 13.67   Line making specified angles with two intersecting lines.

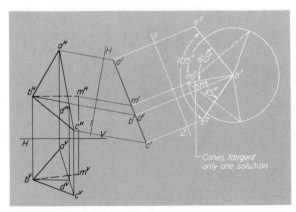

Fig. 13.68   Line making specified angles with two intersecting lines. One solution only.

structed lines may then be drawn intersecting the two given skew lines.

Let it be required to construct a line intersecting AB and CD in Fig. 13.69 making 60° with AB and 45° with CD. The solution is as follows:

a. Through any point O construct two lines, OE and OF, respectively parallel to AB and CD. Figure 13.69(a).

b. Project both lines on plane 1 to get the edgewise view at $o^1e^1f^1$ and on plane 2 to get the true size at $e^2o^2f^2$ in Fig. 13.69(a).

c. In the second auxiliary view construct one view of the desired sphere, and using o^2e^2 and o^2f^2 as axes draw the cones using the specified angles. Figure 13.69(b).

d. Set up a third auxiliary plane parallel to either one of the bases of the cones and draw the circle representing that base. Figure 13.69(b).

e. In the second auxiliary projection the bases of the cones intersect at m^2n^2. Lines OM and ON are lines through point O parallel to the required line, and they may be projected back to the H- and V-projections. Figure 13.69(b).

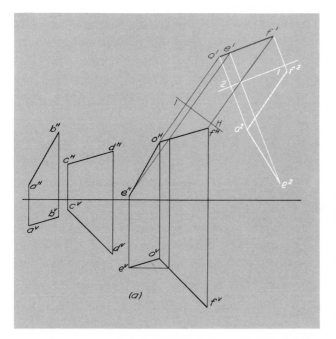

(a)

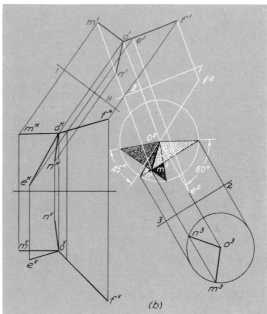

(b)

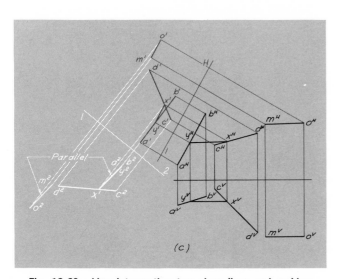

(c)

Fig. 13.69   Line intersecting two skew lines and making specified angles with them.

f. In Fig. 13.69(c) draw the H- and V-projections of MO, one of the lines just found. This is shown at the far right in Fig. 13.69(c).

g. With AB and CD in Fig. 13.69(c) parallel to their original positions, draw an auxiliary plane 1 parallel to AB (a^Hb^H) and find all three lines AB, CD, and MO on this plane.

h. Set up an auxiliary plane 2 perpendicular to a^1b^1 and get the projections of all three lines AB, CD, and OM on this plane.

i. From a^2b^2 draw a line parallel to m^2o^2 until it intersects c^2d^2 at x^2.

j. Project x^2 back to x^1 on c^1d^1 and from x^1 draw x^1y^1 parallel to m^1o^1.

k. From this view project x and y back to the H- and V-projections in the usual manner.

13.9.6 Plane through a given line making a specified angle with a given plane. *Space analysis. The plane may be made tangent to a construction cone, which has been set up so that the elements make the required angle with the given plane.*

a. Given plane horizontal. As an example, let it be required to construct a plane containing line *AB* in Fig. 13.70 and making 60° with the horizontal plane.

  1. Choose any point on *AB* and make that point the apex of the cone. In this case, the apex is at *A* and a cone whose elements make 60° with the *H*-plane has been constructed.
  2. Next find the point *P*, where *AB* pierces the plane of the base.
  3. From this point, construct a line *PC* tangent to the base of the cone. Lines *AP* and *PC* determine the required plane. Line *PC* can be drawn tangent to the circle on either side.

b. Given plane oblique. Let line *AB* be the given line and *CDEF* the given oblique plane as shown in Fig. 13.71.

  1. The procedure is the same as for the problem in Fig. 13.70, except that an edge view of the plane along with the line must be first obtained, as shown in the first auxiliary view of Fig. 13.71.
  2. Second, find a true-shape view of the plane *CDEF* in which the base of the cone lies. Then

the piercing point of the line with the plane must be obtained, in a second auxiliary view.

  3. On this view, second auxiliary view, the tangent line *p²r²* can be drawn from the piercing point to the circle of the base.
  4. The two lines *AP* and *PR* determine the plane.

13.9.7 Planes making specified angles with two given planes. *Space analysis. If two lines are constructed making angles with two planes that are complements of the required angles, the required plane may be constructed perpendicular to either of these lines.*

In Fig. 13.72 the planes *ABCD* and *CDEF* have been placed so that the line of intersection of the planes is perpendicular to the *H*-plane and therefore both planes appear edgewise. In a more general case it might be necessary to make one or two auxiliary projections to get the edge view of the planes. Let it be required to draw a plane that makes 60° with *ABCD* and 45° with *CDEF*.

The construction is as follows:

a. Determine the complements of the specified angles

$$30° \text{ with } ABCD \text{ and}$$
$$45° \text{ with } CDEF.$$

b. By means of construction cones making the above angles with each plane find the lines *OM* and *ON* that meet the required condition as shown in Fig. 13.72(*b*).

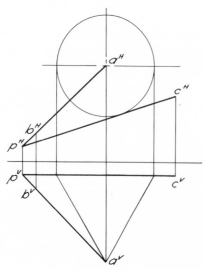

Fig. 13.70 Plane containing a given line and making a specified angle with the *H*-plane.

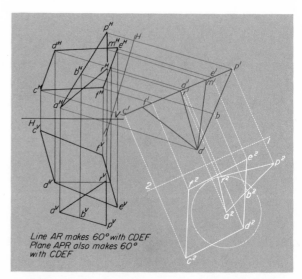

Line AR makes 60° with CDEF
Plane APR also makes 60° with CDEF

Fig. 13.71 Plane through a given line making a specified angle with an oblique plane.

c. Construct planes perpendicular to *OM* and *ON* by drawing two lines perpendicular to *OM* as shown in Fig. 13.72(*c*) and likewise for *ON* as shown in Fig. 13.72(*d*). See Art. 13.3.12 for drawing lines perpendicular to a given line. Plane *ORS* is one solution and *OXY* is the other.

13.9.8   Line making a specified angle with a given line and a given plane. Let it be required to draw a line making 60° with line *AB* and 30° with plane *MNO*. *Space analysis. If a construction cone with vertex at any point on the line AB is made having the elements at 60° with the line AB as an axis and then a second cone with the same apex and having elements that makes 30° with plane MNO is drawn, the intersection of these cones will give the required line.*

a. In Fig. 13.73 obtain first an edge view of the plane and in the same view a true length projection of the line. In Fig. 13.73 this requires three auxiliary views. In some problems two auxiliary views might be enough.

b. Draw the standard sphere with center at point *E* on line *AB* extended. This extension of *AB* was made to prevent too much overlapping of the views.

c. Draw the appropriate construction cones as shown in Fig. 13.73.

d. The intersection of the cones gives the required lines, *EC* and *ED*.

e. Return them to the original views in the usual manner. In Fig. 13.73(*c*) lines $b^2c_1{}^2$ and $b^2d_1{}^2$ have been drawn through *B* parallel to e^2c^2 and e^2d^2. Line *BD* only has been returned to the front and top views.

13.10   LOCUS PROBLEMS. The concept of loci appears in some descriptive geometry problems. The solution of such problems usually requires that the general locus be determined first and then further limiting conditions be applied. For example, let it be required to find the locus of points equidistant from two given points and in a given plane. The general locus of points equidistant from two given points is the

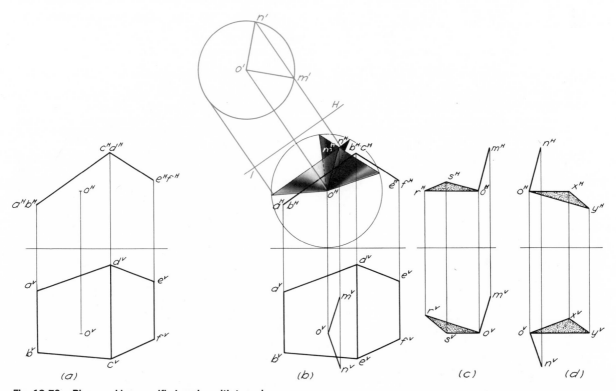

Fig. 13.72   Plane making specified angles with two planes.

plane-perpendicular bisector of the line joining the points. This plane must be determined first. The second condition limits the locus to points lying in a particular given plane. Hence the answer is the line of intersection of the two planes. The loci most commonly used are listed below.

a. The locus of points equidistant from two given points is the plane-perpendicular bisector of the line joining the points.

b. The locus of points equidistant from three given points is the line of intersection of the two plane-perpendicular bisectors of the two lines joining the three points. This line will be perpendicular to the plane of the three points.

c. The locus of points equidistant from four given points (not lying in a plane) is a single point, which is the center of a sphere having the four points on its surface. This problem can be solved by finding the locus of points equidistant from three points as in (b) above and then finding the piercing point of this line with the plane-perpendicular bisector of the line joining the fourth point to any one of the first three.

d. The locus of points at a given distance from a plane is two parallel planes, one on each side of the given plane at the specified distances from it.

e. The locus of points at a given distance from a line is the surface of a right circular cylinder having the line as an axis and a radius equal to the specified distance.

f. The locus of points at a given distance from a given point is the surface of a sphere with the given point as its center and a radius equal to the given distance.

g. The locus of lines making a specified angle with a given line is the surface of a right circular cone having the given line as an axis, and whose elements make the specified angle with the line.

h. The locus of lines making a specified angle with a given plane is the surface of a right circular cone whose axis is perpendicular to the plane and whose elements make the specified angle with the plane.

13.11 WARPED SURFACES. A warped surface is one that is generated by a straight line moving according to certain specifications that vary with the different surfaces. No two positions of the generating line will lie in the same plane. These surfaces are nondevelopable; that is, they cannot be formed from metal without stretching or warping the metal. Some of these surfaces are illustrated in Fig. 14.1 in Chapter 14 and will be discussed briefly in the following paragraphs.

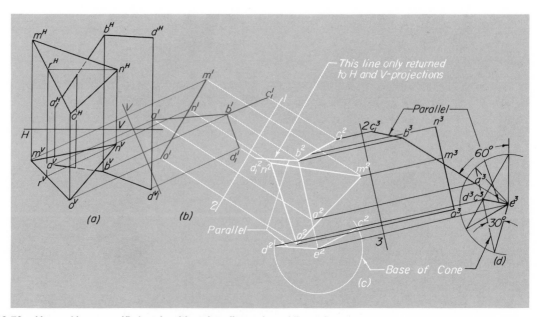

Fig. 13.73 Line making a specified angle with a given line and an oblique plane.

13.11.1 Hyperbolic paraboloid.

The hyperbolic paraboloid or warped quadrilateral is a surface generated by a straight line, called a generatrix, moving so that it always touches two nonparallel, nonintersecting lines, called linear directrices, and remains parallel to a plane director. It is a doubly ruled surface because it has two sets of linear directrices, two plane directors, and two sets of generating lines.

If the surface is defined by giving four bounding lines such as *ABCD* in Fig. 13.74, it is called a warped quadrilateral. Elements may be drawn in the surface by dividing either set of linear directrices (opposite sides) into the same number of equal spaces and drawing lines connecting the division points. If a plane is passed through *AB* parallel to *CD*, this plane will be one of the plane directrices and one set of elements will all be parallel to that plane. The other plane may be found by passing a plane through *AD* parallel to *BC*.

The hyperbolic paraboloid is sometimes used as the basis or framework of some practical structure and as such should be recognized by the student. The hyperbolic paraboloid is also used in the design of the bow of a boat, or in any transition surface connecting planes of different slope.

Figure 13.75 shows the projections of a hyperbolic paraboloid having two lines *AB* and *CD* as linear directrices and the horizontal plane as the plane director. Since the horizontal reference line represents the edgewise view of the horizontal plane in the vertical projection, that projection of the elements may be drawn parallel to the reference line. Therefore, to construct one view of any hyperbolic paraboloid, it is only necessary to find the edgewise view of the plane director by means of one or more auxiliary planes and draw the elements in that view. They may then be projected to the other views by means of their intersections with the linear directrices as was done in Fig. 13.75.

It is interesting to note that the true-length line of various slopes in Fig. 13.60 are elements of a hyperbolic paraboloid which are perpendicular to and intersect the line *OP*.

13.11.2 Hyperboloid of revolution of one sheet.

This surface is generated by a right line that revolves about another nonparallel, nonintersecting right line as an axis. It may also be generated by a line touching three circles whose planes are perpendicular to a common axis through their centers. When the radius of the middle, or gorge, circle becomes zero, the surface is a cone, and when this radius becomes the same as the radius of the other two circles, the surface is a cylinder. Thus the cone and cylinder become the limits of the hyperboloid of revolution. Since this is a surface of revolution, a plane passed perpendicular to the axis of revolution cuts a circle from the surface.

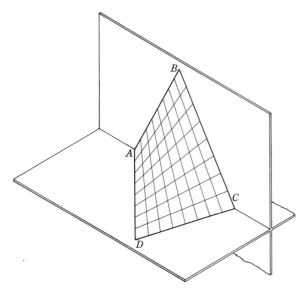

Fig. 13.74 Warped quadrilateral.

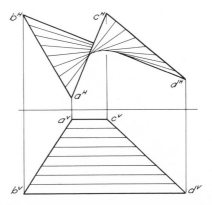

Fig. 13.75 Hyperbolic paraboloid with the *H*-plane as a plane director.

The surface is doubly ruled, since two different lines may be revolved about the axis to give the same surface. These lines make equal angles with the base but slope in opposite directions. Figure 13.76 gives the projections of a hyperboloid of revolution, showing both sets of generatrices, *AB* and *CD*. The other elements shown are of the *AB* generation, no other positions of *CD* being shown.

The hyperboloid of revolution may be generated also by revolving a hyperbola about its conjugate axis. The surface is sometimes represented by showing its contour lines as illustrated in Fig. 13.77, these contour lines being the opposite branches of the hyperbola.

a. Construction 1. Given three curvilinear directrices, as in Fig. 13.76, divide the base circle into a number of equal parts in the plan view and draw the horizontal projection of the elements through these

points tangent to the gorge circle. Project the ends of the elements to the elevation and draw in the elements.

b. Construction 2. Given the axis *OM* and the generatrix *AB*, as in Fig. 13.77, draw the gorge circle with a radius *CN* equal to the perpendicular distance from *OM* to *AB*. Project c^V up to c^H on $a^H b^H$, and through c^H draw the vertical projection of the gorge circle perpendicular to the axis. Then locate the limiting points *D* and *E* on the gorge circle, the vertices of the contour hyperbola. By drawing other circles in the horizontal projection this process is repeated and other points on the hyperbola obtained.

The hyperboloid of revolution has practical applications in mechanism, the most important being found in the pitch surfaces of skew gears. If any two right

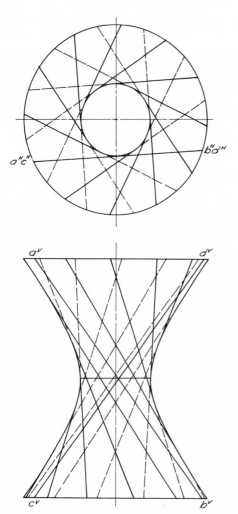

Fig. 13.76   Hyperboloid of revolution.

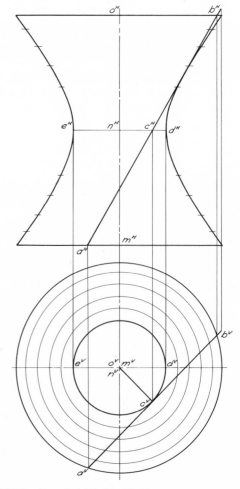

Fig. 13.77   Hyperboloid of revolution.

lines not in the same plane are taken as axes, a third line may be taken in a plane parallel to the other two lines so that the hyperboloids formed about the two axes by using the third line as a generatrix will be tangent to each other. They will operate together as the pitch surface of gears, since all elements will in turn assume positions common to both surfaces. Figure 13.78 illustrates this use of the hyperboloid of revolution or rolling hyperboloid.

13.11.3   The helicoid. A surface generated by a right line moving so that it always touches a helix and its axis, and making a constant angle with its axis, is called a helicoid and is the warped surface most frequently encountered in drafting. It occurs in the surface of screw threads, screw propellers, conveyors, circular staircases, and chutes. If the generatrix is perpendicular to the axis of the helix, the surface is a right helicoid as illustrated by the surface of a square thread. If the generatrix is inclined to the axis, it is an oblique helicoid such as the surface of a V-thread. The helicoid is actually a limitless surface, but is usually considered only as the portion contained within a cylinder concentric with the helix.

a. *Construction of a right helicoid.* The first step is to construct the helix with a given pitch on the surface of a given cylinder. To do this the pitch is divided into equal parts, and the circle representing the cylinder is divided into the same number of

equal parts (24 parts is very convenient), as shown in Fig. 13.79. The points on the circle are then projected up to the horizontal line drawn through the corresponding point on the axis. From the points on the helix, lines are drawn intersecting the axis and perpendicular to it. These lines form elements of the right helicoid.

b. *Construction of an oblique helicoid.* Given the limiting cylinder, the pitch of the helix, and the angle that the elements make with the axis, first construct the helix in the same manner as explained for Fig. 13.79. Then draw in the element *AB* (Fig. 13.80), making it parallel to the horizontal plane. In this position the true angle that the element makes

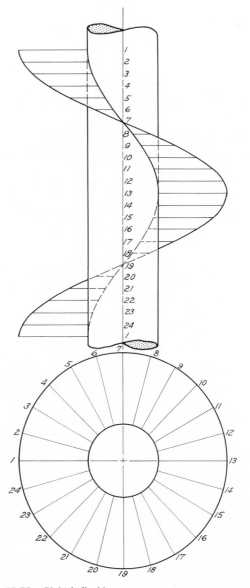

Fig. 13.79   Right helicoid.

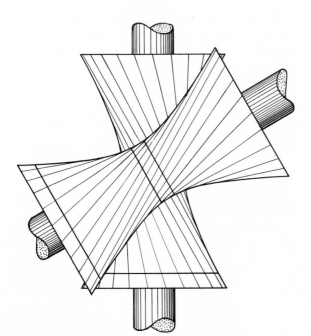

Fig. 13.78   Rolling hyperboloids.

with the axis shows in the horizontal projection, and the horizontal projection $a^H b^H$ can be drawn. Because each element must move the same proportionate distance along the axis as it does along the curve, the other elements are drawn by laying out horizontal distances starting at b^H equal to the horizontal distances between the points on the helix, and joining these points on the axis to the corresponding points on the helix.

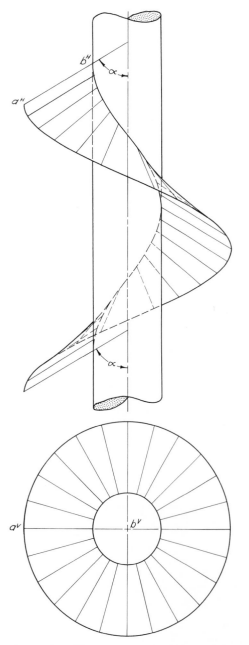

Fig. 13.80   Oblique helicoid.

13.11.4   Conoids. A conoid is a warped surface having a plane director and two linear directrices, one of which is a straight line and the other a curve. The curve may have any form, but closed plane curves are most commonly thought of.

If the straight-line directrix is parallel to the plane of the curved directrix and also perpendicular to the plane director, the surface is called a right conoid, as shown in Fig. 13.81(a). A common application of this form is shown in Fig. 13.81(b), where a roof must change from a curved to a flat section.

When the linear directrix, the curved directrix, and the plane director are oblique to each other, the surface is called an oblique conoid. Figure 13.82 shows the projections of an oblique conoid.

13.11.5   Cylindroid. A surface generated by a straight line moving so that it always remains parallel to a plane director and at the same time touches two plane curves, not lying in the same plane, is called a cylindroid. These curves are usually parts of circles or ellipses. See Fig. 13.83.

Construction. Since this problem is more frequently encountered in arch construction where the plane director is likely to be the horizontal plane, it is so illustrated here. However, it should be clear that any plane director and any plane curves, not lying in the same plane, can be used. Elements of the surface can be found by obtaining the edgewise view of the plane director and drawing elements in that view to intersect the two curvilinear directrices. See Fig. 13.83.

In Fig. 13.83, the two curvilinear directors ABC and DEF are to be joined by a cylindroid whose plane director is the H-plane. This means that elements can be drawn in the vertical projection by making them parallel to the reference line. They may then be carried to the H-projection to complete the required views.

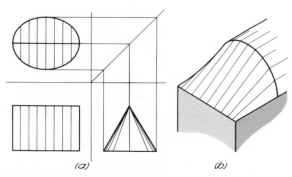

(a)   (b)

Fig. 13.81   Right conoid.

13.11.6 General procedure in drawing warped surfaces. There are many more varieties of warped surfaces and other methods of generation, but the drawing of the surfaces usually consists of drawing elements touching certain curved or right-line directrices or parallel to certain directors. With a general knowledge of engineering geometry the student should be able to follow any of the necessary constructions. Accurate development of warped surfaces is not pos-

sible, but it is frequently necessary to get an approximate development. This is done by dividing the surface into small triangles and laying out these triangles side by side in true size. This is called the method of triangulation.

Intersections of warped surfaces with other surfaces may be found by following the general procedure given in Chapter 14 for all intersections. Usually the best method is to find the points where elements of the warped surface pierce the other surface.

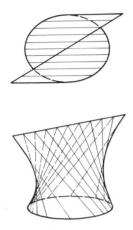

Fig. 13.82 Oblique conoid.

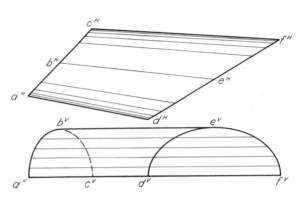

Fig. 13.83 Cylindroid.

SELF-STUDY QUESTIONS

Before trying to answer these questions, read the chapter carefully. Then, without reference to the text, answer as many questions as possible. For those that cannot be answered, the number, in parentheses following the question number, gives the article in which the answer can be found. Look it up and write down the answer. Check the answers that you did give to see that they are correct.

13.1 **(13.2.1)** The slope of a line is the angle that the line makes with the _____ plane.

13.2 **(13.2.1c)** For an oblique line the slope may be found on an auxiliary view, with the auxiliary plane _____ to the line and perpendicular to the *H*-plane.

13.3 **(13.2.2b)** In structural work the slope of a line is given by stating or showing the _____ and rise.

13.4 **(13.2.3)** The bearing of a line is the smaller of the two angles that the _____ projection of the line makes with a _____ and south line.

13.5 **(13.2.4)** The azimuth of a line is the angle that the _____ projection makes with a north and south line measured clockwise from the north.

13.6 **(13.3.1)** By definition, parallel lines are said to meet at _____ .

13.7 **(13.3.1)** In drawing two lines, they are parallel when their _____ on any and all planes are _____ .

13.8 **(13.3.3)** If two lines intersect, the crossing point of the horizontal projections must be in _____ with the crossing point of their vertical projections.

13.9 **(13.3.5)** The true value of the angle between two intersecting lines will show on a plane _____ to the two lines.

13.10 **(13.3.6)** The shortest distance between two parallel lines is the distance between their point projections on a plane _____ to them.

13.11 **(13.3.7)** The true distance between two parallel lines will show on the _____ shape view of the plane of the two lines.

13.12 **(13.4)** A vector is a line that is used to represent any quantity that has both _____ and direction.

13.13 **(13.6.3)** The angle that an inclined or oblique plane makes with the *H*-plane shows in any view in which the _____ planes appear _____ wise.

13.14 **(13.6.6)** The strike of a plane is the direction or bearing of a _____ line in the plane.

13.15 **(13.6.7)** In geology and mining the slope of a plane in a downward direction is called the _____ of the plane.

13.16 **(13.6.10)** The distance between two parallel planes can be measured in a view where _____ planes appear _____ wise.

13.17 **(13.7.1)** The piercing point of a line with a plane can be located by inspection in a view that shows the plane _____ along with the corresponding projection of the line.

13.18 **(13.7.6)** A plane can be drawn parallel to a line by making it pass through a second line that is _____ to the first line.

13.19 **(13.7.5)** A line is parallel to a plane when it is _____ to any line in the plane.

13.20 **(13.7.10)** A plane can be drawn perpendicular to a line by passing it through two lines each of which is _____ to the given line.

13.21 **(13.7.10)** A plane can be passed perpendicular to a line by making the _____ _____ of the plane perpendicular to the true-length view of the line.

13.22 **(13.7.13)** The intersection of two planes is a straight line passing through two points each _____ to both planes.

13.23 **(13.7.15)** When two planes show edgewise in the same view, the _____ between them shows in this view in true size.

13.24 **(13.8)** Two lines that are nonparallel and nonintersecting are called _____ lines.

13.25 **(13.10a)** The locus of points equidistant from two given points is the plane perpendicular _____ of the line joining the points.

13.26 **(13.10d)** The locus of points at a given distance from a plane is two parallel _____, one on each side of the given plane.

13.27 **(13.10e)** The locus of points at a given distance from a straight line is the surface of a _____ circular _____ having the line as an axis and the given distance as a radius.

13.28 **(13.11.3)** A surface generated by a right line moving so that it always touches, a helix and the axis of the helix, and makes a constant angle with the axis, is called a _____.

13.29 **(13.11.3)** The _____ is the surface found on screw threads, screw propellers, and conveyors.

13.30 **(13.11.4)** A conoid is a warped surface having a plane director and two linear directrices, one of which is a _____ line and the other a curve.

PROBLEMS

Sheet layout. In Figs. 13.84 and 13.85 the borderline layouts for two standard-size sheets have been given. Most of the problems in this chapter, as well as those in Chapters 14, 15, 16, and 17, have been designed to fit the smaller-size sheet. The larger sheet will accommodate more problems or make possible the use of a larger scale.

On the following pages layouts for various problems have been presented on a grid format. The problems can easily be drawn at a suitable size for solving by considering the squares to be one-half inch on a side. Where a point or the end of a line comes at the center of the space, it should be made exactly at the center.

In order to conserve the time for both students and instructors the authors recommend the use of printed workbooks. Four separate workbooks have been prepared by the authors and others. These are designated "Engineering Geometry Workbooks," Series 1, 2, 3, and 4. They may be purchased from the Stipes Publishing Co., 10 Chester Street, Champaign, Ill. Solution files are available for instructors if orders are placed with the publisher.

The layouts of points, lines, and planes on the following pages can be used for more than one problem.

Group I. Line or Point and Line Problems
Figures 13.86(a) through (m) and 13.87(a) through (d).

13.1 Find the profile view of point C and line AB in any problems assigned from the figures in Group I.

13.2 For any problem assigned from the figures in Group I find the true length and slope of line AB. Ignore point C. Dimension the line and angle. Measure the angle with a protractor from point A.

13.3 For any problems assigned from the figures in Group I determine the true length of the line and its bearing measured from A.

13.4 For any problems assigned from the figures in Group I find the true length and the angle φ. (Angle with the vertical plane).

13.5 Same as Problem 13.4, except find the angle π with the profile plane.

13.6 In the following verbal problems find the bearing, slope and true length of line AB. All measurements are to be made from point A.

Locate point A at 1¼″ below the H-plane and 1½″ behind the vertical plane.
   a. Bearing N. 30° E. slope −45° length 2″
   b. Bearing N. 45° W. slope −30° length 1½″
   c. Bearing S. 60° E. slope +30° length 1½″
   d. Bearing S. 45° W. slope −45° length 1½″
Dimension angles and lengths.

13.7 For any problems assigned from the figures in Group I find the true distance from point C to line AB. Use the point projection method.

13.8 Same as Problem 13.7, except use the plane method.

13.9 For any problem assigned from the figures in Group I draw a line through C parallel to AB.

13.10 For any problems assigned from the figures in Group I draw a line CM intersecting line AB at any point except the ends.

13.11 For any problems assigned from the figures in Group I draw a line CM perpendicular to AB. Point M does not necessarily have to fall between A and B. Use any method you prefer.

13.12 For any problems assigned from the figures in Group I draw a line CM from point C making 45° with line AB. Line AB may be extended if necessary.

Group II. Parallel Line Problems
Figures 13.87(e) through (m).

13.13 For any problem assigned from the figures in Group II determine whether lines AB and CD are parallel by making a third view.

13.14 For any problems assigned from the figures in Group II find the true distance between the lines by the point projection method, if the lines are parallel.

13.15 Same as Problem 13.14, using the plane method of solution.

Group III. Line, Angle, and Plane Problems
Figures 13.88(a) through (m).

13.16 Find the true value of the angle ABC. Ignore point D.

13.17 Through point D draw a line parallel to plane ABC.

13.18 Through point D draw a line perpendicular to plane ABC.

13.19 Find where a perpendicular from D pierces plane of ABC.

13.20 Find the true length of the shortest distance from point D to plane ABC.

13.21 Draw a plane DEF through point D parallel to plane ABC.

13.22 Draw a plane through point D perpendicular to plane ABC.

13.23 Through point D draw a line making 45° with plane ABC.

Group IV. Planes at Specified Angles with the H-, V-, and P-plane.
Figures 13.86(a) through (m) and 13.87(a) through (d). Ignore line AB and use point C only.

13.24 Draw a line through point C, making an angle of 45° with the H-plane.

13.25 Same as Problem 13.24, except that the line shall make 60° with the V-plane.

13.26 Same as problem 13.24, except that the line shall make an angle of 60° with the P-plane.

13.27 Through point C draw a line making an angle of 45° with the H-plane and 30° with the V-plane.

13.28 Same as Problem 13.27, except that the line shall make 45° with the V-plane and 30° with the P-plane.

13.29 In any problem of Fig. 13.88 draw a line through point D making an angle of 45° with the plane ABC.

Group V. Vector Problems

Figures 13.89(*a*) through (*m*).

13.30 In any problem from Figs. 13.89(*a*) through (*d*) find the resultant of the forces shown. Use a scale of $1'' = 100$ lbs. Note that lines *BA* and *BC* represent the direction of the forces only and not the magnitude, which is given beside the line.

13.31 In any problem from Figs. 13.89(*e*) through (*m*) find the stress in the supporting members due to the indicated load. Scale $1'' = 100$ lbs.

Group VI. Line and Plane Problems

Figures 13.90(*a*) through (*f*).

13.32 Find the piercing point of line *DE* with plane *ABC*. Use the edge view method.

13.33 Same as Problem 13.32, using the cutting plane method.

13.34 Find the angle between line *DE* and plane *ABC*.

13.35 Find the projection of line *DE* on plane *ABC*. *Note*: This projection may fall outside of *ABC*.

13.36 Draw a line making 45° with line *DE* and 30° with plane *ABC*.

Group VII. Intersection and Plane Problems

Figures 13.90(*g*) through (*m*).

13.37 Find the intersection of the two planes.

13.38 Find the angle between the two planes.

13.39 Draw a plane at right angles to each of the two planes.

Group VIII. Skew Line Problems

Figures 13.91(*a*) through (*h*).

13.40 Find the shortest common perpendicular between the two skew lines *AB* and *CD*.

13.41 Find the shortest horizontal line between the two skew lines. *Note*: Make the first auxiliary view on a plane perpendicular to the *H*-plane.

13.42 Draw the shortest line making an angle of 30° with the horizontal. As stated, this problem is indetermin-

ate. Draw first an auxiliary plane perpendicular to the *H*-plane as in Fig. 13.60. Then draw a sloping line parallel to auxiliary plane 1 and proceed.

Group IX. Warped Surfaces

Figures 13.91(*a*) through (*h*).

13.43 Draw nine elements of a warped quadrilateral having *AB* and *CD* as directrices. Show visibility of elements.

13.44 Having drawn the warped quadrilateral in Problem 13.43, find the plane director.

13.45 In any one of Figs. 13.91(*a*), (*b*), or (*e*) draw a warped surface having the lines *AB* and *CD* as linear directrices and the *H*-plane as a plane director. If necessary, extend either line.

13.46 In any one of Figs. 13.91(*a*), (*c*), or (*e*) draw a warped surface having *AB* and *CD* as linear directrices and the *V*-plane as a plane director. If necessary extend either line.

13.47 In Fig. 13.91(*j*) draw a rolling hyperboloid of one sheet. Show at least 12 straight line elements equally spaced.

13.48 In Fig. 13.91(*k*) draw an oblique conoid having the circle and the line *AB* as directrices and the vertical plane as a plane director.

13.49 In Fig. 13.91(*l*) draw a right helicoid between the two cylinders.

13.50 In Fig. 13.91(*m*) draw a cylindroid having the two curves as directrices and the *H*-plane as a plane director.

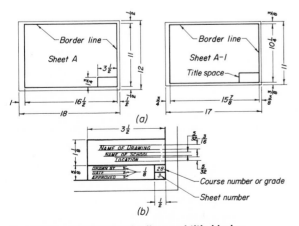

Fig. 13.84   Standard border lines and title blocks.

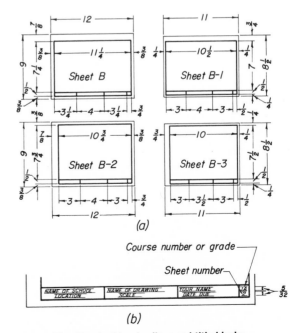

Fig. 13.85   Standard border lines and title blocks.

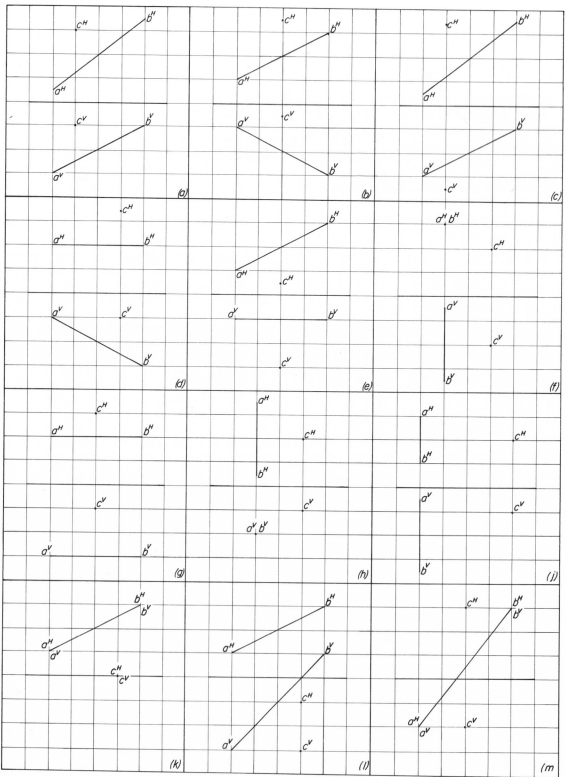

Fig. 13.86

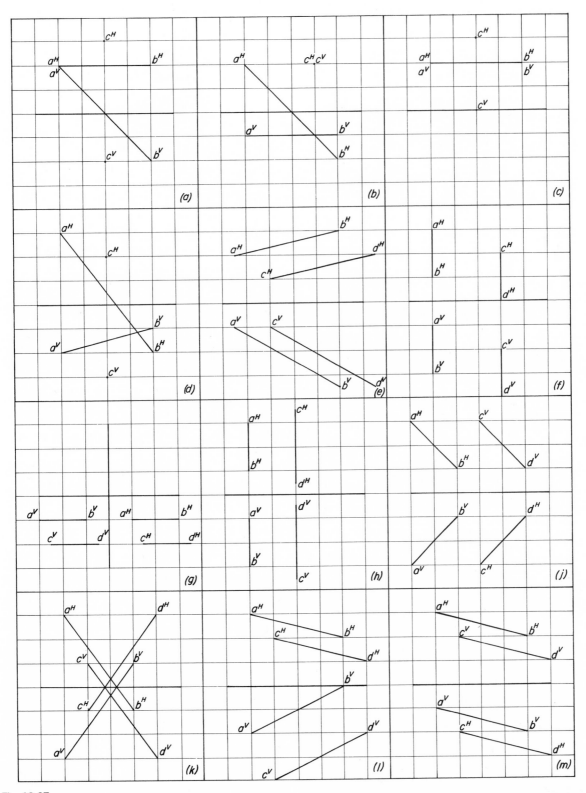

Fig. 13.87

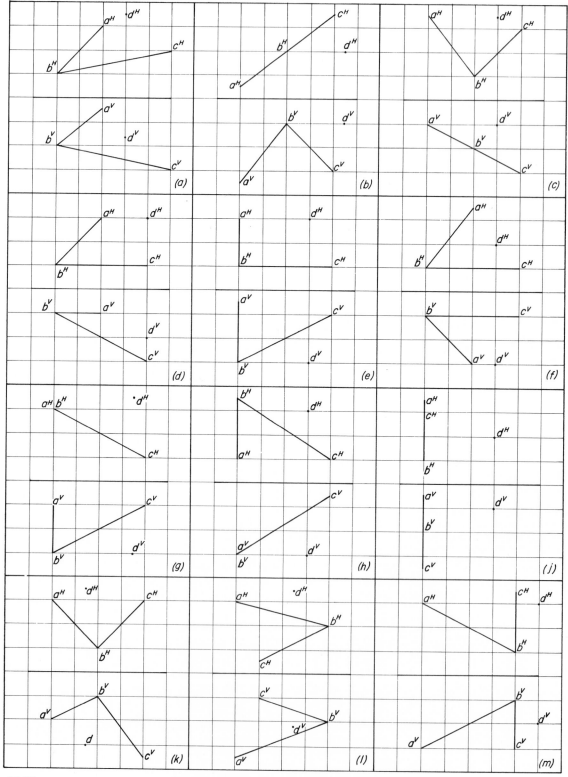

Fig. 13.88

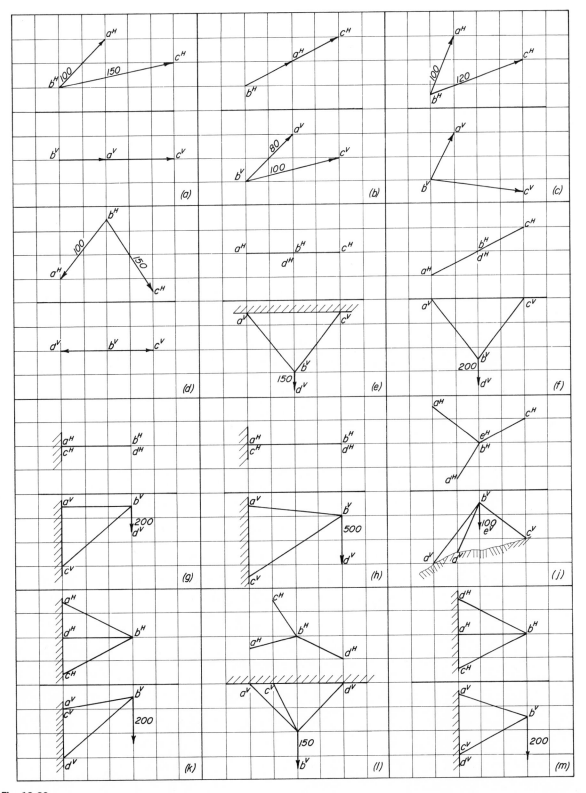

Fig. 13.89

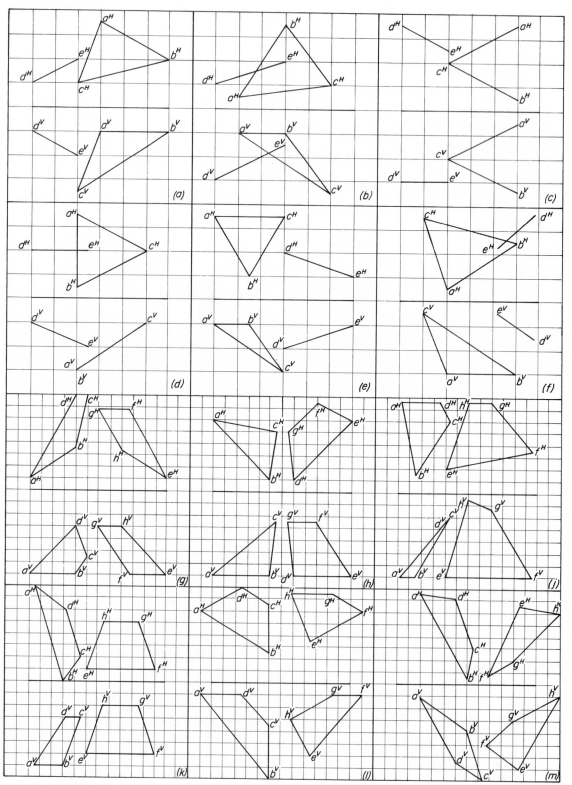

Fig. 13.90

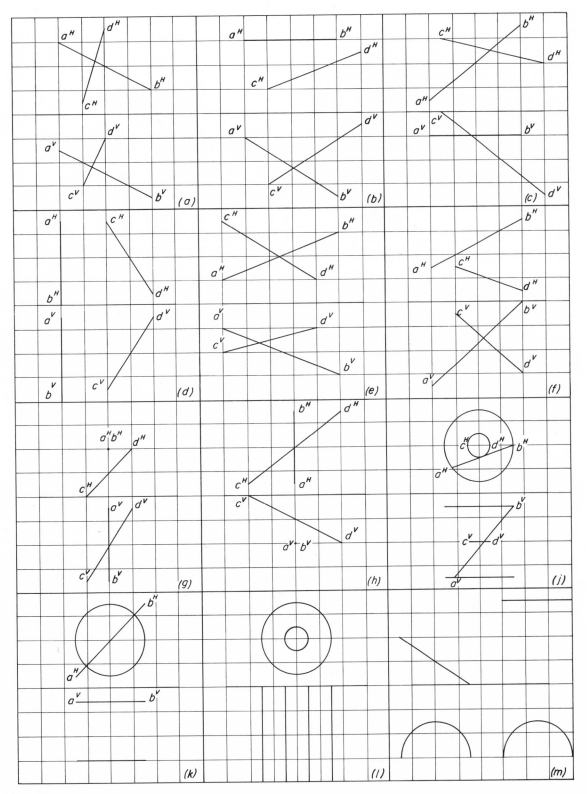

Fig. 13.91

Intersections and Developments

OLD: 18th century engraving of a blast furnace (The Granger Collection)

NEW: Stressed skin aluminum dome building erected in Oklahoma City. (Kaiser Aluminum)

Chapter 14 Intersections and Developments

14.1 The problems involved in finding the intersections of surfaces and in developing surfaces of various kinds into flat patterns and templates have many applications in a wide range of industries. In some instances intersections are shown in a conventional way as discussed in Art. 14.20, but in other cases it is necessary to find these intersections with accuracy. Boilers, smokestack breeching, ducts, and ventilators also involve problems of this kind. In ship, automotive, and aircraft drafting the problems are numerous and the intersections must be laid out full-size. In aircraft work the layouts on the loft floor are held to a very close tolerance.

In this chapter we discuss not only a variety of practical problems but also the general method of procedure that may be used to solve any problems of this type.

14.2 GEOMETRICAL SURFACES. Most structures involved in engineering practice are bounded by simple geometric surfaces or more complex combinations of them. The engineer should be familiar with these surfaces and the terminology connected with them. A classification of the more common surfaces shown in Fig. 14.1 is given in Table 14.1.

Many of the surfaces in the table are often found in practice to exist as the surface of solid objects. In dealing with them, however, the engineer is concerned only with their properties as surfaces. In this book the prisms and pyramids are treated as solids, and cylinders and cones are considered hollow surfaces without ends.

14.3 FINDING INTERSECTIONS. *The intersection of two surfaces is the locus of all points common to both surfaces.* The usual process of finding this line consists of passing planes that cut elements from both surfaces and finding the points where these elements intersect.

An element of a surface is any line lying wholly in that surface. It may be either curved or straight. In all ruled surfaces, the straight line element is preferable since it is easiest to draw. On double-curved surfaces, the circle is the most practical element that may be used. The general method of finding intersections may be stated in the following steps.

a. Pass a cutting plane that cuts elements from both surfaces. These elements should project as straight lines or circles.

b. Find the several projections of each element.

c. Locate the points where these elements intersect. These are points on the line of intersection.

d. Repeat the process with as many cutting planes as necessary to obtain a good intersection.

e. Connect the points in the proper order and with the correct visibility.

In order that the construction be as easy as possible, the following rules of procedure should be observed.

f. The first cutting plane should be tangent to one or both surfaces, when possible.

g. The planes should be numbered in order from the first to the last. The last plane should also be tangent to one or both surfaces when possible.

h. The elements should be drawn showing the proper visibility in their own surface only.

i. The elements should be given the same number as

TABLE 14.1   CLASSIFICATION OF SURFACES

Ruled surfaces (which can be generated by moving a straight line)	Plane surfaces	Five regular polyhedrons Prisms Pyramids	
	Single-curved	Cylinders Cones Convolutes	
	Warped surfaces	Cylindroids Conoids Hyperbolic paraboloid Hyperboloid of revolution of one sheet Helicoid	
Double-curved surfaces (generated by revolving a curved line)		Sphere Spheroids Hyperboloid of two sheets Paraboloid Torus	oblate prolate

433

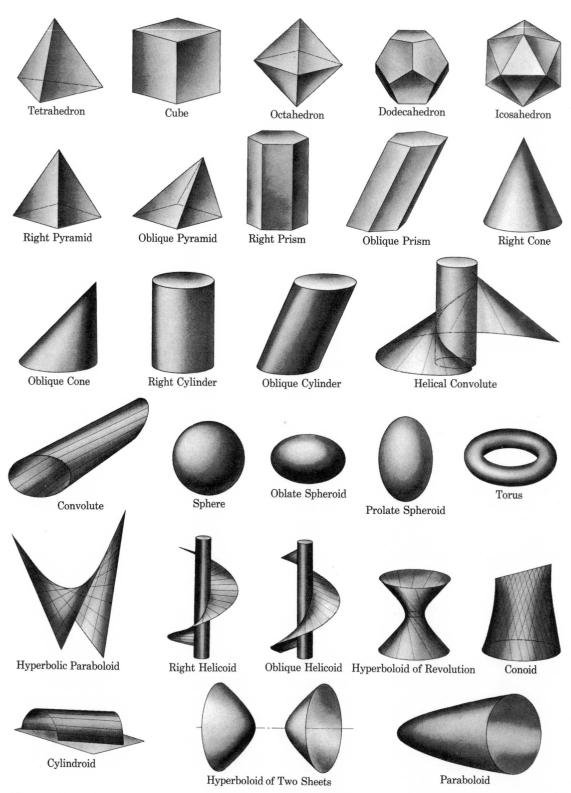

Fig. 14.1 Geometric surfaces.

the plane. There may be four elements having the same number.

j. The points where these elements cross should be given the same number as the plane and the elements.

k. The visibility of each projection of a point should be indicated. In this text a visible point is marked with a very small solid circle, ●, and an invisible point is marked with an open circle, ○.

l. When two visible elements cross, the point is visible. Any other combination gives an invisible point.

m. Connect the points in numerical order showing the proper visibility of the line of intersection.

n. The line of intersection can change visibility only where the curve of intersection touches a limiting element or crosses an open base.

o. The visibility of limiting elements must be determined and drawn properly.

p. The visible portion of the line of intersection must be a continuous line from one surface to the other unless it is interrupted by an open base.

14.4   INTERSECTION OF TWO PLANES. For a discussion of this topic, see Art. 13.7.13, Chapter 13.

14.5   INTERSECTION OF PLANE AND PRISM. There are two convenient methods for finding the line of intersection between a plane and a prism. The first is the edgewise view method and the second is the cutting plane method. The particular conditions of the problem will determine which method is the best.

14.5.1   The edgewise view method for plane and prism. The edgewise view method is illustrated in Fig. 14.2. *The general analysis for applying this method is to find the edge view of the given plane and in that view locate the piercing points of the edges of the prism*

and the plane. These are then projected to the various views to determine the line of intersection.

In Fig. 14.2(*a*), the plane *ABCD* projects as an edge view in the vertical projection. The edges of the triangular prism pierce the plane at e^V, f^V, and g^V as can be determined by inspection. These points can be projected to the side view on the corresponding edges of the prism determining the profile projection of the line of intersection as $e^P f^P g^P$. The true shape of the intersection can be found by an auxiliary projection off the front view, as shown in $e^1 f^1 g^1$.

When the given views of the plane and prism do not show edgewise, as in Fig. 14.2(*b*), an auxiliary projection is necessary to obtain an edgewise view of the plane. In this case the auxiliary plane is passed perpendicular to line *AB* since *AB* is parallel to the *H*-plane and therefore projects true-length in the *H*-plane. In the auxiliary view the given plane *ABCD* appears as an edge view. The piercing points of the edges of the prism with plane *ABCD* are determined by inspection to be $e^1 f^1 g^1$. These points *E*, *F*, and *G* are projected back to the corresponding edges of the prism in the *H*- and *V*-views as shown in Fig. 14.2(*b*). To determine the true shape of the intersection *EFG*, a second auxiliary plane parallel to $e^1 f^1 g^1$ would have to be used and *EFG* projected upon it.

14.5.2   The cutting plane method for plane and prism. The cutting plane method is illustrated in Fig. 14.3 and follows the general procedure outlined in Art. 14.3. The steps are as follows:

a. Pass a cutting plane through an element of the prism as in Fig. 14.3(*a*). In this case a horizontal projecting plane is used and is called cutting plane *1*.

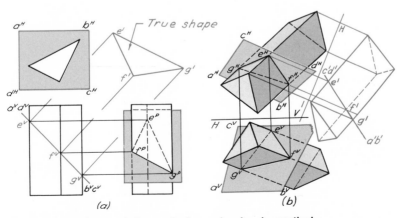

Fig. 14.2   Intersection of plane and prism—edgewise view method.

b. Determine the line of intersection of cutting plane *1* with the given plane *ABCD* in the horizontal view as $e^H f^H$.

c. Project *EF* to the vertical view, $e^V f^V$, to determine point *O*, the piercing point of element *1* with plane *ABCD*.

d. Project point *O* to the horizontal view.

e. Repeat the above process by passing cutting planes *2* and *3* as shown in Fig. 14.3(*b*) to determine points *M* and *N*.

f. Points *OMN* determine the line of intersection between plane *ABCD* and the prism, which is shown with its proper visibility in Fig. 14.3(*c*).

14.6   INTERSECTION OF A PLANE AND A PYRAMID.

The same methods of procedure as discussed in the preceeding article for prisms may be used for pyramids.

14.6.1   The edgewise view method for plane and pyramid.

The edgewise view method for finding the line of intersection between a plane and a pyramid is illustrated in Fig. 14.4. In Fig. 14.4(*a*) the plane shows edgewise in the front view. The piercing points between the edges of the pyramid and the plane are determined by inspection in front view. They are then projected to the respective views on the corresponding elements of the pyramid to determine the line of intersection in the other views.

When the plane does not appear edgewise in the given views, such a view must be obtained. In Fig.

14.4(*b*), for example, a horizontal line can always be drawn lying in the plane by making the vertical projection $b^V d^V$ horizontal. From this the horizontal projection $b^H d^H$ is then located and the auxiliary plane set up perpendicular to *BD* by drawing the *H-1* reference line perpendicular to $b^H d^H$. The plane then shows edgewise at $a^1 b^1 c^1 d^1$ and the piercing points may be found by inspection and projected back to the other view as shown in Fig. 14.4(*b*).

14.6.2   The cutting plane method for plane and pyramid.

This method follows the procedure outlined in Art. 14.3 and is illustrated in Fig. 14.5. The steps are as follows:

a. Pass a cutting plane through an element of the pyramid as in Fig. 14.5(*a*). In this case a vertical projecting plane is used and is called cutting plane *1*.

b. Find the line of intersection of cutting plane *1* with the given plane *PMNO* in the vertical view as $e^V f^V$, as shown in Fig. 14.5(*a*).

c. Project *EF* to the horizontal view, $e^H f^H$ to determine point *1*, the piercing point of element *1* with plane *PMNO*.

d. Project point *1* to the vertical view.

e. Find the piercing points of each of the other two limiting elements of the pyramid with the given plane *LMNO* as shown in Fig. 14.5(*b*) by using cutting planes *2* and *3*.

f. Connect these piercing points to determine the line

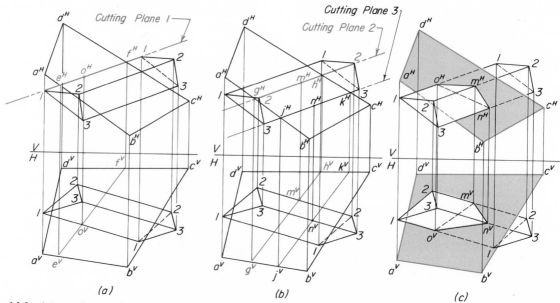

Fig. 14.3   Intersection of plane and prism—cutting plane method.

of intersection between the pyramid and plane and show proper visibility as in Fig. 14.5(c).

14.7   INTERSECTION OF A PLANE AND CYLINDER.

To find the line of intersection of a plane and cylinder requires the same procedure as followed in the example above. The main difference is that a cylinder has no edges and therefore a series of elements must be chosen lying in the surface of the cylinder. The line of intersection is determined by finding where these elements pierce the given plane. As a rule, 12 equally

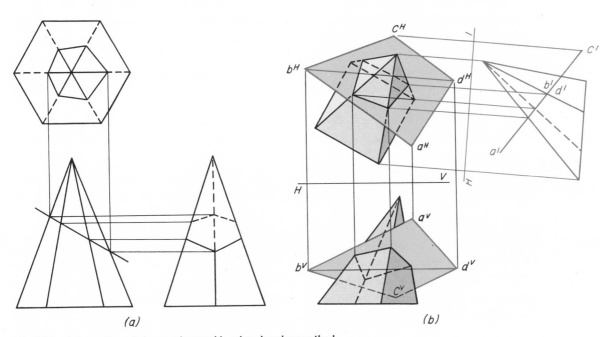

Fig. 14.4   Intersection of plane and pyramid—edgewise view method.

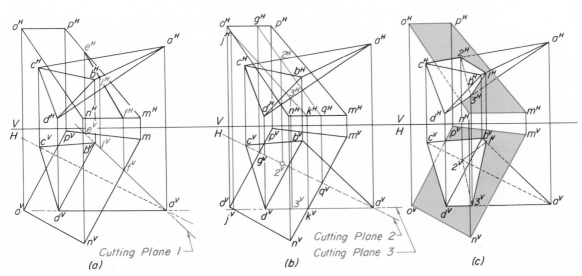

Fig. 14.5   Intersection of plane and pyramid—cutting plane method.

spaced elements will suffice as is shown in Fig. 14.6(a). Note that, if the upper part of the cylinder is detached and rotated 180°, a right-angled elbow is formed as shown.

14.7.1   Edgewise view method for a plane and cylinder. In Fig. 14.6(a), the edge view of the plane appears in the front view. The 12 equally spaced elements are assumed in the top view and projected into the front and side views. The piercing points of these elements with the plane are determined by inspection in the front view. These are projected to the side view to determine the right side view.

When the plane does not appear as an edge view, the first step is to pass an auxiliary plane to obtain the edge view. In Fig. 14.6(b) this has been done by passing the auxiliary view perpendicular to $a^H b^H$ since AB is parallel to the horizontal plane and is in true length in the top view. In the auxiliary view the piercing points of the elements with plane $ABCD$ can be determined by inspection. These are then projected back to the respective view on the corresponding elements to determine the line of intersection in the top and front views.

14.7.2   Cutting plane method for a plane and cylinder. The method of obtaining the intersection of a cylinder and a plane by the cutting plane method is illustrated in Fig. 14.7. The cutting planes used in this case are horizontal projecting planes and are passed at regular or irregular intervals. They are passed closer together where the degree of curvature is changing rapidly and farther apart where the curve is flat. The procedure is as follows:

a. Pass the first projecting plane tangent to the cylinder. In Fig. 14.7(a), plane 1 is a horizontal projecting plane that cuts one element from the cylinder.

b. Get both projections of this element as shown in Fig. 14.7(a). Show the proper visibility of the element.

c. Find the line of intersection of the cutting plane with plane $ABCD$, as shown in Fig. 14.7(b).

d. Find the point where the line of intersection crosses the element cut by plane 1. See Fig. 14.7(b). The elements and point are both numbered 1 to agree with the number of the plane. Mark the projections of visible points with a solid circle and the invisible points with an open circle.

e. Pass successive planes such as planes 2 and 3 as shown in Fig. 14.7(c) and find points on the intersection in the same manner.

f. Pass other planes at the desired intervals to obtain the complete intersection. The last plane will be the one that is tangent to the other side of the cylinder. Only a part of the curve is shown.

g. Connect the points to form the complete line of intersection. The open circles will be connected with a dashed line and the solid circles with a solid line. The visibility of the curve can change only on the limiting element of the cylinder.

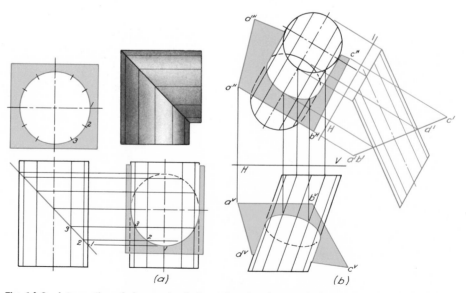

Fig. 14.6   Intersection of plane and cylinder—edgewise view method.

14.8   INTERSECTION OF PLANE AND CONE. The problem of finding the intersection of a plane and a cone is the same as for a plane and a pyramid. Elements are assumed in the cone. These are used to find where they pierce the given plane. These piercing points determine the line of intersection between the cone and plane.

14.8.1   Edge view method for plane and cone. The edge view method for determining the line of intersection of a plane and a cone is shown in Fig. 14.8. In making an auxiliary projection to obtain an edgewise view of the plane, it will facilitate the solution a great deal if the base of the cone (cylinder, prism, or

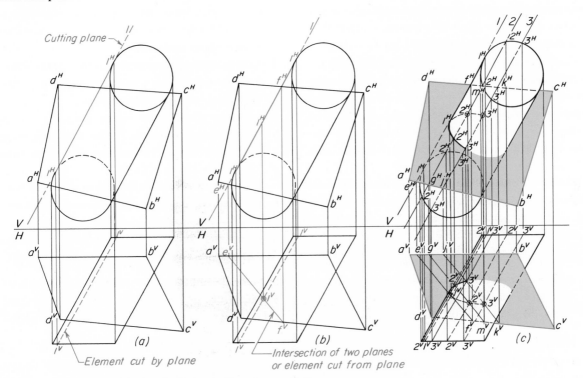

Fig. 14.7   Intersection of plane and cylinder—cutting plane method.

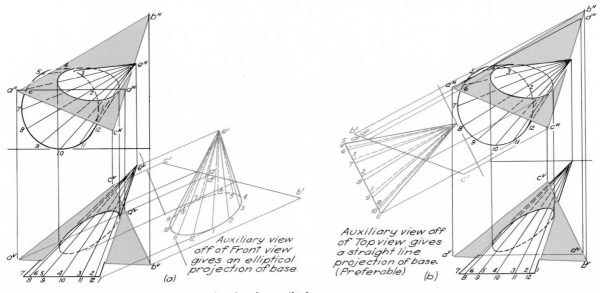

Fig. 14.8   Intersection of plane and cone—edgewise view method.

pyramid) also appears edgewise in the auxiliary view. In Fig. 14.8, two solutions have been presented, the first of which, Fig. 14.8(*a*), shows the auxiliary plane perpendicular to the *V*-plane, thus making the base of the cone an elliptical figure.

The position of the auxiliary plane was determined by drawing line *AD* in the plane parallel to the *V*-plane and making the auxiliary plane perpendicular to this line. Although this solution is correct, a less tedious solution is shown in Fig. 14.8(*b*).

In the second solution, line *AD* was drawn in the plane parallel to the *H*-plane and the auxiliary plane placed perpendicular to this line. It can be observed that since the base of the cone is parallel to *H*, it will also appear as a straight line or edgewise in the auxiliary projection, thus making the solution much simpler.

14.8.2 Cutting plane method for plane and cone.
The cutting plane method follows the same pattern as given for the plane and cylinder. The method is as follows:

a. Pass the first cutting plane tangent to the cone as shown in Fig. 14.9(*a*). Plane *1* is a vertical projecting plane that cuts one element from the cone.

b. Get both projections of this element as shown in Fig. 14.9(*a*). Show the proper visibility of the element.

c. Find the line of intersection of the cutting plane with plane *ABC*, as shown in Fig. 14.9(*b*).

d. Find the point where the line of intersection crosses the element cut by plane *1*. See Fig. 14.9(*b*). The element and point are both numbered *1* to agree with the number of the plane. Mark the projection of a visible point with a solid circle and an invisible point with an open circle.

e. Pass successive planes such as cutting planes *2* and *3* as shown in Fig. 14.8(*c*) and find points on the line of intersection in the same manner.

f. Pass other planes at the desired intervals to obtain the complete intersection. The last plane will be the one that is tangent to the other side of the cone.

g. Connect the points to form the complete line of intersection. The open circles will be connected with a dashed line and the solid circles with a solid line. The visibility of the curve of intersection can change only on a limiting element or where the curve crosses an open base.

14.9 INTERSECTION OF PLANE AND SURFACE OF REVOLUTION.
To find the intersection of the plane *ABCD* and the sphere in Fig. 14.10(*a*), a cutting plane

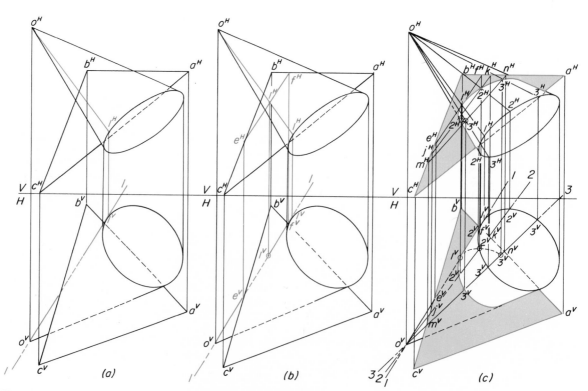

Fig. 14.9 Intersection of plane and cone—cutting plane method.

MN has been passed through both surfaces. This cuts a circle from the sphere which appears as a straight line in the front view and a circle in the top view. The two planes intersect in the line *GH*. The intersection of the line and circle can be seen by inspection at $e^V f^V$ in the front view and e^H and f^H in the top view. A sufficient number of points to determine the curve of intersection may be obtained by repeating this process as shown in Fig. 14.10(*b*). The curve is tangent to the great circle in the top view at points a^H and b^H where the cutting plane crosses the great circle at a^V and b^V in the front view.

The curve of intersection of a plane and sphere is always a circle but in our illustration it appears as an ellipse. In Figs. 14.10(*c*), (*d*), and (*e*), the plane forming the intersection has been shown edgewise in three different positions. Note the effect on the visibility of the ellipse and its tangency to the great circle in the different positions of the intersecting plane. In Fig. 14.10(*c*), the intersection lies entirely above the great circle, which means that it is all in the upper half of the sphere. Therefore, it is entirely visible in the top view. In Fig. 14.10(*d*), the intersecting plane passes through the center of the sphere and the curve is tangent to the great circle at the ends of the corresponding diameter in the top view. The upper half is visible but the lower half is invisible. The student should study these illustrations and clearly visualize each situation for himself.

A similar construction for the intersection of a plane and torus is shown in Fig. 14.11. In this case the true outline of the curve of intersection is not a circle. It may have a wide variety of shapes, depending on the position of the intersecting plane. The method of construction, however, is the same as for the sphere and is clearly shown in the figure. It should be noted that each construction plane, except the top and bottom ones, cuts two circles from the torus. Open circles indicate invisible points, and black circles indicate visible points.

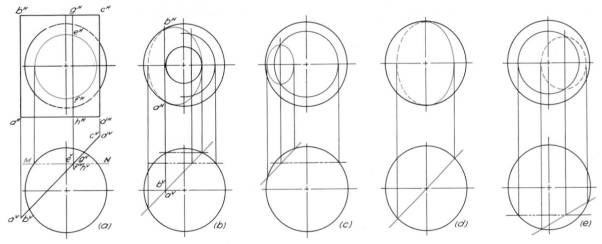

Fig. 14.10   Intersection of plane and sphere.

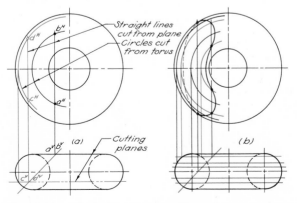

Fig. 14.11   Intersection of plane and torus.

14.10   INTERSECTION OF PLANE AND DOUBLE-CURVED SURFACE. Many practical problems involve finding the intersection of planes with curved surfaces that are considerably more complex, for example, the determination of station lines and waterlines in ship and aircraft construction. The principles involved, however, are exactly the same, the only difference being that in many surfaces straight-line elements cannot be drawn. For example, the simplest elements that may be drawn on a sphere or torus are circles. Figure 14.12 shows an aircraft surface that is determined by the body plan view and side view. To work with these surfaces, certain terms must be understood. In ship and aircraft drafting, a waterline represents the intersection of a horizontal plane with the hull or fuselage. A buttock line is the intersection of a vertical plane, running lengthwise, with the hull or fuselage, and a station line is the intersection of a transverse vertical plane with the hull or fuselage at right angles to the other two planes. All of them represent the intersection of a curved surface and a plane. These lines are used to define the shape of the surface. See Fig. 14.12.

The intersection of an inclined plane *MN*, shown edgewise in the side view with the surface, represented in Fig. 14.12, appears in the plan view and the body plan view. The central buttock line that pierces the plane at a^V is projected to a^P and a^H. The intersection

of station line *4* with plane *MN* appears at b^V which is projected at b^P and b^H. Any number of points required to determine the curve can be found in the same manner, using waterlines, buttock lines, and station lines.

14.11   INTERSECTION OF TWO PRISMS. When it becomes necessary to find the intersection of two prisms, certain points can usually be found directly. This occurs when any of the planes appear edgewise in any view. Other points can be found by use of the analysis of Art. 14.3. Figure 14.13 shows the intersection of two prisms. The top view shows the four faces of the square prism edgewise. Therefore, the projections of the points in which the three edges of the triangular prism pierce these faces are shown directly in the top view at points *1*, *2*, and *4* and *6*, *8*, and *9*. The projections *1*, *2*, *4*, *6*, *8*, and *9* in the front view are located on the corresponding projections of the same edge lines of the triangular prism. (Note that numbered points in this illustration and in succeeding ones are not given superscripts since the connection between the views is obvious.) It remains then to find where the two edges *AE* and *CG* of the square prism pierce the faces of the triangular prism. The construction is as follows:

a. Extend the plane of the face *AEDH* and use it as a cutting plane.

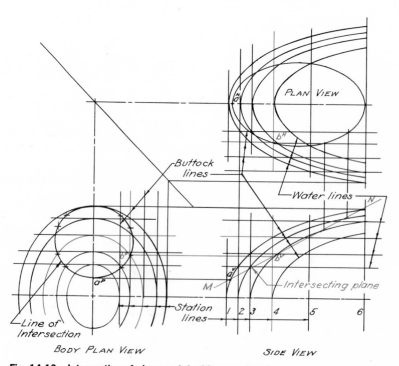

Fig. 14.12   Intersection of plane and double-curved surface.

b. Find the intersection, *4UT*, where this cutting plane intersects the triangular prism.

c. The points where element *AE* intersects triangle *4UT* give points *3* and *5* on the intersection of the two prisms.

d. Using a cutting plane through *BCGF*, the same procedure can be used to locate points *7* and *10* on the right half of the intersection.

When one of the prisms is shown endwise, as in Fig. 14.13, it is possible to determine the general shape of the intersection and also to number the points consecutively so that they may be connected in order. In this case it can be seen that the triangular prism goes completely through the square prism, which shows that there will be two completely separate parts to the intersection. Since the square prism shows endwise in the top view, all lines of the intersection must show on the outline of the square in the top view and cannot cut across the square. Thus planes *ABEF* and *ADEH* will form one part of the intersection and these planes must intersect the top part of the triangular prism, planes *MNOP* and *OPRS* first and then the bottom part, plane *MNRS*.

To number the points properly, it is best to start with point *1* in the top view and proceed around the square prism and on the top faces of the triangular prism first. Therefore, the numbering would go from *1* to *2*, on plane *OPRS*, *2* to *3* and *3* to *4*, on plane

MNOP. From *4* the intersection will go to *5* and from *5* to *1* on plane *MNRS*. When the two points *3* and *5* have been obtained, as previously explained, it is essential that the higher point in the front view be marked *3* because this was taken as the point on the upper surface of the triangular prism.

In the same manner, points *6, 7, 8, 9,* and *10* may be numbered on the right side of the intersection. When they have been numbered in this manner, they may be connected in order to give the correct intersection. If the end view of one of the prisms is not given, it is usually best to take enough auxiliary views to obtain an endwise view.

For visibility each line must be checked to see if it is on the front or back of both surfaces. If on the front of both surfaces, the line will be visible. All other combinations give an invisible line in the front view.

14.12   RULES FOR VISIBILITY. The visibility of points on each of two lines is determined simply by ascertaining which of the points is closest to the observer. Thus, in Fig. 14.14(*a*), it can be observed from the top view that at the crossing point of the two rods in the front view the point *1* on rod *AB* is in front of point *2* on rod *CD*. Therefore, rod *AB* is visible in the front view and must be shown passing in front of *CD*. In Fig. 14.14(*b*), an examination of the front view shows that rod *AB* is higher than *CD* at the crossing point shown in the top view. In the top view *AB* is entirely visible and must be shown passing over *CD*. The

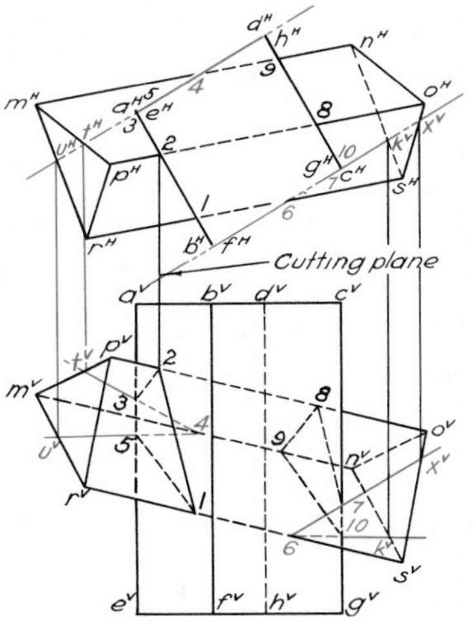

Fig. 14.13   Intersection of two prisms.

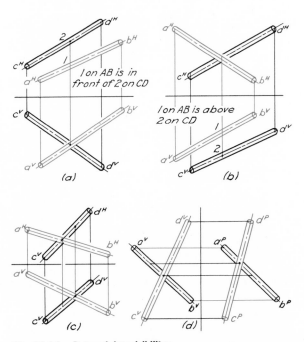

Fig. 14.14   Determining visibility.

student should verify the visibility of the rods as shown in Figs. 14.14(c) and (d).

It will be noted from the foregoing discussion that the visibility of a line in any view is always determined by reference to the adjacent view. In Fig. 14.13, since line BF is in front of line RS, the latter enters the prism at point 1 and emerges again at point 6. Between these two points it is invisible. For the same reason line PO enters the prism at point 2 and emerges at point 8. Point 8, however, is invisible since it lies on the rear surface of the vertical prism, and line PO does not become visible again until it passes the edge CG of the vertical prism.

From Fig. 14.13 and subsequent figures, the following principles can be observed:

1. To be visible a point must lie on a visible edge or element of both intersecting surfaces.

2. For a line of intersection to be visible it must connect two visible points. If it connects one visible and one invisible point, it is entirely invisible.

3. A line of intersection can change from visible to invisible or vice versa only upon the outlines of one or the other of the two intersecting surfaces.

14.13 INTERSECTION OF PRISM AND PYRAMID.

To find the intersection of a prism and a pyramid, certain points can be found directly if any plane shows edgewise. Other points can be found by using the analysis of Art. 14.3. In Fig. 14.15, the cutting plane

method is illustrated. The steps are as follows:

a. Pass a cutting plane AB through two edges of the pyramid. See Fig. 14.15(a).

b. Find the triangle ABC that this plane cuts from the prism. See Fig. 14.15(a).

c. Find the points 1, 2, 3, and 4 in the front view where this triangle crosses the edges of the pyramid. See Fig. 14.15(a). Project these points to the top view. These are points on the line of intersection.

d. Pass another plane CD as in Fig. 14.15(b).

e. Find the intersection DEF where this plane intersects the prism.

f. Find the points 5, 6, 7, and 8 where this triangle crosses the edges of the pyramid. These are points on the line of intersection.

g. Pass plane EF through the lower edge of the prism. See Fig. 14.15(c).

h. Find the line of intersection, MNOP, of this plane with the pyramid. See Fig. 14.15(c).

i. Find the points 9 and 10 where MNOP crosses the lower line of the prism. See Fig. 14.15(c). These are points on the line of intersection.

j. Connect the points in the proper order and with the proper visibility to obtain the complete line of intersection.

The first points 1 to 8 in the problem could have been found quite conveniently by making an endwise view of the prism in an auxiliary projection. The

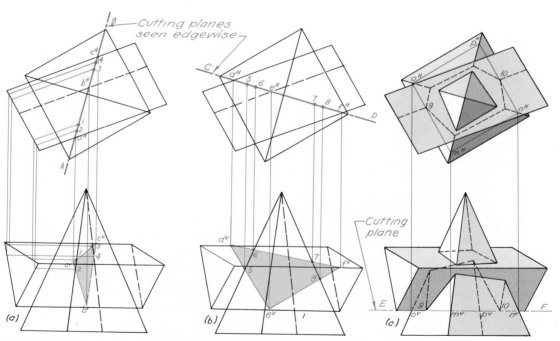

Fig. 14.15   Intersection of prism and pyramid.

simplest method for the remaining two points, *9* and *10*, is by the cutting plane method used in Fig. 14.15(*c*).

Had the prism in Fig. 14.15 been inclined to both *H* and *V*, the auxiliary plane method would have required two auxiliary views, whereas the cutting plane method could be applied without additional work.

14.14   INTERSECTION OF TWO PYRAMIDS. The method of cutting planes, to obtain elements of both surfaces that intersect each other, is further illustrated in determining the intersection of two pyramids as shown in Fig. 14.16. The cutting plane *AB* passing through the front edge of the horizontal pyramid in Fig. 14.16(*a*) cuts the shaded quadrilateral $a^Vb^Vc^Vd^V$ from the other pyramid. The front element of the horizontal pyramid crosses this area at points *1* and *2* of the intersection.

In Fig. 14.16(*b*), plane *CD* cuts a line from the up-right pyramid and the shaded triangle *RST* from the other, thus locating points *3* and *4* of the intersection. Other points obtained in a similar manner give the final intersection shown in Fig. 14.16(*c*).

14.15   POSSIBLE TYPES OF INTERSECTIONS. It is of considerable value to the draftsman if he knows, before beginning construction, what general form the intersection will have. Only four forms are possible, and the type that any problem will give may be easily determined for cylinders, if an endwise view of one of the cylinders is obtained. The four types are shown in Fig. 14.17, with the cylinders placed in the most ad-

vantageous positions possible relative to the principal coordinate planes. With a complete penetration of one cylinder by the other, as in Fig. 14.17(*a*), two closed curves are formed. With a partial penetration, as shown in Fig. 14.17(*b*), one continuous closed curve is formed. With a partial penetration in which one cutting plane is tangent to both cylinders, as in Fig. 14.17(*c*), a crossed curve with one point common to both parts like a figure 8 is formed. Finally, with a complete penetration of two cylinders of the same size with two cutting planes tangent to both cylinders, as in Fig. 14.17(*d*), two closed curves are formed that cross each other at two points. In right circular cylinders and cones these curves are ellipses. The above statements concerning intersecting cylinders apply equally to two cones, to a cone and a cylinder, or to prisms and pyramids, when under the same conditions as regards penetration and tangency of cutting planes. The determination of the form of the intersection can be readily made either from an auxiliary view or from the position of the limiting cutting planes, as shown in Fig. 14.33, where the first cutting plane, No. *1*, is tangent to both cylinders and the last is tangent to one and cuts the other, thus giving a crossed loop as in Fig. 14.17(*c*).

14.16   THE INTERSECTION OF TWO CONES. The intersection of two cones is a common practical problem. In this case, if straight-line elements are to be cut from both surfaces, the cutting planes must pass

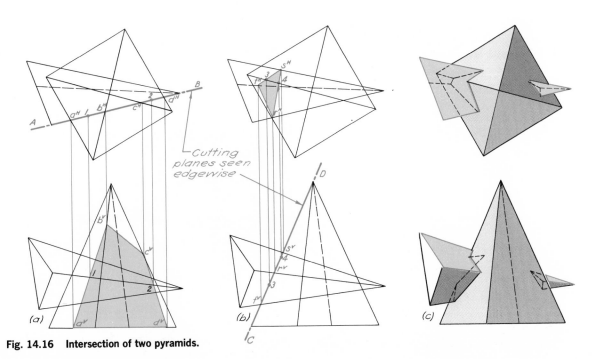

Fig. 14.16   Intersection of two pyramids.

through the vertices of both cones.

Thus in the pictorial drawing of Fig. 14.18, line *AD* passes through the vertices of *B* and *C*. Any plane such as *ADE*, which contains the line *AD*, will cut straight lines from both cones if it cuts the cones. Line *ED* in the plane of the base of cone *B* intersects the foot of elements *1* and *2* from this cone, and line *EA* in the plane of the base of cone *C* intersects the foot of elements *3* and *4* of cone *C*. The two pairs of elements, all lying in this one cutting plane, cross each other to give four points on the curve of intersection.

From Fig. 14.18 it can be observed that the crux of this problem lies in finding the foot of the elements cut by one plane. The method of procedure will depend on the situation in which the cones occur. In general the steps of the solution are as follows.

1. Draw a line through the vertices of both cones.
2. Find the piercing points of this line with the base of each cone.
3. Pass a cutting plane through this line and find the elements cut from each cone. These elements cross in points on the curve of intersection. A variety of procedures may be required to accomplish this second step. These are illustrated in the five following examples.

14.16.1   Endwise view of the line joining the apexes.

If the line joining the vertices of the cones is an *H*- or *V*-parallel, an endwise view of this line can be obtained in a first auxiliary view as shown in Fig. 14.19. The cutting planes then appear edgewise in the auxiliary view, and the foot of the elements cut from the cones

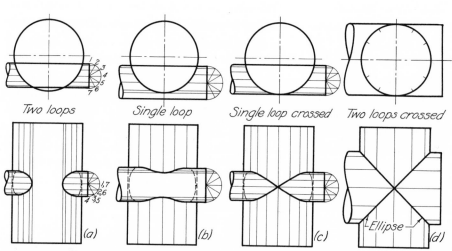

Two loops   Single loop   Single loop crossed   Two loops crossed

(a)   (b)   (c)   (d)

Fig. 14.17   Four types of intersections.

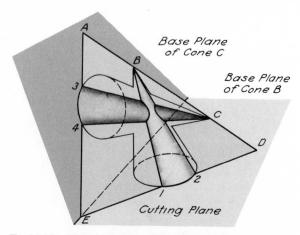

Fig. 14.18   Pictorial drawing of the intersection of two cones.

can be obtained by inspection. See elements *1* and *4* in this figure.

14.16.2   Both bases in the same plane. When the bases of both cones lie in the same plane, the cutting planes may be located by constructing a line joining the two apexes and finding the point where this line pierces the plane of the bases. In Fig. 14.20, line *AB* pierces the plane of the bases at point *C*. When a series of planes is passed through line *AC*, they will intersect the plane of the bases in a series of lines that meet at point *C*. From this point *C*, any number of lines may be drawn on the base plane so that they cut across both bases. Each of these lines when taken with the line *AC* determines an inclined plane containing both

apexes. One such line is shown in Fig. 14.20, which locates points *D*, *E*, *F*, and *G* on the bases of the cones. From each of these points elements of the cones may be drawn to locate four points on the line of intersection of the two cones. The elements should be drawn showing their proper visibility in their own surface only, without regard to the other cone. Then when two visible elements cross, the point on the intersection will be visible. All other combinations will give an invisible point.

The problems occurring in engineering practice often involve frustums of cones. In cases of this kind the vertices must be found by extending two or more elements. An illustration of this type of problem is

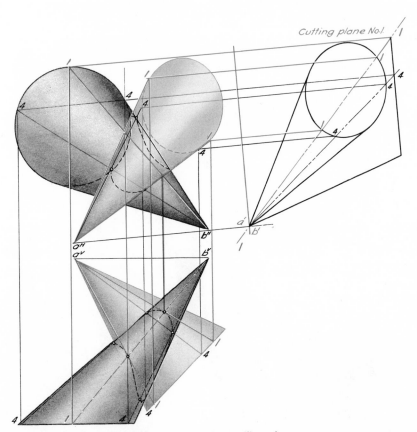

Fig. 14.19   Intersection of two cones—using auxiliary view.

shown in Fig. 14.21. Here the two cones have a common base, which is, of course, one of the lines of intersection. When cones have a common base or common base plane, the solution is much simplified because elements cut out by any cutting plane are very easily found. The procedure is as follows. Extend the line joining the two vertices until it pierces the plane of the bases as at *P*. From this point draw a line across the bases. The intersections of this line with the curve of the bases locate the foot of all elements lying in the cutting plane determined by the two intersecting lines, that is, the one through the vertices and the one drawn across the bases. The elements cut by one such plane intersect in points on the curve of intersection. The construction for one cutting plane is shown in the figure. Line *XZ* pierces the plane of the bases at point *P*. *PB* is the line across the bases. Elements *XB* and *ZA* are cut from the cones. They intersect at point *3* on the surfaces of the cones. The other two elements that intersect at *A* and *B* on the common base have not been shown. Other points on the curve of intersection were obtained in a similar way.

14.16.3 Bases edgewise in the same view. In Fig. 14.22, two cones are illustrated with bases that

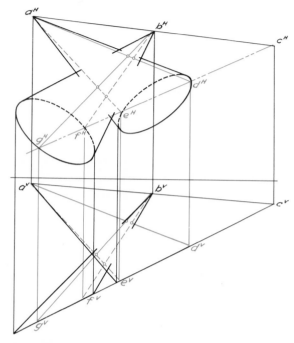

Fig. 14.20   Intersection of two cones—bases in same plane.

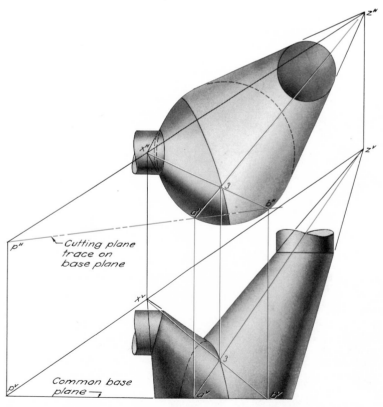

Fig. 14.21   Intersection of two cones with common bases.

appear edgewise in the top view. To determine the elements that lie in a cutting plane, proceed as follows:

a. Draw a line AB connecting the vertices of the cones and extend it until it pierces the planes of both bases at C and D.

b. Find the line of intersection EF of the planes of the bases. It appears endwise at $e^H f^H$ in the top view and as a vertical line $e^V f^V$ in the front view.

c. Draw a line from d^V across the base of the cone up to the line of intersection at g^V and from this point across the other base to point c^V. These lines determine the elements 3 on both cones and the points on the curve of intersection, as shown in the figure. The entire curve has not been shown. As many planes as desired can be found in the same manner. A line is drawn through d^V intersecting the base of cone B to the point where it crosses $f^V g^V$. From this point another line is drawn to c^V crossing the base of the cone A. Through the points on the base, elements can be drawn and points on the line of intersection determined.

14.16.4 Bases edgewise in different views. In Fig. 14.23, one cone has its base edgewise in the top view and the other cone has its base edgewise in the front view. The procedure is exactly the same as in the preceding problem. It should be noted that the

projections of the line of intersection of the base planes lie in the edgewise views of the bases since one is an H-projecting plane and the other a V-projecting plane. Line EF is the line of intersection of the base planes. Any line such as DE may be drawn in the plane of base 1 until it crosses the line of intersection at point E. Line EC can then be drawn in the plane of the other base, from e^H to c^H. If this plane is numbered 4, the elements 4 can be drawn in each cone through the points on the base of the cones where these lines DE and EC cross the respective bases. These elements locate four points on the line of intersection. Any other similar lines such as DF and FC can be drawn to locate other points which are marked 1.

14.16.5 Only one base shown edgewise. When the base of only one cone shows edgewise, the elements determined by a single cutting plane may be found as illustrated in Fig. 14.24. The procedure is as follows:

a. Extend the line AB joining the vertices of the two cones until it pierces the plane of the base of the cone that shows edgewise as at D.

b. Choose an element in the other cone as AC in Fig. 14.24 and extend it until it likewise pierces the plane of the edgewise base at E.

c. Draw the line DE that crosses the base of the cone at F and G in the front view. The cutting plane

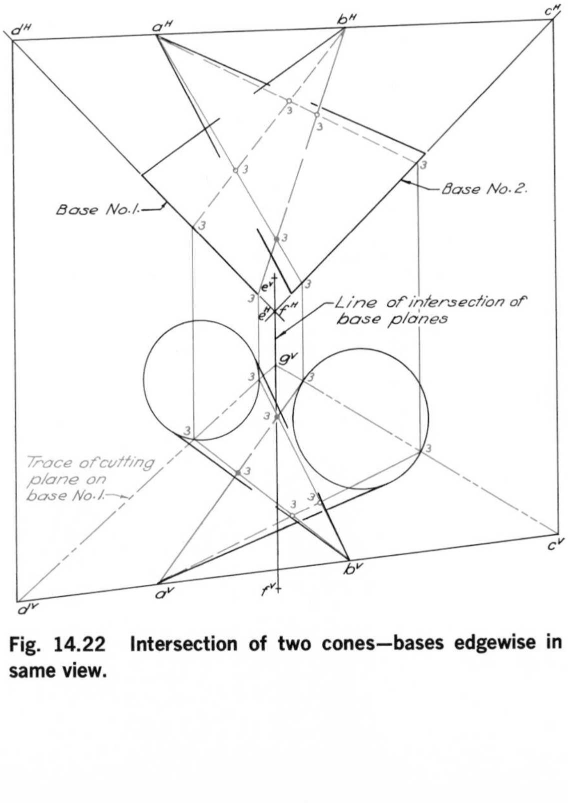

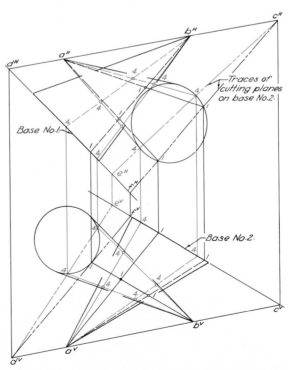

Fig. 14.22   Intersection of two cones—bases edgewise in same view.

Fig. 14.23   Intersection of two cones—bases edgewise in different views.

through the vertices is thus determined by lines *DE* and *AE*.

d. Draw the elements *BF* and *BG* that cross element *AC* at two points *1* on the curve of intersection. The curve is not shown in the figure.

e. Repeat the process with a succession of elements in cone *A*.

14.16.6   Neither base edgewise. If neither base appears edgewise in any view, an auxiliary plane can be set up perpendicular to one of the bases and both cones projected to this auxiliary plane. When this is done, the procedure of Art. 14.16.5 can be followed. Another method of solution would be to extend both cones to some common base plane and then proceed as in Fig. 14.20.

14.17   INTERSECTIONS OF CYLINDERS AND CONES. To cut straight lines from both a cone and a cylinder at the same time requires (1) *that the cutting plane pass through the vertex of the cone* and (2) *that it be parallel to the elements of the cylinder.*

14.17.1   Endwise view of cylinder method. The line of intersection of a cone and cylinder can be obtained with relative ease if the end view of the cylinder can be obtained. Passing the required cutting planes can be accomplished by inspection if an endwise view of the cylinder can be obtained as in Fig. 14.25. Here the points obtained with one typical cutting plane have been shown.

14.17.2   Right circular cone with cylinder parallel to base of the cone. When the cone is right circular and the cylinder is parallel to the base of the cone, as in Fig. 14.26, the cutting planes can be chosen so that they cut straight lines from the cylinder and circles from the cone that intersect in pairs to locate points on the curve of intersection.

14.17.3   Oblique cutting plane method. When the cone and cylinder are so situated that neither of the schemes used above can be readily applied, the cutting planes must be passed through a line drawn from the vertex of the cone and parallel to the elements of the cylinder. Any plane through this line will cut straight lines from both cone and cylinder if it cuts them at all. This is illustrated pictorially in Fig. 14.27. To understand the theory and construction of this problem, it is necessary to follow both Fig. 14.27 and Fig. 14.28 at the same time. The steps required for the solution are as follows:

a. Construct a line through the apex of the cone parallel to the elements of the cylinder. In Fig. 14.27 this line is lettered *CAB*. In Fig. 14.28 the line is lettered *ACB*.

b. Find the point where this line pierces the plane of the base of the cylinder. In Fig. 14.27 this point is lettered *C*. In Fig. 14.28 the point is also labeled *C*, but in this figure it is located by its projections c^V and c^H.

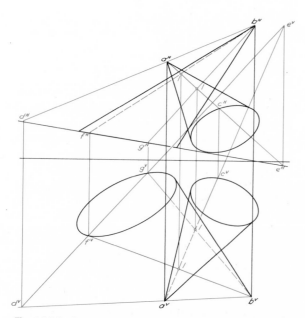

Fig. 14.24   Intersection of two cones—one base edgewise.

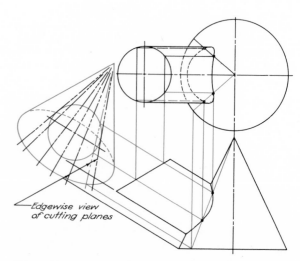

Fig. 14.25   Intersection of cone and cylinder—end view of cylinder.

c. Find the point where the line pierces the base of the cone. In Fig. 14.27 this point is labeled B. In Fig. 14.28 the point is also labeled B, but it is located by means of the two projections b^H and b^V.

d. Find the line of intersection of the plane of the base of the cone with the plane of the base of the cylinder. In Fig. 14.27 it can be seen that this line of intersection is the reference line. In Fig. 14.28 this line of intersection has its vertical projection in the reference line and also its horizontal projection in the reference line. Any two points on the reference line such as E and F will locate the line.

e. In Fig. 14.27, construct a line from C crossing the base of the cylinder and intersecting the line of intersection at point D. In Fig. 14.28 the horizontal projection of a line through C, intersecting line EF at D, is constructed at c^Hd^H. This line crosses the base of the cylinder at two points marked 4. The vertical projection of this line is c^Vd^V in the reference line.

f. In Fig. 14.27 another line can be drawn through D to B crossing the base of the cone. In Fig. 14.28 a corresponding line can be drawn by constructing the vertical projection through b^V and d^V. The line in this case must be extended to cross the base of the cone at the two points marked 4.

g. In Fig. 14.27, plane BCD must cut elements from both the cone and the cylinder because the plane passes through the apex of the cone parallel to the elements of the cylinder. These elements must pass

through the points already found on the bases of the two surfaces. In Fig. 14.28 the plane is defined by lines BD and DC and cuts elements from both surfaces starting at the points marked 4. The elements should be drawn with the proper visibility in their own surface only.

h. Locate the points where the elements of the cone cross the elements of the cylinder. These points show plainly in the pictorial of Fig. 14.27. In Fig. 14.28 locate the points where the vertical projections of the elements of the cylinder cross the vertical projection of the elements of the cone. The same thing can be done in the horizontal projection.

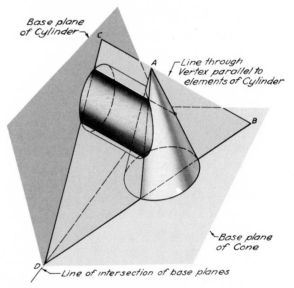

Fig. 14.27   Intersection of cone and cylinder—pictorial drawing.

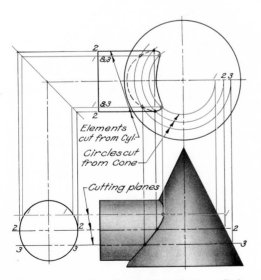

Fig. 14.26   Intersection of cone and cylinder—cylinder parallel to base of cone.

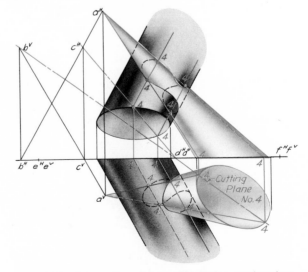

Fig. 14.28   Intersection of cone and cylinder—cutting plane method.

If the work is accurate the horizontal projection of each point must be directly above its vertical projection. If both elements are visible, the point will be visible. Any other combination will give an invisible point.

i. Pass a series of planes in the same manner, each of which will go through a different point on the reference line.

j. Number the planes, elements, and points in order.

k. Connect the points in numerical order to form the line of intersection.

l. The final line of intersection is shown in Fig. 14.28 without all of the complicated construction.

14.18   INTERSECTION OF TWO CYLINDERS. An-

other illustration of the general method involving the intersection of two cylinders is shown pictorially and orthographically in Fig. 14.29. When obtaining the intersection of two cylinders, the cutting planes must be constructed parallel to the elements of both cylinders. This is illustrated pictorially in Fig. 14.30 where *CD* is parallel to one cylinder and *OA* is parallel to the

other cylinder. These two lines determine the guide plane. All other cutting planes must be parallel to the guide plane.

14.18.1   Cutting planes edgewise. The cutting plane *AB* shown edgewise in the top view of Fig. 14.29 cuts elements numbered *3* and *7* from one cylinder and

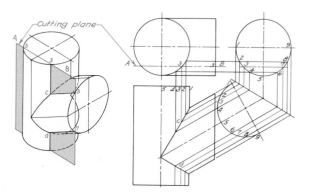

Fig. 14.29   Intersection of two cylinders.

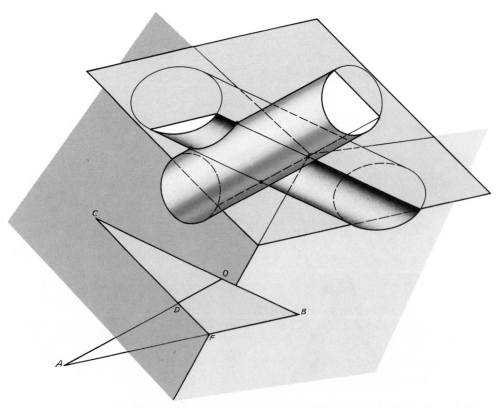

Fig. 14.30   Intersection of two cylinders—pictorial drawing.

the element *3* only from the other. These elements cross each other at two points *c* and *d* on the curve of intersection. If the inclined cylinder passed entirely through the other, four points would have been determined by this one cutting plane. Other cutting planes are passed parallel to the first one until enough points have been obtained to determine a smooth curve. Two other common situations are shown in Figs. 14.31 and 14.32, with the method of solution indicated. When the two right circular cylinders are of the same size and their axes intersect, the curve of intersection is one half of each of two ellipses, unless the penetration is complete, in which case the two ellipses are also complete.

In the preceding illustrations the cylinders were so placed that planes that cut straight lines from both cylinders could be drawn by inspection. Although the draftsman can, many times, draw intersecting cylinders in positions like these, sometimes this may not be convenient. To cover other situations, four illustrations are shown and discussed in the following paragraphs.

14.18.2 Bases in the same plane. In Fig. 14.33, two oblique cylinders are shown having a common vertical base plane. Up to this point it has been possible to draw the cutting plane by inspection since all of them have been *H-* or *V*-projecting planes. In this problem and those that follow, the cutting planes are oblique; hence they cannot be determined by inspection. It is necessary, therefore, to determine the position of the cutting planes that will cut straight lines from the cylinders or cones.

The following steps are necessary for this solution. See Fig. 14.33.

a. Assume point *A* and construct two lines *AB* and *AC* parallel respectively to the elements of the two cylinders. These lines determine a guide plane that is parallel to the elements of both cylinders.

b. Find points *B* and *C* where these two lines pierce the plane of the bases of the two cylinders.

c. Draw the line $b^V c^V$ which is the trace of the guide plane on the plane of the bases.

d. Construct other planes parallel to the guide plane by drawing traces parallel to *BC*, that is, parallel to $b^V c^V$. Cutting plane *3* in Fig. 14.33 is an example. It is understood that the other projection of these traces lies in the edgewise view of the bases. If the two cylinders intersect, it will be possible to draw these traces so that they cross both bases. The first plane should be tangent to one or both bases and the others numbered consecutively.

e. From the points where the guide traces cross the bases of the cylinders, draw the elements of the cylinders. For cutting plane *3* there are two elements in each cylinder. These elements should be drawn with the proper visibility in their own surface only. The elements should be given the same number as the plane.

f. The points where these elements cross determine points on the line of intersection. When two visible elements cross, the point will be visible. Any other combination will locate an invisible point. The

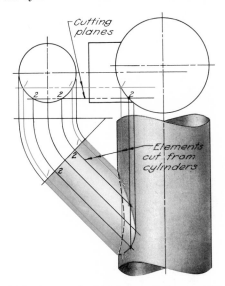

Fig. 14.31   Intersection of two cylinders—cutting plane method.

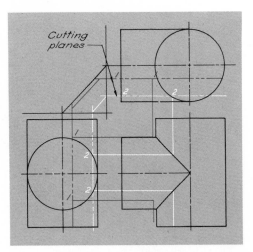

Fig. 14.32   Intersection of two cylinders of same size.

points should be given the same number as the plane and elements.

g. Connect the points in numerical order to obtain the curve of intersection. Visibility of the curve can change only on the limiting element of one of the cylinders or where the curve crosses an open base.

14.18.3 Bases edgewise on one projection but not in the same plane. In Fig. 14.34, the bases of the cylinders are in different planes but both appear edgewise in the top view. To find the intersection of these two surfaces it will be necessary to apply a procedure very similar to that used in Art. 14.8.2.

a. Assume point O at any convenient place on the sheet, as shown in Fig. 14.34, on the left side of the figure. See also small illustration for guide plane at right side of figure.

b. Through point O at left construct a line BOC parallel to the elements of one of the cylinders. Then through point O construct another line AOD parallel to the elements of the other cylinder.

c. Find the points A and B where the two lines pierce the plane of the base of one of the cylinders.

d. Find the points C and D where the two lines pierce the plane of the base of the second cylinder.

e. Locate the line FG which is the line of intersection of the planes of the two bases.

f. Through a^V and b^V draw one trace of the desired guide plane on the plane of the base of cylinder 1.

g. Through c^V and d^V draw the trace of the desired guide plane on the plane of the base of cylinder 2.

h. These traces must intersect at f^V on line FG.

i. Traces of parallel planes may be drawn so that they intersect the bases of the cylinders. The two traces of all of these planes must intersect on the vertical projection of line FG. Plane 1 will be the first usable plane. Others should be numbered in order.

j. Through the points where the traces cross the bases elements of the cylinders may be drawn. Show their visibility in their own cylinder only.

k. Find the point where these elements intersect. When two visible elements intersect, the point is

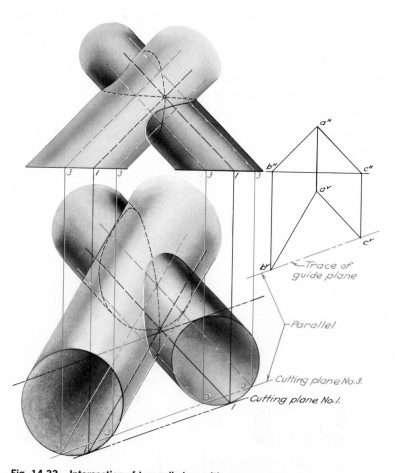

Fig. 14.33 **Intersection of two cylinders with common base plane.**

visible. All other combinations give invisible points.

l. Join the points in numerical order. Visibility of the intersection can change only on a limiting edge of one of the cylinders or where the curve crosses an open base.

When it is not convenient to use the actual bases of the cylinders, parallel bases can be set up to locate the direction of the traces of the guide plane. This construction is shown at the right side of Fig. 14.34.

14.18.4   Bases edgewise in different views. A third situation is shown in Fig. 14.35, where the base of one cylinder shows edgewise in the top view and the base of the other appears edgewise in the front view. The direction of the traces of the cutting plane on the base planes is shown in the construction at the right. In this construction it should be noted that one actual base plane has been used (base *1*) and for convenience a second plane parallel to base plane *2* has been set up. The required steps are as follows:

a. Through point *A* construct two lines parallel respectively to the elements of the two cylinders.

b. Find the points where each line pierces the plane of base *1*. These are points *B* and *C* in Fig. 14.35.

c. Find the point where each line pierces the plane that was set up parallel to base *2*. These are points *D* and *E* in Fig. 14.35.

d. The projection $d^H e^H$ is the trace of the guide plane on base *2*.

e. The projection $b^V c^V$ is the trace of the guide plane on base *1*.

f. The line of intersection of the planes of base *1* and base *2* is line *PN*. The *H*-projection of this line must lie in the edgewise view of base *1*. The *V*-projection of this line must lie in the edgewise view of base *2*.

g. Construct a series of cutting planes similar to plane *6* in Fig. 14.35. Make a trace parallel to $b^V c^V$ cutting base *1* in the points marked *6*.

h. Extend this trace until it crosses $p^V n^V$ at f^V.

i. Project f^V to f^H on $p^H n^H$.

j. From f^H draw a trace parallel to $d^H e^H$ until it crosses base *2* in the points marked *6*.

k. Proceed from this point just as in *j*, *k*, and *l* in Art. 14.8.3.

14.18.5   Neither base edgewise. In Fig. 14.36, two cylinders are shown in which neither base appears

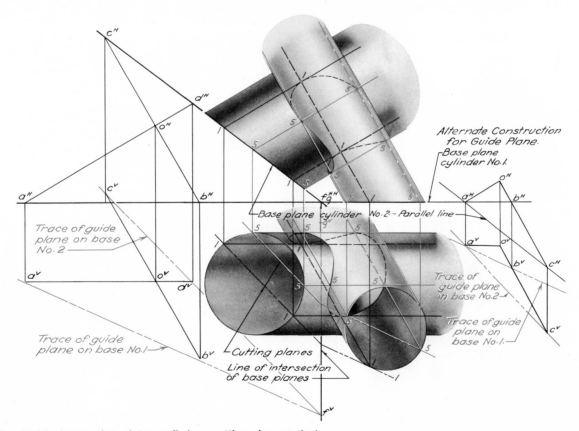

Fig. 14.34   Intersection of two cylinders—cutting plane method.

edgewise. As before, the problem is to determine cutting planes that will cut straight lines from both cylinders.

Several methods of solution are possible.

a. A plane could be chosen arbitrarily to cut across both cylinders, and the intersection of this plane with both cylinders could be found, thus making the new bases of both cylinders lie in the same plane, similar to the situation in Fig. 14.33. This having been done, the problem would be reduced to that of Fig. 14.33.

b. A second method consists of constructing the guide plane *ABC* in Fig. 14.36. An auxiliary plane perpendicular to this guide plane will show the edgewise view of all cutting planes. By making the views of both cylinders on this auxiliary plane the elements may be determined.

In Fig. 14.36, the direction of the horizontal trace of the guide plane has been determined at $b^H c^H$. The reference line *H-1* is drawn perpendicular to this line.

Both cylinders are then projected in the auxiliary view. Here cutting planes like *4* and *7* are drawn edgewise to determine the foot of the elements in both cylinders. From an inspection of the auxiliary view it can be seen that the intersection will be a single continuous curve.

14.19 CYLINDER WITH A DOUBLE-CURVED SURFACE.

A simple illustration of the intersection of a cylinder and sphere is shown in Fig. 14.37. Here the cylinder and sphere have been chosen in such position that the planes, which cut straight lines from the cylinder, cut circles from the sphere that project as circles in the top view. Two typical cutting planes are shown. In this position the problem becomes very simple. By the use of one or two auxiliary views the draftsman can always reduce the problem to the situation shown in Fig. 14.37.

A more complex situation is shown in Fig. 14.38, where a curved pipe (geometrically a partial torus) passes through a double-curved surface. In this case, by a careful selection of the cutting plane and the aux-

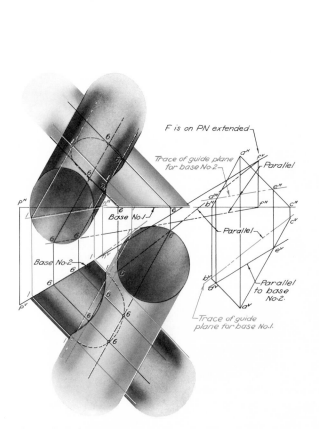

Fig. 14.35 Intersection of two cylinders—cutting plane method.

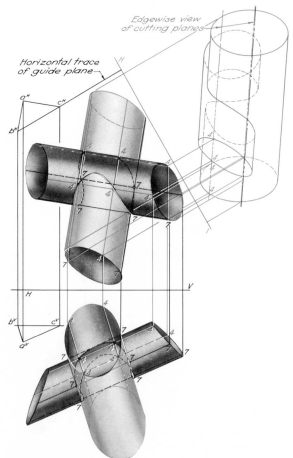

Fig. 14.36 Intersection of two cylinders—cutting plane method.

iliary view, parts of circles are cut from the pipe and more complex curves from the other surface. The method for finding the curve on the larger surface is illustrated for two cutting planes in Fig. 14.38. The process must be repeated a sufficient number of times to determine the curve. In any event, it is a long and tedious process.

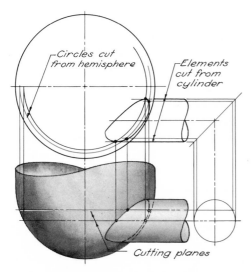

Fig. 14.37   Intersection of sphere and cylinder.

14.20   CONVENTIONAL INTERSECTION. On many machine parts, intersections occur that are automatically produced by machining operations. Thus a small hole drilled into a tube, for example, produces the intersection of two cylinders. Such intersections can be shown conventionally, as in Fig. 14.39. If the intersection is relatively large, an approximation may be made by locating three points and using an irregular curve, as shown in the lower right-hand illustration of Fig. 14.39. These conventional intersections are used to save time, but the actual intersections could have been found by the methods described in the previous article

14.21   DEVELOPMENT OF SURFACES. Another practical problem that arises frequently in construction work and is commonly associated with the work in intersections is the development of surfaces. The term development means the laying out of flat patterns from which curved surfaces can be formed without stretching the material.

The method of making developments is best explained by concrete examples. *One fundamental principle, however, may be noted, namely, that every line used in making a development must represent the true*

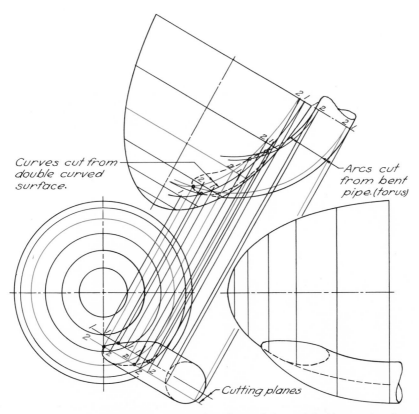

Fig. 14.38   Intersection of curved pipe and double-curved surface.

length of that line on the actual surface.

The two methods of finding the true length of a line will be found in Arts. 7.7 and 13.2.5, which should be thoroughly reviewed at this time.

14.22   DEVELOPMENT OF A PRISM. *A right section of a prism develops as a straight line, known as a stretchout line. The elements of a prism develop as lines perpendicular to the stretchout line. The elements and the stretchout line both show in true length in the development.*

14.22.1   Right prism. If the prism in Fig. 14.40 is cut along the edge *AE* and unfolded into a flat surface, the resulting pattern is called a development. In this case all the edges show in their true lengths in one or the other of the two original views. The plane of the base is perpendicular to the edges; hence this base line develops into a straight line perpendicular to the edges as shown in Fig. 14.40. The true size of the right section is laid out on the stretchout line at *ABCDA*. The true length of each element is then placed on perpendiculars to the stretchout line as shown for *AE* and *BF*.

14.22.2   Oblique prism parallel to a coordinate plane. When neither base of a prism is perpendicular to the elements, it is called an oblique prism. In this case it is necessary to find the true size of a right section. The best method of doing this is by setting up an auxiliary plane perpendicular to the elements as shown at $a^Vb^Vc^Vd^V$ in Fig. 14.41(a). In Fig. 14.41(a), the ele-

ments show in their true length in the front view. The stretchout line *ABCDA* can be laid out on a perpendicular to the vertical projection of the elements. The length of the stretchout line is obtained from the true size of the right section $a^1b^1c^1d^1$. The elements will then be laid out perpendicular to the stretchout line and their length can be projected from the front view.

14.22.3   Oblique prism not parallel to a coordinate plane. In Fig. 14.41(b), none of the edges of the prism show in true length in the front and top views. The true lengths of the four corner edges, however, are obtained in the first auxiliary view and the true shape of the right section in the second auxiliary view. These true lengths have then been used to obtain the development as shown. For convenience the development has been projected from the first auxiliary, but it could have been laid out in any position by the use of dividers.

14.23   DEVELOPMENT OF A PYRAMID. *A pyramid is developed by finding the true size of the base and the true length of all elements. These values are combined by building up a series of triangles in true size.*

14.23.1   Development of a right pyramid. Figure 14.42 shows two projections of a right square pyramid. The true size of the base shows in the top view. The faces of the pyramid are triangles. The true size of these triangles can be found by auxiliary projection or by finding the true length of each line as has been done in Fig. 14.42(b). To find the true length of *AE* the pro-

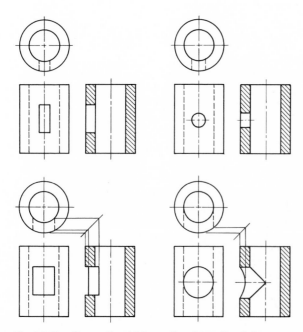

Fig. 14.39   Conventional intersections in sectional views.

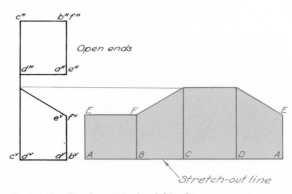

Fig. 14.40   Development of a right prism.

jection a^H is revolved to $a_r{}^H$ and then projected to $a_r{}^V$. The true length of AE shows at $a_r{}^V e^V$.

The development is made by laying out each complete triangle such as EDC, by using the true length of each line. Then the upper part of the pyramid that has been cut away is laid out in the same manner as for triangle EFG. The portion $CDFG$ is the development of one face of the truncated pyramid.

14.23.2   Oblique pyramid. In the oblique pyramid in Fig. 14.42(b), it was necessary to obtain the true

length of the four edges by rotation as shown. The edges of the base appear in true length in the top view. Study carefully the method of obtaining the true lengths of the truncated portions. The true lengths having been obtained, the development is made as in the foregoing example. As in previous cases, the pyramid is cut on the shortest element FA of the truncated portion.

14.24   DEVELOPMENT OF A CYLINDER. The cylinder is a very common surface encountered in design.

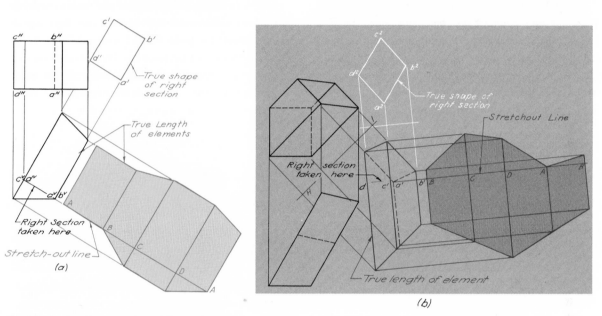

Fig. 14.41   Development of an oblique prism.

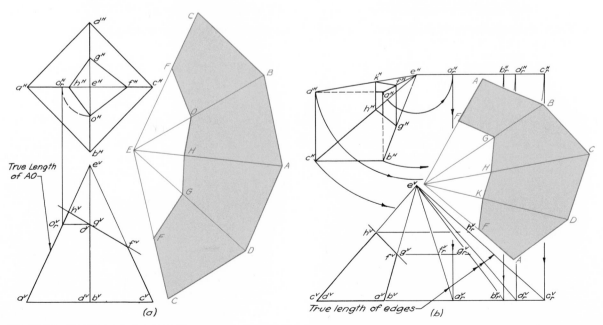

Fig. 14.42   Development of a pyramid.

If its bases are parallel and perpendicular to the axis, it is easily seen that when split along any element and rolled out flat, as in Fig. 14.43, a rectangle is formed. The width of this rectangle is equal to the length of the cylinder, and its length is equal to the circumference of the cylinder. Both measurements are easily found from a working drawing. The development of a cylinder is the same as that of the prism. The cylinder is divided into a number of parts which actually form a prism that approximates the surface of the cylinder.

14.24.1 Truncated right cylinder. A truncated right circular cylinder has been developed in Fig. 14.44. Here the elements, 12 in number, show in their true length in the front view and may be projected directly to the development. The lower base shows the true size of the right section as a circle in the top view, and the true shape of the inclined face may be ob-

tained by auxiliary projection if desired.

In stepping off the 12 spaces between elements with a divider, it is well to check the accuracy of the setting by stepping it off six times halfway around the true size of the base. If this does not check with the semicircle, the setting should be adjusted until a perfect check is obtained. The true size of the right section is laid out on the stretchout line and the length of each element is projected to a line perpendicular to the stretchout line.

14.24.2 Oblique cylinder parallel to a coordinate plane. An oblique cylinder, that is, one that has its bases inclined to the elements, requires, first, the true length of all elements and, second, the true size of a right section similar to that explained in the discussion of the oblique prism. The right section may be taken at any convenient point and its true size may be ob-

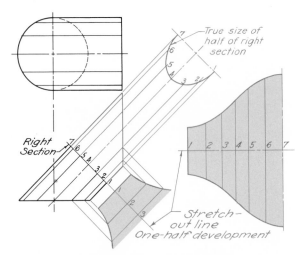

Fig. 14.45 Development of an oblique cylinder.

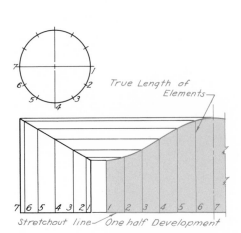

Fig. 14.43 Pictorial drawing of development of a right cylinder.

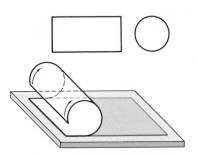

Fig. 14.44 Development of a right cylinder.

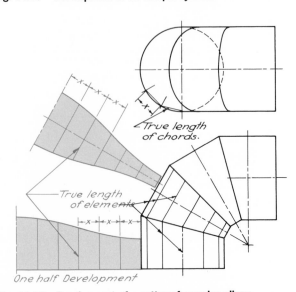

Fig. 14.46 Development of a pattern for a pipe elbow.

tained by auxiliary projection as in Fig. 14.45. In this case the elements show in their true length in the front view; they may be projected to the development in a direction at right angles to their length as illustrated for three of them or they may be transferred into another position with dividers as shown for the half development. The right section rolls out as a straight line, and the spaces between elements, obtained from the auxiliary view, may be laid out on this line. A practical application is shown in Fig. 14.46.

14.24.3 Oblique cylinder inclined to all coordinate planes. A still more general case of the oblique cylinder is shown in Fig. 14.47. In this instance it is necessary to obtain the true length of the elements in the first auxiliary view and the true size of the right section by a

second auxiliary view. These having been determined, the construction follows in the usual manner.

14.25 DEVELOPMENT OF A CONE. *A cone may be regarded as a pyramid with an infinite number of sides.* In practice it is divided into a practical number of parts which form a close approximation to the surface of the cone. Each section is developed as a triangle, as was explained for the pyramid.

14.25.1 Right circular cone. The right circular cone develops into a sector of a circle as shown in Fig. 14.48. The front view shows the true length of the elements as y. The lengths of the chords of the base may be obtained from the top view. With y as a radius, an arc of indefinite length is drawn and on it a length equal to the chord x is stepped off 12 times. If these points are connected to the center we have in reality 12 small triangles which approximate very closely the actual cone. This is the usual graphical method of development. A closer approximation can be obtained by dividing the base into a greater number of parts or the length of the base of the cone may be computed and laid out on an arc. The development of a cone intersected by a cylinder is shown in Fig. 14.49.

14.25.2 Oblique cone. The oblique cone requires that the true length of all elements be found, and if the base is not parallel to one of the planes of projection, the true length around the base may also be found, preferably by auxiliary projection. Figure 14.50 illustrates the first type with the base parallel to *H*. Note again that the development consists of a series of triangles, the length of whose sides has been determined and which have been joined in consecutive order, beginning with the shortest element.

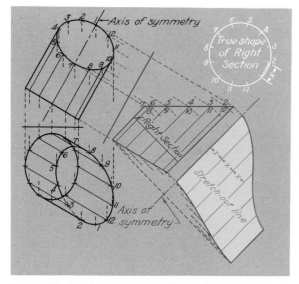

Fig. 14.47 Development of an oblique cylinder.

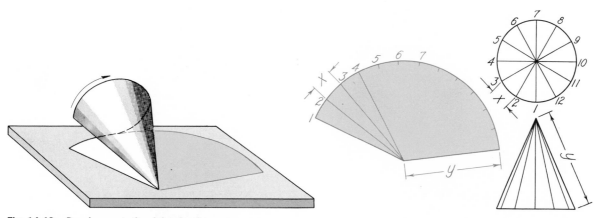

Fig. 14.48 Development of a right circular cone.

A second cone is shown in Fig. 14.51, in which the true shape of the base has been determined by auxiliary projection and the true length of the elements by rotation as usual. As soon as these things have been accomplished, the solution follows the customary procedure.

In several of the preceding figures the development has been begun on the shortest element. This is a practical feature. By splitting the part on the shortest element the least labor is required in welding or riveting the seam. Whenever possible, therefore, the shortest element should be chosen as the beginning of a development or template.

14.26   DEVELOPMENT OF TRANSITION PIECES.
A large amount of sheet metal layout work consists of transition pieces or reducers as they are sometimes called. When it becomes necessary to join ducts of different shapes, the portion by which this change is accomplished is called a transition piece. If there is a change in size, the sections are commonly called reducers. Thus one may connect rectangular parts in different planes or change a section from square to round and so on through a wide range of combinations.

The problem in making these pieces lies, first, in recognizing and identifying the various component shapes. The transition pieces are composed of planes, cones, cylinders, and convolutes. The second step is the development of the several parts and connecting them in the proper order. It is also desirable to identify axes of symmetry since a pattern of one half will suffice if there is one axis of symmetry and one fourth

may be enough if there are two axes of symmetry.

14.26.1   Rectangular sections.
A series of reducers connecting rectangular sections is shown in Fig. 14.52. In the first three of these the reducer is composed entirely of plane sections. In the last, Fig. 14.52(d), two of the faces are warped quadrilaterals. Theoretically, warped surfaces cannot be formed without stretching the material but, practically, a development can be made if the warping is not too severe. In Fig. 14.52(d), the warped surface can be made into two plane-triangular surfaces by bending slightly along the line between the triangles.

The axes of symmetry have also been shown in Fig. 14.52 by center lines. A little study of these illustrations and those that follow will be an aid in analyzing similar problems in practice.

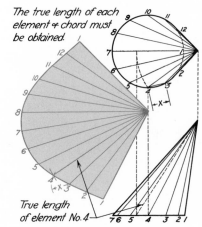

Fig. 14.50   Development of an oblique cone.

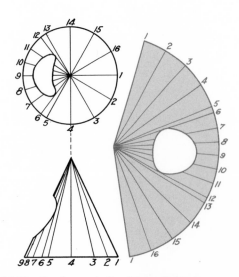

Fig. 14.49   Development of an intersected cone.

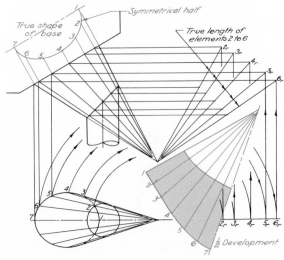

Fig. 14.51   Development of an oblique cone.

The development of a reducer similar to that in Fig. 14.52(*b*) is shown in Fig. 14.53. Each part consists of a quadrilateral. To lay these out it is necessary to have the true length of the edges and a diagonal, unless some of the edges are at right angles to each other. This piece, having only one plane of symmetry, will be split on that plane and only one half need be developed. Parts *1* and *4* each have two edges perpendicular to the central plane of symmetry, hence a diagonal is not essential. Face *2-3*, however, cannot be developed without one of the diagonals as shown.

The three parts must be laid out in their proper relationship to each other. Although it would seem impossible for anyone to put them together in the wrong order, nevertheless this sometimes happens. If the draftsman is not sure of himself, it is suggested that the corners be lettered on the two views and that these letters be carried through to the development as shown in Fig. 14.53.

14.26.2 Circular sections. In Fig. 14.54, transition pieces connecting circular cylinders have been shown. In the first two cases the connector is a part of a cone because the circles at the top and bottom lie in parallel planes. In the last two cases, Figs. 14.54(*c*) and (*d*), the surfaces are convolutes and may be developed by dividing the circular ends into an equal number of parts, beginning at any known element of the surface and then connecting the points on each end, making a series of quadrilaterals that can be developed by dividing each quadrilateral into two triangles as explained in Art. 14.27.

14.26.3 Circular and rectangular sections. Reducers that change in shape from rectangular to circular are shown in Fig. 14.55. These are commonly found on the roofs of buildings as ventilators. In each case the reducing section consists of four partial cones and four triangular plane surfaces. The vertices of the cones lie at the corners of the rectangle. A typical de-

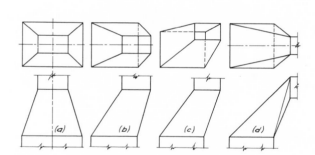

Fig. 14.52   Typical rectangular reducing sections.

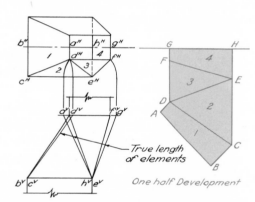

Fig. 14.53   Development of one half of a reducing section.

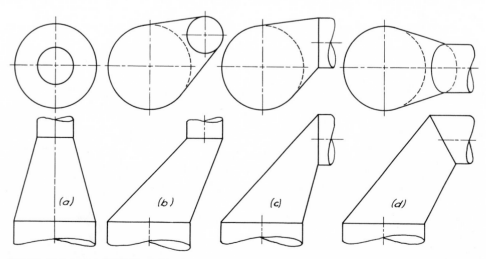

Fig. 14.54   Reducers between cylindrical surfaces.

velopment is shown in Fig. 14.56.

Another group of transition pieces involving parts of cylinders and planes and cones is shown in Fig. 14.57. The end part of the one in Fig. 14.57(*d*) is a portion of an oblique cone. With the vertex downward the chords of both bases show in true length in the top view; hence it is only necessary to obtain the true length of the segments of the elements.

In all cases developments should be made exactly to the planes of symmetry. If additional material is needed to make a joint, this should be added as a narrow strip in the developed pattern and not on the original two- or three-view drawing.

The reducer shown in Fig. 14.58 consists of parts of

two oblique cylinders and two triangular plane sections. Note that the auxiliary view used to determine the length of the elements of the cylinder could be projected from either the front or top view. The top view was chosen because this makes the bases come out as straight lines in the auxiliary view, rather than curves. The right section is obtained in the second auxiliary view. Again, care must be exercised to connect the two triangular parts to the cylinder in proper order.

When it becomes desirable to design a transition surface to connect two cross sections composed of straight lines and curves, the surface must be divided into planes, cones, cylinders, or convolutes as necessary. In each case there will be only one solution that

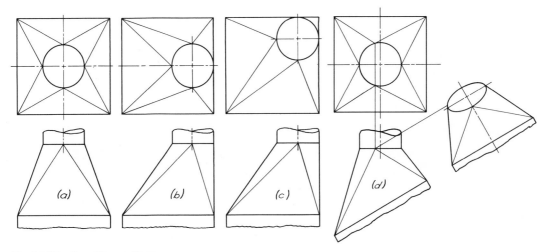

Fig. 14.55   Transition sections.

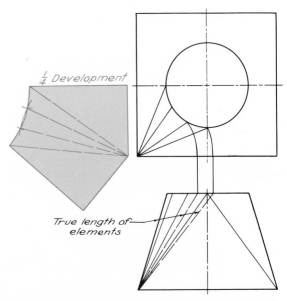

Fig. 14.56   Development of one fourth of a transition piece.

will give a perfectly smooth surface, although other subdivisions might be used to form a closed surface. The best procedure is to determine the plane surfaces first, after which the remaining surfaces are usually quite evident. A few simple rules will help in making the divisions.

a. Every straight line in either base must lie in a plane surface. Determine the plane surfaces first.
b. When there are curves in one base but none in the other, there will be cones in the surface.
c. When there are circles in both bases of equal radius, there will probably be cylinders in the surface.
d. When there are circles of different radii or other

curves in both bases or when the bases are not parallel, there may be frustums of cones or convolutes.

14.26.4 Mechanical aid in surface development.
Any surface made up of planes, cones, cylinders, or convolutes can be developed by means of the mechanical aid illustrated in Fig. 14.59. The bases are interchangeable and any plane figure can be used for either base. The bases can make any angle with each other or with the elements. Plane figures with reentrant angles and reverse curves are very difficult to use as bases and should be avoided. The mechanical aid illustrated in Fig. 14.59 must be rolled along with both bases in contact with the paper.

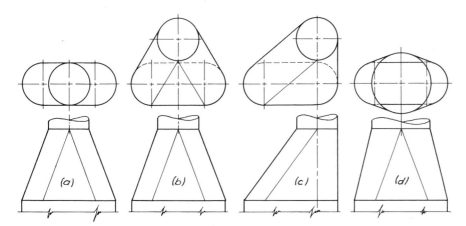

Fig. 14.57 Transition pieces between cylindrical surfaces.

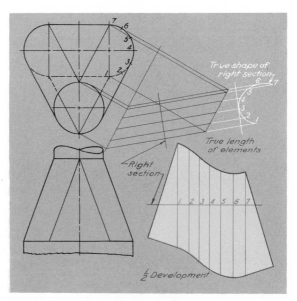

Fig. 14.58 Development of one half of a reducing section.

14.27 DEVELOPMENT BY TRIANGULATION. In many cases a transition piece cannot be divided into cylinders, cones, and planes. For example, Fig. 14.54 is composed entirely or in part of frustums of cones or convolutes. Such surfaces can be developed by a method commonly called triangulation. This method is frequently applied to cones if the vertex is too far removed for practical use. The method consists in dividing the surface into small triangles that will approximate the surface and then laying out these triangles in their true size and proper relative order.

This method is illustrated for a reducer connecting a circular and an elliptical section in Fig. 14.60. Be-

ginning at any common element, usually on a plane of symmetry, the upper and lower bases are divided into the same number of equal parts and these points are connected in a manner similar to that for the elements of a cone. This divides the surface into a series of quadrilaterals. Next these quadrilaterals are divided into triangles by drawing diagonals. It is customary to keep all diagonals running in the same general direction. This method is simple but it cannot be regarded as a shortcut since it is still necessary to find the true length of every line used in the development. The method of finding the true length has again been illustrated for a few of the lines in Fig. 14.60.

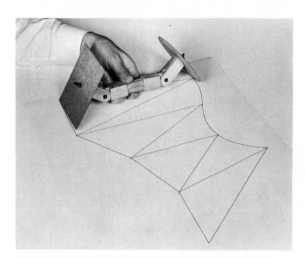

Fig. 14.59   Mechanical developing model.

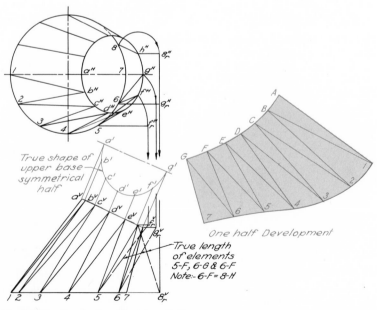

True shape of upper base — symmetrical half

One half Development

True length of elements 5-F, 6-G & 6-F
Note:- 6-F = 8-H

Fig. 14.60   Development by triangulation.

14.28 DEVELOPMENT OF DOUBLE-CURVED SUR-FACES. Spheres and other double-curved surfaces can be only roughly approximated by development. If these surfaces are to be accurately reproduced, as many of them must be in aircraft work, the material must be stretched by forming in dies with a drop hammer, or hydropress, or by spinning.

The construction of these dies involves a knowledge of intersections as illustrated in Fig. 14.61, where the templates used in forming a plaster mold for a paraboloid of revolution are shown. The sections are taken at right angles to each other. The templates are cut from sheet metal and firmly joined together. Circular sections may be added to give accuracy to the shaping of the plaster cast. The spaces between the templates are filled with wire netting and excelsior over which the plaster can be placed. As the plaster dries it can be

scraped to the exact contour. It is then used to make a metal die, and from the die a metal punch similar to the plaster mold can be made. Allowance must be made for the thickness of metal to be formed.

Surfaces of revolution may be approximated in one or two ways, as illustrated in Figs. 14.62 and 14.63. When the sections are cut along meridian curves as in Fig. 14.62, the method is called the gore method and each section is referred to as a gore. When the sections are cut perpendicular to the axis of revolution as in Fig. 14.63, the scheme is referred to as the zone method. In either case the accuracy will obviously depend on the number of sections made. The greater the number, the closer will be the approach to the true surface. True lengths must again be used throughout.

The zone method of development is in general similar to the polyconic system of map projection used

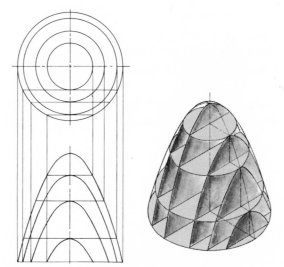

Fig. 14.61   Section of a paraboloid of revolution.

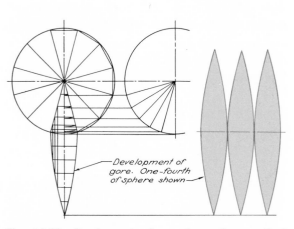

Development of gore. One-fourth of sphere shown

Fig. 14.62   Development of a sphere. Gore method (approximate).

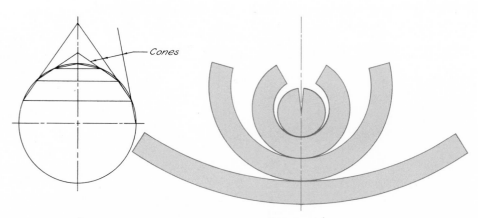

Cones

Fig. 14.63   Development of a sphere. Zone method (approximate).

for topographic maps of the United States and gives a good basis for further study of that system of map making.

14.29 SHEET METAL JOINTS. Sheet metal developments and templates would be of little value unless the ends could be fastened together. A wide variety of methods are used in sheet metal work. Seams may be made by bending, welding, or soldering and riveting, as shown in Fig. 14.64. Allowance must be made beyond the theoretical line of development to provide the necessary overlap to make these joints.

14.30 BEND RADII AND BEND ALLOWANCE. In bending or forming sheet metal parts the minimum radius to which the sheet can be bent is determined by the type of material, the thickness, and the equipment available. In any bend, the material on the outer portion of the bend is stretched and that on the inside is compressed. Somewhere between the two sides there is a line that has not been changed in length. This is referred to as the neutral line or surface. Experience has shown that this line is approximately 44 per cent of the thickness from the inner or compressed side. In making a flat pattern, therefore, this line will develop in its true length.

Since the circumference of a circle is $2\pi r$, the length

of a curve of 1° will be $(2\pi r)/360$ or $(\pi r)/180$. This reduces to $0.01745r$, where r is the radius to the neutral surface and is equal to $(R + 0.44t)$. If this quantity is multiplied by the angle of bend in degrees, the total length of material required to make the bend may be readily computed as $0.01745rA$, where A is the angle of bend. A simple illustration is shown in Fig. 14.65. To save the labor of computation, tables of bend allowances for 1° are usually used.

14.31 DEVELOPMENT BASED ON MOLD LINES. It will be noted in the preceding illustration that the distance to the bend line must be known to make use of the formula and table mentioned in the preceding article. Frequently, however, the distance to the mold line is known, rather than that to the bend line. Under these conditions it is simpler to use the distance between mold lines, called the setback, in determining the length of a flat pattern.

The mold line is the line of intersection of the two faces on each side of the bend, as shown in Fig. 14.66. Although there is a mold line for the inside surfaces as well as the outside surface, the outside mold line is generally used. It will be noted that, although there is only one outside mold line for the part in its bent condition, there are two mold lines in the flat shape. In

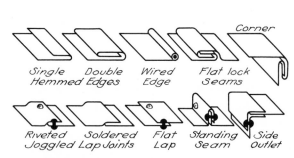

Fig. 14.64 Sheet metal joints.

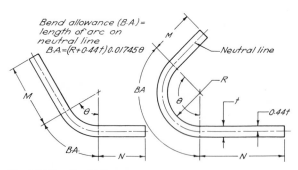

Fig. 14.65 Bend allowances.

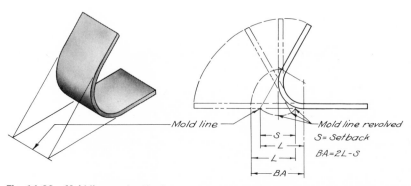

Fig. 14.66 Mold lines and setback.

other words, there is a mold line for each face. The method of computing the setback and of using it in determining the developed length is shown in Fig. 14.66. The meaning of open and closed bevels is illustrated in Fig. 14.67.

14.32   BEND RELIEF. When two edges of a flat pattern are bent up, the corner is subjected to stresses that may tear the material. In order to avoid tearing, the corner is cut out on a circular arc to relieve this strain. This curve is frequently drawn tangent to the bend lines although it need not be. The chief purpose is to remove material that is subject to bending in two directions. A few simple layouts for the development of patterns are shown in Fig. 14.68.

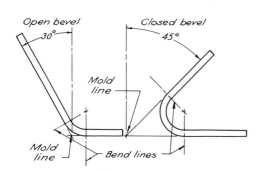

Fig. 14.67   Open and closed bevels.

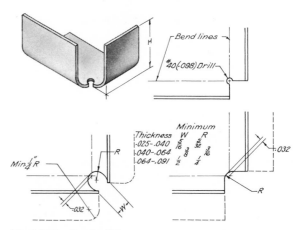

Fig. 14.68   Bend relief.

SELF-STUDY QUESTIONS

Before trying to answer these questions, read the chapter carefully. Then, without reference to the text, answer as many questions as possible. For those that cannot be answered, the number, in parentheses following the question number, gives the article in which the answer can be found. Look it up and write down the answer. Check the answers that you did give to see that they are correct.

14.1 **(14.2)** In this book prisms and pyramids are treated as _____ .

14.2 **(14.2)** Cylinders and cones are considered to be _____ without ends.

14.3 **(14.3)** The usual process of finding intersections consists of passing _____ _____ which cut elements from both surfaces.

14.4 **(14.3)** The first cutting plane should be _____ to one or both surfaces.

14.5 **(14.3)** The cutting planes should be _____ in order.

14.6 **(14.3)** The elements should be drawn showing their proper _____ in their own surface only.

14.7 **(14.3)** The elements should be given the same _____ as the plane.

14.8 **(14.3)** The points should be given the same _____ as the elements.

14.9 **(14.3)** The points should be connected in _____ order.

14.10 **(14.3)** The line of intersection can change visibility only where the curve of intersection touches a _____ _____ or crosses an _____ _____ .

14.11 **(14.5)** The intersection of a plane and prism can be solved by the _____ _____ method or by the _____ _____ method.

14.12 **(14.5.1)** When the intersection of a plane and object is found by getting the edgewise view of the plane, the _____ _____ method is being used.

14.13 **(14.5.2)** The first step in the _____ _____ method of finding intersections is to pass a plane through an element.

14.14 **(14.9)** When working with a surface of revolution, the planes should be passed to cut _____ from the surface.

14.15 **(14.11)** When finding the intersection of a prism and some other surface, it is usually best to find the _____ _____ of the prism.

14.16 **(14.12)** In the top view the _____ points are visible.

14.17 **(14.12)** In the vertical projection the _____ points are visible.

14.18 **(14.16)** In getting the intersection of two cones, the _____ _____ method should be used.

14.19 **(14.17)** In finding the intersection of a cone and cylinder, the plane should be passed through the _____ of the cone and be _____ to the elements of the cylinder.

14.20 **(14.16)** In finding the intersection of two cones, the plane should be passed through _____ _____ .

14.21 **(14.15)** If the first and last planes are tangent to both surfaces, the curve of intersection will be two _____ curves with _____ points in common.

14.22 **(14.21)** In developing a surface, every line in the development must show _____ _____ .

14.23 **(14.22 to 14.22.3)** In developing a prism or a cylinder it is necessary to find the true size of a _____ _____ and the _____ _____ of the elements.

14.24 **(14.25.2)** In developing a cone it is best to find the _____ _____ of the elements and the true size of the _____.

14.25 **(14.28)** The development of a double-curved surface can only be _____.

14.26 **(14.29)** When laying out a sheet metal development _____ _____ must be allowed for joints.

14.27 **(14.32)** When material is cut out to relieve stress while bending a flat pattern, this is known as _____ _____.

PROBLEMS

All of the problems in this group have been laid out to be drawn on an 8½ × 11″, sheet with the front and top views arranged along the long dimension of the sheet. Dimensions have been given to border lines so that the student may make his layout to come within the borders of the sheet. Space between border lines is assumed to be 7½ × 10½″ by allowing a ¾″ margin on the left long edge and a ¼″ margin on the other three edges.

If it is desired to include developments with the intersection problems, an 11 × 17″ sheet should be used, the intersection portion of the problem being kept at the left.

In each problem the student must reproduce the figure as shown and then find the intersection specified. These instructions are not repeated in the problem statements.

The location of reference lines for making auxiliary views to show the true shape of some intersections have also been definitely located. In some instances these reference lines are center lines. In the intersections of surfaces the elements are not terminated where they actually disappear. The student is to determine this as a part of his problem.

14.1 Find the intersection of plane A and the square pyramid of Fig. 14.69. Show the true shape of the intersection.

14.1a Develop the lower portion of the pyramid.

14.2 Same as Problem 14.1, using plane B.

14.3 Same as Problem 14.1, using Fig. 14.70. Plane A.

14.3a Develop the lower portion of the pyramid.

14.4 Same as Problem 14.1, using Fig. 14.70. Plane B.

14.5 Same as Problem 14.1, using Fig. 14.71. Plane A.

14.5a Develop the lower portion of the cone.

14.6 Same as Problem 14.1, using Fig. 14.71. Plane B.

14.7 Same as Problem 14.1, using Fig. 14.71. Plane C.

14.8 Find the intersection of plane A with the hexagonal prism of Fig. 14.72.

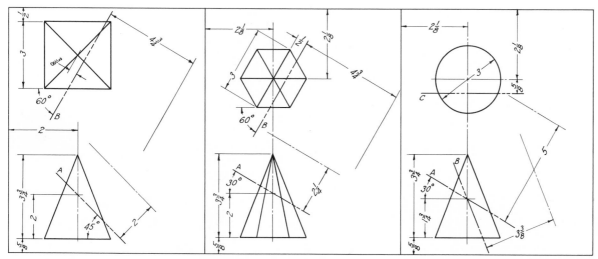

Fig. 14.69   Plane and prism.   Fig. 14.70   Plane and prism.   Fig. 14.71   Plane and cone.

14.8a Make a development of the prism in Fig. 14.72.

14.9 Find the intersection of plane *A* with the cylinder of Fig. 14.73.

14.9a Make a development of the cylinder.

14.10 Find the intersection of plane *A* and the pentagonal prism of Fig. 14.74.

14.10a Make a development of the prism in Fig. 14.74.

14.11–14.13 Find the intersection of the surfaces as assigned from Figs. 14.75 through 14.77. Show visibility correctly on your finished drawing. Note that the edges of the prisms and pyramids are not necessarily terminated where they actually disappear.

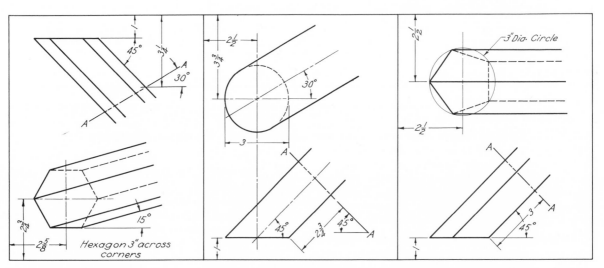

Fig. 14.72   Plane and prism.   Fig. 14.73   Plane and cylinder.   Fig. 14.74   Plane and prism.

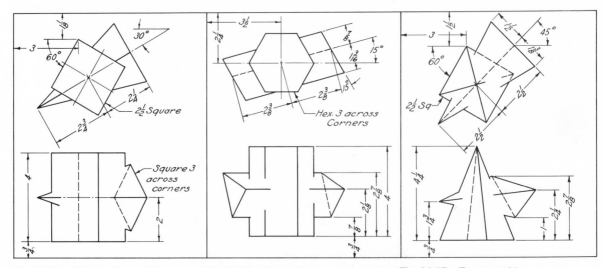

Fig. 14.75   Prism and pyramid.   Fig. 14.76   Two prisms.   Fig. 14.77   Two pyramids.

14.14–14.16 Find the intersection of the cylinders as assigned from Figs. 14.78 to 14.80. Show visibility.

14.17–14.19 Find the intersection of the surfaces as assigned from Figs. 14.81 to 14.89.

14.20 Make a three-view working drawing of the connecting-rod end shown in Fig. 14.90. Find accurately all curves of intersection in your drawing.

14.21 Same as Problem 14.20, using the connecting-rod end of Fig. 14.91.

14.22 Make a development of the object shown in Figs. 14.92 to 14.101. Use B scale for 8½ × 11 sheet and A scale for larger sheet.

14.23 The cylindrical bar, shown in plan and elevation, is clamped on the work table of a milling machine as indicated. The size, shape, and location of the axis of the cutter are also given. Find the shape of the cut after the bar has passed the cutter.

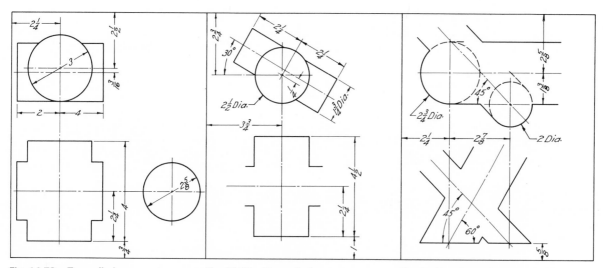

Fig. 14.78 Two cylinders.   **Fig. 14.79 Two cylinders.**   **Fig. 14.80 Two cylinders.**

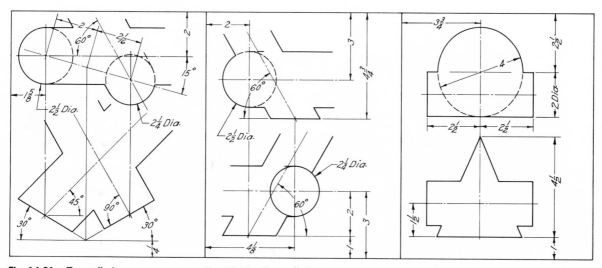

Fig. 14.81 Two cylinders.   **Fig. 14.82 Two cylinders.**   **Fig. 14.83 Cone and cylinder.**

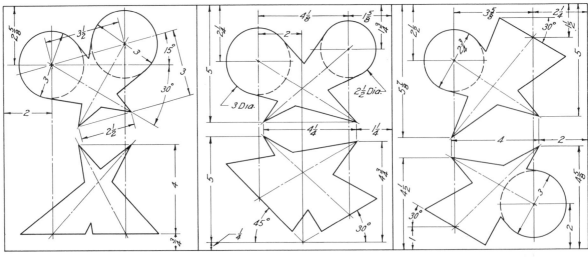

Fig. 14.84 Two cones.   **Fig. 14.85 Two cones.**   **Fig. 14.86 Two cones.**

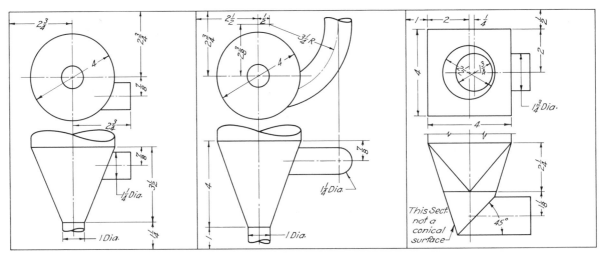

Fig. 14.87 Reducer section.   **Fig. 14.88 Reducer section.**   **Fig. 14.89 Transition section.**

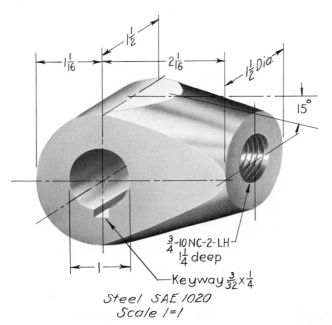

Fig. 14.90 Connecting-rod end.

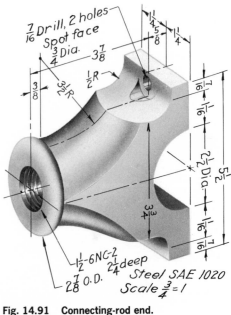

Fig. 14.91 Connecting-rod end.

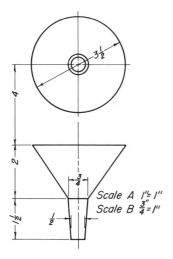

Fig. 14.92   Funnel.

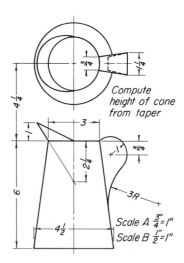

Fig. 14.93   Pitcher.

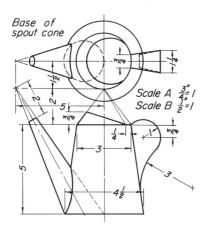

Fig. 14.94   Watering can.

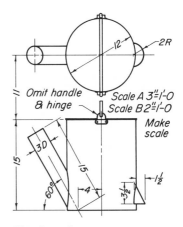

Fig. 14.95   Watering pail.

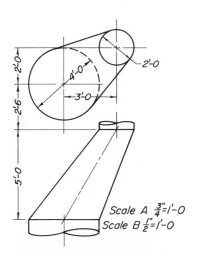

Fig. 14.96   Pipe reducer section.

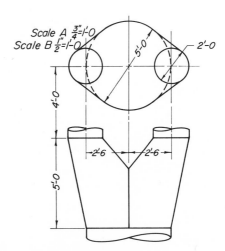

Fig. 14.97   Pipe transition section.

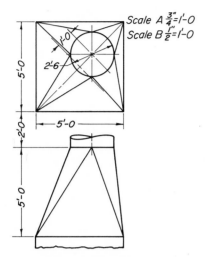

Fig. 14.98 Sheet metal transition section.

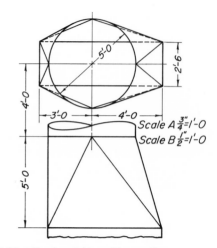

Fig. 14.99 Sheet metal transition section.

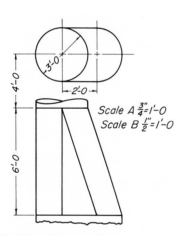

Fig. 14.100 Pipe reducer section.

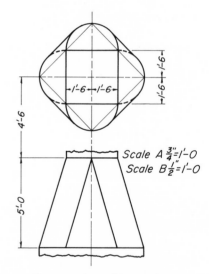

Fig. 14.101 Sheet metal transition section.

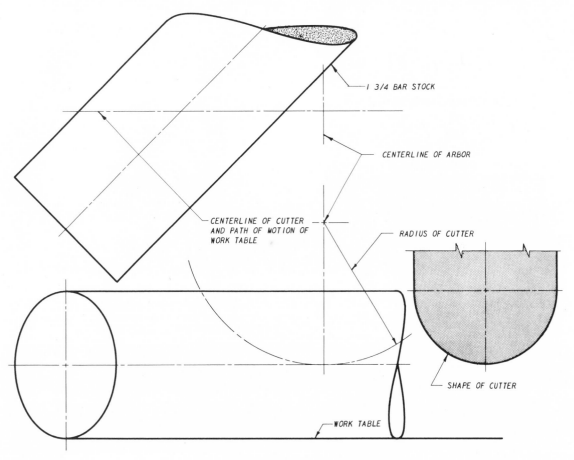

I 3/4 BAR STOCK

CENTERLINE OF ARBOR

CENTERLINE OF CUTTER
AND PATH OF MOTION OF
WORK TABLE

RADIUS OF CUTTER

SHAPE OF CUTTER

WORK TABLE

Fig. 14.102

CHAPTER 15

Axonometric Projection

OLD: American locomotive of 1870's. (The Granger Collection)

NEW: Japanese electric trains which travel up to 125 miles per hour. (© 1966, Japanese National Railways)

Chapter 15 Axonometric Projection

15.1 INTRODUCTION. The term axonometric projection or drawing includes three forms of pictorial drawing that are widely used for the illustration of catalogues, assembly diagrams, piping diagrams, and proposals for engineering projects. The three forms are isometric, dimetric, and trimetric projection.

15.2 ISOMETRIC PROJECTION BY ROTATION. An isometric projection shows three faces of an object in equal proportion, since the faces make equal angles with the plane of projection as illustrated for the cube in Fig. 15.1. The cube is in its normal position for orthographic projection in Fig. 15.1(*a*). In Fig. 15.1(*b*) it has been rotated about the vertical edge *OC* (see top view) until the sides make 45° with the vertical plane. In Fig. 15.1(*c*) the cube has been tilted up until the body diagonal is perpendicular to the vertical plane, which is sometimes referred to as the picture plane. This places the three front edges of the cube at an angle of 35° 16′ with the picture plane. The angle marked in the side view of Fig. 15.1(*c*) is the only one

to the body diagonal. The isometric views in both Figs. 15.1 and 15.2 are true projections. An examination of the two foregoing figures will show that for objects more complicated than a cube the process of making a true projection by either method would be quite tedious and time-consuming.

15.4 ISOMETRIC DRAWING COMPARED WITH ISOMETRIC PROJECTION. By observing certain facts from Figs. 15.1 and 15.2 it is possible to make a drawing that looks like an isometric projection but is not a true projection.

At this point the student should be cautioned not to permit himself to quibble over the fact that any projection is a drawing. Every illustration in this book, regardless of kind or scale or object represented, is a drawing but only certain ones are also true projections.

15.4.1 Isometric projection. In an isometric projection the lines are foreshortened in a mathematical proportion, which can be obtained graphically by any one of four methods.

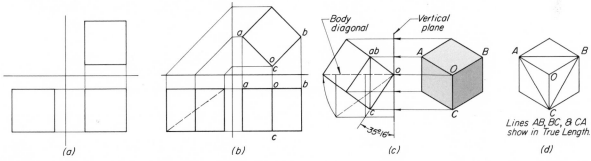

(a)   *(b)*   *(c)*   *(d)*

Fig. 15.1 Isometric view by turning cube.

that shows in true size. In the pictorial all edges project in equal length but not in the true length. Hence measurements can be made along these edges or axes at the same scale. In Fig. 15.1(*d*) the face diagonals *AB*, *BC*, and *AC* appear in true length.

15.3 ISOMETRIC PROJECTIONS BY AUXILIARY VIEWS. The same result can be more easily obtained by making an auxiliary view of a cube with the first auxiliary view parallel to the body diagonal as shown in Fig. 15.2. The second auxiliary plane is perpendicular

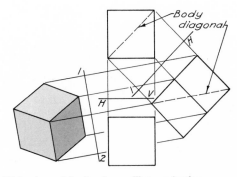

Fig. 15.2 Isometric view by auxiliary projection.

481

a. By rotation as in Fig. 15.1.

b. By auxiliary views as in Fig. 15.2.

c. By the use of an isometric scale as in Fig. 15.3.

d. By direct orthographic projection from properly placed orthographic views, as explained near the end of this chapter. See Art. 15.21.2.

Direct projections can be made from the orthographic view of an object by methods (*a*) or (*b*). Method (*c*) although possible, is quite impractical

since the isometric scales are not on the market and it is too time-consuming to make a scale like those of Fig. 15.3.

Method (*d*) is very accurate and useful for complicated objects. It is explained in Art. 15.21.

15.4.2   Isometric drawing. It is the common practice to make isometric, dimetric, and trimetric drawings rather than true projections. The axonometric drawings are made by "rule of thumb" based upon a careful study of axonometric projections. These methods are explained in the following paragraphs.

The only visual difference between isometric drawings and isometric projections is in their relative size. If an isometric drawing is constructed from a three-view orthographic drawing at the same scale as the three-view drawing, it will be 1.224 times as large as a direct projection made from the same three-view drawing. See Fig. 15.4.

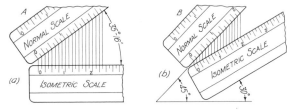

Fig. 15.3   Construction of isometric scales.

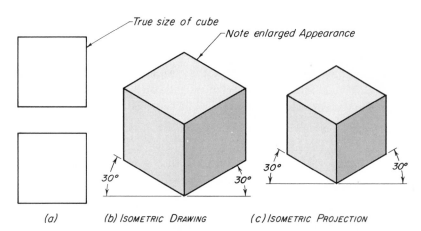

Fig. 15.4   Isometric projection and isometric drawing compared.

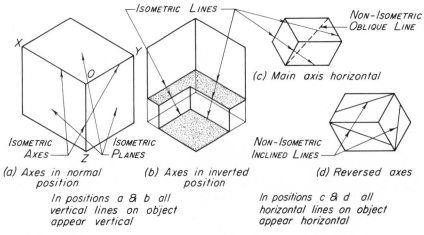

Fig. 15.5   Meaning of terms.

In the case of dimetric and trimetric drawings there is an additional factor of a slight distortion because the scales used on the three axes are usually only convenient approximations of what they should be for true projection. In appearance, however, they may be equally satisfactory.

15.5 DEFINITION OF TERMS. At this point some of the more common terms used in this chapter are defined.

Axes. In Fig. 15.5(*a*) the three edges of the cube *OX, OY,* and *OZ* are referred to as axes. Much of the construction is built around these three lines.

Axonometric. This term includes isometric, dimetric, and trimetric. In all of these, the three edges of a box that are perpendicular to each other are called axes.

Isometric. This term literally means equal measurement. Measurements along the axes are made to the same scale.

Dimetric. The word implies two scales of measurement. The same scale is used along two axes but a different one is used on the third. The construction is the same as that for isometric except that two scales are used.

Trimetric. The term implies three scales of measurement. Different scales are used on each of the three axes. The construction is the same as that for isometric except that three scales are used.

Isometric lines. Lines parallel to any one of the isometric axes. See Figs. 15.5(*b*) and (*c*).

Non-isometric lines. Any lines not parallel to one of the axes. See Figs. 15.5(*c*) and (*d*).

(*a*) Inclined—in an isometric plane but not parallel to any axis. See Fig. 15.5(*d*).

(*b*) Oblique—not in any isometric plane nor parallel to one. See Fig. 15.5(*c*).

Isometric plane. Any plane containing two isometric axes or two lines each parallel to one of two axes. See Fig. 15.5(*a*).

Nonisometric planes. It is useful to identify two types of nonisometric planes: (1) those that are inclined to two isometric planes and perpendicular to the third as in Fig. 15.6(*a*); (2) those that are oblique to all isometric planes as in Fig. 15.6(*b*).

15.6 ISOMETRIC OF PLANE FIGURES COMPOSED OF STRAIGHT LINES. The isometric drawing of a solid object consists mainly in representing three, more or less irregular plane faces, which are parallel or inclined to the faces of the isometric cube. As a prelude to the drawing of more complicated solids the construction of plane figures in isometric is presented first.

15.6.1 Details of constructing a plane figure. The construction proceeds as follows:

a. In Fig. 15.7(*a*), an irregular seven-sided figure is shown in true shape.

b. In Fig. 15.7(*b*), this figure has been enclosed in a rectangle and the coordinates of the corners of the figure relative to the box have been indicated.

c. In Figs. 15.7(*c*) and (*d*), an isometric of the rectangle has been made in two different positions in order to show more than one arrangement.

d. Locate the points *m, o, p, q, r* and *s* that lie in the edges of the rectangle. This is done by transferring the distances such as *1, 5, 4, 7,* and *8* from Fig. 15.7(*b*) to both isometric rectangles on the proper sides.

e. Locate the corner *n* by transferring the distances *3* and *6* to the sides of the rectangle. Then draw isometric lines across the figure until they intersect at *n*.

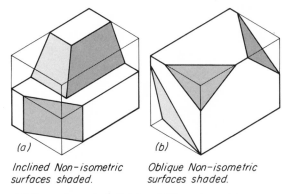

(a) Inclined Non-isometric surfaces shaded.

(b) Oblique Non-isometric surfaces shaded.

White surfaces in both (a) and (b) are isometric

Fig. 15.6 Definition of terms.

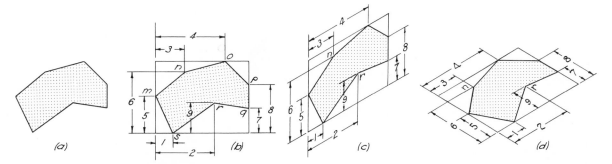

Fig. 15.7 Construction of plane figures in isometric.

f. Repeat the process for point *r* using distances *2* and *9* as shown in Figs. 15.6(*c*) and (*d*).

g. Connect the plotted points.

15.6.2 Angles in isometric. It should be noted that angles cannot be drawn at their true value in isometric drawing. Two points must be used. One may be assumed and the other laid out by coordinates from the first. For angles of 15, 30, 45, and 60° the values of the sine and tangent may be used to plot the points as shown in Fig. 15.8.

15.7 CIRCLES AND CURVES IN ISOMETRIC. A circle will appear as an ellipse in isometric. Several methods of constructing an ellipse in isometric are

available. Some are exact and some approximate. Coordinate methods are exact.

15.7.1 Isometric of circles. Coordinate method 1. A circle may be constructed by the coordinate method as shown in Fig. 15.9. The procedure is as follows:

a. Divide the circle into 12 equal parts with a 30–60° triangle as shown in Fig. 15.9(*b*).

b. Enclose the circle in a square as shown in Fig. 15.9(*c*) and draw horizontal and vertical lines through the points on the circle to determine the coordinates of each point.

c. Draw the isometric square as shown in Fig. 15.9(*d*). Note that the horizontal coordinate lines have been extended across from the circle in Fig. 15.9(*c*).

d. Draw the vertical coordinates by transferring distances *a*, *b*, *c*, etc., from the circle in Fig. 15.9(*c*) to the parallelogram as shown in Fig. 15.9(*e*).

e. The intersection of the coordinates locates points *1*, *2*, *3*, etc., on the ellipse.

f. Draw a smooth curve through the points.

15.7.2 Isometric of circles and curves. Coordinate method 2. Another very convenient method of drawing an ellipse that represents a circle in isometric or any kind of projection is illustrated in Fig. 15.9(*f*).

a. First draw a parallelogram which is the projection of a square circumscribing the circle.

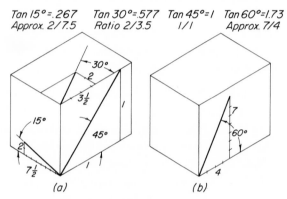

Tan 15°=.267 Tan 30°=.577 Tan 45°=1 Tan 60°=1.73
Approx. 2/7.5 Ratio 2/3.5 1/1 Approx. 7/4

Fig. 15.8 Angles in isometric.

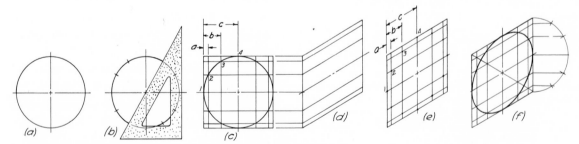

Fig. 15.9 Construction of a circle in isometric by the coordinate method.

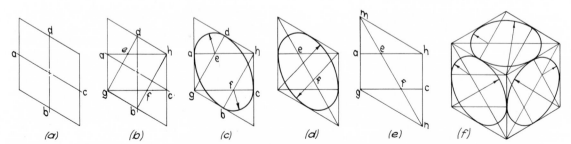

Fig. 15.10 Four-center method of constructing a circle in isometric.

b. Then draw a semicircle, using one of the sides of the parallelogram as a diameter.

c. Divide the semicircle into an even number of parts and project them perpendicularly to the side of the parallelogram.

d. From these points draw lines in the parallelogram parallel to the adjacent side.

e. Draw a diagonal of the parallelogram.

f. Draw lines from the points of intersection of the diagonal, parallel to the side of the parallelogram on which the semicircle is drawn.

g. The intersections of those two sets of parallel lines give points on the isometric of the circle. This method may be used in any type of pictorial drawing.

15.7.3 Isometric of circles by the four-center approximate method. An approximate isometric of a circle may be drawn by the method shown in Fig. 15.10. This construction depends on the fact that *the center of a circle which is tangent to a straight line lies on the perpendicular to the line at the point of tangency.* Hence if we erect perpendiculars at the midpoints *a, b, c,* and *d* of the sides of the isometric square, as in Fig. 15.10(*b*), these perpendiculars will intersect in pairs, thus locating the centers of the four arcs, *e, f, g,* and *h,* as in Fig. 15.10(*c*). This will approximate the

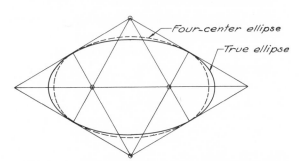

Fig. 15.11   True ellipse and four-center ellipse compared.

correct ellipse. It will be noted that in isometric two of these centers lie on the corners of the square and the other two lie on the long diagonal. Use of these facts enables the draftsman to shorten the construction considerably by drawing only the lines *ah, gc,* and *mn,* as in Fig. 15.10(*e*). This construction can be used in any isometric face of a cube, as illustrated in Fig. 15.10(*f*). The method involves less labor than the coordinate method and is sufficiently accurate for most isometric work. This approximate ellipse has a shorter major axis and longer minor axis than the true ellipse, as shown in Fig. 15.11.

15.7.4 True-diameter four-center method. A careful examination of Fig. 15.1(*d*) will indicate that the diagonals of the faces of a cube project in true length because they are parallel to the isometric plane or plane of projection. This construction, which produces a more accurate ellipse than the standard four-center method, is based on this fact. Only the location of the center and the size of diameter need be known. The construction is as follows:

a. Through the center *E* draw a 30° line as *MN* in Fig. 15.12(*a*) and mark off the diameter to the scale being used for the isometric drawing, as at *M* and *N.*

b. Through *E* draw a 45° line *PO* as in Fig. 15.12(*a*). Note the similarity between *PO* and the normal scale in Fig. 15.3(*b*).

c. At *M* and *N* erect vertical lines until they cross the 45° line at *O* and *P.*

d. With center at *E* and radius *EO* or *EP* draw arcs to the vertical line at *A* and *B.* See Fig. 15.12(*b*). These points are two of the centers for the arcs of the ellipse.

e. From *A* and *B* draw 60° lines until they touch the sides of the isometric square near (but not at) *M* and *N.* Note that the square is not essential to the

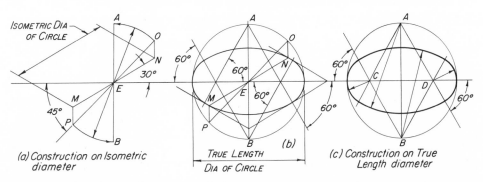

Fig. 15.12   True-diameter four-center method.

construction. It has been drawn to show that the tangent points of the arcs are not at the exact centers of the sides of the square.

f. In Fig. 15.12(c), the intersection of the four 60° lines locates the two other centers C and D on the major axis of the ellipse, which is in true length. The minor axis is also correct.

15.7.5 Isometric of irregular curves. In Fig. 15.13, a section of an ogee molding is shown in orthographic and then in isometric. The coordinates to be used are shown in both the orthographic and the isometric. These may be transferred with dividers. The second curve is made parallel to the first by offsets as noted.

15.7.6 Limitation of the four-center approximate method. The four-center method may be used for tangent circles or arcs only when they are tangent to each other at the midpoint of the sides of their enclosing rectangles, as shown in Fig. 15.14(a). If the tangency points occur at other places, the circles will overlap or miss, as shown in Fig. 15.14(b), because of their departure from the true ellipse. In such cases the coordinate method should be used or other approximations made.

The four-center method may be used in pictorial forms other than isometric but only when the scale on the two adjacent sides of the enclosing square is the same. Thus it can be used in the following cases:

a. In dimetric in one face only.
b. Not at all in trimetric.
c. Only in the cavalier form of oblique projection.

15.7.7 Accuracy of the true diameter method. The ellipse construction shown in Fig. 15.12 and applied to three tangent circles in Fig. 15.15 indicates very little error. The departure from the true ellipse is no more than those produced by normal instrumental drawing, when compared with points plotted by the coordinate method.

15.8 ISOMETRIC DRAWING OF SOLIDS. BOX METHOD. From the drawing of plane figures to the drawing of solid objects in isometric is but a simple step, involving only the use of a third coordinate distance. The steps in the procedure are as follows:

a. Draw the orthographic views of the object to the same scale as that to be used on the isometric.
b. Enclose the views in the smallest enclosing rectangular box.
c. Draw the enclosing box in isometric in the position that will best reveal the shape of the object, making the three edges at 120° with each other.
d. Draw the simple parts of the object that lie in or adjacent to the faces of the box.
e. Plot the curves and interior points, if any, by the coordinate method.
f. It is the usual practice to omit all invisible lines in pictorial drawing.

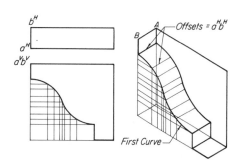

Fig. 15.13 Curves by the coordinate method.

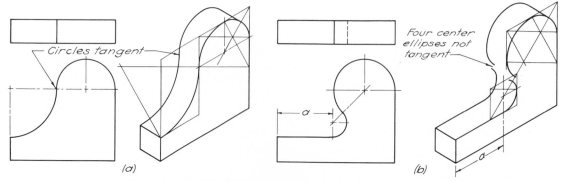

Fig. 15.14 Limitations of the four-center approximate method.

15.8.1   Isometric of a block. Box method of construction.

An isometric drawing of the block, shown by three orthographic views in Fig. 15.16(a), may be readily constructed in the following manner. The first step as outlined above consists of enclosing the orthographic views of the object in the smallest rectangular box that will just enclose it as shown by the light lines of Fig. 15.16(a). This box serves as a reference frame from which dimensions can be measured in the orthographic views and plotted in the isometric.

The second step consists of drawing the isometric of the enclosing box in the position desired, as shown in Fig. 15.16(b). Here the front orthographic view has been made the left face. The various parts that have been cut out of the block can now be cut from the isometric box in any order desired. Thus, in Fig. 15.16(c), the distance $(a^H$-1) on the top view has been measured on the same line, AC, in the isometric and the distance $(a^H$-2) along the line AB. The diagonal line 1-2 can now be drawn in the isometric view. From the points 1 and 2 in the isometric, vertical lines can be dropped to the bottom of the box and then the diagonal in the bottom face can be drawn.

In a similar manner the other cutouts can be transferred by direct measurement from the orthographic to the isometric, as illustrated in Figs. 15.16(d) and (e). It should be carefully noted that in all cases measurements are made *on or parallel to the three isometric axes.* They can be made in no other manner for no other lines are foreshortened in the same ratio as these lines.

15.8.2   Solids involving nonisometric lines.

As a second illustration, the construction of a truncated hexagonal pyramid is shown. This object has only two isometric lines. The remainder are all nonisometric. In Fig. 15.17(a), the object is shown enclosed in a rectangular box; in Fig. 15.17(b), the box has been drawn in isometric and the hexagonal base is shown in the bottom of the box. The measurements a and b for constructing this plane figure are obtained from the top view, as shown in the figure.

Whenever an object has a plane of symmetry, advantage should be taken of this fact to speed construction. Hence, in Fig. 15.17(c), the central plane of symmetry has been established and the two points 2 and 9 located in it to give the center line of the truncated face (2-9). For example, point 2 is located by measuring the coordinate 1-2 in the central plane as indicated. Point 9 is located by going up along the center line from 0 to 9, using the distance 0-9 in the front view. Points 3, 4, and 5 are located by taking the measurements (1-3), (1-4), and (1-5) from the top or front views. By dropping perpendiculars from 3, 4, and 5 to

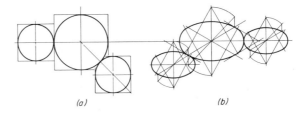

(a)   (b)

Fig. 15.15   Tangent circles by the true-diameter four-center method.

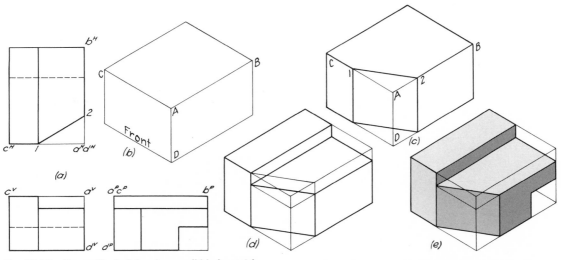

Fig. 15.16   Box method of drawing a solid in isometric.

the center line (*2-9*), points *6, 7,* and *8* are located as shown in Fig. 15.17(*c*). Isometric horizontal lines can then be drawn through points *6* and *7*. Points *10* and *11* can be located by stepping off from point *6* on these lines the distances (*6-10*) and (*6-11*), which are equal. A similar procedure locates points *12* and *13* as shown in Fig. 15.17(*d*). All these measurements are taken from the top view. The six points in the truncated face are then connected to form the sloping truncated face. The corners of this face are then joined to the corresponding corners of the base, thus completing the isometric as shown in Fig. 15.17(*e*). It is customary in isometric drawing, as in all other pictorials, to omit hidden lines unless they are necessary to make clear the shape of the object. *Note again that all measurements were taken on or parallel to isometric lines.*

15.9 SOLID OBJECTS INVOLVING CIRCLES. The objects illustrated thus far have been composed entirely of straight lines. Many objects, however, involve circles either singly or in groups. The following suggestions will assist in speeding construction and in avoiding common errors.

15.9.1 Parallel circles or other curves. In actual drawing, circles nearly always occur in pairs. Since rapidity in construction is always important, the suggestions for speeding the layout of circles parallel to each other, as shown in Fig. 15.18, are valuable.

In the four-center method the centers for the first circles are found in the usual way. Circles parallel to the first may be quickly found by drawing isometric lines from the original four centers and stepping off on them the distance between the circles, to locate the new centers, as shown in Fig. 15.18.

The same scheme may be used for a curve plotted by the coordinate method, as shown in Fig. 15.19, for a noncircular curve. One curve is drawn in the usual way, and isometric lines are drawn from the plotted points. Each successive curve may be stepped off with one setting of the divider.

15.9.2 Common errors in drawing circles. Two common errors are frequently made by the student in drawing circles on various objects. One of these consists of drawing the circle out of the proper isometric plane, as shown in Fig. 15.20(*a*). This can be avoided by making sure that the sides of the enclosing parallelogram are parallel to the isometric lines of the plane in which the circle lies, as shown for the circle in the lower face of the object in Fig. 15.20(*a*).

A second error occurs in the drawing of short cylinders or cylindrical parts where the student fails to put in the isometric tangent line between the circles, as shown in Fig. 15.20(*b*). The far side of small holes is omitted many times.

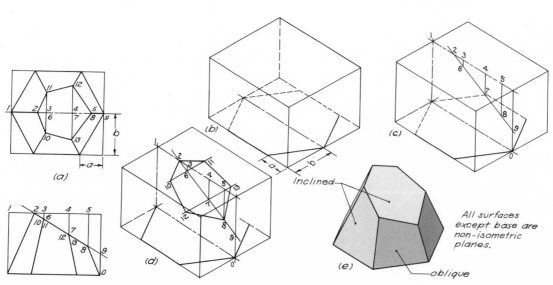

Fig. 15.17 Truncated pyramid in isometric by the box method.

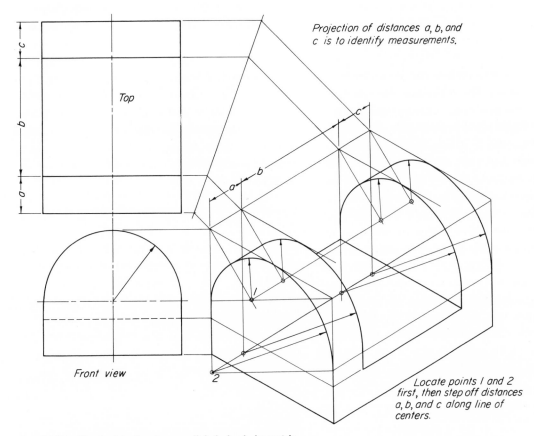

Projection of distances *a, b,* and
c is to identify measurements.

Locate points *1* and *2*
first, then step off distances
a, b, and *c* along line of
centers.

Fig. 15.18   Shortcut in drawing parallel circles in isometric.

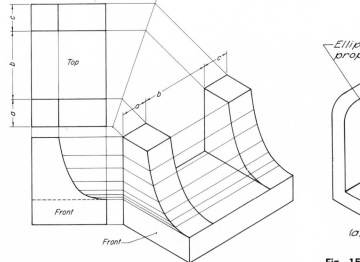

Fig. 15.19   Shortcut in drawing parallel curves in isometric.

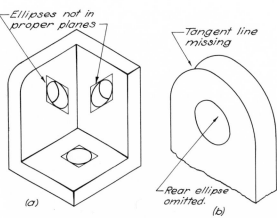

**Fig. 15.20   Common errors made in drawing circles in
isometric.**

15.10 USE OF ISOMETRIC PLANES IN CONSTRUCTION. The simple bearing bracket shown in Fig. 15.21(a) will serve to illustrate further the method of construction, which has again been broken down into a series of successive steps, following the method previously suggested. Figure 15.21(a) shows the orthographic views enclosed in a box. Figure 15.21(b) shows the box in isometric with the base and cylindrical bearing partly completed. The circles are drawn in their proper planes by the four-center method based on the enclosing rectangles, which are shown.

In an object of this kind, considerable time can be saved by noting that much of the construction falls naturally into isometric planes. To plot the vertical and sloping webs, a series of horizontal planes d, e, f, etc., are drawn in the orthographic views locating points 1 to 12 on the curves. In Fig. 15.21(c), the end view of the vertical web is drawn in the end of the isometric box, and on it the points d, e, f, etc., are located by measurements (0-d), (0-c), etc. From these points d, e, f, etc., isometric horizontal lines are drawn and measurements (d-1), (e-2), etc., made on them, thus

locating points 1, 2, 3, etc., on the curve, which can then be drawn as in Fig. 15.21(c).

The *front view of the sloping web* is next constructed in the right face of the isometric box, as shown in Fig. 15.21(d). It is a simple matter to carry the m, n, o, p horizontal planes around the box from d, e, etc., to locate the points (5, 6, 9, and 10), etc. From these points horizontal lines can be drawn in isometric, and the distances (m-5), (n-6), etc., obtained from the three-view drawing in Fig. 15.21(a), can be measured on them, thus establishing points 5, 6, 7, etc. The other curves may be found in a similar manner. The completed drawing with all construction removed is shown in Fig. 15.21(e).

15.10.1 Use of isometric cutting planes in finding the intersection of a plane and cylinder. In Fig. 15.22 a right circular cylinder is shown inside a box having an oblique plane for its top face. The intersection of the top with the cylinder can be found as follows:

a. Draw the circle of the base by any suitable method in the bottom of the box.

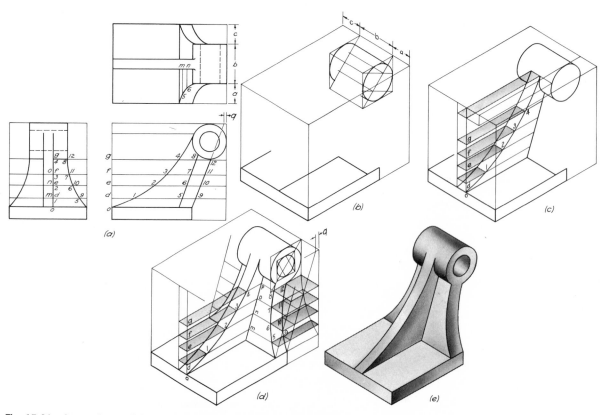

Fig. 15.21 Layout in parallel isometric planes that speeds construction.

b. Draw a series of well-spaced lines across the bottom of the box locating points *1* to *12* on the circle.

c. From points such as *m, n, o, p,* where the lines drawn in (*b*) above cross the bottom of the box, erect perpendiculars and then connect them across the top.

d. Erect perpendiculars from the points like *12* and *2* on the circle until they cross the lines in the top, like line *jt* on the top.

e. A smooth curve through the points in the oblique top gives the curve of intersection.

15.11 INTERSECTION OF CYLINDERS IN ISO-METRIC. The intersections of three cylinders shown in Fig. 15.23 illustrate in another manner the use of cutting planes in isometric construction.

Figure 15.23(*a*) shows the two orthographic views of the cylinders with the end circles divided into 12 equal parts and cutting planes shown by light solid lines cutting across the three cylinders in the top view. The elements cut from each cylinder are shown in the front view. The intersection of these elements determines the curve of intersection.

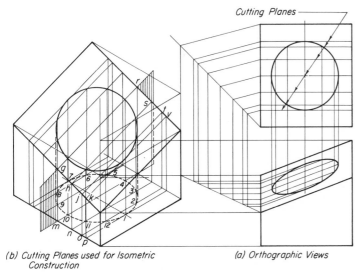

(*b*) Cutting Planes used for Isometric Construction

(*a*) Orthographic Views

Fig. 15.22 Intersection of an oblique plane with a cylinder using isometric cutting planes.

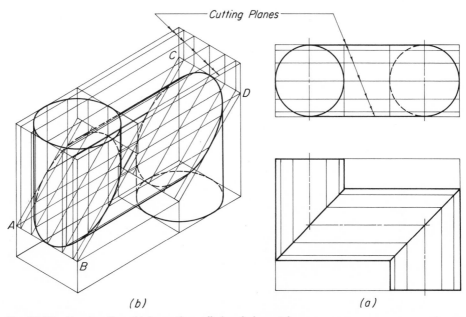

(*b*)

(*a*)

Fig. 15.23 Construction of intersecting cylinders in isometric.

The construction is as follows:

a. Draw the enclosing box in isometric as shown in Fig. 15.23(*b*).

b. Lay out the boxes enclosing each of the two vertical cylinders and the two sloping planes of intersection as shown in Fig. 15.23(*b*).

c. Draw the ellipse for the top of the left vertical cylinder by the true-diameter four-center method of Fig. 15.15 or the four-center approximate method.

d. Locate the cutting planes in the top of the box.

e. Draw the elements of the left-hand cylinder as located by the cutting plane.

f. Carry these elements down to the plane of intersection.

g. The intersection of these elements with the inclined plane is found where the cutting plane line in the inclined plane intersects the elements.

h. Note that the continuous cutting plane lines are carried:

    (1) down the side of the box to line *AB*,

    (2) then up the inclined plane,

    (3) across the top and bottom of the box to the back side,

    (4) down the back to line *CD*,

    (5) then down the inclined plane at the right;

    (6) thus the lines cut by any one plane can be traced throughout the entire system and all intersections can be found.

i. Draw the visible part of the curve of intersection.

j. Draw the elements of the horizontal cylinder over to the sloping plane of the right-hand intersection.

k. Draw the visible portion of the lower ellipse for the right end cylinder by the same four-center method used in step (*c*) above.

l. Complete the figure.

15.12 CONSTRUCTION BY CENTER LINE LAYOUT. The box method of construction discussed in preceding paragraphs may be used for any type of object. However, when the object consists of a number of circular faces lying in the same or parallel planes, the

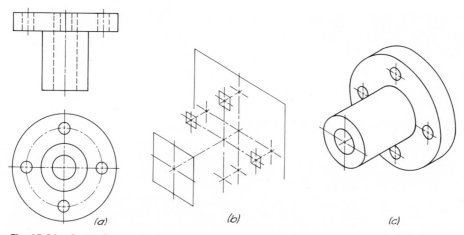

(*a*)   (*b*)   (*c*)

Fig. 15.24 Center-line method of constructing cylindrical objects in isometric.

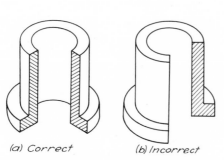

(*a*) Correct   (*b*) Incorrect

Fig. 15.25 Sectional views in isometric.

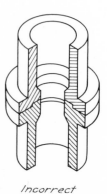

Incorrect

Fig. 15.26 Incorrect crosshatching.

center line layout shown in Fig. 15.24 is a convenient and rapid method of construction. In Fig. 15.24(*a*) the orthographic views are shown, and in Fig. 15.24(*b*) the isometric layout of the principal center lines are drawn. In Fig. 15.24(*b*) the parallelograms for some of the circles are drawn, and in Fig. 15.24(*c*) the drawing is completed.

In general, center lines for holes and cylinders will be shown so far as they do not make the drawing more difficult to read.

15.13   SECTIONAL VIEWS IN ISOMETRIC. The interior construction of complicated objects is best

shown by sectional views. Half and full sections may be made by removing one fourth or one half of the object, respectively. The cutting planes should always be isometric planes as shown in Fig. 15.25(*a*). In a half section the crosshatching lines should be drawn in a position to give the effect of coincidence if the two sectioned faces were revolved together. Correct and incorrect examples are given in Figs. 15.25 and 15.26 to illustrate this point. No new principles of construction are involved in making section views.

The step-by-step construction of a sectional view is shown in Fig. 15.27. By beginning with the sectioned

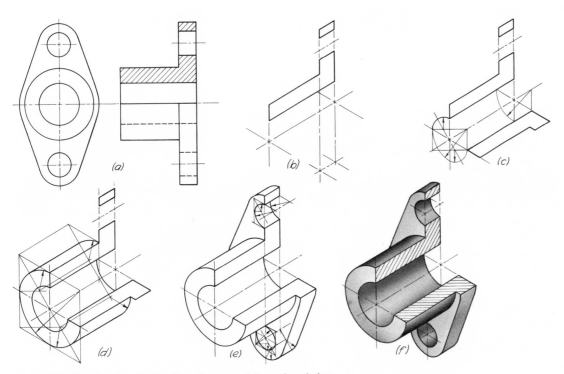

Fig. 15.27   Step-by-step construction of an isometric sectioned view.

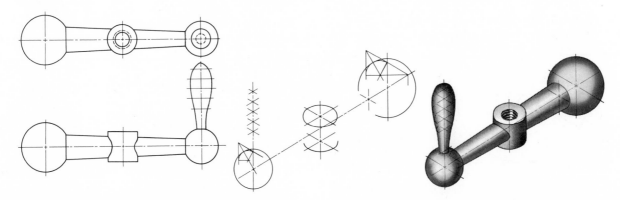

Fig. 15.28   Construction of object with curved surfaces.

parts, as shown in Figs. 15.27(b) and (c), a minimum number of construction lines need be used. Careful study of the figure will show the procedure. The finished sectional drawing is shown in Fig. 15.27(f).

15.14   SPHERES AND OTHER CURVED PARTS IN ISOMETRIC. Spherical parts occur on pieces of machinery and can readily be drawn in isometric. The sphere appears as a true circle. A simple lever involving spheres and curved handle is shown in Fig. 15.28.

In some objects, such as gears and conveyors, it is desirable to divide a circle into a large number of equal parts. This must be accomplished first in the orthographic layout and then transferred to the isometric, using the outlines of the isometric square as shown in Fig. 15.29. Isometric protractors are on the market, and where such an instrument is available, it may be

used to make the divisions directly in the isometric.

15.15   ISOMETRIC OF DOUBLE-CURVED SURFACES. On some objects, such as the pipe return bend shown in Fig. 15.30, an enveloping curve representing the outstanding contour of the object must be drawn. This curve does not lie in a single plane, hence it cannot be constructed by plotting points in the usual way.

Since a sphere projects as a circle in isometric, a simple method of making this, or any similar construction, is shown in Fig. 15.30(a). A series of spheres may be imagined lying in the bend just tangent to it. The centers of five or six of these spheres may be located on the isometric of the center line circle, as shown in the illustration by points a, b, etc. Next the size of the isometric sphere is obtained, as shown in Fig. 15.30(b), by making the circle tangent to the isometric ellipse. Only

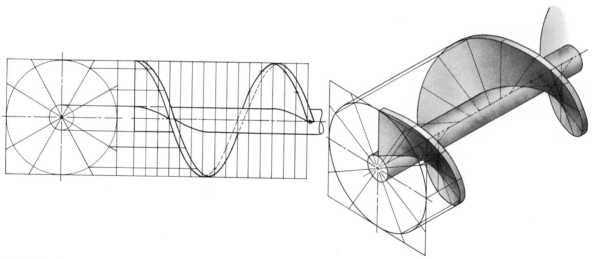

Fig. 15.29   Construction of a right helicoid in isometric.

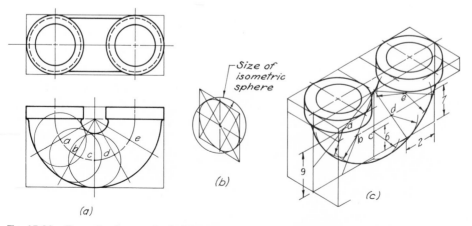

Fig. 15.30   Tangent sphere method of drawing a double-curved surface.

the major axis of the ellipse needs to be drawn to determine the diameter of the spheres. With the radius thus determined, the arcs and a smooth curve tangent to them may be drawn.

15.16 SCREW THREADS IN ISOMETRIC. Screw threads could be accurately drawn in isometric, but the process is so laborious that a conventional scheme which is quite satisfactory has been adopted. Arcs of a series of parallel circles are used to represent the crest lines only because the root lines need not be shown. Any method of drawing the circles may be used, but the construction for the four-center approximate method is illustrated in Fig. 15.31.

Because of symmetry of construction, Square threads and Acme threads cannot be clearly shown in isometric. Dimetric or trimetric layouts are much more suitable for this purpose.

15.17 POSITION OF ISOMETRIC AXES. Thus far we have considered isometric drawing with the object always in one position. The three axes, however, may be drawn in an infinite number of positions so long as

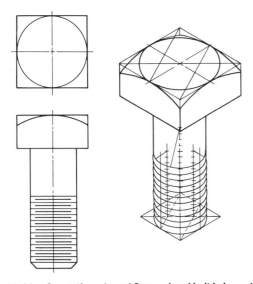

Fig. 15.31   Screw threads and Square head bolt in isometric.

they always make equal angles with each other. Four easily drawn positions, as shown for the object and enclosing box in Fig. 15.32, are most commonly used.

The choice of the position of these axes will depend on the nature of the object. When the top and sides of the object contain most of the details, the position used thus far is best. If, on the other hand, the bottom contains the more important details, the position of Fig. 15.32(*b*) is by far the best. The object should, of course, be shown in the natural or normal position if it has one.

15.18 ADVANTAGES OF ISOMETRIC. As compared with two- and three-view orthographic projections, isometric has the advantage of showing three sides of the object in one view, thus giving a more realistic picture of it.

As compared with other forms of pictorial drawing, isometric has the advantage of being easily constructed since the same scale is used on all sides. Circles can be readily approximated by the four-center method. It can be scaled and dimensioned. It is flexible in the position in which an object may be shown but not as flexible as other types, particularly oblique projection described in a later chapter. Circles are not distorted as in oblique and sometimes in perspective.

Against these advantages may be placed definite disadvantages that limit its usefulness in certain situations. Long objects with parallel sides show a disagreeable distortion since the eye is accustomed to the perspective effect of long parallel lines that appear to approach each other. There is also an exactness of symmetry causing an overlaying of lines in some symmetrical objects, which makes the isometric difficult to read.

15.19 DIMENSIONING ISOMETRIC DRAWINGS. For shop purposes, other than assembly work, an isometric drawing must be dimensioned. The regular rules and suggestions for dimensioning two- or three-view working drawings hold for isometric drawing in a

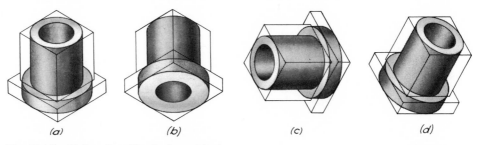

(a)   (b)   (c)   (d)

Fig. 15.32   Choice of position for isometric views.

general way, but in addition the following rules must be observed.

15.19.1 Pictorial plane dimensioning. Dimensions on isometric drawings should be placed in such a way that they can be read from one point of view, which should be from the bottom of the sheet. This may be said to encompass all other rules in regard to the direction on which dimensions should read, and it is the only safe one to follow at all times. It is best to dimension the visible faces.

a. All dimension lines must be isometric lines and lie in isometric planes. This point must be carefully observed. Difficulty usually occurs in objects having nonisometric lines. Figure 15.33(*a*) illustrates a very common error. The dimension line and the two witness lines do not lie in an isometric plane even though the dimension line is vertical. Figure 15.33(*b*) illustrates the correct method.

b. Figures and lettering of notes should be made to lie in isometric planes. Only vertical-style lettering should be used in isometric. Figure 15.34 shows how the parallelogram enclosing a letter or figure may be used as an aid in isometric lettering. The front views of the small cubes show the letters and their enclosing parallelograms orthographically; the two isometrics of the cubes show the six possible positions in which these parallelograms and figures may appear. Figure 15.35 illustrates the dimensioning of a rectangular object, placing the numerals in one or another of the positions shown in Fig. 15.34.

15.19.2 Unidirectional dimensioning. The United States of America Standards Institute has recently approved the placing of all dimensions and notes in one plane, as illustrated in Fig. 15.36. When using this system, only vertical letters or numerals should be employed. This method is simple and more rapid for production purposes.

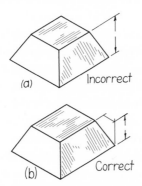

Fig. 15.33 Dimension lines in isometric planes.

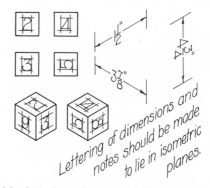

Fig. 15.34 Lettering and numerals in isometric.

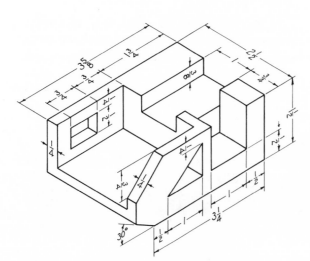

Fig. 15.35 Aligned system of dimensioning.

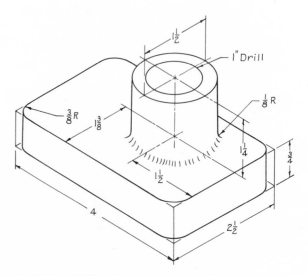

Fig. 15.36 Unidirection system of dimensioning.

15.20   DIMETRIC DRAWING. Somewhat the same distinction exists between dimetric projection and dimetric drawing as obtained between isometric projection and isometric drawing, namely, that scales approximating the projected scales are used in making the drawing. In Fig. 15.37(*a*) the conventional cube has been shown rotated from the position for isometric projection to a convenient dimetric position. The dimetric projection is shown in (*b*).

In Fig. 15.38, four convenient positions for the dimetric axes are illustrated, with the approximate proportion of angles and scales for each axis indicated. The construction in conventional dimetric is carried on in the same manner as in isometric, except that on one axis the scale is changed. The simplest way of making a dimetric drawing is to proceed in the following manner.

15.20.1   Construction of a dimetric drawing. For the construction of Fig. 15.39 the axes have been chosen in the position of Fig. 15.38(*c*). The scale on the vertical edge and the left receding axis is full-size. The

scale on the right receding axis is as shown, namely, ⅝ of the full scale used on the front face. The construction is as follows:

a. Make the orthographic views to the scale desired for the two equal dimetric axes and then enclose the views in the smallest possible rectangular box, as shown in Fig. 15.39.

b. Draw the box in the desired dimetric position by transferring overall dimensions with dividers directly from the orthographic views for the equal axes and to the proper scale for the third axis. The scale to be used for this third axis is shown in Fig. 15.39 at the left side of the top view. In this case the scale on the short axis was made ⅝ that of the other axes.

c. Plot points locating the corners and curves of the object just as in isometric, taking care to use the proper scale.

d. *It should be noted that the four-center method of drawing circles can be used only in the face having equal scales on both sides.*

15.21   TRUE AXONOMETRIC PROJECTION. A simple method of making true axonometric projections was published by Theodor Schmid in 1922 and L. Eckhart in 1937. This method was presented in the United States by the authors in 1942 and has since been widely used. The method is applicable to isometric, dimetric, and trimetric projections and is particularly useful when orthographic views of an object are available. The question of scale on the various axes is automatically determined.

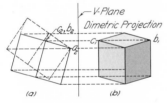

Fig. 15.37   Dimetric projection by rotation.

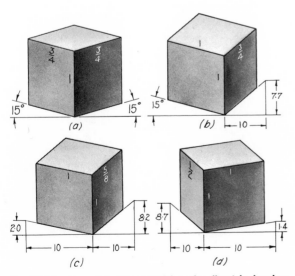

Fig. 15.38   Four convenient positions for dimetric drawing.

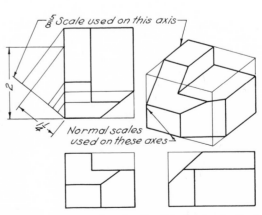

Fig. 15.39   Construction of a dimetric drawing by the box method.

15.21.1 Definition of terms. An axonometric projection may be defined as an orthographic projection upon a plane oblique to the three principal planes, as shown in Fig. 15.40. The object represented is usually assumed to have its principal faces parallel to the three principal planes of projection. Three types of views or projections may be obtained by varying the position of the axonometric plane. *When this plane makes equal angles with the principal planes, an isometric projection results.* The axes, or edges of the cube, are therefore equally foreshortened and make angles of 120° with each other in the projection.

When the axonometric plane is equally inclined to two of the principal planes, a dimetric projection is produced. Two of the axes project equally and the third is foreshortened by a different amount. In this case two of the angles between the axes are equal, whereas the third is different.

When the plane is unequally inclined to all three principal planes, a trimetric projection results. When this happens, the axes are all foreshortened by different amounts and the angles between the axes are all unequal. In no case can any of these angles be 90° or less.

15.21.2 Theory of axonometric projections. In Fig. 15.41, the position of the axonometric plane relative to the three principal planes is shown pictorially for each of the three types of projection. In each case the picture plane coincides with the axonometric plane. Therefore the axonometric triangle in each drawing is true-size. The relative positions of the three principal views and the axonometric view are also

shown. It should be noted at the beginning that *axonometric projection as here discussed is orthographic projection, that is, the projection lines are perpendicular to the plane of projection.* The basic principles of orthographic projection are involved in an understanding of axonometric projection. These principles are illustrated in the step-by-step solution in Art. 15.22.

a. If a point is projected orthographically upon any two intersecting planes, as in Fig. 15.42, the two projections, when one of the planes is revolved into coincidence with the other, fall on a line which is perpendicular to the line of intersection of the two planes. Thus in Fig. 15.42, the two projections o^H and $o_r{}^A$ lie on the same perpendicular to AB.

In Figs. 15.43 and 15.44, the three principal

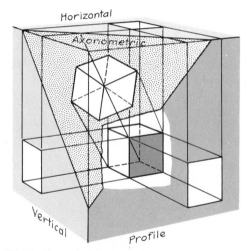

Fig. 15.40 Exact theory of isometric projection.

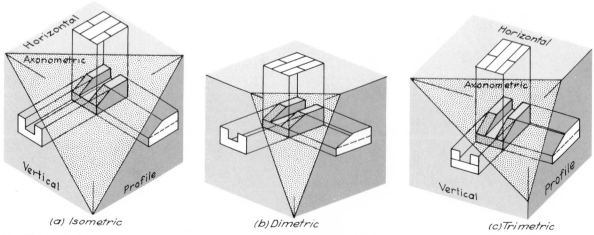

Fig. 15.41 Position of axonometric plane for isometric, dimetric, and trimetric projection.

planes, together with the projections of an object on them, have been revolved into the plane of the axonometric triangle. From Fig. 15.45, it can be seen that the axonometric projection can be obtained by direct projection from any two of the three revolved views.

b. The projecting lines are always perpendicular to the axis of rotation, which is the edge of the axonometric plane.

c. In each case, the revolved positions of the orthographic views have their principal edges parallel to the edges of the corresponding revolved plane.

d. One other geometric principle is involved. If three mutually perpendicular lines, for example, three intersecting edges of a cube, ox, oy, and oz, in Fig. 15.43(a), are made to pass through the three corners of a triangle, xyz, the projections of these lines on the triangle will be perpendicular to the side opposite the corner through which the line passes. That is, ox will be perpendicular to yz, oy will be perpendicular to xz, and oz will be perpendicular to xy. This is shown in Fig. 15.43(a).

e. Finally, in order to determine the position of right triangle XOY, of Fig. 15.43(b), when revolved into the plane XYZ, it is necessary to use the geometric principle that any two lines drawn from the ends of a diameter of a circle to a point on the circumference make a right angle with each other. Then, since it is known that the angle XOY is a right angle, its true size must show where the plane has been revolved into the axonometric plane that has been set up to show in its true size.

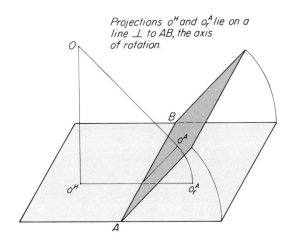

Fig. 15.42 Orthographic projection of a point on an inclined plane.

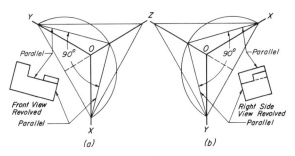

Fig. 15.44 Rotation of coordinate planes into the axonometric plane.

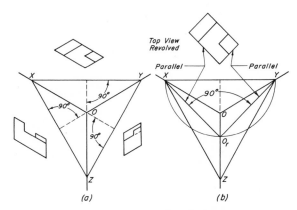

Fig. 15.43 Axonometric triangle for isometric projection.

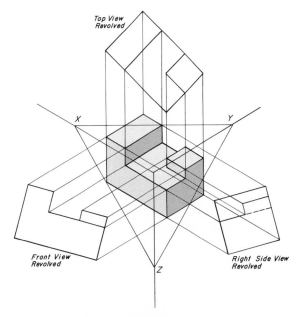

Fig. 15.45 Axonometric projection of a solid.

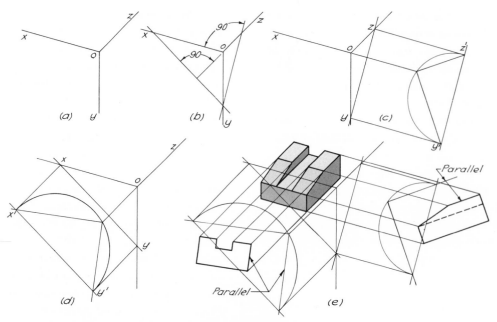

Fig. 15.46 Step-by-step construction of a trimetric projection.

15.22 CONSTRUCTING AN ISOMETRIC PROJEC-TION. Making use of the principles outlined in the preceding article, an isometric projection may be made as shown in Figs. 15.43, 15.44, and 15.45.

a. Draw the equilateral triangle XYZ that represents the isometric plane as in Figs. 15.43(a) and (b).

b. With XY as a diameter draw the semicircle XO_rY. The point O has thus been revolved into the isometric plane at O_r, making a right angle XO_rY.

c. Draw the orthographic top view with the edges of the view respectively parallel to the lines O_rX and O_rY as shown in Fig. 15.43(b).

d. Follow the same procedure as given in (b) and (c) to obtain the position of the orthographic front view as shown in Fig. 15.44(a).

e. Follow the same procedure as in (b) and (c) to obtain the position of the orthographic side view as in Fig. 15.44(b).

f. Having the three orthographic views located as in Fig. 15.45, draw projecting lines from each view perpendicular to the corresponding edge of the isometric plane.

g. Find the intersection of these projectors as shown in Fig. 15.45 to obtain the isometric projection of the object.

15.23 CONSTRUCTING A TRIMETRIC PROJEC-TION. Having these principles in mind, a step-by-step construction for making a trimetric projection may be made as follows. See Fig. 15.46.

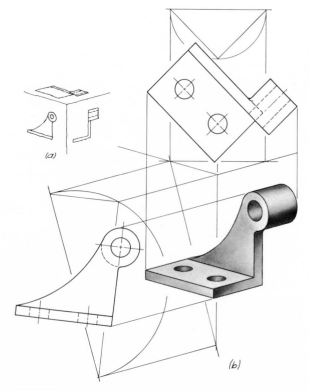

Fig. 15.47 Dimetric projection of a bearing bracket.

a. Select the position of the three axes as in Fig. 15.46(a). Note that the edges of the object in the finished drawing will be parallel to these lines. The angles between the lines may have any value greater than 90° except 180°. For trimetric the three angles must be unequal.

b. Draw lines at right angles to the axes across the opposite angles as shown in Fig. 15.46(b). All three may be used but any two will be sufficient.

c. Determine the revolved position of the axes as shown in Figs. 15.46(c) and (d). Note that this construction has been translated to a parallel position in order to leave the central area free.

d. Place the front and side views with the edges parallel to the revolved positions of the respective axes, as shown in Fig. 15.46(e). Project from these views to form the axonometric projection.

As a further illustration of this method, the bearing bracket in Fig. 15.47 has been drawn in dimetric. In this case two angles between the lines are equal.

The details of projection have been omitted. In order to orient the orthographic views properly, it is best to make a freehand thumbnail sketch of the axes and orthographic views in the position in which they are to be shown, as in Fig. 15.47(a).

In Fig. 15.47(b) the top and front views have been used to make the construction. In drawing the circles with ellipse guides or by the trammel method, it is only necessary to find the location of the center and the major and minor axes in the pictorial. The length of the major axis is always equal to the diameter of the circle and its direction will be perpendicular to the axis of the right cylinder of which the circle is a base.

15.24   EXPLODED PICTORIAL ASSEMBLIES. The three forms of axonometric projection lend themselves very well to the preparation of so-called exploded assemblies. These drawings are very useful in assisting persons who are not skilled in reading regular multiview drawings to perform work at the assembly bench. An illustration of this type of drawing is shown in Fig. 15.48. They can be made by direct projection from two orthographic views of each part as shown in Fig. 15.48. The parts must be arranged in the proper order for assembly.

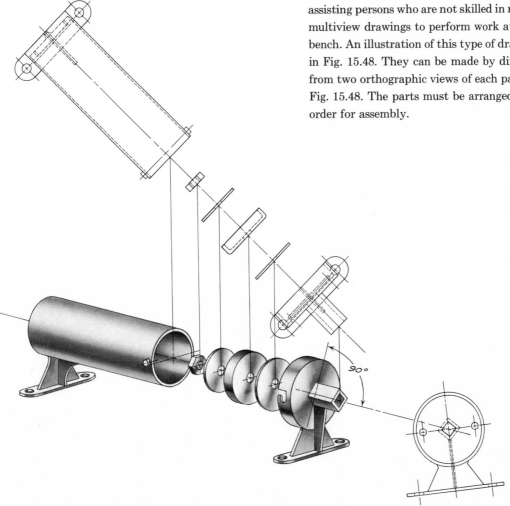

Fig. 15.48   Arrangement of views for an exploded assembly.

15.25 PRACTICAL CONSIDERATION. In most pictorial drawings or exact projections the drawing of circles is one of the most time-consuming parts of the work. This can be speeded up by using mechanical aids such as the Lietz ellipse templates, as shown in Fig. 15.49.

To use the ellipse guides properly the axes of the projection must be carefully selected. For isometric projection there is only one choice, as shown in Fig. 15.50. The notes in the upper left part of the figure indicate the 35° Lietz ellipse guide and give the ratio of the major to minor axes. The position of the orthographic views is indicated and the scale comes directly as a result of projection from any two of the three orthographic views.

In Fig. 15.51 the same information is given for three different positions of the axes for dimetric projection. Note that in each case two faces have the same Lietz guide.

In Fig. 15.52 similar information is given for three positions of the axes for trimetric projection.

15.26 OTHER MECHANICAL AIDS. When numerous pictorial drawings are to be made, other mechanical aids in addition to the Lietz ellipse guide are very valuable as timesaving devices.

15.26.1 Special boards. Several special drawing boards have been developed at the University of Illinois, chiefly by Wayne L. Schick, to make the use

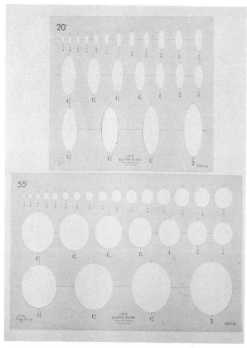

Fig. 15.49 Lietz ellipse template.

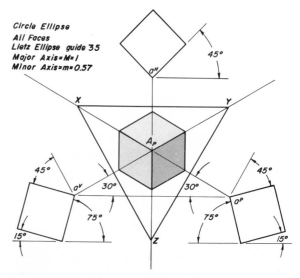

Fig. 15.50 Position of orthographic views for isometric projection.

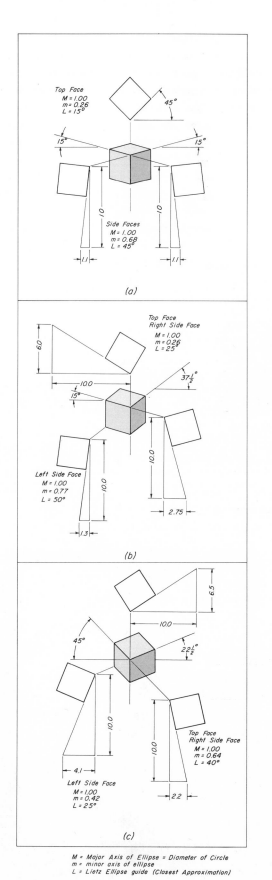

M = Major Axis of Ellipse = Diameter of Circle
m = minor axis of ellipse
L = Lietz Ellipse guide (Closest Approximation)

Fig. 15.51 Three positions for orthographic views for dimetric projection.

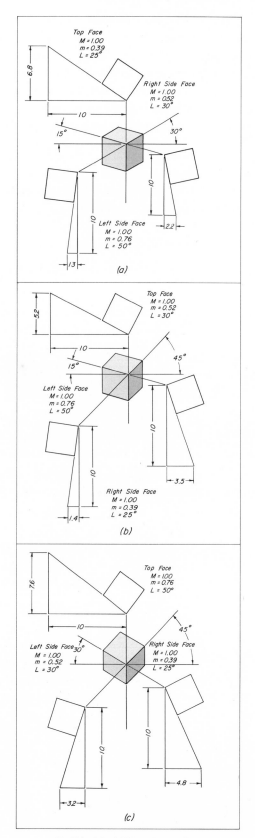

M = Major Axis of Ellipse = Diameter of Circle
m = Minor Axis of Ellipse
L = Lietz Ellipse Angle (Closest Approximation)

Fig. 15.52 Three positions for orthographic views for trimetric projection.

of axonometric projection simpler and more comprehensive. Boards similar to the one shown in Fig. 15.53 may be designed for any set of axes. The positions of the various views and the ellipse guides to be used on the various faces are marked clearly on the face of the board. The corners of the board are cut off perpendicular to the three axis so that all projection lines can be drawn with a T-square. If a blueprint of the object is available, the use of this board to make a trimetric projection may save up to 50 per cent of the time required to make an isometric drawing of a complicated object.

15.26.2   Special board and quadrangle for isometric. By means of the specially designed board, shown in Fig. 15.54, it is possible to construct three ortho-

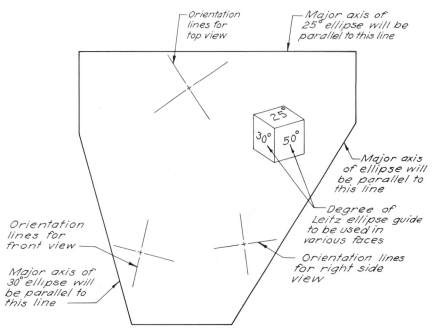

Fig. 15.53   Convenient trimetric board.

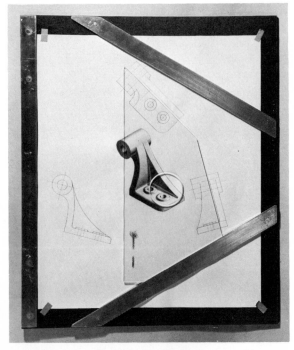

Fig. 15.54   Isometric board and drafting quadrangle.

graphic views of an object and an isometric projection at the same time. This board was invented and patented by Wayne L. Schick of the University of Illinois. It consists of a basic equilateral triangle on which the quadrangle slides. The quadrangle is a transparent plastic tool so designed that two sides may be used for projecting between two of the orthographic views, whereas the third side projects from one view to the isometric view. Since the angles are all equal in isometric, the quadrangle may be used on each of the three sides of the triangle for projection purposes. The advantages of the system are that direct projection is obtained between any two views and also that the isometric acts as a very positive check on the accuracy of all projections. The disadvantage is that the three-view drawings are not arranged in horizontal and vertical alignment as is customary in regular multiview projection.

15.26.3 Isometric stencil. One ellipse stencil designed particularly for isometric drawings is shown in Fig. 15.55. Marks showing the major and minor axes and other marks showing the location of the isometric axes are marked along the edges of the ellipse. These marks enable the draftsman to align the ellipse properly.

Fig. 15.56 shows a set of ten stencils which are very useful for making dimetric and trimetric drawings. The angles shown in the layouts of Figs. 15.51 and 15.52, as L = 25, L = 30, and so forth, are marked on these stencils.

15.26.4 Ellipsograph. This instrument for drawing ellipses of various sizes and shapes is shown in Fig. 3.44, Chapter 3.

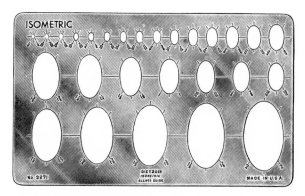

Fig. 15.55 Isometric stencil.

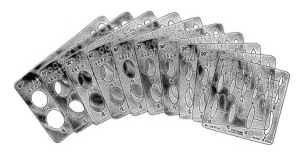

Fig. 15.56 Dimetric stencils. (Courtesy Eugene Dietzgen Co.)

SELF-STUDY QUESTIONS

Before trying to answer these questions, read the chapter carefully. Then, without reference to the text, answer as many questions as possible. For those that cannot be answered, the number, in parentheses following the question number, gives the article in which the answer can be found. Look it up and write down the answer. Check the answers that you did give to see that they are correct.

15.1 **(15.1)** The three forms of axonometric projection are _____, _____, and trimetric.

15.2 **(15.2)** A true isometric projection can be made by rotating the views of a cube until its body diagonal is _____ to the picture plane.

15.3 **(15.3)** Two _____ views of a cube can be made to produce an isometric projection.

15.4 **(15.5)** The three foremost edges of a cube drawn in isometric are called isometric _____.

15.5 **(15.5)** Lines parallel to the isometric axes are called _____.

15.6 **(15.5)** An isometric plane is one determined by two _____ lines.

15.7 **(15.5)** Any lines not parallel to the isometric axes are called non-_____ lines.

15.8 **(15.7.1)** Circles can be drawn in isometric by plotting points on the circle by the _____ method.

15.9 **(15.7.3)** A rapid way to draw circles in isometric by the use of a compass is the _____ _____ approximate method.

15.10 **(15.21.2)** All axonometric projections are true _____ projections.

15.11 **(15.7.6)** The four-center approximate method can be used in only one face of a _____ _____ and not at all in a trimetric projection.

15.12 **(15.8.1)** The _____ method of construction is useful for any type of axonometric drawing.

15.13 **(15.12)** For objects composed entirely of concentric cylindrical parts the _____ line method of construction is appropriate.

15.14 **(15.19.1)** Two methods of placing dimensions on an isometric drawing are the _____ method or the _____ method.

15.15 **(15.2)** In an isometric projection of a cube, face diagonals of the visible faces show in _____ length.

15.16 **(15.13)** In making sectional views in isometric, the cutting planes should be _____ to the isometric planes.

PROBLEMS

These problems may be made as axonometric drawings by the conventional method or as true projections by the exact method.

The scales given under each figure are for the solution of isometrics on 8½ × 11″ paper by the conventional method. When dimetrics or trimetrics are made, the other scales should normally be smaller than the one given.

For exact projections the original orthographic views may

be made at a slightly larger scale, since the projected axonometric is foreshortened in all its dimensions. Thus, for example, a problem with scale specified as ⅜″ = 1″ may have the orthographic views made at ½″ = 1″ for the construction of true projections.

15.1 Make an isometric drawing by the conventional method of an object assigned from Figs. 15.57 to 15.77.

15.2 Make a dimetric drawing of an object assigned from Figs. 15.57 to 15.77. Use axes as assigned.

15.3 Make a trimetric drawing of an object assigned from Figs. 15.57 to 15.77. Use axes as assigned.

15.4 Make a true isometric projection of an object assigned from Figs. 15.57 to 15.77. Note that two correct ortho-

graphic views must first be made for this method.

15.5 Make a true dimetric projection of an object assigned from Figs. 15.57 to 15.77. Use axes as desired.

15.6 Make a true trimetric projection of an object assigned from Figs. 15.57 to 15.77. Use axes as desired.

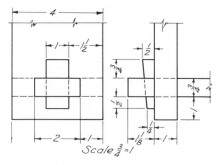

Fig. 15.57   Tenon joint.

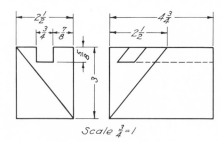

Fig. 15.58   Cut block.

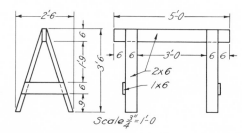

Fig. 15.59   Carpenter's horse.

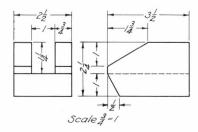

Fig. 15.60   Cut block.

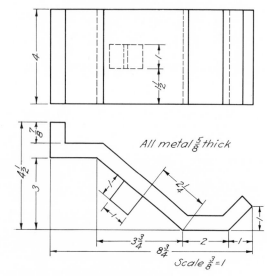

Fig. 15.61   Truss bearing strap.

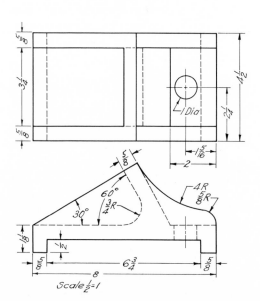

Fig. 15.62   Truss block.

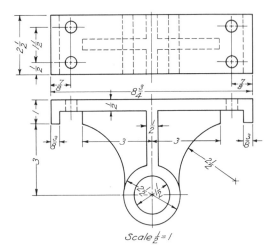

Fig. 15.63   Conveyor-bearing support.

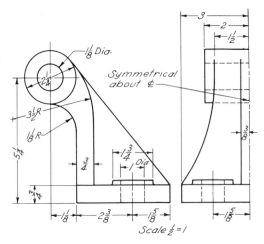

Fig. 15.66   Bearing bracket.

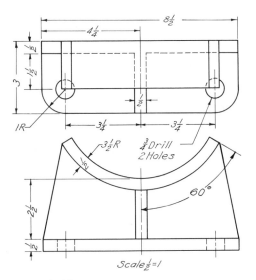

Fig. 15.64   Saddle.

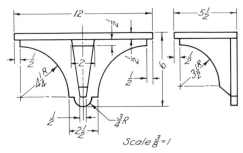

Fig. 15.67   Shelf.

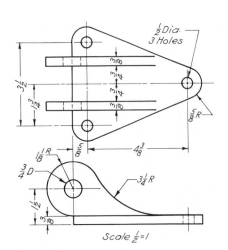

Fig. 15.65   Hinge.

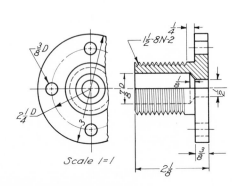

Fig. 15.68   Stuffing box body.

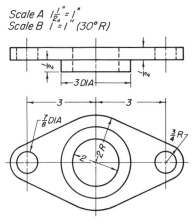

Scale A $1\frac{1}{2}"=1"$
Scale B $1"=1"$ (30°R)

Fig. 15.69 Coupler.

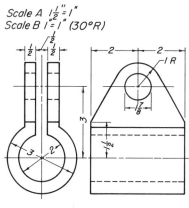

Scale A $1\frac{1}{2}"=1"$
Scale B $1"=1"$ (30°R)

Fig. 15.70 Clamp.

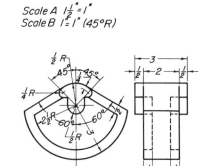

Scale A $1\frac{1}{2}"=1"$
Scale B $1"=1"$ (45°R)

Fig. 15.71 Rocker.

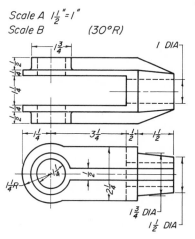

Scale A $1\frac{1}{2}"=1"$
Scale B   (30°R)

Fig. 15.72 Clevis.

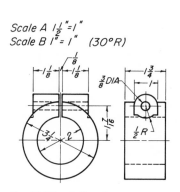

Scale A $1\frac{1}{2}"=1"$
Scale B $1"=1"$ (30°R)

Fig. 15.73 Collar clamp.

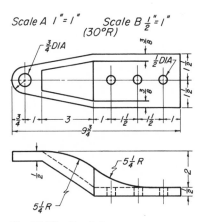

Scale A $1"=1"$ Scale B $\frac{1}{2}"=1"$
                    (30°R)

Fig. 15.74 Bracket.

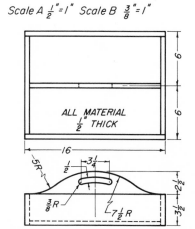

Scale A $\frac{1}{2}"=1"$ Scale B $\frac{3}{8}"=1"$

ALL MATERIAL $\frac{1}{2}"$ THICK

Fig. 15.75 Knife box.

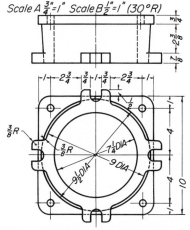

Scale A $\frac{3}{4}"=1"$ Scale B $\frac{1}{2}"=1"$ (30°R)

Fig. 15.76 Exhaust nozzle.

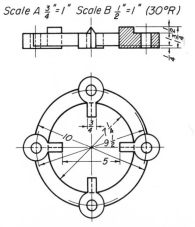

Scale A $\frac{3}{4}"=1"$ Scale B $\frac{1}{2}"=1"$ (30°R)

Fig. 15.77 Exhaust nozzle breakup wedges.

CHAPTER 16

Oblique Projection

OLD: 17th century excavation project. (The Bettmann Archive)

NEW: Irrigation project in Tracy, California powered by diesel electricity. (Philip Gendreau)

Chapter 16 Oblique Projection

16.1 FUNDAMENTAL PRINCIPLES. In both ortho- graphic and axonometric drawing, already discussed in previous chapters, the projecting lines have been at right angles to the plane or planes of projection. We now consider a kind of drawing in which, as in axono- metric, only one plane of projection is used, but in which the lines of sight, although parallel to each other, are oblique to the plane of projection. The ob- ject may be placed in any position, but, for conven- ience and to obtain the full advantage of this method of drawing, it is customary to have the front face of the object parallel to the vertical plane or picture plane as it is sometimes called.

The lines of sight in any one drawing are always parallel to each other; therefore, the point of sight is at infinity. Because the lines of sight are parallel to each other, any line that is parallel to the picture plane will project in its true length. It will also be parallel to the original position of the line as shown in Fig. 16.1. Consequently, any face of an object that is parallel to the plane of projection will have exactly the same ap- pearance in both oblique and orthographic projection. This feature is one of the chief advantages of oblique projections over other forms of pictorial drawing.

16.2 PRACTICAL AND THEORETICAL METHODS OF CONSTRUCTION. Using the facts stated in Art. 16.1, it is possible to make an oblique projection by drawing lines of sight from the object to the plane of projection. This theoretical method will be explained at the end of this chapter in Arts. 16.14 and 16.15.

It is possible, however, to make an oblique projec- tion by using a few simple rules of construction, which will be called the practical method. This method, which is very easy, is explained in the following articles and is used in solving all problems in the remainder of this chapter except Arts. 16.14 and 16.15.

16.3 TYPES OF OBLIQUE PROJECTION. There are several types of oblique projection. Theoretically, they are distinguished from each other by the angle that the lines of sight make with the plane of projection. In the practical construction that we shall follow, they are distinguished by the ratio of the scale used on the

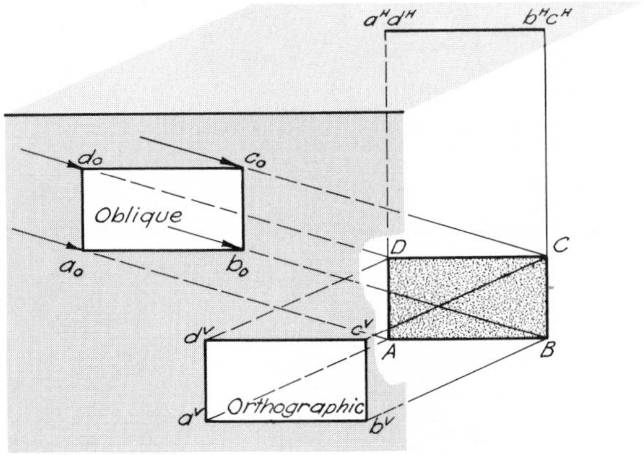

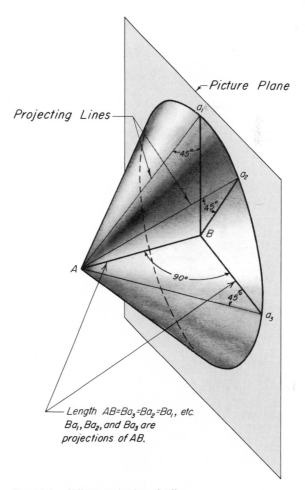

Fig. 16.2 Oblique projection of a line.

Fig. 16.1 Oblique projection of lines parallel to the plane of projection.

513

receding axis as compared to the scale used on the front face.

16.3.1 Cavalier projection. In Cavalier projection the theoretical lines of sight make an angle of 45° with the plane of projection. Thus in Fig. 16.2 line AB, which is perpendicular to the plane of projection, is shown projected upon the vertical or picture plane in three places at Ba_1, Ba_2, and Ba_3. The lines of sight all make an angle of 45° with the picture plane, as indicated in the figure, but the projections of line AB

thus found may have any position relative to the horizontal.

As noted in the figure, the projections of AB, namely Ba_1, Ba_2, and Ba_3, are all equal to the true length of the perpendicular line AB. This is true because the two sides of a 45° isosceles triangle, ABa_3 for example, are equal. Thus the same scale can be used on all three axes of the oblique projection. This is the chief advantage of Cavalier projection over other forms of oblique projection.

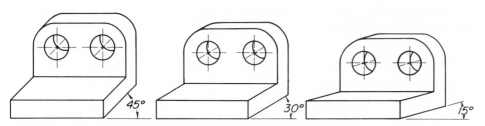

Fig. 16.3   Cabinet drawing with receding axis at various angles.

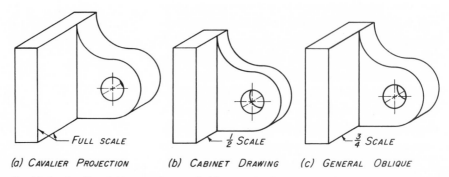

(a) CAVALIER PROJECTION   (b) CABINET DRAWING   (c) GENERAL OBLIQUE

Fig. 16.4   Cavalier, Cabinet, and general oblique projections compared.

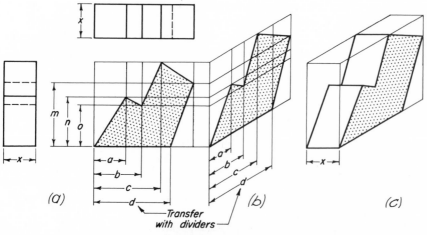

Fig. 16.5   Coordinate method of construction for plane figures.

16.3.2   Cabinet drawing. A second type of oblique projection, which has been specifically named, is produced when the angle that the lines of sight make with the plane of projection is 63° 26′. See Fig. 16.3. The tangent of this angle is 2, which means that a line perpendicular to the picture plane is just twice as long as its projection on the plane. Stated in another way, the projection is just one-half as long as the line. In making a projection of a perpendicular line, this result will be produced automatically if the scale used on the receding axis is just one-half that on the front face. A drawing made in this way is called a Cabinet drawing. Note again that the angle that the lines of sight make with the plane of projection has nothing to do with the angle that the receding axis makes with the horizontal. Thus in Fig. 16.3 all three figures are Cabinet drawings, but the receding axis has a different angle in each case.

16.3.3   General oblique drawing. Obviously, angles that the lines of sight make with the picture plane, other than the 45° and 63° 26′ angles, could be used to make oblique projections. From a practical point of view this simply means that different scales, other than full scale or one-half scale, can be used on the receding axis.

Any oblique drawing made on this basis is called a general oblique projection or drawing. A comparison of a drawing of a simple object representing each of the foregoing types of oblique projection is shown in Fig. 16.4. Note that in each case the receding axis has been made at the same angle with the horizontal.

16.3.4   Clinographic projection. In this type of oblique there is not only a different angle for the lines of sight, but the basic cube is also turned at an angle to the picture plane. This type is used in crystallography. The drawing is made by exact projection. See Art. 16.15 and Figs. 16.22 and 16.23.

16.4   CONVENTIONAL CONSTRUCTION OF CAVALIER PROJECTIONS. As discussed in Art. 16.3.1, the advantage of using Cavalier projection lies in the fact that the same scale is used on the receding axis as on the front face. Cavalier projections, however, though easy to draw, have a distorted appearance. Suggestions for reducing distortion are given in Art. 16.5.2.

16.4.1   Plane figures. One of the advantages of oblique projection is that plane figures in the front face of an object, or parallel thereto, project in their true shape just as in the orthographic views, hence require little further explanation.

In Fig. 16.5 a plane figure composed of straight lines

is shown. In Fig. 16.5(*a*) the true shape appears exactly as it would in the front view of the orthographic projection. Coordinates designated by letters have been indicated to locate the corners of the plane figure.

These coordinates can be used to draw the same figure in the side face of a box as shown in Figs. 16.5(*b*) and (*c*). For a Cavalier projection these can be transferred from Fig. 16.5(*a*) to either of the other views with dividers, since the same scale is used on all axes.

16.4.2   Circles in the front face of an object. In oblique projection, circles in the front face of an object can be drawn as true circles with a compass as shown in Fig. 16.6(*a*). Figure 16.7 also shows circles and parts of circles in the front face of a link.

16.4.3   Circles in faces parallel to the vertical plane. In any face of an object parallel to the *V*-plane, circles will also show as true circles, like those of the rear face of the link in Fig. 16.7(*c*).

16.4.4   Circles in the side or top faces of oblique drawings. Such circles will always project as ellipses, as shown in Figs. 16.6(*a*) and (*b*). They may be accurately drawn by the coordinate method.

Thus in Fig. 16.6(*a*) the ellipse representing the side face has been constructed as follows:

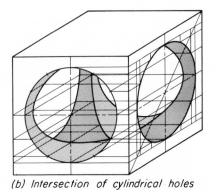

(b) Intersection of cylindrical holes

(a) Constructing circle in side face

Fig. 16.6   Construction of circles by coordinates.

a. Divide the circle in the front face into a suitable number of parts. In this case 12 equal spaces were used.

b. Project these points to the right vertical edge.

c. From these points draw lines parallel to the receding axis across the side face.

d. Draw either diagonal of the side face. The long diagonal was used in this case.

e. Where the diagonal crosses the horizontal coordinates, draw vertical lines representing the other coordinates. Thus *a'b'* in the side face represents a coordinate similar to *ab* in the front face.

f. Mark the points and draw a smooth curve through them.

Figure 16.6(*b*) represents the cube with two cylindrical holes through it. The intersection of the cylinders was found by drawing the corresponding elements of both cylinders to their crossing points as shown in the figure.

16.4.5   Circles by the four-center approximate method. A circle may be enclosed in a square, and since it is always tangent to the square at the midpoint of the sides, the Cavalier projection will show an ellipse that is tangent to the midpoint of the sides of the enclosing rhombus. Hence, to find the centers of the four arcs, erect perpendiculars to the midpoints of the four sides of the rhombus and find their intersections, as shown in Fig. 16.8. It should be noted that as the ratio of the major to the minor axis increases, the approximation becomes less accurate. In oblique projection the four-center method can be used only in Cavalier projection.

16.5 . DRAWING SOLID OBJECTS IN CAVALIER PROJECTION. The drawing of solid objects involves more than adding a third dimension to the plane figures discussed heretofore. Some of the important considerations are:

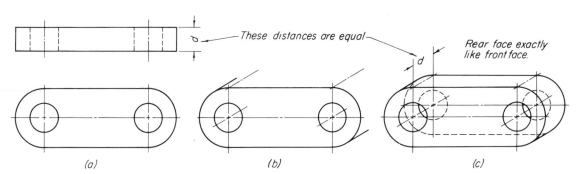

Fig. 16.7   Front face in true shape in oblique.

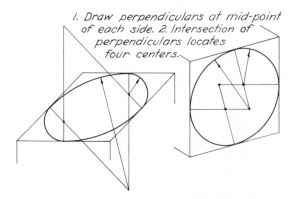

Fig. 16.8   Four-center approximate method of representing circles in Cavalier projection.

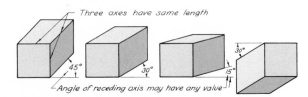

Fig. 16.9   A few positions of the receding axis in Cavalier projection.

a. The selection of the axes. In oblique a wide choice is available. The proper selection is discussed in the following paragraphs.

b. The position of the object. This involves two things. One is to find the simplest construction and the other is to find the best appearance of the object. See Art. 16.5.2.

16.5.1   Position of the axes. As illustrated in Fig. 16.9, the receding axis may make any angle with the horizontal. This angle is not to be confused with the 45° angle that the lines of sight make with the plane of projection. The lines of sight that extend from the object to the plane of projection do not show in any illustration or construction except the theoretical. See Art. 16.14.

As shown in Fig. 16.9, any face of the object may be emphasized by the proper selection of the receding axis. This must be considered first in beginning the layout of a drawing.

16.5.2   Position of object.

a. For simplicity of construction. Since any face of an object that is parallel to the picture plane appears in its true shape in an oblique projection, the con-

struction of many drawings can be kept quite simple by showing the face of the object that has the most circles, arcs, or other curves as the front face. This rule should be adhered to whenever possible, for it can be readily seen that the object in the position of Fig. 16.10(*a*) is not only easier to draw but also looks much better than the same object as represented in Fig. 16.10(*b*).

b. To reduce distortion. Unpleasant distortion in Cavalier projection frequently can be reduced by placing an object that has one dimension much greater than the others with this long dimension parallel to the picture plane, as shown in Fig. 16.11. Some discrimination must be exercised, however, for this may not work so well with some objects as it does with others. A better method to reduce distortion is to reduce the scale on the receding axis, thus selecting a different type of oblique projection.

16.5.3   Drawing the object by the box method. With the foregoing paragraphs in mind, the steps in making a Cavalier projection of a solid or three-dimensioned object are illustrated in Fig. 16.12. They may be listed as follows:

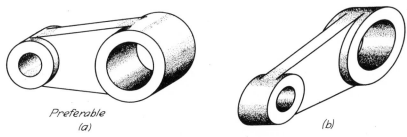

Preferable
(a)   *(b)*

Fig. 16.10   Circles preferably parallel to the front face or plane of projection.

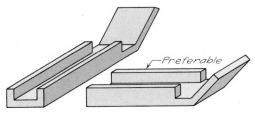

Preferable

Fig. 16.11   Long dimension of objects preferably parallel to the plane of projection.

a. Enclose the orthographic views of the object in the smallest possible rectangular box whose faces are parallel to the principal faces of the object. See Fig. 16.12(*a*).

b. Draw this enclosing box in Cavalier projection, making the front of the box like the orthographic front view and the receding axis to the same scale as the front and at an angle that will show the side and top to the best advantage. See Fig. 16.12(*b*).

c. Draw lightly all lines in the front face and establish position of planes parallel to the front face. See Fig. 16.12(*c*).

d. Draw all lines in faces parallel to the front at the proper distances from the front face, as shown in Fig. 16.12(*d*).

e. Construct coordinates for curves not in front face in the orthographic view as shown at *1-a, 2-b, 3-c*, etc., in Fig. 16.12(*a*) and then transfer these coordinates to the oblique as shown for one curve in Fig.

16.12(*e*). Since the second curve is parallel to the first, points on it may be located by stepping off the thickness of the web (see front view) as *bb'* in Fig. 16.12(*e*).

f. Complete all lines, and erase construction. After erasure make heavy the visible outlines of the drawing, producing the finished drawing of Fig. 16.12(*f*).

16.6 CONSTRUCTION OF A CABINET DRAWING.

A Cabinet drawing may be made in the same manner as a Cavalier projection, with the exception that the scale on the receding axis must be reduced one-half. The steps in this procedure are shown in Fig. 16.13, which, though not a Cabinet drawing, illustrates the method of construction. Where curves are involved in the receding faces, a convenient scheme for obtaining the foreshortened or one-half-scale dimensions from the orthographic views is shown in Fig. 16.13(*a*).

Thus, for a Cabinet drawing, if the total length *ab* on the receding axis is 3 inches, line *ac* will be 1½ inches

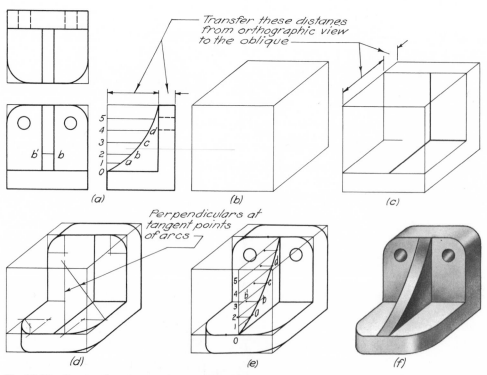

Fig. 16.12 Construction of curves in a receding plane.

long. This line may be laid out in any convenient direction from either end of line *ab*, as illustrated. Point *c* is then connected with *b*, and all other points to be plotted are transferred to line *ac* by lines parallel to *bc*. This device for making proportional divisions of any line should be thoroughly understood by the student.

The four-center approximate method of drawing circles cannot be used in Cabinet drawing since the sides of the enclosing parallelogram are not equal. A circle can be plotted, however, without referring to the original orthographic projections except to obtain the dimensions and position of the enclosing parallelogram. The method of plotting coordinates by means of a semicircle and a diagonal of the parallelogram is shown in Fig. 16.6.

16.7   GENERAL OBLIQUE. Obviously, scales other than those mentioned could be used on the receding axis. For example, if the scale on the front face were

$1'' = 1''$, a scale of $\frac{3}{4}'' = 1''$ could be used on the receding axis. A drawing made in this manner is neither a Cavalier projection nor a Cabinet drawing and is simply referred to as an oblique projection. The angle that the projecting lines make with the plane of projection can be determined by comparing the length of a perpendicular with the length of its projection. Thus, in Fig. 16.13, a perpendicular 1 inch long would project $\frac{3}{4}$ inch long. Hence the tangent of the angle that the projecting line makes with the plane of projection would be $1 \div \frac{3}{4}$ or 1.333. This angle is 53° 8″. Its value, of course, is of theoretical interest only, since it does not enter into the actual construction of the drawing.

The construction of any oblique drawing follows the same pattern as the construction of a Cavalier projection, with the exception that the scale on the receding axis is changed to suit the conditions.

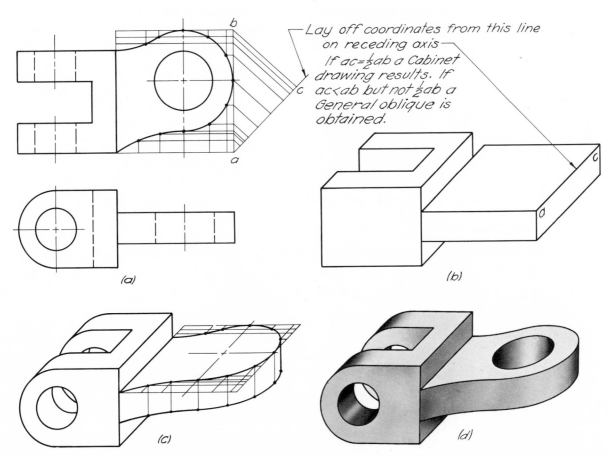

Fig. 16.13   Method of foreshortening the scale on the receding axis.

16.8 CENTER-LINE LAYOUT. When an object is composed of cylindrical parts, like the rocker arm in Fig. 16.14(*a*), the construction can be based upon a center-line framework instead of the box construction previously explained. With the direction of the three axes chosen, the centers of all circular parts can be laid out as illustrated in Fig. 16.14(*b*), using the proper scale on all axes. At each center, circles of the proper size can be drawn, as shown in Fig. 16.14(*c*). The straight lines tangent to them can be drawn quickly, giving the final result shown in Fig. 16.14(*d*).

16.9 SECTIONING OBLIQUE DRAWINGS. As in all pictorial drawing, hidden lines are not shown since it is very difficult to interpret them. Interior construction is best shown by making sectional views with either one-fourth or one-half the object removed. The cutting planes, in general, should be parallel to the oblique planes or faces of the enclosing box, as shown in Fig. 16.15. Other illustrations may be found in the problem sections of various chapters.

The crosshatching lines lying in two planes that are at right angles to each other should be sloped in such a way that they would seem to coincide if the planes were rotated together. Correct section lining is shown in Fig. 16.15.

16.10 DIMENSIONING OBLIQUE DRAWINGS. The principles of dimensioning studied in connection with working drawings apply in general to oblique projections, but with the following additions:

a. Dimensions should be made to read from the bottom and right-hand side of the sheet so far as possible. See Figs. 16.14 and 16.16(*b*).

b. Dimension lines and witness or extension lines must lie in the same oblique plane. See Figs. 16.16 and 16.17.

c. Dimensions must lie in the oblique plane determined by the dimension lines and extension lines.

d. Only vertical lettering and numerals should be used. Numerals and letters may be made to lie in oblique planes in the same manner as shown for isometric. The unidirectional system is also approved.

e. As far as possible, dimensions should be placed in the front face or parallel thereto since this makes the dimensioning similar to that in the orthographic views.

f. When notes are extensive and are not on the figure, they may be lettered neatly in slant style. In general, however, vertical lettering is preferred.

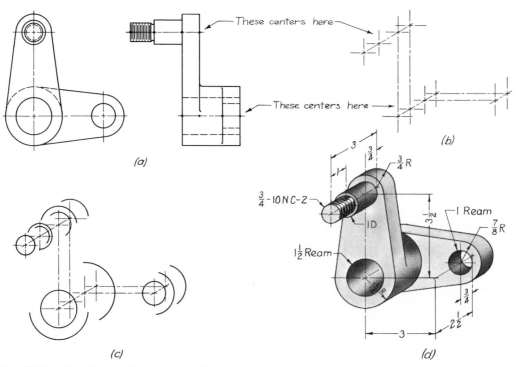

Fig. 16.14 **Center-line method of construction.**

16.11 SCREW THREADS IN OBLIQUE PROJECTION. Since circles that are parallel to the plane of projection show as true circles in oblique projection, screw threads may be easily represented by a conventionalized scheme, if the axis of the thread is made parallel to the receding axis of the drawing. The axis of the bolt or nut, as in Fig. 16.18, becomes the line of centers for a series of circles representing the crests of the threads. The root line does not show. The spacing of the circles is made the same as the pitch of the thread until the pitch becomes too fine, in which case the smallest convenient spacing is used.

Whenever possible, bolts, screws, or nuts should be drawn in the position shown in Fig. 16.18. When placed with the axis parallel to the picture plane, the circles representing the thread crests must be plotted as ellipses and drawn with an irregular curve or ellipse guide, which is a slow process.

16.12 THREE-DIMENSIONAL CURVES. Three-dimensional curves, such as the conveyor shown in Fig. 16.19, can be drawn with comparative ease if the axis of the conveyor is placed on the receding axis of the drawing. The method is illustrated in the figure. The circles are first divided into 12 equal parts, and the pitch is likewise divided into the same number of parts. On the center line, step off intervals equal to one-twelfth the pitch. From these points radial lines can be drawn parallel to those used in dividing the circles. The construction is shown for the first four points on the curve. After the first turn has been completed, successive turns can be made by stepping off distances equal to the pitch from the previous curve. The thickness of the blade can also be stepped off at equal intervals from the first curve. In cases of this kind orthographic views are not required to make the construction, except to obtain the dimensions of the part.

If, on the other hand, the three-dimensional curve is irregular in shape, it may be necessary to resort to the box construction and plot three rectangular coordinates.

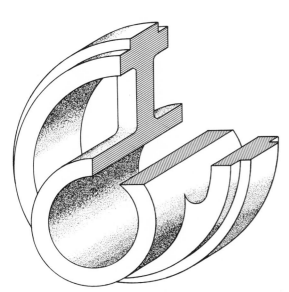

Fig. 16.15 Sectional view in oblique projection.

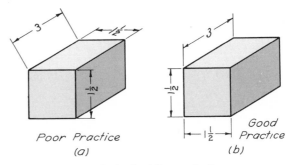

Fig. 16.16 Dimensioning in oblique projection.

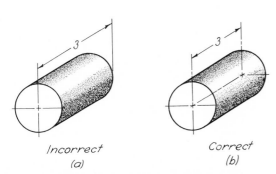

Fig. 16.17 Dimensions must lie in an oblique plane.

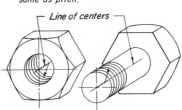

Fig. 16.18 Screw threads in oblique projection.

16.13   DOUBLE-CURVED SURFACES. The outline of a double-curved surface is represented by an enveloping curve tangent to imaginary curves in the surface. Thus a return pipe bend can have a series of semicircles drawn on its surface, as shown in Fig. 16.20(a). These curves are then drawn in oblique and the enveloping curve is drawn tangent to them.

16.14   THEORETICAL CONSTRUCTION OF AN OBLIQUE PROJECTION. In order to give a more thorough understanding of oblique projection, the following discussion for making a projection from the orthographic views is presented. From this the rule-of-thumb methods used heretofore can be derived.

16.14.1   Theoretical construction. An oblique projection of an object may be constructed from its orthographic views by drawing the oblique lines of sight from these views and finding where they pierce the plane of projection, as shown in Fig. 16.21. Any two views could be used, but all three have been shown in the figure in order to illustrate the theory.

Since the vertical plane appears edgewise in both the side and top views, the piercing points of the projecting lines can be seen in these views by inspection. Thus, in the pictorial top view of Fig. 16.21(a), the lines of sight from a^H pierce the plane at $a_0{}^H$, and the

front view of this piercing point must lie in the perpendicular from $a_0{}^H$. Likewise, in the side view the projecting line from a^P pierces the picture plane at $a_0{}^P$, and the front view of this piercing point must lie horizontally across from $a_0{}^P$. The intersection of these two perpendiculars determines $a_0{}^V$, which is the oblique projection of point A on the object. The same procedure is used for all other points.

The orthographic construction of an oblique projection and the completed oblique projection are shown in heavy outline in Fig. 16.21(b). Although this theoretical method can be used for so simple an object as a cube, it would be too cumbersome for more complicated objects. A conventional method of construction similar to that used in isometric has been used throughout all previous paragraphs.

It may be noted, in passing, that the true value of the angle that the lines of sight make with the V-plane does not show in any one of the three views of Fig. 16.21(b). It may be found, however, by dropping a perpendicular to the V-plane from b^H in Fig. 16.21(b) and revolving the shaded triangle to $b^H c^H b_0{}^H$ around line BC until it is parallel to the H-plane. The true value of the angle then shows in the H-projection at $b_{or}{}^H$.

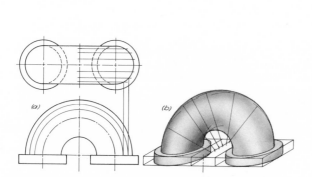

Fig. 16.20   A double-curved surface in oblique projection.

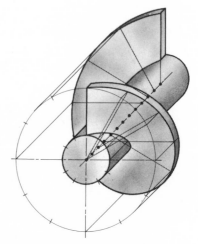

Fig. 16.19   Helicoid in oblique projection.

16.15 CLINOGRAPHIC PROJECTION. In the first part of this chapter, the object to be drawn was always placed with one face parallel to the plane of projection; this is an essential element in oblique projection, as there discussed. Although the advantages to be obtained by this means are of considerable practical importance in the way of convenience and speed, it must be borne in mind that oblique projections of an object can be made regardless of its position relative to the plane. The essential fundamental concept in oblique projection lies in the fact that the projecting lines are parallel to each other and oblique to the plane of projection. The position of the object relative to the plane may or may not facilitate the work of construction, but this does not change the method of projection.

For some purposes it may be desirable to turn the object at an angle to the plane of projection, particularly if there are no curved edges in its outlines. In fact, just such a system of oblique projection, called clinographic projection, has become firmly established in the field of mineralogy and crystallography in representing the various mineral crystals.

In clinographic projection, the angles that the three principal axes of the crystal make with the plane of projection, and the angle that the lines of sight make with the plane, have become fixed by usage, although there is no inherent reason why other angles might not have been used just as effectively.

These angles are shown in Fig. 16.22 in the clinographic projection of a cube. For construction purposes, it is well to remember that the tangent of 18° 26′ is ⅓ and the tangent of 9° 28′ is ⅙. From an observation of the figure it is clear that the vertical line projects in true length, while the others are foreshortened, each by a different amount. In clinographic projection these foreshortened scales are determined accurately; approximations of scales or arbitrary assumptions are

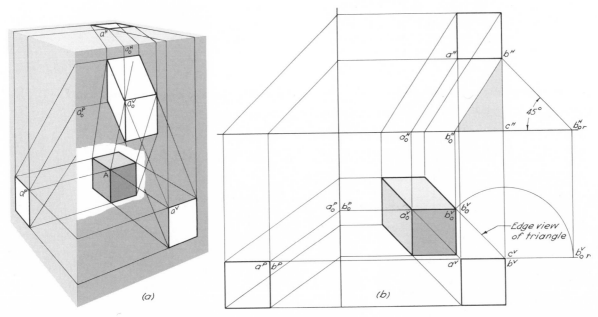

Fig. 16.21 Theory of oblique projection.

not permitted. In practice, the three coordinate axes shown inside of the cube are used as the skeleton upon which the crystal is drawn, as illustrated in Fig. 16.23.

Three of the six principal systems of crystals have their three axes of varying lengths and at right angles to each other. The other three systems have axes that make angles with each other, differing from 90°, as shown in Fig. 16.24. All six sets of axes are drawn upon the cubic axes as a basis.

Clinographic projection is strictly an oblique projection, and although three different scales are used upon the axes, it is not for this reason to be called a trimetric projection, any more than we should call a Cavalier projection an isometric projection for the same reason. So far as appearance and actual construction are concerned, however, oblique projections can be made to appear quite similar to dimetric projection, as is evident from a comparison of the clinographic projection of the cube in Fig. 16.22 and the dimetric of the cube in Fig. 15.51 of Chapter 15.

16.16 ADVANTAGES OF OBLIQUE DRAWING.

From the foregoing paragraphs it is clear that oblique drawings have several distinct advantages over other pictorial forms.

a. The front face of an object or any face parallel to it may be drawn like its true orthographic projection, hence circles may be drawn as true circles.

b. Distortion may be largely overcome by a careful foreshortening of the scale on the receding axis.

c. Dimensioning is simpler since only one set of dimensions need to be made in an oblique plane.

d. There is a greater range of choice of positions of the axes than in the other forms except trimetric. See Fig. 16.9.

To offset these advantages it should be noted that oblique projections, even though foreshortened on the receding axis, have an unpleasing distortion. This is particularly true when circles must be shown in the receding faces.

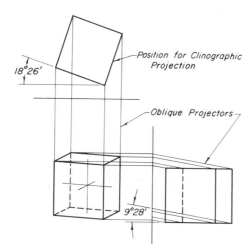

Fig. 16.22   Clinographic projection of a cube.

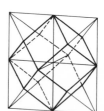

Rhombic Dodecahedron

Fig. 16.23   Crystal in clinographic projection.

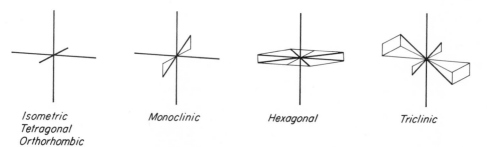

Isometric
Tetragonal
Orthorhombic   *Monoclinic*   *Hexagonal*   *Triclinic*

Fig. 16.24   Axes in six crystal systems.

SELF-STUDY QUESTIONS

Before trying to answer these questions, read the chapter carefully. Then, without reference to the text, answer as many questions as possible. For those that cannot be answered, the number, in parentheses following the question number, gives the article in which the answer can be found. Look it up and write down the answer. Check the answers that you did give to see that they are correct.

16.1 **(16.1)** In oblique projection the projecting lines are _____ to the plane of projection.

16.2 **(16.1)** The face of an object that is parallel to the vertical plane (picture plane) shows in _____ _____ in an oblique projection.

16.3 **(16.3.1–16.3.4)** Two of the four types of oblique projection are _____ and _____.

16.4 **(16.3.1)** In Cavalier projection the projecting lines make _____ _____ with the plane of projection.

16.5 **(16.3.1)** The _____ scale must be used on all axes of a Cavalier projection.

16.6 **(16.3.2)** In Cabinet drawing the scale on the receding axis is _____ _____ that on the front face.

16.7 **(16.4.2)** Circles in the front face of an object show as _____ in oblique projection.

16.8 **(16.4.5)** Circles in the side and top faces of an object can be drawn by the _____ _____ method in Cavalier projection.

16.9 **(16.6)** The four-center approximate method for drawing circles cannot be used in _____ drawing.

16.10 **(16.5.1)** The receding axes in a Cavalier projection can be made at _____ _____. It does not have to be at _____ degrees with the horizontal.

16.11 **(16.5.2)** For ease in construction, the front face of an object should be _____ to the plane of projection.

16.12 **(16.5.2)** To reduce distortion the _____ dimension of an object should be parallel to the plane of projection.

16.13 **(16.3.3)** In a general oblique projection, if the scale on the front face is $1'' = 1''$, the scale of the receding axis could have _____ value except $1'' =$ _____ or $\frac{1}{2}'' =$ _____.

16.14 **(16.8)** If an object consists mostly of parallel circular parts, the _____ method of construction is very convenient.

16.15 **(16.9)** In making sectional views the cutting planes should preferably be _____ to the oblique faces of the enclosing box.

16.16 **(16.10)** Dimension lines and extension lines must be in the same _____ plane.

16.17 **(16.11)** If a bolt showing screw threads must be drawn in oblique, it is simplest to make the _____ of the bolt on the _____ axis of the drawing.

16.18 **(16.15)** In mineralogy and crystallography the shape of crystals is shown by a form of oblique drawing called _____ projection.

PROBLEMS

Problems in the following group may be assigned as Cavalier projections, Cabinet drawings, or general oblique projections. The student should note that the only practical difference in drawing the different types of projection lies in the scale used on the receding axis. The angle that the receding axis makes with a horizontal line may have any value, unless specified in the figure or by the instructor.

In Figs. 15.69 to 15.77 and 16.25 to 16.36 two scales have been specified. The larger scale A is for the A-size sheet (11 × 17 or 12 × 18). Scale B is for the B-size sheet (8½ × 11 or 9 × 12). In Figs. 16.37 to 16.47 no scale is given and the student may select his own scale unless it has been given by the instructor.

For general obliques it is recommended that the scale on the receding axis be in the ratio of ¾ to 1 of that used on the front face. The most convenient slope for the receding axis is 30° up to the right, but any other direction may be used.

Sheet sizes and borderline layouts are shown in Figs. 13.84 and 13.85 of Chapter 13. Use the one assigned by your instructor.

16.1 Make a Cavalier projection of an object assigned from Figs. 15.69 to 15.77 and Figs. 16.25 to 16.47.

16.2 Make a Cabinet drawing of an object assigned from Figs. 15.69 to 15.77 and Figs. 16.25 to 16.47.

16.3 Make a general oblique projection of an object assigned from Figs. 16.25 to 16.47.

16.4 Make a Cavalier, Cabinet, or general oblique projection as assigned for any specified part of an object or assembly shown in the problems of Chapters 6, 8, or 15, as directed by your instructor.

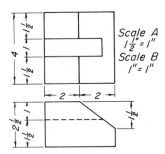

Scale A
$1\frac{1}{2}'' = 1''$
Scale B
$1'' = 1''$

Fig. 16.25   Block.

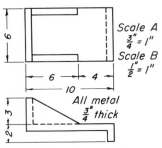

Scale A
$\frac{3}{4}'' = 1''$
Scale B
$\frac{1}{2}'' = 1''$

All metal
$\frac{3}{4}''$ thick

Fig. 16.26   Truss end block.

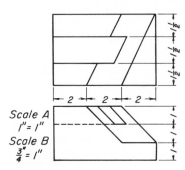

Scale A
$1'' = 1''$
Scale B
$\frac{3}{4}'' = 1''$

Fig. 16.27   Block.

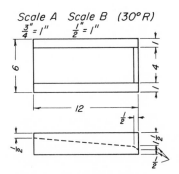

Scale A   Scale B   (30°R)
$\frac{3}{4}'' = 1''$ $\frac{1}{2}'' = 1''$

Fig. 16.28   Bearing wedge.

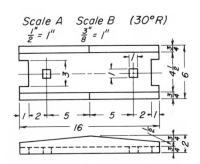

Scale A   Scale B   (30°R)
$\frac{1}{2}'' = 1''$ $\frac{3}{8}'' = 1''$

Fig. 16.29   Anchor block.

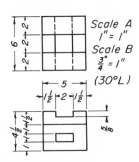

Scale A
$1'' = 1''$
Scale B
$\frac{3}{4}'' = 1''$
(30°L)

Fig. 16.30   Block.

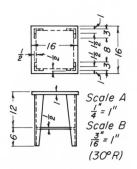

Scale A
$\frac{1}{4}'' = 1''$
Scale B
$\frac{3}{16}'' = 1''$
(30°R)

Fig. 16.31   Taboret.

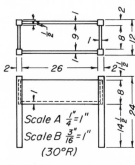

Scale A $\frac{1}{4}'' = 1''$
Scale B $\frac{3}{16}'' = 1''$
(30°R)

Fig. 16.32   Fern box.

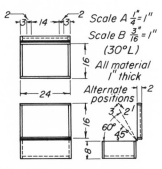

Scale A $\frac{1}{4}'' = 1''$
Scale B $\frac{3}{16}'' = 1''$
(30°L)
All material
$1''$ thick
Alternate
positions

Fig. 16.33   Box.

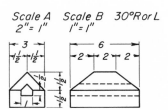

Scale A   Scale B   30°R or L
$2'' = 1''$ $1'' = 1''$

Fig. 16.34   Block.

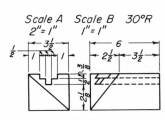

Scale A   Scale B   30°R
$2'' = 1''$ $1'' = 1''$

Fig. 16.35   Block.

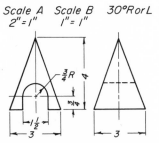

Scale A   Scale B   30°R or L
$2'' = 1''$ $1'' = 1''$

Fig. 16.36   Pyramid.

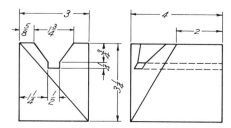

Fig. 16.37   Cut block.

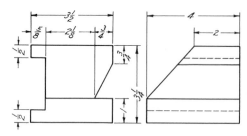

Fig. 16.38   Cut block.

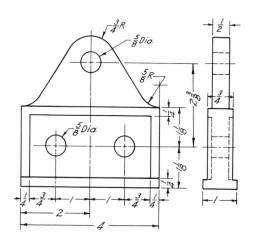

Fig. 16.39   Conveyor attachment.

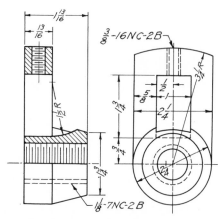

Fig. 16.40   Flue hole cutter holder.

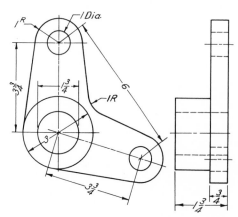

Fig. 16.41   Rocker arm.

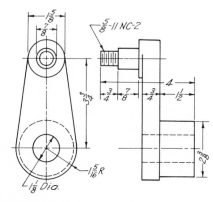

Fig. 16.42   Bell crank.

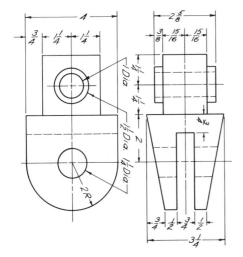

Fig. 16.43 Link.

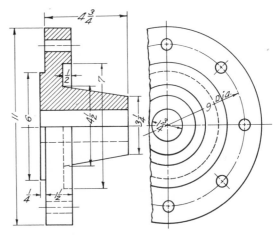

Fig. 16.44 Cylinder end.

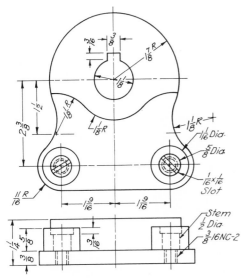

Fig. 16.45 Cam follower.

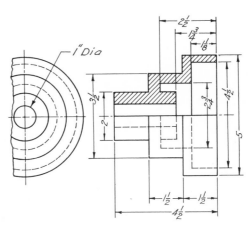

Fig. 16.46 Step pulley.

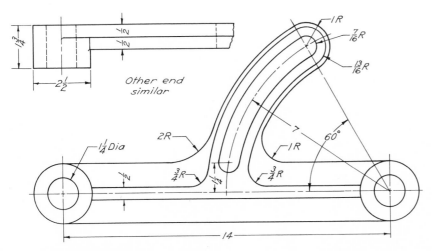

Fig. 16.47 Belt tightener.

CHAPTER 17
Perspective

NEW: Alcoa Building in Pittsburgh, Pennsylvania (Alcoa Aluminum)

OLD: 17th century engraving (New York Public Library Picture Collection)

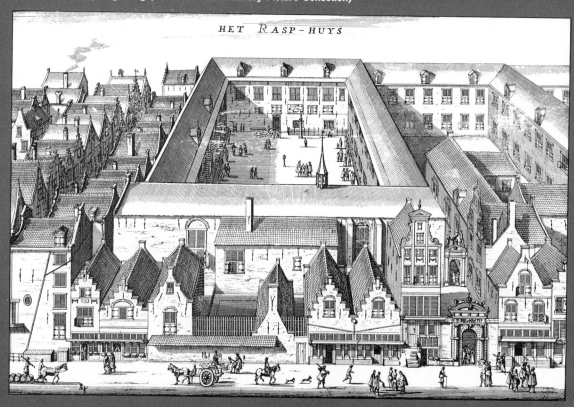

Chapter 17   Perspective

17.1   DEFINITION OF PERSPECTIVE. When a person looks at an object, the light rays (visual rays) from the object are focused by the eye so that the picture is formed on the spherical rear surface of the eye known as the retina. Perspective is the form of pictorial drawing that most nearly approaches the picture as seen by the eye. Thus if we imagine a vertical plane between the eye and the cube, as in Fig. 17.1, the visual rays from the cube to the eye, if intercepted by the vertical or picture plane, will form an image that exactly coincides with the edges of the cube. This produces the same image as the cube itself if viewed from this one particular position. This image is called a perspective.

From Fig. 17.1 it will be observed that the major difference between perspective projection and the forms of projection studied heretofore lies in the fact that the point of sight is at a finite distance from the object. The visual rays or lines of sight from the object, therefore, converge to the point of sight instead of being parallel to each other as in other forms of projection. This type of drawing is sometimes called scenographic projection or central projection since the lines of sight converge to a single point or center.

The picture or perspective obtained will depend on the relative position of the object, picture plane, and point of sight.

17.2   BASIC TERMS AND RELATIONSHIPS OF PERSPECTIVE. Certain terms and the relationships between them are commonly used in a discussion of perspective. Some of these are presented in the following paragraphs.

17.2.1   The point of sight. The position of the eye of the observer in making a perspective is called the point of sight. It is sometimes referred to as the station point. In the illustrations and problems of this book the point of sight will be designated by the letter S. Its projections will be s^H, s^V, and s^P, as is customary in orthographic projection. See Fig. 17.1.

17.2.2   Visual rays. Visual rays are the straight lines from the object to the point of sight that represent the light rays that produce the image in the eye. They are the lines of sight used in making the actual construction of perspectives.

17.2.3   Picture plane. The picture plane is the plane surface on which the perspective is drawn or projected. It could have any position. For a bird's-eye view a horizontal plane would be used. For most perspectives a vertical plane is used as the picture plane. Only this type will be discussed here.

17.2.4   Vanishing points. Vanishing points are the points in space where, by definition, parallel lines meet. On the drawing the vanishing point, designated by the letters VP, is the perspective of the meeting point of the lines in space. Every set of parallel lines not parallel to the picture plane has a vanishing point.

17.2.5   Horizon line. The horizon line is a horizontal line that always passes through the vertical projection of the point of sight.

17.3   LOCATION OF THE PICTURE PLANE. If we assume the point of sight and the object in Fig. 17.2 to be fixed in position, the picture plane may have several positions relative to them.

17.3.1   Enlarged perspective. When the object is between the point of sight and the picture plane, an enlarged perspective is produced as in Fig. 17.2(a). This arrangement is very rarely used.

17.3.2   Normal perspective. When the picture plane is between the object and the point of sight, the perspective is smaller than the object. The closer the plane is to the point of sight the smaller the perspective becomes, as can be seen by comparing Figs. 17.2(b) and (c). This is the arrangement usually used and it is therefore called a normal perspective.

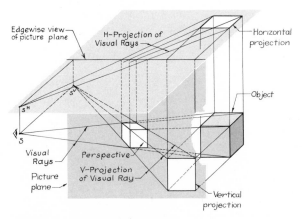

Fig. 17.1   Theory of perspective.

17.3.3 Reversed perspective. When the point of sight is between the object and the picture plane as in Fig. 17.2(*d*), the perspective is inverted and reversed as in a camera. In the camera the lens represents the point of sight. In drawing this arrangement is not used.

17.4 LOCATION OF THE POINT OF SIGHT. With the picture plane and the object in a definite relationship to each other the perspective can be greatly altered by a change in the position of the point of sight. The choice of the location of the point of sight is there-

fore very important in making an attractive perspective. A careful selection of the position of the point of sight makes it possible to emphasize the features in any visible face of the object. This is discussed in the following paragraphs.

17.4.1 Distance of the point of sight from the object. It has been observed from experience that when the viewer is at a certain point, the eye will see clearly all the picture contained within a right circular cone having its apex at the eye and an interior angle at the

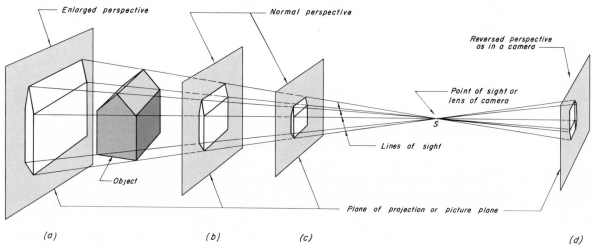

Fig. 17.2 Relationship of object, picture plane, and point of sight.

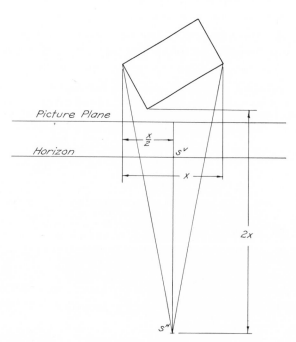

Fig. 17.3 Location of point of sight.

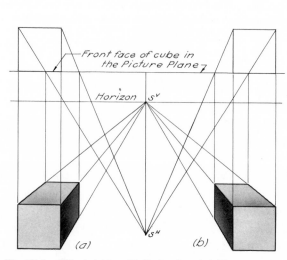

Fig. 17.4 Object right and left of point of sight.

apex of approximately 30°. This condition is satisfied when the point of sight is placed at a distance from the object at least twice the longest dimension of the object, as shown in Fig. 17.3. For a good perspective, the point of sight should be located in front of the center of the object. Keeping these conditions in mind, the location of the point of sight may be selected to show prominently the more important faces of an object.

17.4.2   Position to the right or left of the object. In Fig. 17.4(a) the point of sight is to the right of the cube, thus revealing the right face. By moving the point of sight farther to the right, the right side of the cube could be made still more prominent.

In Fig. 17.4(b) the left side of the cube is revealed by having the point of sight to the left of the cube.

17.4.3   Elevation of the point of sight. In Fig. 17.5(a) the lower portion of the figure, the point of sight shown by projections s^V and s^P, is above the top of the cube. This can be seen in the side view at the left. The shaded perspective therefore shows the top of the cube.

In Fig. 17.5(b) the point of sight shown by the same projections s^V and s^P is below the side view of the cube. The perspective therefore shows the bottom of the cube.

17.5   POSITION OF THE OBJECT. One more preliminary consideration should be presented before proceeding with the actual construction of an object, namely, the effect of the position of the object.

By changing the position of the object relative to the picture plane, other changes in the appearance of the perspective can be made. These changes are so different from each other that they have been given special names.

17.5.1   Parallel or one-point perspective. When the principal face of the object is parallel to the picture plane, as in Fig. 17.4, a parallel or one-point perspective is formed. The term one-point refers to the fact that such perspectives have only one principal vanishing point.

17.5.2   Angular or two-point perspective. When two faces of the object are inclined to the picture plane, as in Fig. 17.5, an angular or two-point perspective is formed. There are two principal vanishing points.

17.5.3   Oblique or three-point perspective. When all faces of the object are oblique to the picture plane, an oblique or three-point perspective results. There are three principal vanishing points, as shown in Fig. 17.6.

17.6   DEFINITION OF THE METHODS OF CONSTRUCTING A PERSPECTIVE. Four methods are commonly used for constructing perspective drawings.

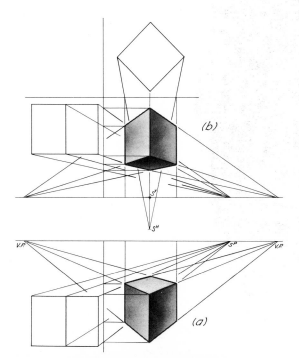

Fig. 17.5   Object above and below point of sight.

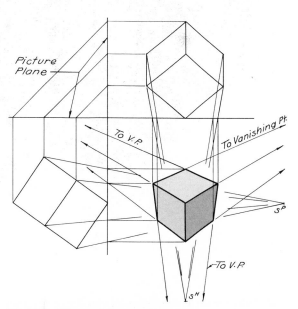

Fig. 17.6   Three-point perspective.

Each has its own advantages. A complete discussion of each method is given in later articles of the chapter.

17.6.1 Visual-ray method. This method is based directly on the definition of a perspective. See Art. 17.1 and Fig. 17.1. This method is very simple to understand and particularly useful for simple objects. It clarifies the meaning of perspective. See Fig. 17.7. It involves finding the piercing point of the visual ray with the picture plane. For the method of finding piercing points see Art. 13.7.2.

17.6.2 Vanishing-point method. This method consists of finding the perspective of two points in each line of an object. One of the points is the vanishing point for any series of parallel lines. This one point suffices for every line in the parallel group. See Fig. 17.8.

The other point is the piercing point of the lines on the object that are extended until they pierce the picture plane. The piercing point and the vanishing point determine the perspective of an infinite line. There is a separate piercing point for each line. See Fig. 17.14.

17.6.3 Combination method. This is the method most commonly used. In this method both the visual-ray method and the vanishing-point method are combined to obtain the greatest advantage from each. In Fig. 17.9 the perspective of the infinite line, of which AB is a segment, has been found by means of the vanishing-point method. The segment AB has been cut from the infinite line by visual rays. It is designated A_pB_p in Fig. 17.9.

17.6.4 Measuring-point and measuring-line method. This is a more sophisticated method for finding perspectives. The orthographic views are used only to obtain dimensions and are otherwise not directly involved in the construction. See Art. 17.16.3.

17.7 CONSTRUCTION BY THE VISUAL-RAY METHOD. Two methods of procedure may be employed, namely, by using the front and top views of both the object and the point of sight or by using the top and side views of both.

17.7.1 Front and top views. By this method it is only necessary to draw the visual rays from the object to the point of sight and find where they pierce the picture plane. This method has been used in Fig. 17.10 where visual rays from A to the point of sight S have been drawn in the top and front views. The vertical projection A_p of the point where this line pierces the vertical plane is the perspective of A. The remaining visible corners of the cube have been found in the same manner. They are then connected in the proper sequence to make the perspective. Only visible outlines are shown in perspective drawings.

17.7.2 Top and side views. In this method as in the preceding one it is necessary to lay out the top and side views of the object and of the point of sight all in proper relationship to the reference planes as shown in Fig. 17.11. As an example, note the following:

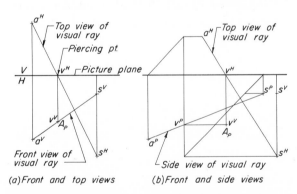

Fig. 17.7 Perspective of a point by the visual-ray method.

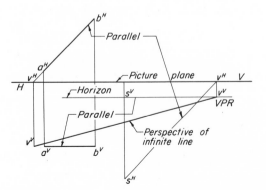

Fig. 17.8 Perspective of an infinite line by the vanishing point method.

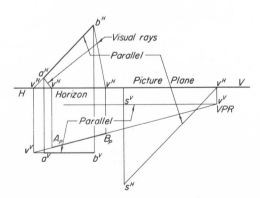

Fig. 17.9 Perspective of a line segment AB by the combination method.

a. In the top view the visual ray goes from a^H to s^H and pierces the vertical plane at v^H.

b. In the side view the visual ray goes from a^P to s^P and pierces the vertical or picture plane at v^P.

c. The vertical projection of the piercing point v^V is found by projecting down from v^H and across from v^P in the same manner as the front view of any point would be obtained from the top and side views.

It will be noted that the entire construction is simply orthographic projection throughout. The problem resolved itself into the simple one of finding the piercing point of visual rays with the *V*-plane.

17.8 CONSTRUCTION BY THE VANISHING-POINT METHOD. This method consists of the two operations listed in Art. 17.6.2. Before proceeding with the perspective of an object it is necessary to be able to find the vanishing point for any kind of line.

17.8.1 General principles for finding vanishing points. It can be observed in a number of the preceding figures that lines that are not parallel to the picture plane converge to a point in the perspective. By definition parallel lines meet at infinity. The perspective of this meeting place is called the vanishing point of the lines. To find the perspective of the vanishing point for any group of parallel lines it is necessary to do the following:

a. To construct a line through the point of sight parallel to the group of parallel lines. This new line meets the others at the same point at infinity.

b. To find the point where this new line, through the point of sight, pierces the picture plane or vertical plane.

It should be noted that two projections of the given line or group of parallel lines must be available or must be drawn. There must also be two projections of the line through the point of sight.

17.8.2 Vanishing points for horizontal lines. The identifying feature of horizontal lines is that their vertical projections are always parallel to the *H-V* reference line. Given the projections of line *AB* in Fig. 17.8 and the projections of the point of sight, proceed as follows:

a. Through s^H draw a line parallel to $a^H b^H$ and extend it to the picture plane as seen edgewise in the top or plan view.

b. Through s^V draw a line parallel to $a^V b^V$.

c. The vertical projection v^V directly below v^H is the piercing point of the line with the picture plane. It is marked *VPR* since it is a vanishing point at the right. For all horizontal lines the vanishing point is always in the horizon line.

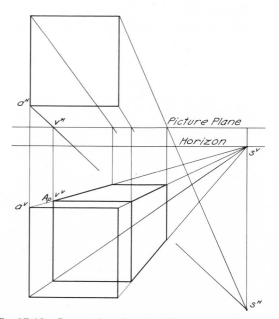

Fig. 17.10 Perspective of a cube. Visual-ray method using front and top views.

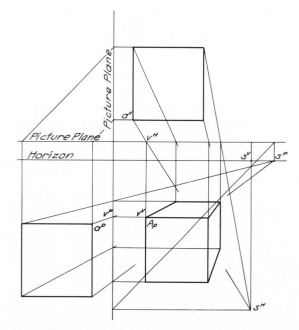

Fig. 17.11 Perspective of a cube. Visual-ray method using top and side views.

17.8.3   Vanishing point of oblique and inclined lines.

a. In Fig. 17.12(a) line *CD* is inclined upward to the rear and left. Follow the same three steps as in Art. 17.8.2. Note that the vanishing point *VPL* is to the left of the point of sight and above the horizon line.

b. In Fig. 17.12(b) line *EF* is inclined downward to the right and rear. Follow the same three steps as in Art. 17.8.2. Note that the vanishing point, marked *VPR*, is to the right of the point of sight and below the horizon line.

c. In Fig. 17.13 line *AB* is horizontal and also perpendicular to the picture plane. Following the same procedure as in Art. 17.8.2, it will be observed that *the vanishing point for lines perpendicular to the picture plane is always at the vertical projection of the point of sight s^V.*

17.9   CONSTRUCTION OF A PERSPECTIVE OF AN OBJECT BY THE VANISHING-POINT METHOD.

This method is well adapted to the construction of angular perspective. With a cube shown in the position of Fig. 17.14 proceed as follows:

a. Find the vanishing points for the two sets of parallel lines like *AB* and *AC*. These are marked *VPL* and *VPR* in Fig. 17.14. See Art. 17.8.2.

b. Extend all horizontal lines like *AB* and *AC* in Fig. 17.14 until they pierce the picture plane at v^H. There are eight lines, four in each direction, and eight piercing points all marked v^V.

c. Note that it is not necessary to have either a complete front or side view of the object. The elevation of the piercing points is obtained from the partial elevation of the cube at the left of Fig. 17.14.

d. We now have two points in every horizontal line on the cube, *VPR* being a point on all horizontal lines in the direction of *AC* and *VPL* being a point on every line in the direction of *AB*.

e. The crossing points of these lines in pairs locate the corners on the perspective of the cube such as A_p, B_p, and C_p.

f. Connecting the upper and lower corners of the cube by vertical lines completes the perspective. Note that vertical lines on the object are always vertical in the perspective since they are parallel to the picture plane.

17.10   COMBINATION METHOD.

This method makes judicious use of both the visual-ray method and the vanishing-point method. The combination makes

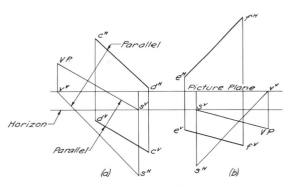

Fig. 17.12   Method of finding vanishing points.

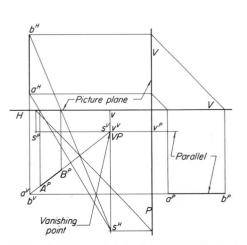

Fig. 17.13   Vanishing point for lines perpendicular to the picture plane.

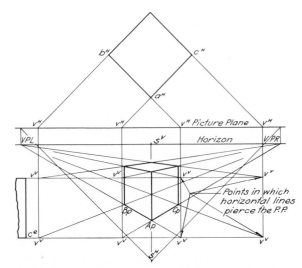

Fig. 17.14   Perspective by the vanishing-point method.

the most rapid and efficient use of both methods.

17.10.1   Perspective of an inclined line. To find the perspective of a finite segment of an inclined or oblique line proceed as follows:

a. From the two projections, s^H and s^V of the point of sight S, draw lines parallel to the corresponding projections of AB, as in Fig. 17.15(a).
b. Find where this line pierces the picture plane. The vertical projection of this point v^V is the vanishing point VP for line AB. Since this line is oblique, the VP is not in the horizon line.
c. Extend line AB until it pierces the picture plane at v_1^H. A perpendicular from v_1^H to $a^V b^V$ extended lo-

cates v_1^V, the vertical projection of the piercing point of the line with the picture plane.
d. Connect VP and v_1^V. This is the perspective of the infinite line.
e. In Fig. 17.15(b) draw the visual rays from s^H to a^H and b^H.
f. Where these rays cross the reference line, drop perpendiculars to the infinite line cutting off the line segment $A_p B_p$, which is the required perspective.

17.10.2   Perspective of a horizontal line on an object by the combination method. In the preceding problem it should be noted that two complete projections of the oblique line were required. For this problem and

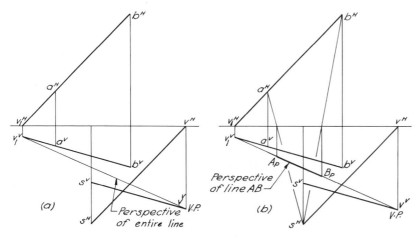

Fig. 17.15   Perspective of an inclined line by the combination vanishing-point and visual-ray method.

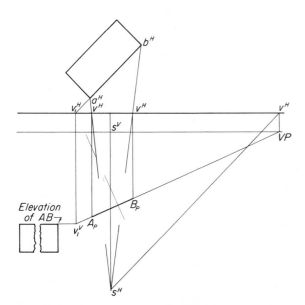

Fig. 17.16   Perspective of a horizontal line by the combination method.

all problems involving horizontal lines it is not necessary to have the correctly located vertical projection of the horizontal lines on the object. It is only necessary to have a view that will give the correct elevation of the horizontal lines as shown in Fig. 17.16. Proceed as follows:

a. Find the vanishing point of line AB. This will be in the horizon line. See Fig. 17.14. It is therefore not necessary to have a true front view of the box.
b. Extend $a^H b^H$ until it pierces the picture plane at v^H. The actual piercing point v^V is at the level of AB in the view at the left and is simply projected across to the vertical line from v^H.
c. Draw a line from v^V to VP.
d. Draw visual rays from s^H to a^H and b^H.
e. Drop perpendiculars from the points v^H, where the visual rays cross the picture plane, to the infinite line from v^V to VP.
f. This locates the perspective of the line segment $A_p B_p$.

17.11 KINDS OF PERSPECTIVE. The two common types of perspectives are the parallel perspective and angular perspective. The first is used mostly for interior views of buildings while the latter give more attractive results for the exterior views of buildings or larger civil engineering projects. A third type three-point perspective is discussed in Art. 17.17.

17.12 PARALLEL OR ONE-POINT PERSPECTIVE. When the object is placed so that one face is parallel to the picture plane and the others perpendicular to it, the resulting picture is known as parallel or one-point perspective. Except for interior views this is not usually the most desirable position for the object. It tends to move the point of sight over to one side in order to show two exterior sides of an object as shown in Fig. 17.17 and thus distorts the picture.

For this construction the more practical combination method will be used.

It is necessary to have the horizontal projection drawn in the proper relation to the reference or picture plane and any elevation in its proper relation to the horizon. The horizontal and vertical projection of the point of sight must also be given. This information for a small house is shown in Fig. 17.17(a).

The first step in the solution is always to find the vanishing points of the principal lines of the figure. In this case the lines parallel to the picture plane will have vanishing points at infinity, which means that any face parallel to the picture plane will show in the perspective in true shape but reduced in size, depending on the distance of the object behind the picture plane. The lines perpendicular to the picture plane will have a vanishing point that may be found by the method explained in Art. 17.8.3(c). In this case the lines drawn through S parallel to the given line must pierce the picture plane at a point whose vertical projection is at s^V, which therefore becomes the vanishing point for all lines perpendicular to the picture plane, as in Fig. 17.17(a). In other words, *the vertical projection of the point of sight is always the vanishing point for lines perpendicular to the picture plane.*

The next step is to extend one of these lines until it pierces the picture plane. Since this is a horizontal line, the piercing point will be at the level of the line as shown in the given elevation. This piercing point is marked v^V in Fig. 17.17(a). By joining the piercing point to the vanishing point the perspective of the complete line is formed. By visual rays the required points A_p and B_p on the line may be found to give one line on the building, as shown in Fig. 17.17(a). Other lines on the building may be found in the same manner, as illustrated in Fig. 17.17(b). It should be noticed that the front face of the building is true-shape but not true-size. The photograph in Fig. 17.18 is a parallel perspective.

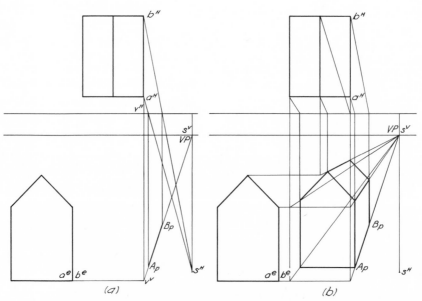

(a)   *(b)*

Fig. 17.17 Perspective of a building. Vanishing-point and visual-ray method.

17.13   ANGULAR OR TWO-POINT PERSPECTIVE BY THE COMBINATION METHOD. When one of the principal axes of the object is parallel and the other two are inclined to the picture plane, the resulting picture is called two-point perspective. In this case the required information, which is the same as that for parallel perspective, is shown in Fig. 17.19(*a*). Note

that a true profile projection is not required.

To find the perspective of any point it is necessary to find the perspective of a line through the point and then locate the point on the line by a visual ray. Any two points on the line will determine the line, but the best ones are the vanishing point and the *V*-piercing point.

Fig. 17.18   One-point photographic perspective of McGregor Lounge, Wayne State University.
(Courtesy of Minoru, Yamasaki and Associates, Archs., and Baltazor Korab, Photographer.)

a. The first step is to find the vanishing points of both sets of inclined horizontal lines that are parallel respectively to AB and AC. These vanishing points have been located at VPR and VPL in Fig. 17.19(b).

b. Then any line of the drawing such as AB in Fig. 17.19(b) may be extended to find its V-piercing point at v^V.

c. By connecting v^V with VPL, the vanishing point of AB, the perspective of the entire line is found.

d. Visual rays drawn to points A and B will serve to locate points A_p and B_p on the perspective of the line. These will be the perspectives of two corners of the building.

e. Another corner of the building, such as C in Fig.

17.19(c), may be located by connecting A_p with VPR, which is the vanishing point of line AC, and drawing the visual ray through C, thereby locating C_p on line AC.

f. Corner D of the building must be located exactly as was done for point A. Any horizontal line through D may be used if its vanishing point has been located.

17.14   PERSPECTIVE OF CIRCLES OR CURVES.
Thus far all objects shown have been made up of straight lines. In buildings, however, some circular parts such as arches are frequently involved. The circle will form the basis for the construction of many other curves.

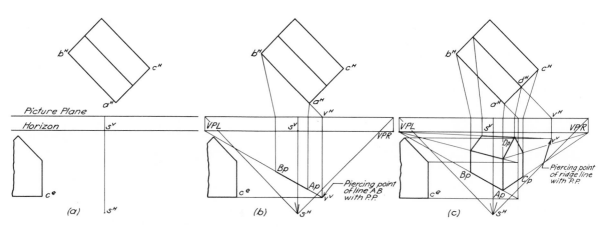

Fig. 17.19   Angular perspective. Vanishing-point and visual-ray method.

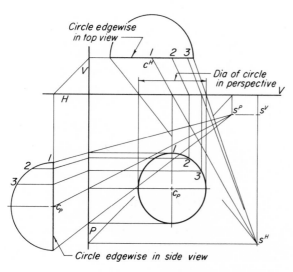

Fig. 17.20   Perspective of a circle parallel to the picture plane.

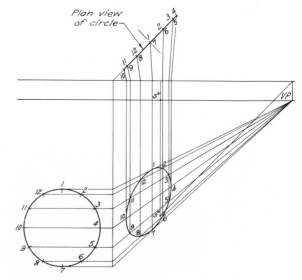

Fig. 17.21   Perspective of a circle in a vertical position inclined to the picture plane.

17.14.1 Circle parallel to the picture plane. If a circle is parallel to the picture plane as in Fig. 17.20, the horizontal projection is the edge view which is a straight line parallel to the V-plane. If visual rays are drawn from s^H to the circle, they form an oblique cone. The intersection of the picture plane and the cone is a circle having a diameter as shown in Fig. 17.20. With the center line piercing the plane at C_p and a diameter as shown, the circle can be drawn with a compass.

17.14.2 Circle in a vertical position. Figure 17.21 shows a circle in a vertical plane inclined to the picture plane. A series of points (12 in this case) are located and numbered in each view. Imaginary horizontal lines are drawn through these points and the perspective of the lines found in the usual way. The points are then located on these lines by visual rays. For this construction it is desirable to have all points located in each view.

17.14.3 Circle in a horizontal position. In Fig. 17.22 the perspective has been found by the vanishing-point method only.

Twelve points have been located on the plan view of the circle. Only the elevation shown by the heavy line at the lower left is needed. Draw two sets of imaginary horizontal lines through the points as shown in Fig. 17.22. Find the perspectives of these two sets of lines by means of the piercing points and the vanishing points. Where the lines intersect in pairs locates the points on the perspective.

17.15 VANISHING-POINT TRACES. In perspective a vanishing point may be found for any line.

Ordinarily they are useful only when it is necessary to find the perspective of a group of parallel lines. When two or more lines lie in a plane, the intersection of that plane with the plane of projection or picture plane forms a line. That line is the locus of vanishing points of all lines lying in that plane and is called a vanishing-point trace. Thus plane $ABCD$ in Fig. 17.23 is a vertical plane that intersects the picture plane in the vertical line marked VPL-$VPCD$. This line then becomes a locus on which the piercing point or vanishing point of every line in plane $ABCD$ will be found.

Any two points will determine a straight line; therefore, if it is possible to find any two vanishing points in a plane, the line joining them will be the vanishing point trace for that plane. Thus since the vanishing point of CD is at $VPCD$ and the vanishing point of DN is at VPR, the line joining $VPCD$ with VPR will be the vanishing-point trace for plane $CDNM$. In a similar manner it can be shown that VPL-$VPGK$ is the vanishing point trace for plane $GKNM$. It follows that the intersection of these two traces will be the vanishing point for line MN, which is the line of intersection of the two planes.

This principle is frequently useful in finding intersections of planes and in locating shadows in perspective.

17.16 MEASURING-POINT METHOD. The great advantage of this method over all other methods of perspective is that it is not necessary to set up the projections in any particular position and work from them by projection or visual rays.

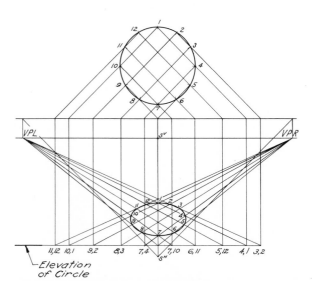

Fig. 17.22 Perspective of a circle in a horizontal position.

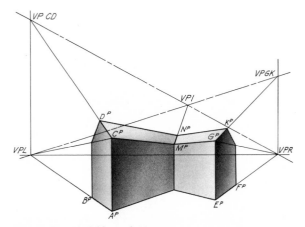

Fig. 17.23 Vanishing-point traces.

17.16.1 Measuring points and lines. When a vertical face that is inclined to the picture plane, such as face $ABCD$ in Fig. 17.24, is rotated until it lies in the picture plane, the vertical projection of this face in the revolved position $a_r{}^V b_r{}^V c_r{}^V d_r{}^V$ is coincident with the perspective of the revolved position. If the vanishing point of the line joining b^H to $b_r{}^H$ in Fig. 17.24 is found, the perspective of this line can be used to carry points from the revolved position to their correct position in the perspective. The vanishing point MPR, of line $b^H b_r{}^H$ is therefore called a measuring point. Since the vertical projection of the revolved position $a_r{}^V b_r{}^V c_r{}^V d_r{}^V$ is in true size, the horizontal lines $a_r{}^V b_r{}^V$ and $c_r{}^V d_r{}^V$ are true-length and any desired distances from A or D can be laid off along these projections. The projection $a_r{}^V b_r{}^V$ is therefore called a measuring line. The projection $c_r{}^V d_r{}^V$ could have been used equally well as a measuring line. In fact, a horizontal line can be drawn through any point that lies in the picture plane and used as a measuring line.

A simpler method for finding the measuring point MPR is illustrated in Fig. 17.24. If, through v^H, the H-projection of VPR, an arc having a radius $v^H s^H$ and center v^H, is drawn from s^H to the picture plane, this point on the picture plane may be projected straight down to MPR on the horizon.

Proof. Since $a^H b^H b_r{}^H$ was constructed as an isosceles triangle and since $v^H s^H v_1{}^H$ has its sides respectively parallel to $a^H b^H b_r{}^H$, the triangle $v^H s^H v_1{}^H$ is similar and is also an isosceles triangle. Therefore, $v^H s^H$ is equal to $v^H v_1{}^H$, and $v_1{}^H$ may be located by constructing the arc shown on the figure.

17.16.2 Selection of conditions for the perspective by the measuring point.

a. The vanishing points right and left are usually taken as far apart as convenient.
b. The picture plane and horizon are made to coincide.
c. The angles that the sides of the object make with the picture plane are chosen.
d. A front corner of the object is selected at a certain place on the picture plane.
e. If the vanishing points are chosen first, s^H is located by drawing lines from the vanishing points parallel to the sides of the object, which are usually at right angles to each other.

17.16.3 Construction of a perspective by the measuring-point method. In Fig. 17.25(a) the projections of an object are given. The problem is to draw the perspective so that the corner marked A will be in the picture plane 6 inches below the horizon and 1 inch right of the point of sight as in Fig. 17.25(d). Side AB is to make an angle of 60° with the picture plane, and the

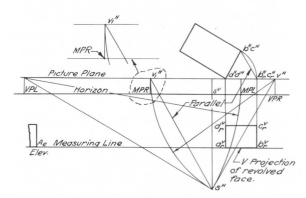

Fig. 17.24 Finding measuring points.

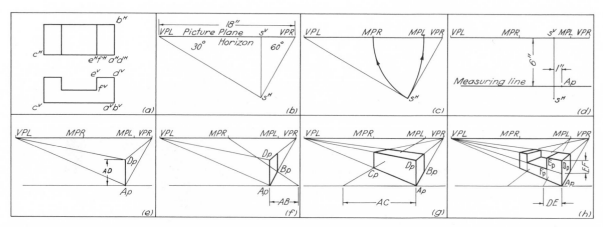

Fig. 17.25 Perspective by the measuring-point method.

vanishing points are to be 18 inches apart. The construction will then proceed in the following steps:

a. Figure 17.25(b). Draw a horizontal line near the top of the sheet and mark off the vanishing points 18 inches apart.

b. Figure 17.25(b). Through *VPR* construct a line at 60° with the picture plane and through *VPL* a line making 30° with the picture plane. The intersection of these two lines will locate s^H. The vertical projection s^V will be on the horizon. This assures that the faces of the block will form the specified angles with the picture plane.

c. Figure 17.25(c). Using *VPR* as a center, swing an arc through s^H to the picture plane to locate *MPR*. Using *VPL* as a center, swing an arc through s^H to the picture plane to locate *MPL*.

d. Figure 17.25(d). Measure 6 inches below the horizon and 1 inch right of the point of sight to locate the perspective of point *A*. Through this point draw a horizontal line, which is the measuring line for horizontal distances.

e. Figure 17.25(e). On a vertical line through A_p, lay out the height of the object *AD* to locate D_p. Draw lines from these points to *VPR* and *VPL*.

f. Figure 17.25(f). Lay out the distance *AB* on the horizontal measuring line to the right of A_p. From this point draw a line to *MPR* to intersect line from A_p to *VPR*, thus locating B_p. Erect a vertical line through B_p to give the right edge of the object.

g. Figure 17.25(g). Lay out the distance *AC* on the horizontal measuring line to the left of A_p. From this point draw a line to *MPL* to intersect the line from A_p to *VPL*. This locates C_p. Erect a vertical line through C_p to give the left edge of the object. Complete the outline of the figure by drawing to the proper vanishing points.

h. Figure 17.25(h). From D_p lay out on the vertical line the distance *FE*, which is the depth of the slot. From this point draw a line to *VPL*. From A_p lay out the distance *DE* on the horizontal measuring line to the left of A_p. Connect this point to *MPL* to intersect the line from A_p to *VPL*. Erect a perpendicular to locate points E_p and F_p, which establishes the right side of the slot. In a similar manner locate the left side of the slot.

i. Connect these points to the proper vanishing points to complete the picture.

17.16.4   Perspective of a vertical circle by the measuring-point method. By taking measurements from the orthographic projections, points on a circle may be located in perspective by the use of coordinates, but this is a tedious process and should be avoided if possible.

The better method is to find the perspective of a square circumscribing the circle and then obtain the ellipse by the diagonal method. For a circle lying in a vertical face the procedure is illustrated in Fig. 17.26 and the steps are listed below.

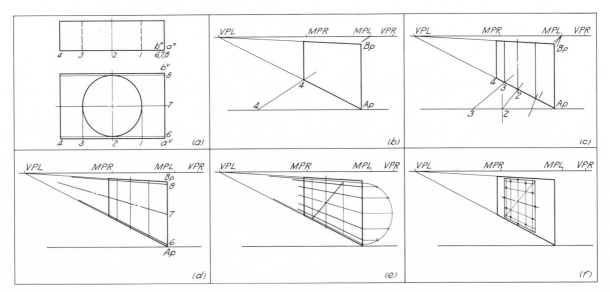

Fig. 17.26   Circle in a vertical plane by the measuring-point method.

a. Figure 17.26(*b*). Find the perspective of the front face of the object shown in Fig. 17.26(*a*) by the method given in the preceding paragraph.

b. Figure 17.26(*c*). On the measuring line through A_p lay out the horizontal distance *A-2*, from *A* to the center line of the circle, to the left of A_p. On either side of this point lay out the radius of the circle to locate points *1* and *3*. Carry the three points back into the picture by drawing lines to *MPL*.

c. Figure 17.26(*d*). From A_p lay out the vertical distance *A-7*, from *A* to the center line of the circle, on the front corner of the object. On either side of this point lay out the radius of the circle to locate points *6* and *8*. From these three points draw to *VPL* to form the perspective of the square circumscribing the circle.

d. Figure 17.26(*e*). On either of the vertical lines construct a semicircle as shown. Divide the semicircle into six equal parts and project these points hori-

zontally to the vertical line that was used as the diameter of the construction circle. From these points on the vertical line draw lines to *VPL*.

e. Figure 17.26(*f*). Construct the diagonal of the square and complete the grid by constructing vertical lines through the points where the horizontal lines cross the diagonal of the square and mark the points as shown in the figure.

17.16.5   Perspective of a horizontal circle by the measuring-point method. When the circle lies in a horizontal plane, the procedure is similar except that the semicircle must be drawn on the measuring line, as illustrated in Fig. 17.27. When the points have been carried back into the perspective by means of the measuring points and vanishing points, the grid is constructed by using the diagonal as previously explained.

17.16.6   One-point measuring point and line. It is sometimes convenient to use the same measuring point for distances on both sides of an object in perspective. However, to be able to do this, it is necessary to locate a new measuring line.

The construction for this method is illustrated in Fig. 17.28. The steps are as follows:

a. Figure 17.28(*a*). This figure shows the two-vanishing-point method for finding a perspective. The vanishing point, *VP* 45°, for a line making 45° with the two principal lines has been added. In all of this construction the picture plane and the horizon are coincident.

b. Figure 17.28(*b*). With *VPL* as a center, an arc is drawn through *VP* 45°. The intersection of this arc with the two-point measuring line locates point *X*.

c. Figure 17.28(*c*). A line is constructed from *VPL* through *X* and is continued until it intersects an arc drawn through s^H with its center at *VPL*. Through the point of intersection marked *y* the one-point

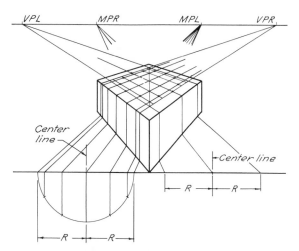

Fig. 17.27   Horizontal circle by the measuring-point method.

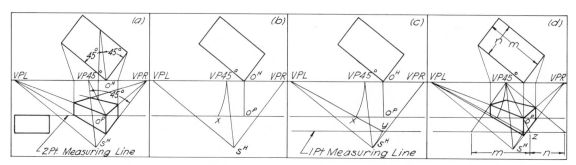

Fig. 17.28   One-point measuring point and line.

measuring line may be constructed parallel to the picture plane.

d. Figure 17.28(d). If a line is drawn from *VP* 45° through O^p and continued until it intersects the one-point measuring line, point *Z* is located. *Z* is the point from which distances *m* and *n* may be laid out in opposite directions on the one-point measuring line. From the points thus obtained lines may be drawn to *VP* 45° to cut off the perspective lines through O^p to determine the size of the perspective. Visual rays have been added to show that both methods give the same results.

17.17 THREE-POINT PERSPECTIVE. When all three of the principal axes of an object are oblique to the picture plane, the resulting picture is called a three-point perspective. The theory of perspective as it has been developed for one- and two-point perspective can be extended to three-point. However, the actual construction is more complicated because the picture plane does not appear edgewise in the top view. It is possible to solve the problem by visual rays, as shown in Fig. 17.6, but the solution is tedious and will not be discussed here. If it is desired to specify the angle of tilt of the picture plane and the angle of rotation of the object, the reader should refer to *Industrial Production Illustration* by R. P. Hoelscher, C. H. Springer, and R. F. Pohle, McGraw-Hill Book Co., New York, 1943; and *Handbook of Perspective* by J. C. Morehead and J. C. Morehead, Jr., Pittsburgh, 1941.

The customary procedure is to select the three vanishing points as far apart as convenient and work from these points in the manner illustrated in Fig. 17.29 and explained below.

a. Figure 17.29(a). Select the three vanishing points and draw the triangle connecting them. Through each corner construct a line perpendicular to the opposite side of the triangle. These three lines intersect at point *S*, which is the projection of the point of sight as determined by the selected vanishing points.

b. Figure 17.29(b). Revolve the top plane into the picture plane as explained in Art. 15.21.2 for axonometric. With *VPR* as a center and *VPR-s_r* as a radius, swing an arc to locate *MPR*. With *VPL* as a center and *VPL-s_r* as a radius, swing an arc to locate *MPL*.

c. Figure 17.29(c). Revolve the right-side plane *S*, *VPR*, *VPV* into the picture plane as explained in

Art. 15.21.2. With *VPV* as a center and *VPV-s_r* as a radius, swing an arc to locate *MPV*. If desired, another *MPR* may be located, but this is not necessary since one has already been found.

d. Figure 17.29(d). Select A_p as a point in the picture plane in such a position that the center of the picture will come approximately at *S*.

Through A_p, draw a line parallel to *VPL-VPR*. This is a measuring line, and distances may be laid out for right or left distances and front or back distances just as explained for two-point perspective in Art. 17.16.3. The top of the box is obtained as shown in Fig. 17.29(d).

e. Figure 17.29(e). Construct a line through A_p parallel to *VPR-VPV* and on this line lay out the height of the box from A_p. From the point draw to *MPV* to intersect the line from A_p to *VPV*. This determines the height of the box in the perspective.

f. Figure 17.29(f). From the points already located draw to the proper vanishing point to complete the perspective of the box.

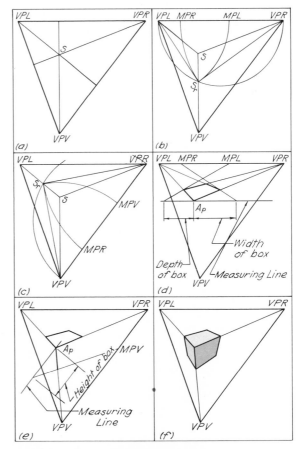

Fig. 17.29 Three-point perspective.

17.17.1   Isometric three-point perspective.* For the special case of three-point perspective in which the three principal vanishing points lie on the corners of an equilateral triangle, an easy construction has been developed that has the same relation to the theoretical three-point perspective that isometric drawing has to isometric projection.

The construction is as follows:

a. Figure 17.30(a). Lay out an equilateral triangle of the size desired, usually the maximum a drawing board will accommodate, and let the corners be the three vanishing points.

b. Figure 17.30(b). Select a point A_p in the picture plane and through this point construct two measuring lines, one parallel to *VPL-VPR* and the other parallel to *VPR-VPV* (or *VPL-VPV*).

c. Figure 17.30(c). On the horizontal line lay out the right and left or length dimension of the box to the left of A_p. Lay out the front and back dimensions or depth of the box to the right of A_p. Draw to the vanishing point as shown. This determines the top of the enclosing box for any object.

d. Figure 17.30(d). On the measuring line parallel to *VPR-VPV* lay out the height of the box and draw to the vanishing point *VPR* as shown. The lower corner of the box is located at the point where this

line crosses the line from A_p to *VPV*. Complete the box by drawing to the proper vanishing points. Other dimensions of an object may be laid out in the same manner.

17.17.2   Alternate method for three-point perspective. When the orthographic projections of the object are available at a scale that is convenient for use, the method illustrated in Fig. 17.31 is very expedient. In using this construction it is best to work on tracing paper placed directly over the appropriate views of the object. The procedure is as follows:

a. On the tracing paper lay out the three vanishing points as far apart as convenient and join them to form the triangle, *VPL-VPR-VPV*.

b. Revolve the top plane as shown in Fig. 17.31 to obtain s_r.

c. Assume point A^P, which is one corner of the object, in the picture plane.

d. Arrange the horizontal projection or plan view under the tracing paper with sides parallel respectively to s_r-*VPR* and s_r-*VPL*.

e. Join A^P to *VPR* and *VPL*.

f. Join a^H, b^H, c^H, and d^H to s_r.

g. The perspective of B is located at B^P where $b^H s_r$ intersects A^P-*VPR* and the perspective of D at D^P where $d^H s_r$ intersects A^P-*VPL*.

h. This locates the top plane of the object at $A^P B^P C^P D^P$.

i. By revolving one of the side faces and proceeding in

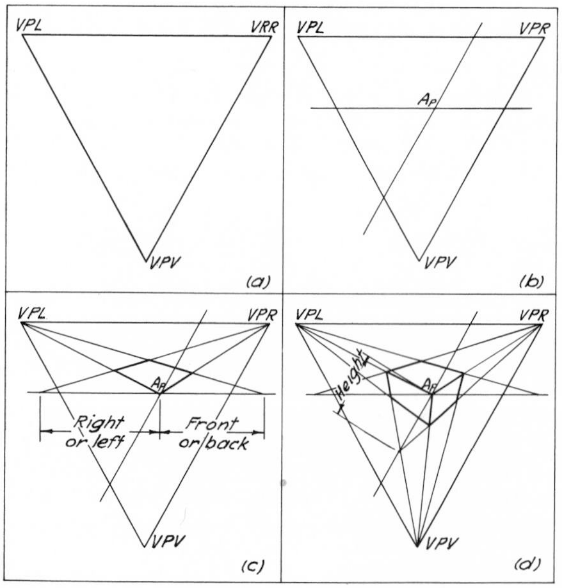

*This method was developed by Wayne Shick of the University of Illinois and is reproduced by his permission.

Fig. 17.30   Three-point perspective drawing.

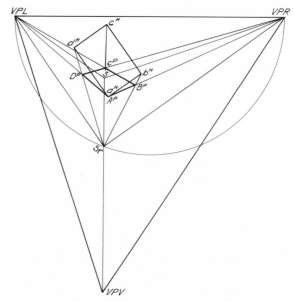

Fig. 17.31   Alternate method of three-point perspective.

a similar manner, the vertical faces of the object can be located.

17.17.3 Three-point perspective board. The big disadvantage of three-point perspective is that it is very difficult to get the vanishing points far enough apart to avoid excessive perspective effect. Even on a very large drawing board the triangle is so small that the lines vanish too rapidly for a good appearance. To avoid this, it is fairly easy to construct a special board by means of which the vanishing points can be widely separated. The board is shown in Fig. 17.32. The three arcs are constructed with their centers at the three vanishing points. Then by means of a special T-square so arranged that one edge is exactly centered between the two bearing points of the head, lines may be drawn that always point to the center of the circle. The use of this T-square is illustrated in the figure.

By means of the construction explained in Art. 17.16.6, the 45° vanishing points are located for each face together with the corresponding one-point measuring lines. These lines are marked off in unit divisions as illustrated, and from these divisions the accurate perspective can be found directly. In this figure a rectangular solid 3 × 4 × 5 has been drawn. With three measuring points and lines, it is possible to make each measurement in two different ways. Lines showing both sets appear in the figure.

17.18 SHADES AND SHADOWS IN PERSPECTIVE.
When light shines on an object, a part of the surface will be lighted and the remaining part will be dark.

That part of the surface on which no light shines is said to be in shade. The lines on the object that separate the light areas from the shaded areas are called shade lines. When the object rests on or is adjacent to some other object, it casts a shadow, which may be outlined by finding the shadow of the shade lines. To find the shadow of an object, therefore, two things are necessary; first, to pick out the shade lines and, second, to find the shadow of these lines on the surfaces on which the shadow falls.

To recognize the shade line requires a knowledge of the direction of the light ray and the ability to visualize the object as it stands in space. In case of doubt it is possible to find the shadow of every line on the object, after which the largest area outlined by these shadows will be the shadow of the object.

When the light rays are tangent to any surface, that surface is said to be in shade.

17.18.1 Shadow of a vertical line. A vertical line resting on a horizontal plane is used as the basic line in determining shadows. One reason for this is that, since the horizontal projection of a vertical line is a point, the horizontal projection of the shadow of the line must coincide with the horizontal projection of a light ray. When the direction of the light ray is specified by two projections of one ray, as MN in Fig. 17.33, the shadow of line AB in the horizontal projection must be a line through $a^H b^H$ parallel to $m^H n^H$. Since that shadow is a horizontal line, it must have its vanishing point on the horizon. That vanishing point may be found at VPS in the usual manner, as shown in Fig.

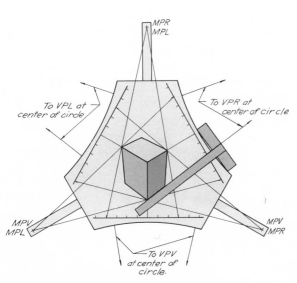

Fig. 17.32 Three-point perspective board.

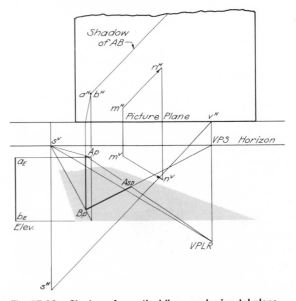

Fig. 17.33 Shadow of a vertical line on a horizontal plane.

17.33. Then the shadow of AB on the horizontal plane must vanish at VPS and, since B is on the horizontal plane, the shadow must start at B_p. By joining B_p to VPS, the shadow of a vertical line of infinite height is obtained. To find the shadow of A, it is then necessary to draw the perspective of the light ray through A and find the point where it intersects the shadow line. The vanishing point of the light ray MN, found as explained in Art. 17.8.3, is located at the point marked $VPLR$. Then, by joining A_p to $VPLR$, point A_{sp} is located, and the actual shadow of the line lies between B_p and A_{sp}.

In finding shades and shadows in perspective, *it is always necessary to locate first the vanishing points VPS and VPLR. Always remember that VPS is the vanishing point of the shadow of the vertical line on a horizontal plane* and nothing more.

When the vertical line casts a shadow on a vertical plane, the shadow must be parallel to the line and in two-point perspective will show as a vertical line. The best way to find this shadow is to find the shadow of

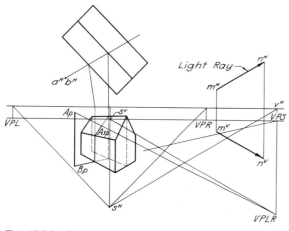

Fig. 17.34 Shadow of a vertical line on a vertical and an inclined surface.

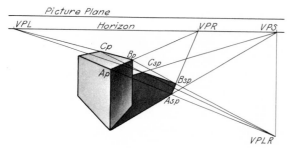

Fig. 17.35 Shadow of a horizontal line on a horizontal plane.

the line on the horizontal base plane until it crosses the base line of the vertical plane. From there the shadow will be vertical, as illustrated by the shadow or the flagpole in Fig. 17.34. The location of this vertical shadow can also be found by means of a visual ray from the plan or top view, as indicated in the figure.

When the shadow falls on an inclined surface such as the roof of the building in Fig. 17.34, it is necessary to locate two points on the shadow of the line or the line extended. One point on the eave line has already been located, and another can easily be located on the ridge line. One method is by visual ray, as shown in Fig. 17.34. The other method, which is better since it can also be used when working by measuring-point method, involves cutting a vertical plane through the center of the building, as indicated by the dotted line. Then by imagining the front of the building removed the shadow on the section plane can be found, which will locate the desired point on the ridge line. This construction is shown in dashed lines in Fig. 17.34. The shadow of the flagpole on the roof will be the line joining the point on the eave line to the point on the ridge line, and a light ray through the top of the flagpole to $VPLR$ will locate the end of the shadow.

17.18.2   Shadow of a horizontal line. When a horizontal line casts a shadow on a horizontal plane, the shadow will be parallel to the line itself. In perspective this means that the two lines will have the same vanishing point. Thus, in Fig. 17.35, line AB vanishes at VPR, and consequently its shadow must also vanish at VPR. BC vanishes at VPL, and its shadow also vanishes at VPL.

When a horizontal line casts a shadow on a vertical or inclined plane, the shadow of two points on the line, or one point and the direction, must be found on the given plane. Thus, in Fig. 17.36, line AB casts a shadow

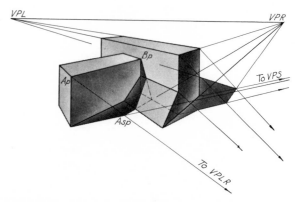

Fig. 17.36 Shadow of a horizontal line on various planes.

on the horizontal, inclined, and vertical planes. The shadow on the horizontal plane vanishes at *VPR*, and if the inclined plane were removed, it would continue to the base of the vertical plane and from there would go to B_p because B is actually on the vertical face. The intersection of this shadow on the vertical face with the top line of the inclined face gives a second point on the inclined plane to determine the shadow of the horizontal line on the inclined plane. A vertical line through A_p can be used to locate A_{sp}, which is the shadow of A on the ground. The shadow of the inclined line AB is found by joining A_{sp} to *VPR*.

17.18.3 Shadow of an inclined line on a horizontal surface. To find the shadow of an inclined line it is usually best to assume as many vertical lines as necessary through points on the line and find the shadows of these vertical lines. For example, in Fig. 17.37 a vertical line was assumed through B_p. By means of this vertical line the shadow of B_p on the ground was found at B_{sp}. Note that the vertical line through B_p is an imaginary line.

17.18.4 Shadow of an inclined line on horizontal, vertical, and inclined planes. The conical structure in Fig. 17.38 will cast a shadow on the house, but the actual lines that cast the shadow, called the shade lines, are elements of the cone and must be found as a part of the first step. As in the preceding illustration, it is necessary to establish a vertical line, which in this case is the altitude of the cone called AB. The shadow of AB on the ground is found in the usual manner, by drawing from B^P to *VPS* and from A^P to *VPLR*. The intersection of these two lines $A_s{}^P$ gives the shadow of A on the ground. Since the base of the cone rests on the ground, the entire shadow of the cone on the ground can be found by drawing from $A_s{}^P$ tangent to both sides of the base. The points of tangency C^P and D^P of those lines with the base locate the shade lines A^PC^P and A^PD^P on the cone. The problem then is to find the

shadow of these inclined shade lines on the various planes.

The shadow of the shade lines on the ground has already been determined, and from these shadows points E^P and F^P at the base of the wall may be located. Next the imaginary shadow of A on the wall extended is found at A_{sw}^P by use of the vertical line AB. By joining this point with E^P and F^P the shadow of the cone on the vertical wall is found.

The shadow of AB on the inclined roof is found to be K^PN^P, as explained in Art. 17.18.1. By extending K^PN^P until it intersects the light ray through A^P, the shadow of point A on the inclined roof extended is located at A_{SR}^P. By connecting A_{SR}^P to R^P and S^P the shadow of the cone on the inclined roof is completed. The various parts of the shadow may be shaded to give the complete picture as shown in Fig. 17.38.

17.18.5 Shadow of a curved line. The shadow of a curved line may be found by assuming a series of vertical lines through points on the curve. The shadow of these vertical lines may be found in the usual manner and the shadow of the point located on the shadow of the line. This is illustrated in Fig. 17.39.

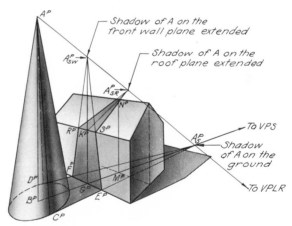

Fig. 17.38 Shadow of an inclined line on various planes.

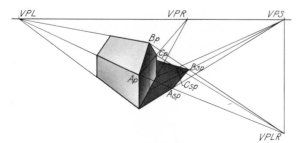

Fig. 17.37 Shadow of an inclined line on a horizontal plane.

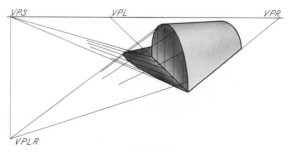

Fig. 17.39 Shadow of a curved line.

17.18.6 Reflections. Whenever water appears in the foreground of a perspective, the building or structure shown in the picture will also show in the water as a reflection. To obtain the perspective of the reflection, the elevation of the structure being shown may be reversed about the waterline and the complete perspective of this inverted object may be constructed in the same manner as the original perspective. Figure 17.40 shows the elevation of the corner of a building standing on the bank of a body of water, with the picture plane and water surface shown edgewise. Point C is the corner of a building, C_w is the projection of C on the surface of the water, and C_R is the position of C in the reversed elevation.

Point S is the point of sight for the perspective and, therefore, the piercing points of the visual rays in the picture plane will locate the perspectives of C, C_w, and C_R at C_p, C_{wp}, and C_{Rp}, respectively. By plane geometry it can be shown that, since the two distances, y, were constructed equal, the three angles marked $\propto$ must be equal. Then the perspective of C_R must coincide with the perspective of the reflection of C on the

water surface, thus proving that the reflection of an object may be obtained in this manner.

By geometry it can also be shown that, since the two distances marked y were constructed equal, the two distances marked y' must also be equal. Since these distances are measured directly in the perspective, it becomes possible to locate the reflection of any point in a two-point perspective by measuring the distance, y', from the perspective of the point, C_p, to the perspective of its projection on the water surface, C_{wp}, and laying that distance below C_{wp} on the water surface to locate C_{Rp}, which is the reflection of point C. This gives a rapid method of finding the reflection of any point, without drawing the reversed elevation. In a three-point perspective, the reversed elevation must be drawn and the reflection found in the same manner as the real perspective.

The lines in the reflection should be made irregular and broken to represent wave action. The surface of the water can be indicated by a series of irregular horizontal lines whose spacing increases toward the front of the drawing. Figure 17.41 shows a perspective with shades, shadows, and reflections. Figure 17.42 shows

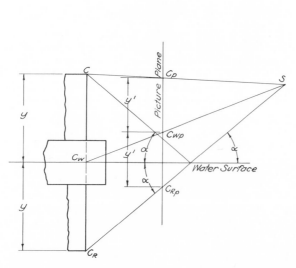

Fig. 17.40 Theory of reflections.

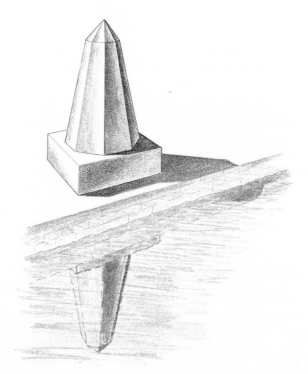

Fig. 17.41 Shades, shadows, and reflections in perspective.

the method for finding reflections by reversing distances in the perspective.

17.19   SKETCHING IN PERSPECTIVE. Sketching in perspective is more difficult than sketching in any of the other pictorial forms. The student should be thoroughly familiar with the technique of sketching as discussed in Chapter 5.

17.19.1   Proportioning. As in all other sketching, proportioning of the sketch is the most important phase. Since the enclosing box method gives the best approach to the problem, the first step is to obtain the proper proportions for the box. Since dimensions are not the same along the three axes of the box, the construction is best made on the basis of a cube. The following suggestions give a choice of two positions of the basic cube and the proportions of the sides to the chosen height as shown in Fig. 17.43. The steps in Fig. 17.43(a) are as follows.

a. Select the two vanishing points as far apart as desired. Note that they must be on the same horizontal line.

b. Halfway between the vanishing points sketch a ver-

tical line to represent the height of the basic cube you wish to draw.

c. Place the upper end of this line as far below the horizon line as you wish if the top of the cube is to be shown. The farther below the horizon line, the more the top shows.

d. Draw lines from the top and bottom of the vertical line to both vanishing points.

e. Sketch two other vertical lines on opposite sides of the center, each at a distance of ½h from it as shown in Fig. 17.43(a).

f. From corners E_p and F_p draw lines to the vanishing points, thus completing the top of the cube.

This now represents a cube whose faces make 45° with the picture planes.

If it is desired to have a cube in the position shown in Fig. 17.43(b), which makes the faces at 30° and 60° with the picture plane, use the same steps as given for the 45° cube but use the dimensions given in Fig. 17.43(b).

17.19.2   Proportioning a box by repeating the basic cube. The basic cube must have been constructed on the smallest dimension of the box if the repetitive method is to be followed.

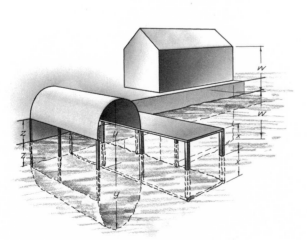

Fig. 17.42   Method of finding reflections.

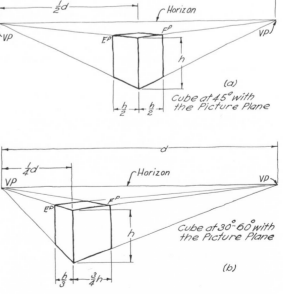

Fig. 17.43   Proportioning a cube in perspective sketching.

a. Repeating the cube. When the sketch of the cube has been completed as in Fig. 17.44(*a*), the general proportion of the object can be obtained by extending the lines and building other similar cubes. In Fig. 17.44(*b*) the diagonals and main center lines of one face of the original cube have been drawn. Next the diagonal line *AB* is drawn joining the top center point to the left center point and is continued to locate *C*. Through *C* the vertical line *CDE* is drawn to locate *D* and *E*. The procedure is continued until the desired number of cubes have been formed. In this case the proportion desired was $1 \times 1 \times 3$. In Fig. 17.44(*c*) the beginning of the same steps is shown in order to place another cube on top of the first one. When completed, this will give a box whose proportions are $1 \times 2 \times 3$. This method is discussed in Chapter 5.

b. Proportioning a box by subdividing a cube. Figure 17.45 shows a more accurate method for obtaining a box in the proportions of $1 \times 2 \times 3$. In this case the original cube is made large enough to represent the largest dimension. By subdividing this cube, using the method explained in Art. 4.2.11 and illustrated in Fig. 17.45, the proper proportion is ob-

tained. This construction can be continued to locate the details of the object. The use of the construction is more important in perspective than in axonometric, because distances decrease in size as they get farther behind the picture plane.

17.19.3 Sketching circles in perspective. The best method for sketching a circle in perspective is to sketch the square circumscribing the circle and then draw the circle inside the square. It is well to locate the center point of the sides by means of the diagonals and center lines. This is illustrated in Fig. 17.46(*a*).

The proportions of circles in horizontal planes vary as the circle is placed above or below the horizon. When the circle is on the horizon it will show in perspective as a straight line. As it moves away from the horizon, the circle appears as an ellipse. The minor axes of the ellipse increase with respect to the major axes as the circle is moved farther from the horizon. This process is shown in Fig. 17.46(*b*).

17.19.4 Steps in sketching a perspective. When a perspective sketch of an object such as that shown in Fig. 17.47(*a*) is to be made, the draftsman should follow the steps listed below.

a. Establish a basic proportion. In this case it would be approximately $1 \times 2 \times 3$.

b. Draw a horizontal line to represent the horizon and pick two points on it as far apart as possible to represent the vanishing points. See Fig. 17.47(*b*).

c. Establish the front corner of the object for position and size.

d. Construct the basic cube and, from that, block in the outline of the object as discussed in Art. 5.14. See Fig. 17.47(*c*).

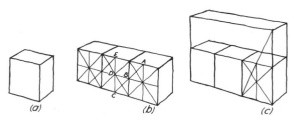

Fig. 17.44 **Proportioning a box in perspective sketching by adding cubes.**

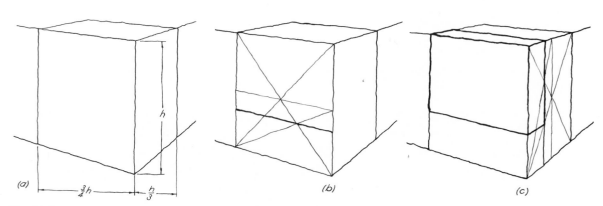

Fig. 17.45 **Proportioning a box in perspective sketching by subdividing a cube.**

e. Locate the position of the slot by subdividing the left front face. See Fig. 17.47(*d*).

f. Locate the center of the circle and construct a square circumscribing the circle by methods of proportions. This is illustrated in Fig. 17.47(*e*).

g. Draw the circle. See Fig. 17.47(*e*).

h. Clean up the drawing and make the lines heavy. Shade if desired. See Fig. 17.47(*f*).

17.20 PERSPECTIVE GRID. It is possible to purchase sets of ruled sheets similar to the one shown in Fig. 17.48 for the purpose of making perspective drawings. This grid is designed so that the faces make 30° and 60° with the picture plane.

The best way to use the grid is to draw the perspective plan of the building on the grid at the bottom of the figure. These points may then be projected up to the perspective. It must be remembered that the vertical line marked zero is the only line on which vertical dimensions may be measured. Therefore, everything must be referred to that line. Thus to locate the perspective of point *A* it is necessary to start at a point on the zero vertical line at the proper elevation. From that point it is possible to move to the left on a line vanishing to the left, to the vertical line marked *10*.

From that point a line can be drawn to the right vanishing point and the perspective of *A* is directly above the plan of *A* in the lower grid.

The same procedure must be followed for every point.

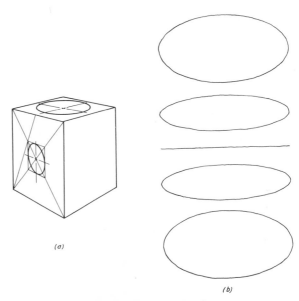

Fig. 17.46 Sketching circles in perspective.

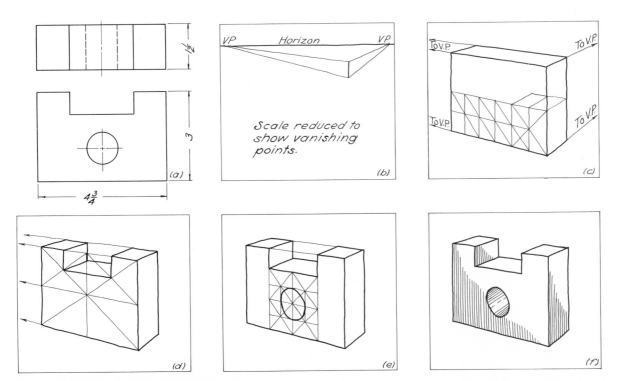

Fig. 17.47 Steps in making a perspective sketch.

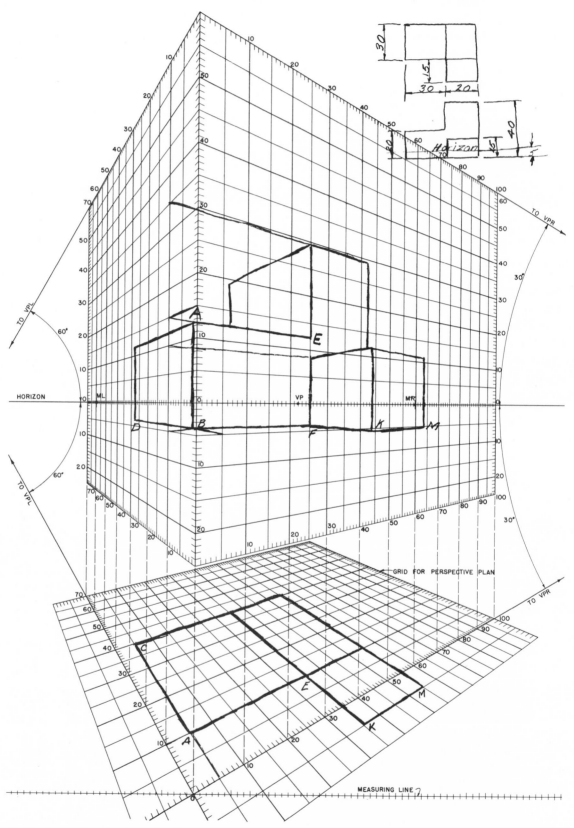

Fig. 17.48 Perspective sketch on grid. (Courtesy of Grace Wilson.)

SELF-STUDY QUESTIONS

Before trying to answer these questions, read the chapter carefully. Then, without reference to the text, answer as many questions as possible. For those that cannot be answered, the number, in parentheses following the question number, gives the article in which the answer can be found. Look it up and write down the answer. Check the answers that you did give to see that they are correct.

17.1 **(17.1)** The major difference between perspective and other forms of projections is that the point of _____ is at a _____ distance from the object.

17.2 **(17.2.2)** Visual rays are the lines connecting a point on the object with the _____ of sight.

17.3 **(17.2.3)** The _____ _____ is usually used as the _____ plane for most perspectives.

17.4 **(17.2.4)** Each set of parallel lines on an object, except those that are parallel to the picture plane, has a _____ point.

17.5 **(17.2.5)** The horizon line always passes through the _____ projection of the point of sight.

17.6 **(17.3.2)** For normal perspectives the picture plane is _____ the point of sight and the object.

17.7 **(17.4.1)** For good perspective the point of sight should be _____ the width of the object from it.

17.8 **(17.5.1)** If the object has one principal face _____ to the picture plane, a parallel or _____ _____ perspective will be produced.

17.9 **(17.5.2)** If two faces of an object are at _____ _____ with the picture plane, an angular or two-point perspective will be produced.

17.10 **(17.5.3)** An oblique perspective has _____ faces of the object inclined to the picture plane.

17.11 **(17.6.1)** The visual-ray method of finding a perspective involves finding the _____ point of the visual ray with the picture plane.

17.12 **(17.7.1; 17.7.2)** Either the front and top views or the _____ and side views may be used in making a perspective by the visual-ray method.

17.13 **(17.8.1)** By definition _____ lines meet at infinity.

17.14 **(17.6.2)** To find the perspective of a line, the vanishing point, and the point where the line extended _____ the picture plane must be found.

17.15 **(17.8.2)** The vanishing points for horizontal lines are always in the _____ line.

17.16 **(17.8.3)** The vanishing points of oblique lines are either above or _____ the horizon line, never on it.

17.17 **(17.8.3c)** Lines that are perpendicular to the picture plane have their vanishing point at the _____ projection of the point of sight.

17.18 **(17.14.1)** The perspective of a circle that is parallel to the picture plane is a _____.

17.19 **(17.18.1)** The shadow of a vertical line on a horizontal plane will coincide with the _____ projection of the visual ray through the line.

17.20 **(17.18.2)** The shadow of a horizontal line on a horizontal plane will be _____ to the line. Therefore, the line and its shadow will have the same _____ point.

PROBLEMS

In the following problems the location of the views is given with reference to the border-lines of standard A- and B-size sheets.

Size *A* is 11 × 17 or 12 × 18

Size B is 8½ × 11 or 9 × 12

The scale for each size sheet is given within the problem. These layouts if carefully followed should bring the horizontal projection S^H of the point of sight and both vanishing points, where there are two, within the border lines.

Make all construction lines lightly but clearly so that your problem can be checked for accuracy and method of construction.

17.1–17.6 Make a parallel perspective of a problem assigned from Figs. 17.49 through 17.54. In your construction use only the top and side views. It will be necessary to find the side view of the point of sight.

17.7–17.12 Make an angular perspective of an object assigned from Figs. 17.55 through 17.60. Use the method assigned by your instructor.

The problems in the following group may be solved by any method discussed in this chapter. The layouts have been made for angular perspective. These can be drawn most rapidly by the combination vanishing-point and visual-ray method.

For parallel perspectives, notes have been added on each of the simpler drawings specifying the location and position of the plan view. In all cases the elevation should be placed out of the range of the perspective at the left or right.

For shades and shadows in perspective, the direction of the light ray has been specified verbally in the figure for some of the simpler objects.

17.13 Make an angular perspective of the outdoor fireplace shown in Fig. 17.61 by the combination visual-ray and vanishing-point method.

17.14 Same as Problem 17.13, using vanishing-point method only.

17.15 Make a parallel perspective of the outdoor fireplace shown in Fig. 17.61. See note in the figure for position of object relative to the picture plane and the point of sight.

17.16 Make the perspective specified in Problem 17.13, and then find the shades and shadows, assuming the light

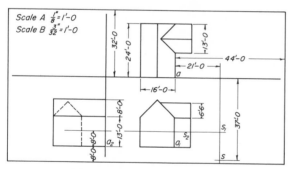

Fig. 17.49   Ell-house outline.

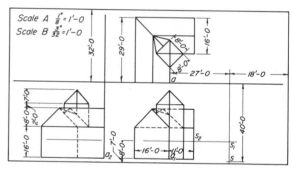

Fig. 17.50   Church outline.

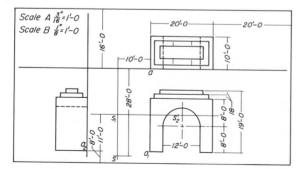

Fig. 17.51   Memorial arch.

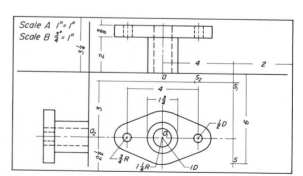

Fig. 17.52   Bearing.

ray to be parallel to the vertical plane and to make an angle of 45° with the horizontal plane, down to the right.

17.17 Make an angular perspective of the cube shown in Fig. 17.53 by any assigned method.

17.18 Make a parallel perspective of the cube shown in Fig. 17.53. See note in the figure for the relative position of the object and point of sight.

17.19 Make a perspective of the monument shown in Fig. 17.62 by the visual-ray method.

17.20 Make a perspective of the monument that is illustrated in Fig. 17.62 by using the combination visual-ray and vanishing-point method.

17.21 Make the perspective assigned in Problem 17.20 and then find the shades and shadows, assuming the light ray to have the following position: horizontal projection 30° with ground line, up to the right; vertical projection 45° with ground line, down to the right.

17.22 Make an angular perspective of the memorial fountain shown in Fig. 17.63 by the combination vanishing-point and visual-ray method.

17.23 Make a parallel perspective of the memorial fountain shown in Fig. 17.63. See note in the figure for the relative position of object and point of sight.

17.24 Make an angular perspective of the arch shown in Fig. 17.64 by the combination vanishing-point and visual-ray method.

17.25 Make an angular perspective of the garage shown in Fig. 17.65 by the combination vanishing-point and visual-ray method. Find and use the vanishing points for the rafters.

Sketching Problems

17.26 In any of the preceding 25 problems make a freehand perspective sketch of the object assigned.

17.27 Make a freehand perspective sketch from an object assigned from Figs. 16.25 to 16.38 in Chapter 16.

Shade and Shadow Problems

In the following problems only the simpler objects should be assigned in order to stay within classroom time.

17.28 Find the shades and shadows of an object assigned by your instructor. The direction of the light ray must be parallel to the V-plane and 45° with the H-plane.

17.29 Same as Problem 17.28, with the horizontal projection of the light ray making 30° with the reference line and the V-projection 45° with the reference line.

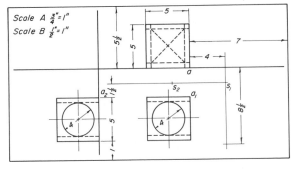

Fig. 17.53   Drilled cube.

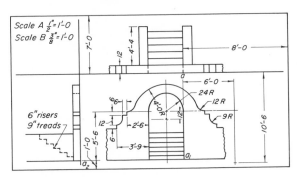

Fig. 17.54   Garden gate.

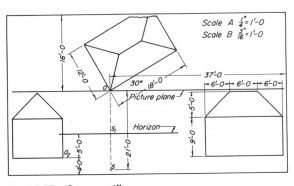

Fig. 17.55   Garage outline.

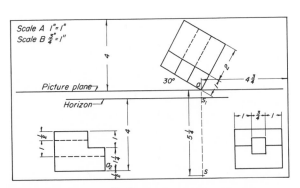

Fig. 17.56   Stepped block.

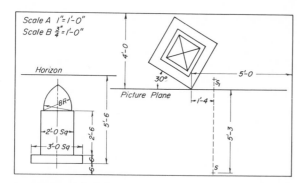

Scale A 1"=1'-0"
Scale B 3/4"=1'-0"

Fig. 17.57 Monument.

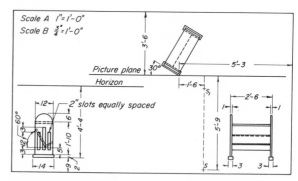

Scale A 1"=1'-0"
Scale B 3/4"=1'-0"

Fig. 17.58 Book rack.

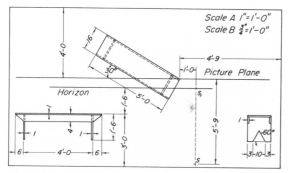

Scale A 1"=1'-0"
Scale B 3/4"=1'-0"

Fig. 17.59 Bench.

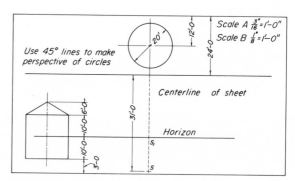

Scale A 3/16"=1'-0"
Scale B 1/8"=1'-0"

Use 45° lines to make perspective of circles

Fig. 17.60 Tank.

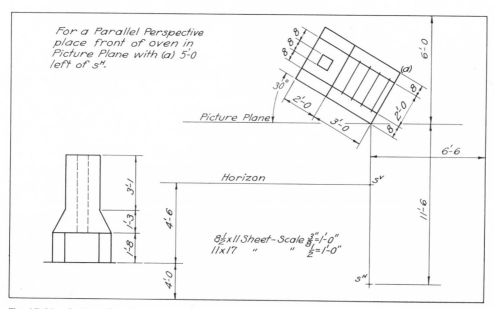

For a Parallel Perspective place front of oven in Picture Plane with (a) 5'-0 left of S^H.

8 1/2 x 11 Sheet—Scale 3/8"=1'-0"
11 x 17   "   "   1/2"=1'-0"

Fig. 17.61 Outdoor fireplace.

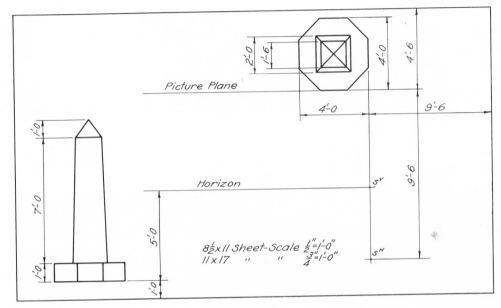

Fig. 17.62 Monument.

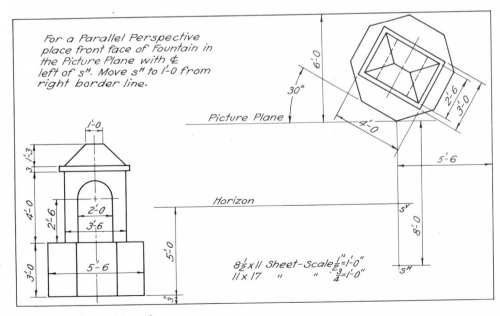

Fig. 17.63 Memorial fountain.

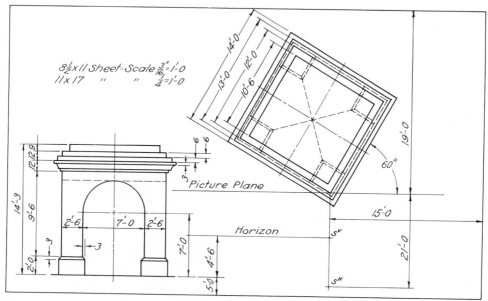

8½ x 11 Sheet–Scale 3/16"=1'-0
11 x 17 " " ¼=1'-0

Picture Plane

Horizon

60°

14'-0
13'-0
12'-0
10'-6
19'-0
15'-0
21'-0
12'-9
14'-3
9'-6
2'-6   7'-0   2'-6
7'-0
4'-6
5'-0
2'-0
3
3
6   6
3
S^V
S^H

Fig. 17.64   Memorial arch.

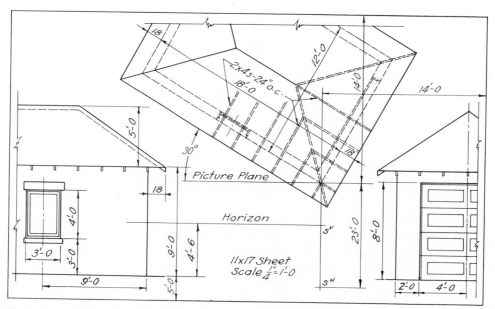

2x4s–24" o.c.
18
18'-0
18
12'-0
14'-0
14'-0
30°
Picture Plane
Horizon
5'-0
18
4'-0
3'-0
3'-0
9'-0
9'-0
4'-6
5'-0
23'-0
8'-0
2'-0   4'-0
S^V
S^H

11x17 Sheet
Scale ¼"=1'-0

Fig. 17.65   Garage.

PART THREE

Technical Charts
and
Graphic Computation

CHAPTER 18
Charts and Diagrams

OLD: Model of the printing press built in 1620 by William Jansen Blaew. (Philip Gendreau)

NEW: Modern newspaper press. (Philip Gendreau)

Chapter 18 Charts and Diagrams

18.1 USES OF CHARTS. The purpose of charts and diagrams is to present facts and their significance in a more easily interpreted form than could be done with words or tabular data. A technical or business publication scarcely appears today without charts of some kind. Some of the more common uses of charts are as follows:

a. To present results of test data obtained in experiments.
b. To correlate the observations of natural phenomena.
c. To present business statistics.
d. To determine trends in business.
e. To present equations graphically for computation uses.
f. To derive empirical equations.

18.2 CLASSIFICATION OF CHARTS. According to the method of presentation or drawing, with which this chapter is primarily concerned, charts may be readily classified in the following form:

a. Plane curves on rectangular coordinates, logarithmic, semilogarithmic, trilinear, polar coordinates, and others.
b. Bar charts of all kinds.
c. Pie or sector charts.
d. Computation charts, vector diagrams, and nomographs.
e. Flow charts and distribution diagrams.
f. Three-dimensional charts.
g. Map or distribution diagrams.

All of these are illustrated in the various figures of this chapter.

18.3 CHARTS ON RECTANGULAR COORDINATES. Charts are more commonly made on rectangular coordinates than on the other forms, as illustrated in Fig. 18.1. They are used to compare quantities. The impression given by such charts will depend on the scales selected for each of the coordinates.

18.4 HOW TO DRAW THE CHART. When one has the data for a chart given or collected in tabular form,

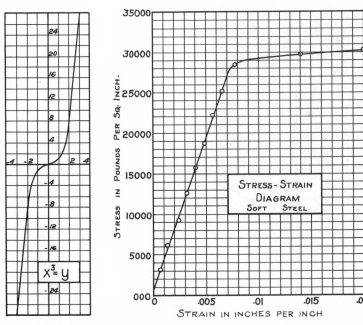

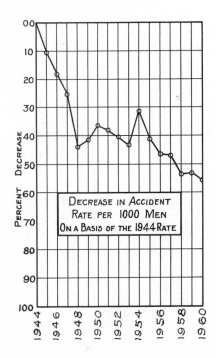

Fig. 18.1   Types of plane curves.

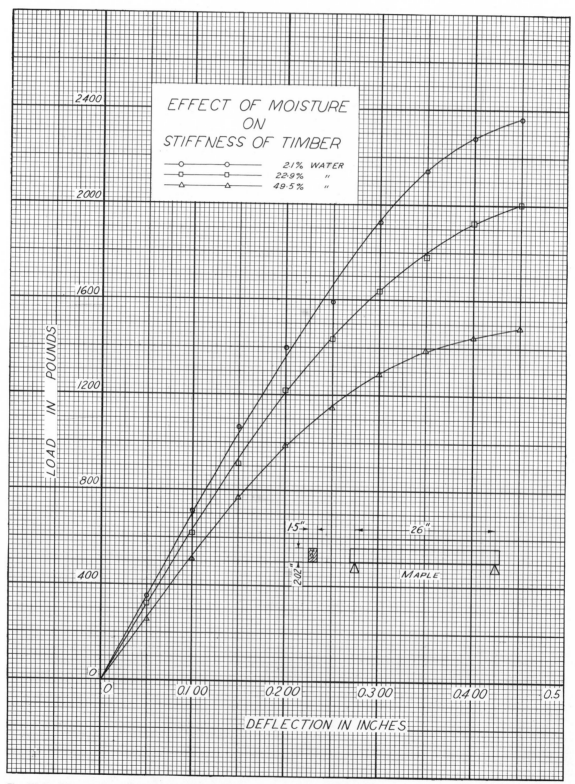

Fig. 18.2 Plane curve—rectangular coordinates.

the steps outlined in the following paragraphs must be taken to produce a chart that will give the desired effect. Two forms of presentation are possible, depending on the purpose of the chart. One form is the test or laboratory report; the other is designed for publication.

In this book we are concerned primarily with those prepared directly on commercially available printed coordinate papers.

18.4.1   Selection of axes. Two variables are usually involved in a chart. It is therefore necessary to decide which variable will be placed on the vertical or *Y*-axis and which on the horizontal or *X*-axis. It is general practice to place the independent or controlled variable on the horizontal axis. One exception to this rule, established by custom, is the so-called stress-strain curve. When time is one of the variables, this is usually placed on the *X*-axis.

The location of the zero point or intersection of the axes must be so chosen that all values of the variables can be plotted. When only positive values are involved, this point is placed in the lower left corner of the chart about 1 inch in from the printed border, as shown in Fig. 18.2. This allows room for numerals and legends.

18.4.2   Choice of scales. The choice of scales materially affects the impression given by the chart. See Fig. 18.3. The scales on the two axes should be chosen to take maximum advantage of the space available. If the chart is to be made on printed coordinate paper, the scale units should be chosen to come upon the heavy printed lines. These units should be multiples of 1, 2, 4, or 5. Interpolation of the smaller divisions on the paper should be easy to make. If the chart is to be made for formal publication, coordinates are usually ruled upon blank paper. For this type of work the reader should consult the USASI publications Y15-1—

1959 *Illustrations for Publication and Projection* and Y15-2—1960 *Time Series Charts.*

18.4.3   Marking coordinates. Unit values of the coordinates should be marked on each axis, as shown in Fig. 18.2. A legend should indicate what the units are and the unit of measurement, for example, inches or feet, or time in days, hours, or minutes. Note in Fig. 18.2 that the smaller-ruled divisions have been used as guidelines for the lettering.

18.4.4   Showing plotted points. The plotted points are indicated by open circles about ⅒ inch or a little less in diameter. If more than one curve is shown on a single chart, squares and triangles may be used for the points on the other curves, as shown in Fig. 18.2. If more curves are needed, solid circles, squares, and triangles may be used. They should be smaller than the open ones. If a curve is to be drawn to represent a mathematical equation, plotted points should not be shown on the finished chart.

18.4.5   Drawing the curve. The nature of the curve to be drawn between plotted points will depend on the data involved. If there is no direct relationship between the variables, as for time and rainfall, straight lines will be drawn from point to point, as shown in Fig. 18.4. When there is a direct relationship, as in Fig. 18.2, a smooth curve will be drawn through the average of the points. The curve should touch but not pass through the circles of the plotted points.

18.4.6   Titles. Every chart must have a well thought-out title stating specifically what is represented. This should be placed in an open area to make the total effect one of a well-balanced sheet.

18.4.7   Sketches. If a small sketch will make the chart more intelligible, this may be placed on the sheet but tables of data and extensive explanatory matter should not be placed within the chart.

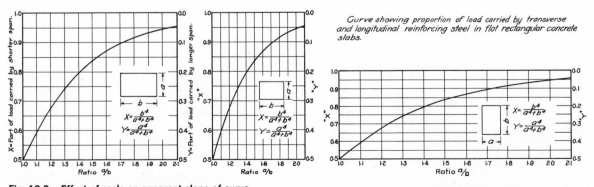

Fig. 18.3   Effect of scale on apparent slope of curve.

18.5   INTERPRETATION OF CHARTS. As indicated in Art. 18.4.2, the choice and location of scales are very important. They can create an erroneous impression unless careful observations are made.

18.5.1   Location of the origin. In Figs. 18.5 and 18.6 both figures have been correctly plotted, but in Fig. 18.6 the origin or zero point has been omitted. At a span of 20 feet, the deflection of a cedar beam would seem to be about three times that of oak. In Fig. 18.5 the deflection seems to be only twice as much for cedar as for oak.

18.5.2   Change of scale. The effect of change of scale can also create an erroneous general impression. In Fig. 18.3 note the apparent flatness of the curve. Again in Fig. 18.7, the two curves of Fig. 18.5 have been placed on separate grids with the vertical scale in Fig. 18.7(b) just twice that in Fig. 18.7(a). The two curves seem to be almost alike even though 18.7(a) is for oak and 18.7(b) is for cedar.

18.6   LOGARITHMIC CHARTS. These charts are most useful in engineering work where the relationship of the variables is more complex, for example, a prod-

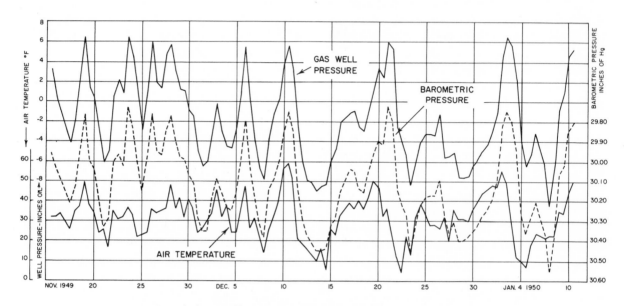

Record of gas-well pressures, barometer readings, and air temperatures during a two-month period, November 1949 to January 1950, for the Alvin Albrecht farm gas well, sec. 34, T. 15 N., R. 9 E., Bureau County.

Fig. 18.4   Gas well pressures. (Courtesy Illinois State Geological Survey.)

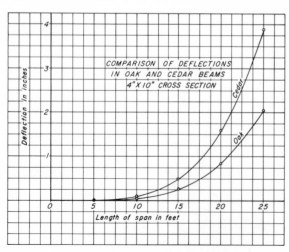

Fig. 18.5   Two plane curves in one chart. (Basic Fig. 16.1.)

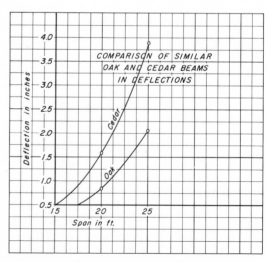

Fig. 18.6   Incorrect impression due to omission of zero line. (Basic Fig. 16.3.)

uct, quotient, or exponential form of the variables. In such cases the chart becomes a straight line on logarithmic paper, as illustrated in Fig. 18.8. By the use of logarithmic charts empirical equations to represent test data can frequently be derived, as discussed in Chapter 20. The ruled lines of this type of paper are spaced according to the logarithms of numbers. Such paper is commonly available with one, two, or three cycles, in each direction.

18.7 SEMILOGARITHMIC CHARTS. When the rate of change in two variables is more important than the quantitative change, semilogarithmic paper is used, since the slope of the tangent to the curve at any point gives the rate of change at that point and the

whole chart indicates a trend in the rate more accurately than does the same data plotted on rectangular coordinates, as may be seen by comparing the two charts of Fig. 18.9. Semilogarithmic paper has a logarithmic scale in one direction and an arithmetic scale in the other. Equations of the general form $y = a10^{MX}$ will plot as straight lines on this paper. Empirical equations can frequently be determined by plotting data on this type of paper.

18.8 TRILINEAR CHARTS. Trilinear charts are in the form of an equilateral triangle. The coordinates are ruled parallel to the sides, and the altitude perpendicular to any side represents 100. These charts are useful in comparing properties of chemicals or alloys

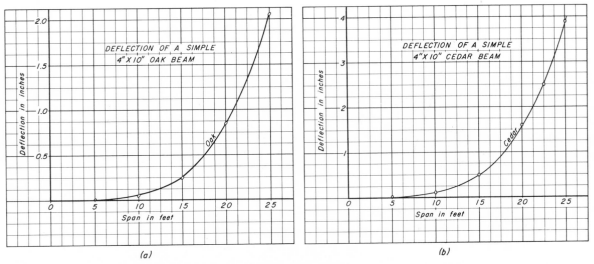

Fig. 18.7   Incorrect impression due to change of scale. (Basic Fig. 16.2.)

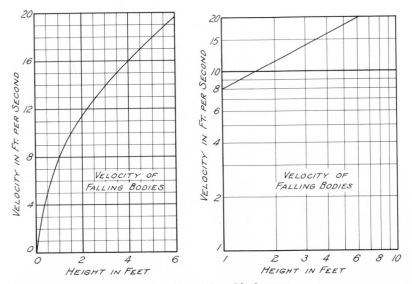

Fig. 18.8   Same curve on rectangular and logarithmic paper.

composed of three substances, as shown in Fig. 18.10. The equilateral triangle has the property that the sum of the perpendiculars to the three sides from any point inside is equal to the altitude of the triangle. It will be noted in Fig. 18.10 that only a portion of the complete triangle has been drawn since the curves lie in one corner and it would be a waste of space to show the remainder of the blank chart.

18.9 POLAR CHARTS. These charts are useful when equations are given in polar coordinate form or when quantities radiating from a center are involved, for example, in illumination or radiation charts as in Fig. 18.11. They are also used in modified form on continuous recording devices, as illustrated in Fig. 18.12. The radiating lines are curved in this case because the recording stylus is pivoted at a fixed center.

18.10 PIE DIAGRAMS OR SECTOR CHARTS. These charts, circular in form, are used to show the

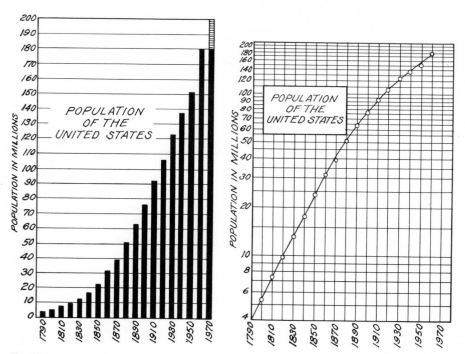

Fig. 18.9 Barograph and semilog chart of same data.

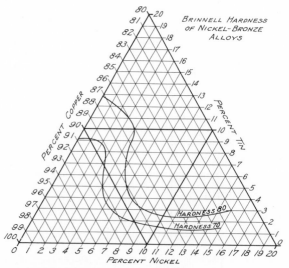

Fig. 18.10 Trilinear curve.

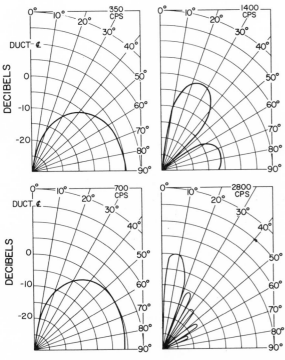

COMPUTED RADIATION

FOR A

THIN RECTANGULAR DUCT

ONE FOOT WIDE

q = 1 MODE

Fig. 18.11 Polar chart. (Courtesy *SAE Journal;* J. M. Tyler and T. G. Sofrin.) (Basic Fig. 16.9.)

relative distribution of the parts of a whole, as illustrated in Fig. 18.13. Other common examples are the distribution of the tax dollar and the costs of production in an industry. They are quite effective and simple to make. If the sector areas are shaded, Zip-A-Tone may be used. The pictorial form of Fig. 18.14 is also very effective.

18.11   BAR CHARTS. Bar charts are more commonly used for the popular presentation of facts since

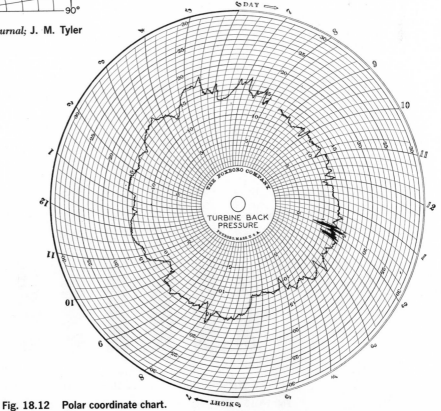

Fig. 18.12 Polar coordinate chart.

they are easy for the average layman to interpret. Bar charts may have the bars either vertical or horizontal, as shown in Figs. 18.15 and 18.16. They may be additive, as in Fig. 18.17, or comparative, as in Fig. 18.18.

The same general rules used for rectangular coordinate charts apply here with only slight modification. Shading of the bars can be done most economically with Zip-A-Tone, a commercial product available from dealers in art and drafting supplies.

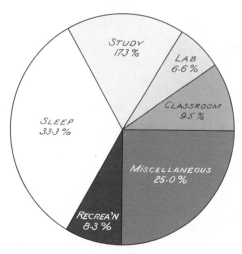

Fig. 18.13 Pie diagram or sector chart showing use of students' time.

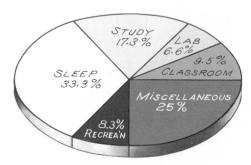

Fig. 18.14 Pictorial pie diagram. (Same data as for Fig. 18.13.)

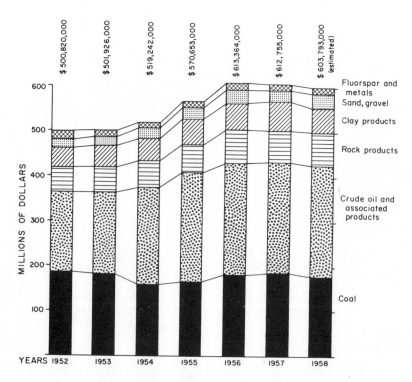

Illinois mineral production for 1952–1958.

Fig. 18.15 Bar diagram. (Courtesy Illinois State Geological Survey.)

18.12   FLOW AND ORGANIZATION CHARTS. In the process industries it is often desirable to trace the raw material through the various stages of handling to the finished product. This is readily accomplished by a flow chart, as illustrated in Fig. 18.19.

Charts showing the lines of authority or responsibility from chief executive to the minor departments can also be shown in this type of chart, which is then called an organization chart. For formal presentation, the lettering on such charts is usually done mechanically with Wrico or Leroy lettering guides.

18.13   DISTRIBUTION DIAGRAMS. These diagrams usually take the form of maps and may show a wide variety of information useful in business operations, such as distribution of sales and density of population. A good map of the area under consideration is a basic requirement. These are usually traced from existing maps in atlases or the like. A typical example is shown in Fig. 18.20. In addition to location, quantitative values are usually involved. These values are shown by different types of shading.

18.14   COMPUTATION CHARTS. Though many of the foregoing charts can be used to simplify calculations, a number of charts are designed specifically for that purpose. Charts of these types are discussed in the next four chapters of this book.

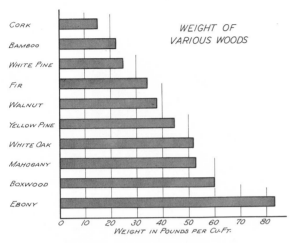

Fig. 18.16   Horizontal bar chart.

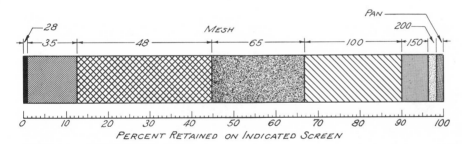

Fig. 18.17   A 100 per cent bar chart.

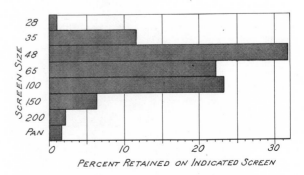

Fig. 18.18   Histogram.

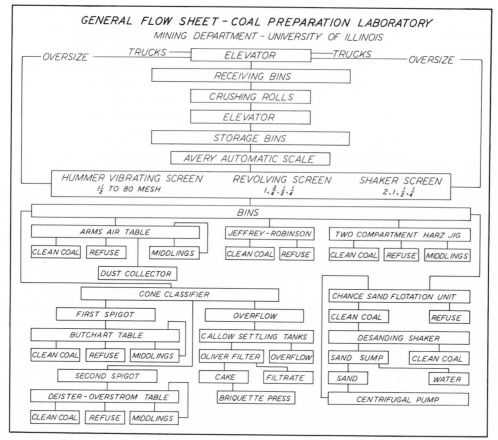

Fig. 18.19   Flow chart.

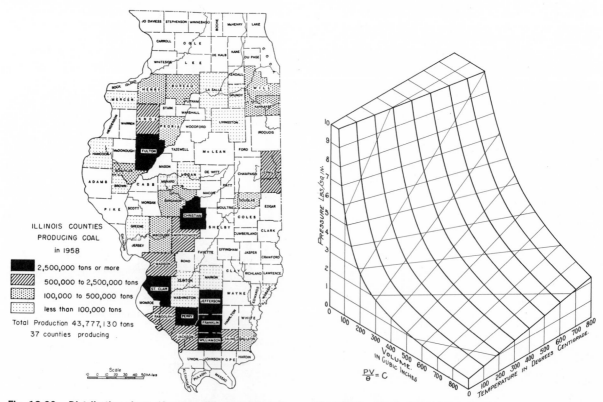

Fig. 18.20   Distribution chart. (Courtesy Illinois Geological Survey.)

Fig. 18.21   Three-dimensional chart.

18.15   THREE-DIMENSIONAL CHARTS. Three-dimensional charts are based on one of the pictorial forms of projection discussed in Chapters 15 and 16. They are useful for illustrating in a popular way the relationship between three variables. Figures 18.21 and 18.22 show a chart of this type.

18.16   CHARTS AND DIAGRAMS FOR PUBLICATION OR LANTERN SLIDES. Many times in teaching or in public discussion it is desirable to have charts prepared for reproduction as lantern slides, as illustrated in Fig. 18.23. For those who have occasion to make drawings for this purpose it is recommended that a copy of United States of America Standards Institute Y15-1—1959 *Illustrations for Publication and Projection* and Y15-2—1960 *Time Series Charts* be obtained.

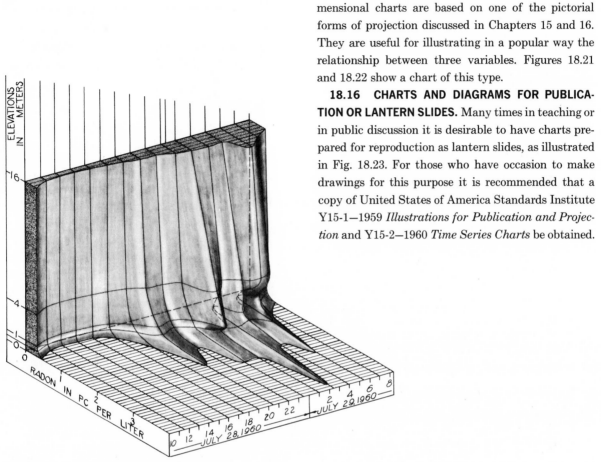

Fig. 18.22   Three-dimensional shaded chart.

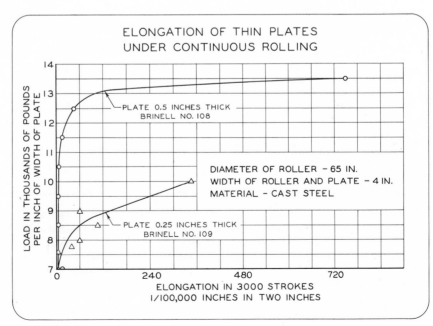

Fig. 18.23   Standard projection slide.

SELF-STUDY QUESTIONS

Before trying to answer these questions, read the chapter carefully. Then, without reference to the text, answer as many questions as possible. For those that cannot be answered, the number, in parentheses following the question number, gives the article in which the answer can be found. Look it up and write down the answer. Check the answers that you did give to see that they are correct.

18.1 **(18.1)** A more understandable way of presenting tabular data is by the use of _____ and _____.

18.2 **(18.3)** To assist in making charts _____ _____ paper is used.

18.3 **(18.4)** One important use of a chart is in _____ reports, and the other in _____.

18.4 **(18.4.2)** The choice of _____ affects the impression given by the chart.

18.5 **(18.4.4)** Empirical data plotted on a chart have the points _____ on the curve.

18.6 **(18.4.5)** When there is a direct relationship between the variables being plotted a _____ _____ is used.

18.7 **(18.6)** Two- or three-cycle _____ paper is commercially available for plotting test data that may be complex in nature.

18.8 **(18.7)** To show data that indicate a rate of change in two variables _____ charts are used.

18.9 **(18.10)** Circular charts showing a distribution of a particular sample are called _____ charts.

18.10 **(18.11)** A popular manner of presenting data to the lay public is by the use of _____ charts.

18.11 **(18.12)** To show an administrative structure of a company an _____ chart is used.

18.12 **(18.12)** The process industries makes great use of _____ charts.

18.13 **(18.13)** A map showing geographic data is called a _____ diagram.

18.14 **(18.9)** Continuous recording devices often use _____ charts.

18.15 **(18.4.2)** In selecting _____ to use in plotting variables, care must be taken to show the data accurately.

18.16 **(18.7)** A change in the slope of a curve plotted on semilogarithmic paper indicates a variation in the _____ of change.

18.17 **(18.8)** A _____ chart is made from an equilateral triangle.

18.18 **(18.2)** An annual report of a corporation uses such charts as _____, _____, and _____.

PROBLEMS

The information contained in the following problems should be shown in chart form according to specifications in the book or from the instructor. If these are not given, the student should select the best form of presentation for any particular data.

Each chart should be complete with proper titles, coordi-

nate markings, and any other necessary information. It is recommended that 8½ × 11″ paper be used for these charts, and commercial coordinate papers should be used when available.

Coordinates are not specified. The student should select his own values to give the best results.

Plane Curves—Rectangular Coordinate Paper

18.1 Plot a curve for the areas of circles, $A = \pi r^2$, of radii varying from 0 to 14'.

18.2 Plot a curve for the areas of spheres, $A = 4\pi r^2$, of radii varying from 0 to 14'.

18.3 Plot a curve for the volume of spheres, $V = 0.5236d^3$, for diameters from 0 to 10'.

18.4 Plot a curve for computing the volume of a liquid at different depths in a segment of a hemisphere 20' in diameter. $V = \pi h(c^2/8 + h^2/6)$, where h = depth of liquid and c = diameter of liquid surface. Show a sketch in your chart to explain the terms in the equation.

18.5 Plot a curve for computing the volume of a liquid at different depths in a cylindrical tank whose axis is horizontal and whose diameter is 10'. Carry the curve from zero to a full tank by 1' intervals. Make a diagram showing the meaning of terms in your equation. Consult a handbook for necessary equations.

18.6 The equation for the bending moment of a beam is $M = \frac{1}{8}WL^2$, where M = the bending moment in foot-pounds, W = the uniform load in pounds per foot of beam, and L = the span in feet. Compute and plot three curves for these values of W, namely, 100, 200, and 300 pounds per foot, for all spans from 5 to 35'.

18.7 Plot a curve for wind pressures on a flat surface normal to the wind as given by Marvin's formula, $P = 0.004\,V^2$, where P is the pressure in pounds per square foot and V is the velocity of the wind in miles per hour. Use values of V from 0 to 100 miles per hour.

18.8 Plot a curve showing the growth in population of your state. Data from U. S. Census.

18.9 Plot a smooth curve showing the maximum rainfall to be expected for any period of time from the following data. *Note:* The curve will pass along the upper boundary of the plotted points. One or two extreme points may be outside of the curve.

Storm Intensity Data

Column A: Duration of storm in minutes.
Column B: Rainfall in inches per hour.

A	B	A	B	A	B
121	0.78	27	3.52	63	2.06
122	1.18	18	4.31	15	3.10
25	1.21	32	2.70	15	3.62
56	1.26	26	2.92	15	4.51
103	2.10	180	0.90	60	1.20
63	1.32	82	0.70	56	2.20
32	2.11	70	1.10	22	3.93
38	1.82	72	1.77	12	4.88
34	2.80	70	1.90	7	5.92
4	5.92	45	1.30	11	2.30
10	5.10	24	1.61	16	3.87
10	4.15	8	1.46		

18.10 Draw stress-strain diagram for mild steel from the data given below. Plot strain on the horizontal axis.

Mild Steel

Unit Stress	Unit Strain	Unit Stress	Unit Strain
0	0	32,800	0.0022
4,080	0.00012	33,500	0.0030
7,670	0.00025	34,400	0.0052
11,100	0.00037	37,000	0.0250
15,400	0.00050	47,000	0.0625
18,700	0.00063	52,000	0.1000
23,200	0.00075	53,400	0.1250
26,700	0.00087	54,100	0.1500
30,100	0.0010	54,800	0.1875
32,800	0.00113	55,100	0.2375
33,800	0.00119	54,700	0.2625
32,700	0.0015	47,500	0.3125

18.11 Draw a stress-strain curve for mild steel from the data above. Plot only as far as the 37,000-pound load. Plot strains horizontally and select coordinates so that the curve goes well across the sheet.

18.12 Same as Problem 18.10. Use data for duralumin.

Duralumin

Unit Stress	Unit Strain	Unit Stress	Unit Strain
0	0	35,700	0.0087
4,520	0.0004	36,300	0.0107
9,100	0.0008	37,300	0.0130
15,820	0.00143	41,300	0.0250
20,300	0.00186	46,100	0.0500
24,900	0.0023	48,000	0.0625
29,400	0.0030	50,100	0.0750
32,000	0.0044	51,500	0.1000
33,500	0.0057	53,300	0.1250
34,500	0.0069	53,500	0.1600

18.13 Same as Problem 18.10. Use data for brass.

Free-Cutting Brass

Unit Stress	Unit Strain	Unit Stress	Unit Strain
0	0	34,900	0.0083
5,750	0.00033	35,200	0.0100
10,600	0.00066	36,600	0.0133
16,800	0.00122	37,500	0.0208
21,600	0.00166	39,100	0.0333
26,300	0.0023	40,800	0.0667
29,200	0.0030	44,200	0.1000
32,200	0.0039	47,500	0.1500
32,200	0.0051	49,400	0.2000
34,000	0.0059	50,500	0.2333

Plane Curve—Logarithmic paper

18.14 Same as Problem 18.1. Plot on logarithmic paper.
18.15 Same as Problem 18.2. Plot on logarithmic paper.
18.16 Same as Problem 18.3. Plot on logarithmic paper.
18.17 Same as Problem 18.6. Plot on logarithmic paper.
18.18 Same as Problem 18.7. Plot on logarithmic paper.

Semilogarithmic Chart

18.19 Same as Problem 18.8. Use semilogarithmic paper.

Bar Charts

18.20 Make a bar chart comparing the loss of weight of various metals in different solutions as given in the table below. Group the three bars for each metal together.

Action of One-Half Liter of 0.2 N Salt Solutions, Renewed Daily for 7 Days, on Metals at 17° to 20° C

Loss in grams per square meter per hour

Metal	MgCl₂	CaCl₂	NaCl
Zinc	0.57	0.21	0.06
Cast iron	0.51	0.12	0.06
Wrought iron	0.51	0.18	0.15
Aluminum	0.10	0.03	0.00
Lead	0.33	0.24	0.01
Copper	0.15	0.12	0.01
Tin	0.10	0.08	0.00
Nickel	0.03	0.05	0.00

18.21 Plot the following information in the form of
(a) a barograph, (b) a pie diagram,
(c) a 100% bar chart, (d) a histogram.

Distribution of the Opening Money of a State University

Item	Amount	Per Cent
Instruction	15,200,000	36
Related activities	2,900,000	7
Organized research	8,400,000	20
Extension and public service	4,200,000	10
Libraries	1,300,000	3
Physical plant	5,830,000	14
Administration	3,002,000	7
Retirement, etc.	1,093,000	3

18.22 Plot the following information in the form of
(a) plane curve, (b) barograph,
(c) 100% bar, (d) histogram.

Screen Analysis of Medium Sand

Screen	Size of Opening	Amount Passing in Pounds
#100	0.0055	0.75
#50	0.011	3.00
#40	0.015	5.75
#30	0.022	10.00
#20	0.034	14.25
#10	0.073	20.50
⅛″	⅛	21.75
³⁄₁₆″	³⁄₁₆	23.25
¼″	¼	25.00

Trilinear Chart

18.23 Make a trilinear chart for the data shown in the following table. Let the upper vertex represent 100% volatile matter, the left vertex 100% moisture. Plot a smooth "coalification curve" through the points. A coalification curve shows the changes from peat to anthracite due to geologic forces. The left wing of the curve shows the loss of moisture due to vertical pressure, the right wing the loss of volatile matter due to lateral pressure.

Analysis of Fuel on Ash-Free Basis

Type	Per Cent Moisture	Per Cent Volatile Matter	Per Cent Fixed C
Anthracite	4.1	4.8	91.1
Semianthracite	4.0	11.2	84.8
Bituminous A	2.8	20.2	77.0
Bituminous B	3.2	36.3	60.5
Bituminous C	12.0	39.1	48.9
Bituminous D	19.8	35.7	44.5
Lignite	37.6	29.6	32.8
Peat	81.6	12.4	6.0

Sector Diagrams

18.24 Make a sector diagram showing the distribution of the various items entering into the cost of government in the island of Puerto Rico.

Items	Per Cent
General government	14.4
Protection	9.6
Education	29.4
Social welfare	9.7
Highways and streets	13.7
Economic development	5.8
Public utilities	10.2
Debt service	7.2

18.25 Secure data and make a chart showing the distribution of the tax dollar in your community.

CHAPTER 19

Graphic Vector Analysis

OLD: Benz automobile of 1902. (New York Public Library Picture Collection)

NEW: Agena missile in combination with an Atlas rocket carrying a Ranger space-craft into orbit. (Lockheed Missiles and Space Company)

Chapter 19 Graphic Vector Analysis

19.1 INTRODUCTION. Many quantities that are important in engineering work are defined by two properties: direction and magnitude. In addition each has a point of application that locates the line of action and gives the quantity a definite position in space. These factors may be represented graphically by a line called a vector. The direction of the vector line represents the direction of the quantity, and the length of the line represents the magnitude. The vector as such has no relation to the line of action of the original quantity.

Such things as force, velocity, acceleration, displacement and magnetic intensity, fall into this class. Therefore, problems involving these factors may be solved graphically by means of a vector diagram. The graphical solution is usually comparatively easy and fast, and it can be made as accurate as necessary by increasing the scale of the drawing. Often the graphical solution is satisfactory, but at other times an analytical approach is preferred, in which case the graphical solution may be a valuable check. The graphical solution also frequently helps to visualize the action.

19.2 DEFINITIONS. In order to be able to understand the use and applications of vector diagrams, it is necessary to define a few terms.

a. *Vector quantity.* Any quantity that may be completely described by direction, magnitude, and a definite position in space.

b. *Line of action.* The line in space along which the vector quantity acts.

c. *Point of application.* The point on the line of action where the action begins.

d. *Vector.* A straight line that represents the vector quantity in direction and magnitude but not in line of action.

e. *Direction.* The specification telling which way along the line of action the vector tends to produce results. It is usually specified by an arrow on the vector.

f. *Concurrent vectors.* When all of the vectors meet in a single point, they are called concurrent.

g. *Coplanar vectors.* When all of the vectors lie in a single plane, they are called coplanar.

h. *Resultant.* A single vector that can be used to replace *or produce the same result* as a group or system of vectors.

i. *Equilibrant.* A single vector that will just balance a group or system of vectors. It has the same magnitude as the resultant but the opposite direction.

j. *Equilibrium.* A condition in a system of vectors where all resultants are zero.

k. *Composition of vectors.* The process of combining a system of vectors into a smaller number, usually one, which is the resultant.

l. *Resolution of vectors.* The process of replacing a given system of forces by another system having a larger number of forces. The most common case of resolution is the breaking down of a single force into two or more components.

m. *Vector diagram.* A continuous polygon of vectors. If the forces are concurrent and the polygon is a closed figure, the system is in equilibrium, provided that the vectors all point in a continuous directional pattern around the polygon.

19.3 COMPOSITION OF TWO FORCES. When two vectors act at a point, they form a concurrent coplanar system and the resultant may be obtained by means of a parallelogram. In Fig. 19.1(*a*), a boat started at *A* and is being driven in the direction *AB* at 10 miles per hour, and the stream flows in the direction *CG* at 4 miles per hour. It is desired to determine the actual direction and speed of travel. The construction shown in Fig. 19.1(*b*) may be done in the following steps:

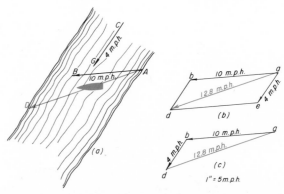

Fig. 19.1 Composition of two concurrent coplanar vectors.

583

a. Construct the vector *ab* parallel to *AB*.

b. Lay off 10 units on *ab* to any convenient scale (an engineer's scale is best).

c. Construct the vector *ae* parallel to *CG*.

d. Lay off 4 units on *ae* using the same scale as for *ab*.

e. Complete the parallelogram of forces.

f. Draw the diagonal *ad*.

g. Measure the length of *ad* using the same scale.

h. The vector *ad* gives the direction and velocity of the boat.

The usual method of solving this problem is by drawing only half of the parallelogram, as shown in Fig. 19.1(*c*). The vector *ab* is constructed and then *bd* is drawn parallel to *CG* and of the proper length to locate *d* and the resultant *ad*. This saves time and is especially convenient when more than two vectors are involved.

Line *AD* in Fig. 19.1(*a*) can be drawn parallel to *ad* to determine the point of landing on the opposite shore. The vector diagram could have been started at *A* to locate *AD* immediately, but this is not always possible or convenient. It is not necessary for the vector diagram to have any definite position with respect to the line of action which is *AD*.

In a coplanar system it is important that the vectors be laid out in the view that shows the true size of all vectors.

19.4 COMPOSITION OF CONCURRENT COPLANAR VECTORS. In Fig. 19.2 there are three ropes, *AB*, *AC*, and *AD*, pulling at point *A*, with the magnitude specified on each rope. Since the *H*- and *V*-projections do not show the ropes in true size, it will be necessary to project the system onto auxiliary plane *1* which is set up parallel to the three forces. In this situation it is customary to letter the spaces between the forces, as *W*, *X*, *Y*, and *Z*. Force *AB* will then be known as *WX*, force *AC* as *XY*, and *AD* as *YZ*. This makes the lettering of the vector diagram very simple. The forces may be taken in any order, but it is customary to take them either clockwise or counterclockwise. The construction is as follows:

a. Set up auxiliary plane *1* with the *1-V* reference line parallel to $d^V a^V c^V e^V b^V$.

b. Project all forces onto plane *1*.

c. Letter the spaces between the forces *XYZW*.

d. Construct vector *WX* parallel to *a'b'*.

e. Using any convenient engineer's scale, measure the 200 pounds along *WX*.

f. Construct *XY* parallel to *a'c'*.

g. Measure from *X* on *XY* a distance of 150 pounds, using the same scale.

h. Lay out *YZ* parallel to *a'd'*.

i. Measure from *Y* on *YZ* a distance of 100 pounds, using the same scale.

j. Measure the length of *WZ*, using the same scale.

The resultant or the force that will replace the three will be *WZ* and the magnitude, *260 pounds, can be determined by measuring line WZ.* If desired, line *AE* may be drawn parallel to *WZ* and carried back to the *H*- and *V*-projections to locate the line of action of the resultant.

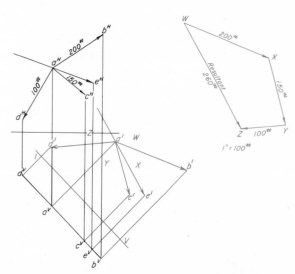

Fig. 19.2 Composition of three concurrent coplanar vectors.

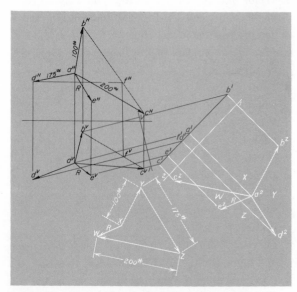

Fig. 19.3 Composition of concurrent coplanar vectors.

If the original forces are so located that the plane does not show edgewise in either the top or front view, two auxiliary projections will be necessary to determine the true size of the plane and the true magnitude of the forces. This construction is shown in Fig. 19.3.

19.5 COMPOSITION OF CONCURRENT NONCOPLANAR VECTORS. When the vectors do not lie in one plane, it is impossible to find the true length of every vector in any one view. Therefore, the vector diagram must be drawn in two views at the same time. In Fig. 19.4(a) it is desired to find the direction and magnitude of the magnetic intensity at point P, due to AB which is a long straight conductor that carries a current (i) and to CD which is a bar magnet having point poles of strength m at each end. The values of H_I, H_C, and H_D represent the magnetic intensities at point P due to the conductor, pole C, and pole D, respectively. These values can be calculated by well-known formula when the current i, the strength of the magnet, and all distances are known. Lines PE, PC, and PD give the respective lines of action of the forces. The values, H_I, H_C, and H_D, may be placed consecutively in a vector diagram whose resultant is the magnetic intensity acting on point P. The following steps, shown in Fig. 19.4, will give the value and direction of the resultant:

a. Letter the spaces between the forces.

b. Assume two projections of the starting point W.

c. Construct WX parallel to PE and lay out on it the value H_i, using any convenient engineer's scale. This can be measured in the V-projection because that shows in true length.

d. Construct XF parallel to PC.

e. Find the true length of XF at x' f'.

f. On x' f' measure the value H_e from X to locate Y.

g. From Y construct YG parallel to PD.

h. Find the true length of YG at $y'g'$.

i. On $y'g'$ measure the value of H_d from Y to locate Z.

j. Construct the vector from W to Z.

k. Find the true length of WZ at $w'z'$.

The resultant then will be the vector from W to Z. Its true length must be determined to obtain the magnitude of the magnetic intensity at point P. By drawing through P in Fig. 19.4(a) a line parallel to WZ, line PO is established, which gives the direction of the magnetic intensity at P.

19.6 RESOLUTION OF FORCES. If it is desired to break a given force into a number of components, this may be done by considering the known force to be the resultant. From Fig. 19.5 it can be seen that there are any number of sets of components that may be drawn. The only conditions are that their lines of action all pass through the same point on the line of action of the original force and that in the vector diagram the original force turns out to be the resultant of all the components.

If the lines of action are given, the number of possible solutions is decreased. When there are only two components and the lines of action are given, there will be only one result. To resolve a known force into a set of components so that the system will be in equilibrium requires that the known force be the equilibrant of all the components instead of the resultant.

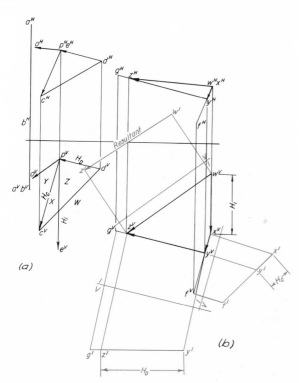

(a)

(b)

Fig. 19.4 Composition of concurrent noncoplanar vectors.

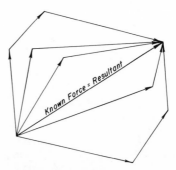

Fig. 19.5 Resolution of a vector.

19.7   EQUILIBRIUM. When a condition exists in a system of vectors in which the resultant is zero, the system is said to be in equilibrium. The vector diagram of a system that is in equilibrium is a closed polygon with the arrows on the vectors all pointing around the polygon in the same direction. In each of the preceding problems an extra vector could have been added that would produce a state of equilibrium in the system. This vector is called the equilibrant and it is equal to the resultant but opposite in direction.

The system of forces in Fig. 19.6 in which a weight is suspended by two ropes is in a state of equilibrium. The vector diagram always considers the forces acting on a single joint, in this case on point A, and here they are concurrent coplanar forces. In considering the forces acting on this joint there are six factors that must be known. They are the magnitude and direction of each of the three forces. When it is known that the joint is in equilibrium, the problem can be solved if there are no more than two unknowns. If there are more unknowns at any one joint, the problem is said to be statically indeterminate. In Fig. 19.6 the magnitude and direction of the load are known, and the direction of each of the other forces is also known, leaving their two magnitudes unknown. Therefore the problem can be solved by the vector diagram shown in Fig. 19.6(b). The steps are as follows:

a. Letter the spaces between the forces.
b. Lay out the vector for the known force by making XY parallel to $a^V b^V$ with a length of 100 pounds to any convenient engineer's scale.
c. From Y construct a vector parallel to $a^V d^V$ of an

indeterminate length.
d. From X construct a vector parallel to $a^V c^V$ of indeterminate length.
e. The intersection of these vectors is at Z. This completes the vector diagram for this joint.
f. Scale the lengths of XZ and YZ to determine the load on each rope. Use the same scale as for XY.

Since in equilibrium the arrows must all point around the diagram in the same direction, the direction of the forces is found to be from Y to Z and from Z to X. The arrows indicate the direction in which the forces act on the original joint in Fig. 19.6(a). From this it can be seen that each force is pulling away from the joint and therefore they are all in tension. If the arrow is found to be pointing toward the joint, the member is in compression.

19.8   RESOLUTION OF VECTORS IN A THREE-DIMENSIONAL SYSTEM. When it becomes necessary to find the loads in a three-dimensional structure, the work of drawing the vector diagram becomes a little more complicated. It has been seen in a plane vector system that it is possible to construct the diagram if there are no more than two unknowns. *In a space or three-dimensional system it is possible to construct the diagram if there are no more than three unknowns.* In Fig. 19.7(a) a three-legged tripod is supporting two known forces of 100 pounds each. There are ten possible factors in this problem, of which seven are known. They are the direction and magnitude of the known forces and the direction of the three components. The unknowns are the magnitudes of the components or, in other words, the load in each leg of the tripod. If the known forces are called AB and BC, the other three may be called CD, DE, and EA. The vector diagram may be constructed in the usual way. Assume point A in both projections of Fig. 19.7(b). Draw AB in a vertical position and measure the length of 100 pounds in the vertical projection. BX can be drawn parallel to the other known force and its true length determined at $b^1 x^1$. On the true length lay out the value of 100 pounds to locate c^1, and project it back to the horizontal and vertical views. Next a line AZ, of any length, must be drawn through point A parallel to leg EA of the tripod. Point E will be somewhere on that line. Then through C a line CY, of any length, must be drawn parallel to leg CD of the tripod. Point D will be somewhere on that line. The final step is to construct a line intersecting AZ and CY and at the same time parallel to leg DE of the tripod. The construction is

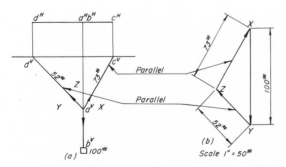

Fig. 19.6   Resolution of forces in equilibrium.

shown in the figure, but the theory is discussed in detail in Art. 13.8.5. In this case the point projection of line MN, which is parallel to leg DE, is found in the second auxiliary projection shown in Fig. 19.7(c).

The vector diagram may be constructed in the usual way by the following steps:

a. Letter the spaces between the forces.

b. Assume two projections of the starting point A.

c. Draw AB parallel to the known vertical force and measure the known 100 pounds on AB.

d. Construct BX parallel to the other known force.

e. Find the true length of BX at b^1x^1 and on b^1x^1 lay out the known value of 100 pounds to locate c^1.

f. Project c^1 back to locate c^H and c^V.

g. From C construct a line CY parallel to leg CD of indeterminate length.

h. From A construct a line AZ parallel to EA of indeterminate length.

i. Construct MN parallel to DE of the tripod.

The next steps give the construction for drawing a line parallel to MN and intersecting AZ and CY.

j. Project MN, AZ, and CY on a plane parallel to MN.

k. Project MN, AZ, and CY on a plane perpendicular to MN.

l. Find the place where a^2z^2 and c^2y^2 intersect. This is the point projection of the line parallel to MN and intersecting AZ and CY.

m. Letter this projection e^2d^2.

n. Carry e^2d^2 back to the H- and V-projections.

o. The vector diagram is complete as $ABCDEA$.

p. Find the true lengths of CD, DE, and EA. These will be the loads in the respective legs when scaled with the same scale as used for AB.

q. Transfer the arrows to the tripod in Fig. 19.7(a) to determine which is tension and which is compression. DE is pointing away from the joint and is in tension. The others are pointing toward the joint and are in compression.

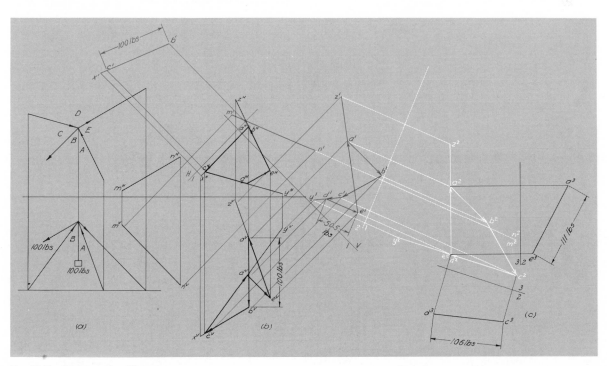

Fig. 19.7   Space vector diagram.

19.8.1 Alternate solution. A somewhat easier solution for this problem may be obtained by solving the following steps:

a. Find the resultant of all known forces. This is AB in Fig. 19.8(a).

b. Construct a vector AX along resultant AB starting at the point where all forces meet. Make it of any length.

c. Find the true length of AX at a^1x^1.

d. On a^1x^1 lay out the true value of the resultant. This gives the vector AB.

Resolve the vector AB into two components. One component must be parallel to one of the legs of the tripod and the other component lies in the plane of the other two legs. The following steps will solve this problem.

e. Through point B construct BY parallel to leg *1*.

f. Find the point, P, where BY pierces the plane of legs *2* and *3*.

g. Through point P construct a line, PC, parallel to leg *3*.

h. Find the point C where the line PC crosses leg *2* of the tripod.

i. The vector diagram is $ABPCA$.

j. Find the true length of each leg of the diagram to determine the load in each leg of the tripod.

By transferring the arrows to the tripod in Fig. 19.8(a), it can be shown that leg *3* is in tension and the other two in compression.

19.9 RESULTANT OF NONCONCURRENT COPLANAR VECTORS. When a series of nonconcurrent vectors lie in a single plane, they must intersect in pairs unless they are parallel. Therefore, the resultant can be found by combining two vectors as V^1 and V^2 in Fig. 19.9 to obtain the resultant R^1. Then V^3 may be combined with R^1 to obtain resultant R^2. The magnitude and direction of each resultant are found in the vector diagram in Fig. 19.9(b) and the line of action in Fig. 19.9(a). If the resultant of the first two forces happens to be parallel and equal in magnitude to the third force but opposite in direction, the resultant will be a couple.

19.10 THE STRING POLYGON. The same result could be obtained by means of a string polygon or, as it is often called, a funicular polygon. This is a very important method of analysis and should be familiar to every engineer. The illustration in Fig. 19.10 is the same as Fig. 19.9, and although in this case the method of Fig. 19.9 may seem easier, the method of the string polygon can be used in many other problems that would be difficult or impossible to solve by the first method.

To solve a problem by the string polygon method, it is necessary to have some direct relationship be-

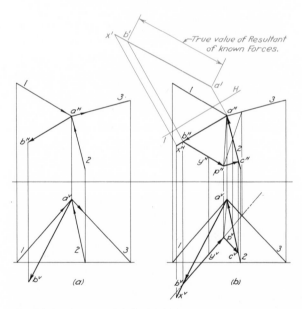

Fig. 19.8 Space vector diagram.

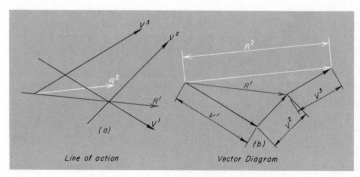

Fig. 19.9 Composition of nonconcurrent coplanar vectors.

tween the original vectors. This is accomplished by re-solving each force into two components in such a way that one of the components of the first force is also a component of the second force but opposite in direction. The vector AB in Fig. 19.10(b) represents the force V^1 of Fig. 19.10(a), and by selecting a pole P at any convenient place the vector AB can be resolved into two components, AP, called string S^1, and PB, called string S^2. The vector BC, representing force V^2, can be resolved into two components BP, which is still called S^2, and PC, which is called S^3. From this it can be seen that PB and BP are equal and opposite and would therefore cancel out, leaving AP and PC as the components of the resultant R^1. In a similar manner the vector CD, representing force V^3, can be resolved into two components—CP, string S^3, and PD, string S^4. Again it can be seen that PC and CP cancel each other, leaving AP and PD as the components of the resultant R^2.

Lines of action of these various components can be determined as in Fig. 19.10(c) in the following steps:

a. Select a starting point, O, as any point on the line of action of force V^1.

b. Through point O construct lines parallel to strings S^1 and S^2 of Fig. 19.10(b).

c. Locate the point, m, where the line parallel to string S^2 crosses the line of action of force V^2.

d. Through point m construct a line parallel to string S^3.

e. Locate the point, n, where the line parallel to string S^3 crosses the line of action of force V^3.

f. Through point n construct a line parallel to string S^4.

g. Locate the point where the line parallel to string S^4 crosses the line parallel to string S^1. This locates point X.

h. Through point X construct a line parallel to R^2 of Fig. 19.10(b). This is the line of action of resultant R^2.

The first point O can be chosen any place on V^1 since any other locations would merely determine a different point on the line of action of R^2.

19.11   RESULTANTS OF VECTOR SYSTEMS. There are several possibilities that must be investigated when determining the resultant of a set of vectors. If, in each case, the vector polygon and the string polygon are drawn, it is possible to tell immediately what the form of the resultant will be. The three possibilities are as follows:

a. *If, as in Fig. 19.10(b), the vector polygon does not close, the resultant must be a force.* A vector diagram is said to close when the end of the last vector coincides with the beginning of the first vector. In this case point D would have to fall on point A for closure.

b. *If the vector polygon closes with the vectors all pointing around the polygon in the same direction, but the string polygon does not close, the resultant will be a couple.* A couple is defined as two forces that are equal and opposite but whose lines of action are parallel and at a definite distance apart. In Fig. 19.11(b) the vector polygon closes, but the string polygon, shown in dashed line, in Fig. 19.11(a) does not close because there are two parallel positions of string S^1. In this case the resultant is a couple whose forces are both S^1 acting at a distance of a from each other.

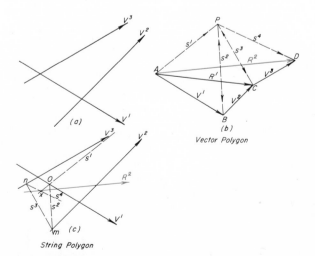

Fig. 19.10   Composition of nonconcurrent coplanar vectors—string polygon method.

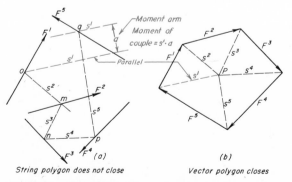

Fig. 19.11   Vector and string polygons of a force system when the resultant is a couple.

c. *If the vector polygon closes with the vectors all pointing around the polygon in the same direction, and the string polygon also closes, the system is in equilibrium.* This condition is illustrated in Fig. 19.12.

19.12 PARALLEL FORCES. The problem of parallel forces is a special case of nonconcurrent forces and may be solved by the same method. Figure 19.13 shows a truss with vertical loads as specified. The appearance of the vector diagram, shown in Fig. 19.13(*b*) is different because it becomes a straight line with the panel loads all pointing down and the reactions pointing up. When in equilibrium, the sum of the reactions must equal the loads, so that the vector diagram will close at the top point of P^1. It will be necessary to determine

the value of each reaction. To do this the following steps are necessary, as illustrated in Fig. 19.13.

a. Construct the vector diagram of all forces. This falls on a straight line as shown in Fig. 19.13(*b*). The loads are downward and the reactions upward.

b. Select a pole at some convenient place such as P.

c. Draw strings S^1 to S^5 so that each force is resolved into two forces represented by strings.

d. Construct the string polygon in the usual manner. Figure 19.13(*c*).

e. Extend strings S^1 and S^5 to their point of intersection. This locates a point on the line of action of the resultant. The value of the resultant can be found on the vector diagram from the beginning of P^1 to the end of P^4.

f. Continue S^1 to its intersection with the line of action of R^1 as in Fig. 19.13(*c*).

g. Continue S^5 to its intersection with the line of action of R^2 as in Fig. 19.13(*c*).

h. Join these two points to locate string S^6.

i. Draw string S^6 in the vector diagram, Fig. 19.13(*b*), to locate a point in the vector diagram, which gives the magnitude of the two resultants. In the string polygon, Fig. 19.13(*c*), strings S^5 and S^6 intersect on R^2. Therefore these strings are components of R^2 and indicate on the vector diagram, Fig. 19.13(*b*), the limits of R^2. R^1 whose components are S^1 and S^6 closes the diagram.

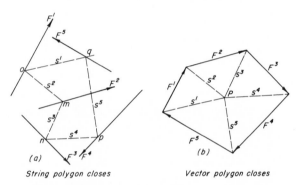

Fig. 19.12 Vector and string polygons of a force system in equilibrium. The resultant is zero.

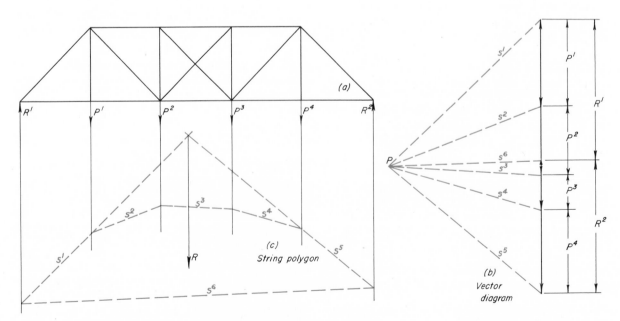

Fig. 19.13   Reactions of a truss.

j. The vector diagram and the string polygon both close, so that the system is in equilibrium.

19.13   CENTROID OF AN AREA. The centroid or center of gravity of an area is defined as that point where the area would act if it were concentrated at a point. For simple figures it is usually quite easy to locate the centroid, but for irregular areas the string polygon forms a convenient method. The method given here is general and may be applied to any area, but for regular figures there are usually easier methods. For instance, if there is an axis of symmetry, the centroid must be on that axis.

The irregular figure shown in Fig. 19.14(*a*) will serve to show the general method. The steps are as follows:

a. Divide the area into fairly small parts by means of vertical lines.

b. Select the approximate center of each area by estimation and judgment. In a triangle the centroid will be one third of the altitude from the base. In a trapezoid the centroid will be near the center but closer to the larger base.

c. Draw a vertical line through the center of each area.

d. Calculate the area of each small part by scaling distances.

e. Construct a vector diagram using the areas as forces. See Fig. 19.14(*b*).

f. Select a pole and draw the strings S^1 to S^5. See Fig. 19.14(*b*).

g. Construct the string polygon in the usual manner in Fig. 19.14(*c*).

h. The intersection of strings S^1 and S^5 locates a point on the resultant. The centroid of the total area must lie on this resultant.

i. Divide the area into small sections by means of horizontal lines. See Fig. 19.14(*d*).

j. Select the approximate center of each part.

k. Draw a horizontal line through each center.

l. Calculate the area of each small horizontal part.

m. Construct a vector diagram using the areas as forces. See Fig. 19.14(*d*).

n. Assume a pole and draw strings S^1 to S^6.

o. Construct the string polygon as in Fig. 19.14(*e*).

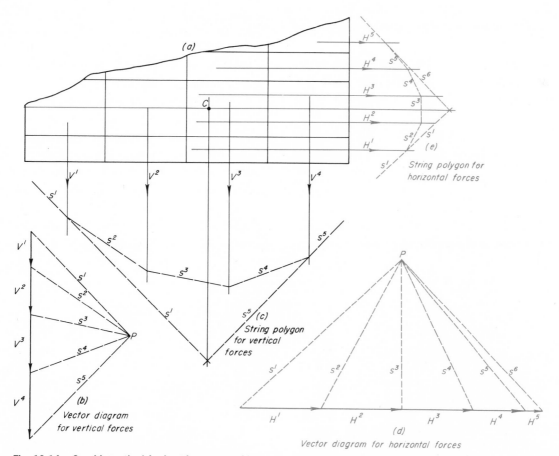

Fig. 19.14   Graphic method for locating a centroid.

p. The intersection of strings S^1 and S^6 locates a point on the resultant of all the forces.

q. The centroid of the entire area must lie on that resultant.

r. The centroid C lies at the intersection of the two resultants.

19.14   MOMENTS OF A FORCE ABOUT A POINT. A moment is defined as the product of a force times the distance measured from the line of action of the force to some point about which the moments are to be taken. It is frequently necessary in engineering problems to find the moment of a force about some point. This may be done graphically as shown in Fig. 19.15. To find the moment of force F about point O, the following steps are necessary. See Fig. 19.15.

a. Construct a vector diagram as in Fig. 19.15(*b*). If possible, the scale should be a convenient one such as 1 inch = 100 pounds. Select the pole so that the pole distance y is an easily used number such as 10 pounds or 100 pounds. The components S^1 and S^2 complete the diagram.

b. Draw the string polygon ABC in Fig. 19.15(*a*). Begin at any point A on the line of action of the force. Make the strings S^1 and S^2 parallel respectively to components S^1 and S^2.

c. Make the scale of the string polygon to some convenient scale such as 1 inch = 10 feet. Using this scale, lay out the distance X from the force to the

point. The base of the polygon, BC, goes through the point O.

d. Scale the distance, m, in feet, using the scale to which the string polygon or force layout was made.

e. Scale the distance, y, in pounds, using the scale to which the vector diagram was made.

f. Multiply m by y to obtain the required moment in foot-pounds.

The theory involved is easily explained by geometry. The two triangles ABC and DEP are similar. Then
$$ED:y::BC:x$$
and $$ED \cdot x = BC \cdot y$$

Since ED is the value of the force and x is the distance from O to the force, $ED \cdot x$ is the desired moment.

$\therefore BC \cdot y$ is the desired moment, which is also called $m \cdot y$.

It must be remembered that two scales are involved, one for m and a different one for y.

In Fig. 19.16 the moment of three forces about line XX is found to be $m \cdot y$ in foot-pounds. In this figure the vector diagram is drawn to a scale of 1 inch = 1000 pounds and the pole distance, y, is scaled as 1400 pounds. The string polygon is drawn to the scale of 1 inch = 10 feet and the distance between S^4 and S^1 on line XX, about which the moments are taken, is scaled as 21.2 feet. The moment is therefore $1400 \times 21.2 = 29,680$ foot-pounds.

19.15   MOMENTS ON A BEAM. One of the most common problems of this kind occurs in finding the moments at various points in a beam. Figure 19.17 shows a beam loaded with a series of concentrated loads. It is desired to find the moment of these forces about the plane XX. First the vector diagram, Fig. 19.17(*b*), is drawn and the pole selected. The string polygon, Fig. 19.17(*c*), is then drawn and string S^6 is located, from which the values of the reactions can be

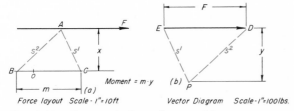

Fig. 19.15   Moment of a force about a point.

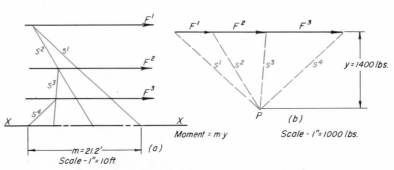

Fig. 19.16   Moment of forces about a line.

determined by means of the vector diagram. It was proved in Art. 19.14 that the moment is the product of the pole distance and the intercept of the two strings of a force on the plane about which the moment is to be taken. Therefore, the moment of R^1 about XX is $R_m{}^1$ in Fig. 19.17(c) times y. In the same manner the moment of W^1 is $W_m{}^1$ times y, of W^2 it is $W_m{}^2$ times y, and of W^3 it is $W_m{}^3$ times y. However, since the moment of R^1 is clockwise and the other three are counterclockwise, they must be subtracted, leaving the actual moment as m^1 times y. It will be noted that m^1 is the vertical intercept on the string polygon, so that the moment at any point on the beam may be found by taking the vertical intercept on the string polygon at that point and multiplying it by the pole distance. It makes no difference whether S^6 is horizontal or not. Either end of the beam may be used and the result will be the same, since the end used may be considered as a free body with the beam broken on plane XX and acted on by the reaction and the specified loads. The free body is then held in equilibrium by means of the moment found on plane XX.

19.16 MOMENT OF INERTIA. Moment of inertia

is defined as the product of the mass or area times the square of the distance from the center of gravity to the point about which moments are to be taken. The equation for the moment of inertia as given in textbooks is $I = \Sigma M(r)^2$, where M is the mass and r is the distance from the center of gravity to the point about which moments are to be taken. If the mass, assumed to be acting in a certain direction, is represented by a vector, F, as in Fig. 19.18(a) and the distance r is marked x, it will be necessary to multiply the vector by $(x)^2$, if the moments are taken about point O. In Art. 19.14 the method of multiplying the vector by x was explained. In Fig. 19.18 a method is shown whereby the vector can be multiplied by $(x)^2$. The necessary steps are shown in Fig. 19.18.

a. Lay out the vector F, which represents the mass to some even scale, such as 1 inch = 100 pounds. See Fig. 19.18(b).

b. Select pole distance y as some even distance such as 100 and draw the components S^1 and S^2, forming the triangle EDP.

c. Construct the string polygon ABC in Fig. 19.18(a) by starting at any point, A, on the line of action of the force F and drawing strings S^1 and S^2 parallel to the components S^1 and S^2 of Fig. 19.18(b). Use some even scale such as 1 inch = 10 feet. Line BC goes through point O.

d. The moment of F about O will be $m \cdot y$. See Art. 19.14.

e. Assume another pole P' at some even distance from BC, using the same scale 1 inch = 10 feet. Figure 19.18(c).

f. Draw the components r^1 and r^2 in Fig. 19.18(c).

g. Using any point G on the line of action of the force F, construct another string polygon GHK by making the strings r^1 and r^2 in Fig. 19.18(d) parallel to the components r^1 and r^2 in Fig. 19.18(c).

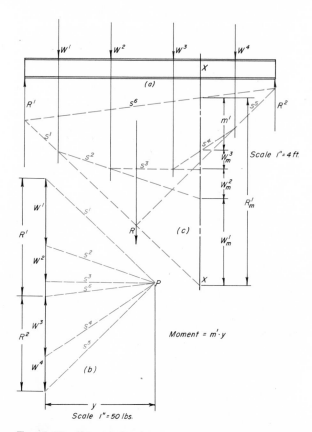

Fig. 19.17   Moments in a beam.

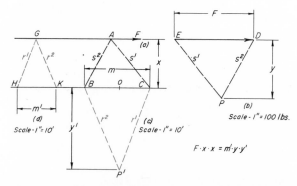

Fig. 19.18   Product of a force times the square of a distance.

h. Scale *HK* (*m'*), using the same scale. 1 inch = 10 feet.

i. Scale *y'*, using the scale to which it was drawn. 1 inch = 10 feet.

j. Scale *y*, using the scale to which it was drawn. 1 inch = 100 pounds.

k. Multiply the terms $m' \cdot y' \cdot y$ to obtain the moment of inertia in terms of pounds (feet)².

The theory can be explained by geometry. *GHK* and *BCP'* are similar triangles. Therefore,

$$BC:y' :: HK:x$$

or

$$m:y' :: m':x$$

multiplying

$$m \cdot x = m' \cdot y'$$

By definition $I = F(x)^2 = F \cdot x \cdot x$

By similar triangles *EDP* and *ABC*

$$Fx = my$$

Then $I = m \cdot y \cdot x$

By substitution $I = m' \cdot y' \cdot y$

For finding the moment of inertia of an area it is necessary to divide that area into rather small parts and to represent each part by means of a vector through the approximate centroid of the area. The method is approximate but becomes more accurate as the number of divisions is increased. To illustrate the effect of more divisions on the accuracy, Figs. 19.19 and 19.20 have been drawn. In each case the moment of inertia of a 4 × 6 rectangle has been found. In Fig. 19.19 the rectangle was divided into two parts and two vectors were used, whereas in Fig. 19.20 four divisions and four vectors were used. It can be seen that two different answers have been obtained, 116 and 126.4, respectively. If an infinite number of divisions could be used, the same result could be obtained as by analytical integration, and the result would be 128. Therefore, for an approximate answer it seems that, in this case, four divisions should be satisfactory.

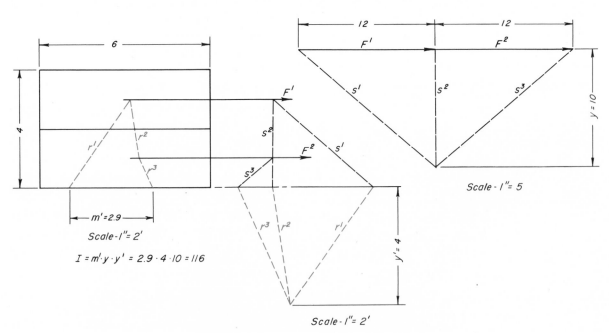

Fig. 19.19   Moment of inertia of a rectangle about one side—two divisions. Culman's method.

Actually, the graphical method would not be used for such simple areas. It is particularly valuable for irregular areas that are hard to solve analytically.

19.17   RADIUS OF GYRATION. The radius of gyration in Fig. 19.21(a) is the distance r from an axis about which moments are to be taken, to a line R representing a summation of a series of parallel forces that is so located that the moment of inertia of the summation about the given axis is the same as the total moment of inertia of all the individual forces about that same axis. In Fig. 19.21, R is a summation of all the forces $(F^1 + F^2 + F^3)$, which acts at a distance r from the plane XX, about which moments are being taken. This distance r is by definition the radius of gyration if the moment of inertia of R about XX is the same as the

sum of the moments of inertia of F^1, F^2, and F^3 about axis XX. By definition

$$I = R(r)^2$$

or

$$(r)^2 = \frac{I}{R}$$

By the previous paragraph

$$I = m^1 \cdot y^1 \cdot y$$

Then

$$(r)^2 = \frac{m^1 \cdot y^1 \cdot y}{R}$$

If the distance y is made equal to R, as has been done in Fig. 19.21(b), the equation becomes

$$(r)^2 = m^1 \cdot y^1$$

The length of the radius of gyration may then be found graphically, as illustrated in Fig. 19.21(e). To do

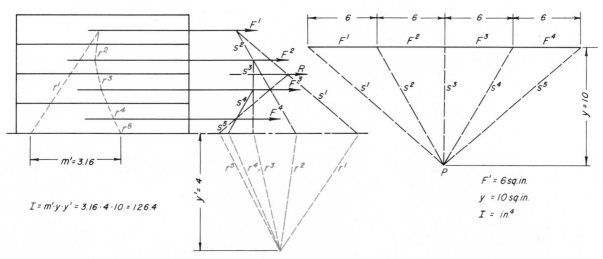

Fig. 19.20   Moment of inertia of a rectangle about one side—four divisions.

this, the distance AB is made equal to m^1, and the distance BC is made equal to y^1. A semicircle is then drawn with AC as a diameter and with a perpendicular to that diameter erected at B. Then by geometry

$$AB:BD::BD:BC$$

or $\qquad (BD)^2 = AB \cdot BC = m^1 \cdot y^1 = (r)^2$

Therefore, the value of r may be scaled at BD on Fig. 19.21(e). The steps needed in this construction are as follows:

a. Construct the vector diagram for the three forces F^1, F^2, and F^3. Use a convenient engineer's scale. Figure 19.21(b).

b. Select the pole P at a distance y from the force. The distance y is made equal to R, which is the sum of F^1, F^2, and F^3. See Fig. 19.21(b).

c. Construct the string polygon in Fig. 19.21(c). Begin at any point on F^1.

d. Assume the pole P' at some even distance, y', from the plane XX. See Fig. 19.21(c). Use any convenient engineer's scale.

e. Draw the components r^1 to r^4 from the points where the strings S^1 to S^4 cross plane XX. Figure 19.21(c).

f. Construct the second string polygon shown in Fig. 19.21(d).

g. Measure the distance m'. Figure 19.21(d). Use the same scale as used in Fig. 19.21(a).

h. On a horizontal line, lay out the distance m' at AB.

i. On the same line lay out the distance y' at BC.

j. Draw a semicircle with AC as a diameter.

k. Erect the line BD perpendicular to AC.

l. Measure BD. This is the radius of gyration r.

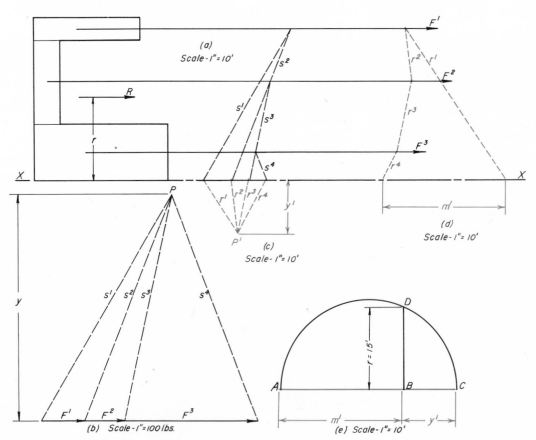

Fig. 19.21 **Radius of gyration.**

SELF-STUDY QUESTIONS

Before trying to answer these questions, read the chapter carefully. Then, without reference to the text, answer as many questions as possible. For those that cannot be answered, the number, in parentheses following the question number, gives the article in which the answer can be found. Look it up and write down the answer. Check the answers that you did give to see that they are correct.

19.1 **(19.2)** A vector can be used to represent any quantity that has _____ and _____ .

19.2 **(19.2)** The line in space along which the vector acts is called the line of _____ .

19.3 **(19.2)** When vector quantities meet in a single point they are called _____ .

19.4 **(19.2)** When vector quantities act in a single plane they are said to be _____ .

19.5 **(19.2)** A single vector that will produce the same result as a group of vectors is the _____ .

19.6 **(19.2)** A single vector that will just balance a group of vectors is called the _____ .

19.7 **(19.2)** The process of combining a group of vectors into a smaller number is called _____ .

19.8 **(19.2)** The process of replacing a system of vectors by another system having a larger number of vectors is called _____ .

19.9 **(19.2)** Any number of concurrent coplanar vectors can be combined into a single resultant: True
False

19.10 **(19.5)** Any number of concurrent noncoplanar vectors can be combined into a single resultant: True
False

19.11 **(19.7)** Equilibrium is the condition that exists in a system of vectors when the _____ is _____ .

19.12 **(19.7)** In a system of concurrent coplanar vectors in equilibrium there can be only _____ unknown quantities.

19.13 **(19.7)** In the vector diagram of a system in equilibrium the arrows must point in the _____
_____ .

19.14 **(19.7)** In the true-size view of the joint, the member is in _____ when the arrow points away from the joint.

19.15 **(19.8)** In a system of concurrent, noncoplanar forces that is known to be in equilibrium there can be _____ unknown quantities.

19.16 **(19.9–19.10)** The string polygon is used in solving a set of _____ _____ vectors.

19.17 **(19.11)** When a vector polygon does not close, the resultant is a _____ .

19.18 **(19.11)** When the vector polygon closes but the string polygon does not close, the resultant is a
_____ .

19.19 **(19.11)** When the string polygon and the vector polygon both close, the system is in _____ .

19.20 **(19.16)** Moment of inertia is the product of the _____ times the _____ of the _____ from the center of gravity to the point about which moments are taken.

PROBLEMS

In solving these problems the student should use as large a scale as possible on the sheet of paper that he is using. If a large sheet of paper is used, the scale can be made large and the accuracy will be better. However, with careful work a reasonable answer can be obtained on an 8½ × 11 sheet. Some of the problems require a knowledge of engineering geometry for solution. Although some of the problems may be solved without a formal study of Chapter 13, it is believed that the students will be able to comprehend the work and get more benefit from it if they first have a good knowledge of geometry.

19.1 A river, 1 mile wide, is flowing due south with a current of 10 miles per hour. A boat traveling 20 miles per hour with respect to the water must land at a point directly opposite the starting point. What direction must it travel and how long will it take to cross?

19.2 A weight of 100 pounds is suspended by two ropes attached to the ceiling at points 10 feet apart. One rope is 8 feet long and the other is 10 feet long. Find the load in each rope.

19.3 A derrick picks up a load of 2000 pounds. The boom of the derrick is at an angle of 45° with the horizontal and the cable connecting the end of the boom with the top of the mast is at an angle of 15° with the horizontal. Find the load in the cable and the boom and indicate whether they are in tension or compression.

19.4 A falling body is acted on by gravity and by a horizontal wind that causes a horizontal acceleration of 2 feet per second per second. What is the magnitude and direction (angle with the horizontal) of the resulting acceleration?

19.5 A 4-foot cube of stone is resting on a fairly smooth surface. Two of the vertical faces of the cube are in a N.-S. direction. A force of 2000 pounds pushing due east is applied at the S.W. corner. Another force of 2500 pounds is applied at the N.E. corner and is pulling N. 45° E. A third force of 1850 pounds is applied at the S.E. corner and is pulling in a direction S. 60° E. These forces are just enough to start motion. What is the direction of the motion? What is the frictional resistance to motion?

19.6 An equilateral triangle, 6 feet on a side, is horizontal and has the west side in a N.-S. position. It is acted on by three forces. One at the N. corner pulls N. 45° E. with a magnitude of 50 pounds. One at the east corner acts in a direction S. 60° W. with a magnitude of 35.4 pounds. The other at the south corner acts in the direction S. 15° W. with a magnitude of 18.3 pounds. Find the resultant.

19.7 Four forces acting at a point have magnitudes of 100 pounds, 200 pounds, 300 pounds, and 400 pounds. They act downward along the edges of a right, regular, rectangular pyramid whose apex is at the point where the four forces act. The altitude of the pyramid is 20 feet and the base is a rectangle 10 feet by 15 feet. Find the resultant of the four forces. Describe it by means of a vertical component and two horizontal components which are parallel respectively to the sides of the base of the pyramid.

19.8 An airplane must take off in a direction N. 30° E. to take advantage of a rising air current of 5 miles per hour. The wind is due south at 20 miles per hour. Flying speed of the plane is 75 miles per hour with relation to the ground and the plane is climbing at an angle of 20°. What is the compass bearing of the flight and the speed? How long will it take to reach an altitude of 10,000 feet?

19.9 A captive balloon is held by three ropes, each 100 feet long. They are fastened to the ground at points A, B, and C. These points are the three corners of an equilateral triangle 75 feet on a side. AB is a N.-S. line. The balloon has a lift of 1000 pounds and a wind blowing S. 45° E. causes a horizontal force of 200 pounds exerted by the balloon. Find the load in each of the three ropes.

19.10 A beam 15 feet long is supported at both ends, and loaded with four concentrated loads. These loads are specified in the table.

Load No.	Magnitude	Distance from the left end
1	1000 pounds	3 feet
2	500	5
3	2000	10
4	300	13

a. Find the resultant of the loads.
b. Find the value of each reaction.
c. Find the moment in the beam at any point specified by the instructor.

19.11 A beam 12 feet long is supported at both ends and loaded with a uniformly increasing load starting with 160 pounds at the left end and increasing to 400 pounds at the right end. Find the reactions and the moment at any point.

19.12 A semicircle has its base on the X-axis. The radius is 2 inches.
a. Find the centroid.
b. Find the moment of inertia about the base.
c. Find the radius of gyration about the same axis.

19.13 A T-section has its top $24'' \times 4''$ and the stem $14'' \times 6''$.

    a. Find the centroid.

    b. Find the moment of inertia about an axis through the bottom of the stem.

    c. Find the radius of gyration about the same axis.

19.14 For the irregular area described below, find the centroid, the moment of inertia, and the radius of gyration about the specified axis.

    The axis is a horizontal line. The base of the area is a horizontal line $1''$ above the axis. The coordinates of the points on the outline of the area are listed in the table and are measured to the right from the left edge of the figure and upward from its base.

Point	Distances	
No.	Right	Vertical
1	1	1.5
2	2	2
3	3	1
4	4	1
5	5	3
6	6	4
7	7	4
8	7	0

CHAPTER 20

Graphic Layouts
for Empirical Equations

NEW: Construction of the Pan American Building, New York (J. Alex Langley, D.P.I.)

OLD: Slaves building the pyramids. (The Bettmann Archive)

Chapter 20 Graphic Layouts for Empirical Equations

20.1 USE OF EMPIRICAL EQUATIONS. Engineers and businessmen deal constantly with equations. Some of these are developed by a logical reasoning process and are called rational equations. Others are developed from observations of natural processes or from data obtained in carefully controlled laboratory experiments. The latter are called empirical equations. These equations are very useful in the design and development of many types of structures, machines, and other equipment. Many natural phenomena follow such equations, and problems relating to them can thus be solved.

20.2 PRESENTATION OF DATA. The purpose of most laboratory experiments is to determine how one variable in a certain situation changes with respect to another while all other factors are held relatively constant. The controlled variable is usually called the independent variable and the other the dependent variable. The results of the experiment may be presented in three forms:

a. As tabulated data.
b. Graphically by a curve that represents the data as accurately as possible.
c. By an equation that represents the curve with a minimum deviation.

Of these methods the first is cumbersome and difficult to use for interpolation or extrapolation. The curve, on the other hand, quickly shows trends and the value of one variable corresponding to another can be found quickly and accurately. The curve can easily be extended, if the data upon which it was based warrants such extension. An equation, if reasonably simple, is compact and can be used as easily as the graph. It also permits extension beyond the range of the original data. An equation can also be used in a computer for rapid solution, if the equation is more difficult or must be used repeatedly. For these reasons, it is often desirable to have an equation.

20.3 LIMITATIONS. No matter how carefully the graphical work is done nor how accurately the mathematical equation is determined, it can never be more reliable that the original data from which it was obtained. Even in a well-controlled experiment there are always possibilities of errors of observation in making readings of the instruments. Some of these errors are self-compensating in that some may be too high, whereas others are too low. Generally such errors do not affect the validity and usefulness of the data. If one reading appears to be entirely out of line, when plotted on graph paper, such a point can simply be ignored in drawing the curve.

On the other hand, errors due to faulty instruments, improper calibration, or inaccurate setting and adjustment may cause all readings to be either too high or too low. Nothing can be done in the graphical layout to compensate for such errors. Instruments must be corrected and the work repeated.

20.4 ACCURACY OF GRAPHICAL WORK. Since the derivation of an equation by the methods of this chapter will depend on the plotting of data and the subsequent drawing of an average straight line or curve through the plotted points, it is obvious that

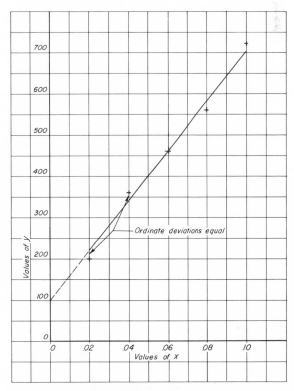

Fig. 20.1 Drawing an average line.

such work must be done with accuracy. To assist in this process the following suggestions are offered.

a. Review Chapter 18 and particularly Art. 18.4 and follow the suggestions therein contained.

b. Make the layout of the chart as large as possible. The customary 8½ × 11-inch printed coordinate papers may be used, but where greater accuracy is desired, it may be advisable to construct large-scale charts.

c. When indicating plotted points make these as sharp and small as possible. Later, if desired, the location can be indicated by a cross mark or a small circle.

d. The average line, whether straight or curved, should have the following features:

1. As many points on the line as possible. Sometimes, of course, none can be on the line.

2. Approximately an equal number of points above and below the line and the summation of ordinate distances above and below the line, within a limited length, equal to zero as shown in Fig. 20.1.

3. When there are dozens of points scattered at random across a rather narrow belt as in Fig. 20.2, it is best to draw very lightly the top and bottom enclosing or enveloping lines, ignoring, of course, any extreme points. Giving consideration to the density of distribution of the points, the average line will be somewhere near the halfway position between the upper and lower boundary lines.

20.5 SELECTION OF THE TYPE FORM OF THE EQUATION. If an average curve drawn to fit plotted data does not result in a straight line on rectangular coordinate paper, it is difficult to select the type of equation that will represent the data accurately. There are no rules for making a selection among the many possible equations. If, however, a convenient working equation, suitable for engineering computations of a practical character, is needed, a few suggestions can be offered. The selection, in this chapter, will be limited to three equations that are relatively simple and can be based upon a straight line. The form of the equation depends on the kind of coordinate paper used for plotting. None of these are too laborious for practical use. Two other equation forms based upon curves on rectangular coordinate paper will also be given, but these are not so readily applied.

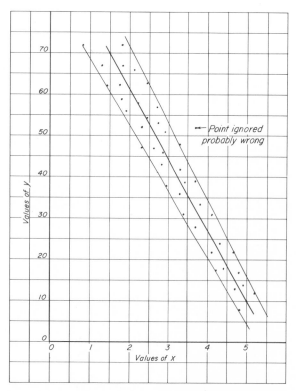

Fig. 20.2 Drawing an average line through scattered points.

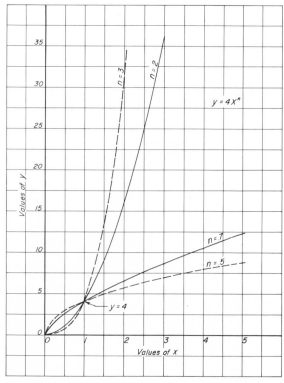

Fig. 20.3 Curves of parabolic form.

a. $y = mx + c$. This is the familiar equation of a straight line on rectangular coordinate paper.

b. $y = a(10)^{bx}$. If this equation is transformed by taking logarithms of both sides, it becomes

$$\log y = \log a + bx \log 10$$

Since $\log a$ is a constant and $\log 10$ is 1, this is the equation of a straight line on semilog paper with y on the log scale and x on the uniform scale.

c. $y = ax^m$. If this equation is also transformed by taking logarithms of both sides, it becomes

$$\log y = \log a + m \log x$$

This is the equation for a straight line on logarithmic coordinate paper.

Two other straight-line types are possible with a little additional computation:

d. $y = a(10)^{mx} + c$; or $y - c = a(10)^{mx}$ which becomes

$$\log (y - c) = \log a + mx$$

thus showing $\log (y - c)$ to be linear with x on semilog paper.

e. $y = ax^m + c$; or $\log (y - c) = \log a + m \log x$
This shows $\log (y - c)$ to be linear with $\log x$ on logarithmic paper.

f. Two other forms that can sometimes be used with curved lines are

$$y = a + bx + cx^2 \cdots (n + 1) x^n$$
$$\text{and} \qquad (y + b)(x + a) = c$$

20.6 RECTIFICATION OF CURVES. From the foregoing paragraphs, with the exception of the last two, it will be noted that the equations are all based on straight lines upon certain kinds of coordinate paper. Examination of the tabulated data from an experiment usually will not reveal the nature of the curve to be drawn. The customary practice therefore is as follows:

a. Plot the data upon rectangular coordinate paper. If a straight line can be drawn, proceed to the development of the equation.

b. If a straight line does not result upon rectangular coordinate paper, a comparison of the curve obtained, with those shown in Figs. 20.3, 20.4, and 20.6 may give a clue for another plotting upon one of the other two types of coordinate paper. Curves in Fig. 20.3 will develop as straight lines with positive slopes on logarithmic paper, and those in Fig. 20.4 will become straight lines with negative slopes as shown in Fig. 20.5. The curves in Fig. 20.6 will

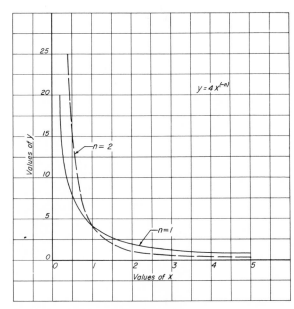

Fig. 20.4   Curves of hyperbolic form.

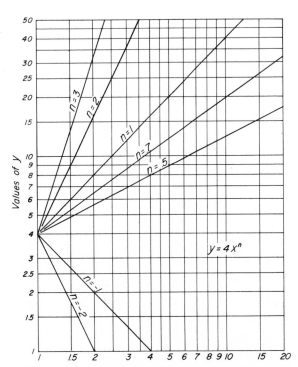

Fig. 20.5   Curves showing as straight lines on logarithmic paper.

become straight lines if plotted on semilog paper as shown in Fig. 20.7. It will be noted that positive exponents give positive slopes and negative exponents give negative slopes.

c. If a second plotting on log or semilog paper does not result in a straight line, the remaining type of coordinate plotting should be tried. If only a very slight curvature exists on either type of paper, equations shown in Art. 20.5(d), (e), and (f) may be tried.

Briefly, then the graphical portion of finding empirical equations to fit tabulated data is as follows:

1. Plot first on rectangular coordinate paper. If a straight line does not result, proceed as in (2).
2. Plot on one or both of the remaining types of coordinate paper until an average straight line can be drawn.
3. Having a straight line, derive the equation by one of the methods discussed in the following paragraphs.

20.7 METHODS OF DETERMINING THE EQUATION. Four methods for finding the equation for a straight line are listed below. The first two are relatively simple, the third requires more labor, and the fourth, though probably more accurate, is quite laborious. It will not be discussed in this chapter.

1. Slope and intercept method.
2. Method of selected points.
3. Method of averages.
4. Method of least squares.

Each of the first three methods will be illustrated with a typical problem. On the last of these problems, all three methods will be used and their relative reliability checked.

20.8 STRAIGHT LINE ON RECTANGULAR COORDINATE PAPER. *Slope and intercept method.* Equation $y = mx + c$. In Fig. 20.8 the tabulated data in the upper left corner give the collapsing pressure Q of steel tubes compared with the ratio S of the wall thickness

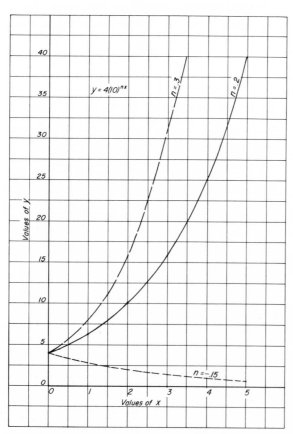

Fig. 20.6 Equations of the form $y = a(10)^{nx}$ show as curves on rectangular coordinate paper.

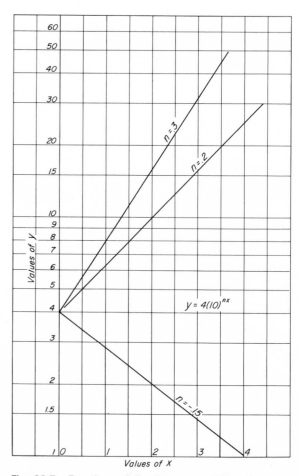

Fig. 20.7 Equations of the form $y = a(10)^{nx}$ shown as straight lines on semilog paper.

of the tube to its outside diameter. The data have been plotted on rectangular coordinate paper with S as the independent variable. The plotted points are well distributed about the selected straight line.

To obtain the equation for the line by the slope and intercept method, two steps are required.

a. Extend the line to the y-axis and read the intercept. This is the constant c in the equation. It will be noted in this problem that when the line was extended, it intercepted the y-axis below the x-axis, therefore giving the constant a negative value, namely, -1330.

b. Determine the slope of the line. The slope is expressed as the tangent of the angle that the line makes with the x-axis.

In analytical geometry the slope is usually determined by dividing the difference of the coordinates of the two points as shown for (a) and (b) in Fig. 20.8.

$$m = (y_2 - y_1)/(x_2 - x_1)$$
$$= (5100 - 1500)/(.075 - .033)$$
$$= 3600/.042 = 85,700$$

The equation therefore is $Q = 85,700S - 1330$.

As a check on the accuracy of this equation we may substitute any value of S, say 0.06, in our equation and compute the value of Q, which in this case comes out to be 3812. This agrees with the position of the line and is reasonably satisfactory. A further method of checking the reliability of an equation is shown in Art. 20.12.

20.9 STRAIGHT LINE ON SEMILOG PAPER. *Method of selected points.* Equation $y = a(10)^{mx}$. The data for the free swing of a pendulum at given intervals after it was started are shown in the upper right corner of Fig. 20.9 and the plotted rectangular coordinates below. Since an average straight line cannot be drawn through the plotted points, a second trial must be made. A comparison of this curve with Figs. 20.3 and 20.4 shows that (1) it does not pass through the origin $x = 0$, $y = 0$ and (2) it is not asymptotic with the x- and y-axes. On the other hand, a comparison with the type of curve in Fig. 20.6 shows a similarity in that both curves intersect the y-axis and appear to be asymptotic with the x-axis.

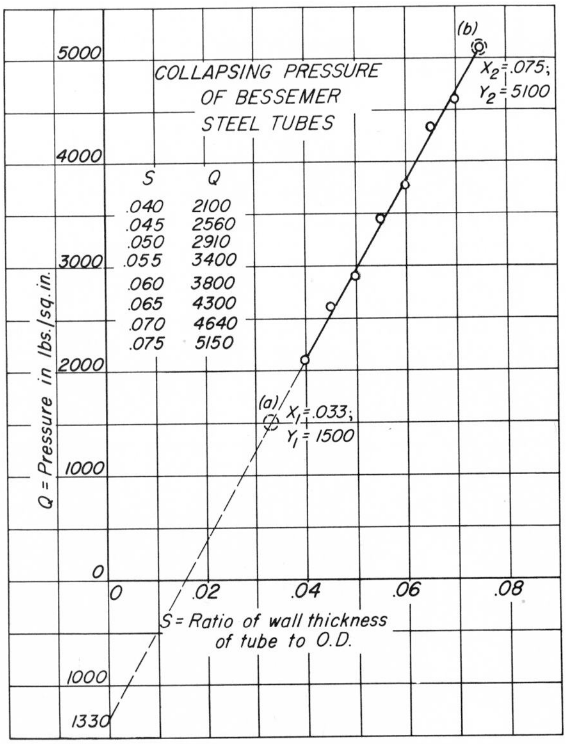

Fig. 20.8 Data that plot as a straight line on rectangular coordinate paper.

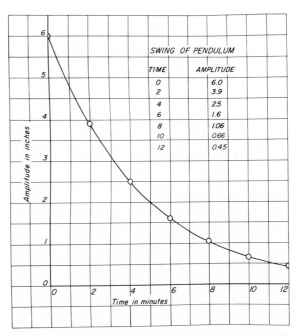

Fig. 20.9 Data that plot as a curve on rectangular coordinate paper.

This suggests that plotting the same data on semilog paper be tried as shown in Fig. 20.10. This does give an excellent straight line. Therefore the equation may be rewritten as $\log y = \log a + mx \log (10)$.

Since there are two constants to determine, two points on the line may be chosen which are not necessarily a part of the data unless by chance the line goes through one point. Then two equations can be written to solve for the constants. Thus for point a

$$x = 3.0 \quad \text{and} \quad y = 3.1$$

gives the equation

or
$$\log 3.1 = \log a + 3m$$
$$0.491 = \log a + 3m$$

Point b

$$x = 12 \quad \text{and} \quad y = 0.44$$

gives the equation

or
$$\log 0.44 = \log a + 12m$$
$$-0.357 = \log a + 12m$$

Subtracting the first equation from the second, we obtain

$$-0.848 = 9m \quad \text{and} \quad m = -0.094$$

Substituting this value in the first equation, gives

$$0.491 = \log a - 0.282$$

Therefore

$$\log a = 0.773 \quad \text{and} \quad a = 5.93$$

Therefore the equation for the line is

$$y = 5.93(10)^{-0.094x}$$

As a check, solve this equation for $x = 8$. Then

$$\log y = \log 5.93 + (-0.094)(8)(\log 10)$$
$$\log y = 0.773 - (0.094)(8) \quad \text{or} \quad \log y = 0.021$$

then $\quad y = 1.05$
which is quite satisfactory.

20.10   STRAIGHT LINE ON LOG PAPER. *Method of averages.* Equation $y = ax^m$. For this illustration, the relationship of the horizontal force H per inch of length of roller bearing on bridges required to produce movement to L, the load per inch of roller, is used. The data are shown in tabular form in Fig. 20.11. When the data were plotted on rectangular coordinates, a straight line could not be drawn through the average of the points as shown in Fig. 20.11.

A comparison with the curves in Figs. 20.3 and 20.6 would seem to point to plotting on semilog paper. This was tried, but a straight line did not result. The data were again plotted on logarithmic paper with the result shown in Fig. 20.12. There is a slight reversal in the curve of the actual plotted points, but the straight line approximates the whole series very well.

The method of averages requires that the data be divided into two equal parts, which has been done in Table 20.1. The summation of each part is then used to obtain the necessary two equations. Note that, except for the summation of two parts of the data, the method is just like the method of selected points as far as the computations are concerned. There is this dif-

TABLE 20.1   SUMMATION OF TWO PARTS OF TABULAR DATA

H	$\log H$	L	$\log L$
8.0	0.903	3	0.477
11.0	1.041	4	0.602
15.0	1.176	5	0.699
20.5	1.312	6	0.778
Summation	4.432		2.556

H	$\log H$	L	$\log L$
26.0	1.415	7	0.845
33.5	1.525	8	0.903
40.5	1.607	9	0.954
48.0	1.681	10	1.000
Summation	6.228		3.702

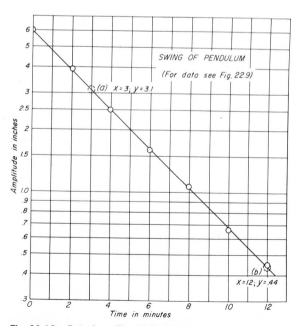

Fig. 20.10   Data from Fig. 20.9 plotted on semilog paper.

ference however, namely, that the straight line is not used at all except to show that the data seem to fit about such a line. Other than this, the line itself is not used.

For the solution, the logarithmic form of the equation is used. Thus

$$y = ax^m \quad \text{becomes} \quad \log y = \log a + m \log x$$

Substituting the summations from the table in this equation, we obtain

and
$$4.432 = 4 \log a + 2.556 \, m$$
$$6.228 = 4 \log a + 3.702 \, m$$

Since each logarithm is the summation of four quantities, $\log a$, which is a constant, must also be multiplied by 4. This coefficient will always be equal to the number of items in the summations. Eliminating $4 \log a$ between the two equations gives

$$1.796 = 1.146 \, m \quad \text{or} \quad m = 1.796/1.146 = 1.567$$

This quantity represents the slope of the line. Substituting this value in the second equation above, we get

$$6.228 = 4 \log a + 5.800$$
$$4 \log a = 0.428 \quad \text{and} \quad \log a = 0.107$$

Therefore
$$a = 1.28$$

and the equation becomes

$$H = 1.28 \, L^{1.567}$$

20.11 SOLUTION OF THE PROBLEM BY THE FIRST TWO METHODS. In order to show the method for checking the accuracy of the equation and to compare results by the different methods, this problem will be solved by the other two methods.

a. Slope and intercept method. By extending the line in Fig. 20.12 to the y-axis where $x = 1$ or $\log x = 0$ it can be seen that the intercept is 1.5 as nearly as it can be read. Selecting points a and b on the line (not from the data) and writing the equation for the slope,

$$(\log y_2 - \log y_1)/(\log x_2 - \log x_1) =$$
$$(\log 60 - \log 10)/(\log 12 - \log 3.6)$$
or $\quad (1.778 - 1.00)/(1.079 - 0.556) = 1.489$
Hence $\qquad m = 1.489$

By this method, therefore, the equation is

$$H = 1.5 \, L^{1.489}$$

b. Method of selected points. Using the same two points a and b on the line in Fig. 20.12 and substituting the values of the coordinates of these points in the equation,

$$\log 10 = \log a + m \log 3.6$$
$$\log 60 = \log a + m \log 12$$

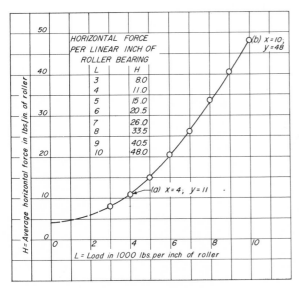

Fig. 20.11 Data that plot as a curve on rectangular coordinate paper.

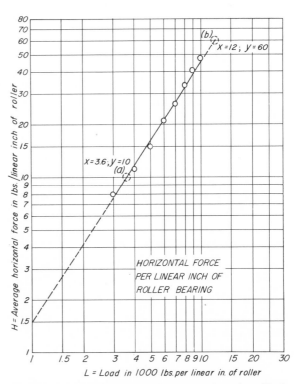

Fig. 20.12 Data from Fig. 20.11 plotted on logarithmic paper.

Inserting the values of the logarithms

$$1 = \log a + m \times 0.556$$
$$1.778 = \log a + m \times 1.079$$

Eliminating log a between these equations

$$0.778 = m \times 0.523 \quad \text{or} \quad m = 0.778/0.523 = 1.49$$

Substituting the value of m in the first equation, it becomes

and
$$1 + \log a = 1.49 \times 0.556$$
$$\log a = 0.173 \quad \text{and} \quad a = 1.492$$

The equation by this method therefore is

$$H = 1.492 \, L^{1.49}$$

20.12   CHECK ON EQUATIONS BY THE METHOD OF RESIDUALS.

In Arts. 20.8 and 20.9 the accuracy of the equations was checked by solving for a single point, which gives only a partial proof. The following procedure gives a more reliable check over the whole range of the data. The method consists of substituting values of the independent variable in the equation and computing the value of the other variable from the equation. The difference between the computed value and the observed value is called a residual. It is designated as plus when the observed quantity is larger than the calculated quantity and minus when the observed quantity is smaller than the computed one. Thus if the plotted point appears above the line, we might expect a plus residual, if below the line, a minus or negative residual. Ideally the sum of the residuals should be zero.

In Table 20.2, the results of computations for residuals, in the last problem, have been shown for each of the three methods. The columns marked H_c under each method give the computed values. To get the residuals these values are subtracted from the observed values under column H. As might be expected from the chart the numbers of plus and minus residuals are equal. The summation for the slope and intercept method comes about as close to the ideal as one could expect. The other two methods, in this particular case, do not give quite as good results. Frequently this works out in the opposite order. It should be noted again that the method of averages makes no use of the plotted line once it has been established that the particular coordinate plotting does result in a good average straight line. It may be observed that the intercepts obtained by the three methods differ by less than 0.01 for two of them and by 0.22 for the third. The slopes likewise differ very little. Any one of the equations would be satisfactory.

20.13   CURVES OTHER THAN STRAIGHT LINES.

Rectangular coordinates. Method of selected points. The method of selected points can be used for curves other than straight lines under certain conditions. For example, the curve in Fig. 20.11 seems to have a parabolic shape, but it does not cross the y-axis at zero. It is, however, horizontal at the intersection with the y-axis. In such cases the general equation

$$y = a + bx + cx^2 \ldots (n+1)x^n$$

TABLE 20.2   CHECKING RELIABILITY OF EQUATIONS

Data from Experiment		Computations for Residuals					
		Slope and Intercept Method		Method of Selected Points		Method of Averages	
L	H	H_c	Residuals	H_c	Residuals	H_c	Residuals
3	8.0	7.66	+0.34	7.67	+0.33	7.14	+0.86
4	11.0	11.70	−0.70	11.78	−0.78	11.27	−0.27
5	15.0	16.50	−1.50	16.45	−1.45	16.00	−1.00
6	20.5	21.75	−1.25	21.58	−1.08	21.30	−0.80
7	26.0	27.00	−1.00	27.23	−1.23	27.04	−1.04
8	33.5	33.20	+0.30	33.12	+0.38	33.42	+0.08
9	40.5	39.50	+1.00	39.45	+0.05	40.27	+0.23
10	48.0	45.20	+2.80	46.14	+1.86	47.21	+0.79
		$\Sigma =$	−0.01	$\Sigma =$	−1.92	$\Sigma =$	−1.15

can be applied with considerable success.

Thus, if the curve in Fig. 20.11 is extended as shown by the dash line, it crosses the y-axis at $y = 4$, thus giving the constant a in the equation. In order to have an equation that is simple to use, the second power of x is about as far as one should go. If greater accuracy is required and machine computations can be used, higher powers could be found.

If it is decided to use only the second power of x, it is necessary to determine only two more constants, namely, b and c in the general equation. Therefore, if points a ($x = 4$; $y = 11$) and b ($x = 10$; $y = 48$) are selected, and these values are substituted in the equation,

$$11 = 4.0 + 4b + 16c$$
$$48 = 4.0 + 10b + 100c$$

Eliminating b between the two equations

$$c = 0.4417$$

Substituting this value in the first equation

$$b = -0.017$$

The equation therefore is

$$y = 4.0 - 0.017x + 0.4417x^2$$

The computation of residuals shown in Table 20.3 indicates that this equation is reasonably close. Since it does not involve logarithms, it is just as easy to use as the straight-line equation. However, if higher powers of x must be used to get a close-fitting curve, the equation becomes somewhat cumbersome.

As a second illustration of the use of the method of selected points to curves other than straight lines, let it be assumed that the curve in Fig. 20.9 is used only from $x = 2$ to $x = 12$. This portion of the curve appears to be hyperbolic in form with the asymptotes somewhere near the x- and y-axes. This type of curve might conform to the equation

$$(x + a)(y + b) = c$$

With three constants to determine it will be necessary to select the two end points $x = 2$ and $x = 12$ and one near the middle $x = 6$ with their corresponding values of y. Three equations can then be written as follows:

$$(2 + a)(3.9 + b) = c$$
$$(6 + a)(1.6 + b) = c$$
$$(12 + a)(0.45 + b) = c$$

Solving these three simultaneous equations gives

$$a = 3, \quad b = 1.275, \quad \text{and} \quad c = 25.875$$

Hence the equation is

$$(x + 3)(y + 1.275) = 25.875$$

If this equation is checked for residuals between points $x = 2$ and $x = 12$ as shown in Table 20.4, the summation of residuals is $+0.01$, which is as close as one could expect to get.

When $x = 0$, the solution of the equation gives $y = 7.35$, which obviously does not fit the curve, hence it is good only between the values of $x = 2$ to 12.

TABLE 20.3   CHECKING RELIABILITY OF EQUATIONS

$y = a + bx + cx^2$
$y = 4 - 0.017x + 0.4417x^2$

Data from Experiment		Computations of Residuals				
x	y	a	$-0.017x$	$0.4417x^2$	y_c	Residual
3	8	4	-0.051	3.975	7.924	$+0.076$
4	11	4	-0.068	7.067	10.999	$+0.001$
5	15	4	-0.085	11.043	14.958	$+0.042$
6	20	4	-0.102	15.901	19.799	$+0.201$
7	26	4	-0.119	21.643	25.524	$+0.476$
8	33.5	4	-0.136	28.269	32.133	$+1.367$
9	40.5	4	-0.153	35.778	39.625	$+0.875$
10	48	4	-0.170	44.170	48.000	$+0.000$

$\Sigma = +3.038$

TABLE 20.4   CHECKING RELIABILITY OF EQUATIONS

Equation $(x + 3)(y + 1.275) = 25.875$

Data from Experiment		Computation of Residuals	
Time (x)	Amplitude (y)	Y_c	Residuals
2	3.9	3.900	0.000
4	2.5	2.420	$+0.080$
6	1.6	1.600	0.000
8	1.06	1.075	-0.015
10	0.66	0.715	-0.055
12	0.45	0.450	0.000

Summation $\Sigma = +0.01$

SELF-STUDY QUESTIONS

Before trying to answer these questions, read the chapter carefully. Then, without reference to the text, answer as many questions as possible. For those that cannot be answered, the number, in parentheses following the question number, gives the article in which the answer can be found. Look it up and write down the answer. Check the answers that you did give to see that they are correct.

20.1 **(20.1)** Equations that are developed by logical reasoning processes are called _____ equations.

20.2 **(20.1)** Equations obtained from carefully controlled experimental laboratory data are called _____ equations.

20.3 **(20.2)** The results of an experiment may be presented in the form of _____ data.

20.4 **(20.4)** Plotted points on a graph are usually shown by a small _____.

20.5 **(20.4)** When drawing a curve or straight line, as many points as possible should _____ the line.

20.6 **(20.4)** When points are not on the line there should be as many _____ the line as there are below it.

20.7 **(20.5)** The equation $y = mx + c$ will plot as a _____ line on rectangular coordinate paper.

20.8 **(20.5)** The equation $y = a(10)^{bx}$ plots as a straight line on _____ paper.

20.9 **(20.5)** The equation $y = ax^m$ plots as a straight line on _____ paper.

20.10 **(20.8)** The equation for a straight line on rectangular paper may be determined by the _____ and intercept method.

20.11 **(20.10)** Another scheme for finding the equation for a straight line on a graph is the method of _____.

20.12 **(20.3)** When attempting to draw a straight line or smooth curve through plotted data and one point seems to be way offside, this point is _____ in drawing the curve.

20.13 **(20.4)** In order to secure the greatest accuracy in graphical work, make the layout as _____ as possible.

20.14 **(20.8)** To solve an equation for a straight line by the slope and intercept method, extend the line to the y-axis and measure the _____.

20.15 **(20.8a)** The intercept on the y-axis determined by a straight line represents the _____ _____ in the equation $y = mx + c$.

20.16 **(20.9)** The equation of a straight line may be obtained by the method of _____ points. Only _____ points on the line are used.

PROBLEMS

In the following problems find the equation that fits the data by the method specified. In each case check your equation by the summation of residuals. Plot the data on $8\frac{1}{2} \times 11$ coordinate paper of the proper type.

20.1 Use data from Fig. 20.8 and solve by the method of selected points.

20.2 Use data from Fig. 20.8 and solve by the method of averages. Omit middle point in your summation for averages and residuals.

20.3 Use data from Fig. 20.9 and solve by the slope and intercept method.

20.4 Use data from Fig. 20.9 and solve by the method of averages.

20.5 Plot the data of Table 20.5 on 2-cycle semilogarithmic paper. Draw an average straight line through the points and determine the equation of the line by the slope and intercept method.

Table 20.5

x	y
10	20
20	36
30	56
40	105
50	170
60	300

Table 20.6

x	y
5	110
15	84
25	62
35	43
45	31
55	23

20.6 Plot the data of Table 20.5 as in Problem 20.5 and determine the equation of the average straight line by the method of selected points.

20.7 Plot the data of Table 20.6 on 2-cycle semilogarithmic paper. Draw an average straight line through the points and determine the equation of the line by the slope and intercept method.

20.8 Same as Problem 20.7, using the method of selected points.

20.9 Plot the data of Table 20.7 on rectangular coordinate paper and draw a smooth curve through the points.

Extend the curve to the X-axis and then determine an equation to fit the curve as nearly as possible by the method of selected points, using the general form of equation $x = a + by + cy^2$.

20.10 Plot the data of Table 20.7 on 2-cycle log-log paper and draw an average straight line through the points. Determine an equation for the line by the slope and intercept method.

Table 20.7

x	y
2	30
6	54
10	74
20	110
30	136
40	155
50	182
60	200

Table 20.8

x	y
40	170
60	105
80	76
100	55
150	36
200	24

20.11 Same as Problem 20.10. Solve by the method of selected points.

20.12 Plot the data of Table 20.8 on rectangular coordinate paper and find an equation of the general form $(x + a)(y + b) = c$ which will fit a smooth curve drawn through the points as nearly as possible. Assume three points on the curve, one near each end and one near the middle. These points should be on the curve and not necessarily a part of the plotted data unless the curve actually passes through the points.

20.13 Plot the data of Table 20.8 on 2-cycle semilogarithmic and/or 2-cycle log-log paper until an average straight line can be drawn through the points. Determine the equation for the line by the slope and intercept method.

20.14 Same as Problem 20.13, using the method of selected points.

20.15 Solve Problems 20.6, 20.7, 20.10, or 20.13 as assigned by the instructor by the method of averages.

CHAPTER 21

Construction and Use of Nomographs

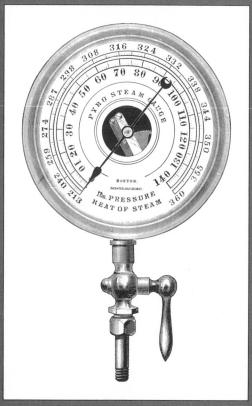

OLD: Pyrometrical Steam Gauge with two sets of graduations. (Culver Pictures, Inc.)

NEW: Control panel of a chemical plant. (Rotkin, P.F.I.)

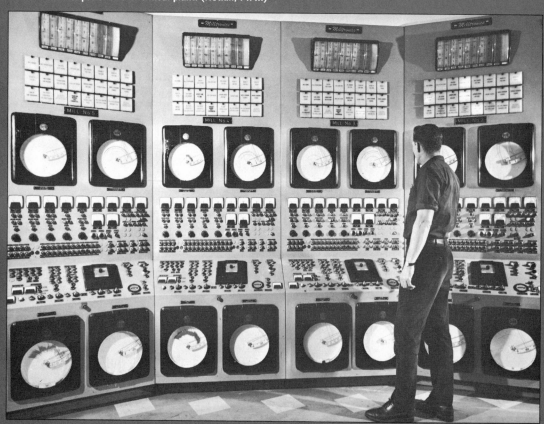

Chapter 21 Construction and Use of Nomographs

21.1 THE NOMOGRAPH. The nomograph or alignment chart, as it is sometimes called, is a graphical device for solving equations by means of a straight line, called an isopleth, laid across three or more calibrated scales which represent the variables in an equation. Nomographs make it possible to save considerable time when it is necessary to solve an equation repeatedly. They can be used by persons who may not have the mathematical skill to solve the equation. These charts have a built-in safety device in that the range of the scales can be limited to values for which the equation is valid. This prevents using them where the equation would not apply.

Nomographs can be designed by means of plane geometry, as will be done in this chapter, or by means of matrix algebra as explained in more advanced texts. The number of variables and forms of equations that can be handled in an alignment chart depends largely upon the skill and ingenuity of the designer. Here we shall limit our discussion to the more common types of charts and equations which will give an adequate basis for further study and development of the subject.

a. Two variables. Two parallel scales in contact or with a turning point between them.

$$f(x) = f(y)$$

b. Three variables. Three parallel scales.

$$\left. \begin{array}{l} f(x) + f(y) = f(z) \\ f(x) - f(y) = f(z) \end{array} \right\} \text{ natural scales}$$

$$\left. \begin{array}{l} f(x) \cdot f(y) = f(z) \\ \dfrac{f(x)}{f(y)} = f(z) \end{array} \right\} \text{logarithmic scales}$$

c. Three variables. N- or Z-charts.

$$\dfrac{f(x)}{f(y)} = f(z) \quad \text{natural scales}$$

d. Four variables. Four parallel scales.

$$f(x) \pm f(y) \pm f(v) = f(z) \quad \text{natural scales}$$
$$f(x) \cdot f(y) \cdot f(v) = f(z) \quad \text{logarithmic scales}$$

e. Four-variable proportionality charts. Parallel scales.

$$\dfrac{f(x)}{f(y)} = \dfrac{f(v)}{f(z)}$$

f. Four-variable combination parallel scale and N-chart.

$$f(x) \pm f(y) = \dfrac{f(v)}{f(z)}$$

21.2 DEFINITIONS. It is assumed that the student has studied algebra and is familiar with the following terms which are briefly defined for review purposes.

a. Constant. A constant is a term in an equation which always has the same value. Thus in the equation $M = \frac{1}{8}wl^2$, $\frac{1}{8}$ is a constant and has this value regardless of values assigned to all other terms.

b. Variable. A variable is a term in an equation which may have different values. For practical purposes these values usually lie between specified limits. If the variable may have all values between the limits, it is said to be continuous over this range.

c. Function of a variable. A function of a variable is any expression involving that variable, for example, a function of x may be $(2x + 1)$, x^3, $1/x^2$, $\sin x$, and $\log x$.

d. Functional modulus. A functional modulus is a proportionality or multiplying factor used to design a functional scale. It is the distance on the functional scale occupied by one unit of the function. The functional modulus is used in laying out the values in the line marked $2x^3$ in Table 21.1. For example, when $x = 3$, the value of the function $2x^3$ is 54. If the functional modulus were 0.1, the distance from the zero point on the scale, which is always the zero value of the function, would be $54 \times 0.1 = 5.4$ inches. The functional modulus is represented by a lower-case m; in this case, the functional modulus is called m_x.

e. Scale modulus. The scale modulus is the functional modulus multiplied by any constant coefficient in the function. The scale modulus is used in laying out the values in the line marked x^3 in Table 21.1. For example, when $x = 3$, the value of x^3 is 27. If the functional modulus were 0.1, in this case the scale modulus would be 0.2. By multiplying $27 \times 0.2 = 5.4$ inches, the same distance from the zero point is obtained as though the functional modulus had been used. The use of the scale modulus will save some time in the layout of the chart. The scale modulus is represented by capital M or in this case M_x.

21.3 FUNCTIONAL SCALES. Any function may be represented by a scale, called a functional scale. The method of constructing such scales is illustrated by two examples. In practical work the range of the variables is always limited. The limits are established either by experience and usage or by experimental procedures that indicate the range over which the equation is valid.

The steps in making a functional scale are as follows:

1. Make a table of the values of the variable that it is desired to have shown on the scale.
2. Compute the corresponding values of the function.
3. Determine the length of the scale to accommodate
   (a) the range of the function,
   (b) the size of the paper it is convenient to use.
4. Choose a modulus or multiplying factor to give the desired length.
5. Lay out the values of the function of the variable using the selected functional modulus as a unit.
6. Mark the division points with the value of the variable.

Thus, if L equals the length of scale and m is the modulus, then

$$L = m_x[f(x_2) - f(x_1)] \qquad (21.1)$$

where $f(x_2)$ is the upper limit of the function and $f(x_1)$ is the lower limit.

Example 1. Let $f(x) = 2x^3$ and let the range be from 3 to 8. Let it be required to show only the integral values on the scale. Steps 1 and 2 are shown in Table 21.1. Using Equation 21.1 the length of the functional scale can be determined. It is possible to proceed in either one of two ways. The length of the scale may be chosen, from which the modulus can be computed, or by reversing the process, the modulus can be chosen and the length computed. The exact length of the scale is rarely important. But it is very convenient to have the modulus an integer or whole number which will permit using commercially available scales for the work. In the given example,

$$L_x = m_x(1024 - 54) = 970m_x$$

If it is desired to have a length suitable for $8\frac{1}{2} \times 11$-inch paper, a functional modulus $m_x = 0.01$ may be chosen. This will give a scale length of 9.70 inches and permit the use of the engineer's 10-scale. Each value shown in the lower row of Table 21.1 may be multiplied by the modulus 0.01 to obtain the length in inches shown in Table 21.2 for each value of the variable.

The scale can now be constructed as shown in Fig. 21.1. If further subdivisions are needed, they can be computed and plotted or a fan chart, as shown in Fig. 21.2, can be used for approximate results, provided that the plotted points are not too far apart and the

TABLE 21.1 CALCULATIONS OF THE VALUES OF THE FUNCTION OF A VARIABLE

Values of the variable x	0	1	2	3	4	5	6	7	8
Values of the function x^3	0	1	8	27	64	125	216	343	512
$2x^3$	0	2	16	54	128	250	432	686	1024

TABLE 21.2 CALCULATIONS OF DISTANCES TO BE LAID OUT TO OBTAIN A FUNCTIONAL SCALE

Values of x	0	1	2	3	4	5	6	7	8
Values of the function $2x^3$	0	2	16	54	128	250	432	686	1024
0.01 by $2x^3$	0	0.02	0.16	0.54	1.28	2.50	4.32	6.86	10.24

change in spacing between successive points does not vary too greatly. The chart can be used to subdivide two adjacent spaces into five parts each. It can be used as an underlay with a light table or as an overlay, punching the points through with a pin. With one division point on the first line, the next on the middle line of the fan chart, and the third on the last line and having the angle of the line in the proper direction, the points may be marked. However, it should be remembered that this method is approximate.

The construction of the preceding functional scale could have been shortened somewhat if a scale modulus had been used instead of the functional modulus. Whenever a function has a constant coefficient, it is possible to multiply the functional modulus by the coefficient to obtain a scale modulus, in which case the coefficient appears in the modulus rather than in the values to be plotted. Thus in Table 21.1 the last step could be omitted and a scale modulus of 0.02 used to give exactly the same result. This is often very convenient. It should be noted in Fig. 21.1 that the divisions on the scale are marked with the values of the variable, not those of the function. This is always true of functional scales. Other illustrations of functional

scales can be seen on the student's slide rule on which many functional scales have been plotted; for example, the C, D, and trigonometric scales.

21.4   CONVERSION CHART. Equation $f(x) = f(y)$. The conversion chart is a graphical device for relating one variable to another in an equation that involves only two variables. This can be done by placing the two functional scales on opposite sides of the same line as in Fig. 21.3. In this case *both scales must have the same modulus, they must run in the same direction, and the zero values of both functions must be at the same point.* On the other hand, if it is more convenient to have different moduli for the two functional scales, these scales may be on two different parallel lines, run in opposite directions, and be related to each other through a turning point, or pole, as in Fig. 21.4.

Both scale arrangements are illustrated in the following examples.

Example 1. Let it be required to make a conversion chart on a single line for the area of a circle in terms of the radius, $A = \pi r^2$, and let the range of r be from 0 to 10 feet. See Fig. 21.3. The standard equation is $f(A) = f(r)$. The computations are shown in Table 21.3.

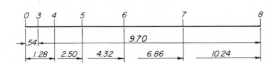

Fig. 21.1   **Construction of a functional scale $F(x) = 2x^3$.**

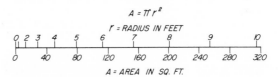

Fig. 21.3   **Conversion chart.**

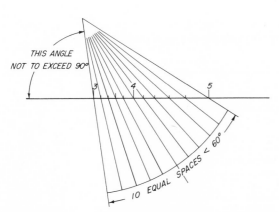

Fig. 21.2   **Use of a fan chart to subdivide two unequal spaces.**

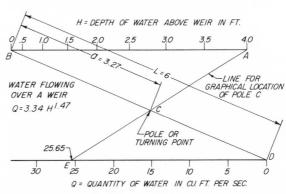

Fig. 21.4   **Conversion chart with pole.**

Using Equation 21.1 for length of scale,

$$L_r = m_r[f(r_2) - f(r_1)]$$

$L_r = m_r(314 - 0) = 314m_r$. If m_r is chosen as $\frac{1}{60}$, then $L_r = 314 \times \frac{1}{60} = 5.23$ inches, which is a convenient length. When we apply the same modulus to the A-scale, $L_A = 320 \times \frac{1}{60} = 5.33$ inches. The scales may then be plotted with the engineer's 60-scale as shown in Fig. 21.3 by beginning each scale at a common point which is the zero value of both functions, and using the values of $f(r)$ and $f(A)$.

Example 2. Let it be required to make a conversion chart with two parallel scales and a turning point for the equation for the discharge of water over a sharp-crested weir, as illustrated in Fig. 21.4. The equation is $Q = 3.34 \cdot H^{1.47}$ where Q is the quantity of water in cubic feet per second and H is the height of the water above the weir in feet with a range from 0 to 4 feet. The standard equation is $f(Q) = f(H)$. The computation of

the necessary data for the functions is shown in Table 21.4. The moduli $m_H = \frac{1}{5}$ and $m_Q = \frac{1}{6}$ are assumed to give the desired length of scale as explained in Art. 21.3. The scales may be placed any convenient distance apart, but must run in opposite directions. The diagonal connecting the zero points should have a convenient length. The location of the turning point can be determined graphically by drawing lines between two sets of related values of the functions. Thus when $H = 0$, $Q = 0$, and when $H = 4$, $Q = 25.65$. The location of the turning point may also be computed from the ratio of the functional moduli.

By similar triangles in Fig. 21.4,

$$\frac{AB}{BC} = \frac{DE}{DC} \quad \text{or} \quad \frac{AB}{DE} = \frac{BC}{CD}$$

If $BC = a$ and the diagonal $L = 6$ inches,

$$\frac{m_H f(H)}{m_Q f(Q)} = \frac{a}{L - a}$$

TABLE 21.3   CALCULATIONS OF THE VALUES OF THE FUNCTION OF THE VARIABLES

Variable r

Values of r	0	1	2	3	4	5	6	7	8	9	10
r^2	0	1	4	9	16	25	36	49	64	81	100
$f(r) = \pi r^2$	0	3.14	12.6	28.3	50.3	78.5	113	154	201	254	314

Variable A

Values of A	0	40	80	120	160	200	240	280	320	Values selected
$F(A) = A$	0	40	80	120	160	200	240	280	320	as desired

TABLE 21.4   CALCULATIONS OF THE DISTANCES TO BE PLOTTED TO OBTAIN THE FUNCTIONAL SCALES

Variable H

H	0.0	0.5	1.0	1.5	2.0	2.5	3.0	3.5	4.0
$H^{1.47}$	0.0	0.36	1.0	1.82	2.77	3.85	5.03	6.30	7.68
$f(H) = 3.34 H^{1.47}$	0.0	1.21	3.34	6.08	9.25	12.84	16.78	21.03	25.65
$m_H f(H) = \frac{1}{5} \cdot 3.34 \cdot H^{1.47}$	0.0	0.24	0.67	1.22	1.85	2.57	3.36	4.21	5.13

Variable Q

Q	0	5	10	15	20	25	30
$f(Q) = Q$	0	5	10	15	20	25	30
$m_Q f(Q) = \frac{1}{6}Q$	0	0.83	1.66	2.5	3.33	4.16	5.00

Since $f(Q) = f(H)$, then

$$\frac{m_H}{m_Q} = \frac{a}{L - a} \quad \text{or} \quad \frac{1\!/5}{1\!/6} = \frac{a}{6 - a}$$

Solving this equation, a equals 3.27 inches measured on the diagonal from the zero point of the H-scale. See Fig. 21.4.

21.5   THREE-VARIABLE PARALLEL-SCALE CHART.
Equation $f(x) + f(y) = f(z)$. If a three-variable parallel-scale chart or nomograph is to be constructed as shown in Fig. 21.5, the relationship between the scale spacing and the functional moduli can be determined by the principles of plane geometry. In Fig. 21.5, AG and CH are drawn parallel to BF, thus giving two similar triangles ACG and CEH. Therefore

$$\frac{EH}{b} = \frac{CG}{a} \quad \text{or} \quad \frac{EF - HF}{b} = \frac{CD - GD}{a}$$

or $a \cdot (EF - HF) = b \cdot (CD - GD)$

When we substitute the functional scale lengths for EF, HF, etc., the equation becomes

$$am_y f(y) - am_z f(z) = bm_z f(z) - bm_x f(x),$$

When we collect terms,

$$bm_x f(x) + am_y f(y) = (a + b)\,m_z f(z)$$

If this equation is to reduce to $f(x) + f(y) = f(z)$, the coefficients must be equal or

$$bm_x = am_y = (a + b)m_z$$

Hence $$\frac{m_x}{m_y} = \frac{a}{b} \qquad (21.2)$$

This equation gives the relationship between the moduli of the outside scales and the scale spacing.

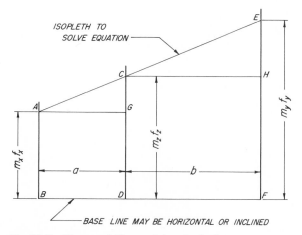

ISOPLETH TO SOLVE EQUATION

BASE LINE MAY BE HORIZONTAL OR INCLINED

Fig. 21.5   Three-variable parallel-scale chart.

Also from the equation

$$am_y = (a + b)m_z$$

$$m_y = \left[\frac{a + b}{a}\right]m_z = \left[1 + \frac{b}{a}\right]m_z$$

But $\dfrac{b}{a} = \dfrac{m_y}{m_x}$ so $\left[1 + \dfrac{m_y}{m_x}\right]m_z = m_y$

Therefore

$$\left[\frac{m_x + m_y}{m_x}\right]m_z = m_y \quad \text{or} \quad m_z = \frac{m_x m_y}{m_x + m_y} \quad (21.3)$$

This equation gives the functional modulus for the scale in the middle, in terms of the moduli for the two outer scales. These calculations must always be made with the functional modulus, not the scale modulus. The equation must be arranged so that the scale that is to be the center scale of the chart is the only variable on that side of the equation.

Example 1. Let it be required to make a nomograph for the equation $E = RI$ which gives the relationship between voltage, resistance, and current in an electric circuit. The range for R is to be from 1 to 20 ohms and the amperage I from 10 to 100 amperes. The following steps can generally be used as a guide in the construction of charts.

Step 1. Write the equation in proper form. $f(x) + f(y) = f(z)$. To get the equation $E = RI$ into the proper form, it is necessary to take logarithms of both sides. The equation then becomes $\log E = \log R + \log I$, and E will be the center scale.

Step 2. Select the moduli to give suitable lengths for the outside scales.

$$L_R = m_R(\log 20 - \log 1) = m_R(1.301 - 0) = 1.301m_R$$

For an $8\frac{1}{2} \times 11$-inch page, approximately 8 inches will make a suitable length; hence, if m_R is assumed as 6, the length will be 7.8 inches.

$$L_I = m_I(\log 100 - \log 10) = m_I(2 - 1) = 1m_I$$

For this scale the modulus may be chosen as 8 which will make $L_I = 8$ inches.

Step 3. Determine the modulus for the center scale. From Equation 21.3

$$m_E = \frac{m_R m_I}{m_R + m_I} = \frac{6 \cdot 8}{6 + 8} = \frac{48}{14} = 3.43$$

Step 4. Determine the scale spacing. From Equation 21.2, $m_R/m_I = a/b = 6/8 = 3/4$. The scales may therefore be spaced so that the distance from the R-scale to the E-scale is $\frac{3}{4}$ of the distance from the I-scale to the E-scale. The ¾ is only a ratio and any suitable numbers having that ratio may be used. In this case the distance from the R-scale to the E-scale may be chosen as 3 inches and therefore the distance from the I-scale to the E-scale will be 4 inches. Table 21.5 shows all the information necessary for laying out the chart in a convenient form that is easy to check.

Step 5. Lay out the scales. All scales must be logarithmic, and it is necessary to construct three scales, one having a 6-inch cycle, one having an 8-inch cycle and the third having a cycle 3.43 inches long for the center scale. To obtain these functional scales of the desired lengths (6, 8, and 3.43 inches), the construction shown in Fig. 21.6 may be used and the chart folded at the cycle whose length is M. To construct this chart pick out the logarithms of the desired numbers from a slide rule or a table of logarithms, multiply them by 10, and plot them in inches to obtain the 10-inch scale shown in Fig. 21.6. Approximately opposite the middle

of the scale and 10 inches away, select a pole P. From each of the divisions on scale AB, draw a line to the pole P. Then draw lines parallel to scale AB at 1-inch intervals until 1 inch from P. Number these lines successively 9, 8, etc., beginning with the first from the 10-inch scale. This chart can now be folded at any one of the lines or between them at the proper place to give a logarithmic scale of any length from 1 to 10 inches.

The 8- and 6-inch scales can now be used to construct the outside scales of the chart in Fig. 21.7 and by folding the chart made similar to Fig. 21.6 at 3.43, the center scale of the chart in Fig. 21.7 can be laid out as shown in Fig. 21.7. A base line must be established to give a starting point for each scale. This is frequently the line through the zero point of each scale and is usually horizontal. However, it may be any line that goes through points that give a solution of the equation. In this case, the base line is horizontal and goes through the points $R = 1$, $I = 10$, and $E = 10$.

TABLE 21.5 DATA NECESSARY FOR LAYOUT OF CHART

Variable	Range of Variable	Function	m	M	L	Direction	Spacing from Center Scale
R	1 to 20	$\log R$	6	6	7.8	↑	3
E	10 to 2000	$\log E$	3.43	3.43	7.9	↑	0
I	10 to 100	$\log I$	8	8	8	↑	4

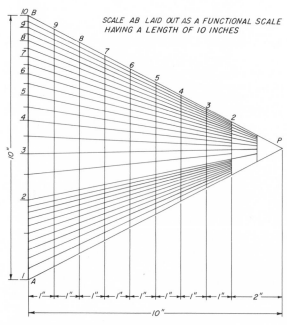

Fig. 21.6 Chart to obtain logarithmic scales.

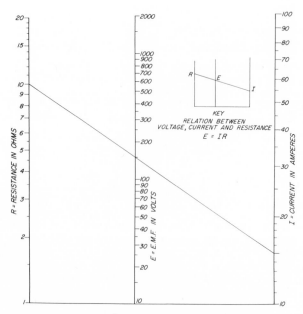

Fig. 21.7 Three-variable parallel-scale chart—logarithmic scales.

See Fig. 21.7. These points are obtained by assuming $R = 1$, $I = 10$, and substituting in the equation to obtain $E = 10$. These points are also the assumed lower limits for the chart.

Step 6. Check the chart. Each chart should always be checked for accuracy by solving the equation for selected values of two of the variables and then testing the chart with an isopleth connecting these values to see if the same answer is obtained. It is important that the check be made on an inclined line to catch any error in spacing.

Example 2. Let it be required to construct a nomograph for the equation for the moment of inertia of a hollow square,

$$I = \frac{(B^4 - b^4)}{12}$$

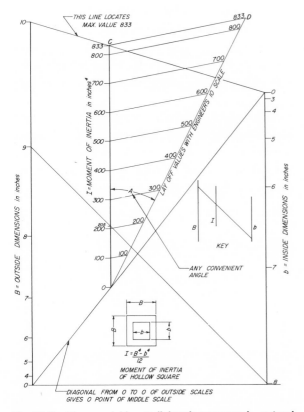

Fig. 21.8 Three-variable parallel-scale nomograph—natural scales.

as illustrated in Fig. 21.8. The outside dimension B is to have a range from 4 to 10 inches and the inside dimension b from 3 to 8 inches.

Step 1. Write the equation in proper form. $12\,I = B^4 - b^4$ is perhaps most convenient.

Step 2. Select the moduli to give suitable scale lengths.

$$L_B = m_B(10^4 - 4^4) = (10{,}000 - 256)m_B = 9744m_B$$

If $m_B = \dfrac{1}{1000}$, then $L_B = 9.744$ inches.

$$L_b = m_b(8^4 - 3^4) = (4096 - 81)m_b = 4015m_b$$

If $m_b = \dfrac{1}{500}$, then $L_b = 8.03$.

Step 3. Determine the modulus for the middle scale. From Equation 21.3, it can be seen that $m_I = m_B m_b / m_B + m_b$.

When we substitute the known values of m_B and m_b

$$m_I = \frac{0.001 \cdot 0.002}{0.001 + 0.002} = 0.000667$$

By solving the original equation using the maximum value of B and the minimum value of b (since b is negative), the maximum value of $12I$ is found to be 9919. In this case, the effect of the small b value is insignificant, so that the I-scale would probably be carried to the point where $12I = 10{,}000$. The minimum value of I will be zero when B and b are equal. Then $L_I = m_I(10{,}000 - 0) = 0.000667 \cdot 10{,}000 = 6.67$ inches.

Since this modulus is uneven, it will be necessary to multiply all the values of the function by the modulus, to get values to plot. However, it will be easier to multiply the modulus by 12 to get a scale modulus rather than to multiply each value of the function by 12.

Hence the scale modulus will be $0.000667 \times 12 = 0.008$. All of the information necessary to lay out the chart is shown in Table 21.6 in a convenient form that is easy to check. When the desired values of I are multiplied by 0.008, they may be plotted in inches. The dimensions on this scale may also be laid out by geometrical construction as shown in Fig. 21.8.

TABLE 21.6 DATA NECESSARY FOR LAYOUT OF CHART

Variable	Range of Variable	Function	m	M	L	Direction	Spacing from Center Scale
B	4–10	B^4	0.001	...	9.744	↑	2³⁄₁₆
I	0–833	$12\,I$	0.000667	0.008	6.67	↑	0
b	3–8	b^4	0.002	...	8.03	↓	4³⁄₈

Step 4. Scale spacing. Using Equation 21.2

$$\frac{a}{b} = \frac{m_B}{m_b} = \frac{.001}{.002} \quad \text{or} \quad \frac{2}{4}$$

which indicates that the distance from the *b*-scale to the *I*-scale must be two times as great as the distance from the *B*-scale to the *I*-scale.

Step 5. Lay out the scales. Since the inside dimension *b* of the hollow square is negative, the scale must run downward. The middle scale must begin on a line joining the zero values of the outside scales even though these may not be included in the final chart, or upon a set of simultaneous values obtained by solving the equation. See Fig. 21.8. Computations for the two outside scales are shown in Table 21.7.

The scale for *B* may be laid out with the engineer's 10-scale using one hundred times the values on the scale since $\frac{1}{1000} = \frac{1}{10} \times \frac{1}{100}$. The first fraction indicates the scale and the second the multiplier. The values opposite B^4 are plotted, but as usual are marked with the values of the variable as shown in Fig. 21.8. For the *b*-scale the engineer's 50-scale may be used since the modulus for *b* is $\frac{1}{500}$ which is equal to $\frac{1}{5} \times \frac{1}{100}$. The values opposite b^4 in Table 21.7 are used and plotted using one hundred times the values on the 50-scale. For the *I*-scale the modulus is 0.000667, but since the function is 12*I* the scale modulus is $12 \times 0.000667 = 0.008$. The values of *I* may be multiplied by 0.008 to obtain distances that may be laid out in inches to obtain the divisions.

Since there is no convenient scale for this modulus, another procedure is possible. Draw the diagonal connecting the zero points of the functions of the two outside scales, which are $6\frac{9}{16}$ inches apart. Draw a vertical line $2\frac{3}{16}$ inches from the *B*-scale. Beginning where this line crosses the diagonal lay off a distance of 6.67 inches, which is the computed length of the *I*-scale.

From the zero point of the *I*-scale draw an inclined line at any convenient angle *A* and with the 10-scale, lay off the equal divisions for the values of *I* ending with 833 which corresponds to the maximum scale length. From this point lettered *D*, draw a line to point *C* and then subdivide the *I*-scale by parallel lines as shown in Fig. 21.8.

Step 6. Check the nomograph by computing the value of I for one set of values for B and b.

Thus
$$I = \frac{9^4 - 8^4}{12} = \frac{(6561 - 4096)}{12} = 205$$

The line connecting 9 and 8 shows this value on the center scale.

21.6   Z- OR N-CHART. Equation $f(x)/f(y) = f(z)$. *Natural scales.* This type of chart can be made in the form of a letter *Z* or *N*. The first shape has been chosen for the derivation of the equations to be used in the layout of the chart. If the *Z* of Fig. 21.9 were revolved 90° clockwise, it would be a letter *N*.

The variable that is by itself on one side of the equation will be plotted on the diagonal line. By shifting terms in the equation, any one of the variables can be placed by itself. If all other considerations are equal, the most complicated function is usually plotted on the diagonal because this makes the layout easier.

From the similar triangles *ABC* and *CDE* in Fig. 21.9, it can be seen that

$$\frac{m_x f(x)}{P} = \frac{m_y f(y)}{L - P}$$

Then

$$\frac{m_x f(x)}{m_y f(y)} = \frac{P}{L - P}$$

TABLE 21.7   CALCULATIONS OF THE VALUES OF THE FUNCTION OF THE VARIABLE

Variable *B*						
Values of *B*	4	5	6	7	8	9	10
$f(B) = B^4$	256	625	1296	2401	4096	6561	10,000

Variable *b*						
Values of *b*	3	4	5	6	7	8
$f(b) = b^4$	81	256	625	1296	2401	4096

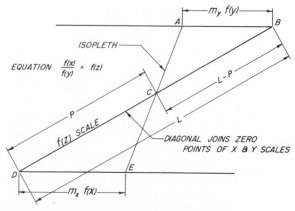

Fig. 21.9   Z or N nomograph—three variables.

But from the given equation

$$\frac{f(x)}{f(y)} = f(z)$$

Therefore

$$\frac{m_x}{m_y}f(z) = \frac{P}{L - P}$$

and $m_x f(z)L - m_x f(z)P = m_y P$

$$m_x f(z)L = P[m_x f(z) + m_y]$$

and $$P = \frac{Lm_x f(z)}{m_x f(z) + m_y}$$

Divide both the numerator and denominator of this fraction by m_x,

$$P = \frac{Lf(z)}{f(z) + \dfrac{m_y}{m_x}} \qquad (21.4)$$

The length of the diagonal and the moduli for the outside scales m_x and m_y can be arbitrarily chosen to give a convenient scale layout. Then for any length L the value of P in Equation 21.4 can be computed for any chosen value of $f(z)$. With these computations a diagonal scale can be constructed. The diagonal scale can also be constructed graphically with somewhat less labor. This method, illustrated in the following examples, is recommended.

Example 1. Let it be required to make a Z-chart for the following equation for bearing sizes

$$d = \frac{Q}{280\ n}$$

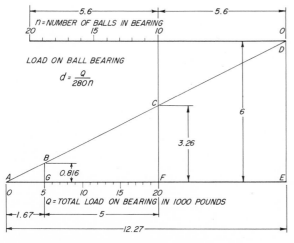

Fig. 21.10   Location of the diagonal scale for a Z chart.

where d equals the diameter of the bearing, Q equals the total load, and n equals the number of balls in the bearing. Let Q vary from 5000 to 20,000 pounds and n from 10 to 20 balls.

Step 1. The equation is in satisfactory form.

Step 2. Select moduli for the outside scales to give a reasonable chart size. It should be noted that although the diagonal scale must connect the zero values of the functions of the outside scales, which run in opposite directions, these points do not have to be included in the chart, as the example in Fig. 21.10 will show.

$$LQ = m_Q(20,000 - 5000) = 15,000\ m_Q$$

If $m_Q = \dfrac{1}{3000}$, $L_Q = 5.0$ inches

$$L_n = m_n(280 \times 20 - 280 \times 10) = 2800\ m_n$$

If $m_n = \dfrac{1}{500}$, $L_n = 5.6$ inches

$$\frac{m_n}{m_Q} = \frac{\dfrac{1}{500}}{\dfrac{1}{3000}} = 6$$

This value is used in Equation 21.4.

In order to lay out the chart shown in Fig. 21.10, it is necessary to compute the length of each outside scale from zero to the minimum value to be used in order to get the overall length of the chart. For the Q-scale the minimum value is 5000 pounds; therefore

$$L_Q = m_Q(5000 - 0) = 5000 \times \frac{1}{3000} = 1.67 \text{ inches}$$

For the n-scale the minimum value is 10; therefore

$$L_n = m_n(2800 - 0) = 2800 \times \frac{1}{500} = 5.6 \text{ inches}$$

From the Fig. 21.10 it can be seen that the overall length, including the zero points, is 12.27 inches. If the zero points had to be included, this would be much too large. By making the width of the chart 6 inches, the location of points B and C on the diagonal can be computed, and the diagonal laid out so that if it were extended, it would pass through the zero values of the functions that are plotted on the parallel scales. A freehand sketch of the entire chart including the zero points should be made to assist in the calculations. The diagonal may be found graphically if the distant zero point can be temporarily located on the table. From similar triangles in Fig. 21.10, ADE and ACF, it can be seen that

$$\frac{DE}{EA} = \frac{CF}{FA} \quad \text{or} \quad \frac{6}{12.27} = \frac{CF}{6.67} \quad \text{and} \quad CF = 3.26 \text{ inches.}$$

Also

$$\frac{DE}{EA} = \frac{BG}{AG} \quad \text{or} \quad \frac{6}{12.27} = \frac{BG}{1.67} \quad \text{and} \quad BG = 0.816 \text{ inch.}$$

The scales are now laid out as in Figs. 21.10 and 21.11.

Step 3. The division points of the diagonal scale may be located by computing the distance of each from the zero point by the use of Equation 21.4. The computations for such spacing are shown in Table 21.8 and the plotting illustrated for one point, $d = 3.0$ in Fig. 21.11. These distances when calculated in this manner will always be measured from the zero point of the function which shows as the numerator of the equation.

Step 4. Scale spacing. The scale spacing and arrangement in this case have been accomplished in Step 2.

Step 5. Lay out the scales. Beginning with the n-scale, it may be seen that the function of n is $280n$. These values are shown in Table 21.9. Since the modulus is $\frac{1}{500}$, the engineer's 50-scale may be used. Thus $\frac{1}{500} = \frac{1}{5} \times \frac{1}{100}$. It is therefore possible to use one hundred times the values printed on the scale. The beginning point for $n = 10$ is therefore at 28 on the 50-scale and the end is at 56. Note that on the chart these points are labeled 10 and 20, not 2800 and 5600.

For the Q-scale the modulus is $\frac{1}{3000}$ and the engineer's 30-scale may be used. Again $\frac{1}{3000} = \frac{1}{3} \times \frac{1}{1000}$ so use one thousand times the values on the scale, and begin at 5000, which is 1.67 inches from the zero point as required.

One method for locating the division points on the diagonal scale has already been described in Step 3. A somewhat easier method is described in the following paragraph.

For the diagonal scale that carries the values for d, it is necessary to choose the major divisions that are to be shown and to arrange them as shown in Table 21.9. Then selecting one convenient value for n, the corresponding values of Q are computed from the original equation for each value of d. In this case, n was chosen equal to 20. It is best to choose this pole in such a place that the rays will intersect the diagonal line as nearly perpendicularly as possible. Having the Q-values, isopleths may be drawn from $n = 20$ to the corresponding points on the Q-scale. The intersection of these lines with the diagonal locates points on the d-scale, as shown in Fig. 21.12.

Step 6. Check the scale. Since the layout was made graphically, the check must be made by computing one or two points for direct measurement or by using some point other than $n = 20$. If the direct method had been used to lay out the scale, the check should be made graphically in the usual way.

TABLE 21.8   CALCULATIONS FOR DIRECT MEASUREMENT ON Z-CHART

Direct Measurement $L = 13.66$		$P = \dfrac{Lf(d)}{f(d) + m_n/m_Q}$	
$f(d)$	$f(d) + m_n/m_Q$	$Lf(d)$	$\dfrac{Lf(d)}{f(d) + m_n/m_Q}$
1.5	7.5	20.5	2.73
2.0	8.0	27.3	3.42
2.5	8.5	34.2	4.02
3.0	9.0	41.0	4.55
3.5	9.5	47.9	5.05
4.0	10.0	54.6	5.46

TABLE 21.9

Computations for Layout of n-Scale		Computations for Graphical Layout of d-Scale $Q = 280nd$		
n	$f(n) = 280\,n$	Pole n	d	Values of Q with $n = 20$
10	2800	20	1.5	8,400
11	3080			
12	3360	20	2.0	11,200
13	3640			
14	3920	20	2.5	14,000
15	4200			
16	4480	20	3.0	16,800
17	4760			
18	5040	20	3.5	19,600
19	5320			
20	5600	20	4.0	22,400

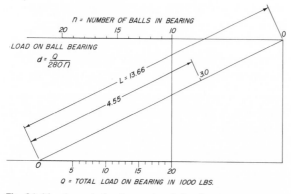

Fig. 21.11   Layout of a diagonal scale by direct measurment.

21.7   FOUR-VARIABLE PARALLEL-SCALE CHART.

The standard form of the equation is:

$$f(v) + f(x) + f(y) = f(z) \quad \text{natural scales}$$
$$f(v) \cdot f(x) \cdot f(y) = f(z) \quad \text{logarithmic scales}$$

This type of chart is based upon the three variable charts; hence no new derivations are required. The equation is simply divided into two parts, each of which is set equal to a new term. Thus

$$f(v) + f(x) = f(p) = f(z) - f(y)$$

A three-variable parallel-scale chart can be made for each equation, and they will have a common scale for $f(p)$ which will be a pivot scale and need not be calibrated. This scale must

(1) have the same modulus in both charts,
(2) run in the same direction in both charts,
(3) have the same zero point for $f(p)$ for both charts.

It is often convenient to have the pivot scale in the same position in both equations. In many cases, placing the pivot scale in the center will reduce the width of the chart and make the lengths of the scales more uniform.

Example 1. As an illustration we shall use the equation for the weight of steel plates such as may be used for beam or column bearings, as shown in Fig. 21.13.

$$W = 0.282\ LBT$$

where

L = the length with a range from 18 to 36 inches
B = breadth with a range from 12 to 30 inches, and
T = thickness with a range from ½ to 2.0 inches.

Step 1. Rewrite the equation in proper form.

$$\log W = \log 0.282 + \log L + \log B + \log T$$

For the time being, it is possible to ignore the log of the constant and take care of it when placing the last scale because the effect of the constant is merely to move the last scale up or down. Therefore, the equation may be written:

$$\log W - \log L = \log p = \log B + \log T$$

or, making two equations,

$$\log W - \log L = \log p$$
and
$$\log B + \log T = \log p$$

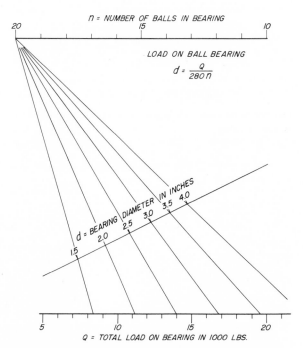

Fig. 21.12   Layout of a diagonal scale by graphical method.

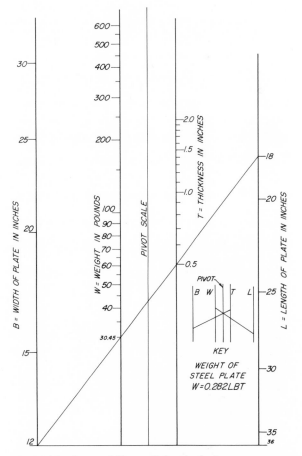

Fig. 21.13   Four-variable parallel-scale chart.

Step 2. Determine the moduli for the outside scales of the first chart. For the W-scale it is first necessary to compute the range of the function corresponding to the other functions.

$$W \text{ min.} = 0.282 \times 12 \times 18 \times 0.5 = 30.45$$
$$W \text{ max.} = 0.282 \times 30 \times 36 \times 2.0 = 609.12$$
$$L_W = m_W(\log 609.12 - \log 30.45)$$
$$= m_W(2.7847 - 1.4835) = 1.3012 \ m_W$$

If $m_W = 5$, then $L_W = 6.506$ inches.

$$L_L = m_L(\log 36 - \log 18)$$
$$= m_L(1.5563 - 1.2553) = 0.3010 \ m_L$$

If $m_L = 20$, then $L_L = 6.02$.

Step 3. Since we have the moduli for the outside scales, then by Equation 21.3 the modulus for the middle scale p is

$$m_p = \frac{(m_W \times m_L)}{(m_W + m_L)} = \frac{(5 \times 20)}{(5 + 20)} = 4$$

The length of the p-scale need not be computed since it is a pivot scale only and is not calibrated.

For the second equation the moduli must be worked out in somewhat different order.

$$L_B = m_B(\log 30 - \log 12)$$
$$= m_B(1.477 - 1.079)$$
$$= 0.398 \ m_B$$

If $m_B = 20$, then $L_B = 7.96$ inches

Since m_p must be the same for this chart as the preceding one, it is necessary to compute the modulus for the scale of function T which is an outside scale by means of Equation 21.3.

$$m_p = \frac{(m_B \times m_T)}{(m_B + m_T)} \quad \text{or} \quad 4 = \frac{(20 \times m_T)}{(20 + m_T)}$$

By solving the above equation, it is found that $m_T = 5$. Therefore $L_T = 5[0.301 - (-0.301)] = 5 \times 0.602 = 3.01$ inches.

The fulfillment of the conditions for this chart can best be checked by arrangement in tabular form as shown in Table 21.10. Note that the term L is negative in the equation and the direction of the scale is therefore downward. All others are positive and therefore upward. The scale for p is in the middle for both equations.

Step 4. Scale spacing. From Equation 21.2 it may be seen that

$$\frac{m_W}{m_L} = \frac{5}{20} = \frac{1}{4}$$

Since the same moduli occur in the second equation, the spacing is also the same. In making the chart, however, it makes a very good solution to reverse them as shown in Fig. 21.13. In order to get a chart that is not too wide, we shall choose as our 1 to 4 ratio the terms 0.6 and 2.4 which gives a total chart width of 4.8 inches.

Step 5. Lay out the scales. Using logarithmic scales 4 inches, 5 inches, and 20 inches long, the chart can be constructed as shown in Fig. 21.13. For the 20-inch log-scale distances may be taken from a 10 inch-scale with dividers and doubled. Note that the minimum values are aligned along the diagonal which is used as a base line. Since this is a correct solution of the equation, this alignment takes care of the constant. The spacing of the scales is such that they could all have been plotted on two lines, but by reversing the distances and using four lines, the danger of mixing up the variable was reduced. Spacing of the scales could be in a variety of forms as shown in Fig. 21.14.

Step 6. Check the chart. The equation can be solved by choosing values of three variables and solving for the fourth. The chart should give the same answer.

21.8 PROPORTIONALITY CHART. *Four variables.* Equation $f(v)/f(x) = f(y)/f(z)$. From Fig. 21.15 by similar triangles

$$\frac{m_v f(v)}{m_x f(x)} = \frac{a}{b} = \frac{m_y f(y)}{m_x f(z)}.$$

TABLE 21.10   DATA NECESSARY FOR LAYOUT OF CHART

Variable	Function	Range	m	L	Direction	Spacing from Pivot Scale
W	$\log W$	609.1 to 30.45	5	6.505	↑	.6
L	$\log L$	36 to 18	20	6.02	↓	2.4
p	$\log p$		4		↑	.0
B	$\log B$	30 to 12	20	7.96	↑	2.4
T	$\log T$	2.0 to 0.5	5	3.01	↑	.6

If the original equation is to hold true, then

$$\frac{m_v}{m_x} = \frac{a}{b} = \frac{m_y}{m_x} \qquad (21.5)$$

Example 1. Let it be required to construct a chart for the equation

$$D = \frac{WS^2}{8H}$$

which is used in computing the sag of a cable. See Fig. 21.16. Where D = the sag of cable in feet,

W = weight of cable from 0 to 2.0 pounds/feet
S = span of cable from 0 to 900 feet
H = horizontal tension from 0 to 10,000 pounds

Step 1. Write the equation in proper form $D/S^2 = W/8H$.

Step 2. Select moduli to give suitable scale lengths and spacing. Any three moduli may be chosen arbitrarily and the fourth computed from Equation (21.5). Since this will be an N-shaped chart, the zero values of the functions of the variables represented on the four scales must be at the ends of the diagonals. The zero

points need not necessarily be included in the chart, but the diagonal must be positioned so it would join them.

$$L_W = m_W(2.0 - 0) = 2\,m_W$$

If $m_W = 2$, then $L_W = 4$ inches.

$$L_H = m_H(80,000 - 0) = 80,000\,m_H$$

If $m_H = \dfrac{1}{20,000}$, then $L_H = 4$ inches.

$$L_S = m_S(810,000 - 0) = 810,000\,m_S$$

If $m_S = \dfrac{1}{200,000}$, then $L_S = 4.05$.

Step 3. Determine the modulus and length of the last scale. By solving the original equation for maximum and minimum values, the range for D is found to be $0 - 20.25$. Greater theoretical range could be obtained by making H a minimum when W and S are maximum. However, this would be an impossible condition since the horizontal force could not be a minimum when the weight and span are maximum. Since

$$\frac{m_D}{m_S} = \frac{m_W}{m_H},$$

then $\quad m_D = \dfrac{(m_W m_S)}{m_H} = \dfrac{2 \times \dfrac{1}{200,000}}{\dfrac{1}{20,000}} = \dfrac{1}{5}$

$$L_D = m_D(20.25 - 0) = \frac{1}{5} \times 20.25 = 4.05$$

Step 4. Scale spacing. Since the middle scale is a diagonal, uncalibrated, and merely a pivot, axis spacing is not involved except that the diagonal must connect the zero points of the other scales.

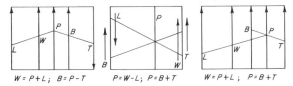

$W = P+L; \quad B = P-T$ $P = W-L; \quad P = B+T$ $W = P+L; \quad P = B+T$

Fig. 21.14 Other arrangements of four-variable parallel-scale charts.

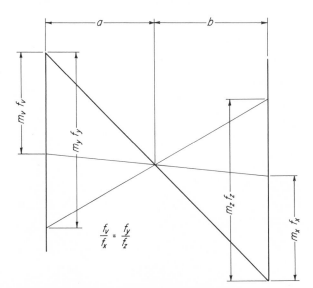

Fig. 21.15 Geometry for proportionality chart.

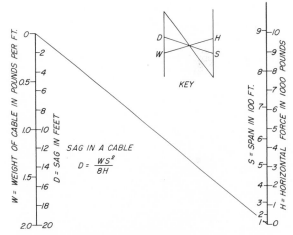

Fig. 21.16 Proportionality chart.

Step 5. Lay out the scales. As will be noted from Fig. 21.16, the terms of the first half of the equation are on the inside of the scales and run in opposite directions. The terms on the other side of the equations are on the outside and in the same order. Considerable variation in the position of the scales is allowable as long as the key shows clearly how the chart shall be read.

Step 6. Check the chart. Assume $W = 2.0$, $S = 500$, and $H = 8000$; then

$$D = \frac{(2.0 \times 250{,}000)}{(8 \times 8000)} = \frac{500{,}000}{64{,}000} = 7.8 \text{ feet}$$

The same answer may be obtained from the chart. As stated above, these charts can be made in a variety of forms as illustrated in Fig. 21.17.

21.9 COMBINATION CHART. Four variables. Equation $f(v) + f(x) = f(y)/f(z)$. This equation can be divided into two parts with a new term p set equal to each.

$$f(v) + f(x) = f(p) = \frac{f(y)}{f(z)}$$

These two equations can be solved by two charts having a common scale for $f(p)$. The first equation $f(v) + f(x) = f(p)$ can be solved by a three-variable parallel-scale chart, and the second $f(p) = f(y)/f(z)$ by an N-chart. The scale or axis common to both charts must have the same modulus and run in the same direction in both charts.

Example. Let it be required to make a chart for the equation for train resistance due to grade

$$R = \frac{2000\,(B - E)}{L}$$

with the following ranges for the various terms, as shown in Fig. 21.18.

B = elevation at high end of section. Range 0 to 20 feet.

E = elevation at low end of section. Range 0 to 20 feet.

L = 1000 to 3000 feet length of section

R = resistance 0 to 40 pounds per ton.

Step 1. Rewrite the equation in the proper form.

$$\frac{RL}{2000} = p = (B - E)$$

For the first equation $B - E = p$ the term p becomes the middle scale and is positive upward. In order to have the p-scale on the outside of the N-chart and also the same direction as in the parallel-scale chart, the other equation must be written $L/2000 = p/R$.

Step 2. Choose moduli to give suitable scale lengths.

$$L_B = m_B(20 - 0) = 20\,m_B$$

If $m_B = \frac{1}{4}$, then $L_B = 5$ inches.

$$L_E = m_E(20 - 0) = 20\,m_E$$

If $m_E = \frac{1}{4}$, then $L_E = 5$ inches.

Step 3. Compute modulus for the middle scale.

$$m_p = \frac{m_B \times m_E}{m_B + m_E} = \frac{\frac{1}{4} \cdot \frac{1}{4}}{\frac{1}{4} + \frac{1}{4}} = \frac{1}{8}$$

Then $\qquad L_p = \frac{1}{8}(20 - 0) = 2\frac{1}{2}$ inches

For the N-chart, the graphical method for calibrating the diagonal scale for L is used and it is therefore only necessary to choose a modulus for the R-scale.

$$L_R = m_R(40 - 0) = 40\,m_R$$

If $m_R = \frac{1}{8}$, then $L_R = 5$ inches

For the N-chart, it will be convenient to keep it inside the parallel-scale chart. We shall therefore choose a width of 2 inches and let the diagonal be what it will. The scales may now be laid out as shown in Fig. 21.18.

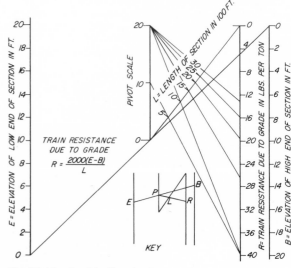

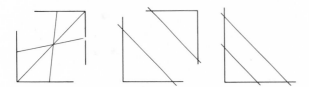

Fig. 21.17 Other arrangements for proportionality charts.

Fig. 21.18 Combination chart.

Since the R-, B-, and E-scales are natural scales and should give no trouble, only the calibration of the L-scale will be discussed.

It will be necessary to solve the equation $p/R = L/2000$ for the values of L which we wish to have on the diagonal scale. One or more poles may be used on the p-scale. They are taken on the p-scale because it will then be unnecessary to plot any other points on that scale.

In Table 21.11, 10 and 20 on the p-scale have been used for the poles. By drawing an isopleth from the pole to the corresponding value of R, the location of the corresponding point on the L-scale is located. The computations are shown in Table 21.11.

TABLE 21.11   COMPUTATIONS FOR SOLUTION BY POLE METHOD $\dfrac{p}{R} = \dfrac{L}{2000}$

L	p	R
500	10	40
1000	20	40
1500	20	26.7
2000	20	20
2500	20	16
3000	20	13.3

SELF-STUDY QUESTIONS

Before trying to answer these questions, read the chapter carefully. Then, without reference to the text, answer as many questions as possible. For those that cannot be answered, the number, in parentheses following the question number, gives the article in which the answer can be found. Look it up and write down the answer. Check the answers that you did give to see that they are correct.

21.1 **(21.1)** A nomograph is used to solve an _____ by a graphical method.

21.2 **(21.2)** A term in an equation that always has the same value is called a _____.

21.3 **(21.2)** A term in an equation that may have different values is called a _____.

21.4 **(21.2)** A mathematical expression that involves a variable in any form is called a _____ of the variable.

21.5 **(21.2)** The proportionality factor used in designing a functional scale is called a _____ _____.

21.6 **(21.2)** The distance on a functional scale occupied by one unit of the function is the functional _____.

21.7 **(21.2e)** When the function of a variable includes a constant coefficient a _____ modulus can be used.

21.8 **(21.3)** A convenient method for constructing a functional scale is to make a _____ specifying the values to be shown on the scale.

21.9 **(21.4)** When two variables are plotted on the same line, they must

(1) have the _____ functional modulus,

(2) run in _____ _____ direction,

(3) have the zero values at the _____ point.

21.10 **(21.4)** A nomograph having only two variables is called a _____ chart.

21.11 **(21.5)** In a three-variable parallel-scale nomograph the standard form of the equation is

$$f(x) \text{_____} \text{_____} = f(z)$$

21.12 **(21.5)** In the equation $\dfrac{m_x}{m_y} = \dfrac{a}{b}$ the values of a and b give the relationship of the moduli of the _____ scales and the scale spacing.

21.13 **(21.5, step 2)** In a three-variable parallel-scale chart the moduli of the outside scales can be chosen to make the scales of the _____ _____.

21.14 **(21.5)** In a three-variable parallel-scale chart the equation $m_z = \dfrac{m_x m_y}{m_x + m_y}$ gives the _____ for the center scale.

21.15 **(21.5)** In the equation in Question 21.14 the term m_z is the _____ modulus and not the scale _____.

21.16 **(21.5)** The base line for a three-variable parallel-scale nomograph may be any line that goes through three points (one on each scale) which represent a _____ solution of the _____.

21.17 **(21.6)** When an equation has the form $f(x)/f(y) = f(z)$, a _____ or _____ chart should be used.

21.18 **(21.6)** In an N-chart the parallel scales run in _____ directions.

21.19 **(21.6)** In an N- or Z-chart the diagonal scale connects the _____ _____ of the outside parallel scales.

21.20 **(21.7)** A four-variable parallel-scale chart can be broken down to two _____ _____ scale charts having a common _____ scale.

21.21 **(21.7)** The pivot scale in a four variable parallel scale chart must

(1) have the _____ modulus in both charts,

(2) run in the _____ direction in _____ charts,

(3) have the same _____ point for both charts.

21.22 **(21.8)** The equation $f(x)/f(y) = f(v)/f(z)$ can be solved by a _____ chart.

21.23 **(21.8)** For a proportionality chart the diagonal joins the _____ points of the other scales.

21.24 **(21.8)** For a proportionality chart the diagonal is an _____ scale.

21.25 **(21.9)** The equation $f(x) + f(y) = \dfrac{f(v)}{f(z)}$ can be solved by combining a three variable _____ scale chart and an _____ chart.

PROBLEMS

The problems below have been grouped according to the number of variables involved. The instructor may assign the type of chart he wishes the student to make, or if no specification is made the student may select the type that fits the situation.

The range of variables given is for general guidance only and may be altered if a better nomograph will result. Unless otherwise specified by your instructor only the major scale markings shall be shown. Each scale must be given a name or legend describing it and the entire chart should be given a title. Those charts with three or more variables will have a key showing how to use the nomograph.

Functional Scales

Make a single functional scale for one of the functions assigned from the problems in the following group. Make the scale 6″ long or if drawn lengthwise of the sheet (8½ × 11) make it 8″ long.

21.1 $f(x) = \sin x$ from $x = 10°$ to $60°$
21.2 $f(x) = (x^2 + 2)$ from $x = 2$ to 10
21.3 $f(x) = 1/x$ from $x = 1$ to 20
21.4 $f(x) = \tan x$ from $x = 10°$ to $45°$
21.5 $f(x) = \text{Log } x$ from $x = 1$ to 10
21.6 $f(x) = \text{Log } x$ from $x = 2$ to 20

Two-Variable Charts

Make an adjacent scale chart, or two scales with a pole or turning point between them, from the following group as assigned by your instructor.

21.7 $Y = \dfrac{D}{\pi}$

$Y =$ distance of the centroid of a semicircular arc of wire from the diameter.
$D =$ diameter, 2 to 20 inches.

21.8 $t = 2\pi \sqrt{\dfrac{l}{g}}$

$t =$ time in seconds for complete oscillation of a pendulum.
$l =$ length of pendulum, 3 to 6 feet.
$g =$ acceleration due to gravity (32.2).

21.9 $P = 0.0036V^2$

$P =$ pressure on an area perpendicular to the direction of the wind in pounds per square feet.
$V =$ velocity of the wind, 10 to 100 miles per hour.

Three-Variable Charts

21.10 $A = \pi rh$

$A =$ area of the surface of a cone in square feet.
$r =$ radius of the base, 1 to 10 feet.
$h =$ slant height, 5 to 50 feet.

21.11 $V = \frac{\pi}{6}(D^3 - d^3)$

$V =$ volume of a hollow sphere in cubic inches.

$D =$ outside diameter, 2 to 20 inches.

$d =$ inside diameter, 1 to 18 inches.

21.12 $I = \frac{\pi}{64}(D^4 - d^4)$

$I =$ moment of inertia of an open circular area about a centroidal axis.

$D =$ outside diameter, 6 to 10 inches.

$d =$ inside diameter, 4 to 8 inches.

21.13 $I = \frac{\pi}{64}Dd^3$

$I =$ moment of inertia of an elliptical disk about its major axis.

$D =$ length of major axis, 5 to 20 inches.

$d =$ length of minor axis, 4 to 16 inches.

21.14 $F = \mu N^{0.97}$

$F =$ frictional resistance in pounds.

$\mu =$ coefficient of friction, 0.20 to 0.60.

$N =$ normal force, 10 to 100 pounds.

21.15 $Q = 0.385 BH\sqrt{2gH}$

$Q =$ cubic feet of water passing over a rectangular weir per second.

$B =$ width of weir, 2 to 20 feet.

$H =$ depth of water above bottom of weir, 1 to 10 feet.

Four-Variable Charts

21.16 $p = \frac{2tf}{D}$

$p =$ internal pressure in cylindrical tank in pounds per square inch.

$t =$ thickness of plate, ¼ to 1½ in.

$f =$ tensile stress, 10,000 to 20,000 pounds per square inch.

$D =$ internal diameter of cylinder, 48 to 120 inches.

21.17 $W = 0.286\, LBT$

$W =$ weight of cast iron base plate in pounds.

$L =$ length in inches, 12 to 24.

$B =$ width in inches, 8 to 20.

$T =$ thickness, ½ to 2½ inches.

21.18 $E = \frac{\mu W \pi D N}{12}$

$E =$ work absorbed in revolving bearing in foot pounds per minute.

$\mu =$ coefficient of friction, 0.15 to 0.30.

$W =$ total load on bearing, 100 to 1000 pounds.

$D =$ diameter of bearing, 0.75 to 2.50 inches.

$N =$ number of revolutions per minute, 400 to 2000.

Five-Variable Charts

21.19 $I = \frac{BD^3 - bd^3}{12}$

$I =$ moment of inertia of a hollow rectangle about a centroidal axis perpendicular to the depth.

$B =$ outside width, 6 to 16 inches.

$b =$ inside width, 4 to 14 inches.

$D =$ outside depth, 8 to 18 inches.

$d =$ inside depth, 6 to 16 inches.

21.20 $HP = \frac{0.786\, PLD^2 N}{33,000}$

$HP =$ horsepower of a reciprocating steam engine.

$P =$ steam pressure, 50 to 150 pounds per square inch.

$L =$ length of stroke, 8 to 24 inches.

$D =$ diameter of cylinder, 6 to 16 inches.

$N =$ number of strokes per minute, 40 to 240.

D

CHAPTER 22
Graphical Mathematics

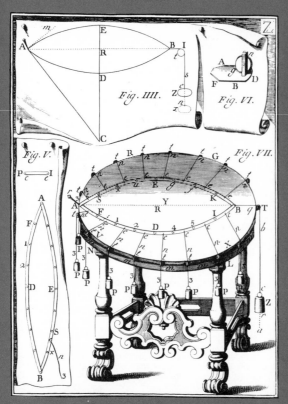

OLD: Graphical calculations of Bernoulli in Johannis Boleni, *Epistolarum Mathematicarum Foscoculus.* (New York Public Library)

NEW: Plotter displaying graphical output hooked up to magnetic tapes. (Courtesy of CALCOMP)

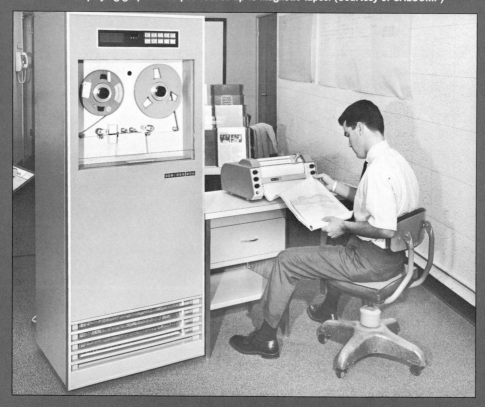

Chapter 22   Graphical Mathematics

22.1   INTRODUCTION. Graphical solutions to mathematical problems have some advantages and some disadvantages that must be considered carefully when they are to be used. One of the principal advantages is speed, and as a general rule graphical solutions are not used unless they save time or provide a necessary check on the analytical method. When the analytical solution is complicated and time-consuming or impossible, the engineer should look for a convenient graphical device. If a highly accurate result is desired, the analytical solution should be used. However, fair accuracy can be obtained by graphical methods if a large scale is used.

Graphical solutions are available for many problems in arithmetic, algebra, trigonometry, calculus, and differential equations. The engineer should be familiar with all of them so that he can use them when conditions are suitable.

22.2   ARITHMETIC. The best known and most used graphical method for solving arithmetical problems is the slide rule. Other methods, such as network charts and proportional charts and nomographs, are available for such operations as addition, subtraction, multiplication, and division. The desirability of their use as tools depends on the condition of the problem.

22.2.1   Addition. The network chart shown in Fig. 22.1(a) is based on the equation of a straight line, $y = mx + b$. In this equation m represents the slope of the line. If the slope (the tangent of the angle with the x-axis) is made equal to -1, the equation becomes $y = -x + b$ or $y + x = b$. Since the slope of the line is -1, the line makes an angle of $45°$ with the horizontal and slopes down to the right, if the scales are both the same. To construct this chart the steps are as follows:

$a.$ Lay out the desired values of y on the vertical axis.

$b.$ Using the same scale, lay out the desired values of x on the horizontal axis.

$c.$ Draw the $45°$ diagonals from the numbers on the vertical axis to the same numbers on the horizontal axis.

$d.$ To solve the chart, take the desired values of y, for example 3.3 in Fig. 22.1(a), and the value of x, for example 5.2 in the figure. The sum may be found by projecting horizontally and vertically from these points to locate point c. From point c, a $45°$ line can be drawn to intersect the vertical axis at 8.5. This is the sum of the two numbers.

A practical example of the use of this chart is shown in Fig. 22.1(b). This is to solve the equation $F = F_1 \cos 45° + F_2 \sin 30°$. Substituting numerical values for the sine and cosine, the equation becomes $F = 0.707F_1 + 0.5F_2$.

Then $\qquad\qquad 0.707F_1 + 0.5F_2 = F$

and $\qquad\quad F_1 + 0.5/0.707F_2 = 1/0.707F$

Or $\qquad\qquad F_1 + 0.707F_2 = 1.414F$

and $\qquad\qquad F_1 = -0.707F_2 + 1.414F$

If we let $b = 1.414F$, the equation becomes

$$F_1 = -0.707F_2 + b$$

This is the form of the equation $y = mx + b$. Then $m = -0.707$.

The chart will be plotted in the following steps:

$a.$ Lay out a scale for F_1 on the vertical axis.

$b.$ Lay out a scale for F_2 on the horizontal axis. Use the same scale for both axes.

$c.$ Since $m = -0.707$, plot a series of inclined lines for the F-scale. Make the tangent of the angle with the horizontal axis equal to 0.707.

$d.$ If read on the vertical scale, the inclined line would give the value of b or $1.414F$.

$e.$ Construct another scale either inside or outside the chart that will read F directly as shown in Fig. 22.1(b).

Graphical addition or subtraction of three numbers can be accomplished by combining two of these charts on a common scale. In the equation $x = a + b + c$, a new factor can be added by letting $y = a + b$. Then by substitution we obtain another equation, $x = y + c$. In these two equations the y-scale is common and can be made the joining side of the two charts. This scale does not have to be graduated since the term does not appear in the original equation.

22.2.2 Subtraction. It is possible to use the network chart shown in Fig. 22.1 for subtraction, but a more convenient one can be found as shown in Fig. 22.2(a). In this figure the equation of the straight line $y = mx + b$ is used. When $m = 1$, the equation becomes $y - x = b$. Using this equation, a series of straight lines are plotted for various values of b. The solution is shown for $y = 16.5$ and $x = 8.75$. The interpolation is made by drawing an extra line through point C, located from the values of x and y, and reading the answer, 7.75, on the Y-axis.

An example of the use of this network is shown in Fig. 22.2(b), which gives the solution of the equation $B = W - T$ for the buoyancy of an object suspended in water. In this case $W = 7.5$ and $T = 2.3$, which locate point C from which the B line may be drawn parallel to the others and the answer, 5.2, read on the W-scale. It should be observed that the inclined lines in this chart would be 45° only if the horizontal and vertical scales were the same.

The use of these charts is limited since the analytical solution is usually easier and faster. They are valuable when similar operations of some complexity are to be repeated many times or for a quick check on the analytical solution.

22.2.3 Addition and subtraction. Another convenient method of solving this problem is based on the fact that the three sides of an equilateral triangle are equal. An equation such as $x + \sqrt{x + 2}$ can be solved readily as shown in Fig. 22.3(a).

In this chart the values of x are placed along the vertical axis. The values of $\sqrt{x}$ are plotted as a curve by measuring along the 30° diagonal solid line. Then if it is desired to find the value for the expression $x + \sqrt{x}$ for any known value of x, it can be done by starting at the value of x on the vertical line to the left and following down the solid inclined line to the curve and then back to the vertical line parallel to the dashed inclined line. This is shown on the chart for the value of $x = 4$. The value of the expression is shown to be 6 on the chart.

To add a constant to this, another vertical line can be drawn parallel to the first and at a distance of twice the constant measured along the solid inclined line. The numbers on this line are made opposite the numbers on the original vertical line. The solution of $x + \sqrt{x} + 2$ can be found by starting with the known value of x on the vertical line at the left. Follow the solid inclined line to the curve and then parallel to the dashed inclined line to the vertical line on the right. The solution is shown for the value of $x = 5$. The answer as shown by the chart is 9.2.

This chart can also be used to solve the expression $x + 2 + \sqrt{x + 2}$. For this solution start with x on the vertical line to the right. Follow parallel to the solid inclined lines to the curve and then parallel to the dashed inclined lines to the vertical line on the left. The solution for this expression is shown when $x = 2.5$. From the chart the answer can be found to be 6.6.

When used in this latter manner, the chart is known

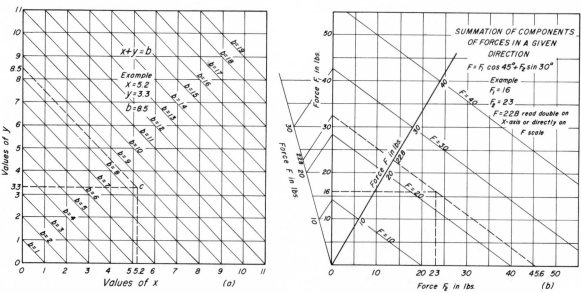

Fig. 22.1 Network chart for addition.

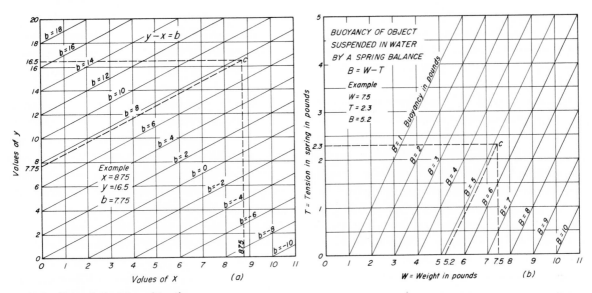

Fig. 22.2   Network chart for subtraction.

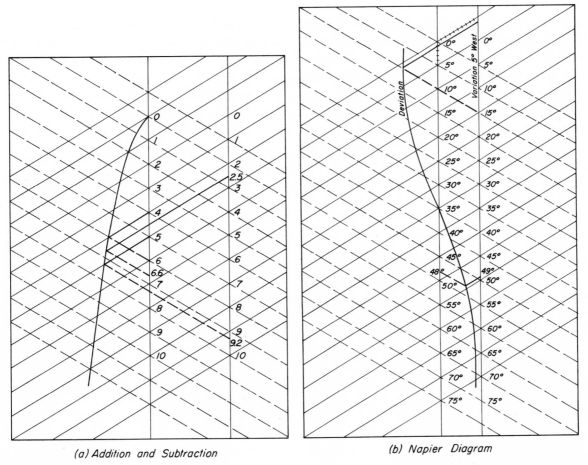

(a) Addition and Subtraction

(b) Napier Diagram

Fig. 22.3   Napier diagram.

as a Napier diagram and is used in navigation for correcting compass headings for variation and deviation. Fig. 22.3(b) shows a portion of a Napier diagram. Deviation varies with the heading and has been plotted as the curve. Variation is a constant over a fairly large area; therefore, twice the variation has been plotted to obtain the straight line on the right. In this figure assume that the variation is 6° W. and the true heading is 1°. The compass heading can be obtained by starting with the 1° on the vertical line at the left. Follow parallel to the solid inclined lines to the curve and then parallel to the dashed inclined lines to the vertical line on the right. This gives a reading of 15°, which is the compass heading. In this case deviation and variation are both west, but if the deviation should be east as for 49°, the same procedure can be followed and the compass heading is found to be 48°. This is the same as adding the variation and subtracting the deviation.

22.2.4 Multiplication. A network chart for multiplication can be formed by plotting curves for various values of the equation $xy = c$. If these curves are plotted on rectangular coordinate paper, they form a series of hyperbolas as shown in Fig. 22.4. This chart is not very practical since the curves require considerable time to plot and interpolation is not easy. However, if logarithms are taken of both sides, the equation becomes $\log x + \log y = \log c$ or $\log x = \log c - \log y$, which is in the form of the equation of a straight line, $y = mx + b$. Therefore, if the equation is plotted on logarithmic paper, as in Fig. 22.5(a), the curves become straight lines and solutions are easily obtained. Interpolation is easy, as shown in the figure for values of $x = 1.6$ and $y = 0.55$, where a new line is constructed through point C, as determined by the values of x and y. The answer is read on the Y-axis as 0.88.

The network chart to solve the equation $F = ma$ for finding the force necessary to cause acceleration a in a mass m is shown in Fig. 22.5(b). In the example $m = 2.7$ slugs and $a = 1.9$ feet/second² locate point C. From C a line is drawn parallel to the F lines and the answer is read as 5.1 pounds on the Y-axis.

22.2.5 Division. The same principles apply for division as for multiplication. When the equation $y/x = c$ is plotted on logarithmic paper, the chart shown in Fig. 22.6(a) is obtained. Interpolation is easy by drawing an inclined line through the point O, obtained from the coordinates, and reading the answer at the point of intersection of the Y-axis with the inclined line. The solution is given for $x = 1.5$ and $y = 6.3$. The answer shows $C = 4.2$.

The network chart to solve the equation $S = F/2l$,

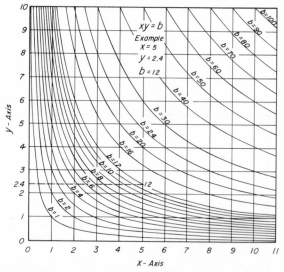

Fig. 22.4 Network chart for multiplication—rectangular coordinate paper.

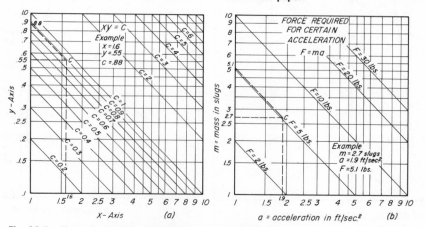

Fig. 22.5 Network chart for multiplication—logarithmic paper.

to determine the surface tension of water, is shown in Fig. 22.6(*b*). The example shows the solution for $l = 4$ centimeters and $F = 500$ dynes. These two values locate the point C from which the diagonal is drawn parallel to the S lines until it intersects the axis at 125. The correct answer for S in this case is found by dividing 125 by 2 to get 62.5 dynes per centimeter, or by reading the answer directly on the vertical scale through $l = 5$. These divisions must be marked as one tenth of the values on the F-scale.

22.2.6   Combinations. Continuous operations may be performed by combining two or more charts. In the equation $x = ab/c$, a regrouping may be done by making $y = a/c$. Then by substitution $x = by$. By constructing these two charts with the *y*-axes coincident, the original equation may be solved as shown in Fig.

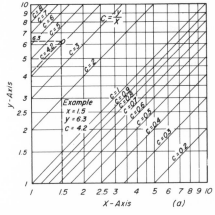
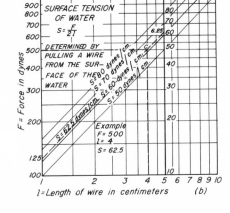

Fig. 22.6   Network chart for division.

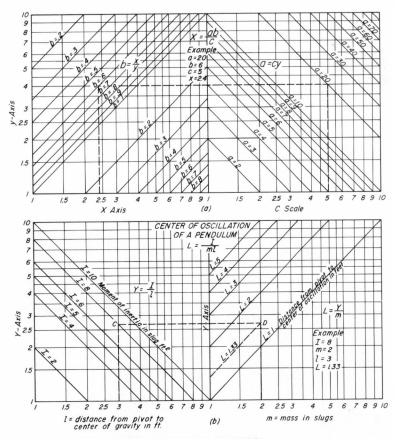

Fig. 22.7   Network chart for multiplication and division.

22.7(a). The solution is given for $c = 5$, $a = 20$, and $b = 0.6$, where it is shown that $x = 2.4$.

To find the center of oscillation of a pendulum, the equation is $L = I/ml$. The network chart to solve this equation is shown in Fig. 22.7(b). In this case the equation is divided into two equations, $y = I/c$ and $L = y/m$. In the example the terms $I = 8$ and $l = 3$ locate the point C. From point C and the term $m = 2$, point

D may be located from which an L line may be drawn parallel to the other and the value of L may be read from the vertical axis at 1.33 feet.

22.2.7   Proportion. Problems in proportion can be easily solved by nomographs as explained in Art. 21.8. These may be arranged for very complicated functions of four variables, or they may be as simple as two uniform scales at right angles to each other when only a simple arithmetical proportion is involved. Fig. 22.8 shows this method of solving the proportion $X/a = b/c$ when a, b, and c are known by plotting the numerators on one scale and the denominators on the other scale. Thus if $b = 6.8$ and $c = 3.5$, the diagonal line joining these points can be drawn as in Fig. 22.8. Then by constructing a line through $a = 2.2$ parallel to the diagonal, the answer $y = 4.3$ can be read on the vertical scale. This is actually a very simple nomograph, but it can be used only for simple arithmetical proportions. In fact, all the charts that have been discussed in this chapter up to this point are sometimes considered to be nomographs.

22.3   ALGEBRA. When the analytical solution of two simultaneous equations is difficult, the graphical solution may save time. If each curve is plotted on rectangular coordinates, the points of intersections of the two curves will locate points that satisfy both equations. Those points are therefore the required values. This is shown in Fig. 22.9.

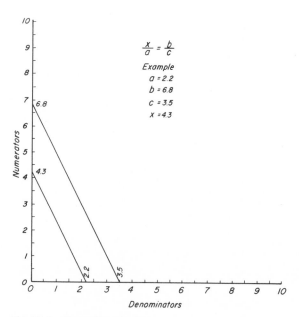

Fig. 22.8   Proportion chart.

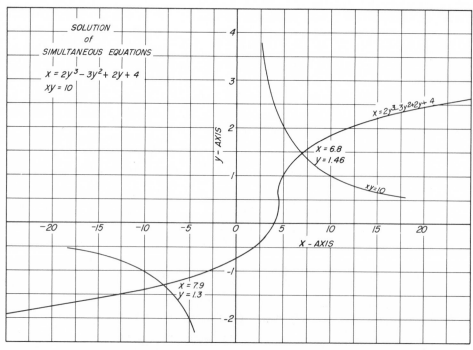

Fig. 22.9   Solution of simultaneous equations.

The graphical solution may also be used to find the roots of a complicated equation like $y^3 - 4y^2 + y - 10 = 0$. By plotting the curve on a rectangular coordinate paper, with the $f(y)$ on the X-axis the roots are found at the points where the curve crosses the Y-axis where $f(y) = 0$. This is illustrated in Fig. 22.10. Some-

times it is more convenient to form two simultaneous equations and plot both curves. The point or points where the curves cross will then be the answer. Thus if $x = y - 10$, then by substitution $y^3 - 4y^2 + x = 0$. Figure 22.11 shows that by plotting the two curves the point of intersection gives the same point that was ob-

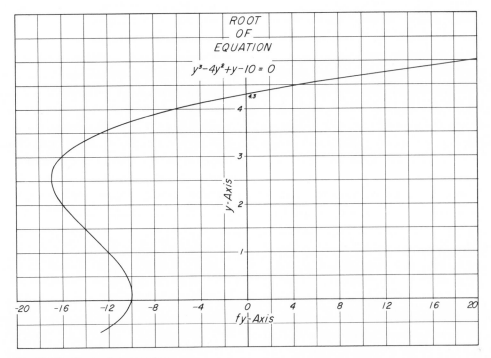

Fig. 22.10   Roots of an equation.

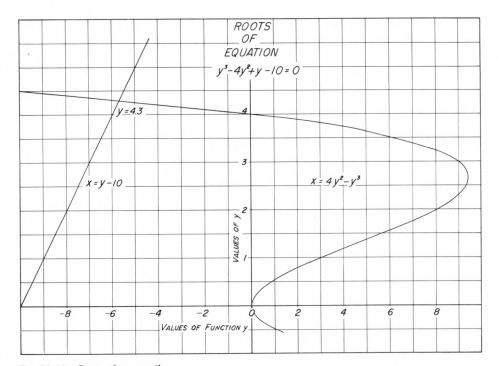

Fig. 22.11   Roots of an equation.

tained in Fig. 22.10. This method is very useful in the solution of transcendental equations in which there is only one variable which appears in two different forms. In the equation $\tan \alpha = 1.5\alpha$ it is necessary to form two equations $\tan \alpha = y$ and $y = 1.5\alpha$. Figure 22.12 shows the solution of this equation as the intersection of the two curves.

22.4 GRAPHICAL CALCULUS. Graphical calculus is a tool that is very useful to every engineer, not only because many very difficult problems may be solved by this method but also because it gives a graphical picture of the fundamental processes of differentation and integration. Basically it can be said that differential calculus provides a method for determining the rate of change of a function of a variable with respect to the variable. Integral calculus may be thought of as a process of summing up a series of increments to obtain a total between certain specified limits. Each process is the reverse of the other and the graphical procedure used in either case may be worked backward to give the other solution. However, the idea of summing up a series of areas may be easier to understand; therefore, integral calculus will be considered first.

22.5 INTEGRAL CALCULUS. Integration is a process of adding a series of increments to obtain the total value between two specified limits. Graphically the easiest way to think of integration with respect to x is that it is a method of obtaining the area between a curve and the X-axis, between certain values of x. This is done by dividing the area under the curve into small segments and adding these segments together, either graphically or analytically, to obtain the total area. By the graphical method, this involves drawing another curve so that the arithmetical difference between any two ordinates is equal to the area under the original curve between those same two ordinates.

In Fig. 22.13(a) it can be seen that the area under the original curve between the points A and B is equal to 8.8×1 if the horizontal line is placed so that the two shaded triangles are equal. In Fig. 22.13(b) the difference between the ordinates A and B is also 8.8, and this curve is therefore the integral of the original curve. The integral curve has an equation of a higher order and therefore is plotted above the original curve.

22.6 INTEGRATION BY THE AREA METHOD. The best method for determining the area of a segment under a curve is to find an equivalent area by drawing a horizontal line in such a position that the two small shaded areas of each segment shown in Fig. 22.13(a) are equal. This can usually be done by eye, but the original segments must be selected carefully to give the proper accuracy. Where the curve is fairly straight, the segments can be rather large, but when the curve is changing direction rapidly, the division points must be taken closer together. As a check on the work or for using this method for differentiation, it can be seen that the point where the perpendicular bisector of the chord in Fig. 22.13(b) crosses the curve may be pro-

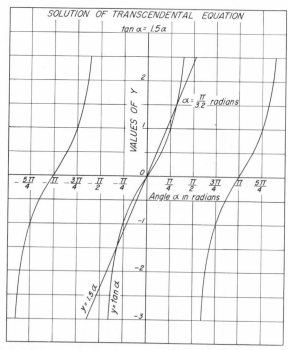

Fig. 22.12 Solution of a transcendental equation.

jected to Fig. 22.13(a) to locate the point on the curve where the horizontal line crosses. This is illustrated by point O in Fig. 22.13. If this does not work out, smaller divisions should be taken. When the horizontal line has been drawn properly, the area under the curve will be equal to the area of the rectangle ABCD in Fig. 22.13.

It is then possible to calculate the area of each small increment and plot the integral curve by making the difference between two ordinates of the integral curve equal to the area under the original curve between those ordinates. This is illustrated in Fig. 22.14. Since the integral curve is always taller than the original curve, the scale on the vertical axis of the integral curve is usually made smaller as shown in Fig. 22.14(b).

To solve this problem analytically, it is necessary to take a small vertical segment of width dx and height y. The area of this segment is $y\,dx$ and the summation of these segments between certain limits such as $x = 0$ and $x = 40$ will give the area under the curve. The original equation $x = 3y^2$ may be changed to $y = x^{1/2}/3^{1/2}$. Then if each side is multiplied by dx, the equation becomes $y\,dx = x^{1/2}/3^{1/2}\,dx$. But $y\,dx = A$, so $A = x^{1/2}/3^{1/2}\,dx$. The integral of this expression is $A = 1/3^{1/2}[\tfrac{2}{3}x^{3/2}] + C$. When $C = 0$ the curve goes through the origin and the equation becomes $A = 0.385x^{3/2}$. This is the equation of the curve shown in Fig. 22.14(b), and plotting the equation will give practically the same results obtained by adding the increments arithmetically.

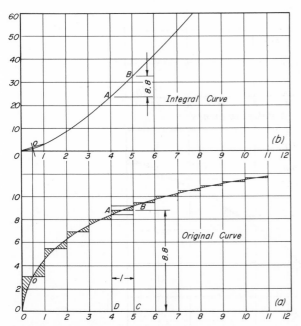

Fig. 22.13   Graphical integration—area method.

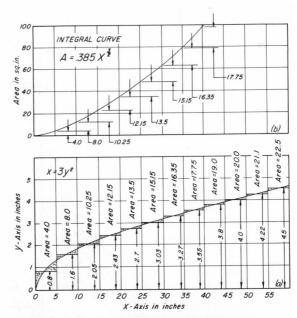

Fig. 22.14   Graphical integration—equivalent areas.

22.6.1 Integration by the area method using a string polygon. A method of integration that is all graphical and involves the use of a string polygon is illustrated in Fig. 22.15. The problem in this case is to integrate the area under the curve in Fig. 22.15(a). The procedure is as follows:

a. Divide the area under the curve into vertical segments making them narrow enough so that it is possible to set up a comparatively accurate equivalent area rectangle for each segment as shown in Fig. 22.15(a). In this case it would have been better to subdivide the first space between $x = 0$ and $x = 2$, but this would have made the construction so small that it would be hard to follow. For this reason there is some error in this portion of the curve.

b. Establish the equivalent area rectangle for each segment. These are shown shaded in Fig. 22.15(a).

c. Project the top of each rectangle to the Y-axis.

d. Establish a pole on the X-axis at some convenient distance from the Y-axis. This distance, d in Fig. 22.15(a), should usually be some multiple of the unit value on the X-axis. In Fig. 22.15(a) it is made eight times this unit distance.

e. Draw rays from the pole to each of the points on the Y-axis. See Fig. 22.15(a).

f. Beginning at the origin in Fig. 22.15(b), construct a string, s_1, parallel to the first ray, s_1, until it crosses the division line between the first and second segments at v.

g. From v in Fig. 22.15(b) construct string s_2 parallel to ray s_2 and extend it until it crosses the division line between the second and third segments at t. Continue in this manner for the rest of the strings.

h. Draw a smooth curve through these points. Notice that the strings become chords of the curve, which

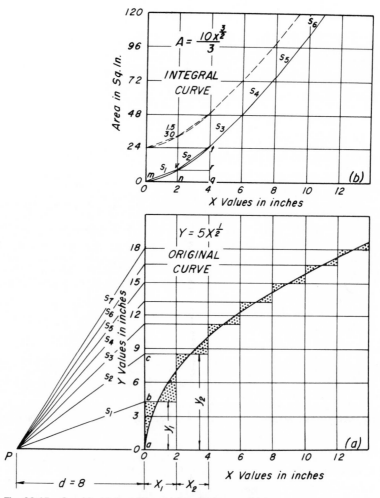

Fig. 22.15 Graphical integration—string polygon method.

gives rise to the name the "chord method" by which it is known.

i. Determine the vertical scale for Fig. 22.15(*b*) by the following method.

Area of the first strip = x_1y_1. By definition of the integral curve $vn = x_1y_1$ to some scale that can be determined. *Pab* is similar to *mnv*

then $\qquad Pa:ab::mn:nv$

or $\qquad d:y_1::x_1:nv$

$$x_1y_1 = nv \cdot d$$

$d = 8$ units on the *X*-scale.

Then the scale on the *Y*-axis will be ⅛ of the scale on the *Y*-axis of the original curve. In other words, where one division represented 3 on the original, the same division will represent 24 on the integral curve. *Pac* is similar to *vrt*

then $\qquad Pa:ac::vr:rt$

or $\qquad d:y_2::x_2:rt$

$$x_2y_2 = d \cdot rt$$

$$x_1y_1 + x_2y_2 = nv \cdot d + rt \cdot d = tq \cdot d$$

Thus it can be seen that the vertical intercept at any point on the integral curve represents the entire area under the original curve to the left of that point.

22.7 CONSTANT OF INTEGRATION. In the previous examples it has been assumed that the integral curve began at the origin, but this is not always true. By the original statement, the difference between two ordinates on the integral curve gives the area under the original curve between those two ordinates, but this does not place the integral curve at any particular height on the axis. It could be raised or lowered by any amount and the difference in the ordinates could still be the same value. Some other information must be known to give the integral curve a definite position. One method of locating this curve would be to say that it has to pass through a certain point, and from this information the value of the constant can be determined.

In Fig. 22.15(*b*) the integral curve has been drawn through the origin which makes the constant zero. If it is desired to have the curve go through a point whose coordinates are $x = 1.5$ and $A = 30$, the coefficient may be determined as follows.

Substitute the values in the equation $A = 10x^{3/2}/3 + C$ to obtain $30 = 10 \cdot 1.5^{3/2}/3 + C$. Then

$C = 23.9$ and the integral curve may be started at a point on the area axis where the value is 23.9. The dashed line shows this curve.

22.8 INTEGRATION OF IRREGULAR CURVES. All examples used up to this point have been such that they can be solved easier by analytical methods than by graphical. Their purpose has been to develop a method. It is usually well for the beginner to start with a simple case that can be checked analytically. There are two reasons for this: first, to give confidence in the method and, second, to show the degree of drafting accuracy that is necessary to obtain a reasonable answer. The graphical method is most useful when the curve is of such a shape that it is very difficult or impossible to write the equation. This frequently occurs with observed data. In Fig. 22.16(*a*) the plotted curve shows the speed of a boat in cruising through a chain of lakes. The speeds were read every five minutes on a Pitot tube speedometer. To find the distance

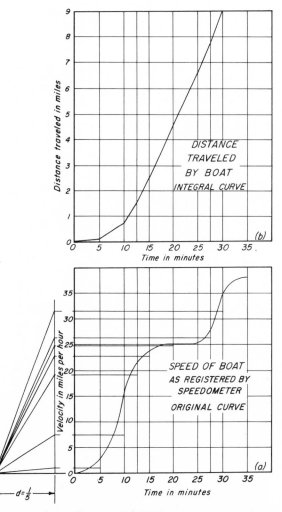

Fig. 22.16 Application of graphical integration.

traveled, it is necessary to integrate the area under the original curve. This has been done in Fig. 22.16(b), which shows that the boat traveled 9 miles in the first 30 minutes.

22.9 DIFFERENTIAL CALCULUS. Differentiation is the process by which the derivative of a function of a variable with respect to the variable is obtained. A derivative is defined as the limit of the ratio of an increment of a function of a variable to the increment of the variable when the increment of the variable approaches zero as a limit. In the equation $x = y^2$, y^2 is a function of x and the curve in Fig. 22.17 shows the relationship between the two variables. If a very small increment of x called $\triangle x$ is considered, there will be a corresponding increment of y called $\triangle y$. As the $\triangle x$ becomes smaller, that is, as it approaches zero as a limit, the $\triangle y$ also becomes smaller and the ratio $\triangle y/\triangle x$ approaches the tangent of the angle that the curve makes with the X-axis at that point, as a limit. The limit of the ratio $\triangle y/\triangle x$ is therefore the derivative of the function at that point with respect to x or,

in other words, the tangent of the angle that the curve makes with the X-axis is the derivative of the curve at that point. It is therefore possible to construct another curve using the same abscissae but with ordinates at each point representing the value of the tangent of the curve at that point. This tangent represents the slope of the original curve or the rate of change of the function of the variable with respect to the variable at that point. The ordinate of the new curve will be the derivative of the original curve at each corresponding point. Fig. 22.18(a) shows a curve where the function of x is $x^3 - x^2/50$. At point A the tangent of the curve has been determined graphically to be 13.3/5 or 2.66/1. By making a new curve, Fig. 22.18(b), whose ordinate at a corresponding point on the X-axis is 2.66, a point on the derivative curve is obtained. Other points may be plotted in a similar manner. The derivative curve is placed below the original curve because the function is of a lower order. The scale used should be as large as possible for accuracy. This is particularly true when the angles become large. For very large angles, it is frequently better to use the reverse of the area method as explained for integration.

22.10 DIFFERENTIATION BY THE TANGENT METHOD. For practical purposes some convenient method must be found to determine the tangent of the curve at various points. If a series of points on the original curve are selected and the chords drawn between them, the tangent will be parallel to the chord if the curve is a circle or a parabola between two adjacent points. If the points are taken sufficiently close together, it is usually possible to find a center that will make that particular part of the curve a circle; in that case the tangent will be parallel to the chord at a point

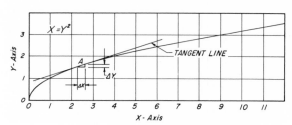

Fig. 22.17   Graphical differentiation—tangent method.

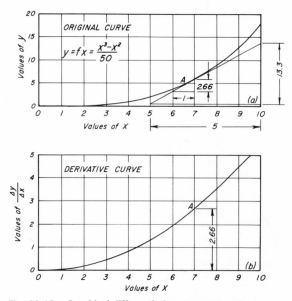

Fig. 22.18   Graphical differentiation—tangent method.

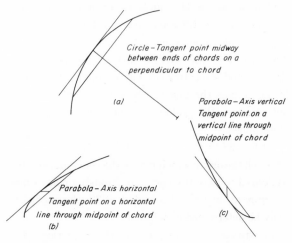

Fig. 22.19   Location of the point of tangency on a curve.

on a perpendicular bisector of the chord as in Fig. 22.19(a). If the curve cannot be considered as a circle, it can usually be fitted as a parabola with the axis either horizontal or vertical. If the axis is horizontal, the tangent will be parallel to the chord at a point that may be found by drawing a horizontal line from the midpoint of the chord until it intersects the curve as in Fig. 22.19(b). When the axis of the parabola is vertical, the tangent is parallel to the chord at a point that is found by constructing a vertical line through the midpoint of the chord until it crosses the curve as in Fig. 22.19(c). The circle is best and should be used whenever possible.

The method is illustrated in Fig. 22.20, in which the chords are made longer than desirable in order that the construction will be easier to follow. By drawing the chords mn and np in Fig. 22.20(a) and erecting perpendicular bisectors of these chords, points a and b are located. These are the points where lines parallel to the chords will be tangent to the curve. The slope of the line through a may be measured by the tangent of the angle, which for this will be $1.15/3 = 0.38$. This is plotted in Fig. 22.20(b) directly below a. Likewise the tangent of the angle that the line through b makes with the horizontal is $6 - 1.15/3 = 4.85/3 = 1.62$. This is plotted directly below b on Fig. 22.20 (b). The derivative curve can then be drawn through those points. For the sake of accuracy, the derivative curve

should usually be plotted to a larger vertical scale than the original curve.

One very common use of differential calculus is to find the velocity of a moving body when the conditions of its motion are known. Thus, the velocity is the differential of distances with respect to time. It is then possible to find the differential of the velocity with respect to time to determine the acceleration.

This is illustrated in Fig. 22.21 where it is assumed that a body is moving according to the equation $S = t^3 + t^2$ where S is the distance traveled in feet and t the time in seconds. In this equation, t is the independent variable and S is the dependent, so that the slope of the curve at any point will be ds/dt. To determine a convenient measure of the tangent at certain points, equal divisions are taken along the X-axis close enough together so that the curves between adjacent points will approximate an arc of a circle. Then a line parallel to the chord will be tangent to the curve at a point where the perpendicular bisector of the chord intersects the circle. In Fig. 22.21(a) the points were chosen at $1, 2, 3, 4$, and 5 seconds and the chords drawn

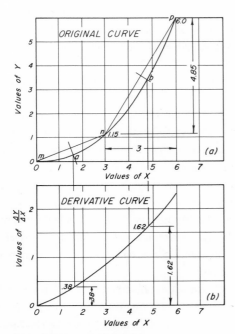

Fig. 22.20 Graphical differentiation.

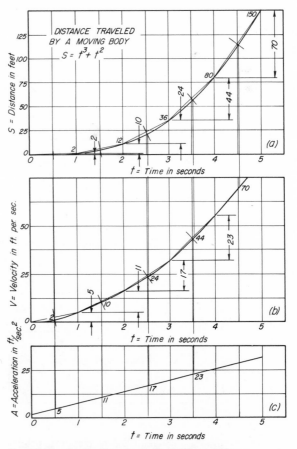

Fig. 22.21 Application of graphical differentiation.

between the points. The tangents have not been drawn, but the perpendicular bisectors of the chords are shown to locate the points of tangency.

The values of S for each of the chosen points are given on the curve in Fig. 22.21(a). The tangent of the angle that the first chord makes with the horizontal axis is 2/1. This value is plotted as shown in Fig. 22.21(b).

The tangent of the second chord will be $12 - 2/1 = 10$, the third $36 - 12/1 = 24$, the fourth $80 - 36/1 = 44$, and the fifth $150 - 80/1 = 70$. These values are plotted directly below the points of tangency to obtain the curve shown in Fig. 22.21(b).

By using the curve found in Fig. 22.21(b), the same process may be used to get the second derivative shown in Fig. 22.21(c). The first derivative gives the velocity time curve and the second derivative gives the acceleration time curve.

22.11 USE OF THE STRING POLYGON FOR DIFFERENTIATION. A method that is somewhat easier and entirely graphical is illustrated in Fig. 22.22. This method involves the use of the funicular polygon or string polygon that was explained in Art. 19.10.

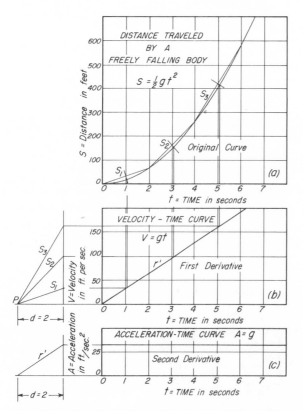

Fig. 22.22 Graphical differentiation by the string polygon method.

The method of procedure may be divided into the following steps:

$a.$ Divide the original curve into segments that are small enough so that they are approximately arcs of circles. See Fig. 22.22(a).

$b.$ Draw the chords between these points. See Fig. 22.22(a). Mark the chords S_1, S_2, and S_3. Erect perpendicular bisectors of the chords.

$c.$ Below the original curve, lay out another set of coordinates, using the same values as on the horizontal axis. See Fig. 22.22(b).

$d.$ Assume a pole, P, so that the pole distance d is equal to 2 units on the horizontal axis. Draw rays S_1, S_2, S_3 parallel respectively to the chords S_1, S_2, and S_3.

$e.$ From the points where the rays cross the vertical axis, draw horizontal lines.

$f.$ From points where the perpendicular bisectors cross the curve in Fig. 22.22(a) project vertically till they intersect the horizontal lines in Fig. 22.22(b) that were drawn in part e. Care must be taken to intersect the corresponding horizontal lines.

$g.$ Through these points of intersection, construct the first derivative curve. In this case the curve is a straight line, as shown in Fig. 22.22(b). This means that the velocity increases uniformly.

A second derivative may be found by using Fig. 22.22(b) as the original curve and repeating the process to obtain Fig. 22.22(c). In this case the second derivative is a horizontal line, which means that the acceleration is constant.

An important part of this solution is the determination of the scale on the vertical axis of the derivative curve. If the pole distance d in Fig. 22.22(b) is made equal to the values of one unit on the horizontal axis, the vertical scale of the derivative curve will be the same as the vertical scale on the original curve. However, in this case the pole distance has been made equal to two times the value of one unit so that the scale on the derivative curve will be twice as large as the original curve. This is shown in Figs. 22.22(a) and 22.22(b). In Fig. 22.22(c) the pole distance is again equal to two units on the horizontal scale so that the vertical scale in Fig. 22.22(c) is twice as large as the vertical scale in Fig. 22.22(b).

22.12 DERIVATIVE OF AN IRREGULAR CURVE. As in the study of integration, the preliminary problems have been simple ones that can be checked analytically. However, the most important use for

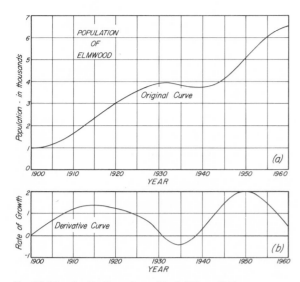

Fig. 22.23   Application of graphical differentiation.

graphical differentiation is when it is difficult or impossible to determine the equation of the curve.

It should be remembered that the derivative curve gives the rate of change of one variable with respect to the other variable. Maximum or minimum values of the rate of change will occur when the tangent to the derivative curve is horizontal or, in other words, at the high and low points on the derivative curve. For instance, in Fig. 22.23(a) the population of a certain town has been plotted by years. Certain factors, such as the building of a railroad or the development of new industries, affected the growth of the town. It is desired to know when the greatest rate of growth occurred. The derivative curve shown in Fig. 22.23(b) was plotted as previously described. It can be seen at a glance that the highest point on the derivative curve is at the year 1950. Therefore the greatest rate of growth was at that time. There was another high point in the rate of growth about 1915.

There was a high point in the population about 1931 and a low point about 1938. These points are indicated on the population curve in Fig. 22.23(a) by high and low points and on the derivative curve in Fig. 22.23(b) by points where the ordinate is zero.

22.13   DIFFERENTIATION BY THE AREA METHOD.

Since the processes of integration and differentiation are reversible, it is possible to use either the area method or the slope method for either process. In most cases the area method is best for integration and

the slope method for differentiation. However, the area method is also quite usable for differentiation, particularly for the steep parts of the original curve. The slope method can be used for integration but is not so convenient and its use will not be discussed here.

The procedures in the area method for differentiation are the same as for integration but taken in the reverse order. The principal difference is that the equivalent areas for integrations are estimated so that the area of the equivalent rectangle is equal to the area under the curve, whereas for differentiation the curve is drawn so that the area under the curve is equal to the area of the equivalent rectangle. Figure 22.24 gives an example where both integration and differentiation were performed on the same curve. The original observed data are plotted in Fig. 22.24(a) and the equivalent areas are established in that figure. Then by taking a pole at P the rays can be drawn as shown in Fig. 22.24(a). The strings in Fig. 22.24(b) are made parallel to the respective rays to give the integral curve in Fig. 22.24(b). Thus the daily fallout of strontium 90 has been added to give the cumulative fallout.

To differentiate the curve shown in Fig. 22.24(a), the first step is to draw the chords so that the curve between the points will be either circles or parabolas. Then the pole P_1 is selected for the left half of the curve and P_2 for the second half. The pole distances are the same, but two poles were used for the sake of clarity to give the desired vertical scale. In Fig. 22.24(a) the pole distance was selected as five times the unit value on the X-axis, whereas in Fig. 22.24(c) the pole distance is two times the unit distance. The rays are then drawn from the pole parallel to the corresponding chords. The intersections of the rays with the vertical axis give the heights of the various equivalent rectangles. The curve can then be drawn so that the small black triangles in each segment are equal. It is also necessary to keep in mind that the perpendicular bisector of the chords in Fig. 22.24(a) will intersect the arc at a point directly above the place where the curve in Fig. 22.24(c) crosses the top of the equivalent rectangle. It should also be remembered that the points of greatest slope in Fig. 22.24(a) will be in projection with the high or low points of the curve in Fig. 22.24(c), and that the high and low points in the curve of Fig. 22.24(a) will be in projection with the points where the curve in Fig. 22.24(c) has the greatest slope.

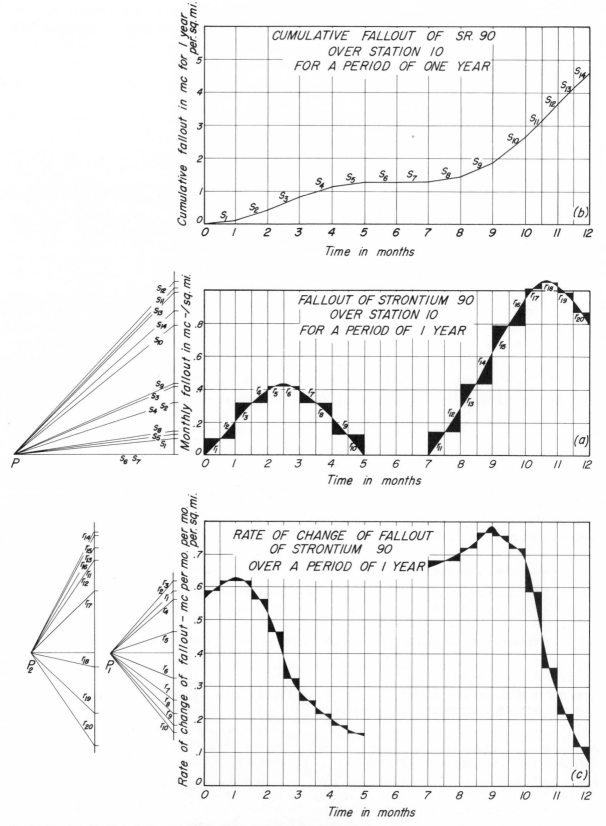

Fig. 22.24   Graphical integration and differentiation by the area method.

SELF-STUDY QUESTIONS

Before trying to answer these questions, read the chapter carefully. Then, without reference to the text, answer as many questions as possible. For those that cannot be answered, the number, in parentheses following the question number, gives the article in which the answer can be found. Look it up and write down the answer. Check the answers that you did give to see that they are correct.

22.1 **(22.1)** One of the principal advantages of graphical solutions is _____ .

22.2 **(22.1)** Accuracy in graphical solutions can be improved by using a _____ scale.

22.3 **(22.2.1)** The network chart for addition is based on the equation for a _____ line.

22.4 **(22.2.1)** In the straight line equation $y = mx + b$ the term m represents the _____ of the line.

22.5 **(22.2.1)** To add or subtract three terms graphically, two _____ may be joined together.

22.6 **(22.2.1)** For addition, the slope of the line is commonly made equal to _____ .

22.7 **(22.2.3)** The Napier diagram is used in navigation for correcting _____ headings.

22.8 **(22.2.4)** The best form for the equation $xy = c$ for multiplication is the _____ form log x + _____ = log c.

22.9 **(22.2.6)** In constructing a network chart for the equation $x = ab/c$, the equation must be _____ into _____ parts.

22.10 **(22.2.7)** To solve a simple arithmetic proportion, the four variables may be plotted with _____ sets of uniform scales at _____ angles to each other.

22.11 **(22.3)** The solution of two simultaneous equations may be found at the point of _____ of the two graphs for the equations when plotted on the same rectangular coordinate grid.

22.12 **(22.3)** A transcendental equation is one in which _____ variable appears in two different _____ .

22.13 **(22.4)** Differential calculus determines the rate of _____ of a function of a variable with relation to the variable.

22.14 **(22.4)** Integral calculus is the process of _____ up a series of increments between specified limits.

22.15 **(22.6)** The best method for finding the area between the x-axis and a curve is to add up the area of a series of small rectangular _____ which will equal the area under the _____ .

22.16 **(22.5)** The difference between two ordinates on the integral curve is equal to the _____ under the original curve between those ordinates.

22.17 **(22.6.1)** An all-graphical method of integration involves the use of the string _____ .

22.18 **(22.6.1)** The pole distance of the string polygon should be some _____ of the unit value used on the X-axis.

22.19 **(22.8)** Graphical integration is most useful when the _____ of the curve is such that it is difficult or impossible to write the equation of the curve.

22.20 **(22.9)** The ordinates on the derivative curve represent the value of the _____ to the curve at that point.

22.21 **(22.9)** For the sake of accuracy the ordinates of the derivative curve should be plotted at a _____ scale than the original curve.

22.22 **(22.11g)** When the derivative curve of a time-distance graph is a straight inclined line, the velocity _____ uniformly.

22.23 **(22.11)** If the second derivative curve of a time-distance graph is a horizontal line, the acceleration _____ _____ .

22.24 **(22.12)** The derivative curve gives the _____ _____ change of one variable with respect to the other variable.

22.25 **(22.12)** The highest point on a derivative curve represents the _____ rate of change.

PROBLEMS

In the solution of these problems, the student must select the proper kind of coordinate paper and choose scales that will enable the problem to be solved on the sheet. Careful plotting is essential and all work must be accurately done if a reasonable answer is to be obtained.

22.1 Design a network chart to solve the equation

$$W = 75E + 150C$$

This equation gives the total weight, W in pounds, of a filled abutment where E is the number of cubic feet of earth and C is the number of cubic feet of concrete. W is the total weight. Use the following limits: $E = 0$ to 2000 and $C = 0$ to 400.

22.2 Design a network chart for the equation

$$W = Q_2 - Q_1$$

This equation gives the amount of heat W in calories that is converted to mechanical work in an engine. Q_2 gives the amount of heat supplied in calories and Q_1 is the heat rejected.

Limits $Q_2 = 0$ to 1000 calories
$Q_1 = 0$ to 500 calories

22.3 Design a network chart to solve the equation

$$A = 3/4X + 10/3Y + 12Z$$

This equation gives the square feet of window area in a building when $X =$ the number of $9'' \times 12''$ panes, $Y =$ the number of $20'' \times 24''$ panes, and $Z =$ the number of $36'' \times 48''$ panes.

Limits $X = 0$ to 100
$Y = 0$ to 20
$Z = 0$ to 10

22.4 Design a network chart for the equation

$$V = 1.3C + 0.5L + 2T$$

This equation gives the approximate cost of floor covering when $C =$ the number of square feet of car-

pet, $L =$ the number of square feet of linoleum, and $T =$ the number of square feet of tile.

Limits $C = 0$ to 1500
$L = 0$ to 400
$T = 0$ to 200

22.5 Design a network chart for the equation

$$F = pA$$

This equation gives the total force, in pounds, exerted by a liquid on an area A in square inches when p is the pressure in pounds per unit of area.

Limits $A = 0$ to 20 square inches
$p = 0$ to 200 pounds per square inch

22.6 Design a network chart for the equation

$$I = \frac{E}{R}$$

This equation gives the current I in amperes when E equals the potential difference in volts and R is the resistance in ohms.

Limits $E = 1/10$ to 10 volts
$R = 1$ to 10 ohms

22.7 Design a network chart for the equation

$$P = i^2R$$

This is the equation for the power absorbed as heat when the circuit is pure resistance R and the current i.

Limits $i = 1$ to 10 amperes
$R = 1$ to 10 volts

22.8 Design a network chart for the equation

$$w = \frac{300 \text{ HP}}{V}$$

This equation gives the width of single ply belting

necessary to transmit a specified horsepower with a certain velocity.

Limits HP = 0.1 to 6.7 horsepower
V = 10 to 200 feet per minute

22.9 Design a network chart for the equation

$$X = \frac{M \cdot P}{N}$$

This equation determines the resistance of a circuit by means of a Wheatstone bridge.

Limits M = resistance in ohms   1 to 10
       N = resistance in ohms   1 to 10
       P = resistance in ohms   1 to 10
       X = resistance in ohms

22.10 Design a chart for the equation

$$y = x + \sqrt[3]{x} + 3$$

22.11 Design a proportion chart for the equation

$$\frac{f}{a} = \frac{F}{A}$$

This equation gives the ratio of hydrostatic pressure to area.

F = 1250 pounds A = 23.5 square inches

Find the corresponding values of pressure, f, when area, a, varies from 1 to 10 by single units.

22.12 Solve the two given simultaneous equations graphically.

$$xy^2 = 43$$

$$\frac{x^2}{2} + \frac{y^3}{3} = 22$$

22.13 Solve the two given simultaneous equations graphically.

$$3x + 4y = 18$$
$$x^2 + y^2 = 20$$

22.14 Find the roots of the given equation graphically.

$$x^3 + 5x^2 - 7x - 18 = 0$$

22.15 Find the roots of the given equation graphically.

$$3x^2 + 4x - 16 = 0$$

22.16 Find the solution for the given equation graphically.

$$2x - 4 = \log x$$

22.17 Find the area of the irregular plot of land by graphical integration. The north-south and east-west lines are on the section lines which are at right angles to each other and the south line is on the shore of a lake. Measuring from the section corner the following points are located on the shore of the lake. From the last point on the shore line, the property line runs due north.

Point No.	Distance East	Distance South
1	0	650
2	200	660
3	400	547
4	500	530
5	600	583
6	700	630
7	800	600
8	1000	300

22.18 The monthly fallout in micro-curies per square mile of strontium 90 over Pittsburgh is listed in the table. Plot the fallout curve and find the cumulative fallout by graphical integration.

Date	Fallout	Date	Fallout	Date	Fallout
Jan.	0.3	May	0.6	Sept.	0.3
Feb.	0.2	June	1.0	Oct.	0.5
Mar.	0.2	July	0.4	Nov.	0.7
Apr.	0.4	Aug.	0.3	Dec.	0.4

22.19 A certain city pumping station tabulates the rate of pumping each hour as follows:

Time	Rate Gallons per Minute	Time	Rate Gallons per Minute
6:00 A.M.	50,000	1:00 P.M.	50,000
7:00 A.M.	60,000	2:00 P.M.	20,000
8:00 A.M.	90,000	3:00 P.M.	25,000
9:00 A.M.	70,000	4:00 P.M.	40,000
10:00 A.M.	30,000	5:00 P.M.	70,000
11:00 A.M.	35,000	6:00 P.M.	60,000
12:00 noon	60,000		

Find the total water used during the 12-hour period by graphical integration.

22.20 With the equation $xy = 8$, find the area above the X-axis and below the curve between the values of $x = 1$ and $x = 8$ by graphical integration.

22.21 With the equation $x = 0.5y^2$, find the area between the X-axis and the curve between the values of $x = 0$ and $x = 8$ by graphical integration. The integral curve shall go through the point $x = 2$ and $y = 4$.

22.22 A moving object travels according to the equation $d = t^2/3$. Plot the time distance curve and find the time velocity curve and the time acceleration curve from $t = 0$ to $t = 5$.

22.23 The population data for Mayview is listed below.

Date	Population	Date	Population
1900	2420	1940	7228
1910	2100	1950	7300
1920	4032	1960	6000
1930	6150		

Plot the population curve and find the time of greatest growth by graphical differentiation.

22.24 The cam follower on a rotating cam is at the following distances from the center at intervals of one second.

Time in Seconds	Distance in Inches	Time in Seconds	Distance in Inches
0	1.50	9	2.64
1	1.64	10	2.64
2	1.85	11	2.64
3	1.88	12	2.34
4	1.88	13	1.97
5	1.88	14	1.60
6	2.00	15	1.50
7	2.24	16	1.50
8	2.48		

These figures make one complete revolution of the cam. Plot the time distance curve and find the time velocity curve and the time acceleration curve.

22.25 Construct a Napier diagram for the following data. Variation = 3°W. (Hint, the variation should be added to the true heading to get the magnetic heading before plotting the deviation curve.)

True Heading	Deviation	True Heading	Deviation
000°	8° W.	210°	9° E.
030°	7° W.	240°	6° E.
060°	3° W.	270°	7° W.
090°	3° E.	300°	10° W.
120°	7° E.	330°	9° W.
150°	10° E.		
180°	11° E.		

Determine the deviation for the following headings: 045°, 075°, 132°, 243°, 275°.

PART FOUR

Professional Applications

CHAPTER 23
Map Drawing

OLD: Map of 1599 showing Northeast Africa, Arabia, Persia, and India. (Map collection, New York Public Library)

NEW: Topographic Sheet of Washington County, Maine. (U.S. Geological Survey)

Chapter 23 Map Drawing

23.1 For the planning and construction of many engineering undertakings, it is necessary to have representations of the earth's surface. Such representations are called maps. When the area to be shown is small, a map is essentially a one-view orthographic projection, hence only two dimensions can be shown. This is frequently sufficient. Where the third dimension, namely, the difference in elevation of the earth's surface, is essential, symbols are used to give this information. If the area to be shown is large or if extreme accuracy is desired, other types of projection are used. Such projections are beyond the scope of this book.

23.2 CLASSIFICATION OF MAPS. Maps are conveniently classified on the basis of their purpose or intended use. On this basis maps may be divided into four classes: geographic, topographic, cadastral, and engineering. Although no hard and fast lines can be drawn between the various classes of maps, the distinctions are usually quite clear, as may be noted from the descriptions in the following paragraphs.

23.3 GEOGRAPHIC MAPS. Maps of this group show a comparatively large area and must, therefore, be drawn to very small scales, which means, of course, that only the more important features of the earth's surface can be shown, such as the larger rivers and lakes, mountains, cities, and railroads. On these maps, the cities are located by small circles, and only the larger curves in streams and the principal changes of direction of the railroads are shown. Examples of such maps are to be found in any atlas or geography textbook, hence they are familiar to everyone. The scales vary from a few miles to the inch to several hundred miles to the inch. Relief, or difference of elevation, is shown in a very general way, usually by hachures or shading.

23.4 TOPOGRAPHIC MAPS. The term topography means the configuration or shape of the land surface of any area. Because of the details that must be shown, the area covered by such maps is quite small as compared to geographic maps. The most widely known maps of this class are those prepared by the United States Geological Survey. A small portion of such a map is shown in Fig. 23.1. Figure 23.1 is taken from the Urbana Quadrangle in Illinois in flat country.

U. S. Geological maps are made to the following scales, determined by the needs in the economic development of the area shown. These maps are always bounded by meridians of longitude and parallels of latitude.

The larger scales shown below are used in the more highly developed areas and the smaller ones in more sparsely settled or desert regions. The arc of latitude and longitude covered is the same in both directions. A scale of 1:24,000, $1'' = 2000$ feet, covers 7½ minutes of latitude and longitude.

$$1:62,500, \quad 1'' = \text{nearly 1 mile.}$$
$$1:125,000, \quad 1'' = \text{nearly 2 miles.}$$
$$1:250,000, \quad 1'' = \text{nearly 4 miles.}$$

Index maps and circulars of each state and Puerto Rico showing the areas covered by topographic and planimetric maps are available without charge from the United States Geological Survey, Washington 25, D.C. The charge for individual maps is given in the circulars.

The large-scale maps show all the natural features down to little streams that run dry in the summer. City streets, country roads and trails, tunnels, aqueducts, pipelines underground, bridges, houses and all the works of man together with permanent vegetation such as forest areas are shown. A portion of a privately made topographic map is shown in Fig. 23.2.

23.5 CADASTRAL MAPS. Maps of this class are used primarily for showing political and civil boundaries, together with property lines, and are used for the purposes of taxation and the transfer of property. Hence, because of the accuracy required, such maps must be drawn on a still larger scale than either of the preceding classes. They contain, besides the property lines, only enough of the natural features, such as streams and roads, to enable one to locate the corresponding lines on the ground. Plats of city additions, mineral rights, farm surveys, and the like fall in this group. The scale for such maps is usually greater than 6 inches to 1 mile.

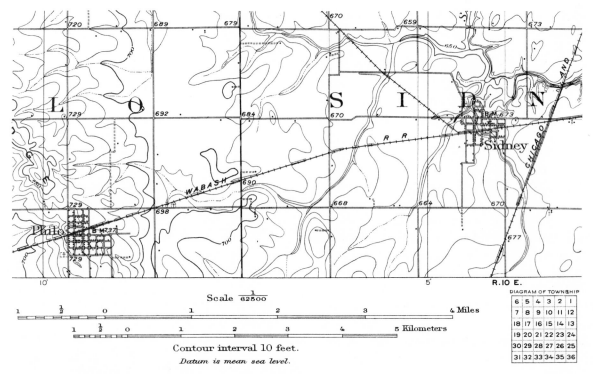

Scale $\frac{1}{62500}$

Contour interval 10 feet.

Datum is mean sea level.

Fig. 23.1 Topographic map. Part of Urbana, Illinois, Quadrangle.

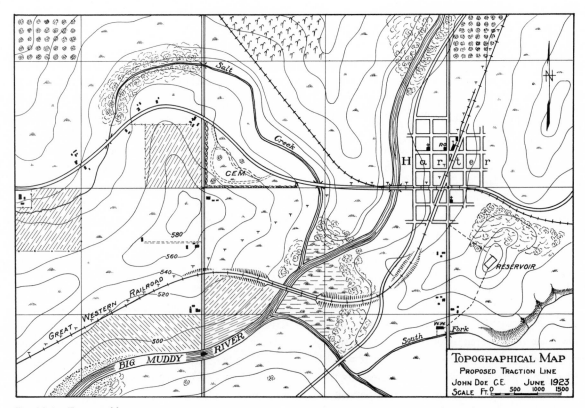

Fig. 23.2 Topographic map.

23.6 ENGINEERING MAPS. Maps drawn for reconnaissance, construction, or maintenance purposes are called engineering maps. The scale is seldom smaller than 1 inch equals 400 feet, and it may approach the architectural scales as the other limit, for example, ⅛ inch equals 1 foot. Maps for railroad, highway, canal, or hydroelectric construction are excellent examples of this class of maps. Such maps frequently have the character of topographic maps in that they include the contour lines, the natural features, and works of man. Being on a larger scale, they are, of course, much more accurate in detail than the usual topographic map. A portion of a highway construction map is shown in Fig. 23.3.

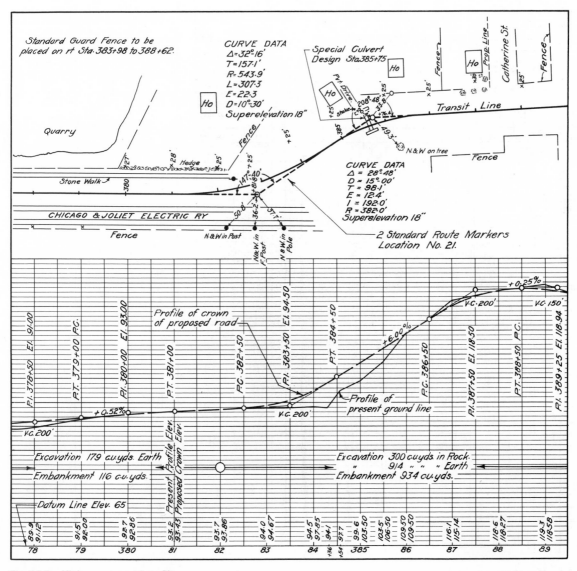

Fig. 23.3   Highway map and profile.

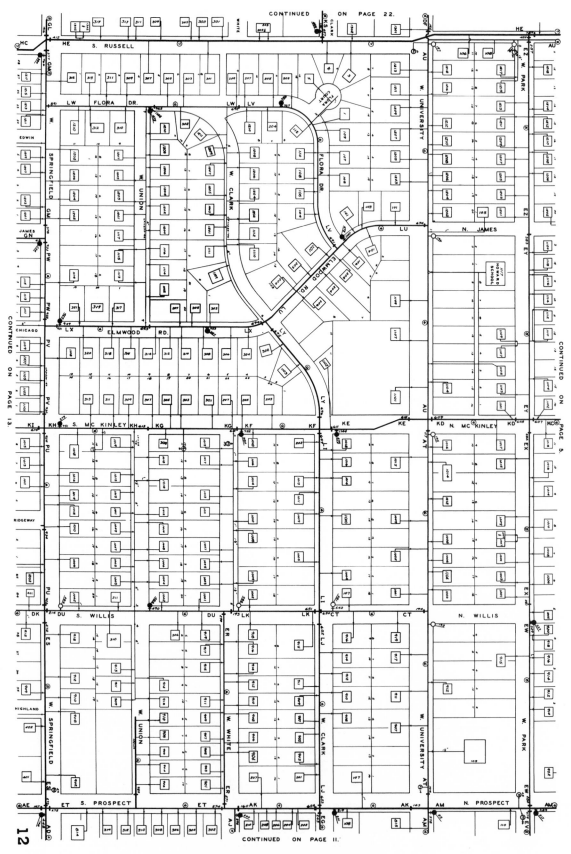

Fig. 23.4 Map of city water supply system. (Courtesy Northern Illinois Water Corp.)

Public utility companies use what are in effect large-scale cadastral maps to show the location of their lines and connections thereto. Figure 23.4 is a portion of a water company map showing the location of the water mains, fire hydrants, and connections to private property.

Contour maps, showing principally the elevation of the land, are used for location, estimating costs, and construction. A map of this type is shown in Fig. 23.5. Further details concerning the use of contour maps are discussed in Art. 23.7.

23.7   MILITARY MAPS. This book is concerned primarily with engineering maps for civilian use, but there is a close connection between topographic maps for this use and military maps. Military maps may be classified according to the scale, which definitely determines the area that can be represented and the use of the map.

Small-scale maps with scales ranging from 1:1,000,000 to 1:7,000,000 are used for strategical planning by commanders of large forces.

Intermediate-scale maps with scales varying from 1:200,000 to 1:500,000 are used for planning operations, troop movements, concentrations, and supply.

Medium-scale maps with scales running from 1:50,000 to 1:125,000 are required for tactical and administrative studies for units of the size of regiments. U.S. Geological maps (1:62,500) are suitable for this purpose.

Large-scale maps of about 1:20,000 are used for tactical and technical battle needs.

Symbols for military maps are quite extensive and may be found in a booklet called *Military Symbols*.

23.8   MAP SCALES. From the foregoing classification of maps it will be noted that scales are used ranging from 0.1 inch equals 1 foot as the largest to 1 inch equals several hundred miles as the smallest. The scale of a map is shown both graphically and numerically at some place near the title or as a part of it, as shown in Fig. 23.1. Sometimes the numerical scale is stated as a ratio. Thus a scale of 1 inch to the mile is expressed as 1:63,360.

Survey measurements are made in feet and fractions of feet, which are expressed in feet and decimals of a foot instead of in feet and inches; hence the engineer's scales on the boxwood rules are in the decimal system—and have 10, 20, 30, etc., divisions to the inch. These units may also represent 1, 2, or 3 feet to the inch, 10, 20, or 30 feet to the inch, or 100, 200, or 300 feet to the inch. All these scales occur frequently in engineering work.

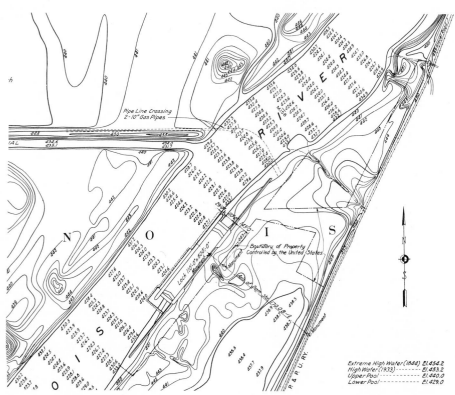

Fig. 23.5   Contour map of construction.

The selection of a scale for a map will be influenced by many factors, chief among which are the size and character of the area to be shown, the form in which the map is to be presented, and the purpose for which it is to be used. Cost of preparation and length of service must sometimes be considered.

23.9 MAP SYMBOLS. Since the scale of any map is small, relatively speaking, the representation of objects upon it must be highly conventionalized. On all but the largest-scale engineering maps, even the largest objects must be shown by symbols rather than by plan views of them. The purpose of a map is, after all, not to show the exact appearance from above, but, rather, to show the comparative size of objects and their position relative to one another. Hence conventional symbols have been devised which bear some resemblance, where possible, to the objects themselves. The purpose of having this resemblance is for convenience in interpretation.

A well-standardized system of symbols, used by practically all map-making departments of the gov-

ernment, is published in a small booklet called *Military Symbols* published by the Departments of the Army and the Air Force.

23.10 SIZE AND PROMINENCE OF SYMBOLS. The size of symbols should vary only slightly with the scale of the map, since, to almost any scale, most symbols are exaggerations, no matter how small they are made. The symbols shown in Figs. 23.6 to 23.17 are the proper-size for the usual engineering maps.

Since the variation in size of symbols is quite limited, prominence may be secured by a variation in the weight of lines used. The purpose of the map will determine which symbols are to be made most prominent. On an oil property map, for example, flowing wells, dry wells, railroads, roads, and property lines are the important features. In practically all cases, the vegetable symbols are least important (military maps excepted) and therefore should be drawn lightly and not too closely together.

23.11 HOW TO DRAW SYMBOLS. There are two distinct steps in learning how to draw symbols, the

Fig. 23.6 Symbol for water lining.

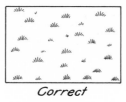

Fig. 23.7 Grass.

Fig. 23.8 Deciduous trees.

Fig. 23.9 Palm trees and tropical grass.

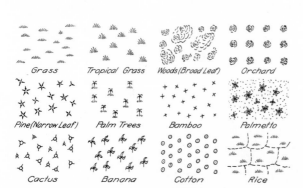

Fig. 23.10 Vegetation symbols (green).

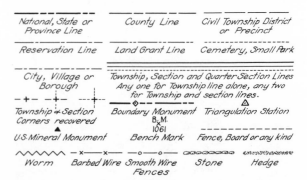

Fig. 23.11 Civil boundaries (black).

first of which is a careful examination of a correct model or sample of the symbol, and the second, an endeavor to reproduce it. The more important of these steps is the examination of the sample, for upon the keenness and accuracy of the observation depend the effort at reproduction. For example, an examination of the water lining at the right in Fig. 23.6 will make clear that the first lines are drawn very near the shoreline and follow it around very closely, whereas the lines become farther apart and less irregular as we approach the center of the body of water. Examples of both correct and incorrect water lining are shown in Fig. 23.6.

Similarly, a careful examination of the symbol for grass in Fig. 23.7 will show that it consists of about seven short strokes, ranging in length from almost a dot at the ends to about $\frac{3}{32}$ inch at the center. It will also be observed that these strokes are slightly curved and seem to meet in a common center. The individual symbols are arranged at random and not in rows. The careless observer would fail to note many of these essential points, and consequently his attempts at imitation would lack the things that he overlooked. Common errors in making the symbols for grass are shown in Fig. 23.7, in contrast with a correct execution. Likewise, the result of poor observation of the tree symbol is shown in Fig. 23.8.

A large variety of map symbols, printed on cellophane for pasting on a drawing, may be obtained from the trade.

23.12   COLORS OF SYMBOLS. On a finished map the symbols should be shown in colors. The color for each symbol in Figs. 23.10 to 23.17 is indicated in the figure title. These colors may be readily remembered by four simple groupings: the artificial features, or works of man, are made in black; water features in blue; contours, sand, washes, etc., in brown; and vegetation in green. In printing maps, each color requires a separate printing; therefore a reduction in the number of colors used reduces the cost. Since vegetation, except for very large forests, is not permanent, the green is usually omitted.

23.13   SPACING OF SYMBOLS. One of the greatest difficulties in drawing symbols is to learn how to space those that do not have plotted locations. The general tendency is to cover the sheet too thickly. The draftsman must constantly be on his guard against this practice for two reasons. First, the more symbols are drawn the longer it takes and the more it costs to produce the map. Second, it is more difficult to produce uniformity of texture when the symbols are crowded. The heavy and light areas on the map are disagreeably noticeable when symbols are placed too closely together. When there are large areas to be covered with symbols involving the use of parallel lines, as in the case of marshlands, a section liner should be used.

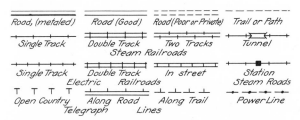

Fig. 23.12   Road and communication symbols (black).

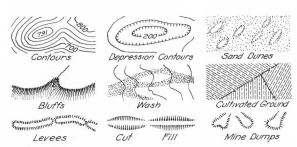

Fig. 23.14   Relief symbols (brown).

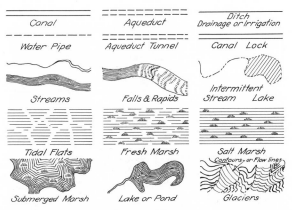

Fig. 23.13   Hydrographic symbols (blue).

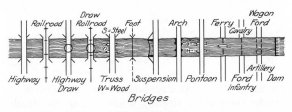

Fig. 23.15   Bridges and fords (black).

23.14 POSITION OF SYMBOLS. Another very important point is the position of the symbols on the sheet. All symbols that have a definite base, for example, grass, marsh, palm trees, and corn, should be drawn with the base parallel to the bottom of the sheet so that the symbols appear in a natural upright position. They should never be placed with their bases parallel to roadways or property lines that run diagonally across the sheet. An illustration of this point is shown in Fig. 23.9. Symbols for vegetation that occur in rows, however, may have the rows running in any direction.

23.15 SPECIAL SYMBOLS. For some purposes, special symbols must be devised. Thus for purposes of aerial navigation a map must show clearly the landing fields of various kinds, beacon, and other aids to navigation, as well as those objects that project up into the air and may be obstructions to flight. Some of these symbols are shown in Fig. 23.16. Such objects as roads, railroads, railway stations, rivers, lakes, woods, and telegraph lines, which will not interfere with flight, are shown by the usual symbols.

Property maps of various industries may also require the engineer to devise symbols to show certain features that are not included among the standard symbols. It should be the engineer's purpose always to make such symbols unmistakable as to meaning and easy to interpret.

23.16 DEFINITION OF TERMS. The following terms are commonly used in surveying and map drafting.

a. *Azimuth.* The azimuth of a line is the angle the line makes with a north and south line measured clockwise from the north. See Fig. 23.18. In older survey notes the azimuth angle is frequently given from the south. See problems at the end of this chapter.

b. *Back azimuth.* The angle measured to the line running in the opposite direction from the azimuth measurement. The back azimuth is therefore equal to the azimuth plus or minus 180°. See Fig. 23.18.

c. *Bearing.* The angle that a line makes with a north and south line measured either from the north or south. It is always less than 90°. The bearing of a line making 57° to the east of north would be specified as North 57° East or N. 57° E. See Fig. 23.18.

d. *Backsight.* A sight looking back to the last point or station previously occupied. It is 180° from the foresight. See Fig. 23.19.

e. *Foresight.* In occupying a new point the surveyor orients his transit by sighting back on the point previously occupied. This is the backsight. The telescope of the transit is then plunged 180° to give the foresight. See Fig. 23.19.

f. *Deflection angle.* The angle of a line in a survey measured to the right or left of the foresight. See Fig. 23.19.

Fig. 23.17 Building symbols (black).

Fig. 23.16 Aeronautical symbols, Departments of the Army and Air Force (black—friendly, single line; enemy, double line); (color—friendly, blue; enemy, red).

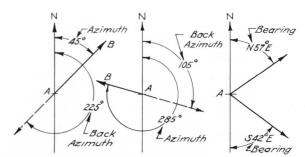

Fig. 23.18 Azimuth and bearing of a line.

g. *Magnetic north.* The north point as indicated by the needle of a magnetic compass which points toward the magnetic North Pole. This varies from place to place.

h. *True north.* A north line established by observations on Polaris, the North Star.

i. *Traverse.* A broken line measured by observation of angles and distances in the field. In property surveys it is usually the boundary line. A traverse may be open or closed. See Fig. 23.19. It is said to be closed when it ends upon the point of beginning or upon a point whose location has been previously determined.

j. *Stations.* The turning points of a traverse. In railroad and highway surveys points on the center line at 100-foot intervals are also called stations and are identified during the survey and construction by stakes with the station numbers on them. Points between stations are given the last station number with the distance from that station as a plus quantity.

The following abbreviations are commonly used on maps and map notes:

P.C. Point of curvature: the point at which the tangent ends and the curve begins on a highway or railroad.

P.T. Point of tangency: the point where the curve ends and the tangent begins.

P.I. Point of intersection: the point where the tangents to a curve intersect.

P.S. Point of switch: the point at which a switch diverges from the main line of a railroad.

P.R.C. Point of reverse curve: the point at which one curve ends and another of opposite curvature begins.

23.17 PLOTTING A MAP TRAVERSE. The method of plotting map notes depends upon that of making the survey and upon the accuracy required. In gen-

eral, the plotting on a map indicates or duplicates in miniature the work carried out in the field. Thus an angle measured in the field with a transit may be measured on the map with a protractor, and a distance measured by tape or stadia in the field is measured on the map with a boxwood scale.

The three most common methods of plotting transit surveys, in an ascending order of accuracy, are (1) protractor and scale method; (2) tangent method; and (3) rectangular coordinate method.

23.18 PROTRACTOR AND SCALE METHOD. Where great accuracy is not required, the survey notes may be plotted by means of the protractor and scale. The degree of accuracy depends both on the kind of instruments used and on the skill of the draftsman. Any errors made are, of course, carried forward, but are not necessarily cumulative, since the possibility of error in either direction is the same, and in a large number of measurements these errors will to some extent balance each other, unless the errors are due to a personal and constant tendency of the draftsman to overestimate or to underestimate in plotting angles or distances.

For ordinary work, nothing less than a 6-inch celluloid protractor should be used, and this should be tested to see that the 180° and 90° angles, at least, are correct. Steel protractors, with straight edge and vernier attached, are, of course, much more desirable.

A portion of a page of survey notes is shown in Fig. 23.20. Let it be required to lay out the angle at Sta. *2* to locate Sta. *3* from these notes. Assume the point *B* in Fig. 23.21 to be Sta. *2* and the line *BC* the "backsight." The first step, then, in laying out the angle is to extend the line *CB* so far past *B* that both ends of the protractor may be on the line when the center is at *B*. Deflection angles are measured to the right and left of the sight line produced; that is, a deflection angle marked right should be laid off to the right of the extended line (Foresight) *BA* when looking forward along that line in the direction *A*. Hence the protrac-

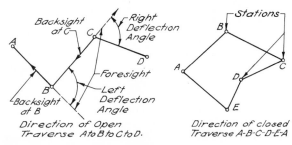

Fig. 23.19 Traverse stations.

	79°40′L	603′
₵ of R.R. bridge	79°40′L	603′
₵ of Park Road bridge	138°50′L	231′
Shore of island at fork	171°20′L	220′
⊙ 3	59°40′R	652′
₵ of Park Road No.1. on curve	151°45′R	119′
North corner of boat house	121°25′R	575′
⊙ 2		

Fig. 23.20 Survey notes.

tor must be laid on the right or left side of the line from which the angle is measured, according as the notes describe the angle, as measured in the field, to the right or left of the line. Having the protractor set as described above, mark off the angle of 59°40′ as accurately as possible, with a very sharp pencil, at the point D. With a straight edge and pencil, draw the line through the point B and the new point just located, and on this line scale off the proper length, namely, 652 feet to locate Sta. *3*.

23.19 TANGENT METHOD. This method is more accurate for the plotting of angles, but requires more time; hence it is generally used for plotting traverses; the protractor method may be used for plotting in the details. The tangent method requires a table of natural tangents and is, in brief, simply the plotting of an angle on the basis of the definition of the tangent. Again assuming the same angle as in the previous case, draw the line AB (see Fig. 23.22), extend it beyond B, and lay off on it ten units with any one of the engineer's scales. The larger the scale the greater the accuracy. At the end of these ten units, erect a perpendicular to the right of the line, since the deflection is marked right, and on it scale off the natural tangent

of the angle multiplied by 10, which is 17.0901. Then through the point thus located and the point B, draw the line required, and on it scale off the distance 652 feet.

If the deflection angle is much greater than 45°, greater accuracy may be obtained by first erecting a perpendicular at B and laying off on it ten units, and then at the end of this ten-unit line erecting another perpendicular on which may be laid off a distance equal to ten times the tangent of the complement of the angle, as shown in Fig. 23.23.

If the deflection angle is greater than 135°, the ten-unit line should be laid off between B and E, as shown in Fig. 23.24, and the tangent of the supplementary angle must be used.

23.20 RECTANGULAR COORDINATE METHOD. Inasmuch as this method requires considerable trigonometric calculation and is used only when great accuracy is required, it will not be discussed in this

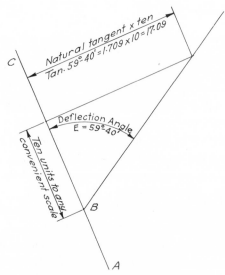

Fig. 23.22 Plotting angles by the tangent method.

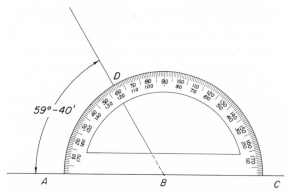

Fig. 23.21 Plotting angles by the protractor method.

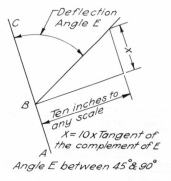

Fig. 23.23 Plotting angles from 45 to 90° by the tangent method.

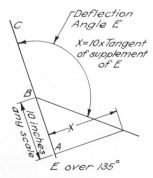

Fig. 23.24 Plotting large angles by the tangent method.

book. Complete information concerning this method may be found in surveying texts.

23.21 REPRESENTATION OF ELEVATION ON MAPS. A one-plane projection can show only two dimensions, but for many purposes it is highly desirable that a map shall show three dimensions, namely, length, breadth, and difference of elevation. This object may be attained by two conventional schemes, that is, by the use of hachures or contours.

23.22 HACHURES. If only a general idea of the elevation of the country is desired, the method of hachures is satisfactory, since it gives the effect of relief and is readily understood by the average person. Differences in elevation between any two points, however, can be shown only in a very relative manner. An example of this method of representation is shown in Fig. 23.25, from an examination of which it will be noted that the strokes are short, heavy, and close together where the slope is steep, becoming gradually longer, lighter, and farther apart as the slope becomes

more gentle and approaches the horizontal. The direction of the stroke should be the same as that in which water would flow on the slope. Care should be exercised not to have a continuous white line between the several rows of short strokes.

23.23 CONTOUR LINES. A contour line on a map is the projection of an imaginary line on the earth's surface which passes through all points of the same elevation. The meaning of a contour line may perhaps become a little clearer from an examination of Fig. 23.26, the lower part of which shows a landscape in perspective, and the upper part of which shows the same landscape in map form with elevations indicated by contour lines at intervals of 20 feet. The shoreline is in reality a contour line. The first contour line above the shore represents what the shoreline would be if the water rose vertically 20 feet. To put it in other words, if a man could walk along such a line on the ground, he would go neither up nor down but proceed always on a level and eventually he would return to the place from which he started.

With a little reflection the following rules will be observed to be true, both of imaginary contour lines on the ground and of their projection on a map. The rules are stated as applied to a map.

a. Every contour line must either close upon itself or extend to the edge of the map.
b. When a contour line closes, it usually indicates a summit but it may indicate a depression. When it indicates a depression, this is made clear by the symbol shown in Figs. 23.14 and 23.27.
c. Contour lines never cross, except for an overhanging ledge or a cave.
d. Where contour lines are close together the surface

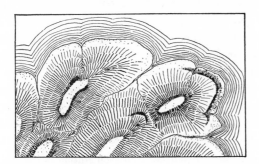

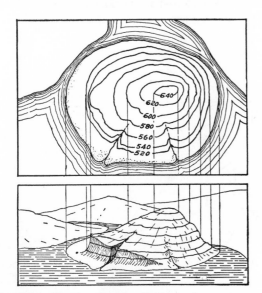

Fig. 23.25   Hachures (brown).

Fig. 23.26   Meaning of contour lines.

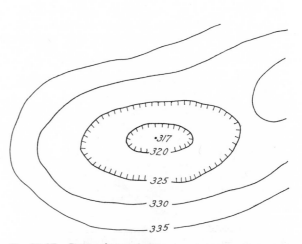

Fig. 23.27   Depression contours.

is steep, and where they are far apart the surface is gently sloping.

e. When contour lines are close together, they are in a sense parallel to each other (not parallel in a strictly mathematical sense). When they are far apart they need not necessarily be parallel.

f. Contour lines approaching a stream go upstream before reaching the water's edge, where they stop at points directly opposite each other at right angles to the stream. If the stream is shown by a single line, they cross it at right angles; if shown by two lines, they do not cross.

g. Contour lines cannot run into the shore of a lake or other still body of water, since the water surface is at the same level at all points.

h. The first contour lines from the water's edge, on opposite sides of a still body of water, must be of the same number or elevation.

i. It is customary to make every fifth contour line heavier than the rest. This line is broken at some convenient place, and the number representing its elevation is inserted in the break in ink of the same color as the line. Where the contour lines are far apart each one may be numbered.

The numbers indicating the elevation of the contour lines are lettered parallel to the contour line, and, where possible, the numbers for consecutive lines are placed in rows, as shown in Fig. 23.26. If it is possible, these numbers should read from the bottom of the sheet. Contour lines may be drawn with a lettering pen or with a pen designed especially for the purpose and called a contour pen. The point of this pen is on a swivel which allows it to turn freely in any direction.

The contour interval may be any desired value, from 1 foot in very flat country up to 200 feet in rough mountainous country. By contour interval is meant the vertical distance between the planes of consecutive contour lines; 5, 10, 20, 100, and 200 feet are the intervals most frequently used.

On a summit or depression, the last contour line is numbered, or the elevation of the high or low point within the contour is given. See Figs. 23.26 and 23.27.

23.24 PLOTTING CONTOUR LINES. The data for making a contour map may be obtained in the field by obtaining the horizontal location and the elevation of a series of points sufficiently close together so that reasonable interpolations may be made between them. These points may be taken in a rectangular pattern at intervals suitable to the terrain. They may also be taken in radial patterns from traverse points. In the latter case it is usual to choose points on the surface where there is a change in slope. Thus, in Fig. 23.28 elevations were obtained at four points as indicated at the top of the figure. A sectional view shows the slope of the ground surface, and the light horizontal lines are contour planes at 1-foot intervals. A sectional view, of course, is not necessary since the horizontal distance between points can be divided proportionately. Thus in Fig. 23.28 the 605 contour is two-thirds the distance from 603 to 606.

With this explanation, the actual work of plotting contour lines from survey data is illustrated in Fig. 23.29. Here the traverse stations *1, 2,* and *3* have been shown with the observations of elevations on the earth's surface plotted from each station in the usual radial pattern. Assuming the ground slope to be uniform between plotted points, the space between points can be divided into a number of spaces equal to the

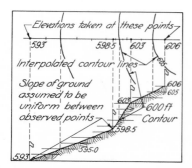

Fig. 23.28 Plotting contour lines by interpolation.

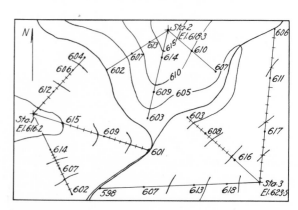

Fig. 23.29 Plotting contours.

difference in elevation between points as indicated for a number of spaces in Fig. 23.29.

In the upper portion of the map completed contours have been shown, and in the other portions the lines are sketched in only between plotted elevations. In general, it will be noted that between the radial lines of plotted points the contour lines follow the stream pattern.

23.25 USE OF CONTOUR MAPS. Contour maps are used in engineering work to make preliminary estimates of excavations for structures, in locating dams and computing the volumes of water stored behind them, in computing the area of watersheds, and in many other kinds of work. Figure 23.1 shows a portion of a topographic map taken from a United States Geological map of the Urbana Quadrangle in Illinois.

23.26 OUTCROP FROM CONTOUR MAPS. Contour maps also are used extensively in geology and mining. Figure 23.30 illustrates the use of a contour map to determine data concerning a stratum of limestone. The upper surface of the layer was observed to outcrop on the 500-foot contour indicated at a^H. At other places the stratum was covered by overlaying material. Borings were made at B and C at elevations shown on the map. At B the top surface was encountered at elevation 580 and the bottom at 465. At C these values were, respectively, 420 and 305.

Using the map, an elevation view was made of the three points a^V, b^V, and c^V at the known elevations of the top surface of the stratum. A horizontal line drawn across this triangle from a^V to d^V determines the strike line $a^H d^H$, which upon measurement from the north line shows the strike to be S. 52°E. By making an endwise view of the strike line and again plotting

the known points as at (b) the stratum is shown edgewise and its thickness and slope or dip can be determined as shown in Fig. 23.30(b). The dip is shown on the map by drawing an arrow perpendicular to the strike line pointing in the downward direction with the value of the dip lettered on it.

Having the edgewise view of the stratum, the outcrop can be determined by finding where the top and bottom surfaces of the limestone bed cross the 400–700-foot contour planes in the edge view and projecting these back to the corresponding contour lines. These are shown by the small circles at the edge of the shaded area for the top surface and the black dots for the bottom.

If, on the other hand, an outcrop of a bed is shown on a contour map, the strike can be determined at once by connecting the points where any one contour line crosses the upper line of the outcrop. Having the strike line, an edge view of the bed or layer may be obtained and from this the dip and thickness.

23.27 CUT AND FILL FROM CONTOUR MAPS. Contour maps are also used to determine the cut and fill required in the construction of a railroad or highway, as illustrated in Figs. 23.31 and 23.32. Since the sides of a cut or fill are plane surfaces, contour lines on them will be parallel and equally spaced. Finding the outline of a cut or fill therefore is simply a problem in the intersection of surfaces. Having the contours on the map, it is only necessary to draw the contours in the cut or fill at the same levels as the map contours and find where these lines intersect.

If the roadbed is level, the contour lines in cut or fill are parallel to the edge of the roadbed. The spacing of these contour lines depends on the slope of the cut

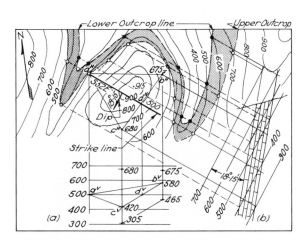

Fig. 23.30 Finding strike and dip from on outcrop.

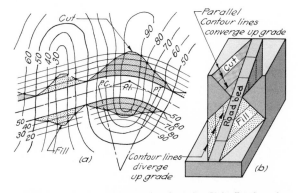

Fig. 23.31 Cut and fill on (a) level grade, (b) inclined grade.

or fill. If the slope is 45° or 1:1, the spacing will be the same as the contour interval of the map, whereas if it is 1½:1, the spacing will be 1½ times the contour interval. The solution of a problem of this type is shown in Fig. 23.31(a).

In hilly country, however, level roadbeds seldom occur. There is usually a definite slope, and this slope or grade is expressed in per cent. Thus a slope or rise of 1 foot in 100 feet of horizontal distance is called a 1% grade. A rise of 2 feet in 100 feet is a 2% grade, and so on. An ascending grade is marked plus and a descending grade minus.

When the roadbed is on a grade, the contour lines of the cut and fill are not parallel to the edge of the roadbed, as can be seen in Fig. 23.31(b). On an up-grade, the contour lines in a cut converge toward the edge of the roadbed and those on a fill diverge. The rate of divergence depends on the grade and the slope of the cut. On a 1:1 slope the divergence will be equal to the grade. Thus in a 1% grade and a 1:1 slope the contour line will diverge 10 feet from the edge of the roadbed in 1000 feet. With the same grade and a 1½:1 slope the divergence in 1000 feet would be 15 feet. On curves, the divergence must be plotted at each station and a smooth curve drawn. This has been done on one side of the line shown in Fig. 23.32. Theoretically, cut and fill will meet at the edge of the roadbed on each side. In order not to complicate the illustration, the culvert necessary for drainage was omitted.

Where necessary, additional contours may be interpolated on the map as well as on cut and fill.

A more customary method for determining the outline of the cut and fill is by taking cross sections in the field. This is done by establishing a line perpendicular to the center line at each station and obtaining elevations at selected points on this perpendicular line. These cross sections are then plotted on paper and the roadway placed in its proper position, as shown for the two sections in Fig. 23.32. These sections can be used to determine the edge of the cut or fill and to calculate the quantities of earth to be moved.

23.28   PROFILES. A profile is a line showing the elevations of the ground along some one particular line on the earth's surface. Although a profile represents something entirely different from a contour, the two are nevertheless related in such a manner that one may be obtained from the other. A profile usually accompanies a map showing a road, railroad, sewer, water-supply line, or canal location. If the profile is to be made very accurately, the elevation of points on the line should be obtained by means of a level in the field. However, a profile for preliminary purposes may be obtained from a contour map as shown in Fig. 23.33.

When elevations are obtained with an instrument in the field, readings are taken every 100 feet in flat country and at closer intervals of 50, 25, or 10 feet in rough country, depending on the ruggedness of the slope. These readings are then plotted on a special coordi-

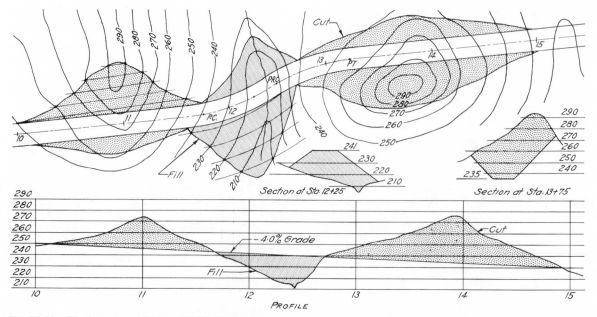

Fig. 23.32   Plotting cut and fill on an inclined grade line.

nate paper called profile paper, in which the spacing of coordinates is different in the two directions.

When the elevations are obtained from a contour map, the proposed line is drawn on the map and the intersections of this line with the contour lines give the elevations of points whose distances apart are obtained by scaling the map. These points are then plotted on the profile paper.

Profiles, as indicated in a preceding paragraph, are usually plotted to two different scales, the larger of which is used on the vertical axis. The purpose of the two scales is to show the variations of elevation more clearly. Since a profile is usually thousands of feet or

several miles in length, whereas the difference of elevation varies only over a few hundred feet, the scale that would bring the horizontal length within workable limits would make the vertical distances so small as to be insignificant.

23.29   PROFILE ON CURVES. When a profile is made of a line, a portion of which is curved, like a railroad line, for example, the developed length of the curve is shown in profile and not the projected length. In other words, the length of the profile is the same as the true length of the line. The beginning and ending of the curve are shown, and the degree of curvature is indicated, as in Fig. 23.34.

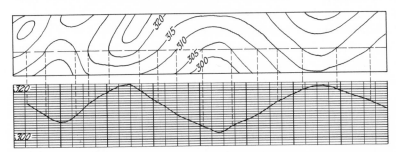

Fig. 23.33   Profile determined from a contour map.

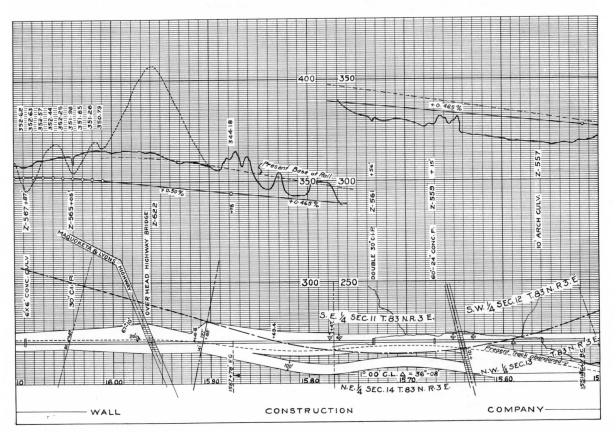

Fig. 23.34   Railway profile.

23.30 GRADE LINES. In engineering work, where maps are used, a profile is seldom drawn except for the purpose of establishing the grade line of some such structure as a railroad, highway, sewer, or other engineering project. The grade line is the controlling line in construction of the types of structures mentioned. It establishes the slope or deviation from the horizontal. The grades of lines are specified in percentages, and represent the number of feet of vertical rise or fall in 100 feet horizontal distance. Grades are specified as plus when the slope is upward, and minus when the slope is downward, in the direction in which the line is laid out. See Fig. 23.32. Thus a −4% grade means a fall of 4 feet in 100 feet horizontal distance.

23.31 VERTICAL CURVES. In lines of any considerable length a uniform grade cannot be maintained from end to end. Although two grade lines of different slope will intersect in a point, in actual construction they must be joined by a vertical curve in order to smooth out the otherwise abrupt change of direction which would be disastrous on highways and railroads. These vertical curves are usually laid out as parabolas in the following manner and as indicated in Fig. 23.35. Lay out on opposite sides of the point of intersection of the grade lines the same number of 10-, 25-, or 50-foot spaces. In practice both the length and number of these spaces are arbitrarily selected to suit the length of the curve and the nature of the work. The elevation of the end points E and D of the curve, Fig. 23.35, may be determined from the grade lines, and the elevation of the midpoint C of the line ED computed. The parabola passes halfway between A and C at B. With this point established, other points on the

parabola may be determined by the fact that the offset from the tangent to a parabola varies as the square of the distance along the tangent. The value of the offset at B being known, offsets at the other points may be computed as shown in Fig. 23.35.

23.32 HORIZONTAL CURVES. When railroads and highways change direction, the change is accomplished by means of circular curves that join the straight parts of the line which are called tangents. The curvature is specified in degrees, as for example, a 3-degree curve. A 3-degree curve is one on which a chord of 100 feet subtends an angle of 3 degrees at the center. Circular curves are joined to the tangent by an easement or spiral curve, but this spiral portion is not shown in the usual map. The radii of curves for various degrees is given in the Appendix.

23.33 LETTERING. Engineering maps, particularly those drawn to a large scale for the purpose of construction, are usually lettered in single-stroke Reinhardt letters, either slant or vertical, except the titles, which may be made in a more ornamental style. On geographic and United States Government maps, the lettering is in modern roman with certain variations designed for special purposes. A competent map draftsman must be a master of this style of lettering.

Although the lettering is about the last thing to be inked on a map, the placing of it must receive attention during the preliminary pencil work; otherwise, there will often be no place to put some very essential information when the work is nearing completion. As in all other types of drawing, lettering should be placed, as far as conditions will permit, so that it may be readable from the bottom and right-hand side of a drawing.

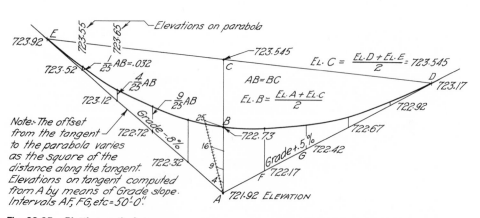

Fig. 23.35 Plotting vertical curves.

23.34   TITLES. The title of a map is usually placed in the lower right-hand corner, if possible. It should contain a statement of what the map is, that is, Plat of Jones Subdivision, the location of the ground, the name of the person or company for whom the map was made, the date of the survey, the scale, the north point, and the name or initials of the draftsman. The name of the surveyor may be in the title or it may occur only in a statement that certifies that the survey and map are correct. This statement and signature must be written. They are usually placed near the title but are not a part of it. The scale is frequently represented graphically below the title. In no case should the title be enclosed in a box.

On engineering maps Gothic letters are used; on the more highly finished maps the roman style is preferred.

23.35   NORTH POINTS. Every map should have the direction of the meridian indicated by means of a suitable arrow. Unless otherwise specified, this arrow points true north. The south portion of the arrow should be somewhat longer than the north portion to give it a balanced appearance. The barb and tail should be narrow and graceful, thus avoiding an arrow that is too bold or conspicuous. Sample arrows are shown in Fig. 23.36.

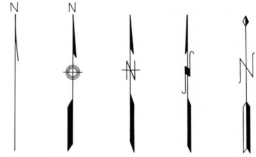

Fig. 23.36   North points.

SELF-STUDY QUESTIONS

Before trying to answer these questions, read the chapter carefully. Then, without reference to the text, answer as many questions as possible. For those that cannot be answered, the number, in parentheses following the question number, gives the article in which the answer can be found. Look it up and write down the answer. Check the answers that you did give to see that they are correct.

23.1 **(23.1)** When the area to be shown on a map is small, the map is essentially a one-view _____ projection.

23.2 **(23.3)** Maps that show large areas of the earth's surface are called _____ maps.

23.3 **(23.4)** Maps prepared by the U.S. Geological Survey are classed as _____ maps.

23.4 **(23.6)** Engineering maps are drawn for the purpose of _____.

23.5 **(23.6)** The scale of an engineering map is seldom smaller than one inch equals _____ _____.

23.6 **(23.7)** Many U.S. geological maps have a scale expressed as 1:_____.

23.7 **(23.7)** Large-scale Military Maps have a scale of 1:_____.

23.8 **(23.9)** On even large-scale engineering maps objects are shown by _____ rather than as true projections.

23.9 **(23.10)** The size of symbols should vary only _____ with the scale of the map.

23.10 **(23.12)** When topographic maps are drawn in color the following colors are used:

   (*a*) Water features _____

   (*b*) Contour and sand _____

   (*c*) Vegetation _____

   (*d*) Works of man _____

23.11 **(23.14)** All symbols that have a definite base line should have this line _____ to the bottom of the sheet.

23.12 **(23.16)** The azimuth of a line is the angle that a line makes with a north and south line measured _____ from the north.

23.13 **(23.16)** The bearing of a line is the acute angle that a line makes with a north and south line measured _____ from the north or south.

23.14 **(23.16)** The bearing angle is always _____ than 90°.

23.15 **(23.16)** A deflection angle in a survey is measured to the right or _____ of the _____.

23.16 **(23.18)** Angles may be plotted by the _____ method when great accuracy is not required.

23.17 **(23.19)** The tangent method of plotting angles requires the use of a table of _____.

23.18 **(23.23)** Differences in the elevation of the land can be shown on a map by _____ lines.

23.19 **(23.23)** When contour lines are close together the slope of the land surface is relatively _____.

23.20 **(23.23)** Contour lines _____ cross.

23.21 **(23.23)** Contour lines cannot _____ upon the edge of a still body of water.

23.22 **(23.28)** A profile is a line showing the _____ of the earth's surface along some specific line such as a railroad center line.

23.23 **(23.30)** Grade lines, for example, on highways, are specified as _____ when they go upward in the direction of the survey.

23.24 **(23.32)** When a roadway must change direction, this is accomplished by means of a _____ curve.

PROBLEMS

In the following problems, which have been selected to fit 8½ × 11 and 11 × 17″ paper, great care should be exercised in the layout of traverses and in plotting the artificial features and contour lines. With few exceptions, all plotted points fall within the border lines of the sheets specified. Since these are from older maps, the azimuth, when used, has been plotted from the south instead of north as is the case in more recent practice.

Without being specified it is assumed that the student will put in all necessary lettering in the proper size and style.

Notes and dimensions given in the sketches are not to appear on the finished map except the size of city lots. Symbols of proper size and color are to be used in all cases.

23.1 From the survey notes of Figs. 23.37 and 23.38, plot Map A. (Notes in these two figures read up the page.) Plot the traverse by the tangent method and have it checked by your instructor. When approved, plot the details by the protractor and scale method, using all information given in the sketches.

Plot the data for the contours from Figs. 23.39 and

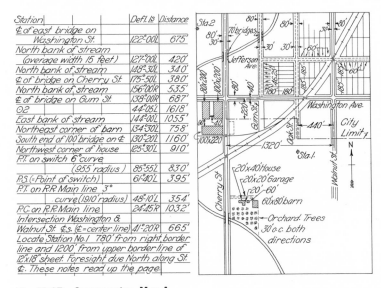

Station	Defl. ∠s	Distance
₵ of east bridge on Washington St.	122°00L	675'
North bank of stream (average width 15 feet)	127°00L	420'
North bank of stream	148°30L	340'
₵ of bridge on Cherry St.	175°50L	380'
North bank of stream	156°00R	535'
₵ of bridge on Gum St.	138°00R	687'
0.2	44°05L	1618'
East bank of stream	144°00L	1055'
Northeast corner of barn	134°30L	758'
South end of 100 bridge on ₵	130°20L	1160'
Northwest corner of house	125°30L	910'
P.T. on switch 6° curve (955' radius)	85°55L	830'
P.S. (=Point of switch)	61°40L	395'
P.T. on R.R. Main line 3° curve (1910' radius)	48°10L	354'
P.C. on R.R. Main line	24°45R	1032'
Intersection Washington & Walnut St. ₵s. (₵=center line)	41°20R	665'
Locate Station No.1 780' from right border line and 1200' from upper border line of 12"x18" sheet. Foresight due North along St. ₵. These notes read up the page		

Fig. 23.37   Survey notes, Map A.

Station	Defl. ∠s	Distance
Scale of map 1"=200'		
0.1	126°30L	1898'
West bank of stream	180°00L	775'
End of R.R. Switch	161°00L	563'
Northwest corner Bldg No.3.	152°00L	862'
West bank of stream	166°30L	514'
West bank of stream	136°30L	417'
Center of R.R. bridge	113°05L	556'
West bank of stream	97°15L	844'
West bank of stream	95°25L	1318'
₵ of R.R. Main line	5°00L	480'
0.3	109°20L	1669'
West shore of lake	45°00L	955'
East shore of lake	45°00L	438'
West shore of lake	51°32L	722'
East shore of lake	51°32L	480'
West bank of stream	60°00L	600'
East bank of stream	60°00L	555'
East bank of stream	89°15L	565'
₵ of west bridge on Washington St.	105°15L	762'
North bank at confluence of streams	113°05L	940'

Fig. 23.38   Survey notes, Map A.

23.40. (Note that these read down the page.) Draw the contour lines, interpolating where necessary. After the map has been checked, ink it in the proper colors. Scale 1″ = 200′ on 11 × 17 sheet.

23.2 Same as Problem 23.1. Use Figs. 23.41 to 23.44 for Map B. Scale, 1″ = 400′.

23.3 On an A-size sheet (8½ × 11 or 9 × 12) draw a map from the notes and sketches in Fig. 23.45. Observe again that the notes read up the page and that the azimuths are plotted from the south instead of north. Scale, 1″ = 400′.

23.4 On an A-size sheet (8½ × 11 or 9 × 12) draw the contour map from Fig. 23.46. The elevations have been given on a large grid for rapid plotting. Parts of a few contour lines have been sketched in as an aid. This contour map may be plotted on the map of Fig. 23.45 by properly locating the grid with reference to the section corner at the left in this figure.

23.5 On an A-size sheet draw the map from the notes and sketch of Fig. 23.47. Azimuths are again given from the south. Scale, 1″ = 400′.

Station	Azimuth	Obs.Dist.	Cor.Dist.	Vert.Angle	Diff.of Elev.	Elev.	
At Sta.1	Elev. 698.8 H.I. 4.6			K=100			
Shot 1	30°30'		1130			690.2	All stations on this traverse are
2	" "		1025			693.1	the same as those in the
3	" "		608			694.5	previous survey.
4	64°25'		1140			693.3	
5	" "		845			693.9	
6	" "		534			694.7	
7	90°00'		1383			693.5	Note:- The azimuth of any line
8	" "		1010			693.8	is the angle which the line
9	" "		490			696.4	makes with a north and south
10	119°15'		1308			693.6	line measured in a clockwise
11	" "		851			694.5	direction from the south.
12	142°05'		1035			693.6	
13	" "		570			696.0	
14	165°10'		1196			693.8	
15	" "		720			698.2	
16	" "		267			700.7	H.I. means height of
17	194°45'		1198			704.2	instrument
18	" "		793			705.3	
19	221°00'		1115			711.9	
20	" "		742			705.6	K is the stadia constant, a
21	240°00'		838			705.6	factor used in computations
22	" "		687			702.1	
23	305°00'		720			697.2	
Δ 2	35°55' H.I.4.7		1618			706.8	

The data in these columns have not been reproduced since they are not essential to plotting the map.

These notes to be read down the page.

Fig. 23.39 Topography notes, Map A.

Station	Azimuth	Obs.Dist	Cor.Dist	Vert.Angle	Diff.of Elev.	Elev.	
At Sta.2							
Shot 1	22°45'		940'			691.0	
2	" "		642'			692.7	
3	31°30'		500'			696.2	
4	46°40'		250'			701.1	Water level of lake 692.3
5	90°00'		358'			693.9	
6	" "		157'			701.3	
7	270°00'		617'			693.6	
8	" "		310'			700.8	
9	335°00'		251'			694.6	
10	" "		148'			698.9	
Δ 3	26°25'		1669'			697.2	
Shot 1	10°00'		520'			699.2	
2	66°50'		530'			706.2	
3	" "		259'			701.4	
4	37°45'		710'			700.6	
5	54°32'		1150'			694.6	
6	" "		512'			698.8	
7	171°05'		1122'			694.5	
8	182°09'		768'			696.0	
9	208°00'		597'			693.6	
10	249°03'		330'			693.4	
11	289°15'		629'			693.2	
12	305°55'		905'			696.1	
13	305°55'		468'			694.0	

Fig. 23.40 Topography notes, Map A.

Station			Defl. ∠s	Distance
West bank at confluence				
of north & south branches			128°30'R	1375'
North bank of south branch			83°45'R	730'
Center of highway bridge			58°30'R	680'
North bank of south branch			26°45'R	905'
West bank of north branch			40°30'L	1560'
South bank of north branch			120°30'L	2290'
North bank of south branch			8°30'R	1170'
⊙2			48°45'R	2700'
P.C. on R.R. line			137°40'R	2420'
P.C. on ₵ of highway			118°15'R	1495'
P.T. on R.R. line			85°00'R	1535'
₵ of R.R. line			7°20'L	1915'
⊙1			50°30'R	3040'
Center of highway bridge			180°00'R	250'
P.S. on R.R.			159°30'R	490'
P.T. on R.R. switch			128°45'R	940'
Southwest corner Bldg No.1			124°30'R	1005'
Northeast corner Bldg No.2			111°15'R	1365'
North bank of stream			107°00'R	550'
North bank of stream			94°45'R	940'
North bank of stream			139°00'L	400'
Locate Station 0, 400' from left and 1100'				
from top border line. Foresight north				
along section line which makes 30° with				
the left border line. Read notes up the page.				

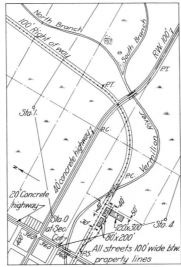

Fig. 23.41 Survey notes, Map B.

Station			Defl. ∠s	Distance
Scale of map 1"=400'				
⊙0			66°00'R	2380'
Southeast cor. bldg No.3			83°00'R	870'
Northeast cor. bldg No.3			90°00'R	1150'
South bank of river			97°00'R	1460'
Center of R.R. bridge			109°00'R	1235'
South bank of river			135°20'R	1022'
South bank of river			163°30'R	1314'
⊙4			56°15'R	3040'
South bank of river			78°00'R	1370'
South bank of river			101°00'R	1185'
Center of highway bridge			118°30'R	1220'
P.T. on ₵ of highway			160°30'R	625'
Section corner			142°40'L	985'
⊙3			94°15'R	2190'

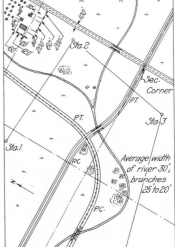

Fig. 23.42 Survey notes, Map B.

23.6 On an A-size sheet draw a topographic map from the data given in Fig. 23.48. Parts of a few contour lines have been shown as an aid in beginning. These contours may be plotted on the map of Fig. 23.47 by properly aligning the section corners at the right of the figure.

23.7 From the contour map of Problem 23.1, Map A, Figs. 23.37–23.48 draw the profile along the railroad or highway center line as specified by your instructor. Use a piece of profile paper 5″ wide and 15″ long. Rule a border ¾″ from the narrow left-hand end and ½″ from the other three edges. Horizontal scale same as

Station	Azimuth	Obs.Dist.	Cor.Dist.	Vert.Angle	Diff.of Elev.	Elevation
At Sta.0	Elev. 448.7	H.I. 4.7	K=98			
Shot 1	135°-40'	720				452.1
2	194°-30'	564				452.6
3	" "	1430				460.0
4	230°-30'	898				455.0
5	" "	1462				461.2
6	" "	1690				469.1
7	" "	2356				474.3
8	331°-30'	712				450.0
9	" "	1344				459.1
Δ1	230°-30'	H.I. 4.3	3040			478.2
10	16°-45'	1200				470.0
11	" "	2000				457.5
12	156°-15'	520				481.3
13	230°-20'	410				477.5
14	" "	1420				470.0
15	" "	2182				460.3
16	254°-15'	1955				462.5
17	" "	2456				470.0
18	296°-45'	984				473.9
19	" "	1714				460.0
20	337°-50'	720				475.0
21	" "	1440				471.8
22	" "	1749				465.0
Δ2	279°-15'	H.I. 4.6	2700			467.6

Notes (in Elevation column area):

Note:- The azimuth of a line is the angle which the line makes with a north and south line measured in a clockwise direction from the south.

Elevation at water line under highway bridge 447.4

Elevation at water line under railway bridge 452.5

The traverse of this survey is the same as that used in the preceding survey.

These notes read down the page.

Fig. 23.43 Topographic notes, Map B.

Station	Azimuth	Obs.Dist.	Cor.Dist.	Vert.Angle	Diff.of Elev.	Elevation
Shot 23	00°-00'	361				463.7
24	" "	1280				470.0
25	58°-30'	775				460.0
26	175°-00'	1889				472.0
27	201°-00'	508				472.4
28	" "	1020				480.0
29	243°-00'	750				473.8
30	264°-45'	834				466.2
31	284°-15'	1100				460.0
Δ3	13°-30'	H.I. 4.8	2190			472.8
32	58°-35'	1770				462.9
33	69°-15'	1715				457.1
34	121°-30'	320				468.6
35	" "	760				463.2
36	173°-40'	978				462.0
Δ4	69°-45'	H.I. 4.3	3040			462.1
37	16°-30'	354				465.0
38	" "	775				468.9
39	" "	1120				472.0
40	69°-20'	682				460.2
41	162°-30'	450				457.3
42	" "	1370				455.0
43	210°-00'	1835				458.4
44	221°-30'	1526				454.7
45	233°-00'	631				457.1

The data belonging in the empty columns have not been reproduced since they are not needed in plotting the map.

Elevation at water line under highway bridge 455.4

Fig. 23.44 Topographic notes, Map B.

map scale. Vertical scale to be selected by the student. This scale should be in units such as 5, 10, or 20 feet to the inch. Make the intersection of the left end of the railroad or highway line with the border line of your sheet Station No. 1. Stations are marked at 100-foot intervals.

23.8 Same as Problem 23.7, using Map B, Figs. 23.41 to 23.44.

23.9 Same as Problem 23.7, using Map C, Figs. 23.45 and 23.46. The length of profile paper required is $5 \times 12''$.

Station	Azimuth	Distance
⊙1 (check back for ∠ & distance	266°-0'	3485'-0"
West bank of stream	325°-30'	940'-0"
P.C. on highway ₵ (Rad.1000')	265°-30'	1245'-0"
₵ of 150' highway bridge	255°-50'	1020'-0"
Southeast corner of barn	197°-45'	1245'-0"
Southeast corner of house	188°-30'	1170'-0"
Intersection of highway ₵s	171°-50'	900'-0"
Northeast corner of house	135°-15'	534'-0"
Southwest corner of barn	108°-45'	610'-0"
⊙3	40°-30'	2945'-0"
Intersection of highway & R.R.₵s	91°-50'	2040'-0"
Northeast corner Bldg.No.1.	38°-0'	810'-0"
Southeast corner Bldg.No.2.	30°-30'	975'-0"
P.T. on R.R. switch (Rad.820')	28°-0'	836'-0"
P.R.C. on R.R. switch	359°-0'	635'-0"
P.S. on R.R. (Rad.820')	312°-45'	815'-0"
⊙2	142°-0'	2530'-0"
East bank of stream	168°-45'	1700'-0"
Intersection of highway & R.R.₵	168°-45'	1305'-0"
₵ of R.R. bridge (200' span)	155°-0'	1510'-0"
East bank of stream	142°-0'	1250'-0"
South bank of stream	104°-15'	430'-0"
P.T. on ₵ of highway (Rad.1000')	104°-15'	895'-0"
⊙1 Locate Sta.No.1 100 ft from right border line & 900 ft from lower border line.		

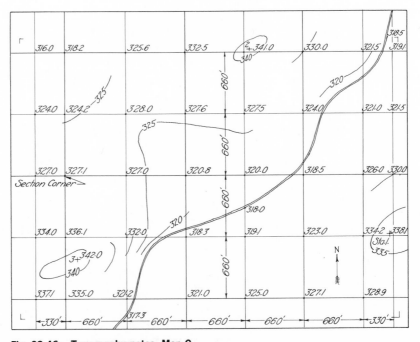

Fig. 23.45   Survey notes, Map C.

Fig. 23.46   Topography notes, Map C.

23.10 Same as Problem 23.7, using Map D, Figs. 23.47 and 23.48. Size of profile paper required 5 × 12″.

23.11 On the profile made as assigned from Problems 23.7 to 23.10, draw a grade line that will balance cut and fill as nearly as possible.

23.12 On an A-size sheet (8½ × 11 or 9 × 12) make a study of six assigned map symbols from Figs. 23.6 to 23.17. Enclose them in neatly balanced rectangles and letter under each the name of the symbol.

Station	Azimuth	Distance
O1 (check back ∠ & distance)	91°0′	3020′-0″
Section Corner	223°0′	575′-0″
P.T. on highway ₵ (1000′ Rad)	192°0′	432′-0″
P.C. on highway ₵	110°0′	569′-0″
₵ of 200′ highway bridge	84°0′	900′-0″
P.T. on highway ₵	67°30′	1775′-0″
East bank of stream	34°0′	1051′-0″
O3	348°30′	1640′-0″
Northwest corner of barn	298°30′	1215′-0″
Northwest corner Bldg No.2	310°45′	564′-0″
Southwest corner Bldg No.1	322°15′	695′-0″
R.R. ₵	110°0′	545′-0″
P.T. on R.R. switch	70°35′	1390′-0″
P.S. on R.R. switch (1200′ Rad)	72°05′	2010′-0″
North bank of stream	47°0′	1620′-0″
East bank of stream	30°0′	1580′-0″
O2	240°0′	3105′-0″
P.C. on highway ₵ (1000′ Rad)	321°0′	1230′-0″
Northwest corner of barn	311°10′	502′-0″
Northeast corner of barn	295°15′	780′-0″
South bank of stream	236°0′	985′-0″
₵ of 150′ R.R. bridge	214°0′	970′-0″
West bank of stream	180°0′	1060′-0″
West bank of stream	168°0′	1550′-0″
O1 Locate Sta No.1. 200′-0″ from left border line & 1200′-0″ from the lower border line		

Fig. 23.47   Survey notes, Map D.

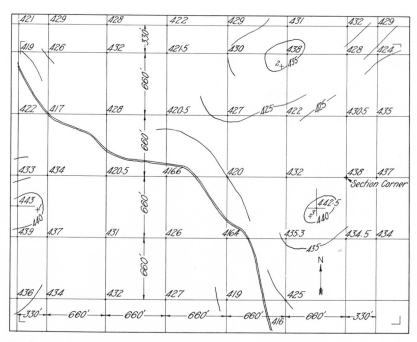

Fig. 23.48   Topography notes, Map D.

CHAPTER 24
Architectural Drawing

OLD: Mausoleum of Hadrian in ancient Rome. (New York Public Library Picture Collection)

NEW: New Madison Square Garden Center. (Courtesy of Madison Square Garden Center)

Chapter 24 Architectural Drawing*

24.1 INTRODUCTION. Architecture is the art and science of building and involves diverse types of structures. Many phases of engineering are integrated in building, construction, and design. These include electrical engineering for power, illumination, and communications; mechanical engineering for elevators, escalators, machinery, and power; and civil engineering for structural design, site planning, and services. Other fields of engineering must be considered for materials and methods, plumbing, heating, and ventilating. Every engineer will have occasion to use architectural drawings. An engineer may draw plans or write specifications for a building or some part of a building. Engineers have designed and built industrial buildings, multistoried structures, bridges, and power projects, whose architecture is good because of the forthright engineered solution of the building's purpose and structure. Architecture constantly changes and advances with progress in science and engineering.

A building is essentially a structural frame which meets certain space requirements and which will endure certain loading conditions. The designer of a building must understand human needs, space requirements, structural elements, form, scale, and proportion. This chapter is concerned with the working drawings or "plans" by which the architect conveys to the builder or contractor the necessary information to erect the complete structure. Building design, specifications, esthetics, and other aspects of architecture are beyond the scope of this book.

As stated elsewhere in this book, the fundamental principles underlying all projection drawing are the same. In general, architectural drawing is third-angle projection, although there are occasions when the first angle is used. Owing to the size of the building, practical sheet size, and the fact that a plan must be made for each floor, the architect cannot relate his views on one sheet as in a machine drawing in third-angle projection. Instead, he uses one plane at a time, placing it parallel to that part of the building which he wishes to show, and then projects upon it. Rather than project

directly from view to view as in machine drawing, the architect must resort to measurements that are made according to the rules of projection.

An architect's drawings may be divided into two general classes, namely, those that are used for study and consultation with clients and those by means of which the building is actually erected. The latter are called working drawings. The former are further subdivided into two classes called preliminary sketches and display drawings. The preliminary sketches are made by the architect for his own study of the problem and for use in discussion with his client; the display drawings represent the completed solution which the architect submits in competition or for public display.

24.2 PRELIMINARY SKETCHES. The draftsman begins his study of a problem by making freehand sketches embodying different ideas that occur to him. From these he selects what appears to be the best and works up a preliminary sketch in pencil to a small scale, say $\frac{1}{16}$ or $\frac{1}{8}$ inch to the foot, for presentation to his client. These sketches may include the main floor plans, an elevation, and a perspective. They are dimensioned for general sizes only and are sometimes embellished in such a way as to make them more attractive to the client. It is essential that they shall be easily understood, since frequently the person who is to inspect and approve them is not proficient at reading drawings. To this end, only the material that will show the general arrangement is included, and the details of construction are omitted. These drawings are often made on tracing paper so that comparison of different floor plans can be readily made by placing one over the other.

24.3 DISPLAY DRAWINGS. In some respects display drawings serve the same purpose as the preliminary sketches, since they make clear to others the general arrangement and appearance of the building. They are made to small scale, the exact choice depending on the size of the building and the desired size of the finished drawing. They usually include a front elevation, the main floor plans, and a perspective. They are rendered in pencil, ink, or water colors, or in a combination of these, and include, besides the building

*This chapter was prepared by Professor Wayne L. Shick, Registered Architect.

itself, some imaginary background, such as trees, shrubbery, gardens, and clouds, the whole drawing being a problem in art, designed to secure the most pleasing effect and to show the building to the best advantage.

An ordinary front elevation may be made quite realistic by projecting the shades and shadows on the building, by material indication, colors in various tones, and by putting in a foreground in parallel perspective.

Display drawings are not dimensioned, but the scale is represented graphically. They contain very little information that could be used by the builder.

24.4 WORKING DRAWINGS. The working drawings developed from the architect's sketches and display drawings are the ones in which the engineer is particularly interested. The purpose of such drawings is to provide information from which, with the written specifications, accurate estimates of cost can be made and the building constructed. They must, therefore, be accurately drawn to scale and include all necessary details and dimensions.

A complete set of working drawings, or set of plans, as they are sometimes called, will include the following six or more sheets: plot plan; basement or foundation plan; floor plans in order—first, second, third, and so on, not duplicating, of course, where the floors are exactly alike; four elevations, if all views of the building are different; sections, as many as may be required; and details, as many as may be required. In addition, large buildings frequently require separate sets of plans for the structural framing, whether it be of timber, steel, or reinforced concrete, and separate plans for the mechanical, electrical, plumbing, heating, and ventilating work.

24.5 PLOT PLANS. The first sheet of a complete set of plans is the plot plan. It shows the property lines and the relation of the proposed building to them. See Fig. 24.1. The building is sometimes represented by a crosshatched area whose shape is that of the outside of the structure at the grade line In addition, there should be shown the drainage sewers and water mains, utilities, walks and driveways, and any outbuildings to be constructed. If the building site is hilly, the elevations are shown by contour lines, and any grading that may be necessary is indicated. This sheet, like the others, contains in the lower right-hand corner the architect's standard title and, at some convenient place on the sheet, an arrow indicating the north point.

24.6 FLOOR PLANS. The floor plan of a building, instead of being a top view as in machine drawing, is in reality a horizontal section as seen from above. The horizontal cutting plane is passed so that it will show the most detail; it need not be a single continuous plane, but may be offset to different heights above the floor at various places. The plan will, therefore, show all openings in the walls in the story through which it it passed. See Figs. 24.2, 24.3 and 24.13. It will show interior walls and built-in features such as the plumbing fixtures, special cases, and cabinets. The location of heat outlets or ventilating ducts may also be shown, as well as the location of steam or hot-water radiators and their connecting lines where space must be provided for them by someone other than the heating contractor. The exact location of the water and drainage pipes for the plumbing is usually not shown on small jobs unless their location presents a problem the solution of which must be provided for in advance.

24.6.1 Stairways. Stairways are indicated by showing approximately one half of the full flight to the floors above and below and by marking upon the drawing the full number of risers. An illustration is shown in the floor plans in Figs. 24.2 and 24.3. Two consecutive floor plans show completely the stairway connecting them. Stairways are frequently worked out to a large scale in order to make sure that they will properly fit in the space allowed. A common rule for proportioning the risers and treads is to make the sum of one riser and one tread approximately 17 inches. Seven to eight inches is a maximum height for a comfortable riser.

24.6.2 Other items on a floor plan. In addition to the items discussed above, which would actually appear in a projection made strictly according to theory, it is customary to indicate certain features that would not appear by the rules of projection. For example, beams and ornamental features, which appear in the ceiling above the floor shown, are indicated on the floor plan. The lintels over wall openings are also indicated, although they are above the cutting plane. In small buildings not requiring separate framing plans, the supporting members for the floor above are shown on the plan of the floor below. Thus the beams or joists supporting the second floor would be indicated on the first-floor plan. This, of course, does not apply where a special set of framing plans is prepared. Ceiling lights and outlets are indicated in the same way, by locating them on the plan of the floor below. The precise location of the wiring is not given, unless openings must be

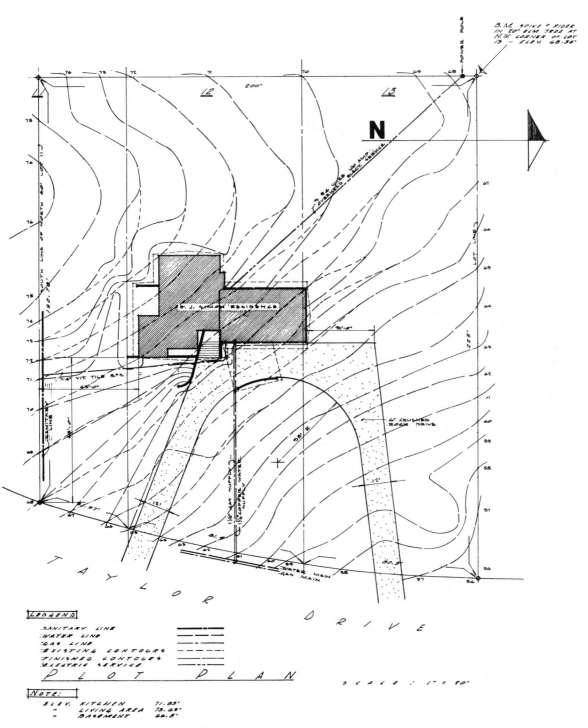

Fig. 24.1   Plot plan. (Courtesy Simon and Rettberg, Archs.)

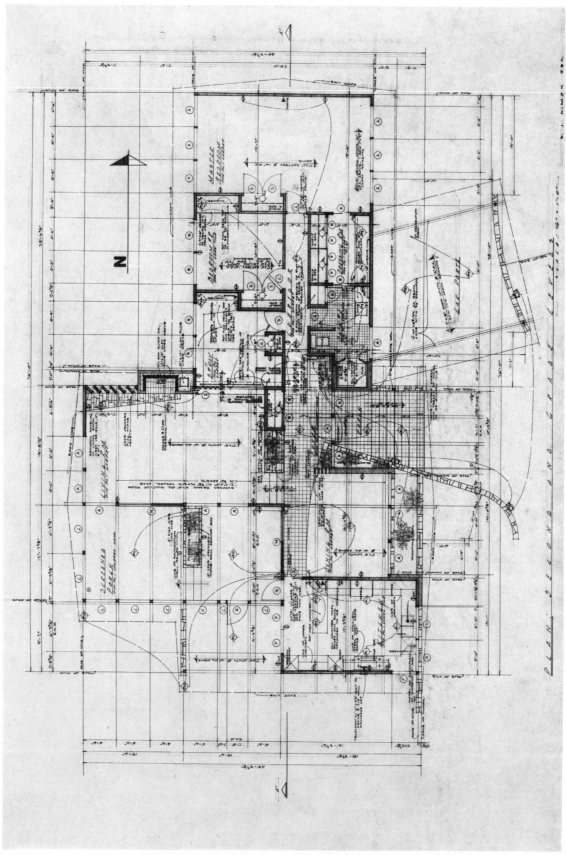

Fig. 24.2 Grade level and second-floor plan. (Courtesy Simon and Rettberg, Archs.)

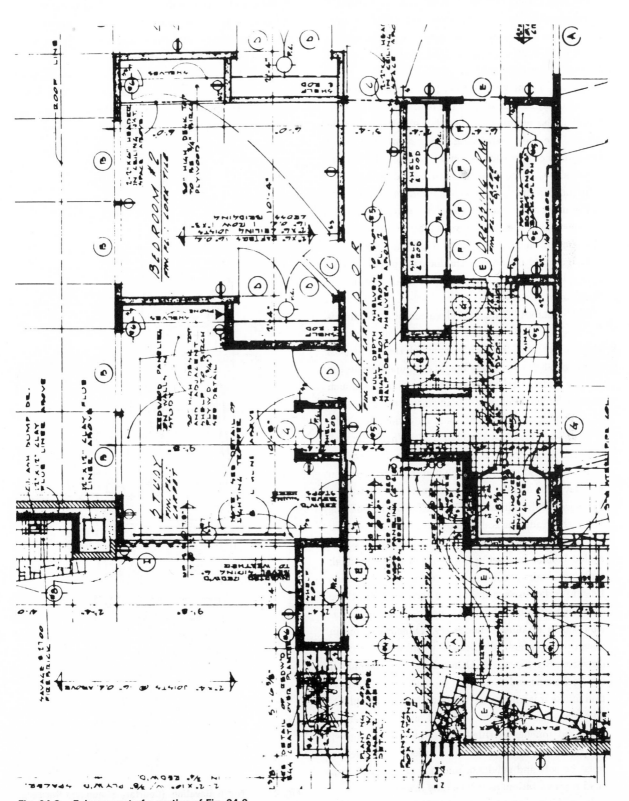

Fig. 24.3   Enlargement of a portion of Fig. 24.2.

allowed for it by others than those who do the wiring. In reinforced concrete and steel work, for example, holes must be provided where wiring conduits and pipes pass through floors or beams, as the cutting of holes after the concrete is poured and set might damage its structural value. For reasons of economy also, space for conduits, piping, and ventilating ducts must be provided in advance.

24.6.3   Position of the floor plan. It has become an established practice to draw the floor plans so that the front of the building is toward the bottom or right edge of the sheet, depending on the shape and size of the building. Elevations should read from the bottom of the sheet, or the right-hand edge in some instances.

In making the floor plans of a building that has several stories, time may be saved by tracing from the first-floor plan the outside walls and interior columns that run through from floor to floor. This also avoids the possibility of error in the location of columns or piers, elevator shafts, and the like, which must line up from story to story.

24.7   ELEVATIONS. The elevation of a building is a projection of the building upon a vertical plane perpendicular to the direction from which the elevation is seen, and shows the story heights, all openings in the outside walls, and the nature of the outside finish, such as wood, stone, brick, metal, and glass. Unless the sides of a building are identical, each elevation should be drawn; see Figs. 24.4 through 24.7. Where the wall material is erected in a certain pattern, the size, arrangement, and location of the material are shown on the elevation, and the exact construction is shown in a large-scale detail drawing. The outline of the building below the grade line is shown by invisible lines, as seen in Fig. 24.14, as are also roof lines which may be concealed behind parapet walls. On elevations of small buildings, stairways are sometimes drawn in invisible lines in order to save drawing a section. With these exceptions, the invisible line is not used on the elevation unless absolutely necessary. Dimensions on an elevation are practically limited to those in a vertical direction. See Fig. 24.14. Other dimensions belong on the floor plans and should not be placed on the elevation unless it is impossible to show them on the plans. The elevations are given life and snap by accented lines and touches of ruled-line rendering to suggest the texture of the surface. This ruled-line rendering must be soft and subdued, and not an attempt at a rigid representation, as in machine drawing.

In making elevations, the plan sheet is taped in

proper projection position, either beneath the tracing paper on which the elevation is to be drawn or at the top of the sheet, whichever is more convenient. Sometimes the elevation is drawn by reading the principal dimensions from the plan view, locating approximate window positions, and then drawing the windows in the best size, style, and arrangement on the elevation. The best fenestration is worked out by a coordinated study of the plan, elevations, and section. This coordinated study applies to the design and detailing of the entire building and its many parts.

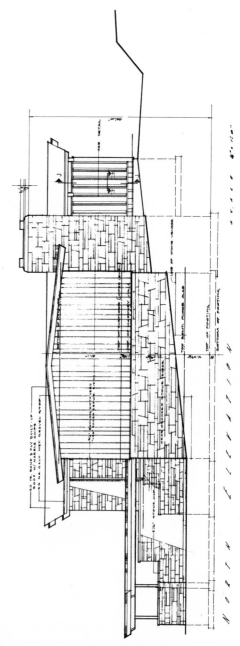

Fig. 24.4   North elevation. (Courtesy Simon and Rettberg, Archs.)

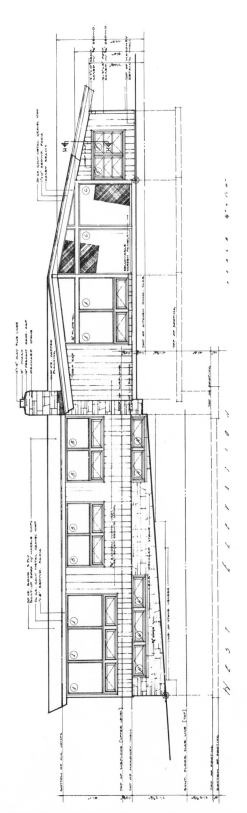

Fig. 24.5   West elevation. (Courtesy Simon and Rettberg, Archs.)

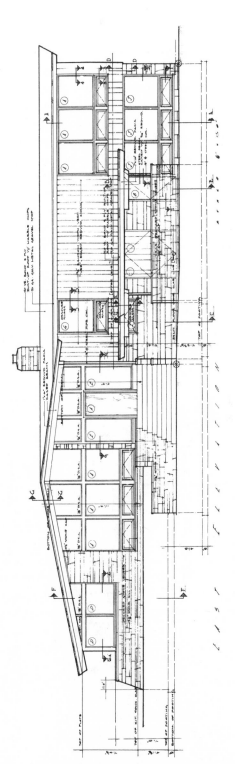

Fig. 24.6   East elevation. (Courtesy Simon and Rettberg, Archs.)

24.8 SECTIONS. The exact details of construction, different kinds of material, and the exact size and integrated placement of the materials are shown in cutaway drawings or sections. Sections cut across the narrow way of a building are called transverse sections, those cutting lengthwise are called longitudinal sections, as shown in Fig. 24.8. Other sections may be taken of parts of the building, showing with exactness the construction of the individual part and how it relates to the building. These sections are called detail sections, that is, a section of a foundation, a doorway, a fireplace, or stairway. The cutting plane for a section may be offset to take in the important features which it is desirable to show. The cutting plane may be shown edgewise on the floor plan by a heavy dash-and-dot line with arrows at the ends indicating the direction in which the view is taken. All parts cut by the plane are shown crosshatched in some characteristic way to represent the material, as shown in Fig.

24.15. All parts behind the cutting plane are shown in the usual way. Invisible lines are avoided.

24.9 STANDARD DETAILS. Many of the details and materials and methods used in building construction have been standardized. An entire building could be erected of materials that are standard, uniformly manufactured and specified by the manufacturer, and erected by standard practices. Such things as brick, tile, structural steel, windows, and doors are furnished in certain standard sizes and fabrications.

The most common uses of brick are as a structural load-bearing wall or partition, or an outer screen wall or veneer facing to a building that has some other structural framing. The brick may be used in a variety of patterns and bonds, and the brick wall may be united with the structure by metal anchors, lintels, and other connectors. Precast concrete slabs, stone, metal sheets, and other materials are also used to "skin" a building over a structural frame, using metal connectors of various kinds.

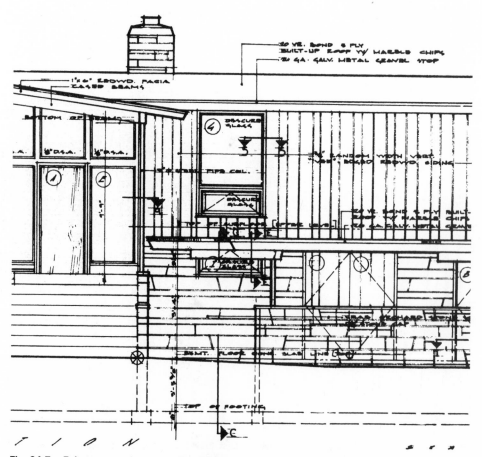

Fig. 24.7 Enlargement of a part of Fig. 24.6.

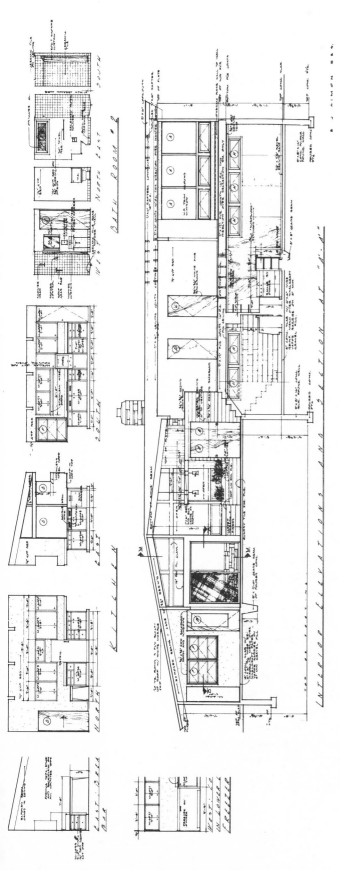

Fig. 24.8   Longitudinal section and details. (Courtesy Simon and Rettberg, Archs.)

a. *Brick.* Bricks may be obtained in several sizes, colors, and textures. Figure 24.9 illustrates two common types of bond, and some types of brick joints. Joints vary from ¼″ to 1″ thick usually by ⅛-″ increments.

b. *Tile.* The word tile applies to two distinct classes of material, namely, the large hollow blocks or building tile, and the smaller solid units used for floors and the covering of walls that are subject to moisture, acid, or other abusive conditions, particularly in kitchens and bathrooms. Tile is also widely used in schools, industrial plants, public buildings, etc. Both kinds may be obtained in standardized dimensions. Figure 24.10 illustrates common building tile sizes.

c. *Structural steel.* A few of the common sizes and dimensions of standard steel beams, channels, and angles are given in the tables in the Appendix. For complete information, consult the American Institute of Steel Construction (AISC) handbook.

d. *Metal sash.* Metal windows are made in stock sizes and are specified by numbers which have the meanings indicated in Fig. 24.11. The details of construction of one type of sash are shown at the left of this figure. See the Metal Window Institute for a complete listing of standard metal window sizes and types.

e. *Wood sash.* Wood windows and metal windows are manufactured in the same types, namely, the projecting or awning types, casement—that is, vertically pivoted; double-hung—that is, sliding up and down and horizontal sliding. Windows can be had in any size of fixed sash. A millwork manufacturer or lumber yard should be consulted for a catalogue of standard types and dimensions of wood sash. For large window openings, the opening is broken up into two, three, or more sashes, separated by a slender vertical member called a mullion. Figure 24.12 gives standard sizes for three types of wood windows.

f. *Doors.* Doors may be obtained in wood, metal, or flexible material types. Common metal and wood doors are manufactured in stock sizes from 1′-8″ to 3′-0″ wide by increments of 2″, and in 6′-6″, 6′-8″, and 7′-0″ heights. The thickness may be 1⅜″, 1¾″, or for very large doors 2¼″. Flush-panel doors having smooth flat faces are most commonly used, although doors paneled in various designs are available. Doors for large openings may be made up of several doors either hinged together or sliding on tracks, or they may be of a flexible folding type.

g. *Wood.* Wood is used in buildings in two ways, as a structural material and as a finish material. Structural lumber comes in several grades, the number 1 and number 2 grades being most commonly used. Lumber is available in lengths varying from 8-foot to 24-foot lengths by 2-foot increments. On special order longer boards can be obtained. The cross-sectional dimensions in greatest demand are 2″ × 4″, 2″ × 6″, 2″ × 8″, 2″ × 10″, and 2″ × 12″. These are nominal dimensions, the exact dimensions of lumber being ⅜″ less than the nominal dimensions up to 5″, and, for 6″ and larger, ½″ less than the nominal. For example: a 2″ × 4″ is actually 1⅝″ × 3⅝″ in cross section, and a 6″ × 8″ is 5½″ × 7½″. One exception is the 1″ board which is about $^{13}/_{16}$″ in thickness. As a finish material, wood is usually employed as boards 1″ ($^{13}/_{16}$″) thick, of various widths and lengths, and in several qualities from nearly perfect boards with no knots, checks, or other defects to the most imperfect of boards which may be used for some decorative effect. Wood can be processed into several other types of finish material such as plywood which comes in many thicknesses and sheet sizes.

24.10   DETAILS. Because of the small scale, it is impossible to show the exact construction of all parts of a building on any of the drawings just discussed. It is necessary, therefore, to draw typical details of all intricate parts of the building for which the construction is not self-evident or in accordance with standard practice. These details are made to a larger scale than the rest of the drawing and may vary from ½ inch to the foot up to full size, as shown in Fig. 24.15. It is quite evident that an architect cannot include everything that may need explanation, but his plans and specifications should embrace enough details to permit the making of an explicit contract. It would be manifestly unfair for him to insist upon some type of construction not fully shown in the plans and specifications, when the contractor had perhaps figured on some cheaper scheme. As the building operations proceed, however, the architect is required, from time to time, to furnish additional detail drawings, which must always be given a title showing clearly to what part of the building they apply.

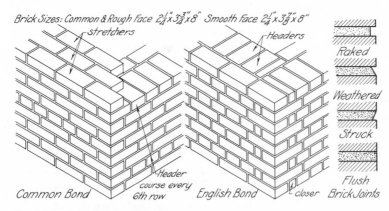

Fig. 24.9   Brick bonds and joints.

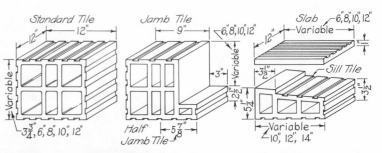

Fig. 24.10   Typical tile blocks.

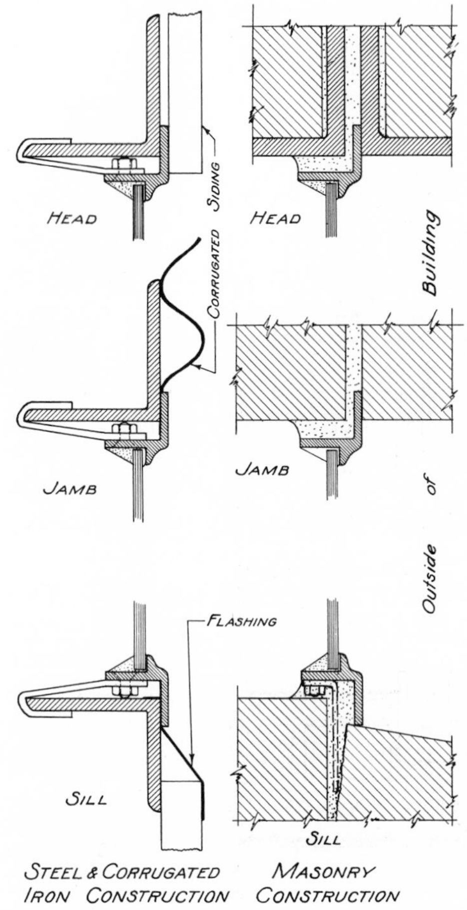
HEAD
SIDING
CORRUGATED
HEAD
Building
JAMB
JAMB
of
Outside
FLASHING
SILL
SILL
STEEL & CORRUGATED IRON CONSTRUCTION
MASONRY CONSTRUCTION

DIMENSIONS - METAL SASH

A TYPE - 20 × 16 BAR CENTERS
B TYPE - 22 × 16 BAR CENTERS

HEIGHT	WIDTH			
	1'-8$\frac{7}{8}$"	3'-8$\frac{7}{8}$"	5'-0$\frac{7}{8}$"	6'-8$\frac{7}{8}$"
2'-9"	A12	B22	A32	A42
4'-1"	A13	B23	A33	A43
5'-5"	A14	B24	A34	A44
6'-9"	A15	B25	A35	A45
8'-1"		B26	A36	A46
9'-5"		B27	A37	A47
10'-9"		B28	A38	A48
12'-1"		B29	A39	A49

MULTIPLE UNITS — OPENING WIDTHS: BAR CENTER DIMENSION (1'-8", 3'-8", 5'-0", 6'-8") TIMES NUMBER OF EACH UNIT, PLUS 4" FOR EACH MULLION, PLUS ONE BRICK JOINT

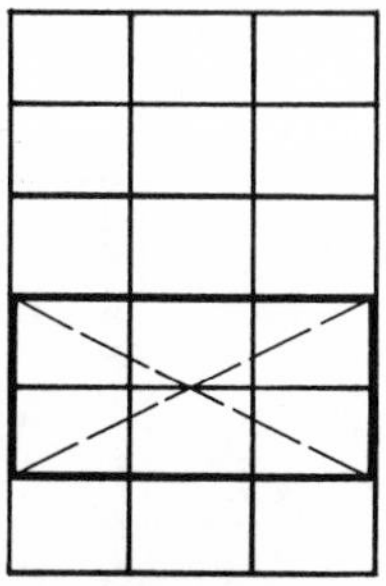

A36161
CODE FOR SASH NUMBERS
A-20×16
3-LIGHTS WIDE
6-LIGHTS HIGH
1-NO. VENTS.
6-LIGHTS IN VENT
1-LIGHTS UP TO VENT

Fig. 24.11 Steel sash details and dimensions.

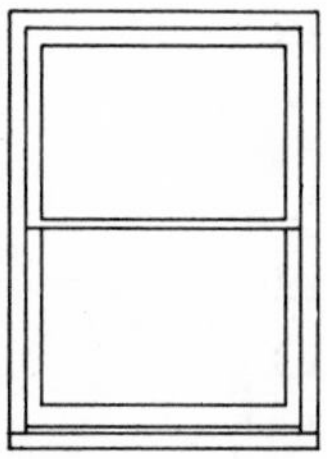

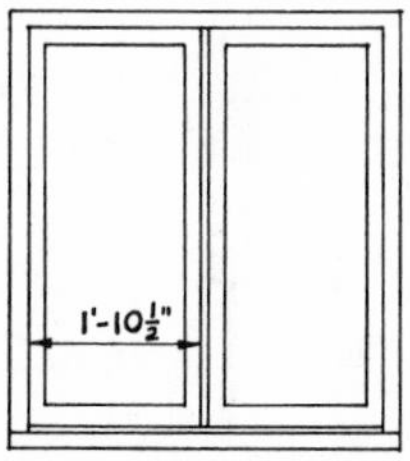
1'-10$\frac{1}{2}$"

DOUBLE HUNG

HEIGHT	WIDTH
2'-10"	1'-8"
3'-2"	2'-0"
3'-6"	2'-4"
3'-10"	2'-8"
4'-2"	3'-0"
4'-6"	3'-4"
4'-10"	3'-8"
5'-2"	
5'-6"	

ONE MANUFACTURER MAKES 54 STOCK SIZES OF LISTED DIMENSIONS~ MULLIONS ARE 3" WIDE~ MUNTINS IN SEVERAL STOCK PATTERNS

CASEMENT (2 SASH)

HEIGHT	WIDTH
2'-2"	1'-10$\frac{1}{2}$"
2'-8$\frac{3}{16}$"	3'-10$\frac{3}{4}$"
3'-2$\frac{3}{16}$"	5'-11"
4'-2$\frac{3}{8}$"	7'-11$\frac{1}{4}$"
5'-2$\frac{9}{16}$"	9'-11$\frac{1}{2}$"

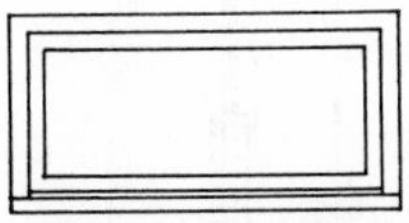

AWNING OR TRANSOM

HEIGHT	WIDTH
1'-0$\frac{1}{8}$"	2'-4$\frac{5}{8}$"
1'-4$\frac{1}{8}$"	3'-2"
1'-8$\frac{1}{8}$"	3'-10"
2'-0$\frac{1}{8}$"	

WOOD WINDOWS - SASH SIZES

ALL WINDOWS MAY BE COMBINED WITH FIXED SASH (PICTURE WINDOWS) OF MANY STOCK SIZES-

Fig. 24.12 Wood window details and dimensions.

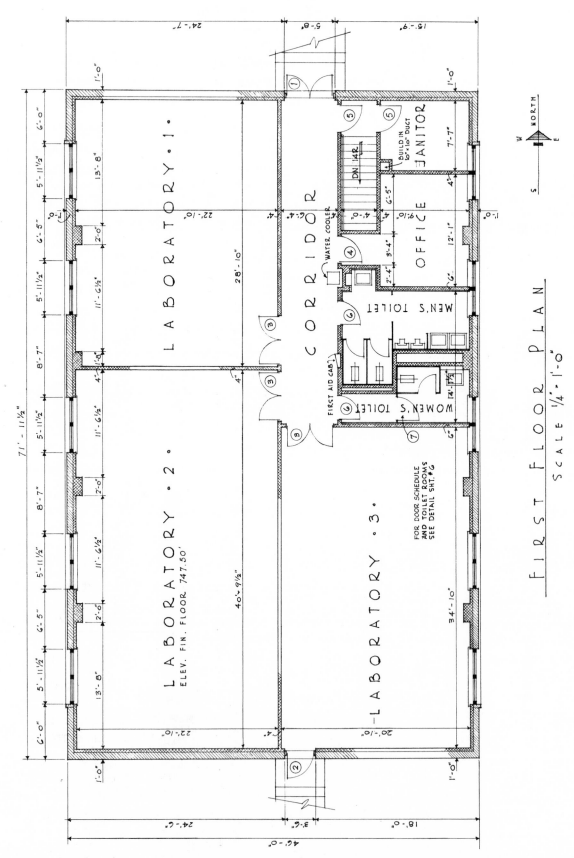

Fig. 24.13 First-floor plan.

The architect does not devise all the details that are shown in his plans but depends upon the manufacturers of the different products that go to make up a building to supply him with information concerning their products. Such information has been collected in a set of volumes, called *Sweet's Architectural File,* published annually. A similar file for engineers is also on the market. The progressive architect or engineer also keeps a file of the catalogues of all the manufacturers of materials in which he is interested.

24.11   DIMENSIONING. The common rules that apply to machine drawing hold in general for architectural drawing. However, it is more difficult to tell

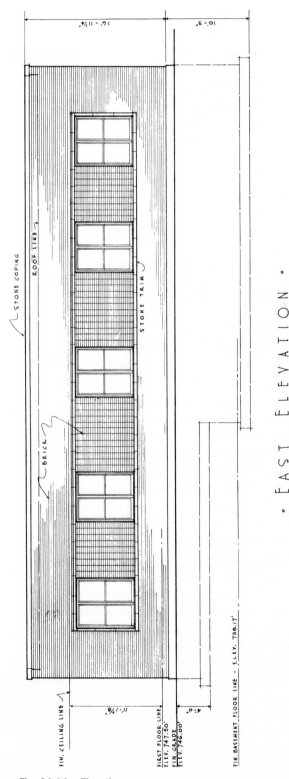

Fig. 24.14   Elevation.

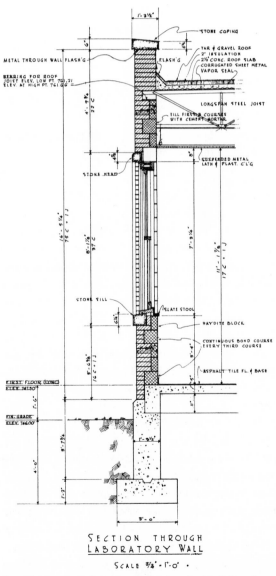

Fig. 24.15   Typical section through wall of building shown in Fig. 24.14.

what to dimension, as it is only by experience that one can learn which dimensions, of the many that might be given on a building plan, are of any value to the workman. The dimensions given must be clear, definite, and unmistakable. Moreover, they must check with one another from place to place and from plan to elevation. The inevitable variation in commercial sizes of material must be taken into consideration. This does not lessen the requirements for accuracy but demands an expert knowledge of building operations on the part of the architect. Several points to be observed in dimensioning are as follows:

a. Keep all outside dimension lines well away from the building lines. The nearest line should be about an inch away from the building line.
b. Dimension to center lines of interior walls or to the outside of walls, and then give the thickness also. Whenever possible, make a series of inside dimensions in one straight line clear across the building.
c. Dimension to the center lines of columns in both directions.
d. Dimension to the center lines of openings in outside walls, or to the sides of the opening, as required by the structural framing.

24.12   NOTES. More notes are used in architectural drawing than in any other branch of engineering drawing. If the meaning of a symbol is doubtful, it should be made clear by a note. When a part is detailed, a brief note, such as "See detail on sheet No. 11," should be placed on the floor or elevation drawings near the part detailed. Then under the detail itself there should be a title stating what it is, and a note referring back to the place where the parts may be found in the drawings. In addition to these notes, the sizes of doors, windows, beams, girders, lintels, columns, etc., must be given. These might be classified as dimensions, but since they do not appear in dimension lines it is better to call them notes.

24.13   SPECIFICATIONS. The contract documents in any architectural project are the agreement, the general conditions of the contract, the drawings, and specifications. The architect prepares specifications to accompany each set of plans. Specifications begin with general statements and conditions, and proceed in a systematic way to consider the work of various trades and materials involved in the construction of the building. The specifications cover those points of construction that cannot be shown in a drawing, namely, kind and quality of materials, manufac-

turer, type of finish, methods of construction, and in addition reemphasize such points as might be overlooked if the drawings alone were used.

The Federal Housing Authority has prepared a booklet on residential construction, *Minimum Property Requirements,* and a short-form type of specifications that are quite good for small-house work. *Architectural Specifications* by Sleeper, John Wiley & Sons, is a most comprehensive book on the subject, and the American Institute of Architects has prepared Specification Sheets as an aid in their writing. The specifications of individual manufacturers of building products and *Sweet's Architectural File* provide specific information.

24.14   SYMBOLS. Since the plans and elevations of working drawings are made to a scale of ¼ or ⅛ inch to the foot, certain conventional representations are employed. These conventions have been generally standardized, and the parts of the building represented by given symbols are specifically described either by detail drawings, notes, or specifications. Windows are commonly indicated by an opening in the wall the width of the sash, and lines representing the glass and sill. Swinging doors are shown by breaking the wall the width of the door, and drawing the door ajar with an arc for the swing of the door. See Figs. 24.2 and 24.3 and Fig. 24.16. Windows and doors are usually coded by a letter in a circle, each window or door of the same kind and size having the same letter as shown in Figs. 24.2 and 24.3. A chart or schedule of doors and of windows is then prepared describing each kind and size used in the building.

It is clear that the smaller the scale the simpler the symbol must become. A common fault of beginners is to make the symbol too large and cumbersome in proportion to the rest of the drawing. See Ramsey and Sleeper, *Architectural Graphic Standards,* for a comprehensive table of architectural indications. Equipment or material which is not standard or for which there is no definite symbol should be identified on the drawing by a noted circle or rectangle, and be explicitly described by note, detail, or specification in the drawings and specifications.

Various kinds of crosshatching indicate different materials as shown in Fig. 24.17. A key, showing the crosshatching and materials represented, may be placed on the drawing, particularly if the materials are uncommon and not generally recognizable. However, to one familiar with building plans and construction, crosshatchings commonly used are readily understood without such a key.

24.15   ELECTRICAL WIRING. The electric outlets and switches that control outlets are shown either on the floor plan, or upon a simplified tracing of the floor plan, in their approximate locations. A line between an outlet and a switch indicates control of the outlet by that switch, as shown in Figs. 24.2 and 24.3. This simplified type of electrical layout is generally used by architects. The type of service, method of wiring, number of circuits, types of fixtures, and other details are exactly described in the specifications. The precise

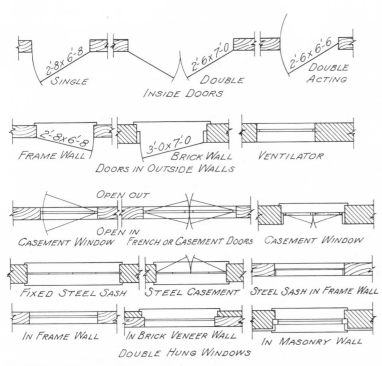

Fig. 24.16   **Window and door symbols.**

Building Material Symbols			
Material	In Plan	In Section	In Elevation
Brick			
Stone			
Concrete (stone)			
Concrete (cinder)			
Hollow Tile	Glazed	Glazed	
Terra cotta			
Marble			
Metal			
Wood			
Plaster	Metal Lath Wood Lath		
Insulation			
Earth	Rock	Cinders	

Fig. 24.17   **Standard material symbols.**

location of outlets, routing of wire and conduit, and the grouping of outlets into circuits can best be accomplished after the structural shell of the building has been erected. This on-the-job location is worked out by the electrical contractor under the supervision of the architect. Such procedure is economic of drafting time and costs, avoids conflicts between the drawing and the practical installation, and gives the contractor a clear picture of the outlets to be installed which with the specifications enables him to figure the contract cost. The National Electrical Code governs the method of wiring and circuit design. Electrical symbols used in building construction are shown in Table 38 in the Appendix.

For buildings that are repeated many times, such as identical units in a housing project or prefabricated houses, or for very large structures in which duct and pipe spaces must be provided for wiring, the electrical layout problem should be integrated with the plan and the structural drawings. In such cases, it may be economical to predetermine the exact location of outlets, wiring, and the grouping of outlets into circuits. Even so, under practical installation difficulties, and unforseen conditions, changes or deviations from the electrical layout will be made. A meticulous electrical design and layout could be made for any building, but this should be done only when it is a practical and economical procedure.

24.16 TITLES. Architectural titles are usually placed in the lower right-hand corner of the sheet, although occasionally one will find a drawing whose title has been put in some other place. The style of lettering usually employed is a single-stroke, free imitation of the roman. The title generally displays the name of the architect, or firm of architects, rather prominently. The name of the building, if public, or the name of the owner, is also given prominence in the title. The contract number, the sheet number, the scale, the names of the draftsman, tracer, and checker, and the approval signature of the architect are also included. The same general title is placed on each sheet, with a change, of course, in the sheet number and other de-

tails where necessary. Other information concerning the drawing on the sheet is placed below the views, as, for example, First-Floor Plan, East Elevation, etc., and not in the title space itself.

24.17 TECHNIQUE. The technique of architectural drawing is similar in many respects to that of machine drawing. Visible outlines, such as walls, beams, and columns, are made heavier than center lines, dimension lines, and crosshatching. All lines should be lighter than those generally used in a first-class machine drawing in order to show adequately the many small details. Contrast between the weights of lines will give the drawings a vigorous and workmanlike appearance.

There is, however, a little greater freedom in the architect's technique, by which he gives expression and life to the drawing, than is permissible in other fields of drawing, although greater freedom does not mean less accuracy. The overunning of corners is a common practice not found in other engineering drawings, and, though it may speed up the work somewhat, care should be exercised not to overrun where confusion might result.

On elevations, accent lines and ruled-line rendering are used for embellishment of the drawing. There are also many details that the architect must put in freehand. These give character to the work, and produce an effect that is entirely different from the hard and rigid appearance of machine drawings. These elements, together with the greater freedom in the style of lettering, constitute the chief differences between the technique of architectural and machine drawing.

24.18 LETTERING. The architect must employ his knowledge of lettering in two ways: first, in the lettering of his drawings, titles, and the like; and second, in the design of inscriptions and display or sign lettering. Such lettering constitutes a problem in design with which the engineer is not concerned. On working drawings, single-stroke modification of the roman alphabet is used for titles and subtitles; the single-stroke Gothic is most frequently employed for notes.

SELF-STUDY QUESTIONS

Before trying to answer these questions, read the chapter carefully. Then, without reference to the text, answer as many questions as possible. For those that cannot be answered, the number, in parentheses following the question number, gives the article in which the answer can be found. Look it up and write down the answer. Check the answers that you did give to see that they are correct.

24.1 **(24.1)** Architectural drawings may be divided into two main groups: those that are used for _____

and those that are used for _____ .

24.2 **(24.2)** The first drawing made by the architect is called a _____ _____ .

24.3 **(24.2)** The first drawing is made to a _____ scale.

24.4 **(24.3)** A well-rendered drawing made for the purpose of explaining or selling the idea is called a

_____ _____ .

24.5 **(24.4)** A drawing from which the building can be constructed is called a _____ drawing.

24.6 **(24.4)** The drawings for construction purposes shall include basement and foundation plans and

_____ plans and elevations.

24.7 **(24.5)** The plot plan should include the _____ lines and the relation of the building to them.

24.8 **(24.6)** The floor plan shall show all exterior and interior walls and _____ in them.

24.9 **(24.6.3)** The floor plan is drawn with the _____ of the building toward the bottom of the sheet.

24.10 **(24.6.1)** The floor plans indicate a stairway by showing the _____ of the risers to the next floor

above and below.

24.11 **(24.6.1)** The risers of a stairway should be approximately _____ inches.

24.12 **(24.6)** The floor plan is really a _____ section as seen from above.

24.13 **(24.7)** An exterior view of a building projected on a vertical plane is called an _____ .

24.14 **(24.7)** The elevation shows the story _____ and all _____ in the outside wall.

24.15 **(24.7)** When stairways are shown in an elevation they should be in _____ lines.

24.16 **(24.7)** The outline of a building below grade should show on an elevation in _____ lines.

24.17 **(24.7)** The elevation usually shows only _____ dimensions.

24.18 **(24.7)** Other dimensions are shown on the _____ _____ .

24.19 **(24.8)** Sections cut across the narrow way of the building are called _____ sections.

24.20 **(24.8)** Sections cut lengthwise of the building are called _____ sections.

24.21 **(24.8)** Sections may be _____ to show important details.

24.22 **(24.8)** The location of a section may be shown on the _____ plan.

24.23 **(24.9)** In wood the actual size is three-eighths inch _____ than the nominal size when under

five inches.

24.24 **(24.10)** A detail drawing is made to a _____ scale.

24.25 **(24.10)** Detail drawings are made of those parts where the _____ is not self-evident.

24.26 **(24.10)** Many details may be obtained from Sweet's _____ Index or File.

24.27 **(24.11)** Outside dimensions should be _____ away from the building line.

24.28 **(24.11)** Dimensions should be given to the _____ line of interior walls.

24.29 **(24.11)** Columns should be dimensioned to their _____ line.

24.30 **(24.13)** Points of construction, such as quality of workmanship and finish of materials, that cannot be shown on a drawing are covered by _____ .

24.31 **(24.14)** Show the symbol for a window in a frame wall by a sketch.

24.32 **(24.14)** Show the symbol for a single swinging door by a sketch.

24.33 **(24.14)** Show the symbol for concrete by a sketch.

24.34 **(24.15)** The electrical _____ and switches are shown on the _____ plan.

PROBLEMS

The plans in Figs. 24.18 to 24.31 show all walls, doors openings, and rooms (some windows and prominent elements are also shown). Other plans may be selected from magazines and books, or a plan may be originally designed. Some variations have been suggested, and the student may develop and modify any particular plan to suit individual needs. Locate and determine the size of windows, built-in features, and other details. Select materials for construction, walls, and partitions. Determine the type of roof, whether flat, shed, gable, or hip. Locate electric outlets, plumbing fixtures, heating, etc., as required. Some details of construction can be worked out by inspection of the building shown in this chapter, and by information from reference books. Select the scale and sheet size to be used for each problem.

Fig. 24-18 Perspective of store. The building may be modified by different arrangements of interior partitions and by changing display space, counters, windows, and doors. The plan will vary with the type of store. From first to second floor is 12′ 0″; second-floor ceiling height is 9′ 0″. The first floor is 4″ reinforced concrete on 12″ fill. The second floor will support 80 lb per sq ft. Outside walls are 13″ thick. See Fig. 25.47 for truss and roof details. Heat is supplied from outside sources.

Each of the following problems may be applied to any one of the buildings shown in Figs. 24.18 to 24.31.

24.1 Draw the floor plan (or plans).

24.2 Draw the foundation or basement plan.

24.3 Draw a vertical section through the outside wall, roof, and foundation.

24.4 Draw one to four elevations, as assigned.

24.5 Draw four interior elevations and a plan of a selected room.

24.6 Draw a detail of some part of the building, such as fireplace, doorway, stairway, or counter and sections or elevations as needed.

24.7 Draw a transverse section through the entire building.

24.8 Draw the plot plan for the building.

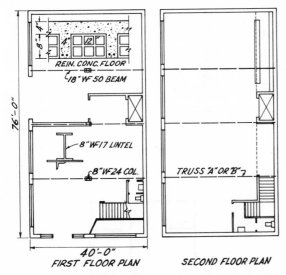

Fig. 24.19 First- and second-floor plans of store shown in Fig. 24.18. The interior of the building may be divided by nonbearing partitions into desired spaces, that is, washroom, office, stockroom, salesroom, etc.

Fig. 24.20 Perspective of factory. Walls of masonry, concrete, or metal panels over masonry. Wall footings are reinforced concrete 2′ 0″ wide and 12″ deep. Column footings are 3′ 0″ square and 15″ deep. The gable end may have truck doors on each side with a large window in the middle. The monitor on top of the building may be extended the full length, or it may be omitted. See Fig. 25.48 for steel framing.

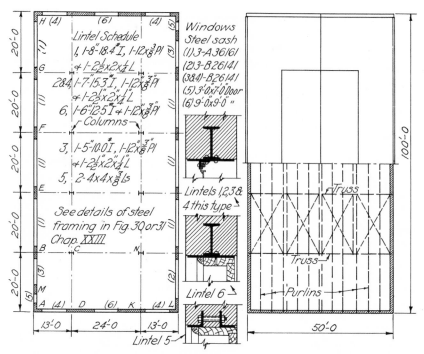

Lintel Schedule
1, 1-8"-18.4# I, 1-12x3/8 Pl
+ 1-2 1/2"x2x1/4 L
2&4, 1-7"-15.3 I, 1-12x3/8 Pl
+ 1-2 1/2"x2x1/4 L
6, 1-6"-12.5 I + 1-12x3/8 Pl
—— Columns ——
3, 1-5"-10.0 I, 1-12x3/8 Pl
+ 1-2 1/2"x2x1/4 L
5, 2-4x4x3/8 Ls

See details of steel
framing in Fig. 30 or 31
Chap. XXIII

Windows
Steel sash
(1) 3-A 36161
(2) 3-B 26141
(3&4) B 26141
(5) 3'-0"x7'-0" Door
(6) 9'-0"x9'-0"

Lintels 1,2,3 &
4 this type

Lintel 6

Lintel 5

Truss

Truss

Purlins

20'-0
20'-0
20'-0
20'-0
20'-0

13'-0   24'-0   13'-0

100'-0

50'-0

Fig. 24.21   Floor plans of factory shown in Fig. 24.20.

Fig. 24.22   First-floor plan of a two-story residence with basement. 30' 0" x 72' 0".

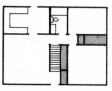

Fig. 24.25   Floor plan of a one and one-half or two-story house with basement. 26' 0" x 36' 0".

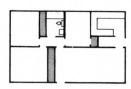

Fig. 24.23   Floor plan of a one-story development house. 24' 0" x 40' 0".

Fig. 24.26   Floor plan of a two-story house with basement. 27' 0" x 33' 0".

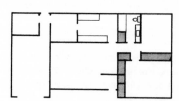

Fig. 24.24   Floor plan of a two-bedroom house. 28' 0" x 56' 0".

Fig. 24.27   Floor plan of a six-room house with basement. 32' 0" x 68' 0". Furniture and interior decoration should be considered. Minimum ceiling height is 10' 0".

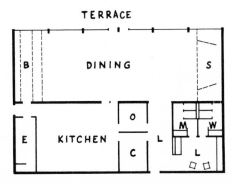

Fig. 24.28   Floor plan of a restaurant or cafe. The building may serve various types of business. Ceiling height is 12′ 0″ for large spaces.

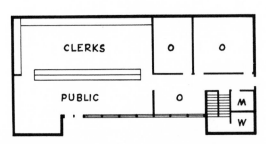

Fig. 24.29   Floor plan of a small office building. 40′ 0″ x 84′ 0″.

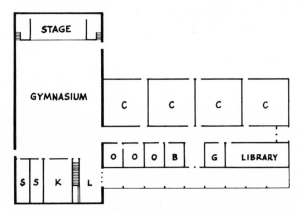

Fig. 24.30   Floor plan of a school. 128′ 0″ x 188′ 0″. The gymnasium truss is 6′ 0″ deep and clears the floor by 24′ 0″. Roof structure over classrooms is 2′ 0″ deep. Ceiling height in all rooms but gymnasium is a minimum of 10′ 0″.

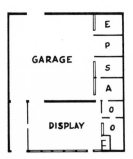

Fig. 24.31   Floor plan of a garage with salesroom. Ceiling height in garage and sales room is 14′ 0″ minimum. Smaller spaces have 9′ 0″ ceilings. Trusses in garage portion average 6′ 0″ deep.

CHAPTER 25
Structural Drawing

OLD: Covered bridge at Brattleboro, Vermont. (Philip Gendreau)

NEW: Golden Gate Bridge, San Francisco, California. (Philip Gendreau)

Chapter 25   Structural Drawing

25.1   INTRODUCTION. Structural drawing includes all layout and detail drawings connected with the design and construction of buildings, bridges, viaducts, and similar structures in which structural steel, timber, concrete, and other building materials are used. Certain standard practices and conventions have been developed in this field of drafting quite unlike those prevailing in machine drawing, although merging somewhat with those found in architectural drawing.

Steel and reinforced-concrete structures are treated here from the drafting viewpoint only. No attempt is made to deal with engineering design of any structure, but the information gained in studying methods of framing, clearances required, and the technical terminology forms an excellent basis for later design courses.

Although a sufficient number of tables are given in the Appendix to solve the problems of this chapter, it is desirable that the student have access to the *Steel Construction Manual* of the American Institute of Steel Construction.

25.2   DEFINITION OF TERMS. In order that the meaning of certain terms used in the later portions of this chapter may be clear, a glossary of the more common terms used in structural work is given below. Where the term member is used in these definitions,

a unit part of some larger structure is meant. This unit part itself may be constructed of numerous pieces of steel, but it functions as a single piece and is designated as such. Thus any part of a structural framework, such as a floor beam or post in a steel bridge, may be spoken of as a member of that particular structure.

Definitions of Common Terms Used in Structural Drafting Rooms and Fabricating Plants

Batten Plate. A small plate used near the ends of built-up members to hold two parts of any member in their proper position. See Fig. 25.1.

Bay. The space between two consecutive sets or tiers of columns and beams, or columns and trusses. See Fig. 25.2.

Bent. A vertical framework, usually columns and beams supporting other members. In Fig. 25.2, the truss and two columns supporting it constitute a bent. Figure 25.3 shows a bent as used in railroad trestles or on viaducts.

Cantilever. A beam, girder, or truss in which one end or both ends project beyond the supports.

Chord. The top or bottom members of a truss. See Fig. 25.2.

Clearance. The space left between members to allow for the slight inaccuracies of cutting, and also to facilitate erection. See Fig. 25.4.

Clip angle. A small angle used to fasten light connections. See angles on top chord of truss in Fig. 25.33.

Column. A vertical compression member, usually supporting beams and girders. See Fig. 25.2.

Cope. To cut out a part of the top or bottom flange of a beam or channel so that it may fit another. See Fig. 25.4.

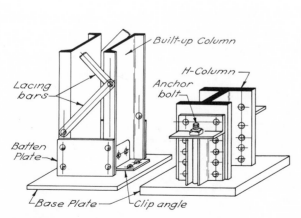

Fig. 25.1   Column bases.

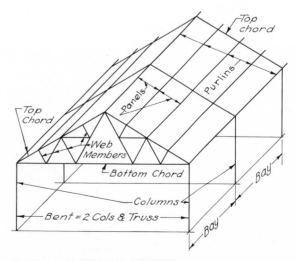

Fig. 25.2   Line diagram, mill building.

Cover plate. A plate riveted to the flanges of a compression member to give it greater area. The plates on the top flange of a plate girder are perhaps the most common examples. See Fig. 25.5.

Filler plate. A plate used to fill in empty spaces through which rivets must pass, as, for example, under stiffeners on a plate girder. See Fig. 25.5.

Flange. The top and bottom projection or outstanding parts of a beam, channel, or girder. See Figs. 25.4 and 25.5.

Gage line. The line along which rivet holes are punched in structural members. See Fig. 25.4.

Girder. A member designed to carry bending stress, usually supporting other members. Figure 25.5 shows one end and a section of a girder.

Gusset plate. A plate connecting the several members of a truss or other structural framework. See Fig. 25.4.

Lattice bar or lacing bar. One of a series of short diagonal bars used to connect the several parts of a member. See Fig. 25.1.

Lintel. A structural member designed to carry the wall over a window, door, or other opening. See Fig. 25.6.

Panel. The space between two purlins in a roof or between two vertical members in a bridge truss. See Fig. 25.2.

Pitch. The ratio of the height of a gabled roof to its width.

Purlin. The horizontal members spanning from truss to truss, upon which the roof is carried. See Fig. 25.2.

Stiffener. An angle riveted to a plate to prevent it from buckling. See Fig. 25.5.

Truss. A steel framework whose members take only tension or compression stresses. See Figs. 25.2 and 25.33.

Web. The portion of an I-beam, channel, or girder, between the upper and lower flanges. See Figs. 25.4 and 25.5.

Web member. The members of a truss between the top and bottom chords. See Fig. 25.2.

25.3   NUMBER AND LOCATION OF VIEWS. As in machine drawing, third-quadrant projections are used entirely, and two or three views of an object are drawn, as may be required. The top view appears above the front view, and the end view to the right or left of the front view. If the top member is inclined, the top view will be an auxiliary projection rather than a projection on the horizontal plane, as, for example, the top chord of the truss in Fig. 25.33. Frequently, however, for very simple pieces, only one view is necessary, since the shapes of the pieces in the other direction are known to have a certain standard form. In blocking out the views, care should be taken to allow ample

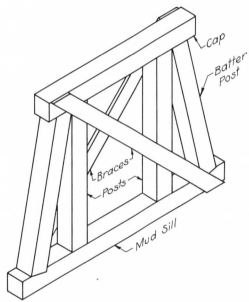

Fig. 25.3   Railroad trestle bent.

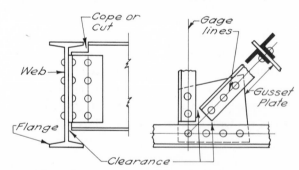

Fig. 25.4   Structural steel riveted connections.

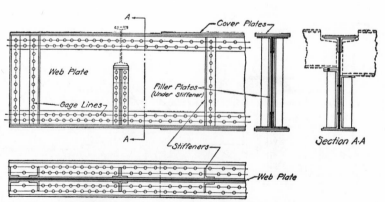

Fig. 25.5   Plate girder.

space for dimensions, more space being required between views for this purpose than is ordinarily necessary in machine drawing.

25.4   BOTTOM VIEW. In addition to the usual three views, it is frequently necessary to show a bottom view of structural members. In structural drafting, such a bottom view is made as a horizontal section looking down, instead of the regular bottom view, such as would be made in machine drawing. The horizontal cutting plane is passed to show as little other detail beside the bottom members as possible. An illustration of this practice is shown in Figs. 25.5 and

25.33. The purpose of this practice is to show the front and back details of a girder, for instance, on the same side of the horizontal center lines in both the top and bottom views. This arrangement shows their actual relation to each other better than if a theoretical bottom view were taken.

25.5   DETAILS. In machine drawing it is customary, in making a detail working drawing to separate the parts of a machine and detail them individually, whereas in structural drafting the opposite may be said to be the common practice. In other words, all the parts of a member are detailed as far as possible in the place they occupy in the structure. For example, the members of an ordinary roof truss are detailed in their proper places in the truss, as are the parts of a plate girder, or the large posts and chords of a bridge. That is to say, beams and girders are detailed horizontally on the sheet, and columns are detailed vertically, unless they are too long to be placed in that position, in which case the bottom end is placed at the left of the sheet and the column detailed horizontally. Inclined or sloping members are sometimes detailed in the position which they occupy, as indicated in Fig. 25.7. When

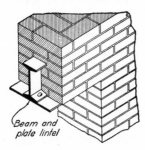

Fig. 25.6   Steel lintel.

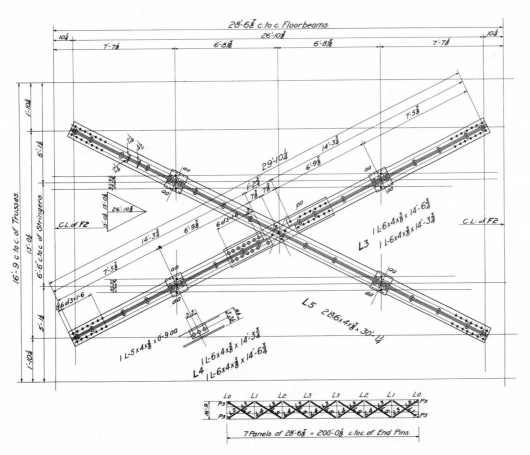

Fig. 25.7   Wind bracing and erection diagram.

they cannot be conveniently detailed in this manner, they are placed horizontally in the position in which they would fall.

If the member detailed is a part of a larger structure, its position in the completed structure is shown by a heavy line in a small sketch on the sheet, as in Fig. 25.7. This holds true for all except plain building work. When connections occur in building work upon the detailing of which other framing depends, sketches are made showing the member connecting with the one detailed, in order to work out dimensions. Connecting members are not shown on the final shop drawing.

25.6   SCALES. Structural drawing differs from machine drawing again in that on simple pieces the drawing is not scaled in one direction. Thus, in Fig. 25.8, the end view is made to scale in both directions and the other view is likewise to scale in all dimensions except the overall length. The details at the ends are made to scale lengthwise, but the total length is not. In machine drawing a break is indicated across a figure that is shortened in this manner, but in structural drawing it is not customary to do this. See Fig. 25.8.

When beams are of the same size and vary only in lengthwise dimensions, the same drawing may be used for several beams by putting on a set of dimensions for each beam as shown in Fig. 25.8. Many companies have printed forms showing the front, top, bottom, and end views of a beam, or any combination of these views which best suits their purpose. On these sheets it is only necessary for the draftsman to put in the details and dimensions.

In structural drawing the architect's scales are the only ones employed. They range from ¼″ = 1′-0″ for framing plans, to 3″ = 1′-0″ for the layout of joints. Almost any combination between these limits may be

used. The more common ones, however, are ¾″ = 1′-0″ and 1″ = 1′-0″.

25.7   SYMMETRICAL MEMBERS. If large members such as trusses and plate girders are symmetrical about a center line perpendicular to their longest dimension, only one half is detailed. It is the standard practice to show the left half when looking toward the side having the principal connections. For a railroad plate girder, this requires that the inside left end of the far girder be shown as the front view. Figure 25.33 illustrates this for a roof truss. As may be noted, the detail should be carried far enough past the center line to show any variation that may occur at the center. In no case should the detail be stopped exactly on the center line, even though there may be no variation beyond. The member should be broken off beyond the center by a ragged or wavy line, or the lines of the drawing may be simply stopped at the same place. The wavy line should be drawn only where there are members actually broken off and not through the space between members.

25.8   SECTIONAL VIEWS. Sections are frequently necessary in structural drawing and may be made in the positions occupied by end views or interpolated sections in machine drawing. When several sections of the same piece are necessary, these may be put in convenient places on the sheet and noted as sections taken at some particular plane, for example, Section AA. The place where this section is taken is then indicated on the drawing by a line AA, with arrows on the end of it to indicate the direction of sight, as in Fig. 25.5. Standard practice as regards crosshatching is also shown in Fig. 25.5. The main part of the member cut is usually made solid black, although cross-section lines may be used. Filler plates, stiffeners, etc., need not be cross-sectioned.

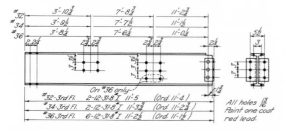

Fig. 25.8   Details for a series of beams.

Fig. 25.9   Structural rolled sections.

25.9   STANDARD DETAILS. Through long years of practice and experience, certain details of steel construction have become standardized. The draftsman and detailer should adhere to these standard details unless it is impossible to do so, or unless some particular advantage is to be gained by departing therefrom. Some of the more important and common standards are discussed in the following paragraphs.

25.10   STANDARD STRUCTURAL SHAPES. The shape, dimensions, and consequently the weight of structural sections are thoroughly standardized, and the general dimensions of the more common pieces should be familiar to the draftsman. Figure 25.9 shows cross sections of the more common shapes, the sizes of which vary through a wide range although the general proportions remain about the same. Thus I-beams may be obtained in sizes from 3 to 36 inches in height, and for each height there are a number of standard weights. The *Steel Construction Manual* lists all of these completely, and the student is referred to it for further information. A list of the standard light sections is given in Tables 27 to 30 in the Appendix.

25.11   GAGE LINES. The lines along which rivets should be placed in the flanges of I-beams, channels, angles, and other structural shapes have become standardized through long usage. These lines are called gage lines. In angles, the gage line is measured from the back of the angle. The gage line in the flange of a channel is also measured from the back of the channel, but in the flanges of an I-beam the gage lines are measured from the center. Edge distances are not given because they vary along the same beam, and they also vary in shapes of different weight, whereas the distance measured from the back or center line always keeps the gage lines in the same relative position. Standard gages for I-beams, channels, and angles are given in Tables 27 to 30 in the Appendix.

25.12   RIVET SIZE AND SPACING. Minimum distances for rivet spacing along the gage lines have also been established. Data on these spacings are given in Table 31 in the Appendix.

Since a certain clearance is required in driving rivets, there is a limit to the size of rivets that may be driven in the standard shapes. Figure 25.10 shows the shape and size of the dies used in driving rivets. The minimum-size rivet is governed by the following rule: the diameter of the rivet should never be less than the thickness of metal to be punched. That is, a hole for a ½-inch rivet should not be punched through ¾-inch metal.

When drawing rivet heads, the diameter is made equal to $1\frac{1}{2}D + \frac{1}{8}$ inch where D is the rivet diameter.

25.13   BEAM CONNECTIONS. The angles for connecting beams to columns or girders have been standardized in six series designated as A, H, HH, B, K and KK to accommodate different loadings and rivet sizes. A portion of the B series for ¾ rivets is shown in Table 32 in the Appendix. The rivet spacings shown should be adhered to.

25.14   CONVENTIONAL SYMBOLS. The use of conventional signs and symbols is limited almost entirely to the representation of rivets. The standard symbols and their meaning are shown in Fig. 25.11. It will be noted that where the operation is to be performed on the near side or outside of the piece the designating marks are on the outside of the circle, whereas, to indicate the same operation on the far side or inside, the marks are on the inside of the circle.

When there is a long line of rivets uniformly spaced, not all the rivets need be drawn in. Usually only those at the beginning and end of a series of uniform spaces need be indicated. The side view of a rivet is not shown except when it will add to the clearness of the drawing.

A departure from the above rule must be observed with field rivets. All field rivets must be shown. They are also shown in the side view unless this will confuse the drawing.

25.15   BILLING MATERIALS. In making a bill of material or in notes, the following symbols are used as abbreviations: the wide-flanged beams are indicated by WF; I-beam is indicated by the capital letter I; the channel by a symbol similar to the cross section of a channel lying on its back to prevent confusion with the symbol for the I-beam if carelessly made; and angle, T-bar, and Z-bar are indicated in the same way by symbols representing their cross section. The

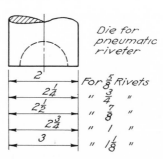

Fig. 25.10   Rivet die.

proper method of billing the various shapes is shown in Fig. 25.12. The weight per foot, or thickness in the case of the angle, must always be given, as all the structural shapes are made in several weights for the same general dimensions.

25.16 DIMENSIONS. Since a single detail may be sufficient for the fabrication of several tons of steel, it is quite evident that a single error in dimensions may spoil tons of steel, not to mention the waste in labor and time and the loss of reputation for reliability. Placing of the dimensions is perhaps the most difficult single problem. An examination of the illustrations in this chapter will give a basis upon which judgment can be formed as to the best placing of dimensions. The rules given apply particularly to drawings that are completely detailed in all respects. The following rules should be observed and applied with common sense and judgment.

25.17 TECHNIQUES

a. Dimension lines should be light, solid, black lines terminating in arrows.

b. The figures should be placed above the dimension lines at or near the center of the space between arrows. *Note:* This differs from the standard practice in machine drawing.

c. Dimensions should be given as shown in *A*, Fig. 25.13.

d. Where a dimension line runs through a rivet whose location it does not give, the dimension line should be broken and an arc drawn around the rivet, as shown in *B*, Fig. 25.13. Avoid this situation whenever possible.

e. The division line in fractions should always be made parallel to the dimension line.

f. When the space between the arrowheads is very

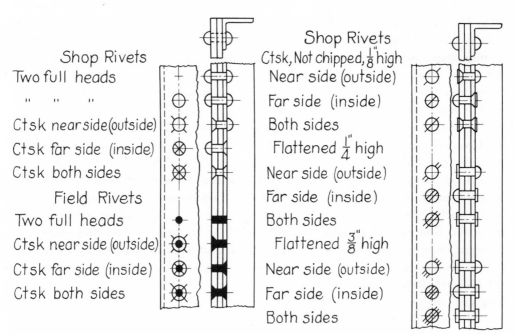

Fig. 25.11 **Conventional symbols for rivets.**

Fig. 25.12 **Method of specifying standard structural shapes.**

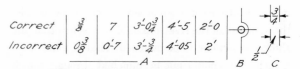

Fig. 25.13 **Method of dimensioning.**

limited, the dimension may be put in as shown in *C*, Fig. 25.13.

25.18 PLACING DIMENSIONS.

a. On truss members, detail dimensions should be placed in a continuous row from end to end of the member, no dimension being omitted.

b. An overall dimension should accompany each set of detail dimensions.

c. Where two or more lines of dimensions are given for the same piece, they should not be placed closer together than ⁵⁄₁₆ inch, and the first line should not be closer to the piece than double this distance. It may be farther away when circumstances demand. Above all things, dimensions should not be crowded upon one another or upon the object drawn.

d. The lettered figures of a dimension should not fall upon the outline of any member, since this makes it almost impossible to read. When other methods fail, a leader should be used and the dimension placed in the clear, where it will be legible.

25.19 FABRICATING DIMENSIONS

a. Dimensions should be calculated to the nearest sixteenth of an inch, except for bevels when it is frequently advisable to work to the nearest thirty second of an inch.

b. The detail dimensions should always be added to see that they check with the overall dimension.

c. The work is completely detailed only when it is unnecessary for the workman to add, subtract, multiply, or perform any other mathematical operation to obtain an essential dimension.

d. The slope of all members should be given in run and rise and not by angles. One of the dimensions of the run and rise should always be 12 inches. The run is the horizontal distance and the rise the vertical distance. See Figs. 25.32 and 25.33.

e. Before the work is submitted to the checker, it should be examined from the point of view of the shop man. All the dimensions and other information needed to lay out the work should be checked.

f. On beams and girders, the position of successive and independent details may be dimensioned consecutively from the left end in one line of dimensions as in Figs. 25.8 and 25.14. Chain dimensioning may be used when the details are continuous from end to end as in Fig. 25.23.

g. End distances and edge distance are usually given by note on light truss members. They are dimensioned on beams, columns, and girders. Gage lines should be dimensioned even though they are standard.

h. Field rivets should be dimensioned independently even though they are located with a series of detail dimensions.

i. The size of each piece is given close to the piece itself.

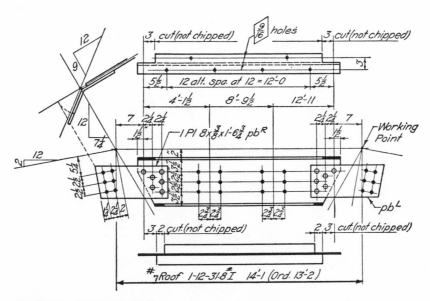

Fig. 25.14   Roof purlin detail.

In dimensioning, as with standard details, many fabricating companies have adopted certain standard practices for their draftsmen to observe, which have been developed through experience in the shop. These vary somewhat in different shops.

25.20 RECTANGULAR FRAMED STRUCTURES. Structural steel fabrication may be roughly divided into two major categories, namely, rectangular framed structures such as tall buildings and those involving triangular framework such as roof trusses and bridges. The framing of buildings consists mainly of vertical and horizontal members which are connected at right angles to each other.

25.21 DESIGN DRAWINGS OR LAYOUTS. The structural draftsman usually works from design layouts or framing plans which show the arrangement of columns, girders, and beams for each floor of a building. This layout gives the size of each member and its location relative to others both horizontally and vertically. The horizontal distances are shown by dimensions and the vertical distances by elevations as shown in Fig. 25.15. A note indicates the distance of the major portion of the framing below the finished floor line. Departure from this general level will be called out as

plus or minus distances above or below the finished floor level as noted for beam *K3* in Fig. 25.15.

25.22 MARKING. In order to provide a systematic procedure for detailing, fabricating, and erection, each member of a structure is given a mark on the design drawing. This mark on the layout is placed on the detail drawing of the piece, painted on the piece in the shop, and used by the erector in the field to place the member in the structure.

In addition to these marks, which can be called erection marks and which must appear on the final finished piece, other marks must be placed upon each piece of steel used to make the composite. The latter marks are for the purpose of assembling the member in the shop and may be called assembly marks.

Each company has its own system in both categories. A common method is to assign capital letters as erection marks to the horizontal members. The letter is followed by a number. This number may refer to the sheet or drawing number on which the member is detailed or it may refer to a floor number.

Columns may be numbered in consecutive order in some systematic arrangement on the plan, or the rows of columns may be given letters in one direction and

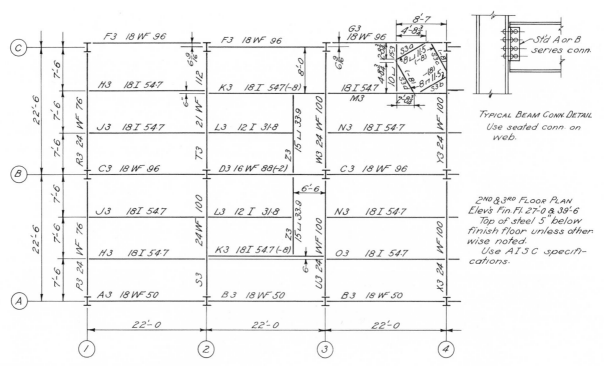

Fig. 25.15 Design layout of floor framing.

numbers in the direction at right angles to the first as shown in Fig. 25.15. Any column is then designated by the intersection of the lettered and numbered rows, as for example, *B-2*, *C-3*, etc., in Fig. 25.15. Since a column will have the same number throughout its entire height, but must be erected in sections, each section must be given a distinguishing mark, as for example, *B-2* Tier One or *B-2 (0-2)*. Tier one would be the mark of the first columns to be erected, usually through two stories. The mark *(0-2)* would indicate the same thing, namely, that the column extended from the footing through story two.

It is customary in many shops to use small letters for assembly marks. The assembly marks originate with the detailer whereas the erection marks are placed on the layout by the designer. The detailer should observe the following rules.

a. Each separate piece should be given a mark.

b. When two or more pieces are identical, they should be given the same mark and need to be detailed only once.

c. When two pieces are similar in all respects except that one is left and the other right, they may be given the same mark with the suffix *R* and *L*. The one drawn is usually marked *R*.

d. The letters *i* and *l* should be avoided since it is difficult to distinguish them on a drawing or in the shop. The prime mark should not be used.

25.23 DETAIL SKETCHES. Before beginning the detail of a member, except perhaps the simplest, it is advisable to make a sketch with straight edge and pencil, or freehand, to work out the connections to other members. The controlling dimensions such as

elevations above or below floor levels, line-up with other members, and actual rather than nominal member sizes form the basis for working out these sketches. Use standard beam connections wherever possible.

Thus for the left end of the beam in Fig. 25.16, which is a sketch of beam *H-3* in Fig. 25.15, a sketch is hardly necessary. But for the right end it is essential to work out the connection very carefully so that beams *H-3* and *K-3* may be erected without difficulty. Note that the top of *K-3* is below *H-3* and also offset horizontally. Such connections may tax the ingenuity of the detailer.

In beginning this sketch, the engineer would first select a standard beam connection. From page 190 of the *AISC Manual*, the load that the beam *H-3* will carry on a span of 22 feet is 54,000 pounds. One half of this load is supported at each end. From the table on page 257, *AISC Manual*, connection *B-4* will be more than ample since it will carry an end reaction of 53,000 pounds, almost double that required. A *B-3* connection would have the necessary strength, but the detailer will normally use the standard for the beam size unless the designer has authorized lighter connections.

The location of this connection on beam *H-3* depends on the size of the beam and type of supporting member. From Table 28 in the Appendix we find that the first rivet cannot be closer than 2¾ inches to the top of the support beam. When possible this distance is made 3 inches to facilitate the use of multiple punches. Since the top of the flange is usually at a specified height, it is customary to dimension rivets from the top flange. This line of dimensions should not be tied in to the bottom flange. The completed shop drawing of beam *H-3* is shown in Fig. 25.17.

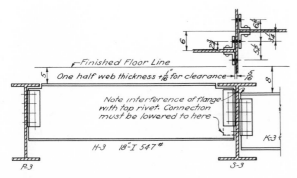

Fig. 25.16 Sketch for detailing beam.

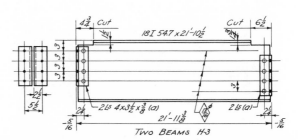

Fig. 25.17 Floor beam detail of Fig. 25.16.

A second detail sketch for a seated connection on a column is shown in Fig. 25.18. This is a detail of beam *C-3* in Fig. 25.15. When a beam must fit between the flanges of a column, standard beam connections are usually not practicable. For the inexperienced draftsman it is a satisfactory rule to make the number of rivets in the seat equal to the number in the outstanding flanges of a standard connection for the size of beam involved. Actually the number of rivets must be carefully computed in design.

The clip angle at the top of the left end of the beam in Fig. 25.18 is used for stability only. On the right end the clip was placed on the web to avoid interference with the connecting beam on the opposite side of the column. The shop drawing of beam *C-3* is shown in Fig. 25.19. Note the −⅝ at each end of the overall dimension. This is the distance from the center line of the column to the end of the beam and gives a check on the center-to-center distance of columns. The 1¹³⁄₁₆″ end distance to rivet holes is obtained as shown in the sketch at the right in Fig. 25.18. The actual clearance is approximately ⁷⁄₁₆ inch instead of ½ inch.

The ±⅛ inch shown opposite the ends of the beam in Fig. 25.19 indicates that the length of beam may be allowed to vary by this amount. In other words, a beam with a minimum length of 21′-10½″ or a maximum of 21′-11″ could be used. The shop would adjust the 1¹³⁄₁₆″ dimension to suit. The net distance between holes as shown on the drawing cannot be varied.

25.24 NONRECTANGULAR CONNECTIONS. Structural members may be skewed, that is, at an angle of other than 90° with each other, as, for example, the 8 inch channels in the upper right-hand part of Fig. 25.15. Members may also have a slope with the horizontal, as, for example, the roof rafters *D* and *E* in Fig. 25.22. The hip rafters *C* in this figure have both skew and slope. If the purlins *P1*, *P2*, etc., had their webs in a vertical plane, they would be canted relative to their supporting members.

Nonrectangular connections usually require some trigonometric calculations in making the layout. In order that these computations may be accurately controlled, working points are established.

25.25 WORKING POINTS. Working points are commonly taken at the intersection of the center lines of members or in the case of trusses at the intersection

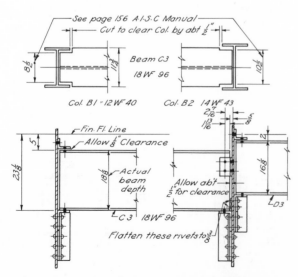

Fig. 25.18 Sketch of beam and column connections.

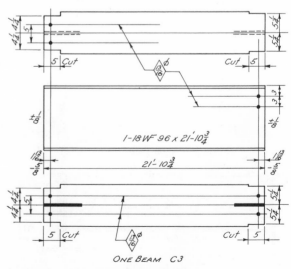

Fig. 25.19 Beam detail of Fig. 25.18.

of gage lines. See Fig. 25.33. It is not necessary that center lines be used. The lines used, however, must be parallel to the center lines. Thus in Fig. 25.20, which is a detail sketch of the channel *S3a* in Fig. 25.15, the center line of the 18 WF 96 beam, and the back of the channels were used to establish the working points. In Fig. 25.22, the intersection of the center lines of the ridge and side beams with the top of the sloping beam were used.

25.26 DETAILING SKEWED MEMBERS. Using the channel *S3a* of Fig. 25.15 as an illustration, the sketch of Fig. 25.20 can be made. The diagonal length between working points is obtained by taking the

square root of the sum of the squares of the two legs of the right-angle triangle, as shown at the bottom of the figure. The squares were obtained from Inskip Table of Squares. Using the same tables, the bevel of the member is found to be 12 to $6^{15}/_{16}$ as shown in the computations in the figure. Minimum bends and rivet distances have been standardized as given in Table 33 in the Appendix. With these data the shop drawing of the channel was made as in Fig. 25.21.

25.27 DETAILING SLOPING MEMBERS. A roof framing plan together with a sketch of the end connections of a rafter is shown in Fig. 25.22. From consideration of the architect's plans the working points were chosen in the plane of the top of the rafter, as shown. The ridge rafter was then located 1½ inches below the working point so that its edge would lie approximately in the plane of the top of the rafter. In a similar manner the top of the side beam and top of the corner column were located to give a reasonable connection. From this sketch the shop detail shown in Fig. 25.23 was prepared.

In some shops sloping members are detailed in the position they occupy. Likewise the elevation of working points rather than the vertical distance between them is sometimes given. The slope of the member is given by the usual right-angle triangle shown on the member.

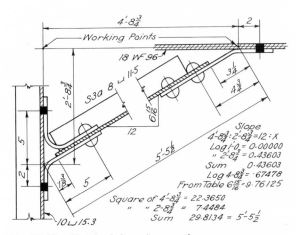

Fig. 25.20 Sketch of skewed connection.

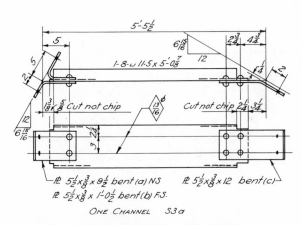

Fig. 25.21 Detail of skewed beam of Fig. 25.20.

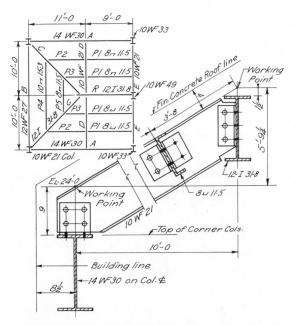

Fig. 25.22 Roof framing plan and sketch of sloping rafter *D*.

In other shops the member is drawn horizontally, in which case the slope or bevel would be given on the end connections as shown in Fig. 25.24. In this figure the purlins have been shown canted for purpose of illustration. Note that the holes for the purlin connections have been kept in lines parallel and perpendicular to the length of the member. This is desirable in multiple-punch operations. Figure 25.25 shows the purlin detail for this situation.

25.28   COLUMN DETAILS. Since the lower-story columns are the first structural pieces to be erected and footings with anchor bolts and base plates must be in position before erection can begin, it is necessary to detail columns first. In order to facilitate detailing, the designer makes a column schedule as illustrated in Fig. 25.26. This schedule shows the elevation of each floor, the size and composition of each column, the point at which the columns are spliced, the elevation of the base plate, and the size of the base plate.

When base plates are shipped loose, as is usually the case, these are detailed separately with proper provision for anchor bolt holes, grouting holes if necessary, and planed surfaces on heavy plates to give full bearing to the milled end of the column. Two typical

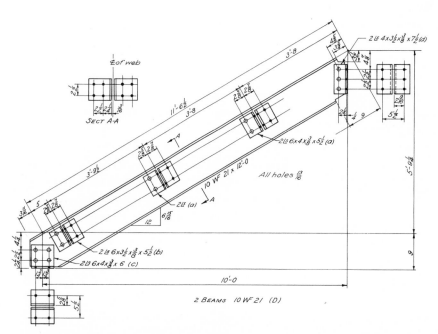

Fig. 25.23   Detail of roof rafter *D* of Fig. 25.22.

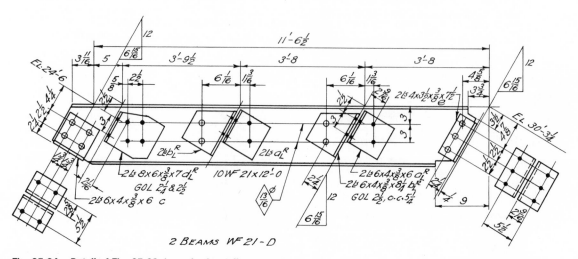

Fig. 25.24   Detail of Fig. 25.23 drawn horizontally.

column bases are shown in Fig. 25.27.

25.29   COLUMN SPLICES. Since the load that columns carry increases from the top downward, the size of columns must be increased accordingly. This is usually done at intervals of two stories, beginning at the bottom. In buildings with an odd number of stories the top section may be either one or three stories in height. Column splices are usually placed far enough above the floor level to clear all beam connections. Two typical splices are shown in Fig. 25.28. Further details are shown in *Structural Shop Drafting*, Vol. I, AISC.

25.30   RIGHT- AND LEFT-HAND COLUMNS. Situations sometimes occur in which columns and other members are similar in detail except that they are in right- and left-hand arrangement as shown for Columns *A2* and *B2* in the upper part of Fig. 25.29. Right- and left-hand arrangements are always relative to a vertical plane, never a horizontal plane.

In situations of this kind considerable drafting time can be saved by detailing one column and calling it out as shown and then by note calling out the second column as opposite hand, as indicated in the lower part of Fig. 25.29.

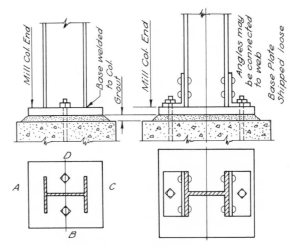

Fig. 25.27   Column-base connections.

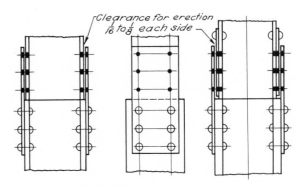

Fig. 25.28   Column splices.

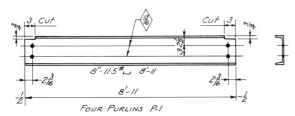

Fig. 25.25   Purlin detail.

	COLUMN SCHEDULE				
	A1	B1 to F1	A2 to A6	B2 to B6	C2 to C6
High Roof line 64'-9					
Fin. Third Floor +39'-6	10 WF 21	12 WF 27 1'-3	12 WF 27 1'-6	12 WF 40	12 WF 40
Fin. Second Floor +27'-0	10 WF 33	12 WF 40	12 WF 40	14 WF 43	14 WF 43
Fin. First Floor +14'-6	12"		1'-6		
Fin. Bsmt Floor +0.0					
COL. BASE PLATE	16x1⅔x18	16x1½x20	16x1½x20	16x1½x22	16x1½x22

Fig. 25.26   Column schedule.

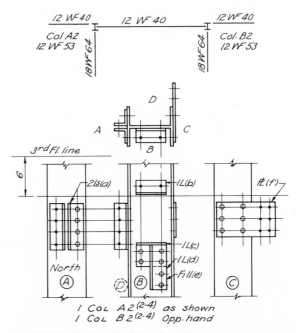

Fig. 25.29   Right- and left-hand details.

In the shop it is customary to mark the faces of a column by the letters *A*, *B*, *C*, and *D* in counterclockwise order, looking down on the column and always beginning with the letter *A* on a flange face as shown in Fig. 25.29. Shop details should show the faces so marked. The direction of one face, for example, the north side, should be so marked.

A shop detail of Column *B2* in the framing plan of Fig. 25.15 and the column schedule of Fig. 25.26 is shown in Fig. 25.30.

The columns having been detailed, the beams framing into them must be detailed to fit.

25.31 DETAILING A TRUSS. In designing trusses, line diagrams similar to the one shown in Fig. 25.31 are used as the bases for the computation of stresses. The intersections of these lines give the working points used in detailing the truss.

Two general schemes for making roof truss details are in use. In one of these only the dimensions between working points are given along with the size of members, the slopes of members, and the number of rivets in each member, as shown in Fig. 25.32. The working out of the details of the joints is left to the template maker.

In the second method, which is more commonly used, all details are worked out and dimensioned on the shop drawing as shown in Fig. 25.33. This method has the advantage of permitting the template maker

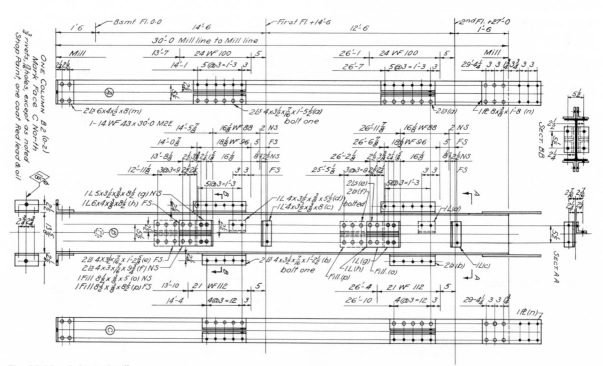

Fig. 25.30 Column detail.

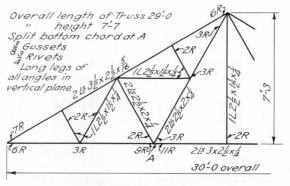

Fig. 25.31 Design diagram of steel truss.

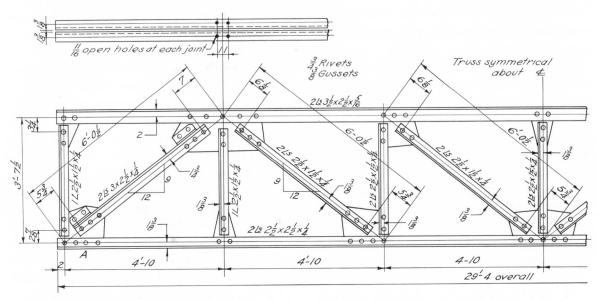

Fig. 25.32   Sketch detail of a flat truss.

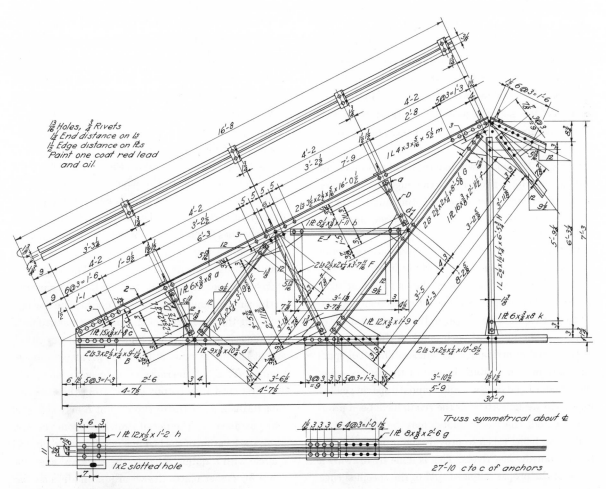

Fig. 25.33   Complete detail of truss in Fig. 25.31.

and the men in the shop to proceed at once to cut, punch, and assemble the work. It also gives a permanent record of the work.

The procedure in making a complete shop drawing is explained in the following paragraphs.

Assume that complete information is given the draftsman in the design sketch, as shown in Fig. 25.31. Since the truss is symmetrical, it will be necessary to show only the left half, up to and including the center points.

The first step, after deciding upon the number and arrangement of views and selecting a scale to fit the requirements, is to lay out the working lines. These working lines correspond to the gage lines shown in Fig. 25.33, which form a group of triangular figures the dimensions of which can be readily computed. It will be noted that all dimensions in Fig. 25.33 are based on the working points. After the working lines are laid out, the members of the truss may be laid out around these lines as gage lines to the same scale, or to a slightly larger one if desired. For example, the bottom chord is composed of two $3'' \times 2\frac{1}{2}'' \times \frac{1}{4}''$ angles placed back to back with the long legs vertical. The standard gage for a $3''$ angle, as obtained from the tables, is $1\frac{3}{4}''$. Hence, we scale down from the working line for the bottom chord a distance of $1\frac{3}{4}''$, and draw a line parallel to the working line which represents the bottom of the angles. A second line, drawn just a little above the first, represents the thickness of the angle. From the bottom line, we may now scale upward a distance of $3''$, and draw a line that will represent the top edge of the vertical leg of the angle. These three lines, which together represent the angle, can be marked off with one setting of the scale and then drawn in very quickly.

In the same way the other angles may be drawn around their corresponding working lines. The ends of the angles should usually be shown cut off at right angles to their length as a matter of economy. When all the angles have been drawn, the proper number of rivets may be put in at each point to the same scale as that used in laying out the angles. The rivet spacings may be scaled from the end of the angles, using the standard end distance and standard spacing called for by the design. After all the rivets have been properly located, the gusset plates may be drawn in to scale, care being taken to provide the proper edge distance from the last rivets. This is done by drawing a circle of the proper radius—equal to the specified edge distance—around the outstanding rivets in each mem-

ber and then drawing the lines representing the edges of the gusset plate tangent to these circles. Gusset plates must be cut from rectangular pieces, and hence it is desirable to make as few cuts as possible to obtain the proper shape for the plates. In no case may re-entrant angles be used. When the gusset plates have been drawn, the truss is ready for dimensioning. The rules for dimensioning are given in Arts. 25.16 to 25.18.

25.32 LAYOUT OF A JOINT. Where structural members meet at an angle other than 90°, the distance from the working point to the first rivet in the sloping member is determined by making a large-scale layout right on the truss detail, as illustrated for one joint in Fig. 25.34, which represents joint A on Fig. 25.32. The truss detail is usually made to a scale of $1'' = 1'0''$, and the joint layout to a scale of $3'' = 1'0''$. The needed dimensions are then scaled off. Although all lines of the large-scale layout have been shown in Fig. 25.34, only those that are useful in obtaining the desired dimensions need be drawn.

To make such a layout, the principal working lines of the joint, as indicated by the lines marked *1, 2,* and *3,* are used. These are the gage lines of the members which form the joint. Around these lines the members are then drawn in to large scale, beginning with the member which runs through the joint, as, for example, the bottom member in Fig. 25.34. The bottom chord, which is composed of two $2\frac{1}{2}'' \times 2\frac{1}{2}'' \times \frac{1}{4}''$ angles, is laid out around line *1* by measuring down at right angles to the line a distance of $1\frac{3}{8}''$, which is the standard gage for the $2\frac{1}{2}''$ leg. With the bottom line of the angle thus determined, the whole angle may now be drawn in. Then, to scale, $\frac{1}{2}$ inch above the top edge, draw a line for clearance. Draw the angles around the working lines *2* and *3.* The sloping member on line *3* is composed of two $3'' \times 2\frac{1}{2}'' \times \frac{1}{4}''$ angles, and the standard gage for the $3''$ leg is $1\frac{3}{4}''$. The angle may then be laid out around the working line as a gage line in the same manner as the bottom chord. The line representing the lower edge of the angle is extended until it intersects the clearance line of the bottom chord, and at the intersection a line is drawn at right angles to line *3.* This last line represents the end of the angle. The first rivet may be put in $1\frac{1}{4}''$ from this line, and then its distance to the working point B may be scaled and put down on the detail drawing. From the first rivet, the location of the last one may be scaled off, and a circle with a radius equal to the standard edge distance for gusset plates drawn around it. In a similar manner, the rivets farthest from the working point B

in each member may be drawn, and then the edges of the gusset plate may be drawn tangent to the edge distance circles around these rivets. Any required distance may now be scaled from this layout, and the size of the gusset plate determined. Such a layout must be made for each different joint, and, although the type of connection may be quite different from the one shown, the general principle is just the same.

25.33 WELDING. In some structures welding is being used in lieu of rivets for fastening members together. As with riveted structures, some of the welding is done in the shop and other portions upon erection in the field. For the correct use of welding symbols and the dimensioning thereof the reader is referred to Chapter 27, Welding Drawing.

25.34 REINFORCED CONCRETE. Only the general principles of detailing reinforced-concrete structures can be covered in this brief treatment, since reinforced concrete is used for such a wide variety of structures each of which involves details not covered in others. The following paragraphs cover items that must always be included. All data, symbols, abbreviations, etc., shown in this section are approved and shown in the *Manual of Standard Practice for Detailing Reinforced Concrete Structures* published by the American Concrete Institute.

25.35 SYMBOLS AND ABBREVIATIONS. The following symbols and abbreviations are recommended by the ACI.

#	To indicate size of deformed bar member
∅	Round—mainly for plain round bars
□	Square
⟷	Direction in which bars extend
Pl	Plain bar
Bt	Bent
St	Straight
Stir	Stirrup
Sp	Spiral
CT	Column tie
IF	Inside face
OF	Outside face
NF	Near face
FF	Far face
EF	Each face
Bot	Bottom
E.W.	Each way
T	Top

Round deformed bars are specified by number from #2 to #8. The number corresponds to the diameter

in eighths of an inch. Thus a #3 bar is approximately ⅜ inch in diameter. The nominal diameter of a deformed bar is the same as a plain bar having the same weight per foot.

25.36 ENGINEERING DRAWINGS. These are the general plans of the structure. They must give all information necessary to build the forms, detail the reinforcing steel, and make the steel placement drawings. Beside the general floor plan showing the location and size of girders, beams, joists, columns, etc., this will require some details, usually sectional views, and typical bar diagrams as shown in Fig. 25.35. In buildings of this type, beam and joist schedules are also required as illustrated in Fig. 25.36. Note that, although these schedules give all necessary information, they are not adequate for bending the steel.

Reinforcement for walls and slabs must be shown either in schedules or on the plans or elevations. A special detail of this type is shown in Fig. 25.37.

The steel for columns is usually shown in schedules together with sufficient detail views to show the typical arrangement of steel, as illustrated in Figs. 25.38 and 25.39.

Typical column splices are shown in Fig. 25.40.

Footings are shown on the general plans as illustrated in Fig. 25.41 and detailed as in Fig. 25.42.

Accessories such as beam bolsters and chairs that support the reinforcing may be shown on the drawing but are usually given by note, referring to some standard, covering the placement of such items.

Anchors for architectural work, such as suspended ceilings, and elevators which require placement before pouring the concrete, must be shown or noted as well as all openings to be provided for plumbing, heating, ventilating, and the like.

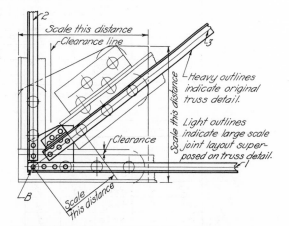

Fig. 25.34 Large-scale layout for obtaining detail dimensions.

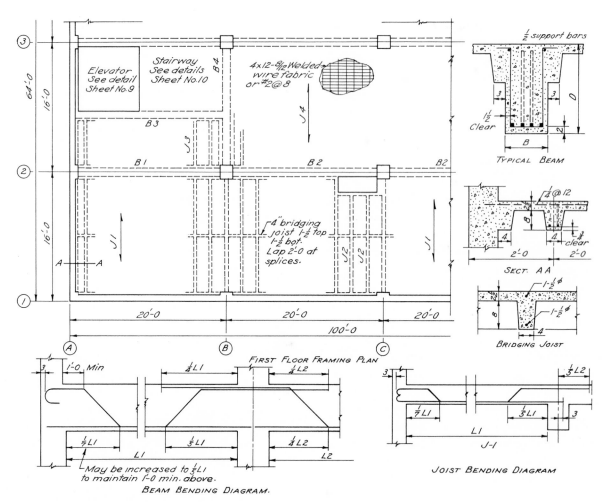

Fig. 25.35   Reinforced-concrete framing plan.

BEAM SCHEDULE									
Mark	B×D	Tee	Reinforcing		Stirrups				Stirrup support
			Bent	Str	No.	Size	Spacing each end.		bar at top
B1	12×25	2 sides	2-$\frac{7}{8}$	2-$\frac{7}{8}$	10	$\frac{1}{2}$	6, 2@8, 10, 12		2-$\frac{1}{2}$
B2	12×25	2 sides	2-$\frac{7}{8}$	2-$\frac{7}{8}$	12	$\frac{1}{2}$	5, 2@7, 9, 12, 12		
B3	10×17	1 side	2-$\frac{3}{4}$	2-$\frac{3}{4}$	8	$\frac{3}{8}$	6, 8, 10, 12		
B4	12×20	2 sides	2-$\frac{7}{8}$	2-$\frac{7}{8}$	10	$\frac{3}{8}$	6, 2@8, 10, 12		
B5	14×25	2 sides	2-1ϕ	2-1ϕ	14	$\frac{1}{2}$	5, 2@7, 2@9, 2@12		

B = Breadth of beam and D = Depth overall.

JOIST SCHEDULE				
Mark	B	D	Reinforcing	
			Bent	Str.
J-1	4	8+2$\frac{1}{2}$	1-$\frac{3}{4}$	1-$\frac{3}{4}$
J-2	4	8+2$\frac{1}{2}$	1-$\frac{3}{4}$	1-$\frac{3}{4}$
J-3	4	8+2$\frac{1}{2}$	1-$\frac{5}{8}$	1-$\frac{1}{2}$
J-4	4	8+2$\frac{1}{2}$	1-$\frac{3}{4}$	1-$\frac{3}{4}$

Fig. 25.36   Beam and joist schedules.

25.37 PLACEMENT DRAWINGS. The instructions in this article are quoted, by permission, from the *ACI Manual of Standard Practice* with such modifications as are necessary to make them fit the illustrations of this textbook.

a. Outline drawing. The detailer should first draw the outline of the floor, which can usually be done by tracing from the engineering drawing. Dimensions are optional on the placing drawings, but, in the case of joist construction, it will be found desirable to show them for convenience and time saving in spacing the joists. Beam and column designations are then added, using the same designations as on the engineering drawing. If there is any variation in beams of the same engineering designation, a letter suffix can be added to differentiate it. On the drawing in Fig. 25.43, the designer has foreseen the reinforcing steel requirements and the detailer is able to use the identical beam designations.

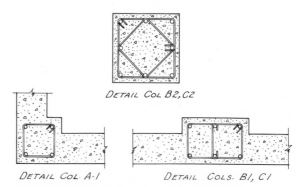

Fig. 25.39   Detail of column reinforcing schedule.

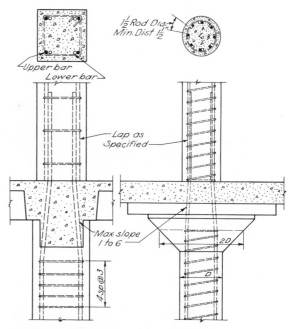

Fig. 25.40   Column reinforcing schedule.

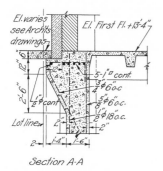

Fig. 25.37   Special reinforcing detail.

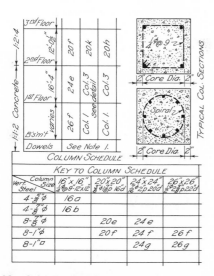

Fig. 25.38   Column schedule.

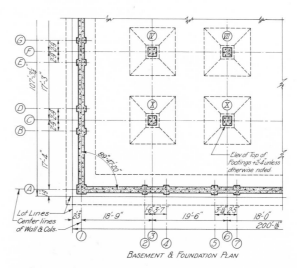

Fig. 25.41   Column and wall footing plan.

b. Metal forms. The next step is the spacing and arrangement of metal forms and concrete joists. It is necessary to draw a few more joists than are shown on the engineering drawing in order to show definitely their location. Joists are generally located directly in line with those in adjacent spans. The 20-inch-wide forms are used wherever possible, but a few 10-inch and 15-inch forms are used to fill out the spaces adjacent to beams and double joists or wherever necessary to adjust the joist spacing to provide continuity. Only these two narrow widths should be used, and, where a space is not sufficient to permit the use of the 10-inch forms, a solid slab with the full depth of the floor system must be used. Tapered forms are not furnished in 10-inch and 15-inch widths.

c. Beam schedule. Since beam bars are the first ones required on a floor, the preparation of a beam schedule is the next logical step. The form of schedule to use is shown in Fig. 25.44. The horizontal type of schedule was chosen because the simplicity in reinforcing steel and the available space on the drawing make this type best suited for the purpose.

d. Beam reinforcement. Beam reinforcement consists of straight bars, trussed bars, and stirrups. The length for the straight bars is usually the same as the center-to-center distance between columns for interior spans, and the distance from the center line of the first interior columns to a minimum embedment of 6 in. into the exterior column or wall for end spans; or, if this embedment cannot be obtained, extend to within 3 in. of the outside face and terminate with a hook. This is shown in the typical beam-bending diagram on the engineering drawing in Fig. 25.35. Bending dimensions for truss bars are calculated from information given on the engineering drawing.

Consider beam *1B9* in Fig. 25.43 as an example. The detailer should draw a simple line detail to show the width of supports and clear span for the

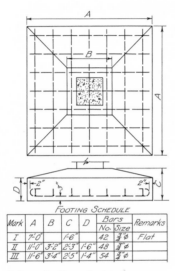

Fig. 25.42   Column footing schedule.

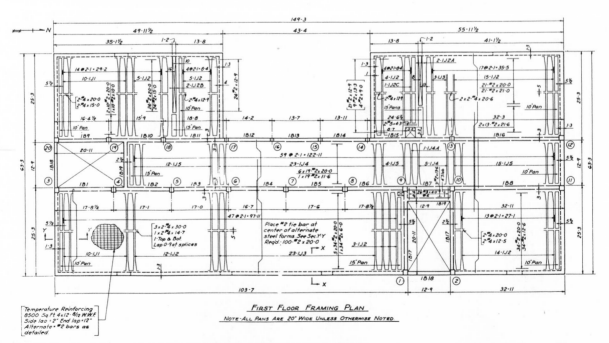

Fig. 25.43   Steel placement drawing. (Courtesy American Concrete Institute.)

beam, as shown in Fig. 25.45, filling in the other dimensions as they are determined.

The various dimensions of the bars are then calculated according to the typical beam-bending diagram and inserted on the line detail. These dimensions are then added up and inserted in the proper space provided in the beam schedule. The height of bend is obtained by deducting the top and bottom concrete protection from the beam depth, in this case, 25 inches less 4 inches (2 inches at bottom for fireproofing and 2 inches at top for fireproofing and joist bars) or 21 inches. The slope dimension is then computed or selected from a table.

e. Stirrups. Dimensions for stirrups are obtained from the size of the beam by deducting the concrete pro-

tection, in this case, 1½ inches from the top, bottom, and sides of the beam. Thus 3 inches is deducted from both the width and depth of the beam. For beam *1B9* which is a 12 × 25 beam, the stirrup dimensions become 9 × 22. The detailer must also determine the direction in which hooks are to extend and indicate this in his schedule. It is usually desirable to turn hooks out into a slab unless prevented from doing so by openings; when used in spandrel beams, one hook is turned in and the other out. In this case, the length of stirrup support bars are specified as approximately the length of the clear span. These support bars are frequently specified as covering the stirrup spacing only.

BEAM SCHEDULE

BEAM				STRAIGHT			BENT					Hook	H	O	Hook	H	O	STIRRUPS						SUPPORT BARS			2" CHAIRS	
MARK	No	B	D	No.	Size	LGTH.	No.	Size	LGTH.	MARK	TYPE							No.	Size	LGTH.	MARK	DIM.	TYPE	SPACING EACH END	No.	Size	LGTH.	No	TYPE
1B1	1	12	25	2	#6	16-8	2	#6	24-3	1B600		8	2-2	2-5½	9-9	2-5½	6-9	1-9	13	#4	4-11	U400	9/22		4,2@6, 2@10,12 Col-3 / 5,2@6, 2@10,12,15 Col-4	2	#4	15-8	4	BB
1B2	1	12	25	2	#7	16-7	2	#7	27-9	1B700			7-6	2-5½	7-10	2-5½	7-6	1-9	7 / 6	#4 / #4	4-11 / 4-11	U400 / U401	9/22 / 9/22		5,2@6, 2@10,12,15 Col-4 / 6,2@6, 10,12,15 Col-5	2		15-7	4	BB
1B3	1	12	23	2	#6	16-6	2	#6	27-8	1B601			7-8	2-3	7-10	2-3	7-8	1-7	16	#3	4-7	U301	9/20		4,3@6, 2@8,10,12	2		15-6	4	BB
1B4	1	12	23	2	#6	16-1	2	#6	27-5	1B602			7-8	2-3	7-7	2-3	7-8	1-7	16	#3	4-7	U301	9/20		Do.	2		15-1	4	BB
1B5	1	12	23	2	#6	17-0	2	#6	28-4	1B603			7-11	2-3	8-0	2-3	7-11	1-7	16	#3	4-7	U301	9/20		Do.	2		16-0	4	BB
1B6	1	12	23	2	#7	16-6	2	#7	27-0	1B701			7-9	2-3	7-10	2-3	6-11	1-7	16	#3	4-7	U301	9/20		Do.	2		15-6	4	BB
1B7	1	12	23	2 / 2	#6 / #7	13-9 / 27-6	Bot. In	Top	Extend	7-8			Info Beam 1B8						10	#3	4-7	U301	9/20		5, 2@7, 10,12				3	BB
*1B8	1	12	33	3	#8	30-8	3	#8	38-8	1B800			8-7	3-2	19-6	3-2	3-2	1-1	2-3	20	#4	6-3	U402	9/30		6,3@6,2@12,2@15,2@18	2		29-9	4 / 6	BBU-1 / BB
1B9	1	12	25	2	#6	15-4	2	#6	22-7	1B604		8	2-1	2-5½	8-9	2-5½	6-2	1-9	12	#4	4-11	U400	9/22		5,2@7, 2@10,13	2		14-4	3	BB

JOIST SCHEDULE

JOIST				STRAIGHT			BENT					Hook	H	O	Hook	H	O	¾" CHAIRS
MARK	No.	B	D	No.	Size	LGTH.	No.	Size	LGTH.	MARK	TYPE							
1J1	20	5	8+2½	1	#7	24-0	1	#6	26-2	1J600		8	3-4	1-0½	16-6	1-0½	3-7	9	24-11	5
1J2	58	5		1	#6	24-0	1	#6	44-11	1J603			3-7	1-0½	15-2	1-0½	24-1	9		5
1J2A	2	Var.		2	#6	24-0	2	#6	31-6	1J607			3-7	1-0½	15-2	1-0½	10-8	9		10
1J2B	2	Var.		2	#6	24-0	1	#6	44-11	1J603			3-7	1-0½	15-2	1-0½	24-1	9		10
1J2C	1	5		1	#6	20-2	1	#6	22-0	1J606		8	2-6	1-0½	13-8	1-0½	3-1	9	20-9	4
1J3	26	5		1	#6	24-0	1	#6	31-6	1J607			3-7	1-0½	15-2	1-0½	10-8	9		5
1J4	28	5		1	#6	13-9	1	#6	21-4	1J604			8-4	1-0½	8-4	1-0½	1-11	8	9	3
1J4A	1	5		1	#6	13-9	1	#6	16-4	1J605		8	1-11	1-0½	9-1	1-0½	1-11	8	9	14-5	3
1J5	31	5	8+2½	1	#5	13-9													

Fig. 25.44   Beam and joist schedules for Fig. 25.43. (Courtesy American Concrete Institute.)

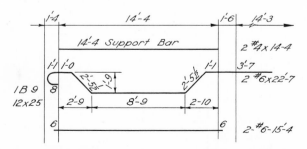

Fig. 25.45   Beaming computation diagram. (Courtesy American Concrete Institute.)

f. Joists. When spacing the joists, it is best to select a principal panel of the floor, then align all other joists in adjoining panels by the use of narrow-width forms where necessary. It is obvious that on the floor shown in Fig. 25.43 the detailer would select the panel bounded by columns *3*, *9*, and *1*.

The general procedure for calculating lengths and bending diagrams for joist bars is the same as for beams except that the typical bending diagrams for joists, as shown on the engineering drawings, are to be followed. The joist schedule is similar to the beam schedule except that stirrups and stirrup support bars are not usually required. Variations in the typical joists shown on the engineering drawings are indicated by suffixes such as *J2*, *J2A*, *J2B*, and *J2C*.

g. Temperature reinforcement. The temperature reinforcement, and reinforcement for bridging joists and around openings, is detailed on the plan view. For ease in handling, and for economy, temperature bars are detailed in 20-foot lengths, using only one odd length in any run with an allowance made for splices. Some fabricators and erectors prefer to have all #2 temperature reinforcement furnished in 20-foot lengths and cut on the job where necessary. Bridging joist bars are detailed in the same manner, except that the bars, being of a larger size, make it more economical to specify greater lengths.

In determining the number of lines of temperature steel, the lines adjacent to beams or walls are located about one-half the standard spacing away from the beam or wall.

Frequently, wire mesh is used for temperature reinforcement instead of straight bars, as the ease of placing often compensates for any difference in cost. The method of indicating the areas to be covered is plainly shown on the placing drawing in Fig. 25.43. Similar methods of detailing can be used wherever wire-mesh temperature reinforcement is required.

25.38 COLUMN-PLACEMENT SCHEDULES. The placement of steel for columns is usually shown in schedules, and bar-bending lists as shown in Fig. 25.46. The straight bars are ordered directly from the schedule, and all bent bars, ties, spirals, etc., are shown in the bar-bending lists. Bent bars are numbered in both schedules to correspond.

25.39 OTHER TYPES OF CONSTRUCTION. The foregoing discussion has applied directly to the beam and joist type of construction. The general principles are the same in all construction, but for specific cases involving other types such as flat slab construction the reader is referred to the *Manual of Standard Practice for Detailing Reinforced Concrete Strucures* ACI 315–51.

COLUMN SCHEDULE

	Col. Mark	A1	A2, A3 B1, C1	B2, B3 C2, C3
Roof				
4th Fl.				
10'-0	Size	12 x 12	12 x 14	15 x 15
	Core			
	Vert. Steel	4-5/8 x 12'-0	2-3/4 x 12'-0 4-C601	8-C602 10 T312
3rd Fl.	Ties or Spirals	10 T301	16 T306 16 T307	10 T313
11'-0	Size	12 x 12	12 x 16	18 x 18
	Core			
	Vert. Steel	4-3/4 ϕ x 13'-0	2-1 a x 13'-8 4-C802	8-C803 11 T310
2nd Fl.	Ties or Spirals	11 T301	17 T304 17 T305	11 T311
12'-0	Size	14 x 14	14 x 18	21 x 21
	Core			
	Vert. Steel	1-1 ϕ x 15'-2 3-C801	1-1¼ □ x 16-4 3-C1001 2-C1002	8-C1003 14-T308
1st Fl.	Ties or Spirals	18 T300	20 T302 20 T303	14 T309
	Top of Footing	6	12	9

BAR BENDS

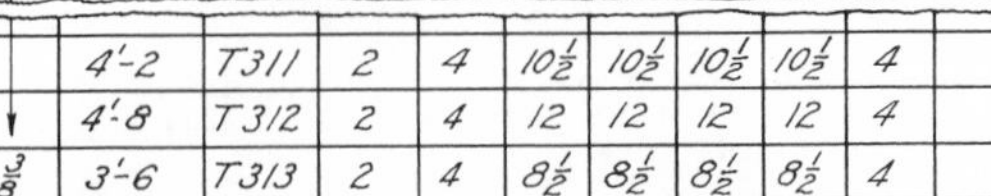

ALL DIMENSIONS ARE OUT TO OUT

Size	Length	Mark	Type	A	B	C	D	E	G	J
3/8	4'-4	T300	2	4	11	11	11	11	4	
	3'-8	T301	2	4	9	9	9	9	4	
	5'-0	T302	2	4	15	11	15	11	4	
	1'-7	T303	3	4	11				4	2¾
	4'-2	T311	2	4	10½	10½	10½	10½	4	
	4'-8	T312	2	4	12	12	12	12	4	
3/8	3'-6	T313	2	4	8½	8½	8½	8½	4	
3/4	12-0	C601	1		8'-6	1-6	2-0			2½
3/4	12-0	C602	1		8'-6	1-6	2-0			2½
1ϕ	15-2	C801	1		11'-0	1'-6	2'-8			2½
1ϕ	13-8	C802	1		9'-9	1'-3	2'-8			2
1ϕ	12-8	C803	1		8'-6	1'-6	2'-8			3
1¼□	16'-4	C1001	1		11-10½	1'-1½	3'-4			2¼
1¼□	16'-4	C1002	1		11-7½	1-4½	3'-4			2¾

Fig. 25.46 Column reinforcing schedule.

SELF-STUDY QUESTIONS

Before trying to answer these questions, read the chapter carefully. Then, without reference to the text, answer as many questions as possible. For those that cannot be answered, the number, in parentheses following the question number, gives the article in which the answer can be found. Look it up and write down the answer. Check the answers that you did give to see that they are correct.

25.1 **(25.2)** In structural work the term member means some _____ of a larger structure.

25.2 **(25.2)** The space between two consecutive sets or tiers of columns and beams or columns and trusses is called a _____ .

25.3 **(25.2)** A beam, girder, or truss in which one or both ends project beyond the supports is called a _____ .

25.4 **(25.2)** A vertical compression member usually supporting beams or girders is called a _____ .

25.5 **(25.2)** The top and bottom projecting or outstanding parts of a beam are called _____ .

25.6 **(25.2)** The lines along which rivet holes are punched in a structural member are called _____ lines.

25.7 **(25.2)** A structural member designed to carry a wall over a door or window opening is called a _____ .

25.8 **(25.3)** In blocking out views, care should be taken to allow ample _____ for dimensions.

25.9 **(25.4)** In addition to the usual three views, it is frequently necessary to show a _____ view in structural work.

25.10 **(25.5)** In structural work all parts of a member are detailed, insofar as possible, in the _____ they occupy in the structure.

25.11 **(25.6)** Structural drawing differs from machine drawing in that simple pieces are frequently not _____ in one direction.

25.12 **(25.7)** If large members such as plate girders are symmetrical about a center line, perpendicular to their longest dimension, only _____ _____ of the member is detailed.

25.13 **(25.9)** Many details of structural steel work have become well standardized. The draftsman should always use these _____ unless there are compelling reasons not to do so.

25.14 **(25.11)** The locations of gage lines have been _____ for beams, channels, angles, and other structural shapes.

25.15 **(25.12)** The diameter of a rivet should never be less than _____ _____ of the metal to be punched.

25.16 **(25.14)** The use of signs and symbols in structural drawing is usually applied to _____ .

25.17 **(25.15)** Indicate by a sketch the symbols used to specify the following:

(*a*) Wide-flanged beams

(*b*) Standard eye beams

(*c*) Channels

(*d*) Angles

(*e*) Tee bars

(*f*) Zee bars.

25.18 **(25.17)** The numerals for dimensions should be placed _____ the dimension line.

25.19 **(25.17)** The division line in fractions should always be _____ to the dimension line.

25.20 **(25.18)** Dimensions should not be _____ upon one another.

25.21 **(25.19d)** The slope of members in a truss should be given by their _____ and _____ .

25.22 **(25.25)** Working points are commonly taken at the _____ of the center lines of members or in the case of trusses at the _____ of gage lines.

25.23 **(25.29)** Column splices are usually placed far enough _____ the floor level to _____ all beam connections.

25.24 **(25.32)** The distance from the working point to the first rivet in a sloping member is determined by making a _____ _____ layout of the joint or connection.

PROBLEMS

The problems for rectangular framed parts and skewed and sloping members are referred to Figs. 25.15 and 25.26 which are to be used together. The truss problem in Figs. 25.47 to 25.48 are for building shown in Figs. 24.18 and 24.20 of the preceding chapter. These should be referred to where necessary.

Beam problems can normally be detailed on an A-size sheet (8½ × 11). Column details will require the B-size sheet (11 × 17), and truss details require the C-size sheet (17 × 22). A scale of $1'' = 1'\ 0''$ should normally be used.

Square Framed Beams

25.1 Make a detail sketch of the connections required for a beam assigned from Fig. 25.15. Refer to Fig. 25.26 for column sizes. Standard beam connections are shown in the Appendix. Study your problem carefully to see that the connection you make can be assembled in the shop and erected in the field.

25.2 Make a complete detail of the beam assigned and sketched in Problem 25.1.

Skewed Beams

25.3 Make a sketch of the connections required in an assigned skewed channel in the upper right corner of Fig. 25.15.

25.4 Make a complete detail of the channel sketched in Problem 25.3.

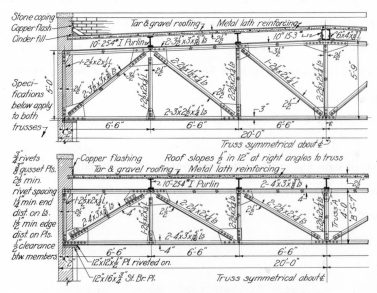

Fig. 25.47   Truss detail for building shown in Figs. 24.18 and 24.19.

Sloping Beams

25.5 Make a sketch of the connections for the sloping rafter *E* in Fig. 25.22.

25.6 Make a complete detail of rafter *E* sketched in Problem 25.5.

25.7 Make a sketch of connections required for the hip rafter *C* in Fig. 25.22. Note that a double auxiliary layout is required to obtain the angle of bend of the connections.

25.8 Make a complete detail of the hip rafter *C* sketched in Problem 25.7.

Purlins

25.9 Make a complete detail of a purlin assigned from Fig. 25.22. Notes should cover number required which are exactly alike.

Trusses

25.10 Make a complete detail of the truss shown in Fig. 25.47 at the top of the figure. This is an architect's drawing. You are not to copy it but to make a detail for fabrication in the shop.

25.11 Same as Problem 25.10, using lower truss of Fig. 25.47.

25.12 Make a complete detail of the truss shown in Fig. 25.48. Scale ¾″ = 1′ 0″.

Although only a few problems have been stated verbally, the selection of beams and columns available make it possible to assign each student in a class of 25 a different problem if desired.

Standard connections can be found in the Appendix.

Where a sketch is called for in the following problems, a pencil layout made with instruments but omitting unessential elements is meant.

Columns

25.13 Make a complete detail of a column assigned from Fig. 25.26. For beam connections to these columns, see Fig. 25.15. Assume first-floor beams to be the same as second-floor beams.

Reinforced Concrete

The following data supplements that given in Figs. 25.49, 25.50, and 25.51.

Columns *C-3*, *C-6*, *F-3*, and *F-6* are 24″ square. The reinforcing consists of eight 1″ square bars with proper ties.

Column *A-1* is 30″ square and has eight ¾″ bars.

Columns *A-2*, *A-4*, *A-5*, *A-7*, *B-1*, *D-1*, *E-1*, and *G-1* are 18 × 30″ in cross section, and each has six ⅞″ bars.

The first-story height floor to floor is 14 feet. The columns above the second floor are 4″ smaller on each dimension. Except for Column *A-1* they are centered over the column below. Column *A-1* has its outside faces flush for the entire height. Reinforcing rods in the second story are ⅛″ less in diameter than in the first story.

25.14 Make a typical cross section of any assigned column.

25.15 Make a typical detail of second-story splice for any assigned column.

25.16 Make a bar-bending schedule for beams *B-101* and *B-102*. See Figs. 25.49 and 25.50.

25.17 Make a bar-bending schedule for joists *J-101*, *J-103*, *J-104*, and *J-105*. See Figs. 25.49 and 25.51.

25.18 Make an engineering drawing (floor framing plan) for the second floor of the building shown in Figs. 24.18 and 24.19. Use 20″ metal pans instead of tile to form joists. Each joist shall have two ⅝-diameter rods, one bent and one straight. See *ACI Manual* for details of framing concrete to steel beams.

25.19 Make a typical detail of the joists of Problem 25.18.

25.20 Make a typical cross-section detail through the 18″-WF 50 pound beam, showing the placing of joist reinforcing rods. See *ACI Manual* for suggestions.

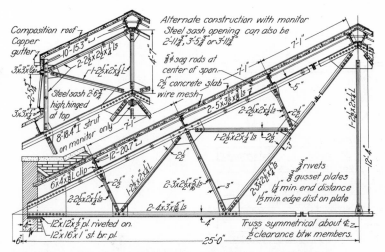

Fig. 25.48   Truss detail for building shown in Figs. 24.20 and 24.21.

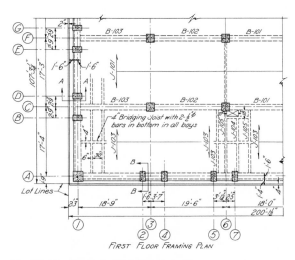

Fig. 25.49   Concrete floor framing plan.

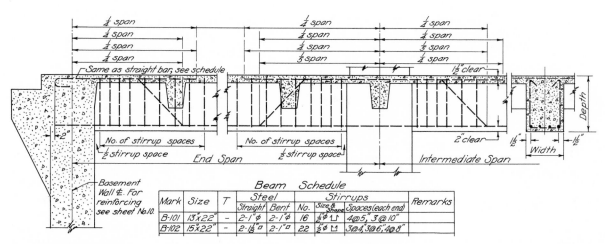

Fig. 25.50   Beam detail.

Beam Schedule

Mark	Size	T	Steel		Stirrups			Remarks
			Straight	Bent	No.	Size & Shape	Spaces (each end)	
B-101	13"x22"	–	2-1"φ	2-1"φ	16	½φ ⌞⌟	4@5", 3@10"	
B-102	15"x22"	–	2-1⅛"□	2-1"□	22	½φ ⊔	3@4,3@6,4@8"	

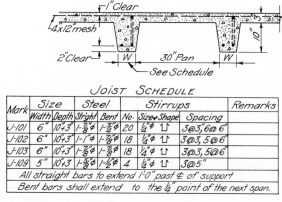

Fig. 25.51   Joist detail.

JOIST SCHEDULE

Mark	Size		Steel		Stirrups			Remarks
	Width	Depth	Stright	Bent	No.	Size+Shape	Spacing	
J-101	6"	10+3	1-⅞"φ	1-¾"φ	20	¼"φ ⌞⌟	3@3,6@6"	
J-102	6"	10+3	1-1"φ	1-⅞"φ	18	¼"φ ⌞⌟	3@3,5@6"	
J-103	6"	10+3	1-⅞"φ	1-⅞"φ	18	¼"φ ⌞⌟	3@3,5@6"	
J-109	5"	10+3	1-⅝"φ	1-½"φ	4	¼"φ ⌞⌟	3@5"	
All straight bars to extend 1'-0" past ₵ of support								
Bent bars shall extend to the ¼" point of the next span.								

CHAPTER 26
Pipe Drawing

OLD: Old wooden pipe gate used in water system of New York in the 18–19th century. (The Bettmann Archive)

NEW: Complex of pipes in petrochemical plant. (Courtesy of the Mobil Oil Company)

Chapter 26   Pipe Drawing*

26.1   INTRODUCTION. Some form of piping is used in most projects with which the engineer is concerned. For that reason he should understand the general functions and characteristics of piping systems. He should also know the proper methods of representation and location of pipes and pipe fittings.

Pipes are normally used for conveying liquids, gases, and solids such as water, oil, steam, air, and minerals. They are sometimes used as structural elements, such as columns and beams.

The material of which pipes are made covers a wide range. In general, they are round but other shapes are frequently used. Sizes range from very small to very large and thickness of walls ranges from very thin to very thick.

The material, shape, size, and wall thickness are not necessarily dependent one upon the other but each depends upon the purpose for which the pipe is used.

In general, a piping system of any extent consists of a succession of individual pieces connected in such a manner as to maintain continuity of flow. Volume of flow is controlled by various devices developed to meet the specific need. Fixtures used to control direction and volume of flow are generally classified as fittings and valves. Fittings and valves may or may not be made of the same material as the pipes to which they are attached.

26.2   PIPE MATERIAL. In ancient times pipe material was limited to bamboo, wood, and stone. As civilization progressed, metals came into common use. At the present time such a wide variety of materials and methods are available that pipes are now made from iron, steel, brass, copper, lead, aluminum, and metal alloys. They are also made from wood, concrete, clay, glass, plastics, and rubber. Insulated, lined, and reinforced pipes are also in common use. Pipes of special materials for special purposes continue to be developed.

It is the purpose of this chapter to consider the drafting problems for pipes made of only the more

common metals such as iron, steel, brass, copper, lead, and their alloys.

26.3   PIPE MANUFACTURE. Much of the pipe used in industry is cast-iron. As the name implies, cast-iron pipe is cast in sand molds placed either horizontally or vertically, or centrifugally cast in metal molds lined with sand or some pulverized material.

The bulk of pipe other than cast-iron is made of wrought metal such as steel, iron, brass, or copper. In principle the methods of manufacture of wrought-metal pipe differ widely from those of making cast-iron pipe. In one common method, pipe-length strips of metal are rolled into cylindrical shapes and the edges are welded together. The electric-weld method is used quite extensively. Another common method is to bring a cylindrically shaped piece of metal to a high forging temperature, force a hole through the center of the cylinder and then roll it down to the desired wall thickness. In general, copper tubing is made by the cold-drawn process.

26.4   PIPE SIZES AND SPECIFICATIONS. Inside diameter depends mainly upon the volume of flow desired. Wall thickness depends upon a number of variables such as internal and external pressure, shock, vacuum, and thermal expansion.

Careful consideration must be given to the meaning of pipe sizes, which are usually indicated simply as ½ inch, 1 inch, 2 inch, etc. When such reference is made to the size of steel or wrought-iron pipe up to 12 inch, the specified size refers to the nominal inside diameter because this is close to, but not, the exact inside diameter. For example, the inside diameter of a nominal 1-inch "standard weight" steel pipe is 1.049 inches, "extra-strong" is 0.957 inch, and "double-strong" is 0.599 inch, yet the outside diameter in each case is 1.315 inches. The great advantage in keeping the outside diameter the same for each nominal diameter, regardless of wall thickness, is the adaptability of standard valves and fixtures to pipes, regardless of the thickness of walls. Figure 26.1 shows the outside diameter, inside diameter, and wall thickness of typical 1-inch steel pipe. See Table 39 in the Appendix for dimensions of wrought-steel pipe.

When reference is made to standard steel or

---

*This chapter was prepared by Professor L. D. Walker of the University of Illinois.

wrought-iron pipe sizes larger than 12 inches, such as 14-inch, 16-inch, etc., the specified size now refers to the outside diameter. Such large pipe is often called O.D. pipe. When outside diameter is used to designate the pipe size, thickness of walls must also be stated so that inside diameter can be determined.

Cast iron pipe is available in a wide variety of standard sizes and weights with the bell-and-spigot joint. It is also available in sizes 1¼ inches to 12 inches with threaded ends. Nominal size of cast iron pipe always indicates inside diameter regardless of size. Terms such as "strong" and "extra-strong" are not commonly used in connection with cast iron pipe; consequently wall thickness or outside diameter or both should be indicated in connection with nominal size. See Table 40 of Appendix for common characteristics of bell-and-spigot-end cast iron pipe.

Brass and copper pipes are available in sizes from ⅛ inch to 12 inches and in two weights called "regular" and "extra-strong." They are very similar in wall thickness and inside diameter to steel pipe classified as "standard" and "extra-strong." Outside diameters are exactly the same as outside diameters of corresponding nominal sizes of steel pipe. Figure 26.2 shows outside diameter, inside diameter, and wall thickness of 1-inch "regular" and "extra-strong" brass pipe. See Table 41 of the Appendix for dimensions of brass and copper pipe.

Copper water tubing is available in sizes from ⅛ inch to 12 inches. Its wall thickness is considerably less than that of most other piping material. Nominal size indicates neither outside diameter nor inside diameter. Actual outside diameter is consistently 0.125 inch greater than nominal size. Consequently, in specifying size of tubing, outside diameter and wall thickness must be given. Three wall thicknesses are available. Figure 26.3 shows outside diameter, inside diameter, and wall thickness of 1-inch Type K, Type L, and Type M copper water tubing. See Table 42 of Appendix for sizes of copper water tubing.

Specifications and recommendations for manufacture, composition, strength, use, size, etc., of pipe and pipe products have been developed by such organizations as the American Water Works Association, American Gas Association, American Petroleum Institute, American Society for Testing Materials. The United States of America Standards Institute is working toward a unification of all pipe specifications in an attempt to eliminate odd sizes and varieties and to develop some coordination applicable to all common types and sizes. Printed copies of complete standards for pipes and pipe products may be obtained from the USASI.

Pipe standards, piping handbooks, manufacturers' manuals, and catalogues are available to supplement the limited amount of data in tables in the Appendix.

26.5 PIPE JOINTS. In order to join properly pipe lengths, fittings, and valves, suitable connections must be provided. These connections must withstand pressures, shock, and stresses to which the pipes, fittings, and valves are subjected.

One of the most common methods of connecting cast iron pipe is by the conventional bell-and-spigot joint. This joint is suitable where there is relatively low pressure and little vibration such as in underground installations. Lead, cement, sulfur compounds, oakum, and jute are the usual packing materials.

Other joints used on cast-iron pipe may be classed as mechanical joints because of the manner in which the jointing material is forced into place. In this type of joint, the jointing material is rolled or pushed along the outside of the inserted spigot end of one pipe into the bell end of the other, either by bolt action or screw action. This type of joint usually requires some modi-

 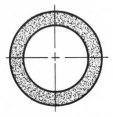

Fig. 26.2 Sections of 1-inch brass pipe.

Fig. 26.1 Sections of 1-inch steel pipe.

Fig. 26.3 Sections of 1-inch copper water tubing.

fications of the conventional bell-shaped end of the pipe. This joint will withstand greater pressure and vibration, and allows for greater lateral deflection and thermal expansion than the conventional bell-and-spigot joint. Additional packing materials especially adaptable to mechanical joints are rubber, composition materials, and bituminous compounds. Frequently these materials are preformed before use.

Still other methods of connecting cast-iron pipe include the use of mechanical joints such as the gland type, ball-and-socket and universal joints, sleeve couplings, and welding. Screwed couplings and fittings similar to those used for steel pipe are not uncommon where small size cast iron pipe is used. The conventional bell-and-spigot joint is illustrated in Fig. 26.4.

Standard steel and wrought-iron pipes are usually connected by flanges, threaded couplings, or welds.

The flange joint can be quite readily disassembled and may be designed to withstand high pressures. Flanges are attached to the pipe ends either by being screwed on, welded, or lapped. To complete the joint the flange faces are drawn tightly together with bolts. Flange design, face type and finish, gasket design and composition, and bolt load are all important factors in this type of joint. One of the more simple flange joints is illustrated in Fig. 26.4.

Welded joints and connections are not uncommon in high-pressure pipe assemblies. They are becoming more common in low-pressure assemblies as less expensive low-pressure valves and fixtures are being developed. Butt welds with conventional modifications are most frequently used. See Fig. 26.4.

Threaded couplings are simply short cylinders, threaded on the inside at each end to form pressure-tight joints for end-threaded pipe. This type of joint is illustrated in Fig. 26.4. These joints are not so readily disassembled as flange joints. They may be designed to withstand relatively high pressures. The thread design of the coupling must conform to the thread design of the pipes to be connected. For pipe sizes over 2 inches the threads are tapered 1 inch in 16 or 0.75 inch per foot measured on the diameter and along the axis. See Fig. 9.28. For pipe sizes of 2 inches and under, straight threads are frequently used on both ends of the coupling. Straight threads on one end and tapered threads on the other, or left-hand threads on one end and right-hand threads on the other are not unusual. To expedite disassembly in a threaded pipe system, couplings called pipe unions are used. See Fig. 26.5 for conventional screwed and flanged unions.

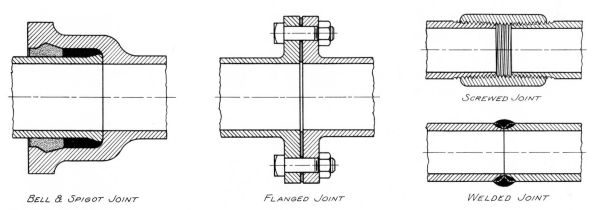

Fig. 26.4 Pipe joints.

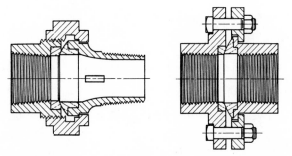

Fig. 26.5 Screwed and flanged unions.

Soldered joints are frequently used on copper and brass tubing, but pressure and temperature restrict the extensive use of solder as a jointing material.

26.6 PIPE FITTINGS. In order to control and change direction of flow in a piping system of any extent, a number of pipe fittings are necessary. Elbows, tees, crosses, laterals, return bends, and reducers are some of many in use. They are made of cast iron, steel, malleable iron, brass, and sometimes of special materials. They are not necessarily made of the same material as the pipe to which they are attached. Connections of these fittings to pipes and valves are made by flanges, screw fittings, welding, soldering, or jointing materials. A number of screw fittings are shown in Fig. 26.6.

Most pipe fittings are specified by material, name, and nominal pipe size. Some fittings such as tees, laterals, and crosses are sometimes used to connect pipes of different sizes. When this occurs, the fitting is called a reducing fitting and sizes of openings must be properly indicated. In the case of the reducing tee, lateral, and cross, the size of the largest opening is given first and then the size of the opening at the opposite end. When the fitting is a tee or a lateral, the third dimension is that of the outlet. When the fitting is a cross, the third dimension is the largest outlet opening and the fourth is the opposite opening. Figure 26.7 indicates the method of specifying sizes of reducing fittings.

26.7 VALVES. Volume of flow in pipes is controlled primarily by valves. The more common types are the gate valve, globe valve, and check valve. Many other types such as the angle valve, relief valve, needle valve, pressure-reducing valve, butterfly valve, and plug valve are not uncommon.

Most valve bodies in the smaller sizes are made of brass or bronze. Those in the larger sizes are usually made of cast iron for intermediate pressures, and cast steel or cast alloy for high pressures. They are not necessarily made of the same material as the pipes to which they are attached. Connections to pipes and fittings are usually made by flanges, screw fittings, or welding.

The gate valve is used more frequently than any other valve. When open it offers little restriction to straight-line flow. It is used on lines conveying water and other liquids.

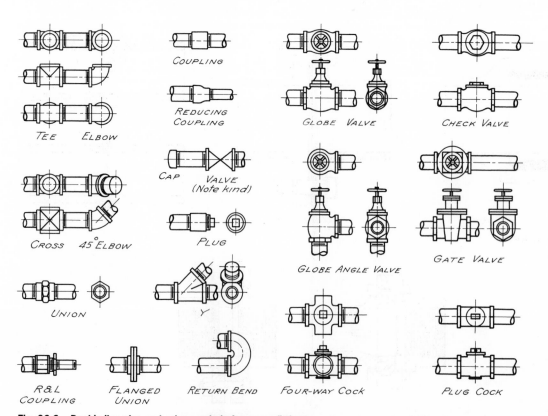

Fig. 26.6   Double-line pipe and valve symbols for screw fittings.

If the design is such that the gate moves out of the body of the valve with the stem, it is called a rising-stem valve. If the gate moves out of the body of the valve along the stem, it is called a non-rising-stem valve. Consideration of the mechanics of these two styles of gate valves is important. The rising-stem type requires more space for stem clearance than does the non-rising-stem type, but an open or closed position of the gate is clearly indicated by the position of the stem.

The globe valve is less expensive than the gate valve. It is used extensively for throttling on steam lines and where close regulation of volume of flow of liquids is necessary. In general, the design requires two changes of direction of flow which causes some loss of pressure in the system. All globe valves are of the rising-stem type. Ample space must be provided for operation to open completely.

The check valve is used to prevent reversal of the direction of flow. The design is usually quite simple, and in most cases gravity plays a part in its operation. The swing check and lift check, with variations, are the two principal types of check valves in common use.

Conventional gate, globe, and check valves are shown in Fig. 26.8.

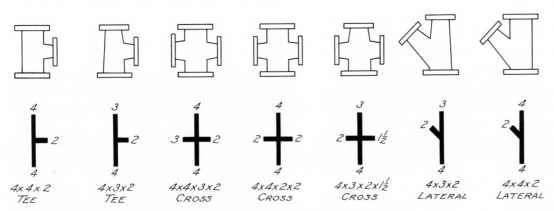

| 4x4x2 TEE | 4x3x2 TEE | 4x4x3x2 CROSS | 4x4x2x2 CROSS | 4x3x2x1½ CROSS | 4x3x2 LATERAL | 4x4x2 LATERAL |

Fig. 26.7   Method of designating sizes of reducing fittings.

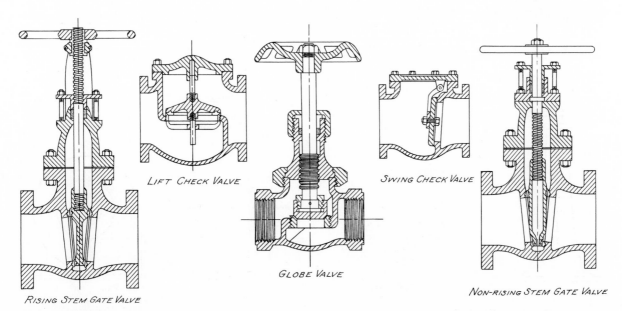

RISING STEM GATE VALVE

LIFT CHECK VALVE

GLOBE VALVE

SWING CHECK VALVE

NON-RISING STEM GATE VALVE

Fig. 26.8   Sections of valves.

26.8 PIPE BENDS. Where conventional long-turn elbows are not suitable for high velocity flow, fabricated pipe bends are frequently used. Lineal expansion and space limitations may also require their use. They may be obtained in almost any size and shape but requirements must be described to the manufacturer in the form of complete drawings and specifications.

Some conventional pipe bends are shown in Fig. 26.9.

26.9 PIPE SUPPORTS AND ACCESSORIES. Pipelines of any considerable extent require hangers and supports to provide for dead weight and stresses due to thermal expansion and vibration. Provision must also be made for adequate drainage of the line. Location, type, and spacing of supports are all important factors which must be given careful consideration. For horizontal runs, rods or straps are usually adequate

where the pipes are relatively small. They are usually attached to joists or steel work in the ceiling. For long vertical runs of considerable weight, bottom supports set on the floor are frequently used. Many types of supports with recommendations for spacing and slope are available from pipe manufacturers. Their recommendations should be carefully considered. A few types of pipe hangers are shown in Fig. 26.10.

In steam lines, special provision must be made for drainage of condensation. The slope of piping in these lines should be in the direction of steam flow. Drip pockets, steam separators, and steam traps are some of the devices used in this connection. A few of the more common accessories on steam and cold water lines are shown in Fig. 26.11. Many other accessories

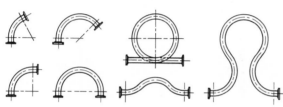

Fig. 26.9 Typical pipe bends.

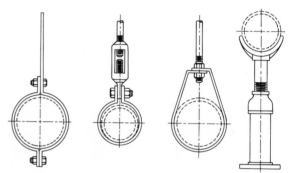

Fig. 26.10 Typical pipe supports.

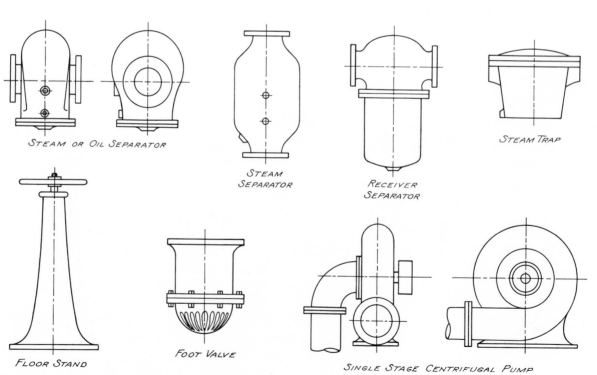

STEAM OR OIL SEPARATOR

STEAM SEPARATOR

RECEIVER SEPARATOR

STEAM TRAP

FLOOR STAND

FOOT VALVE

SINGLE STAGE CENTRIFUGAL PUMP

Fig. 26.11 Devices used in pipelines.

to pipelines are illustrated in manufacturers' catalogues.

26.10   PIPE SYMBOLS. Pipes, fittings, valves, fixtures, and accessories common to piping systems are most frequently represented on drawings by accepted standard symbols. The standard single-line symbols used on small-scale drawings are shown in Fig. 26.12. Shown in the Appendix are standard symbols for plant equipment and plumbing fixtures. These standard symbols are from the United States of America Standards Institute from which complete copies of graphical symbols may be purchased.

26.11   PIPE DRAWINGS AND DIAGRAMS. The purpose of pipe drawings is to show the location and size of pipes and the location and identification of valve fixtures and apparatus which go to make up all or parts of piping systems large or small. In general they are much like other engineering drawings. Orthographic, oblique, and axonometric are the types of projection most commonly used in pipe drawing. The use

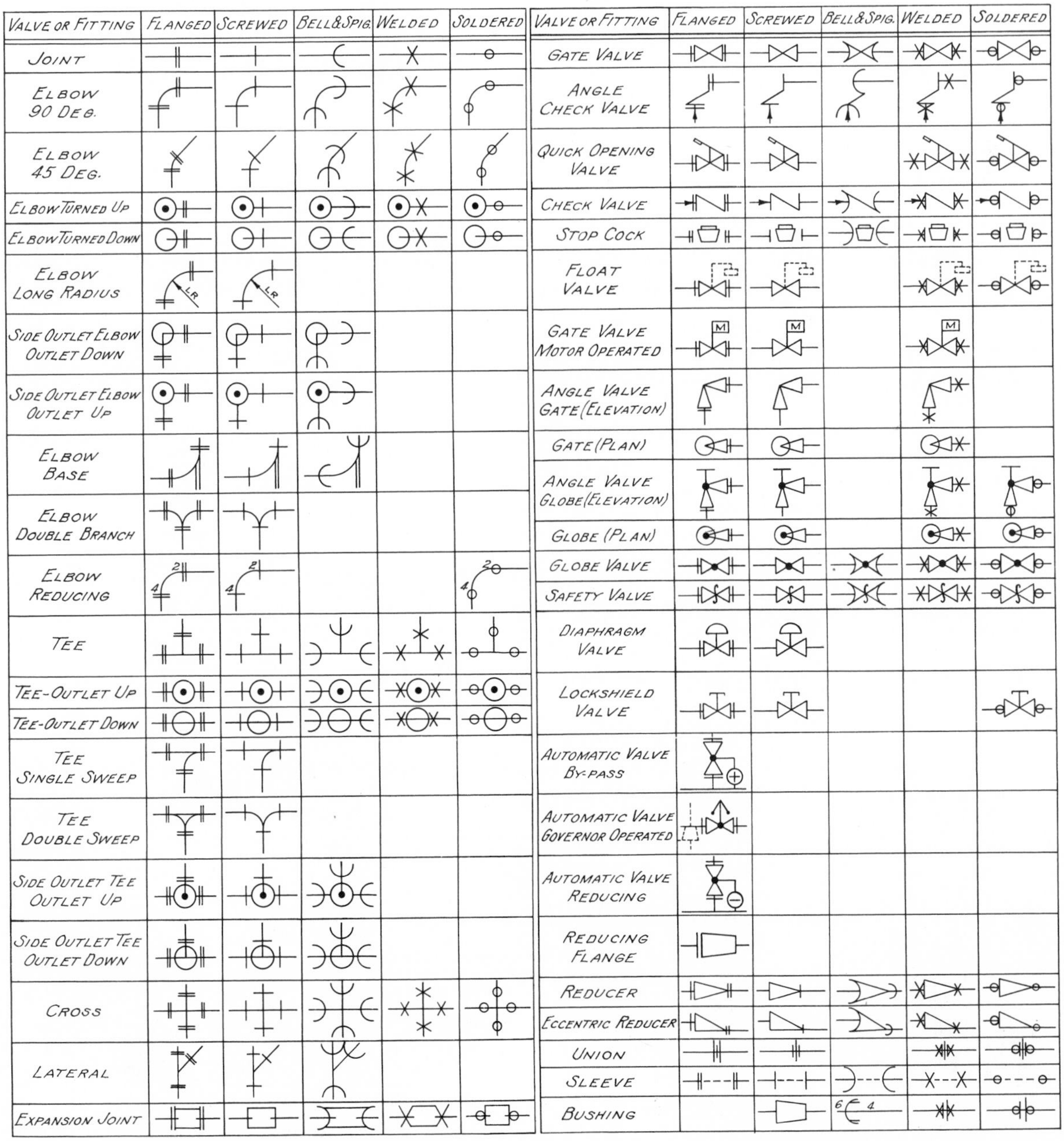

Fig. 26.12   American standard single-line pipe and valve symbols.

of either double-line or single-line representation of pipes, valves, and pipe fixtures is approved.

Orthographic one-, two-, or three-view projections are used in drawings of many installations. Double-line representation is ordinarily used where the system is made up principally of large pipe and where the

drawings may be used a number of times as reference on similar projects. Such a drawing is shown in Fig. 26.13. Single-line representation of small pipe is permissible on double-line pipe drawings. Where the number of pipelines in a system is large, it is good practice to make up several sheets for the same plant layout.

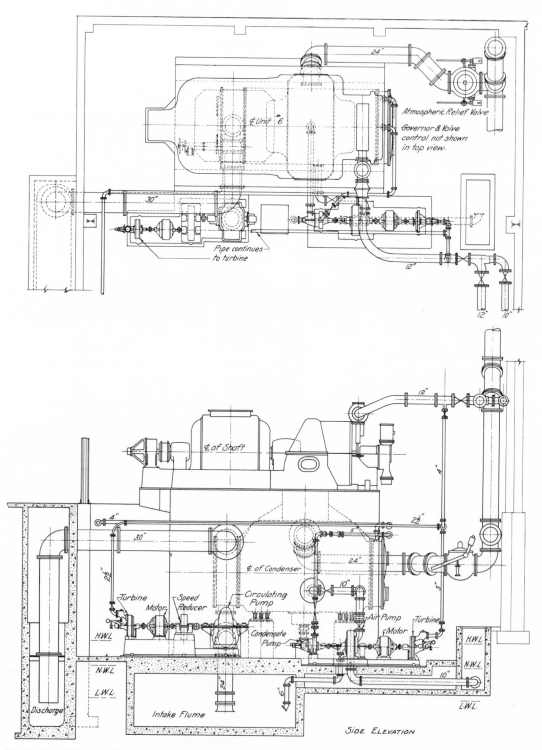

Fig. 26.13 Orthographic layout of a power plant unit.

One or more sheets might properly show the main lines only, others return lines, and still others laterals, etc. Such drawings should be made upon tracing paper or cloth so that they can be checked one over the other to see that no conflicts in the system exist.

For systems in which relatively small pipe is used it is good practice to represent all the pipes and pipe fixtures by single-line representation. This scheme saves much time in drafting and proves very satisfactory in drawings of small units or parts of systems. Figure 26.14 shows such a single-line piping diagram in one-view projection. A modification of the conventional two-view orthographic drawing of a small section of a piping system, sometimes called a developed view, is shown in Fig. 26.15. In this scheme the pipes are imagined to be revolved into a single plane, either the

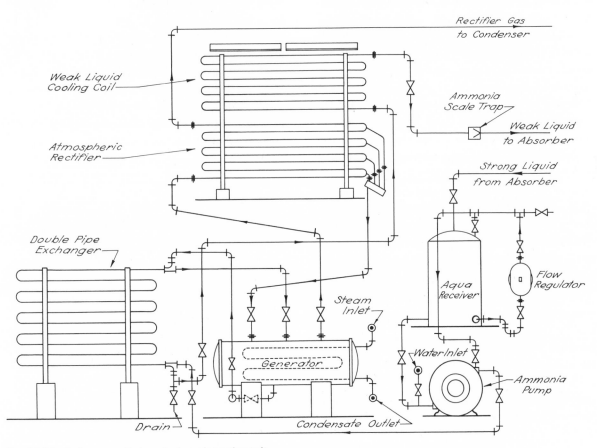

Fig. 26.14   A diagrammatic layout of an absorption unit.

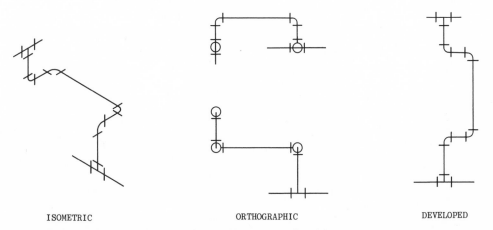

ISOMETRIC   ORTHOGRAPHIC   DEVELOPED

Fig. 26.15   Piping layout in pictorial, orthographic, and developed form.

horizontal or the vertical. This results in a one-view drawing and proves very effective on small-job studies and estimates.

For preliminary layouts and for reference in connection with complete drawings of piping systems, conventional pictorial drawings such as axonometric and oblique are very useful. Rules of projection governing proper pictorial representation of machine parts must be followed in the pictorial representation of piping. An isometric of a small section of piping both single-line and double-line is shown in Fig. 26.16. Single-line isometric is more frequently used than double-line since it serves the purpose equally well in most cases and is much more easily done.

Single-line oblique drawings may be used for the same purpose as isometrics and have advantages in allowable modifications that isometrics do not have. An oblique of a small heat distribution system is shown in Fig. 26.17. It should be noted that the usual method of oblique projection has been modified to allow a clear interpretation of the location of risers and returns in this layout. Such modifications of oblique are used only when necessary to add clearness to the drawing. On almost all pictorial drawings and diagrams of pipe layouts the single-line representation of pipes and pipe fixtures is used regardless of changes of pipe sizes in the system. In single-line pipe drawings for heating systems, the weight of the line representing supply is usually heavier than that representing return. See Fig. 26.17.

26.12   DIMENSIONS ON PIPE DRAWINGS. The general rules for dimensioning orthographic, axono-metric, and oblique apply to pipe drawings. All lengths of straight runs of pipe must be dimensioned. The pipe sizes are indicated by writing the nominal pipe diameter near the side of the pipe, using leaders when necessary. Practically all other dimensions are location dimensions; consequently center lines of pipes, fixtures, and apparatus must be used freely. Overall dimensions of valves and fixtures are seldom shown since their sizes are standard. Valves and apparatus are frequently identified by name or manufacturer's number on the drawing. The material of which the pipes, pipe fixtures, and valves are made is usually indicated in general specifications. Sizes of flanges, length of threads, and similar details are indicated on the drawing by conventional representation. On most pipe drawings, the dimensions are written on the dimension line rather than in a break in the line.

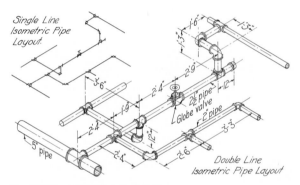

Fig. 26.16   Isometric pipe layout.

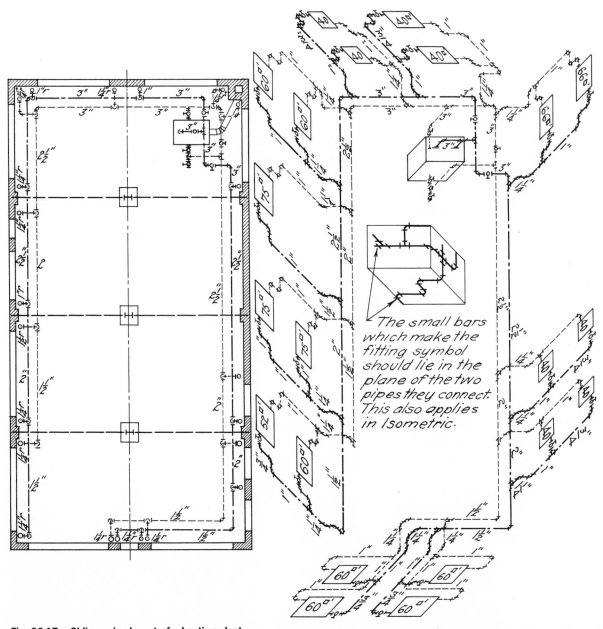

The small bars which make the fitting symbol should lie in the plane of the two pipes they connect. This also applies in Isometric.

Fig. 26.17   Oblique pipe layout of a heating plant.

SELF-STUDY QUESTIONS

Before trying to answer these questions, read the chapter carefully. Then, without reference to the text, answer as many questions as possible. For those that cannot be answered, the number, in parentheses following the question number, gives the article in which the answer can be found. Look it up and write down the answer. Check the answers that you did give to see that they are correct.

26.1 **(26.3)** Much of the pipe used in industry is made of _____ _____.

26.2 **(26.3)** Brass and _____ are also used for making pipes.

26.3 **(26.4)** The inside diameters selected in designing a piping system depend on the volume of _____ desired.

26.4 **(26.4)** For standard steel or wrought-iron pipe in sizes larger than 12 inch the specified size is the _____ diameter.

26.5 **(26.5)** Standard steel pipes are usually connected by _____ or threaded _____.

26.6 **(26.6)** Pipe fittings are specified by name _____ and nominal _____ size.

26.7 **(26.7)** Common types of valves are the gate, _____ and _____ valves.

26.8 **(26.7)** The check valve is used to prevent a _____ of the direction of flow.

26.9 **(26.11)** Orthographic projections _____ and axonometric are used in making pipe drawings.

26.10 **(26.10)** In pipe layout drawings fitting valves, fixtures, and other accessories are represented on the drawing by standard _____.

26.11 **(26.11)** Where a piping system is made up of large pipe, the _____ line symbols are usually used.

26.12 **(26.11)** For systems using small pipes it is good practice to represent all pipes and _____ by _____ line symbols.

PROBLEMS

The following problems are typical of many that can be assigned. Excellent sources of material and references are actual building plans, water treatment systems, valve catalogues, and trade journals.

Sheet sizes, scales, paper, etc., should be chosen to meet the requirements of the problems. In general, 8½″ × 11″ or 11″ × 17″ should be a suitable sheet size.

26.1 Make a one-view freehand sketch of a gate valve, globe valve, or check valve for either flange or threaded connections as assigned.

26.2 Make an orthographic two-view double-line piping drawing of a section of a piping system to include 5 elbows, 3 valves (cross, check, and angle), 2 couplings (R. and L. and union), 1 cross, 1 reducer, 1 plug, and connecting pipe runs. Use either flanged or threaded connections as assigned.

26.3 Make a single-line isometric layout of the section of piping described in Problem 26.2.

26.4 In Fig. 26.18 is shown an isometric single-line piping diagram for a small pump house. In Fig. 26.19 is shown a partial double-line layout for the same system. Standard wrought-iron pipe is to be used in the interior.

Standard cast-iron pipe is to be used underground. Five-inch pipe is to be used from supply to pump. All other pipe is to be 4″. Standard cast-iron valves and fittings are to be used throughout. Flange fittings are to be used from pump to supply and pump to storage tank. Threaded fittings are to be used from the main line to the compound chamber and return. Complete the double-line pipe drawing of the system. Show pipe sizes and all necessary location dimensions and elevations necessary for construction and operation of the system.

26.5 Make a list of the pipe and fittings to be ordered for the system in Problem 26.4. Arrange the list in tabular form under headings of size, pipe lengths, valves (number and kind), fittings (number and kind), material, remarks.

26.6 Following are some typical piping layouts. Make an isometric single-line layout of all, or assigned, portions from any of the given layouts in Figs. 26.20 to 26.22.

26.7 Make a two-view orthographic drawing of portions assigned in Problem 26.6. Show pipe sizes and all necessary location dimensions.

26.8 Make a pipe and fittings list for portions assigned in Problem 26.6. Arrange as suggested in Problem 26.5.

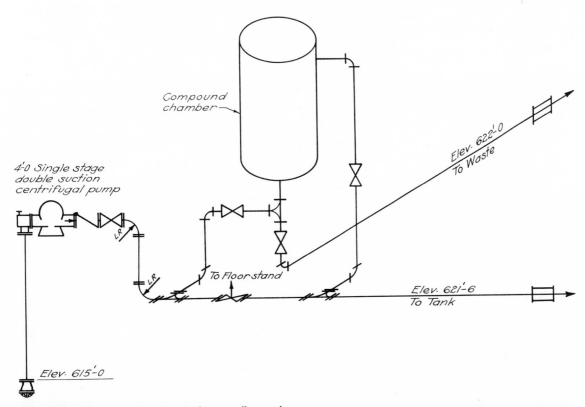

Fig. 26.18   Single-line piping diagram for a small pump house.

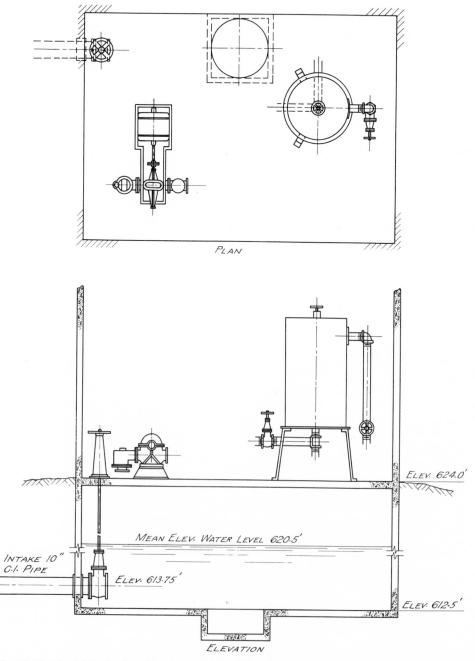

PLAN

ELEV. 624.0'

MEAN ELEV. WATER LEVEL 620.5'

INTAKE 10"
C·I· PIPE

ELEV. 613·75'

ELEV. 612·5'

ELEVATION

Fig. 26.19   Partial double-line piping layout for a small pump house.

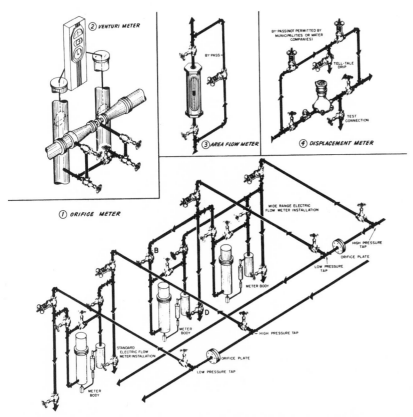

Fig. 26.20 Typical meter connections. (Courtesy Jenkins Bros., Manufacturers of Valves.)

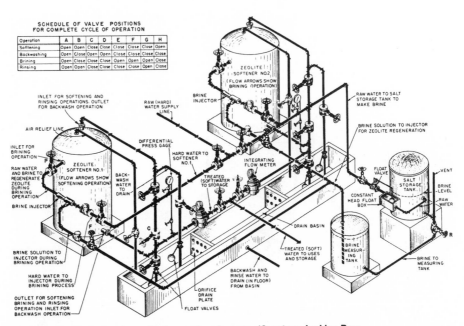

Fig. 26.21 Typical water-softening system layouts. (Courtesy Jenkins Bros., Manufacturers of Valves.)

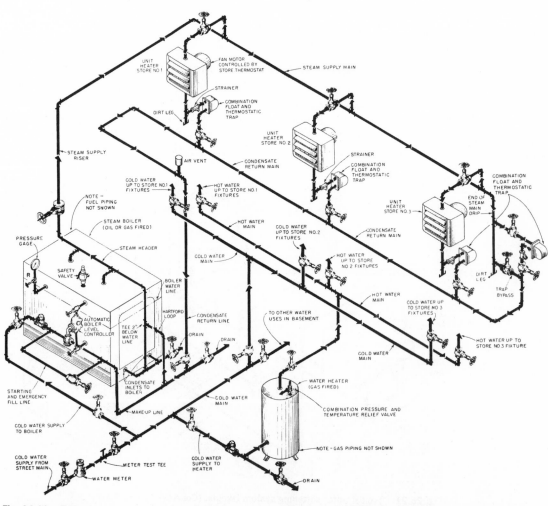

Fig. 26.22 Typical piping layout for plumbing and heating. (Courtesy Jenkins Bros., Manufacturers of Valves.)

CHAPTER 27

Welding Drawing

OLD: Blacksmith of the 1890's. (The Granger Collection)

NEW: Modern welding. (Robert M. Mottar)

Chapter 27 Welding Drawing

27.1 INTRODUCTION. For permanent fastening of parts of a structure, welding is a very important method. Many machine parts are now being constructed by welding various units together, thus making a built-up structure to replace a complicated casting or riveted part.

The earliest form of welding consisted of heating the parts and pounding them together on an anvil until they were joined together. From this stage the process of welding has been developed to its present state of perfection where almost any kind of metal may be satisfactorily welded. The two principal kinds of welding now generally used are fusion welding and forge welding.

a. *Fusion welding* is the term applied to the method of joining two pieces of metal by melting metal into a joint that has been raised to the melting temperature. Thus a fusion weld is actually a process whereby two parts are joined by bringing the metal of each part to a liquid state and adding extra molten metal which forms the joint when cooled.

b. *Forge welding* is the term applied to the method of joining two pieces of metal by heating them to the plastic state and then forcing the parts together either by pressure or by a blow of a hammer. In modern welding various kinds of machines are used to apply the pressure or the hammer blow.

27.2 METHODS OF WELDING. Welding may also be classified according to the method of applying the heat. Under this group there are four main divisions: gas welding, arc welding, resistance welding, and Thermit welding.

27.2.1 Gas welding is that type in which the heat is supplied by burning acetylene or hydrogen gas. The gas under pressure is mixed with oxygen and ignited. This creates a very hot flame which can be regulated to give various characteristics by adjusting the flow of the gas or the oxygen. Temperatures as high as 6000° F may be obtained with the oxyacetylene torch.

27.2.2 Arc welding is that type in which the heat is applied by means of an electric arc. Usually the parts to be welded are wired as one pole of the arc with the electrode held by the operator forming the other pole. Sometimes this is a carbon electrode, in which case the extra metal for the weld is supplied by a welding rod held in the arc in a manner similar to gas welding. More frequently the welding rod is used as the electrode so that the electrode itself gradually melts away, thus supplying the extra metal for the weld. Sometimes the arc is formed between two tungsten points, neither of which touches the metal being welded, in which case extra metal must be supplied by a filler rod. This latter method is used in atomic-hydrogen arc welding. The temperature of the arc is about 6000° F.

27.2.3 Resistance welding. Electric current is also used as a source of heat in a type of welding known as resistance welding. This is usually considered the easiest and cheapest method of fastening the pieces of metal together permanently. It is based on the fact that electric current flowing through metal will heat the metal when the resistance increases. Therefore, since current flowing from one plate to another will encounter the greatest resistance at the joint, whether it be a lap joint or a butt joint, the tendency is to heat the metal at the joint. The temperature at the joint may be regulated by the amount of the current. When the proper temperature is attained, pressure applied by some kind of machine will create a forge weld, thus fastening the two pieces together. This may be done over the entire joint, forming a butt or seam weld, or at particular points forming a spot weld. The term flash weld is sometimes used when the ends of two parts are joined by resistance welding.

27.2.4 Thermit welding is a method based on the strong affinity of aluminum for oxygen. A mixture of finely divided aluminum and iron oxide may be ignited at one spot, and it will then burn rapidly at a very high temperature, leaving a quantity of molten metal and aluminum oxide slag in the container. The temperature resulting from this reaction is about 4500° F. The reaction must be started by lighting a small quantity of special ignition powder.

For the fusion method of Thermit welding, it is first necessary to build a wax mold around the break or joint. A refractory sand mold is then constructed around the wax, which is dried out and preheated by some method such as blowing vaporized kerosene and air into the mold. During this preheating process the wax is burned out, leaving a space into which the metal melted by the Thermit reaction may be poured. This molten metal fuses with the parts to be joined together and upon cooling leaves a welded joint.

In some cases, such as the Thermit pipe weld, only the heat of the Thermit metal and slag is used to make a forge weld. With the ends of the pipe faced and butted together, the slag and the Thermit metal are poured around the joint. The heat of the metal raises the temperature of the pipe to a point where the forge weld can be made by pressing the two pieces together. After cooling the Thermit metal can be broken off because the slag forms a coating on the pipe which prevents the Thermit metal from sticking to the pipe.

27.3 TYPES OF JOINTS. One very valuable feature of welding is that the parts may be fastened together in almost any relative position. However, there are certain standard joints that are most frequently encountered in welding operations. Figure 27.1 shows the joints most commonly found in practice.

27.3.1 Cross section of joint. The thickness of the parts to be joined will have a large bearing on the cross section of the joint. If the plates are thin, the plain butt joint may be used as shown in Fig. 27.2(a). Plates with a little greater thickness might be prepared with a single V butt joint as in Fig. 27.2(b) or a Y type butt joint as in Fig. 27.2(c). Still greater thickness might require a double V butt joint with the welding being done from both sides. See Fig. 27.2(d). Other methods of preparing the parts for welding are shown in Figs. 27.2(e) to (m).

27.4 WELDING SYMBOLS FOR FUSION WELDING. There are so many different conditions under which welding is done and so much information to be conveyed from the office to the welding operator that the

American Welding Society has devised a composite symbol by means of which all this information may be transmitted. This symbol is in the general form of an arrow on which other symbols, letters, and marks may be placed to give complete instructions for fusion welding. The form of this arrow as well as the kind and position of other symbols is given in Fig. 27.3.

27.5 WELDING LEGEND FOR FUSION WELDING. When fusion welding is specified on a drawing by means of the welding symbols, a legend should be placed on the drawing to aid in interpreting the symbols. This legend is shown in Fig. 27.4. To further aid in clarifying the use of the welding symbol, many of the figures shown in Fig. 27.2 are repeated in Fig. 27.5 together with the proper welding symbols.

These symbols may be made either mechanically or freehand.

Fillet, bevel, and groove weld symbols should always be shown with the perpendicular leg to the left.

The size dimension should be to the left of the symbol with length and spacing of increments to the right.

The finish of a weld may be indicated as shown in Fig. 27.5(k). The letters C, G, and M are used to indicate chip, grind, or machine. The standard finish mark f may also be used.

When only one member is to be grooved, it is important that the arrow point specifically to that member as in Figs. 27.5(h) or (i).

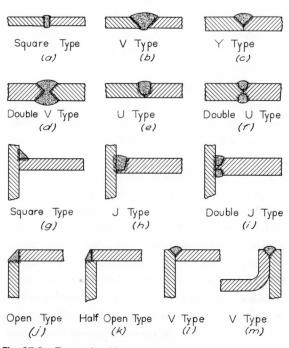

Fig. 27.2 Types of welds.

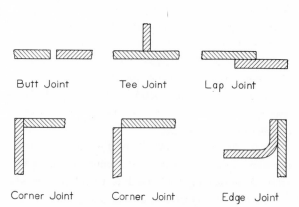

Fig. 27.1 Types of joints.

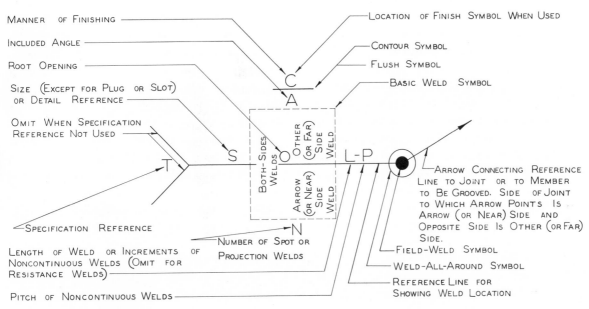

Fig. 27.3   Welding symbol.

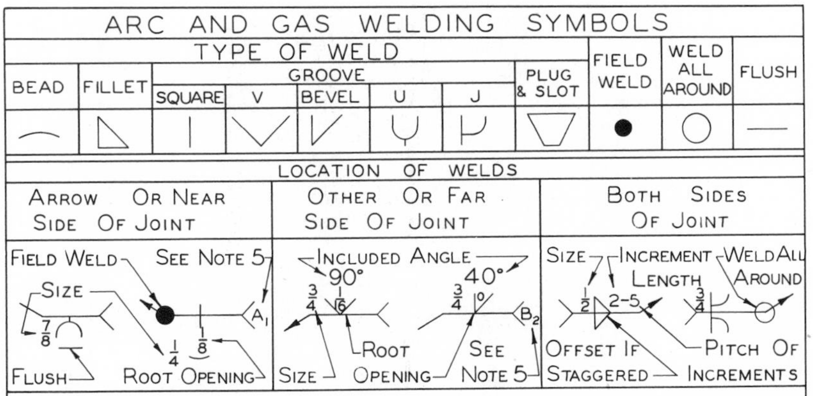

ARC AND GAS WELDING SYMBOLS										
TYPE OF WELD							FIELD WELD	WELD ALL AROUND	FLUSH
BEAD	FILLET	GROOVE					PLUG & SLOT			
		SQUARE	V	BEVEL	U	J				
⌒	◺	‖	∨	⩒	⋃	⊔	⟋⟍	●	○	—

LOCATION OF WELDS

| ARROW OR NEAR SIDE OF JOINT | OTHER OR FAR SIDE OF JOINT | BOTH SIDES OF JOINT |

1. THE SIDE OF THE JOINT TO WHICH THE ARROW POINTS IS THE ARROW (OR NEAR) SIDE.

2. BOTH-SIDES WELDS OF SAME TYPE ARE OF SAME SIZE UNLESS OTHERWISE SHOWN.

3. SYMBOLS APPLY BETWEEN ABRUPT CHANGES IN DIRECTION OF JOINT OR AS DIMENSIONED (EXCEPT WHERE ALL AROUND SYMBOL IS USED).

4. ALL WELDS ARE CONTINUOUS AND OF USER'S STANDARD PROPORTIONS UNLESS OTHERWISE SHOWN.

5. TAIL OF ARROW USED FOR SPECIFICATION REFERENCE (TAIL MAY BE OMITTED WHEN REFERENCE NOT USED).

6. DIMENSIONS OF WELD SIZES, INCREMENT LENGTHS, AND SPACINGS IN INCHES.

Fig. 27.4   Arc and gas welding symbols.

For complete instructions for making these symbols, see the booklet entitled *Welding Symbols* by the American Welding Society, 345 East 47th Street, New York City.

27.6 WELDING LEGEND FOR RESISTANCE WELDING. When resistance welding is specified there must be some difference in the symbols because there is no significance to the terms "arrow" side or "other" side, since the weld always occurs between the two parts. Consequently the symbols are centered on the arrow as shown in Fig. 27.6. Instead of size of the fillet, the weld is specified by strength as indicated in Fig. 27.6. Sometimes the symbol is placed on the arrow and sometimes shown on the drawing in its actual position which may be dimensioned. Figure 27.6 shows the legend to be placed on the drawing when resistance welds are to be specified.

The use of resistance weld symbols is shown in Fig. 27.7. Note that when the welding symbol is placed on the drawing; only the strength specification is placed on the arrow.

27.7 OTHER METHODS OF SPECIFYING WELDS. Although the symbols of the American Welding Society are being used in many industries, welds are still being specified by other means. Probably the most common is to show cross hatching on the drawing at the place where the weld is to be placed. In that case notes and dimensions on the drawing give the required information about the weld. This method is illustrated in Fig. 27.8.

27.8 WELDING SYMBOLS ON WORKING DRAWINGS. An application of fusion welding symbols to a working drawing of a machine part is shown in Fig. 27.9. A second application to a structural joint of a truss is shown in Fig. 27.10.

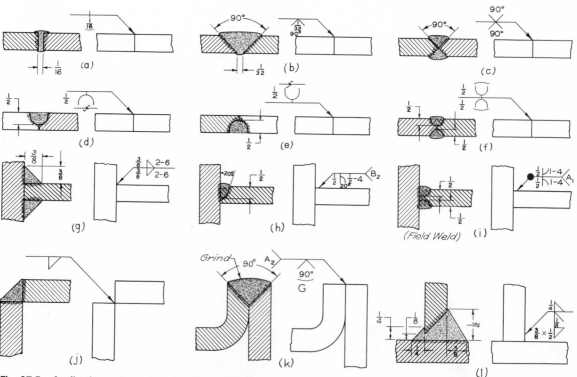

Fig. 27.5 Application and meaning of welding symbols.

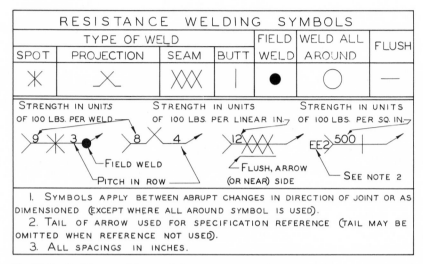

RESISTANCE WELDING SYMBOLS						
TYPE OF WELD				FIELD	WELD ALL	FLUSH
SPOT	PROJECTION	SEAM	BUTT	WELD	AROUND	
✕	✕	✕✕✕	|	●	◯	—

STRENGTH IN UNITS OF 100 LBS. PER WELD

STRENGTH IN UNITS OF 100 LBS. PER LINEAR IN.

STRENGTH IN UNITS OF 100 LBS. PER SQ. IN.

9 ✕ 3 ●   8 ✕ 4   12 ✕✕✕   EE2 500 \|

FIELD WELD

PITCH IN ROW

FLUSH, ARROW (OR NEAR) SIDE

SEE NOTE 2

1. SYMBOLS APPLY BETWEEN ABRUPT CHANGES IN DIRECTION OF JOINT OR AS DIMENSIONED (EXCEPT WHERE ALL AROUND SYMBOL IS USED).
2. TAIL OF ARROW USED FOR SPECIFICATION REFERENCE (TAIL MAY BE OMITTED WHEN REFERENCE NOT USED).
3. ALL SPACINGS IN INCHES.

Fig. 27.6   Resistance welding symbols.

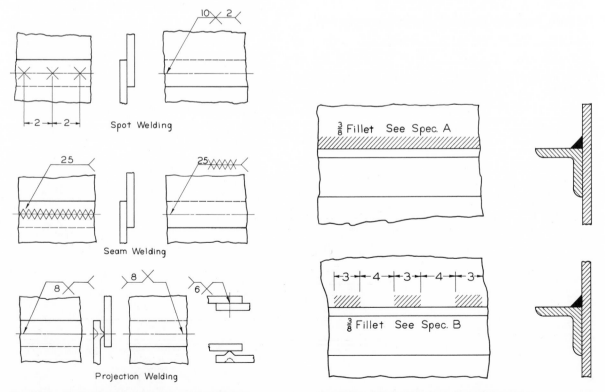

Fig. 27.7   Application of resistance welding symbols.

Fig. 27.8   Alternate method of showing welds.

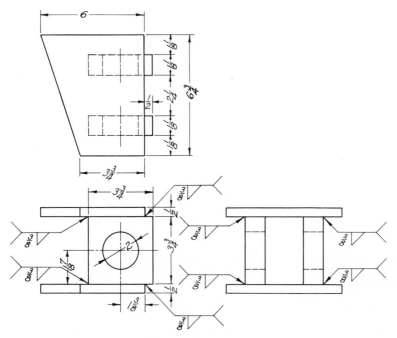

Fig. 27.9 Application of welding symbols to a machine part.

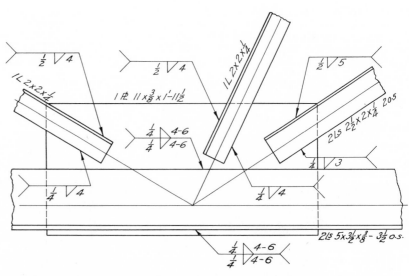

Fig. 27.10 Application of a welding symbol to a structural connection.

SELF-STUDY QUESTIONS

Before trying to answer these questions, read the chapter carefully. Then, without reference to the text, answer as many questions as possible. For those that cannot be answered, the number, in parentheses following the question number, gives the article in which the answer can be found. Look it up and write down the answer. Check the answers that you did give to see that they are correct.

27.1 **(27.1)** When two parts are joined together by melting metal into a joint that has itself been raised to the melting point, this is called _____ welding.

27.2 **(27.1)** When two parts are heated to a plastic state and then joined together under pressure, this process is called _____ welding.

27.3 **(27.2)** Welding may be classified according to the method of _____ the heat.

27.4 **(27.2.1)** When the heat is applied by an open flame the method is called _____ welding.

27.5 **(27.2.2)** When electric current is used for welding the method may be either _____ welding or _____ welding.

27.6 **(27.2.1)** Temperatures as high as _____ degrees may be obtained with the oxyacetylene torch.

27.7 **(27.2.2)** In arc welding, one electric pole consists of the _____ that are to be joined together and the _____ held by the operator is the other pole.

27.8 **(27.2.3)** Electric resistance welding depends on the fact that the _____ is great at the point of contact between two pieces of metal and consequently the heating is greater at this point.

27.9 **(27.2.4)** Thermit welding is based upon the strong _____ of aluminum for _____ .

27.10 **(27.2.4)** A mixture of finely divided _____ and iron oxide can be ignited and will burn at a temperature of about 4500° Fahrenheit.

27.11 **(27.3.1)** For welding thin plates the plain _____ joint may be used.

27.12 **(27.3.1)** For thick plates the _____ V-butt joint may be used.

27.13 **(27.4)** The general symbol for fusion is made in the form of an _____ upon which other symbols, letters and marks may be placed.

27.14 Make a sketch of a welding symbol showing

(a) ½″ fillet weld on both sides,

(b) Noncontinuous weld with welds 2″ long spaced 3″ apart.

PROBLEMS

In these problems the student should decide upon the type of joint to be used and make a welding drawing for shop use. It is not intended that the student design for strength, so in each case he will weld the entire length of contact.

In structural members the weld should be made on both sides of the member.

27.1 Make a complete welding drawing for any joint in the truss specified by the instructor from Fig. 25.47 in Chapter 25.

27.2 Same as Problem 27.1, using Fig. 25.48 in Chapter 25.

27.3 Make a welding drawing for constructing the object in Fig. 15.62, Chapter 15, by building it from flat plates.

27.4 Same as Problem 27.3, using Fig. 15.65 in Chapter 15.

27.5 Same as Problem 27.3, using the object in Fig. 6.93 in Chapter 6.

27.6 Same as Problem 27.3, using the object in Fig. 7.53 in Chapter 7.

OLD: Parallel lathes of 1860's used in metal drilling. (The Bettmann Archive)

NEW: Tape controlled drill. (Courtesy of DeVlieg Company)

Chapter 28 Machine Drawing

28.1   INTRODUCTION. In the design of any mechanism certain elements are always involved in the transmission of motion. Exclusive of linkages of various types, these common elements are shafts, pulleys, gears, cams, bearings and seals for them, keys, splines, and the usual fasteners. To these must be added devices for the lubrication of moving parts.

Bolts, screws, keys, and keyways have been treated in Chapter 9. Tables of sizes of these elements are given in the Appendix.

28.2   STANDARD OR STOCK SIZES. All items mentioned above and many others are carried in stock by companies who specialize in producing them. When production of an item is not to be in sufficient quantity to warrant manufacture of all parts, many can be purchased from suppliers, if this is kept in mind in the original design.

28.3   SHAFTS. Circular steel shafts for power transmission and machine parts may be obtained, finished to close tolerances. For machine parts, stock shafts vary in size, by 1/16 inch, from 1/2 to 2 1/2 inches in diameter. From 2 1/2 to 4 inches, they vary by 1/8 inch intervals. Tolerances are always negative and vary from 0.002 for the smaller size to 0.004 on the larger ones.

28.4   PULLEYS. Pulleys for flat belts offer no problem for the draftsman and can be made as desired. The shape of *V*-belts, however, has been standardized, and the grooves in the pulleys should conform to these standards, as shown in Fig. 28.1 which is taken, by permission, from the SAE *Handbook*.

28.5   GEARS. Gears are used to transmit motion and power from one part of a machine to another. The motion is usually uniform, but this does not imply that the two parts thus connected have the same rates of speed. The speed ratios depend on the relative sizes of the gears. There are many types of gears, but we shall consider here only the spur gear, the bevel gear, and the worm gear and wheel, which constitute the basic types.

A spur gear is simply a short hollow cylinder on which teeth have been cut, cast, or otherwise formed, with their elements (edge lines) all parallel to the axis of the cylinder. See Fig. 28.2. A bevel gear is a frustrum

of a hollow cone on which teeth have been cut, or cast, with their edge lines all meeting at the apex of the cone. See Figs. 28.7 and 28.8. In small gears the tooth cylinder or cone is joined to the hub by a web; on large gears by spokes or arms. A worm gear is a solid cylinder or shaft on which a continuous helical tooth has been cut to mesh with the teeth on a wheel, as shown in Fig. 28.11. The teeth on the wheel resemble those of the spur gear, but each is turned at a fixed angle relative to the plane of the axis of the wheel and the center of the tooth.

The smaller of two meshing spur or bevel gears is called a pinion. See Fig. 28.2. The minimum number of teeth on a pinion is limited by common practice to 12. When gear teeth are formed on a straight thick bar or plate, the product is called a rack. See Fig. 28.4. A rack is simply a gear of infinite radius. The shape of the tooth on a rack is not the same as on the gear, being absolutely straight in the involute system. Racks and gears having the same basic tooth form will mesh properly if the linear pitch of the one is equal to the circular pitch of the other.

A complete discussion of the design and manufacture of gears would constitute a treatise in itself. Limits of space in this book permit the presentation of only such elements of description and design as will enable the draftsman to represent properly the simpler gear types on shop drawings.

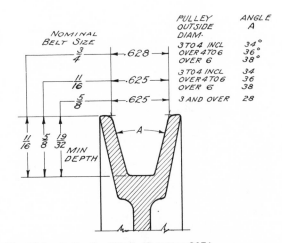

Fig. 28.1   Pulley for *V*-belt. (Courtesy SAE.)

28.6   SPUR GEARS—DEFINITION OF TERMS AND FORMULAS.

In order to make drawings of gears or to understand any discussion concerning them, the meaning of certain common terms must be understood. For coarse pitch gears with up to a diametral pitch of 20 and for either a 20° or 25° pressure angle, the common terms are defined below and illustrated in Figs. 28.2 and 28.3. In the following formulas, N represents the number of teeth in a gear.

Pitch circle. If two gears are in mesh, their pitch circles represent two cylinders in contact which would have the same motion as the gears, provided that the cylinders do not slip.

Diametral pitch (DP). The number of teeth per inch of pitch diameter. $DP = N/PD$.

Pitch diameter (PD). The diameter of the pitch circle. $PD = N/DP$.

Circular pitch (CP). The distance between the centers of two consecutive teeth measured on the pitch circle. $CP = (PD \times 3.1416)/N$ or $3.1416/DP$.

Addendum (A). The radial distance from the pitch circle to the top of the tooth. $A = 1.000/DP$.

Dedendum (D). The radial distance from the pitch circle to the bottom of the tooth space. $D = 1.250/DP$.

Clearance (C). The distance between a tooth and the bottom of its engaging space. $C = 0.250/DP$.

Working depth. The distance a tooth penetrates a space. It is equal to twice the addendum.

Whole depth (WD). The working depth plus the clearance. $WD = 2.25/DP$.

Tooth thickness (TT). The thickness of the tooth measured along the pitch circle. $TT = \pi/2DP$ or $CP/2$.

Pitch point (P). The point where the common normal cuts the line of centers of the gears. The pitch circles of two gears in mesh are tangent at the pitch point.

Tooth face. The portion of the gear tooth outside the pitch circle is called the tooth face.

Tooth flank. The part of the tooth inside the pitch circle is called the flank of the tooth.

Chordal thickness (CT). The thickness of a tooth measured along a chord of the pitch circle. $CT = PD \sin (90°/N)$.

Distance between gear centers (CD). The distance between gear centers is equal to $(N_1 + N_2)/2DP$.

Outside diameter of gears. The outside diameter of a gear is equal to $(N + 2)/DP$.

Base circle. The circle from which the involute curve is formed.

Pressure angle (ϕ). The angle between the common perpendicular of two involute gear tooth profiles in contact and the normal to their center line. See Fig. 28.3.

To find the pitch diameters of two meshing gears when the distance between centers is known and the number of teeth is known:

$$(PD)_1 = [(2CD)/(N_1 + N_2)]N_1$$
$$(PD)_2 = [(2CD)/(N_1 + N_2)]N_2$$

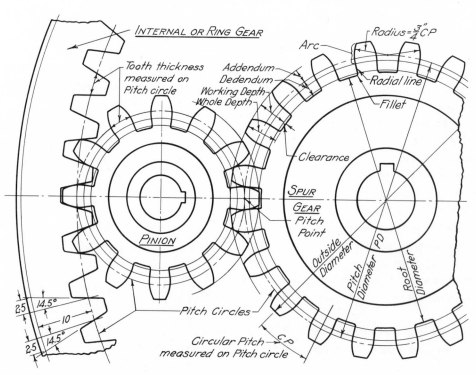

Fig. 28.2   Spur, pinion, and ring gear.

28.7 TOOTH FORMS IN SPUR GEARING AND RACKS. Both the involute and cycloidal systems of tooth profiles are in use, but for many years the involute system has practically replaced the cycloidal. Both are illustrated in Fig. 28.3. The profiles shown are theoretically those obtained by the usual geometrical construction of the involute, the epicycloid, and the hypocycloid curves. Actually, the profiles are close approximations to these curves, slight modifications being made in cutting the teeth to take care of interference and for consideration of strength. Circles are used on the drawings in place of curves.

Figure 28.4 illustrates the details for the racks of four basic gear tooth systems: the 14½° composite system, the 20° stub involute system, the 20° full-depth involute system, and the 25° full-depth involute system. The rack in Fig. 28.4(b) has never been widely used. The gear tooth profiles illustrated in Figs. 28.4(c) and (d) are the ones in most common use today.

Gears made with any of these standard gear tooth profiles and having the same diametral pitch are interchangeable with each other. They are not interchange-

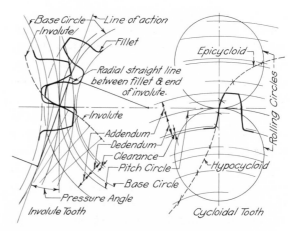

Fig. 28.3   Gear tooth curves or profiles.

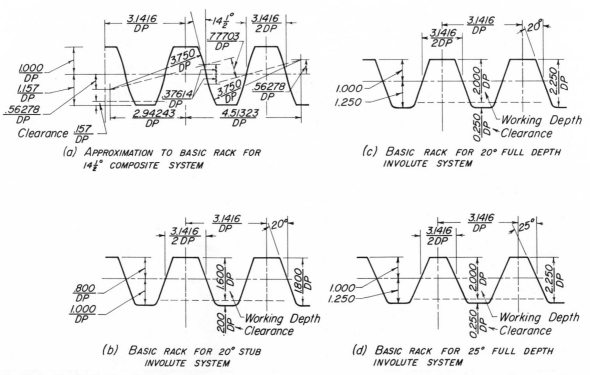

Fig. 28.4   Standard basic rack tooth profiles.

able between one standard and another. Each profile has elements of simplicity both in drawing and cutting the teeth. Only the involute and cycloid are used in the composite tooth profiles and straight line segments in the other three. Close approximation to the actual tooth shape, for drawing purposes, is obtained in the composite system by using circles for the cycloids as shown in Fig. 28.4(*a*). When composite, stub, coarse pitch, or fine pitch teeth are cut on spur gears, the proportions listed in Table 28.1 are used.

28.8 COMPARISON OF INVOLUTE AND CYCLOIDAL GEARS. The cycloidal gear has been largely replaced by the involute. There are, however, advantages for both systems when one is compared to the other.

Cycloidal gears do not have interference, and in general a cycloidal tooth is stronger than an involute tooth because it has spreading flanks in contrast to the radial flanks of an involute tooth. Cycloidal teeth have pure rolling action, whereas with the involute teeth there is sliding action which results in more rapid wear. The center-to-center distance of cycloidal gears must be maintained in order to assume a constant angular velocity between the gears. In general, involute gears can be produced more accurately and more economically than cycloidal gears.

Cycloidal gears are used almost exclusively in watches and fine instruments, whereas in most other applications involute gears are used.

28.9 WORKING DRAWINGS OF SPUR GEARS. The working drawings of gears that are to be cut from blanks are very simple. The drawing itself and the dimensions on it give information only about the gear blank. Information concerning the teeth is usually given in the form of notes, as illustrated in Fig. 28.5. If the gear is small and therefore has a solid web instead of arms, only the sectional view need be drawn. See drawing of pinion in Fig. 28.5. For the design of gear teeth it is recommended that the following American Standards be consulted: USASI-B6.1, USASI-B6, USASI-B6.7, and USASI-B6.8; or the American Gear Manufacturers Association (AGMA) publications 201.2 and 201.02A.

28.10 ASSEMBLY DRAWINGS OF SPUR GEARS. In assembly drawings, especially those intended for display purposes, it is sometimes desirable to repre-

TABLE 28.1 TOOTH PROPORTIONS FOR SPUR GEARS[a]

	$14\frac{1}{2}°$ Composite System and $14\frac{1}{2}°$ Brown and Sharpe	20° Stub System	Coarse Pitch (1–19.99 *DP*) AGMA 201.02 20° or 25° Full Depth	Fine Pitch (20–200 *DP*) AGMA 207.04 20° Full Depth
1. Addendum	$\dfrac{1}{DP}$	$\dfrac{0.8}{DP}$	$\dfrac{1}{DP}$	$\dfrac{1}{DP}$
2. Minimum dedendum	$\dfrac{1.157}{DP}$	$\dfrac{1}{DP}$	$\dfrac{1.250}{DP}$	$\dfrac{1.2}{DP} + 0.002$
3. Working depth	$\dfrac{2}{DP}$	$\dfrac{1.6}{DP}$	$\dfrac{2}{DP}$	$\dfrac{2}{DP}$
4. Minimum total depth	$\dfrac{2.157}{DP}$	$\dfrac{1.8}{DP}$	$\dfrac{2.250}{DP}$	$\dfrac{2.2}{DP} + 0.002$
5. Fillet radius	$\dfrac{0.209}{DP}$	$\dfrac{0.300}{DP}$	$\dfrac{0.300}{DP}$	$\dfrac{0.236}{DP}$
6. Outside diameter	$\dfrac{N+2}{DP}$	$\dfrac{N+1.6}{DP}$	$\dfrac{N+2}{DP}$	$\dfrac{N+2}{DP}$
7. Basic tooth thickness on pitch line	$\dfrac{\pi}{2DP}$	$\dfrac{\pi}{2DP}$	$\dfrac{\pi}{2DP}$	$\dfrac{\pi}{2DP}$
8. Minimum clearance	$\dfrac{0.157}{DP}$	$\dfrac{0.200}{DP}$	$\dfrac{0.250}{DP}$	$\dfrac{0.2}{DP} + 0.002$

[a] In terms of diametral pitch (inches).

sent the gear teeth profiles. A very simple approximate method that is suitable for all diametral pitches and pitch diameters is shown in Fig. 28.6. The steps are as follows:

a. Draw the pitch circle.

b. Draw the addendum circle equal to the radius of the pitch circle plus the addendum.

c. Draw the dedendum circle with radius equal to the radius of the pitch circle minus the dedendum.

d. Locate the pitch point P on the pitch circle and the line of center of the gears.

e. Space off the tooth thickness by laying off one fourth of the circular pitch ($CP/4$) on either side of the pitch point (P) along the pitch circle. The tooth thickness is one half of the circular pitch.

f. Draw the arcs for the tooth face by striking arcs with a radius of ¾ CP with centers on the pitch circle. The arcs are drawn from the addendum circle to the pitch circle.

g. Draw the tooth flank by drawing a radial line from the point where the tooth face arc intersects the pitch circle.

h. Draw the fillet radius tangent to the dedendum circle and the tooth flank radial line.

It must be understood, of course, that this is only a convenient conventional scheme and does not represent the actual shape of the gear teeth. A note will indicate the type of teeth wanted.

The rack is usually represented in conventional form with the sides of the tooth straight, except for the fillet at the bottom, as shown in Fig. 28.4. The 14½° and 20° angles for the composite and stub tooth can be readily laid off by using the tangents which are practically 0.25 and 0.36, respectively.

The teeth of internal gears are also represented with straight sides of the proper slope, as shown in Fig. 28.2. One type of internal gear tooth is actually made in this form.

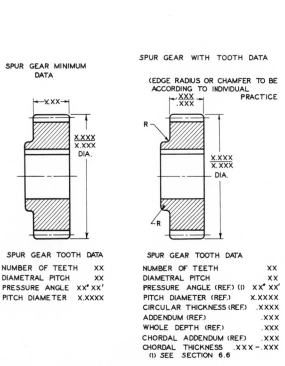

Fig. 28.5   Working drawing of a spur gear.

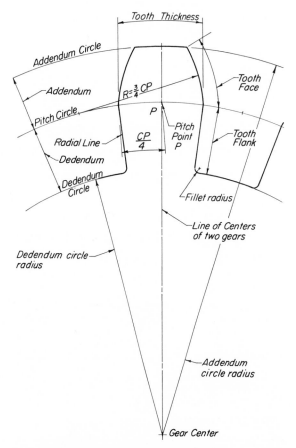

Fig. 28.6   Detail of spur gear tooth profile.

28.11   BEVEL GEARS. A set of bevel gears has the same relation to a pair of rolling cones that spur gears have to rolling cylinders. Bevel gears require the definition of a few new terms, the meanings of which are illustrated on the two common types of gears shown in Figs. 28.7 and 28.8. The equations for computing the value of these terms are given below. The terms and values are the same for all types of bevel gears.

Addendum (A). The addendum is measured at the large end and is the same as for spur gears having the same diametral pitch. $A = 1.000/DP$.

Dedendum (D). The dedendum is measured at the large end and is the same as for spur gears having the same diametral pitch. $D = 1.250/DP$.

Addendum angle (α). The tangent of the addendum angle is expressed as $\tan \alpha = A/CD$.

Dedendum angle (δ). The tangent of the dedendum angle is expressed as $\tan \delta = C/CD$.

Pitch cone radius or cone distance (CD). The pitch cone distance is expressed as $CD = PD/2 \sin \gamma$.

Cutting angle (γ_r). The angle between the center line of the gear and the dedendum line. $\gamma_r = \gamma - \delta$.

Face angle (γ_0). The angle between the center line of the gear and the addendum line. $\gamma_0 = \gamma + \alpha$.

Outside diameter (OD). The largest diameter on the gear. $OD = PD + 2A \cos \gamma$.

Crown height (CH) large end. The distance parallel to the center line of the gear from the apex of the cone to the furthermost point on the addendum line of a tooth. $CH = OD/2 \tan FA$.

Face (F). The face of the gear must be less than ⅓ CD.

Number of teeth, from which to select cutter, $N' = N/\cos \gamma$.

Shaft angle (Σ). The angle between the axes of the shafts of meshing gears.

The following values vary for different gears and for different center angles, as indicated in Table 28.2. The subscript (p) denotes pinion and the subscript (g) denotes the larger of two meshing gears.

28.12   WORKING DRAWINGS OF BEVEL GEARS. Working drawings of bevel gears are usually made with only one view, unless the gear is of such size as to require a wheel with spokes, in which case two views with interpolated sections will be necessary. One view is always a full section, as illustrated in Fig. 28.9. As in spur gears, the dimensions on the drawing are for the gear blank, and the data for cutting the teeth are given in the form of notes. The actual dimensions and the cutting data given will depend on the method of cutting the gears and will be determined by the shop

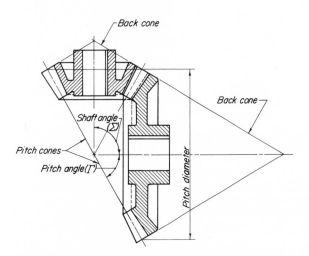

Fig. 28.7   Bevel gear types and terms.

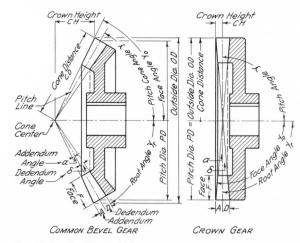

Fig. 28.8   Bevel gear terms.

TABLE 28.2   ANGLE FORMULAS FOR BEVEL GEARS

	Acute Angle between Shaft Axes	Right Angle between Shaft	Crown Gear	Obtuse Angle between Shaft Axes
Pitch cone angle (pinion)	$\tan \gamma_p = \dfrac{\sin \Sigma}{\dfrac{N_g}{N_p} + \cos \Sigma}$	$\tan \gamma_p = \dfrac{N_p}{N_g}$	$\sin \gamma = \dfrac{N_p}{N_g}$	$\tan \gamma_p = \dfrac{\sin (180° - \Sigma)}{\dfrac{N_g}{N_p} - \cos (180° - \Sigma)}$
Pitch cone angle (gear)	$\tan \gamma_g = \dfrac{\sin \alpha}{\dfrac{N_p}{N_g} + \cos \alpha}$	$\tan \gamma_g = \dfrac{N_g}{N_p}$	$\gamma_g = 90°$	$\tan \gamma_g = \dfrac{\sin (180° - \Sigma)}{\dfrac{N_p}{N_g} - \cos (180° - \Sigma)}$

in which the gears are made. Either front or rear face is used as the base for setting the gear blanks in the cutting machines, hence the distance from the front or rear to the outside of the top of the tooth should always be specified in order that all gear blanks may be alike.

28.13 ASSEMBLY DRAWING OF BEVEL GEAR TEETH.

In assembly drawings for display or advertising purposes, it is necessary to represent the actual gear teeth. The following conventional scheme is based on Tredgold's approximation, which consists of drawing the gear teeth upon a development of the back cone, as illustrated in Fig. 28.10. The construction is as follows:

a. Locate the pitch cone center in side view of bevel gear.

b. Draw the pitch cone by laying off the pitch cone angle from the center line of the bevel gear.

c. Lay off the pitch diameter perpendicular to the center line of the bevel gear and determine the intersection with the limiting element of the pitch cone.

d. Draw the limiting element of the back cone by drawing it perpendicular to the limiting pitch cone element from the point at which it intersects the pitch diameter. The apex of the back cone is determined by the intersection of the center line of the gear and the back cone limiting element.

e. Locate addendum and dedendum points on the back cone axis, using the standard spur-gear formulas.

f. Using the back cone apex as a center, draw the developed arc of the addendum, pitch, and dedendum circles (*A*, *PC*, and *D*).

g. Lay out on these arcs a tooth profile by the conventional method for spur gears.

h. Using the front view of the gear, draw the usual three layout circles for both the large and the small ends of the tooth.

i. In the front view lay out the distance *x* and *y* along the projected addendum circle. The distance *x* and *y* are transferred from the spur gear tooth profile construction in step *g* above.

j. Draw radial lines from these points which will locate the corresponding points at the small end of the tooth. The curved outlines through the three points are best drawn with an irregular curve.

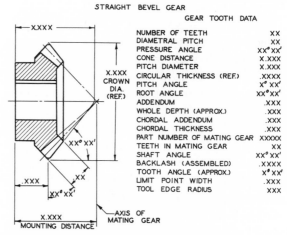

STRAIGHT BEVEL GEAR

GEAR TOOTH DATA	
NUMBER OF TEETH	XX
DIAMETRAL PITCH	XX
PRESSURE ANGLE	XX°XX'
CONE DISTANCE	X.XXX
PITCH DIAMETER	X.XXX
CIRCULAR THICKNESS (REF.)	.XXXX
PITCH ANGLE	X°XX'
ROOT ANGLE	XX°XX'
ADDENDUM	.XXX
WHOLE DEPTH (APPROX.)	.XXX
CHORDAL ADDENDUM	.XXX
CHORDAL THICKNESS	.XXX
PART NUMBER OF MATING GEAR	XXXXX
TEETH IN MATING GEAR	XX
SHAFT ANGLE	XX°XX'
BACKLASH (ASSEMBLED)	.XXXX
TOOTH ANGLE (APPROX.)	X°XX'
LIMIT POINT WIDTH	.XXX
TOOL EDGE RADIUS	XXX

Fig. 28.9 **Working drawing of bevel gear.**

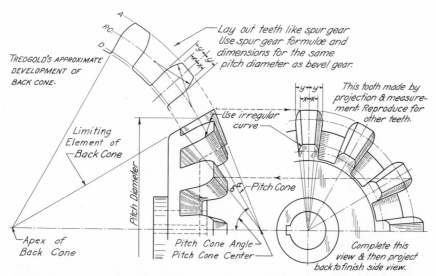

Fig. 28.10 **Representing bevel gears in assembly drawings (Tredgold's approximation).**

Lay out all teeth in the front view in the same way. The side view is then determined by projecting from the front view and locating the same three points as before to determine the tooth curve in each case. In the side view, each tooth curve is a little different from the others except for symmetrically placed teeth which, of course, are alike. In the front view, the draftsman must be careful to use the same part of the irregular curve for each tooth so that they will all look alike. This will be much easier to do, however, than attempting to draw circular arcs with the compass.

28.14 WORM GEAR AND WHEEL. The worm gear and wheel find wide application in the transmission of power when a large speed ratio is desired. The teeth on the worm are based on the standard involute rack which has straight sides with the 14½° slope. The meanings of new terms applying to these gears are illustrated in Fig. 28.11, and the equations for computation are also shown in this figure. Others may be determined from the figure by ordinary trigonometric formulas. In the worm gear the terms linear pitch and lead have the same meaning as they do for screw threads. The linear pitch of the worm is equal to the circular pitch of the wheel.

In practice it is desirable to have thirty or more teeth in the wheel in order to avoid interference. The efficiency varies with the thread angle, with a theoretical maximum of about 45°. For thread or helix angles greater than about 15°, the dimensions of the thread must be based on a section at right angles to the helix.

The pitch at right angles to the helix is called the normal pitch, and is equal to the pitch multiplied by the cosine of the helix angle. This value of the normal pitch should then be substituted in the equations for tooth dimensions.

28.15 WORKING DRAWINGS OF WORM GEARS AND WHEEL. As with other gears, a one-view drawing will suffice for both the worm and the wheel unless the spokes of the wheel make two views essential. For the wheel, one view is a full section, whereas for the worm it may be either a half or full section. The dimensions on the drawings are for the gear blank; the cutting information is given in notes, as shown in Fig. 28.11.

28.16 CAMS. A cam is a mechanism or device in a machine for transmitting a type of motion to another part of the machine that could not readily be transmitted by gears, linkages, and the like. The motion of the cam is usually rotational, being mounted on a shaft like a gear or pulley and turned by the same primary power source. See Figs. 28.12, 28.14, and 28.15. Some cams have an oscillating motion, as shown in Fig. 28.13. The cam has a specially cut periphery or track in its face surface with which a device called a follower is kept in contact. Roller contact between the follower and the cam is desirable on account of the reduction in friction between the two parts. The motion of the follower may be in a straight or curved line, depending on the guides in which it slides or the rocker arms on which it is mounted. Also the motion

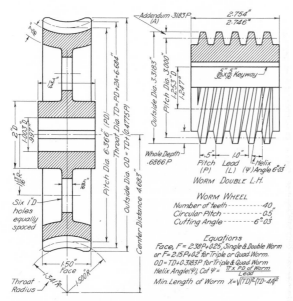

Fig. 28.11   Working drawing of worm gear and wheel.

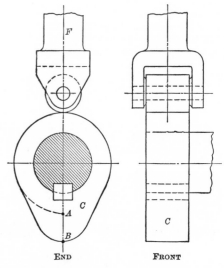

Fig. 28.12   Radial single-acting cam. (After Furman.)

of the follower may be continuous or intermittent as the needs of a particular case may require, and it may be uniform or variable in velocity in each separate phase of its action. In many cam designs, the follower remains at rest over a considerable part of the rotation of the cam. These various qualities and relationships of cams and followers are brought out more clearly in the several illustrations of typical cams of Figs. 28.12 through 28.15.

The cam of Fig. 28.12 is called a radial cam because the follower edge or roller always moves in a radial direction with respect to the cam. The cam of Fig. 28.15 is called a side or cylindrical cam because the action of the follower roller is parallel to the axis of the cam. There are also conical, spherical, and other types of cams, not illustrated in the figures, which usually actuate roller followers mounted on swinging arms. The cam of Fig. 28.14 with the follower groove or track cut in the flat surface of the cam disk is called a face or plate groove cam. Similarly, if the follower track is cut into the surface of a cylinder, the cam is called a cylindrical groove cam.

The positive control of the movement of the follower by the cams of Figs. 28.12 and 28.13 is in one direction only, a spring or weight being relied upon to bring the follower back into starting position at the end of each revolution or stroke. This type of cam is called single-acting. The cams of Figs. 28.14 and 28.15 are called double-acting because they control the action of the follower throughout the entire rotation of

the cam. If the rise of the follower is continuous from the beginning to the end of its stroke, it is said to be a one-step cam. If the rise is broken into two parts by a period of rest, it is said to be a two-step cam.

28.17 EMPIRICAL CAM DESIGN. The technical design of cams involves not only the total range of motion imparted to the follower by the cam and the so-called pressure angle, but also the elements of velocity and acceleration in the follower, elements that can be controlled in shaping the cam. Consideration of the last two factors is beyond the scope of this book. Empirical design, however, in which only range of motion and some phases of the pressure factor are

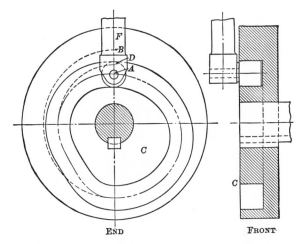

Fig. 28.14   Radial, double-acting, face or plate grove cam. (After Furman.)

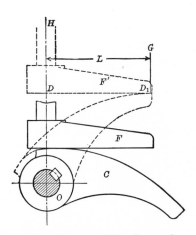

Fig. 28.13   Single-acting cam. (After Furman.)

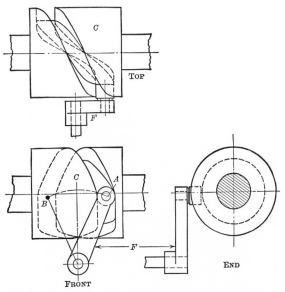

Fig. 28.15   Side or cylindrical, double-acting cam. (After Furman.)

considered, is not a difficult matter, and, with some degree of experience, satisfactory designs can be made on this basis.

28.18 CAM BASE CURVES. The first step in making a working drawing of a cam is to construct the so-called base curves. Their functions will be developed in the next article. Four common base curves used in cam design are shown in Fig. 28.16. The straight line gives a shock to the follower, hence its beginning and end must have a transition curve, which is given a radius equal to the rise if the curve extends 360°. If the rise occupies less distance, the radius is shortened proportionally. See Fig. 28.17.

The crank curve gives simple harmonic motion with a uniformly changing velocity and acceleration. The parabolic curve gives a constant acceleration and deceleration and a uniformly increasing and decreasing velocity, increasing to the center of the curve and then decreasing. The elliptical curve gives variable velocities and acceleration, but it is slower in the starting and stopping portions and faster in the central portion than some of the other curves.

28.19 DRAWING CAMS. The second step in making a working drawing of a cam is the construction of the cam chart. The third step is the construction of the

cam working surface. These two steps are developed together below.

Let it be required to draw the cam curve according to the requirements given in the upper left-hand corner of Fig. 28.17. First, draw the cam chart, as in Fig. 28.17, using the different types of curves as specified in the problem for the rise and fall of the follower. The chart should be to scale vertically, but it may have any convenient length to represent 360°. Subdivide the length according to problem requirements. The various curves are drawn as shown.

The drawing of the cam curve consists in obtaining the line on which the center of the follower roller will run as the cam turns. This is called the pitch surface and is the surface on which the follower roller runs. See Fig. 28.18. If no attention is given to the pressure angle, a radius, *OA*, may be arbitrarily chosen for the pitch circle and the pitch surface may then be constructed from it by dividing the circle into the same proportional parts as the cam chart, Fig. 28.18. If the pitch circle is made to the same scale as the rise, *AG*, of the cam chart in Fig. 28.17, the ordinates to the base curve, measured up and down from the pitch line, may be laid off in a corresponding manner, out and in from the pitch circle, thus locating points on the pitch

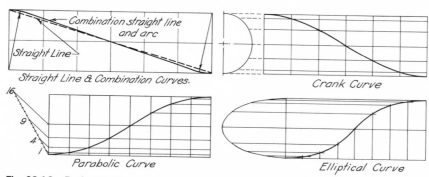

Fig. 28.16 Basic cam curves.

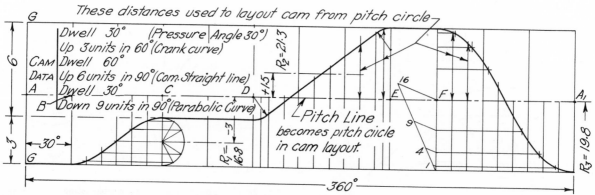

Fig. 28.17 Layout of two-one step cam chart.

surface. A smooth curve is drawn through these points.

If a point follower is to be used, the pitch surface becomes the working surface and the design is complete. A working drawing showing the hub, bore, keyway, and cam curve may then be made in the usual way.

If a roller follower is to be used, the size of the roller may be arbitrarily selected so long as its radius is less than the least radius of curvature of the pitch surface. The working surface is then determined by drawing a series of arcs with centers on the pitch surface and a radius equal to the roller radius, as shown in the upper part of Fig. 28.18. The working surface curve is then drawn tangent to these circles. A working drawing may then be made as before.

If the limitation of a maximum pressure angle is to be observed, the radius of the pitch circle must be computed by the equations shown at the top of Fig. 28.18. The terms d, a, and b are given in the problem data; the pressure angle factor p may be obtained from the chart in Fig. 28.19.

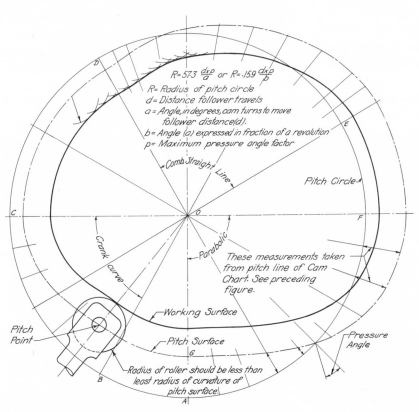

Fig. 28.18   Cam layout for basic curve shown in Fig. 28.17.

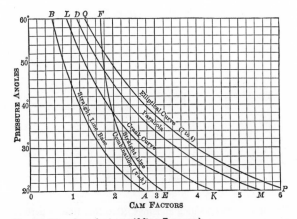

Fig. 28.19   Cam factors. (After Furman.)

If a cam has but one step, the pitch circle is drawn with the radius computed, and the rest of the construction then follows as described before.

If the cam has more than one step, a pitch circle radius can be computed for each step. The pitch line must then be adjusted so that the pitch circle radius is equal to the largest computed radius. The computations for the three steps of the cam of Fig. 28.18 are as follows:

Step one, 3 units.

$$R_1 = \frac{57.3 \times 3 \times 2.72}{60} = 7.77$$

Step two, 6 units.

$$R_2 = \frac{57.3 \times 6 \times 2.27}{90} = 8.66$$

Step three, 9 units.

$$R_3 = \frac{57.3 \times 9 \times 3.46}{90} = 19.8$$

If the largest radius for the parabolic section is used as a trial pitch circle, it can be observed that this circle, being larger than that required by the other two equa-

tions, will be satisfactory since it keeps the pressure angle within the limits specified. The largest pitch radius, $R_3 = 19.8$, is therefore used, and the construction carried out as described before.

28.20   BEARINGS. All rotating parts of machinery are supported in bearings. There are many kinds, and all of them have elements of design beyond the scope of this book. The design of antifriction bearings is a field of specialization in itself. The material here presented consists of those matters that the young engineer should know in representing bearings on drawings.

28.21   JOURNAL OR SLEEVE BEARINGS. Bearings in which the shaft is enclosed by a continuous metal surface in metal-to-metal contact except for clearance and oil films are called sleeve or journal bearings. The shaft is usually made of steel, and the bearing support is lined with Babbitt metal or bronze bushings. Such bearings are shown on drawings as illustrated in Fig. 28.20(a). On schematic layouts, any type of bearing may be shown as in Fig. 28.20(b).

Unless sleeve bearings are of the oil-impregnated type, they must be provided with oil grooves and some means of supplying oil. Under certain conditions they

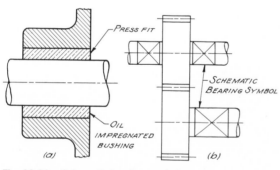

Fig. 28.20   Schematic bearing symbols.

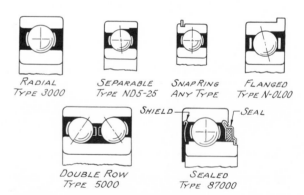

Fig. 28.21   Ball bearing symbols. (Courtesy New Departure Division of General Motors.)

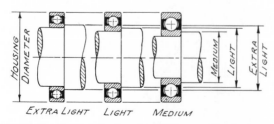

Fig. 28.22   Ball bearing housings. (Courtesy New Departure Division of General Motors.)

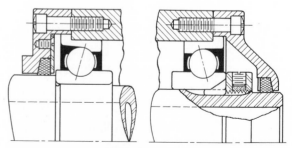

Fig. 28.23   Ball bearing mountings. (Courtesy New Departure Division of General Motors.)

must be protected from dust and dirt by shields or seals. For various types of shields and seals the student is referred to manufacturers' catalogues. Bronze bushings are usually press fitted.

28.22   ANTIFRICTION BEARINGS. Although all bearings have some frictional resistance, ball, roller, and needle bearings are commonly classified as antifriction bearings since the friction has been reduced to a minimum. The material presented here shows the method of representing bearings and a few illustrations of methods of holding them in place. Information concerning the dimensions of a very limited number of smaller-size bearings is given in the Appendix.

Ball bearings are made in a variety of styles and sizes for different purposes. A few of these are shown in Fig. 28.21. The medium, light, and extra-light can be used in different situations to accommodate larger shafts within limited housing dimensions, as shown in Fig. 28.22, when load conditions permit. A few methods of mounting these bearings are shown in Figs. 28.23 and 28.24. Many companies provide full-scale and half-scale sectional drawings of their bearings which can be removed from a loose-leaf catalogue and placed under a drawing on paper or cloth, and traced.

This saves a great deal of time. When press fits are used on either shafts or housing, these must not be so tight as to affect the clearance provided in the bearing.

Roller bearings are of two kinds, namely, those having cylindrical rollers and those having tapered or conical rollers. The inner race of tapered bearings are parts of cones and are called cones. The outer race is called the cup and is also cone-shaped. Several types of roller bearings taken from the Timken Roller Bearing Handbook are shown in Fig. 28.25.

Several methods of mounting these bearings are shown in Fig. 28.26. In Fig. 28.26(a), the cone backing is obtained by a collar pinned to the shaft. The bearing adjustment is obtained by the castellated nut at the other end of the shaft. The cup is supported by a shoulder in the housing which is provided with knock-out grooves for removing the bearing as shown at the top of the figure.

In Fig. 28.26(b), one bearing is supported in a carrier with shoulders. An accurately ground spacer is used between the carrier and housing to obtain adjustment. Split rings with wire clamping rings to hold them in place support the cones at both ends of the bearing. At the right end, a snap ring supports the cup.

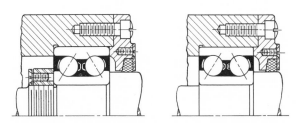

Fig. 28.24   Ball bearing mountings. (Courtesy New Departure Division of General Motors.)

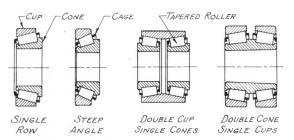

Fig. 28.25   Roller bearing mountings. (Courtesy Timken Roller Bearing Co.)

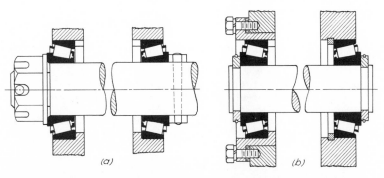

Fig. 28.26   Roller bearing mountings. (Courtesy Timken Roller Bearing Co.)

SELF-STUDY QUESTIONS

Before trying to answer these questions, read the chapter carefully. Then, without reference to the text, answer as many questions as possible. For those that cannot be answered, the number, in parentheses following the question number, gives the article in which the answer can be found. Look it up and write down the answer. Check the answers that you did give to see that they are correct.

28.1 **(28.3)** Tolerances on shafts are always _____ and vary from 0.002 for the smaller sizes to 0.004 on the larger ones.

28.2 **(28.4)** The shape of _____ belts have been standardized.

28.3 **(28.5)** The speed ratios depend on the _____ _____ of the gears.

28.4 **(28.5)** The smaller of two meshing spur or bevel gears is called a _____.

28.5 **(28.5)** The minimum number of teeth on a pinion is limited by common practice to _____.

28.6 **(28.5)** A rack is a gear of _____ radius.

28.7 **(28.6)** The number of teeth per inch of pitch diameter is called _____ _____.

28.8 **(28.6)** The radial distance from the pitch circle to the top of the tooth is called _____.

28.9 **(28.6)** The circle from which the involute curve is formed is called _____.

28.10 **(28.7)** The common tooth forms are the _____ and the cycloidal system.

28.11 **(28.8)** Involute gears can be produced more accurately and _____ than cycloidal gears.

28.12 **(28.8)** Involute gears are _____ than cycloidal gears since the latter have spreading flanks in contrast to the radial flanks of the former.

28.13 **(28.9)** Information concerning the teeth is usually given in the form of _____.

28.14 **(28.10)** A rack is usually represented in conventional form with the sides of the tooth _____, except for the fillet at the bottom.

28.15 **(28.11)** The angle in bevel gears between the axes of the shafts of meshing gears is called _____ angle.

28.16 **(28.14)** The _____ gear and wheel find wide application in the transmission of power when a large speed ratio is desired.

28.17 **(28.16)** A _____ is a mechanism or device for transmitting a type of motion that could not be readily transmitted by gears, linkages, and the like.

28.18 **(28.16)** A cam is usually in contact with a device called a _____.

28.19 **(28.18)** A _____ base curve gives a constant acceleration and deceleration.

28.20 **(28.20)** All rotating parts of machinery are supported in _____.

28.21 **(28.21)** A _____ bearing is a bearing in which the shaft is enclosed by a continuous metal surface in metal-to-metal contact except for clearance and oil films.

28.22 **(28.22)** Ball, roller, and needle bearings are commonly called _____ bearings since the friction has been reduced to a minimum.

PROBLEMS

The following problems are intended only for students who are well grounded in the principles of drawing. Therefore, no directions are given as to scale, choice of views, or arrangement. In some problems considerable latitude for the exercise of common sense and judgment has been allowed, and it is intended that the student do the exercise with as little help from the instructor as possible.

Tooth Profiles

28.1 Draw a 1 *DP* cycloidal gear tooth on a pitch circle of 5″ radius. Construct the tooth profile curves on one side and complete one tooth. The diameter of the rolling circle shall be one-half that of the pitch circle for a 12-tooth pinion. Mark all circles and curves having specific names.

28.2 Same as Problem 28.1. Use a 2 *DP* tooth.

28.3 Draw a 1 *DP* involute tooth on a pitch circle of 6″ radius and having a 20° pressure angle. Construct the tooth profile on one side and complete one tooth. Mark all circles and curves having specific names.

28.4 Same as Problem 28.3. Use a 2 *DP* tooth.

Spur Gears

28.5 Make a working drawing of the gear shown in Fig. 28.27.

28.6 Same as Problem 28.5, Fig. 28.28.

28.7 Same as Problem 28.5, Fig. 28.29. (Note that this is a special type of bevel gear.)

28.8 Same as Problem 28.5, Fig. 28.30.

28.9 Make a working drawing of a gear assigned from Fig. 28.31. The drive gear *A*, when meshed with the right part of double gear *C*, turns the lower shaft in one direction. When *A* is shifted to the left and meshed with *B*, since *B* is always meshed with the left part of *C*, *A* turns the lower shaft in the opposite direction.

28.10 Make a complete set of details for the speed-changing device shown in Fig. 28.31.

28.11 Make a copy of the assembly drawing shown in Fig. 28.32.

Bevel Gears

28.12 Make a working drawing of the large bevel gear assigned from Fig. 28.32. Gears *A* and *B*, with their respective clutch jaws, are free to revolve upon the drive shaft which is keyed to the central clutch jaw *C*. The clutch *C* may be shifted to engage either gear *A* or *B*, thus changing the direction of rotation of the gear *D* and its shaft. The handle for shifting the clutch should have some device for locking the clutch in any one of its three positions.

28.13 Same as Problem 28.12. Pinion gear, Fig. 28.32.

28.14 Make a complete set of details of the reversing mechanism shown in Fig. 28.32.

28.15 Make a copy of the assembly drawing shown in Fig. 28.32.

Worm Gear and Wheel

28.16 Make a working drawing of the worm gear and wheel shown in Fig. 28.33.

28.17 Same as Problem 28.16, Fig. 28.33. Change to double worm.

28.18 Make a complete set of details of the object shown in Fig. 28.33.

Cams

28.19 Draw the cam chart and lay out the cam curve for a cam whose follower moves radially as follows: up 2″ on a crank curve base line in 90°; dwell 120°; down 2″ on a crank curve in 60°; dwell 90°. Use a pitch circle of 3½″ radius; select size of roller followers.

28.20 Same as Problem 28.19. Use a combination straight-line base curve.

28.21 Same as Problem 28.19. Use a parabolic base curve.

28.22 Same as Problem 28.19. Compute pitch circle radius for a 30° maximum pressure angle.

28.23 Draw the cam chart and lay out the cam curve for a cam whose follower moves radially as follows: up 1″ in 45°; dwell 45°; up 1½″ in 90°; dwell 30°; down 1¼″

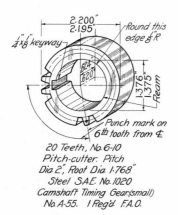

Fig. 28.27   Timing gear.

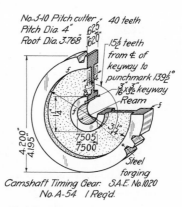

Fig. 28.28   Timing gear.

in 45°; dwell 30°; down 1¼″ in 45°; dwell 30°. Use a crank curve on first two steps and a parabolic curve on the last two. Pitch circle 4″ radius for second step; select size of roller follower.

28.24 Same as Problem 28.23. Use combination straight-line curve throughout.

28.25 Same as Problem 28.23. Compute pitch circle radius for 45° maximum pressure angle.

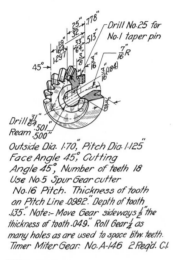

Outside Dia. 1.70″, Pitch Dia. 1.125″
Face Angle 45°, Cutting
Angle 45°, Number of teeth 18
Use No.5 Spur Gear cutter
No.16 Pitch. Thickness of tooth
on Pitch Line .0982″. Depth of tooth
.135″. Note:- Move Gear sideways ½ the
thickness of tooth .049″. Roll Gear ¼ as
many holes as are used to space btw. teeth.
Timer Miter Gear. No.A-146 2 Req'd. C.I.

Fig. 28.29 Miter gear.

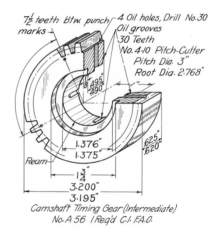

7½ teeth btw. punch marks
4 Oil holes, Drill No.30
Oil grooves
30 Teeth
No. 4-10 Pitch-Cutter
Pitch Dia. 3″
Root Dia. 2.768″

1.376″
1.375″
.625″
.620″

Ream

1¾″
3.200″
3.195″

Camshaft Timing Gear (Intermediate)
No. A 56 1 Req'd C.I. F.A.O.

Fig. 28.30 Timing gear.

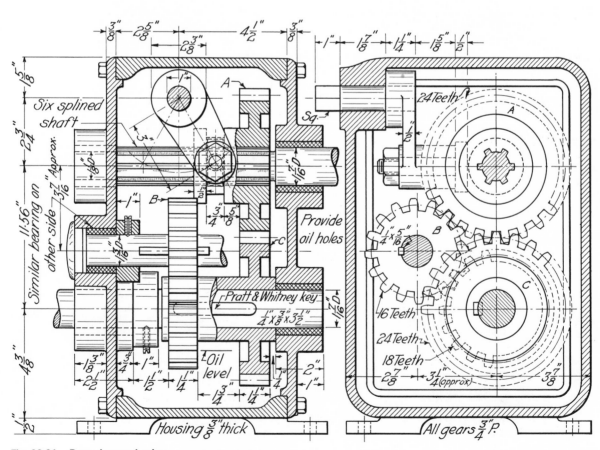

Fig. 28.31 Reversing mechanism.

28.26 Draw a cam chart and lay out the cam curve for a roller follower that moves as follows: up 1″ in 60°; dwell 30°; up 1½″ in 75°; dwell 15°; down 2¼″ in 120°; dwell 60°. Pitch radius 4″ for last step. Select size of roller.

28.27 Same as Problem 28.26. Compute the pitch circle radius for a maximum pressure angle of 30°.
28.28 Same as Problem 28.26. Maximum pressure angle 45°.

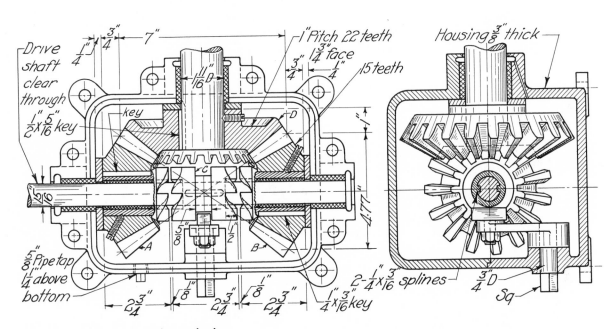

Fig. 28.32   Bevel gear reversing mechanism.

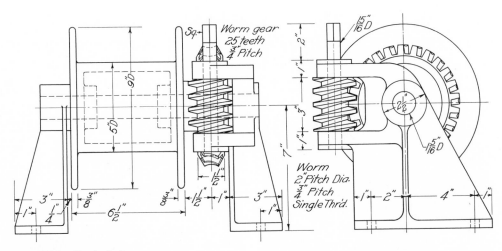

Fig. 28.33   Hand winch.

CHAPTER 29
Tooling for Production

NEW: Steel mill controlled by computers. (Courtesy of the General Electric Company)

OLD: 18th century French foundry. (The Bettmann Archive)

Chapter 29 Tooling for Production*

29.1 MODERN INDUSTRIAL PRACTICE. Companies involved in the production of consumer goods depend heavily on engineering talent to manufacture the final product. Among the functions that must be taken into consideration while producing a product are the following: (1) administration; (2) accounting; (3) marketing; (4) purchasing; (5) industrial and labor relations; (6) research, (7) design and development; (8) facilities and services; (9) manufacturing, planning, and estimating; (10) tool engineering; (11) toolmaking or procurement; (12) manufacturing operation; and (13) quality control.

Some of the functions are very closely related to each other and perhaps the most critical ones are those that occur in the design-drafting rooms. Normally a design engineer is placed in charge of a particular project and it is his responsibility to see that the product is produced. He must generate all the necessary information for the production personnel to enable them to manufacture the product.

The design engineer will work closely with his design engineering staff, the developmental test engineers, and the manufacturing engineering staff. Preliminary drawings are made and a prototype is made very early in the design activity. While detail designing is being done in the design room, the results from the tests performed on the prototype are being fed back to the design room and incorporated into the final design. Before the final product design has been evolved, the work of manufacturing planning begins. The necessary equipment for manufacturing is anticipated, and specifications are written for any equipment that is not immediately available within the plant or from machine tool suppliers. The tool engineers and the tool design department, too, have begun their work.

When the product design has been proved and stabilized, the manufacturing or process engineer determines the exact method of manufacture. He utilizes any manufacturing information gained from the production of the prototype and writes the necessary process sheets. The tool engineer finalizes the tooling requirements, and the tool design department

* This chapter was prepared by Mr. Gerald W. Gladden, Supervisor, Technical Education, Illinois State Board of Vocational and Technical Education.

completes the design of the tooling. If the tools are to be made in the plant, the tool drawings are given to the toolroom where the toolmakers assume responsibility for the manufacture of the tooling.

29.2 IMPORTANCE OF TOOLING IN MANUFACTURE. The importance of tooling as a necessary adjunct to manufacturing operation cannot be overemphasized. Responsibility for the tooling function will vary with the particular organizational structure of a manufacturing company. The determination of tooling requirements, design, procurement, and troubleshooting of tooling problems will be the province of the tool engineer in many organizations, while in others the manufacturing or process engineer and the tool designer will share in this responsibility to varying degrees. Irrespective of the division of responsibility, tool design, tool drawing, and toolmaking or procurement are vital to the manufacturing function.

29.3 RANGE OF COMPLEXITY OF TOOLING. The tooling required for any particular job will vary widely. It will depend on the design of the part, the manufacturing equipment available, the quality of parts desired, and the capability of the skilled workers. The production schedule for tooling will depend on the number of parts to be made, the complexity of the processing to be used, and the production capability of the shop.

When small numbers are involved, as in tooling up for a prototype, the tooling may be conceived, designed, and drawn somewhat informally by the manufacturing engineer. In the case of normal production runs of tooling, rigid quality control standards must be followed. Regardless of the quantity to be made, many parts will require elaborate and complex tooling.

29.4 TERMINOLOGY. A machine tool is any power-operated machine that operates on a workpiece in such a manner as to change its shape. Small tools are expendable tools that through forcible contact with the workpiece change its shape in some manner. A fixture is a device to position and hold a workpiece for inspection, machining, forming, welding, or other manufacturing operation. The fixture may provide a means of setting the cutting tool. A jig also performs the function of positioning and holding a workpiece but in addition serves to guide, or in some manner control, the cutting tool. The aggregate of small tools, jigs, fixtures, templates, gages, and any adaptor used on the machine tool is referred to as tooling.

29.5 MACHINE TOOLS. The tool designer and the tool draftsman must be thoroughly familiar with the principals of operation of all of the standard machine tools used in production, as well as any specially designed machines in the particular company. Although complete specifications for each machine will be available to the draftsman, proper design of a jig, fixture, or tool for the most efficient use of the machine requires a complete understanding of the machine's operation. He must additionally be familiar with those machine tools that are used in the toolroom for the manufacture of tooling. A common precision machine that combines the accuracy of a jig borer and the performance of a heavy milling machine is illustrated in Fig. 29.1. In Fig. 29.2, precision boring work is being performed by a precision boring machine.

An informal discussion between the tool engineer, the tool designer, and the toolroom foreman is a common practice that effects considerable savings to the company. It often happens that a tool design, correct in every detail and well designed, is dimensioned in such a way that much of the work of the tool designer is wasted. The tool drawing must be redimensioned so as to provide necessary information in a form that is usable by the toolroom on particular machines that are available. In a complex tool this additional work can be quite costly.

29.6 UNIVERSAL POSITIONING DEVICES. Many machine tools have a means for positioning the tool relative to the workpiece either by positioning the tool, the workpiece, or both. Work heads that tilt, swivel, or

both can in many cases reduce the complexity of a jig or fixture and in some cases eliminate the need for such a tool. Micrometer and optical positioning devices enable the workpiece to be located relative to the cutting tool with great accuracy after it has been clamped to the machine, eliminating the need for tooling except to meet production requirements. Sine plates, rotary tables, tilting tables, tilting rotary tables (see Fig. 29.3), indexing chucks, dividing heads, and plane and universal vises are all readily available commercially as either machine tool accessories or universal items, which suffice in many cases to position the workpiece and eliminate the need for tooling. The tool designer must be familiar with the capabilities and limitations of all of these auxiliary devices.

29.7 STANDARD JIG AND FIXTURE PARTS. The draftsman working on jig and fixture design must be familiar with component jig and fixture parts that are available commercially. By using these he can materially reduce the cost of the design of jigs and fixtures. Some of these are illustrated in Fig. 29.4. Simple economics requires that these standard items be fully utilized. Standard components are of certified quality and dimensionally accurate within guaranteed tolerances. Many of the available component designs have been standardized and catalogued by the industry.

Purchased items are generally considerably cheaper because of mass-production techniques than would be their counterparts produced individually in the toolroom. Complexity of a tool design is no bar to the use of standard components, since they are highly adaptable to many situations. Standard components such as fixture bases, die sets, chuck jaws, drill bushings, locating pins and jacks, clamps, torque screws, jig feet, rest

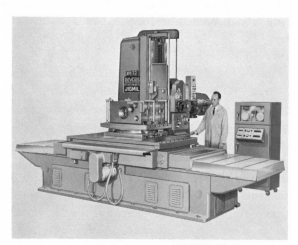

Fig. 29.1   A combination precision boring and milling machine. (Courtesy of DeVlieg Machine Company.)

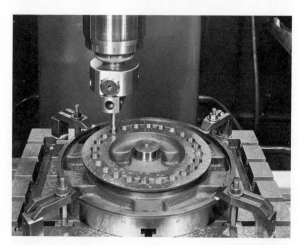

Fig. 29.2   Boring holes with tolerances of 0.0002 on diameter. (Courtesy Kearney and Trecker.)

buttons, tooling balls and buttons, handwheels, knobs, handles, and various screws, studs, nuts, and washers can be modified for any particular application.

Tool design costs are minimized since standard items need only be outlined on assembly drawings and detailed drawings are unnecessary. Such detailing and outlining as are required are facilitated in many cases by templates and design drawings furnished by the component supplier which can be quickly traced directly on the tool drawing.

29.8 STANDARD CUTTING TOOLS. Standard cutting tools are available from several manufacturers to accomplish a vast majority of the tasks for which a cutting tool is required. Of those cutting problems that remain, most can be solved by a relatively simple modification of a standard cutting tool. It is only in extreme instances, and then only when the tool designer has exhausted all of the possibilities of altering standard tools, that a cutting tool should be completely designed and built in the toolroom.

29.9 CUTTER SETTING. Although fixtures do not provide a means of guiding the cutter, they are frequently designed to include setting blocks for locating the cutter relative to the workpiece. The cutter may be located by these setting blocks or by cutter-setting surfaces ground on the workpiece locator or some convenient part of the fixture that can be hardened. See Fig. 29.5. The cutter must clear the surface of the setting block, generally by 0.030″. To insure this the position of the setting block one must allow for the use

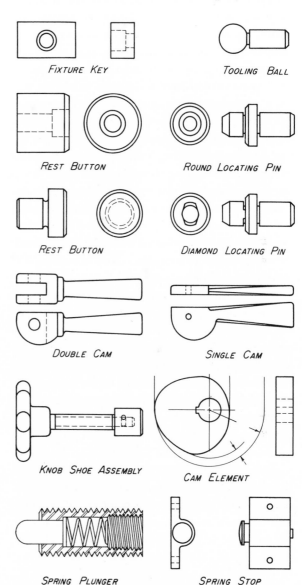

Fig. 29.4 Commercial jig and fixture elements.

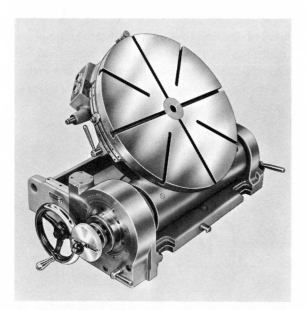

Fig. 29.3 Tilting rotary table. (Courtesy of Pratt and Whitney, Inc.)

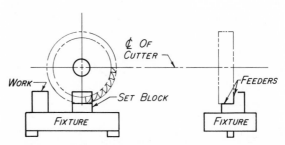

Fig. 29.5 Set block for setting and depth of cut.

of a 0.030″ feeler between the cutter and the surface of the setting block. Where both a rough and finish cut are to be made on a workpiece located in the fixture, the setting block must provide for the use of a one-thickness feeler (generally 0.060″) for setting the cutter for the rough cut, and another thickness (usually 0.030″) for the finish cut. It is usual and desirable shop practice to standardize the thickness of the feelers used to avoid scrap parts caused by the use of a feeler of the wrong thickness.

Fixtures used to locate and position the workpiece for tracing or profiling operations should provide for coordination between tracer template and fixture. An example of such a template is illustrated in Fig. 29.6. For linear positioning this coordination is usually obtained by a locating hole on the template for positioning the tracer stylus and one on the fixture for locating the cutter. Radial coordination is generally obtained by keying both the template and the fixture to the machine. Coordination is also obtained, particularly in those cases where the tracing operation is performed on the lathe, by perpendicular indicating surfaces on the template aligned with its axes while the cutter is positioned either by setting blocks on the fixture or by previously machined surfaces on the workpiece itself.

In making the working drawing for the profile template shown in Fig. 29.6, the necessary instruction must be provided to insure the placing of the notes shown on the finished template.

29.10 TOOL AND CUTTER GUIDING. The device commonly used in jigs to guide the tool is the drill bushing, which is precision-ground of hardened tool steel to resist the abrasive action of chips. Drill bushings are generally placed quite close to the surface of the work to be drilled, as shown in Fig. 29.7(a). This arrangement will allow chip removal by the action of the

drill as it passes through the bushing, resulting in abrasive wear on the drill bushing. An alternative, to this close placement of the drill bushing, is to place it 1½ to 2 drill diameters from the work to permit chip removal in the area between the bushing and the work. This is poor practice for drills of small diameter and for those ductile materials the drilling of which produces long stringy chips. These chips crowd the area between the workpiece and the drill. They become difficult to remove and in some cases they actually dislocate the workpiece within the jig. This alternative bushing placement can be advantageous, however, in the drilling of such materials as brass, magnesium, and cast iron which do not produce a continuous chip when drilled, provided that the drill is of sufficient diameter that deflection is not a problem. Deflection of the drill upon entering an irregular surface is eliminated by grinding the normally squared end of the drill bushing to fit the contour of the surface and placing the bushing as close as possible to that surface.

Drill bushings are of two basic types. The press-fit bushing, shown in Figs. 29.8(a) and (b), is permanently installed directly in the jig and is ordinarily not suitable for long production runs on abrasive materials where the chip passes through the drill bushing. Renewable bushings are used in liner bushings, shown in Figs. 29.8(c) and (d), and are permanently installed in the jig. Fixed renewable bushings, shown in Fig. 29.8(e), are press-fit directly into the liner bushing and are removed only when they become worn. Slip renewable bushings, shown in Fig. 29.8(f), fit the liner bushing with a close slip-fit and are easily and frequently installed and removed. Slip renewable bushings are usually made with a knurled head, a part of which is rotated beneath a retaining screw when it is installed. Bushing liners with slip renewable bushings permit

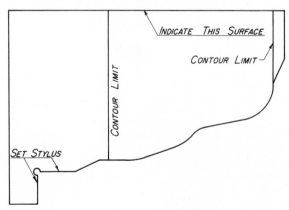

Fig. 29.6 Profile template for tracer lathe.

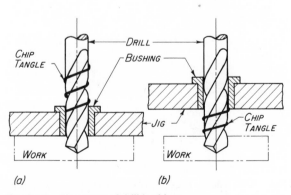

Fig. 29.7 Placement of drill bushings.

the guiding of tools of different diameter, such as a drill followed by a larger diameter reamer, into the workpiece at the same location. This is the most common application of the slip renewable bushing and requires two bushings of different inside diameters and the same outside diameter to fit the one liner bushing.

Pilot bushings are used to guide such tools as counterbores, boring bars, and some reamers. These tools utilize a ground pilot, either ahead of or behind the cutting edge, and it is this pilot that fits the pilot bushing. See Fig. 29.9. The pilot must be of smaller diameter than the cutting tool if placed ahead of the cutting edge and of a larger diameter if placed behind the cutting edge. If the pilot is placed ahead of the cutting edge, it must pass through the workpiece and into the pilot bushing located on the far side before the cutting edge of the tool enters the work. This placement of the pilot ahead of the cutting edge permits piloting directly in previously drilled or reamed holes eliminating the necessity of a pilot bushing in some applications. Pilot bushings are also frequently used to guide locating pins and inspection gages.

29.11 WORKPIECE LOCATING AND POSITIONING. Jigs and fixtures provide a means of producing interchangeable parts within established tolerances by establishing a uniform relationship between the workpiece and the cutting tool. This function of the jig or fixture is accomplished indirectly, by positioning the workpiece to the jig or fixture and by locating the jig or fixture to the cutting tool. Drill jigs may be located

to the cutting tool by manually positioning the jig to bring the drill bushing into alignment with the drill, as must be done with tumble jigs used on a sensitive drill. In the case of individual drilling operations, the jigs once located may be semipermanently clamped to the table of the drill. Lathe fixtures are located concentric with the lathe spindle and the position of the tool relative to the fixture and spindle is controlled by the lathe or the operator. Other fixtures are keyed to the machine table to align the axes of the fixture with the corresponding axes of the machine, and the relative position of the fixture and cutting tool is then controlled by the operator or the machine.

The problem of establishing a uniform relationship between workpiece and cutting tool is thus reduced to the problem of locating the workpiece relative to the jig or fixture. The means that may be utilized to accomplish this is determined by the geometry of the workpiece, by the degree and accuracy of prior machining of the workpiece, by the kind and type of machining operation that is to be performed, by the degree of accuracy required (allowable tolerances), and by the production quantities involved.

In general, the first operation upon a casting or forging or upon rough bar stock should be either a layout operation providing lines scribed on the rough surfaces that have been painted with layout dye for subsequent visual locating or a machining operation that produces holes, surfaces, or external diameters that can be used to position the part by locating devices. Insofar as is practicable, these original locating points should be used for all subsequent operations or new locating surfaces. Such new surfaces are often required after heat-treating operations.

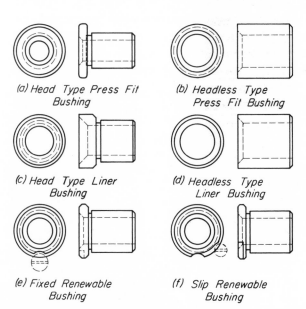

(a) Head Type Press Fit Bushing

(b) Headless Type Press Fit Bushing

(c) Head Type Liner Bushing

(d) Headless Type Liner Bushing

(e) Fixed Renewable Bushing

(f) Slip Renewable Bushing

Fig. 29.8   Types of drill bushings.

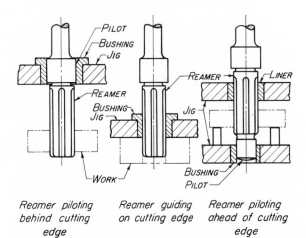

Reamer piloting behind cutting edge

Reamer guiding on cutting edge

Reamer piloting ahead of cutting edge

Fig. 29.9   Piloting and guiding of reamers.

Locators should be of hardened steel to resist wear and abrasion and as small as is consistent with the hardness of the locating surface and the force applied at that point. They should be accessible for easy cleaning when the workpiece is not in place and should be completely covered by the workpiece during machining operations.

When designing the piece, the designer must be familiar with these practices and take them into consideration when the detailed drawings are being made.

29.12 LOCATING METHODS. Many irregular castings and forgings will require location to eliminate the six degrees of freedom of a body in space. This can be accomplished by locating the part against points in three mutually perpendicular planes, namely the H-, V-, and P-planes. Three points must be provided in one plane, two in another, and one in the third. The three points should be located in the base plane. Often it is only necessary to locate a base plane and a major diameter for symmetrical parts, plus additional radial location for those that are asymmetrical.

The base of a workpiece that has been previously machined is often located against a plane surface of the fixture rather than on three points. The area of this locating surface should be reduced or relieved to allow for variations in the workpiece surface, to pro-

vide for easy cleaning, and to prevent misalignment due to chips or burrs on the workpiece. This is illustrated in Fig. 29.10. If possible, clearance should be provided on the locating surfaces of the fixture at all points where burrs may be present from prior machining of the workpiece. Where a workpiece is to rest on three points for plane location, rest buttons are used. These rest buttons are of sufficient surface area to serve the additional function of workpiece support.

Concentric location of a workpiece relative to a machined diameter of the piece, when accomplished by a fixture rather than a chuck, may be attained by virtue of a mating diameter machined on the fixture. Since these two diameters must fit closely (normally within 0.001″ to 0.002″), the length of engagement of the two mating diameters should be kept quite small to prevent jamming or binding that will inhibit engagement or separation of the two diameters. If the locating diameter of the workpiece is a rough-cored hole or a cast projection or is machined to excessive tolerances, cone locators will approximate concentric location, but the accuracy of location will be less than for the method of two mating diameters and will vary with the irregularity of the workpiece diameter. Since the length of engagement of a cone locator and a workpiece diameter must necessarily vary to accomodate a

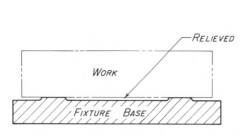

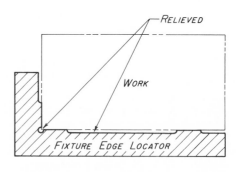

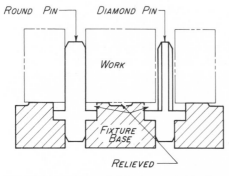

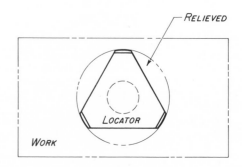

Fig. 29.10 Fixture relief for burr and chip clearance.

range of diameters, the locator must be movable along its axis to allow for positioning of the workpiece against the plane locators. See Fig. 29.11. This is generally accomplished by making the locator spring loaded.

Radial location is used in conjunction with concentric location in those cases where a radial relation must be maintained between the workpiece and the fixture. A pin locator to engage a hole in the workpiece at the greatest distance from the concentric locator will best meet this requirement where the design of the workpiece includes or permits such a hole. A large portion of the locating pin diameter should be relieved on two sides, as in the diamond pin, to allow for any mislocation of the hole relative to its distance from the concentric locating diameter. The diamond pin, shown in Fig. 29.4, should be installed so that a line through its center and through the two unrelieved portions of the pin diameter will be perpendicular to a line through the concentric locator and the radial locator. Where design does not permit a radial locating hole, the fix-

ture must provide a means of radial location to suit a distinctive asymmetrical feature of the workpiece.

Pin and edge locators are frequently used to locate on some edge or external feature of the workpiece, as shown in Fig. 29.12. Where the piece is rectangular in shape and resting on a locating surface or rest buttons, the piece can easily be located by having one edge against two pins and the adjacent edge against a third pin. Round pin locators are much to be preferred for this application over block locators to decrease misalignment due to any out-of-square condition of the two adjacent edges of the workpiece. The locators must be relieved to provide clearance for any burrs on the piece and to prevent the accumulation of chips that would prevent accurate location.

V-blocks are frequently used to locate against cylindrical surfaces, but precautions must be taken if the V-block is to provide accurate locating since a given variation in the radius of the cylindrical surface will cause a larger variation in the workpiece location. See Fig. 29.13. Errors in location are greater with a smaller included angle of the V than with a larger angle, although seating is more positive with the smaller angle. An included angle of 90° for the V is best in most applications. The V should be oriented so that variations in the diameter of the cylindrical surface and consequent mislocation will have the least effect on the accuracy of the finished piece. In many applications, such as location for a hole to be drilled radially through a cylinder, the V can be oriented so that mislocations due to a variation in diameter will have little or no effect on dimensional location. This can be done by locating the workpiece in the V-block, as shown in Fig. 29.13(b), to assure center-line alignment.

Foolproofing to prevent the improper positioning of the workpiece relative to the locators should be a provision of the jig or fixture where possible. A variety of means will suffice to make it impossible to incorrectly position the workpiece. Foolproofing is most

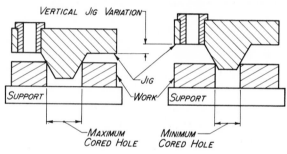

Fig. 29.11   Cone locator.

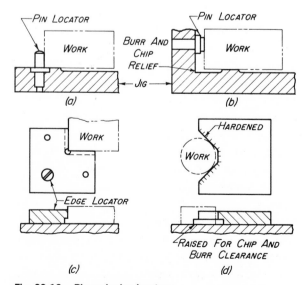

Fig. 29.12   Pin and edge locators.

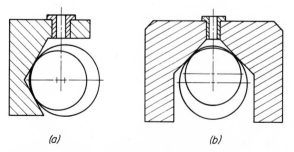

Fig. 29.13   V-block location of cylindrical object.

easily obtained by placing a pin or block on the fixture in such a place that it will prevent the incorrect loading of the workpiece by obstructing some feature of the piece but will clear this same feature when the part is correctly positioned.

When making the tool drawings for these various locating devices, the designer must be fully aware of the above production procedures.

29.13 WORKPIECE SUPPORT AND CLAMPING. Workpiece support is accomplished primarily by the base plane locating surface or rest buttons. The clamping force must be applied perpendicular to the locating surface and directly in line with that surface to prevent distortion of the workpiece by the clamping force. When additional supports are necessary they should be adjustable to conform to variations in the surface of the workpiece. These supports must not themselves exert additional forces on the workpiece, and additional clamping forces should be applied over the support where possible.

Clamps must exert and maintain a force sufficient to counteract the forces of the cutting tool during the machining operation without distorting the workpiece. Clamping forces should be applied at the heavier sections of the workpiece and must be applied directly over either fixed or adjustable supports. The line of force resulting from the clamping action must pass through the support. Clamps should be designed and located so that they will not obstruct loading or unloading of the workpiece and must be placed so that they will clear the cutter and all parts of the machine during normal operation. Required clamping forces can be calculated but are ordinarily determined by experience and experimentation.

Strap clamps are simple rectangular beams and subject to all of the laws of statics. The three forces on a strap clamp are the applied force and the reactions at the fulcrum and the workpiece. The lever principle applies to strap clamps and determines the ratio of applied force to clamping force. Strap clamps may be designed to either slide, swivel, or pivot on a hinge to facilitate loading and unloading of the workpiece.

Cam clamps provide a rapid means of clamping the workpiece but must be properly designed and used if they are to be effective. Two types of cam action are utilized in commercial cam clamps: the spiral cam based on the spiral of Archimedes and the eccentric cam. The eccentric cam is easier to make but the spiral clamp has a more positive locking action and

provides a greater clamping action than does an eccentric clamp with the same applied force.

The wedge clamp utilizes a movable inclined plane to effect the clamping action. When the wedge is restrained from further movement it provides and maintains an effective clamping force, but the determination of this force depends on the coefficient of friction which is difficult to evaluate. Wedge clamps are not recommended where the clamping force is to be applied to a rough casting surface.

Toggle clamps offer an extremely rapid clamping action and provide a large clamping force with a small applied force. These clamps, however, must have provisions for adjustment to allow for variation in thickness of the workpiece. Toggle clamps are available in a multitude of styles and sizes and are rapidly becoming one of the most popular of the clamping methods.

Screw clamps provide a direct clamping action by the advancement of a threaded screw and can accommodate large variations in workpiece thickness. The end of the screw at the point of application is normally fitted with a swivel pad to accomodate irregular workpiece surfaces and to reduce the tendency of the clamp to mar the surface. Screw clamps may become loosened by workpiece vibration and are undesirable where considerable vibration is present. A choice of finer threads for the screw will reduce the tendency for the clamp to loosen but an auxiliary device to bind the screw will be required in some applications.

29.14 CONTOUR LAYOUTS. Although the tool drawing is normally a step in the production of a tool, in one important case the tool itself is solely the work of the tool draftsman. An extremely useful inspection tool is the optical comparator. This device projects a beam of light into a lens system and onto a projection screen. The workpiece that is to be inspected is placed in the path of the beam of light ahead of the lens system, and a magnified silhouette of the workpiece contour is projected on the screen. Available optical comparators have standard magnifications of 10, 20, 50, and 100 with screen sizes up to 30 inches in diameter. Chart gages (contour layouts) are placed on the projection screen and the contour or profile of the workpiece is compared to that on the chart gage. Measurement of the contour features of the workpiece can be accomplished by one of two methods. In one method, direct measurement is made employing micrometer adjustments built into the machine to measure the deviation from a single contour outline on the chart. In the other method, permissible deviation is indicated by a tolerance zone on the chart itself. This tolerance zone is indicated by two concentric outlines on the chart; the distance between the outlines is a magnification of the allowable tolerance.

The chart gage is a very accurately scribed outline on glass or inked outline on plastic or paper with all necessary outlines and dimensions. The outline is an enlarged drawing to the exact magnification power of a particular lens combination and may be laid out by hand-drafting methods or special layout devices. Glass charts provide the greatest dimensional stability, while Mylar films are quite satisfactory for most purposes and paper or vellum is suited only for temporary toolroom use. Layout lines on film or paper should be sharp, black, and 0.006 to 0.010 inch wide with a constant and uniform width. When a single contour line is used the dimension should be to the center of the line. When two contour lines indicate a tolerance zone, the magnification chosen should be great enough to provide a minimum space between the lines of 0.020 inch when projected on the screen, and the workpiece dimensions should be to the two adjacent edges of the two contour lines such that acceptable part contour falls entirely between the two lines.

When the layout must be too large to fit the projection screen or when it is desirable to indicate the different contours of several staging points, the outlines may be superimposed but reference lines for coordination of the outlines must be incorporated in the layout.

29.15   DESIGN LAYOUTS. Often preliminary fixture design layouts are freehand sketches used to record design thinking, reference dimensions, and catalogue information of standard components. More complicated fixtures will require very accurate design layouts in which fixture components and production parts are accurately located. The layout is planned to allow ample space for notes and design information. The design layout is a valuable aid in determining the proper size for fixture components and their placement relative to the workpiece. It is not necessary that this preliminary design include all details of the fixture that will appear in the assembly layout, since it will not be used by the toolmaker in the building of the fixture.

29.16   ASSEMBLY LAYOUTS. The assembly layout is a necessary part of the finished tool drawing, as shown in Fig. 29.14. This layout or drawing should include all fixture components properly placed on the drawing and identified by numbers placed in vertical

or horizontal alignment. These numbers must also be included in a parts list on the drawing which identifies each component and specifies the quantity required. Any standard fixture components used must be properly identified in this parts list. The parts list normally appears above the title block, each component occupying one line of the parts list and numbered consecutively, preferably from bottom to top with the major items specified in the first few lines. These line or item numbers then become the identifying numbers of the fixture components.

The title block requires additional space for information not included on engineering part drawings. See Fig. 29.15. Space is usually provided for recording the tool number; the number of the department in which the tool will be used; the model, part, and operation number of the production part; the machine number; and drawing sheet reference number.

The assembly layout consists of only as many principal views as are necessary, augmented by any explanatory sections or detailed views that may be required. Placement of views does not need to conform to engineering drawing practice and frequently does not, but all views must be clearly identified. The layout drawing of many dies and fixtures will show a front elevation as an edge view, with the top view as a layout of the lower member and the bottom view as a layout of the upper member. See Fig. 29.16. These plan views will show only the fixture member with attached parts and will not include the other member.

The assembly layout should include only those dimensions that are absolutely necessary to ensure clarity and understanding. The production part contour should appear in phantom lines in all views. See Fig. 29.14. Hidden lines tend to confuse the interpretation of the assembly layout and only those that are needed for clarity should be included.

Standard commercial fixture components on any assembly or subassembly drawing are shown in skeletonized outline form only and may be omitted entirely from some views of the assembly.

29.17   DETAIL DRAWINGS. When the design or assembly layout has been completed, all fixture components except standard commercial items are detailed on detail drawings. Modified or altered standard items are detailed only to the extent of the alteration. Unlike product drawings, which have only one detail drawing on a sheet, tool drawing detail sheets are the same size as those used for the assembly drawing, and as many details are placed on each sheet as will give

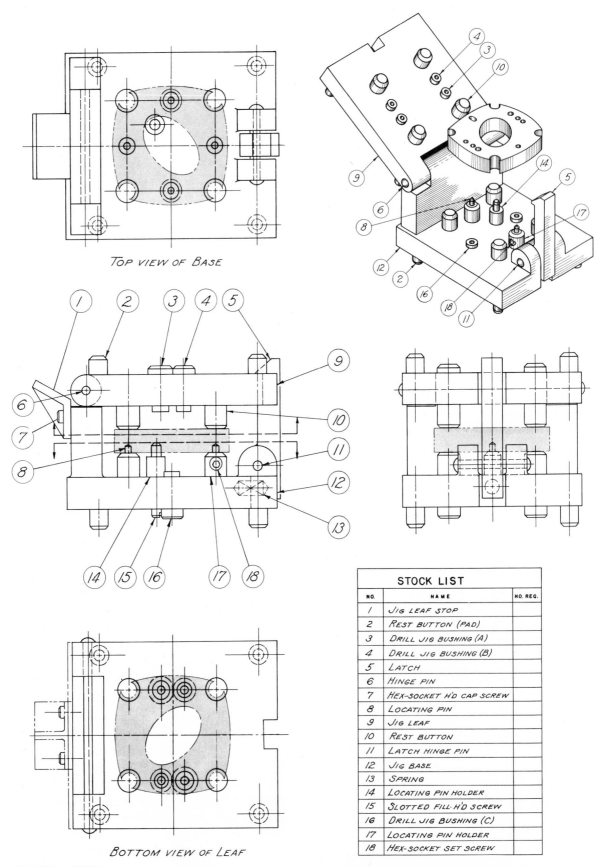

TOP VIEW OF BASE

BOTTOM VIEW OF LEAF

STOCK LIST		
NO.	NAME	NO. REQ.
1	JIG LEAF STOP	
2	REST BUTTON (PAD)	
3	DRILL JIG BUSHING (A)	
4	DRILL JIG BUSHING (B)	
5	LATCH	
6	HINGE PIN	
7	HEX-SOCKET H'D CAP SCREW	
8	LOCATING PIN	
9	JIG LEAF	
10	REST BUTTON	
11	LATCH HINGE PIN	
12	JIG BASE	
13	SPRING	
14	LOCATING PIN HOLDER	
15	SLOTTED FILL·H'D SCREW	
16	DRILL JIG BUSHING (C)	
17	LOCATING PIN HOLDER	
18	HEX-SOCKET SET SCREW	

Fig. 29.14   Drill jig.

TOOL AND DIE DRAWINGS		
DRAWN BY:		DATE:
SCALE:	DEPARTMENT:	
REFERENCE DRAWINGS:		
CHECKED BY:		DATE:
APPROVED BY:		DATE:
PART NAME:		PART NO.
MACHINE NAME:		MACHINE NO.
TOOL NAME:		TOOL NO.
ASSOCIATED DWGS.	DRAWING NO.	

Fig. 29.15   Tool drawing title block.

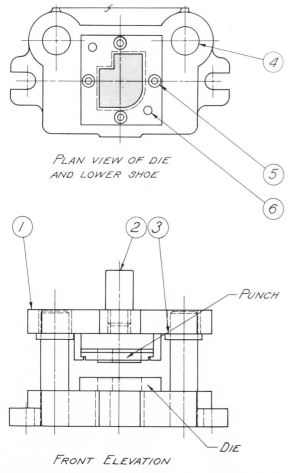

PLAN VIEW OF DIE
AND LOWER SHOE

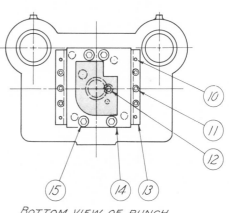

BOTTOM VIEW OF PUNCH
AND UPPER SHOE

FRONT ELEVATION

Fig. 29.16   Die drawing.

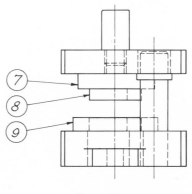

SIDE ELEVATION

desirable spacing. Each detail drawing has the same item number as is assigned to it on the assembly drawing and stock list. This item number, the item name, the material from which it is made, and the condition of heat treatment, and the quantity required for one assembly, are placed directly under the detail drawing or close by. See Fig. 29.17. The name or title of the detail sheets should be the same as that given to the assembly drawing except that the word "details" is substituted for the word "assembly." The identifying number assigned to the jig or fixture is included on all detail sheets, which should be numbered consecutively beginning with 1. Each sheet should contain the note "sheet XX of XX." No other information from the title block of the assembly drawing should be included.

29.18 DIMENSIONING. Although some of the work in the toolroom is done within broad tolerances and on conventional metalworking machines, there is much that is extremely exacting and must be done on precision grinders, die mills, jig mills, and jig borers. See Figs. 29.1 and 29.3. Precision locating dimensions

on jigs and fixtures are normally given a tolerance of 10 per cent of that of the production part.

Even an expert jig borer operator is faced with the possibility of error if he has to recalculate the drawing dimensions in order to position them on the jig borer. He cannot successfully combine shop mathematics with the operation of the machine consistently without error. All calculations that are required for the precise location of features that are to be machined on the tool or component should be made in the drawing room by the draftsman. Since this may result in repetitive work for the draftsman, he should consult with the toolroom before making his first calculations to determine how the dimensions should be specified for the particular machine and toolroom equipment. The features that must be precisely located should then be dimensioned from such tooling points and planes as will be of use to the machinist or toolmaker without further calculations. As many as possible of these precise locating dimensions should be made relative to a common point.

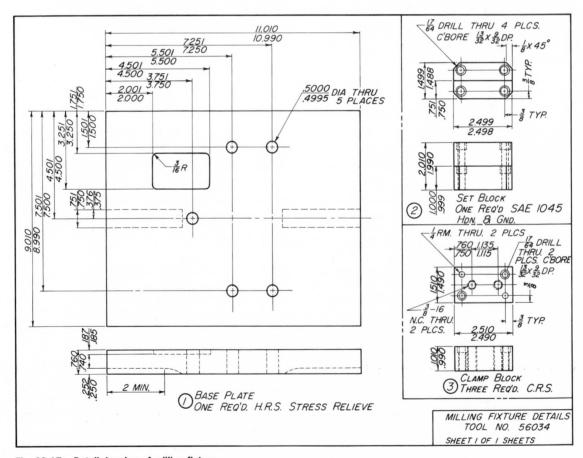

Fig. 29.17 Detail drawing of milling fixture.

Precision rotary tables used on jig borers can maintain an accuracy within seconds of arc, and where holes are to be located radially about a fixed point such as on a bolt circle, dimensioning can be in polar coordinates. For those tools that contain other features as well, or for those that do not have a radial pattern of holes, feature locations should be given in rectangular coordinates with all dimensions related to the same two (or three) axes, as in Item 1, Fig. 29.17. Where a pattern of holes appears symmetrical about a point on a radial line of the fixture, the position of this point is best given in polar coordinates and the hole pattern given in rectangular coordinates with the radial line and a perpendicular line through the point serving as new axes.

Compound angles should be of particular concern to the draftsman because of the large number of ways in which the fixture can be placed in proper alignment with the cutting tool for machining. The spindles of some machines can be made to tilt or swivel in any plane. Rotary tables will rotate a part through 360° in only one plane, while a tilting rotary table will rotate a part through 360° of arc in any plane within a quadrant of 90°. When the axis of tilt is changed, another degree of freedom is obtained. Universal sine plates can tilt a part about two perpendicular axes and require entirely different calculations than those for the tilting rotary table. See Fig. 29.18. It is incumbent upon the tool draftsman to be thoroughly familiar with the trigonometry involved in the necessary calculations that must be made with each of the various means of locating a fixture relative to the cutting tool.

Where compound angles must be located on a fixture, a tooling ball is located at some convenient point and necessary dimensions are related to the center of the ball, providing a means of accurately locating any feature of the jig or fixture in any plane.

The location and dimensions of many features or components of the fixture that are not critical can be left to the discretion of the toolmaker. Where bolts are used to attach some component to the fixture, the location of the bolt and dowel holes can be specified in a general location with short center lines and without the locating dimensions. A note on the detail can then specify "drill and counterbore for ½ inch socket head screws" without specifying either the diameter of the hole or the diameter or depth of the counterbore.

Where the draftsman desires to specify the location of bolt holes used for attaching one or more components to the fixture, it is common practice to indicate

the dimensions on one of the mating parts containing the bolt clearance holes and a note is placed on the other mating parts directing the toolmaker to "locate from item No. XX." This is referred to as locating by transfer. Bolt clearance holes are not normally located by transfer from tapped holes, but rather the tapped holes and any bolt clearance holes of identical pattern are located by transfer from bolt clearance holes. Locating by transfer is accomplished by a transfer punch which has a point ground concentric to its major diameter that fits the bolt clearance hole with a light slip fit and when struck leaves a punch mark in the mating part. The minor diameter of tapped holes is often eccentric to the pitch diameter of the threads, and if this minor diameter is used to locate by transfer, a mislocation will result. Mating dowel holes require extremely precise location and cannot be successfully located by transfer but are customarily drilled and line-reamed in the two mating parts at assembly, ensuring precise location of mating holes.

It should be stated that tool drawings will be used in the toolroom by competent and capable craftsmen and the requirements of mass production and interchangeability do not exist, while production parts are made by less experienced and frequently inept machine operators. For these reasons, wide latitude is allowed and encouraged in the making of tool drawings where this latitude will result in less cost through decreased drawing time or in increased clarity or convenience to the toolmaker, while such latitude cannot be permitted in engineering drawing of mass-produced interchangeable parts. Conversely, since the tool or fixture is to be used as an aid in the production of uniform parts, those features of the jig or fixture that ensure this uniformity must be located with far more precision than is required on the production part.

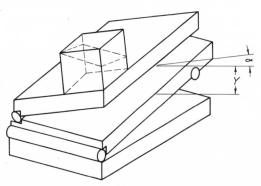

Fig. 29.18 Compound sine plate.

SELF-STUDY QUESTIONS

Before trying to answer these questions, read the chapter carefully. Then, without reference to the text, answer as many questions as possible. For those that cannot be answered, the number, in parentheses following the question number, gives the article in which the answer can be found. Look it up and write down the answer. Check the answers that you did give to see that they are correct.

29.1 **(29.2)** _____ , design, and drawing are vital to the manufacturing function.

29.2 **(29.3)** Normal production runs of most tooling parts require rigid _____ control.

29.3 **(29.3)** Many parts, regardless of quantity, will require _____ and _____ tooling.

29.4 **(29.4)** A fixture is a device to _____ and _____ a workpiece, whereas a jig in addition serves to _____ the cutting tool.

29.5 **(29.5)** Proper design of a tool for the most efficient use of the machine requires a complete understanding of the _____ of the machines.

29.6 **(29.7)** Commercially available machine tool accessories and universal positioning devices enormously extend the _____ of the machine tool.

29.7 **(29.6)** In many cases, _____ are available commercially which suffice to eliminate the need for tooling.

29.8 **(29.7)** Purchased standard fixture components are generally _____ than their counterparts produced in the toolroom.

29.9 **(29.7)** Design costs are minimized because standard components need only be _____ on assembly drawings.

29.10 **(29.8)** Most cutting problems can be solved with a simple _____ of a standard cutting tool.

29.11 **(29.9)** The position of the setting block must allow for the use of a _____ gage between the cutter and the surface of the setting block.

29.12 **(29.9)** Fixtures for tracing or profiling operations should provide for _____ between tracer template and fixture.

29.13 **(29.10)** Drill bushings are generally placed _____ to the surfaces of the work to be drilled.

29.14 **(29.10)** Slip renewable bushings fit the liner bushings with a close _____ fit and are easily and frequently installed and removed.

29.15 **(29.10)** Where a drill and a reamer are to be guided into the same hole location, two slip renewable bushings are required of _____ inside diameters and the _____ outside diameter.

29.16 **(29.10)** The pilot must be of _____ diameter than the cutting tool if placed ahead of the cutting edge.

29.17 **(29.11)** Fixtures are _____ to the machine table to align the axes of the fixture with the corresponding axes of the machine.

29.18 **(29.11)** In general, the first operation upon a casting or forging should be a _____ operation for subsequent visual locating or a machining operation to produce surfaces for positioning by locating devices.

29.19 **(29.11)** New locating surfaces are often required after _____ _____ operations.

29.20 **(29.12)** When locating the workpiece against points in three mutually perpendicular planes, _____ points are required in one plane _____ in another plane, and _____ in the third plane.

29.21 **(29.12)** The base of a workpiece that has previously been machined is often located against a _____ _____ of the fixture rather than on three points.

29.22 **(29.12)** _____ _____ locators are preferred over block locators to decrease misalignment due to out-of-square conditions.

29.23 **(29.13)** The clamping force must be applied _____ to the locating surface and directly _____ _____ with that surface to prevent distortion.

29.24 **(29.14)** _____ charts provide the greatest dimensional stability, while _____ films are quite satisfactory for most purposes.

29.25 **(29.14)** Layout lines of chart gages on Mylar film should be _____ to _____ wide.

29.26 **(29.14)** When a single contour line is used, the dimension should be to the _____ of the line.

29.27 **(29.15)** The preliminary design layout is a valuable aid in determining the proper _____ and _____ of fixture components.

29.28 **(29.16)** Identifying numbers of fixture components should be placed in _____ or _____ alignment on the assembly drawing.

29.29 **(29.16)** The production part contour should appear in _____ lines in all views.

29.30 **(29.16)** Standard commercial components are shown in _____ _____ form only.

29.31 **(29.17)** Tool drawing detail sheets are the _____ _____ as the assembly drawing.

29.32 **(29.17)** The item number, name, quantity, material, and condition of _____ _____ _____ are placed beneath the detail drawing of the item.

29.33 **(29.18)** Precision locating dimensions on jigs and fixtures are normally given a tolerance of _____ per cent of that of the production part.

PROBLEMS

In the following problems the student is expected to make the correct and complete shop drawings. He should first make an assembly layout from which he makes detail drawings of nonstandard parts that cannot be purchased. He also furnishes detailed information for changes in standard parts. Such alterations require a detail drawing of these changes.

The student should first make sketches of his proposed jig, fixture, die, or tool as a means of progressive planning of the final assembly layout. His sketches should be accompanied by catalogue information necessary to the final assembly layout and detail drawings.

Engineering changes may be included at the end of the assignment along with corrections and alterations necessary to bring each detail drawing into compatibility with component parts of the assembly.

All drawing sheets should be of the same size. The size of the drawing sheet chosen for the assembly layout should also be used for detailing. The detail sheets should not be crowded.

The balloon and part number, the part name, the material from which the part is made, and the number required for one assembly should be lettered carefully under each detail drawing. This information should be recorded in the stock list on the assembly layout.

29.1 Make an assembly layout and detail drawings of a fixture to mill or grind the end surfaces of the ½"-diameter bosses on the counterbalance, Fig. 12.83. Include complete stock list for the fixture on the assembly layout.

29.2 Make an assembly layout and detail drawings of a

drill jig to drill the ¼″-diameter hole in the counter-balance, Fig. 12.83. Include a complete stock list on the assembly layout for the jig.

29.3 Make an assembly layout and detail drawings of a drill jig to drill the four ¼″ cap screw holes in the cover, Fig. 10.56, Chapter 10. Locate the workpiece from the outside surface of the flange. Locate workpiece in jig by use of three contact points. Standard parts are not detailed. Include stock list on the assembly layout.

29.4 Make an assembly layout and detail drawings of a jig to drill and ream the ¹⁵⁄₁₆″-diameter center hole in Governor body, Fig. 12.85. The two holes, ⅜″-diameter ream, located 2¾″ apart, are to be used for locating the workpiece in the jig. Include a complete stock list on the assembly layout.

29.5 Make a subassembly drawing of the reservoir baffle plate, Fig. 29.19, and the reservoir cover, Fig. 29.20. Use this subassembly drawing as a workpiece, and

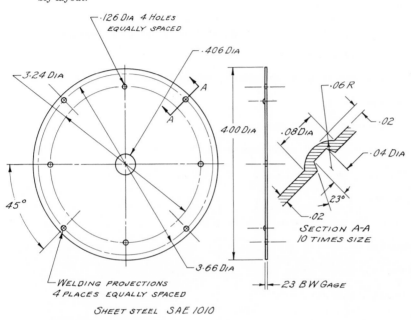

Fig. 29.19   Reservoir baffle plate.

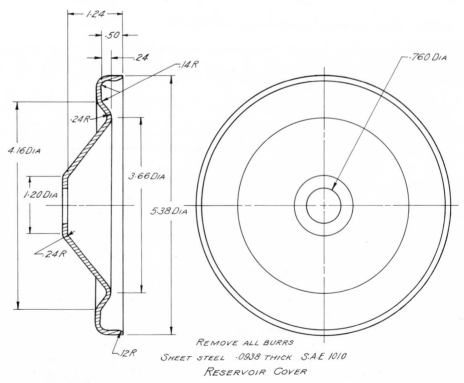

Fig. 29.20   Reservoir cover.

make an assembly layout and detail drawings of a welding fixture to weld these two parts together. Include a complete stock list on the assembly layout.

29.6 Make an assembly layout and detail drawings for a fixture to mill the ½″ slot in the pump plunger, Fig. 12.95. Include a complete stock list on the assembly layout.

29.7 Make an assembly layout and detail drawings of a jig to tap the center hole in the reservoir plate, Fig. 29.21. Include complete stock list on the assembly layout.

29.8 Make an assembly layout and detail drawings of a die to blank and pierce the 0.406″-diameter hole of the reservoir baffle plate, Fig. 29.19. Include a complete stock list on the assembly layout.

29.9 Make an assembly layout and detail drawings of a die to pierce four 0.126″-diameter holes, and emboss four welding projections on the reservoir baffle plate, Fig. 29.19. Include a complete stock list on the assembly layout.

29.10 Make an assembly layout and detail drawings of a die to punch two holes, 0.276″/0.286″ diameter, in the reservoir plate, Fig. 29.21. Include a complete stock list on the assembly layout.

29.11 Make an assembly layout and detail drawings of a die to blank and pierce the two rectangular holes and the two ⅛″ holes adjacent thereto in the ski binding bracket, Fig. 29.22. Include a complete stock list on the assembly layout.

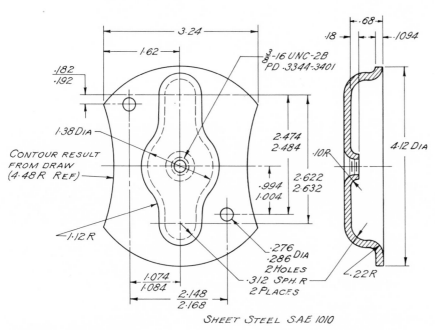

Fig. 29.21   Reservoir plate.

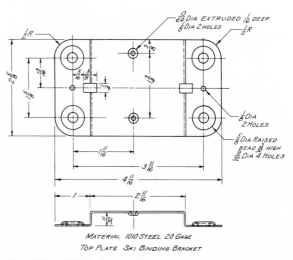

Fig. 29.22   Ski binding bracket.

Shading Drawings

OLD: Early Roman catapult (Philip Gendreau)

NEW: Cutaway drawing of upper stage of Saturn I space vehicle. (Douglas Aircraft Company)

Chapter 30   Shading Drawings

30.1   INTRODUCTION. Occasionally it is necessary to prepare a display drawing that must be made to look as lifelike as possible. These drawings can be used for sales, display, service, or repair. The many uses of production illustration drawings require the draftsman to have a thorough knowledge of pictorial drawing, which is almost always used, and the ability to use some of the various forms and techniques of shading. In most cases for engineering drawings, the shading should be as simple as possible. There are many methods that can be used for the purpose and each requires a different technique. Before learning these techniques it is necessary to make a study of the effect of light on the various surfaces of the object.

30.2   LIGHT. The different faces of an object are largely differentiated by the effects of light. Some surfaces are in direct light, others have indirect or reflected light, and still others are in shade. In previous chapters lines have been used to outline the various faces. There are no lines in nature and the faces are separated by the contrast of lighted surfaces with darker surfaces, by the quality of the material and surface finish, or by color.

30.3   CONTRAST. The surfaces closest to the observer will have the greatest contrast, while the background tends to fade into greys of the same quality and the contrast disappears. In the foreground the blacks will be blacker, the whites whiter, and the colors more brilliant.

A surface on which no direct light falls is said to be in shade. The lighted surfaces will vary in tone because the amount of light reflected from a surface depends on the angle at which the light strikes the surface. The light on a flat face will not usually be constant over the entire surface because of the greying effect of distance and the problem of reflected light.

30.4   ANALYSIS. Before shading a pictorial drawing it is necessary to select a source of light. This is usually chosen so that the face on the right side is in shade. Consequently this face becomes the darkest. The left face is the intermediate tone and the top surface is usually made the lightest. Other sources of light may be used if they will show off the shape of the object to better advantage. Figure 30.1 shows a cube shaded with the standard source of light. The artist makes a careful study of the effects of different lights and takes advantage of all shades and shadows. In engineering work, the shadows are almost always omitted because they tend to obscure some of the details. The effect is obtained by the use of shades and reflected light.

The shape of the object can often be shown to the best advantage by bringing out the reflected light. Thus a cylinder reflects the light in a rectangular form, the cone in a triangular form, and the sphere in a circular or elliptical form. A careful study of the various elements that compose an object must be made. The shades and highlights are then picked out by considering where they will occur with the selected source of light.

30.4.1   Flat surfaces. The shaded surfaces are blackest in the foreground and lighten up a little in the background. The light surfaces are whitest in the foreground and become a little darker in the background. This gives the greatest contrast of black against white in the foreground where it should be. See Fig. 30.1.

30.4.2   Curved surfaces. Rounded surfaces are best shown by bringing out the shades and the highlights. Figure 30.2 shows one cylinder with a polished surface and one with a dull surface. The highlight is in the form of a rectangle which can be very definite when the surface has been polished but quite general when the surface is dull. In that case there is a gradual fading of the highlight into the shades. It is usually considered best to arrange the source of light so that the highlight does not fall in the center of the cylinder.

The same comments can be made about the highlights on a cone except that they are triangular in shape instead of rectangular. The ability to grade a

Fig. 30.1   Airbrush shading of flat surfaces. Choice of light source.

tone from dark to light is one of the first techniques that must be learned. See Fig. 30.3.

The shape and character of the highlights are sometimes the only method of showing the shape of an object. When they are shown in their proper shape, they will always help in the reading of a drawing. A variety of different shapes are shown in Fig. 14.1 of Chapter 14. The best way to learn this is by carefully observing the way light is reflected from all of the objects with which you come in contact.

30.5   TECHNIQUE OF SHADING. The first step in shading a drawing is to analyze it and decide where the shades are to be, which contrasts are to be greatest, where the highlights are to be placed, and what the shape of the highlights will be. After that it is only necessary to use one of the following techniques to produce the desired result.

30.5.1   Line shading. Various tones may be created by drawing straight lines on the surface. To give the desired effect the lines may be varied in weight and spacing. Changing the spacing is usually easier. Figure 30.4 shows a drawing shaded by means of lines. For the flat surfaces the effect is obtained by drawing the lines closer together on the dark face and by omitting some of the lines on the light faces. The analysis previously mentioned will tell where the tones should be dark and where they should be light.

The lines must always lie on the surface. It is well to outline the area where the lines are to be drawn before beginning the shading. See Fig. 30.5. Avoid irregularity in spacing on the same area. Flat surfaces can be made to appear curved or warped by careless shad-

ing. Change in spacing will help the effect on curved surfaces if properly done.

30.5.2   Smudge shading. An overall tone can be produced by dipping a paper stump in finely powdered graphite and spreading it over the drawing. It can be made darker or lighter as desired. Careful work will produce a perfectly smooth or a graded tone. To make it permanent, it should be sprayed with a fixitive. See Fig. 30.6.

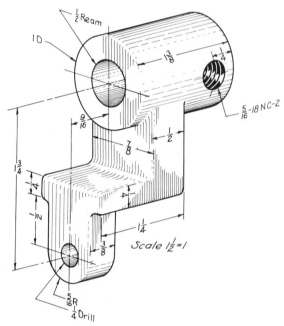

Fig. 30.4   Line shading.

Fig. 30.2   Airbrush shading of curved surfaces.

Fig. 30.3   Airbrush shading of cones.

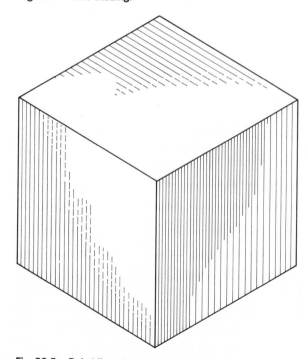

Fig. 30.5   Ruled line shading on flat surfaces.

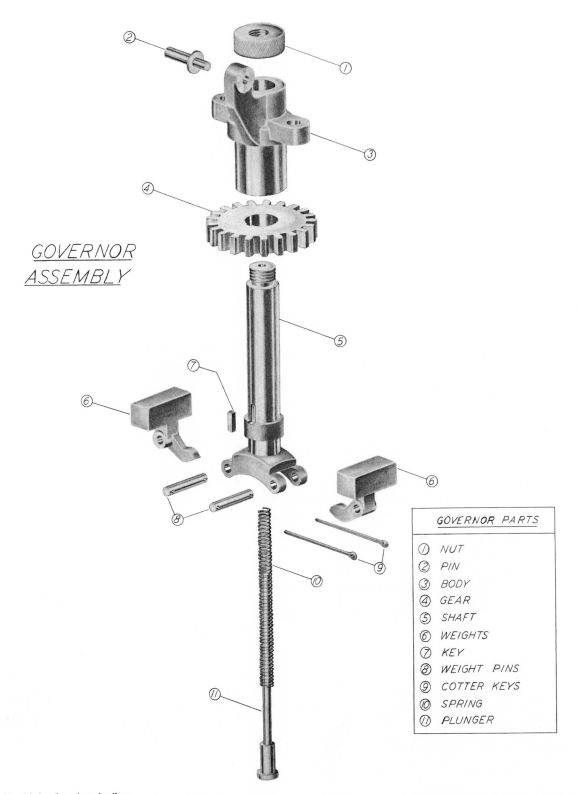

GOVERNOR
ASSEMBLY

GOVERNOR PARTS	
①	NUT
②	PIN
③	BODY
④	GEAR
⑤	SHAFT
⑥	WEIGHTS
⑦	KEY
⑧	WEIGHT PINS
⑨	COTTER KEYS
⑩	SPRING
⑪	PLUNGER

Fig. 30.6 Smudge shading.

810 PROFESSIONAL APPLICATIONS

Fig. 30.7 Broad-stroke pencil shading.

30.5.3   Pencil broad stroke. An effective variation of line shading can be made by sharpening the soft pencils to a bevel point. The shade lines can then be made freehand with a broad stroke using the flat surface of the bevel. A variety of pencils should be used to give different tones. See Fig. 30.7.

30.5.4   Sponge shading. An overall tone can be developed by touching a small piece of sponge to a stamp pad or to a film of printer's ink. The sponge is then used to dab a tone on the drawing in the desired areas. For this method it is best to cut out templates for each individual area so that the rest of the drawing will be protected. This method is shown in Fig. 30.8.

30.5.5   Airbrush. The most effective method of shading is by the use of the airbrush. The airbrush is a little machine that uses compressed air to blow a fine

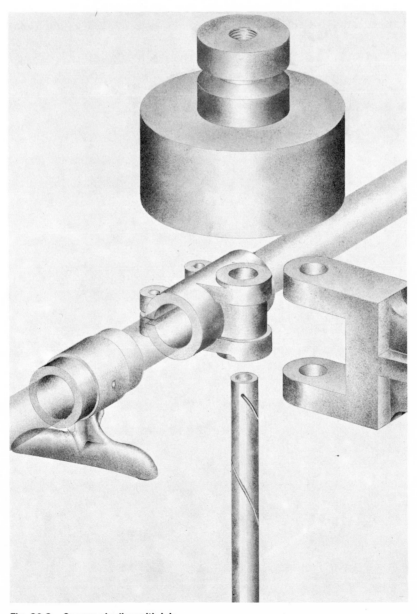

Fig. 30.8   Sponge shading with ink.

spray of ink onto a drawing. Templates may be used to cover the rest of the drawing or a special paper known as frisket paper may be used to cover the entire drawing. This paper has an adhesive on the back so that it sticks to the drawing. The various areas can then be cut out and exposed for shading one at a time. After shading the cover can be replaced on that part. Before trying this method, considerable practice is necessary to learn to make a flat tone and a graded tone. See Fig. 30.9.

30.5.6 Zip-a-tone. It is possible to buy a product that has a wide variety of patterns printed on the surface. One side of the surface is coated with adhesive that will stick to the drawing. Before using this material it is very important to decide just where the shading is to be and what tone is desired. The material is

then placed on the drawing and cut around the desired area. The shading sheet is then pressed down on this area and the rest of the sheet removed. The printed sheet is left on the drawing and provides the shading. It is possible to put on two or more layers to get a darker tone or to obtain a pattern if desired. See Fig. 30.10.

30.5.7 Double tone. This is another patented process that enables the draftsman to obtain four tones. They are black, white, single tone, and double tone. The single tone is a single crosshatching while the double tone is crosshatched in two directions. These lines are printed on a very good grade of paper and two different developers are used to bring out the two tones. The drawing is made directly on the paper or traced on it. Again a careful analysis must be made

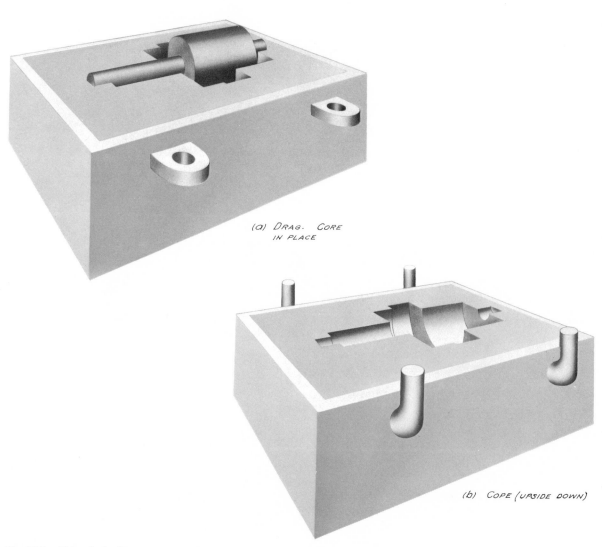

(a) DRAG. CORE IN PLACE

(b) COPE (UPSIDE DOWN)

Fig. 30.9 Airbrush shading.

first to decide where the four tones are to be placed. The white paper provides one tone; black ink can be painted on an area to give the black tone. A brush is used to develop the two chemical tones. They should be blotted as soon as they are developed. The effect obtained by this method is shown in Fig. 30.11.

30.6 ORTHOGRAPHIC PROJECTION SHADING. Occasionally a very simple form of shading is used on the regular views on an orthographic drawing. The light is assumed to come from the upper left side of the view. The lines of the view that are farthest away from the source of light are assumed to be in shade and are made heavier. For a hole the sides nearest the light source are assumed to be in shade and are made heavier. This method is illustrated in Fig. 30.12 and is called shade lining.

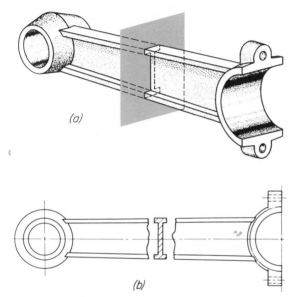

Fig. 30.10   Zip-a-Tone shading.

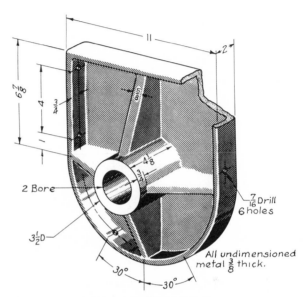

Fig. 30.11   Single- and double-tone shading.

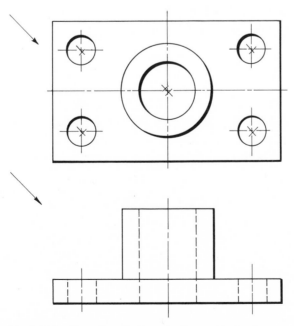

Fig. 30.12   Heavy line shading of orthographic drawings.

SELF-STUDY QUESTIONS

Before trying to answer these questions, read the chapter carefully. Then, without reference to the text, answer as many questions as possible. For those that cannot be answered, the number, in parentheses following the question number, gives the article in which the answer can be found. Look it up and write down the answer. Check the answers that you did give to see that they are correct.

30.1 **(30.1)** Shaded pictorial drawings can be used for many purposes, for example _____ .

30.2 **(30.1)** For engineering drawings the shading should be as _____ as possible.

30.3 **(30.2)** The different faces of an object are largely differentiated by the affects of _____ on the surfaces.

30.4 **(30.3)** The surfaces closest to the observer will have the greatest _____ in shading.

30.5 **(30.3)** The black tones will be black and the lighter tones white in the _____ .

30.6 **(30.3)** A surface on which no direct light falls is said to be in the _____ .

30.7 **(30.3)** In the background contrasts of dark and light tend to _____ .

30.8 **(30.3)** The light on a flat surface will not be the _____ over the entire area.

30.9 **(30.4)** The usual source of light places the darkest face on the _____ .

30.10 **(30.4)** The shadows are almost always _____ when shading engineering pictorial drawings.

30.11 **(30.4)** The shape of an object can often be shown by the character or shape of the _____ light.

30.12 **(30.4.1)** Dark surfaces are made a little _____ in the background.

30.13 **(30.4.1)** Light surfaces become a little _____ in the background.

30.14 **(30.4.2)** Highlights on a polished surface will be more _____ than on an unfinished surface.

30.15 **(30.4.2)** The highlights on a cylinder are _____ in shape.

30.16 **(30.4.2)** The highlights on a cone are _____ in shape.

30.17 **(30.5.1)** In line shading, various tones may be obtained by changing the weight or _____ of the lines.

30.18 **(30.5.2)** Smudge shading is done by rubbing powdered _____ on the drawing by means of a paper _____ .

30.19 **(30.5.3)** In broad-stroke shading a _____ point is used on the pencil.

30.20 **(30.5.4)** In sponge shading the part of the drawing not being shaded will be covered with a _____ .

30.21 **(30.5.5)** The adhesive coated paper used to protect the drawing while shading with the airbrush is called _____ paper.

30.22 **(30.5.5)** The airbrush is used to blow a fine _____ of _____ on the drawing.

30.23 **(30.5.6)** An adhesive coated material that has a pattern printed on it for shading is called _____ _____ _____ .

30.24 **(30.5.7)** Four tones are available for shading with double-tone paper: single _____ , black, _____ , and _____ tone.

30.25 **(30.6)** Making the lines that represent the dark side of an orthographic projection heavier than the others is called _____ lining.

PROBLEMS

For problem material any pictorial drawing in this text may be copied and then shaded by the method assigned by the instructor.

Drawing Control and Reproduction

NEW: Drawing control system with a continuous drawing process using a microfilm aperture card. (Courtesy of Xerox)

OLD: 1769 engraving by C. Hoschel of artist using a camera obscura to draw in essential lines of composition. (Courtesy of Eastman Kodak).

Chapter 31 Drawing Control and Reproduction

31.1 INTRODUCTION. During the past decade there have been many changes in company policies with respect to the manner in which engineering drawings have been handled. These changes have been brought about mainly for economic reasons. The cost of an average-size drawing, 22 inches by 34 inches, has been estimated to be from $22 to $30 per square foot. When this is converted to a weight calculation, it can be justifiably claimed that an engineering drawing is "worth its weight in gold."

Looking at the situation from this viewpoint, one can readily see why the problem of safeguarding engineering drawings becomes a matter of applying strict drawing-control procedures. Such items as standardization of paper sizes, simplified drafting procedures, assignment of drawing numbers, filing of drawings, microfilming, disaster files, printmaking, print distribution, print destruction, drafting costs, drawing change procedures, and drawing retrieval are all important aspects of proper drawing control. In this chapter the more common procedures in use by some of the larger industrial firms making engineering drawings will be discussed.

31.2 DESIGN PROCEDURES. In setting up a drawing-control system, an analysis must be made of the steps through which a drawing passes in going from an original idea to a finished print. The procedures followed by industry will vary, depending on the size of the company. A normal procedure would be to have a project-design group leader work closely with a project-design engineer. As the designer proceeds with the development of the idea, the design-group leader will coordinate the activities of the detailers, who are called on to develop the specific details.

After the drawing is completed it is sent to a clerk-typist for the addition of notes, after which a checker carefully examines it. When all the corrections have been made, the drawing is returned to the project-design engineer, who approves the drawing for reproduction. The prints are then distributed to the appropriate design engineers.

31.3 DRAWING-CONTROL SYSTEM. The purposes of a drawing-control system are (1) to keep an accurate record of the location and status of all drawings, (2) to reduce the handling of original tracings, thereby reducing the hazard of damage to the originals, (3) to minimize printmaking from the original tracings, (4) to insure proper print distribution to qualified persons, and (5) to provide a ready source of information concerning the status of all drawings with respect to their state of completion, location, and obsolescence.

The success of any drawing-control system is dependent upon the engineering drawing-control group having the prime responsibility for the making of drawings, recording of drawings, making changes, making prints, and the storage of drawings. To facilitate the execution of proper drawing control, a drawing schedule and a drawing record card are often used. See Figs. 31.1 and 31.2. Various other aids to drawing control are such printed forms as an Engineering Change Order, an Engineering Change Request, a Change Proposal, a Drawing Release Summary, and Manufacturing Release Orders.

31.4 DOCUMENT-NUMBERING SYSTEM. The drawing-control group has the responsibility of assigning numbers to drawings. Each company has its unique code consistent with its operation. Normally the numbers will be made up of letters of the alphabet and arabic numerals. Such items as the type of drawing, size of sheet, job number, department, and part number are coded into the document-numbering system.

One example of a document-numbering system, in which the numbers have a special significance, is illustrated in Fig. 31.3. The drawing number is made up of eight characters. The first three digits are used to identify the project; the remaining five digits are coded to help identify various characteristics about the particular drawing being numbered. The first digit after the dash indicates the type of document according to the following code:

0—Layout drawings, sketches
1—Specifications, analysis reports, etc.
2—Architectural and engineering drawings
3—Vendor part drawings
4—Detail drawings
5—Detail drawings
6—Assembly and installation drawings
7—Schematics
8—Logistic type drawings—tools, kits, etc.
9—Open

The fifth digit is used to identify a procurement procedure. The last three digits are the actual number of the drawing in its own series for a particular project.

Another example of a drawing-numbering system is illustrated in Fig. 31.4. This system uses a combination of digits and letters. The first letter A, B, C, or D indicates the sheet size. The next number is the job number, which is followed by a letter indicating the department responsible for the drawing, as follows:

A—Architectural
P—Plumbing, heating, and ventilating
H—Hydro
E—Electrical
V—Ventilating
M—Mechanical
S—Structural
Sa—Sanitary

The last digit is coded to identify a particular type of drawing in the department. For example, in architectural drawing, a 1 would indicate a ground floor plan, a 2 would be an operating floor plan, and a 3 would indicate that the drawing was a heater floor plan.

The various drawings are also often numbered as to sheet numbers, such as "Sheet 5 of 7," etc. Some companies add prefixes to the numbers to indicate such things as sketches. Each company has a document-numbering system that satisfies the unique problems

Fig. 31.1 Drawing schedule. (Courtesy American Machine and Foundry Co.)

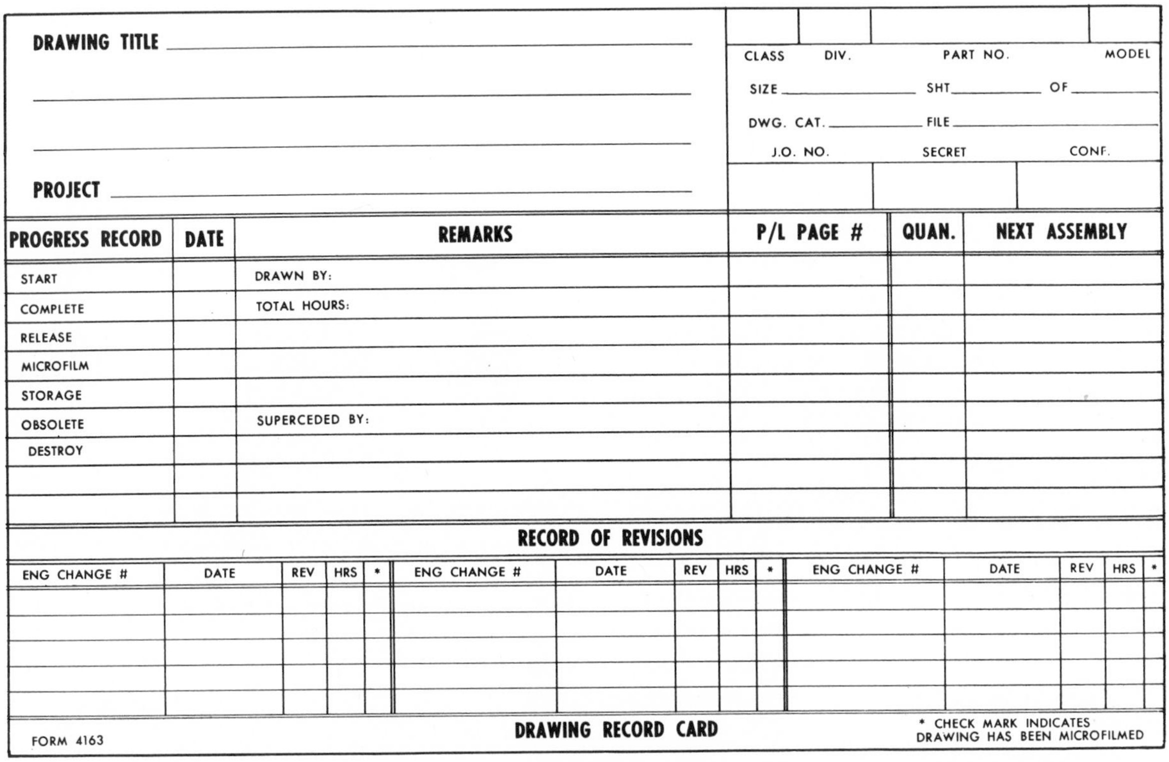

DRAWING TITLE _____

_____

_____

PROJECT _____

CLASS	DIV.	PART NO.	MODEL
SIZE _____	SHT _____	OF _____	
DWG. CAT. _____	FILE _____		
J.O. NO.	SECRET	CONF.	

PROGRESS RECORD	DATE	REMARKS	P/L PAGE #	QUAN.	NEXT ASSEMBLY
START		DRAWN BY:			
COMPLETE		TOTAL HOURS:			
RELEASE					
MICROFILM					
STORAGE					
OBSOLETE		SUPERCEDED BY:			
DESTROY					

RECORD OF REVISIONS

ENG CHANGE #	DATE	REV	HRS	*	ENG CHANGE #	DATE	REV	HRS	*	ENG CHANGE #	DATE	REV	HRS	*

FORM 4163   **DRAWING RECORD CARD**   * CHECK MARK INDICATES DRAWING HAS BEEN MICROFILMED

(a)

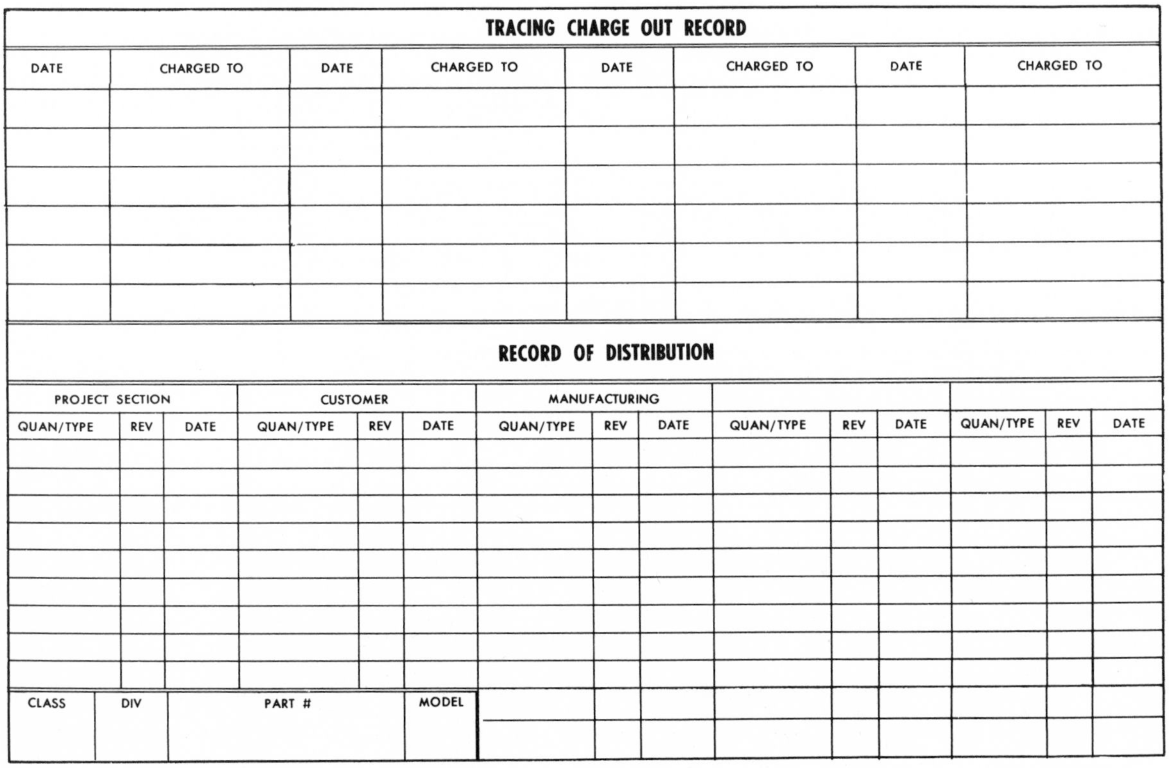

TRACING CHARGE OUT RECORD

DATE	CHARGED TO	DATE	CHARGED TO	DATE	CHARGED TO	DATE	CHARGED TO

RECORD OF DISTRIBUTION

PROJECT SECTION			CUSTOMER			MANUFACTURING								
QUAN/TYPE	REV	DATE	QUAN/TYPE	REV	DATE	QUAN/TYPE	REV	DATE	QUAN/TYPE	REV	DATE	QUAN/TYPE	REV	DATE
CLASS	DIV	PART #		MODEL										

(b)

Fig. 31.2   Drawing Record Card. (Courtesy American Machine and Foundry Co.)

of their operations. Some companies use straight numbering with no special significance assigned to any number.

31.5 DRAWING SCHEDULE. One of the most important functions of the drawing-control group is to be able to tell at any time the status, location, and condition of any drawing while it is being made and after it has been released for prints. Many companies accomplish this by using several types of card records, the most common ones being the Drawing Schedule and the Drawing Record Card.

The Drawing Schedule, Fig. 31.1, as used by the American Machine and Foundry Company, is designed to satisfy the following criteria:

a. To provide a tool for the group leader to assist him in estimating the time required to complete the design and the drafting effort for any project.

b. To coordinate the efforts of the designers and draftsmen and to help alert the shop facilities and thus provide for an orderly scheduling of the work in the shop.

c. To serve as a means for top management to know the day-to-day status of a design in progress.

d. To provide a means for the drafting supervisor to evaluate properly the efforts of his respective draftsman.

e. To provide a ready record of actual time spent on the design and drafting phase of any project, thereby providing an effective cost-control mechanism.

The use of this type of drawing schedule insures positive control and enables the drawing-control group to estimate the length of time required for designing and drafting. This enables the company to submit more accurate proposals when bidding for a project.

31.6 DRAWING RECORD CARD. The Drawing Record Card is used to keep a lifetime history of a particular drawing. This card, Fig. 31.2, shows the

changes, revisions, the location of the original drawing at any given time, and a record of distribution. The front of the card, Fig. 31.2(*a*), includes the title of the drawing, the project name, the drawing number, contract number, type of drawing, time required to make the drawing, the draftsman's name, sheet size, sheet number, file location, security classification, record of revisions, release date, microfilming information, and other pertinent remarks.

The back of the Drawing Record Card, Fig. 31.2(*b*), shows the original tracing charge out and the print-distribution records. It is important to have strict enforcement of drawing-control policies at all times for the system to work. Such items as a record of print distribution are important: when changes and revisions are made, corrected prints can be sent to the persons who received the prints originally.

31.7 DISASTER FILES. The need for maintaining a disaster file is obvious. Most companies follow a procedure of microfilming drawings as soon as they have been released by the engineering design department. These are normally microfilmed on 35 mm rolls with approximately 500 exposures per roll. The rolls of microfilm for the disaster file are then taken to some other location for safekeeping. Naturally a separate file is kept to give the location of a particular picture of a drawing within a microfilm roll.

31.8 STORAGE. Another important function of the drawing-control group is the storage and handling of drawings. A typical file room is illustrated in Fig. 31.5. The file room is normally located close to the reproduction and print-distribution center.

Drawings are filed in a wide variety of filing cabinets. For exceptionally large drawings, provisions are made to store them as rolls. For D-size drawings, large flat drawers are used. The drawings are normally placed in portfolios, which are then filed in the drawers.

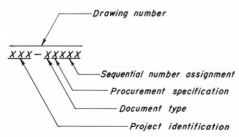

Fig. 31.3 Drawing number—using numerals only.

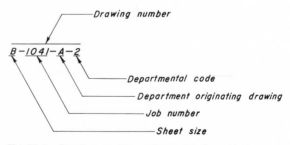

Fig. 31.4 Drawing number—using numerals and letters.

31.9   DESTRUCTION OF OLD DRAWINGS. Companies as a rule are reluctant to destroy their old drawings. Only in recent years has any attempt been made to develop systematically a procedure for the destruction of old drawings. The reason for this is an economic one: storage space becomes so expensive that some attempt at destroying inactive drawings has to be made.

The general criterion for determining which drawings are to be destroyed is the frequency of use of the drawing. Such considerations as the age of the drawing and the product must also be kept in mind. The usual procedure is to review the drawing files periodically and select those that are used infrequently or not at all. After consulting with the people involved, a decision is reached as to whether the drawing should be destroyed. Most companies use some form of microfilming so that a new print or drawing can be made if required.

31.10   DRAWING RETRIEVAL. Another important responsibility of the drawing-control group is to set up an effective retrieval system that will reduce the number of times a drawing is handled and thereby re-duce the hazard of damage to the originals. Only authorized personnel are permitted to take original drawings or tracings from the files. When a change or revision has to be made, the draftsman or designer must present a Change Order Slip and sign out for the drawing. An entry is made on the drawing record card each time the drawing is charged out. The person charged out with the original is responsible for the drawing until it is returned and the charge slip is destroyed.

With the use of microfilming, the need for handling original drawings has been reduced greatly. Prints are readily available from modern reproduction methods. Microfilm aperture cards make retrieval for reproduction a relatively simple problem.

31.11   DRAWING-REPRODUCTION   PROCESSES. The various processes available today for the reproduction of drawings make it possible for companies to select the one that is most economical for their uses. The old blueprint as such is rapidly becoming a thing of the past. Most companies have several methods available to them for making prints, thereby enabling the drawing-control group to provide a wide variety

Fig. 31.5   Drawing file room. (Courtesy Chevrolet Motor Co.)

of services to the draftsman, designer, vendor, customers, production personnel, and top management. See the comparison chart of reproduction processes in Table 31.1, which are discussed in greater detail in the following paragraphs.

31.12 DYE-TRANSFER PROCESSES. The Verifax process is a convenient method of making quick, inexpensive copies of drawings, printed pages, and photographs. It is a two-step, dye-transfer process that can be performed in ordinary room light. The original is exposed in a Verifax copier to a sheet of light-sensitized matrix paper for a few seconds. This matrix is "activated" and then placed in contact with a sheet of copy paper. The two are then stripped apart,

TABLE 31.1   COMPARISON CHART OF REPRODUCTION PROCESSES AND EQUIPMENT

Process	Equipment	Reduces or Enlarges	Characteristics	Comparative Costs
Dye-Transfer	Verifax Constat A. B. Dick	No	Copies are positives on nonsensitized paper. With Verifax, several prints can be made from one matrix.	Verifax: Lowest cost for 3 to 8 copies. Constat and A. B. Dick: Single copies are more costly than Thermofax, but quality is considerably better.
Thermography	Thermofax	No	Copies are positives on buff or colored paper. Waxlike finish. Less sensitive to kinds of ink.	Lowest cost for one or two copies, where quality and permanence are not important factors.
Spirit	Ditto	No	Reproduces typed copy or simple line drawings quickly from a Ditto master. Generally unsatisfactory except for internal purposes.	Lowest cost for runs of 10 to 100 where quality and permanence are not important factors.
Diazo	Ozalid Star Revolute Bruning	No	Copies are transparent, translucent, opaque, and in various colors.	Lowest cost for 1 to 15 prints of transparent or translucent originals, where reduction is not required.
Ektalith	Ektalith	Yes	Makes inexpensive paper masters rapidly for offset masters.	Lowest cost for offset runoff of quantities of 16 or greater.
Xerography	Xerox	Yes	Copies are positives. Process is used to make offset masters.	Lowest cost for offset runoff of quantities of 16 or greater where quality is an important factor, or additions or changes are to be made to the master before runoff.
Offset	Multilith	*	Reproduces clean, clear, high-quality copies up to 20″ x 24″. Color reproductions can be obtained.	Lowest cost for large runs, when used in conjunction with Ektalith or Xerox for the production of masters.
Microfilm	Complete microfilm equipment	Yes	Used to reduce original drawings or records for easy storage and safety. Produces direct copies of convenient size or masters for quantity reproduction by offset.	Not applicable
Photography	Complete photographic and copying equipment	Yes	Reproduces limited numbers of copies of line or halftone drawings or photographs directly, or can be used to make offset plates for quantity reproduction.	Not applicable

* In conjunction with Ektalith, Xerox, or photographic processes, all engineering documents E-size or smaller can be reduced and reproduced as A-, B-, or C-size sheets.

(Courtesy American Machine & Foundry Co.)

with the print on the copy paper. Additional copies can be made quickly from the same matrix sheets by using additional sheets of Verifax copy paper.

This process has the advantage over others in that it will copy anything that is typed, printed, or written in pen, pencil, or crayon. Attachments are available to copy pages in books and magazines. It is a wet process and is relatively slow.

The Contoura Constat is similar to the Verifax. It produces a film positive which is extremely versatile when used with other reproduction processes. It has a removable unit that can be used to copy wall charts, book and magazine pages, and various other bound originals.

31.13   THERMOGRAPHY. Thermofax is an infra-red process that can reproduce one copy of an original in about 6 seconds. Copies are produced dry and may be made from transparent sheets printed on one side or opaque sheets printed on one or both sides. It is a very easy machine to operate.

This process is expensive if more than one or two copies are required and the copy need not be permanent. The copies will not pick up some inks or letterheads. Its great advantage is its ease of operation and the rapidity of obtaining copies.

31.14   DITTO. The Ditto process of reproduction is a spirit duplicating method that uses a ditto master which can be sketched, drawn, or typed. The master is then attached to a duplicator drum and can make up to 100 prints directly from the master. Copies are often fuzzy and grow fainter as the press run continues. Copies also tend to fade, particularly if exposed to light. The Ditto has its greatest advantage in obtaining rapid copies of nonpermanent notes and memos in quantities of 10 to 100.

31.15   MIMEOGRAPH. The mimeograph machine is a common office machine that is normally used to make copies of typed information on a stencil, which is then mounted on the duplicating drum. With care, up to 1000 copies can be made. Drawings can be made directly upon the stencil with a stylus; however, the draftsman has to develop a particular skill to be able to obtain quality. At best, drawings reproduced in this manner have a limited degree of accuracy and sharpness.

The Times Facsimile Corporation makes a Stenafax machine that can cut a stencil from an original drawing electronically, using the same principle as used in wirephotos. It takes about 8 minutes to cut a stencil in this manner.

31.16   DIAZO. The diazo process of making prints depends on the principle of exposing the sensitized paper coated with light-sensitive diazonium salts to actinic light. When the paper is exposed to the light, the diazo compounds are decomposed, thereby rendering them incapable of forming an azo dye.

The Ozalid diazo process is a dry process in which the original drawing, which has to be on a translucent medium, is placed in contact with the diazo-sensitized paper and exposed to the actinic light. The parts of the paper beneath the lines and lettering of the drawing are not exposed to the light and are developed into an azo dye when passed over ammonia fumes. The color on any particular print can be varied by changing the azo-dye component that is used. The normal colors used are red, black, and blue.

The Bruning "Copyflex" process is a wet process whereby the exposed diazo-coated paper is passed through a solution which contains the necessary developing chemicals to convert the unexposed part of the print into an azo dye. The diazo process can be used to make "transparent intermediates" that can be used for printmaking rather than using the original drawing.

31.17   XEROGRAPH. Xerography is a combination photographic and electrostatic process that can produce a direct print or a multilith master for an offset duplicator. It has the advantage of enlarging or reducing the original. The five basic steps in xerography are the following:

a. The charging of the plate.
b. The exposure of the plate.
c. The developing process.
d. The transfer of the image.
e. The fusing of the image.

Figure 31.6 shows a typical xerographic master-making installation.

The original drawing is projected onto a positive electrically charged plate through a camera lens. The positive charges disappear in areas exposed to light, as shown by white space. After exposure the charged plate is placed into a processor where negatively charged particles of granular ink are permitted to flow over the plate. This is often referred to as the powder treatment. The negatively charged particles adhere to the positively charged image on the plate, whereupon a sheet of paper or a Multilith mat is placed over the plate. The paper or master receives the negatively charged particles, thereby transferring the image to the master. The particles are fused to the paper or master by placing it into a fuser where it is heated for a few seconds.

Xerography has its latest application in volume printmaking by using microfilm aperture cards as discussed in Art. 31.23.4. The Xerox Copyflo II continuous printer can be used in making prints directly from the original documents or from microfilms.

31.18 OFFSET. The Multilith offset duplicating method of reproducing drawings is used when large-quantity production runs are required. The process is quite versatile, in that Multilith masters can be made in a number of ways: drawn with a reproducing ink or pencil, by Xerography, by Ektalith, or by photography. The offset process is particularly useful in the preparation of various types of reports.

31.19 BLUEPRINT. The use of the blueprint process for making prints of drawings is the oldest form of reproduction process; however, in recent years it is being replaced rapidly by the various other methods discussed in this chapter. The paper used

in blueprinting is a good grade of white paper free of wood pulp and sulphite. It is coated with a solution of ammonium citrate of iron and potassium ferricyanide. When exposed to light, the ferric salt is reduced to a ferrous state which, when washed in water, produces a blue color called Prussian blue. The portion of the paper not exposed to the light has the water-soluble chemicals washed away, leaving the color of the original paper, or a blueprint with white lines.

The process is slow, requiring a washing and a drying process. It is still used in making prints of large architectural and structural drawings.

31.20 PHOTOGRAPHIC REPRODUCTION. Photography is used in some of the other methods of drawing reproductions as an intermediate step in the process. However, in some instances, the end product from this type of reproduction is a conventional photograph. There are three principal types of photographs that are used: the photostat, the photodrawing, and the conventional photograph.

A photostat machine is used to make enlargements

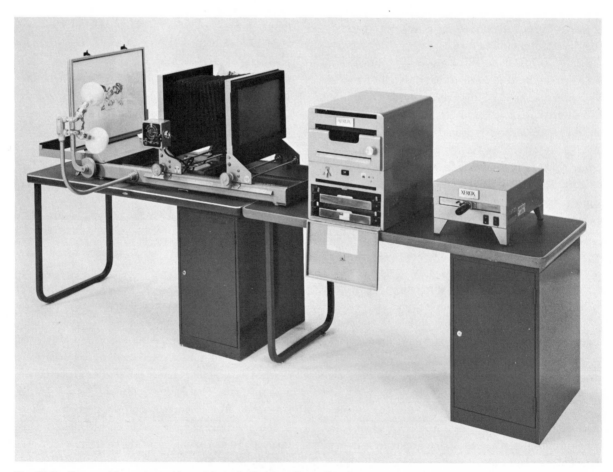

Fig. 31.6   Xerographic master-making equipment. (Courtesy Xerox Corp.)

or reductions of original drawings. The result is called a photostat print. The lens in the machine is oriented to permit the focusing of the image directly upon sensitized paper which is then developed and fixed within the machine. The process is relatively slow and expensive and is used when permanent records are desired.

The photodrawing is a combination of a photograph and line drawing. A photodrawing is used as a supplement to, rather than a replacement of, engineering drawings. It is used primarily in situations where a plant engineering change is to be made. A photograph is made of the particular area of the plant to be remodeled. This photograph is either cut out and pasted on a sheet of paper or reproduced on photosensitized paper. The necessary drawings and corrections are made on both the photograph and the paper.

Photodrawings are used extensively in making instructional assembly drawings. The assembled product is photographed in a convenient position. The various component parts are then labeled as shown in Fig. 31.7. This provides an extremely convenient way of showing an assembly drawing for use by the maintenance technician or the assembly line worker.

The conventional photograph is used when a permanent record for the file is required. It does not lend itself readily to shop use.

31.21 KODOGRAPH AUTOPOSITIVE. The Eastman Kodak Company has developed a process whereby positive prints may be made from tracings or from drawings on opaque paper using ordinary blueprinting equipment. A dark room is not necessary. These prints may be made on cloth or paper. A waterproof cloth has been developed so that the lines may be removed and changes made without spoiling the tracing.

31.22 MICROFILMING FOR SECURITY FILES. The microfilming of drawings for most industrial concerns began in the early 1940s as a security measure during the war. The drawings, engineering data, and supporting specifications were photographed on 35 mm roll film and stored in a remotely located vault. Some type of roll index had to be kept and coordinated with the parts index to facilitate the location of the particular frame. The roll film method of keeping security files is a rather cumbersome one when frequent reference has to be made to the film file. Such things as the revision of drawings often complicate the maintenance of an updated film file.

Today microfilming has completely revolutionized printmaking, the making of drawings, record keeping, and retrieval. In the middle 1950s many companies became aware of the need for streamlining their print distribution system and their drawing storage. The sheer numbers involved caused management to take a close look at ways and means of cutting costs. Guided missiles require 15,000 drawings, jet fighters require 18,000 drawings, and heavy tanks require 30,000 drawings. Another complicating feature was the storage of roll drawings up to 50 inches in width and over 12 feet long.

Some of the problems facing large companies and in particular the Department of Defense with respect to engineering drawings are such items as the following:

a. The difficulty of locating data in a system of massive volume.
b. The slowness of manual drawing retrieval.
c. The use of large areas for storage files.
d. The damage to originals by handling.
e. The time and expense in reproduction and print distribution.

With the experience of roll microfilming methods, many companies began to study ways and means to adapt microfilming to other uses than merely a security file.

31.23 MICROFILMING FOR PRINTMAKING. Once the drawing is stored on a film strip, it can be retrieved by the use of a specially designed viewing machine. After the particular frame is located, it can be printed on paper by an automatic blowback machine which gives an enlarged image. However, the process is time-consuming, and more recent developments make use of modern data-processing methods using punched cards.

In making blowback prints of microfilm photographs, a number of problems had to be solved before good prints could be obtained. Lenses with high resolving power had to be developed for the cameras, and a very fine-grain film had to be produced to permit a large amount of detail to be placed on a small space. In addition to the technical problems associated with the photography of drawings, other items such as the weight and spacing of letters and lines must be considered in the making of the engineering drawings for microfilming.

31.23.1 Drawing technique. In making drawings to be microfilmed, strict drawing technique standards must be adhered to in order to produce high-quality

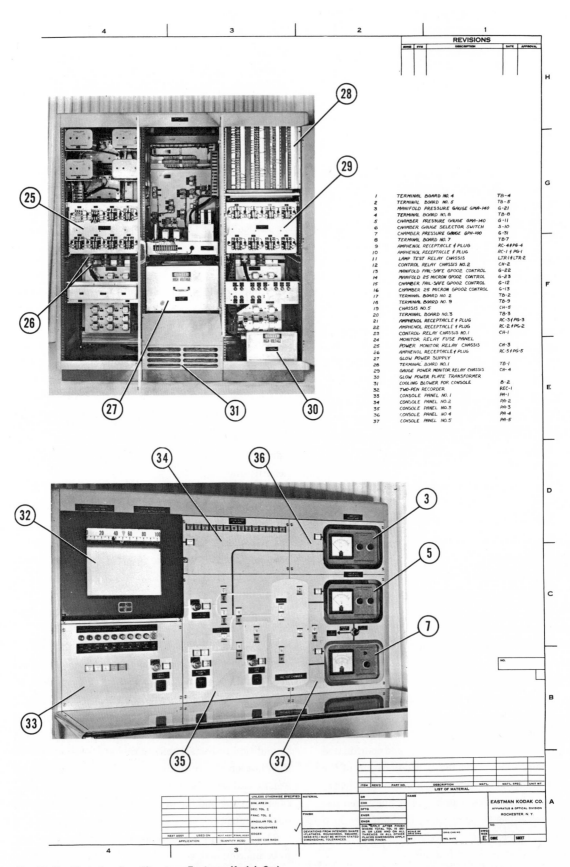

1	TERMINAL BOARD NO. 4	TB-4
2	TERMINAL BOARD NO. 5	TB-5
3	MANIFOLD PRESSURE GAUGE GMA-140	G-21
4	TERMINAL BOARD NO. 8	TB-8
5	CHAMBER PRESSURE GAUGE GMA-140	G-11
6	CHAMBER GAUGE SELECTOR SWITCH	S-10
7	CHAMBER PRESSURE GAUGE GPH-100	G-31
8	TERMINAL BOARD NO. 7	TB-7
9	AMPHENOL RECEPTACLE & PLUG	RC-4 & PG-4
10	AMPHENOL RECEPTACLE & PLUG	RC-1 & PG-1
11	LAMP TEST RELAY CHASSIS	LTR1 & LTR-2
12	CONTROL RELAY CHASSIS NO.2	CH-2
13	MANIFOLD FAIL-SAFE GPOO2 CONTROL	G-22
14	MANIFOLD 25 MICRON GPOO2 CONTROL	G-23
15	CHAMBER FAIL-SAFE GPOO2 CONTROL	G-12
16	CHAMBER 25 MICRON GPOO2 CONTROL	G-13
17	TERMINAL BOARD NO. 2	TB-9
18	TERMINAL BOARD NO. 9	TB-9
19	CHASSIS NO.5	CH-5
20	TERMINAL BOARD NO.3	TB-3
21	AMPHENOL RECEPTACLE & PLUG	RC-3 & PG-3
22	AMPHENOL RECEPTACLE & PLUG	RC-2 & PG-2
23	CONTROL RELAY CHASSIS NO.1	CH-1
24	MONITOR RELAY FUSE PANEL	
25	POWER MONITOR RELAY CHASSIS	CH-3
26	AMPHENOL RECEPTACLE & PLUG	RC-5 & PG-5
27	GLOW POWER SUPPLY	
28	TERMINAL BOARD NO.1	TB-1
29	GAUGE POWER MONITOR RELAY CHASSIS	CH-4
30	GLOW POWER PLATE TRANSFORMER	
31	COOLING BLOWER FOR CONSOLE	B-2
32	TWO-PEN RECORDER	REC-1
33	CONSOLE PANEL NO.1	PA-1
34	CONSOLE PANEL NO.2	PA-2
35	CONSOLE PANEL NO.3	PA-3
36	CONSOLE PANEL NO 4	PA-4
37	CONSOLE PANEL NO.5	PA-5

Fig. 31.7   Photodrawing. (Courtesy Eastman Kodak Co.)

prints. The lettering must be uniformly spaced, consistent in weight and style, and have a minimum of at least ⅛ inch in height on the drawing. Vertical-style lettering is preferred. The space between the lines of lettering must be at least half the height of the letter. When making additions to or changes in the original drawing, conformity to the style of the original must be maintained.

The lines on the drawing must be sharp, even, and uniform in intensity. They are made heavier than on normal tracings. In making individual letters, the space between any actual lines of that letter must be equal to at least twice the thickness of the line used in making the letter. Where possible, the drawings should be simplified to avoid unnecessary details.

The views on a drawing must be spaced in such a manner as to avoid overcrowding in any one part of the drawing. A scale must be selected so that there is adequate space between lines on the drawing. The number of standard drawing forms used is kept to a minimum. Index marks are placed on the drawing to insure centering of the image in the microfilm frame. In some instances, drafting standards have to be modified to meet the needs of microfilming.

31.23.2   Microfilm retrieval. One of the most important steps in providing rapid and updated print service is the facility with which the microfilm can be retrieved from the filing system. The Filmsort Aperture Card is shown in Fig. 31.8. These cards can be punched and filed in specially designed filing units that permit both machine selection and manual, random selection. The aperture cards can be quickly retrieved from the file and forwarded to the print center for making a blowback print or for use as a reference by a designer.

31.23.3   Microfilm for reference. When a designer needs a large number of drawings as a reference for a project on which he is working, it is a relatively simple matter to obtain duplicates of the aperture cards of the drawings he needs. He then uses these duplicate microfilms with a microfilm reader near his work area without requiring a large mass of prints to work from. The "Filmac 200" is a reader-printer that produces a print in a few seconds and can also be used as a reader.

31.23.4   Microfilm for print service. One of the greatest advantages of using microfilm systems is the availability of prints to the user on a demand basis. Storing large quantities of prints becomes unnecessary when microfilms are used. The user of the print can place an order at the print-distribution center by giving the clerk the drawing number. The clerk obtains the aperture card, makes the print in a matter of seconds, delivers the print to the user, and then returns the card to the file. Prints can be made by using Ozalid equipment. Xerox equipment can be used for making quantity reproductions with Offset masters and various other combinations of reproducing equipment.

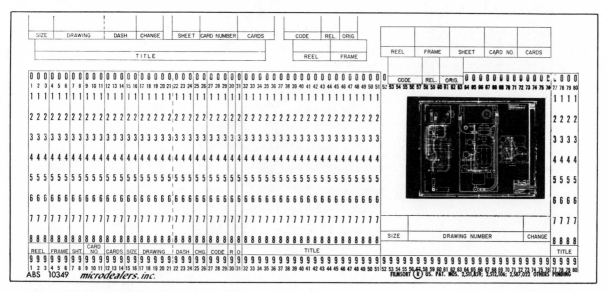

Fig. 31.8   Filmsort Microfilm aperature card. (Courtesy Filmsort.)

The Xerox Corporation makes the Copyflo 24C Continuous Printer that can be used in large-volume production of prints of engineering drawings from microfilm aperture cards. See Fig. 31.9. For smaller or decentralized engineering departments, the Xerox 1824 Printer is convenient for making prints from microfilm aperture cards. See Fig. 31.10. Both machines operate on the principles of xerography. The Copyflo 24C Continuous Printer can produce prints at the rate of 20 linear feet a minute up to $24'' \times 36''$ in size.

A common practice today is to supply a customer with a "deck" of microfilm aperture cards when delivering a particular piece of equipment, thereby enabling the customer to make as many prints for his use as he deems desirable. Large companies that are national in scope with plants in various parts of the country send "decks" of cards to their respective plants from their engineering headquarters.

One of the problems in the use of "decks" is to maintain a continual control over the revisions to original drawings. As soon as a change has been authorized and made by the drawing-control group, care must be taken to replace the outdated microfilm aperture card with microfilm having the revisions on it. Control must be exercised to destroy the obsolete prints and aperture cards.

31.23.5 Steps in microfilm system. In a fully integrated microfilm system the first step occurs when a new or revised drawing is released by the drawing-control group. The drawing is taken to the microfilming center where normally two 35 mm pictures are taken, one for the security files, the other for the making of prints. The film is developed. While this is being done, an aperture card is prepared with the necessary identifying data on it. This information is both typed and punched into the card. After the film is developed, it is cut and mounted in the aperture card.

The original drawings are filed at the end of each day. After the aperture card is made, it is used for making blowback prints by any of the previously discussed methods in this chapter. Duplicate aperture cards are made as needed. These cards are always marked "duplicate."

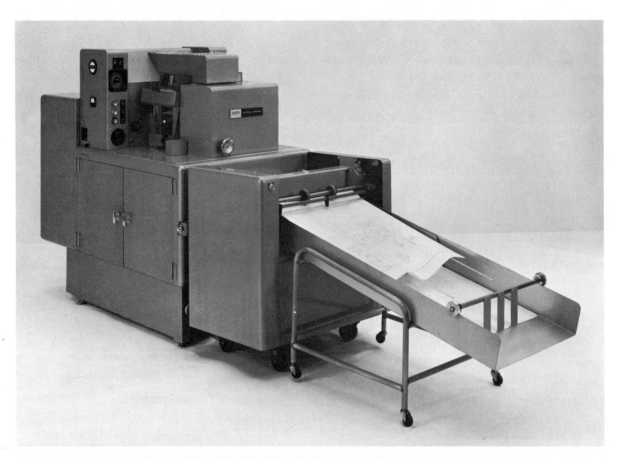

Fig. 31.9 Copyflo 24c Continuous Printer. (Courtesy Xerox Corp.)

After the duplicate cards and the necessary prints have been made, the original aperture card is filed. The original never leaves the print-control center. When a designer requests reference aperture cards, he is given a duplicate. When a drawing has been revised, the revised microfilm aperture card replaces the obsolete microfilm as soon as possible.

Periodically the drawing-control group must review the active drawing files, and sound management policy dictates the destruction of obsolete and inactive drawings. A similar review is made of the microfilm aperture cards, and those that become inactive are placed in an inactive file.

31.23.6   Advantages of microfilming. The advantages of microfilming are many. The accrued advantages will be somewhat dependent upon the type of company involved, the types of products produced, the size of the company, and the acceptance of the general principles by company management. Some

of these advantages are the following:

a. Reduced storage area for drawings.
b. Faster print service.
c. Reduction of print storage space.
d. Faster and easier retrieval.
e. Security file.
f. Economical reference cards for use in viewers.
g. Use of data-processing methods in retrieval.
h. Reduced handling of original drawings.
i. More flexibility with aperture cards.
j. Reduced costs in printmaking.
k. Increased accessibility of data.
l. Improved customer service.

The Department of Defense has been one of the prime movers in the use of microfilm and the development of the various techniques required to produce an efficient workable system. Various Military Standards have been developed.

Fig. 31.10   1824 Printer. (Courtesy Xerox Corp.)

SELF-STUDY QUESTIONS

Before trying to answer these questions, read the chapter carefully. Then, without reference to the text, answer as many questions as possible. For those that cannot be answered, the number, in parentheses following the question number, gives the article in which the answer can be found. Look it up and write down the answer. Check the answers that you did give to see that they are correct.

31.1 **(31.1)** The cost of an average size drawing 22 x 34″ varies from _____ to _____ dollars per square foot.

31.2 **(31.2)** When all corrections have been made, the drawing is returned to the project-design engineer who _____ the drawing for reproduction.

31.3 **(31.3)** The drawing-control group, among other things, must keep an accurate record of the _____ and _____ of all drawings.

31.4 **(31.3)** It is the duty of the drawing-control group to _____ the handling of original tracings in order to reduce the hazard of damage to the originals.

31.4 **(31.4)** The drawing-control group has the responsibility of assigning _____ to drawings.

31.5 **(31.4)** Some companies use a combination of numbers and letters for their drawing numbers. The first letter, such as A, B, C, etc., indicates the sheet _____ .

31.6 **(31.4)** Subsequent letters in a drawing number, after the first one, may indicate the _____ responsible for the drawing.

31.7 **(31.5)** One of the most important functions of the drawing-control group is to be able to tell at _____ time the status, location, and condition of any drawing while it is being _____ .

31.8 **(31.6)** The Drawing Record Card is used to keep a lifetime _____ of a particular drawing.

31.9 **(31.6)** Such items as print distribution are _____ so that when changes and revisions are made, _____ prints can be sent to the persons who received the prints originally.

31.10 **(31.7)** The microfilms of drawings for the disaster file are taken to another _____ away from the original plant office.

31.11 **(31.9)** In destroying old drawings, the usual procedure is to review the files periodically and to select those that are used infrequently or _____ all.

31.12 **(31.10)** Only _____ personnel are permitted to take original tracings from the file.

31.13 **(31.10)** When a change has to be made on a drawing the draftsman must present a "change _____" and sign up for the drawing.

31.14 **(31.11)** Most companies have _____ methods available for the reproduction of drawings.

31.15 **(31.23)** In making copies of a drawing for shop use from microfilm the process is called _____ back.

31.16 **(31.23.1)** In making drawings to be microfilmed, strict drawing technique _____ must be adhered to.

31.17 **(31.23.1)** Lettering on a drawing to be microfilmed must be uniformly spaced, consistent in weight and style, and not less than _____ _____ inch high.

CHAPTER 32
Patent Office Drawings

NEW: Drawing for Vented Mechanical Service patent by J. O. Tennies, Charles M. Allaben, Jr., and Robert H. Mead, 1967. (U.S. Patent Office)

OLD: Drawing for Steam Engine patent by Henry W. Adams, 1871 (U.S. Patent Office)

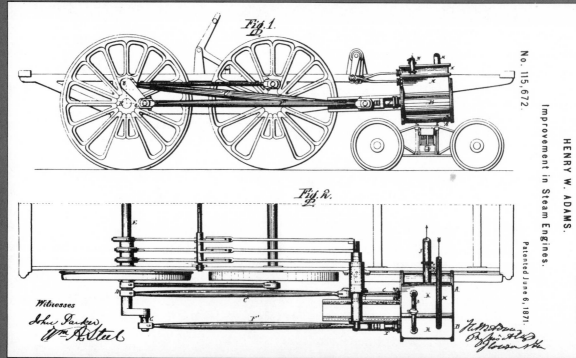

Chapter 32   Patent Office Drawings*

32.1   MEANING OF PATENTS   The patent, as a physical entity (more properly "Letters Patent"), is a document stating the "grant" and including a "specification" describing the invention concerned and ending with one or more claims defining specifically the novel features of the invention. There must also be a drawing, if the invention permits of illustration, which is fully described in the specification.

The Statute limits the field of patentable inventions (other than growing plants and designs) to processes, machines, manufactures, and compositions of matter. It also requires that the invention be "new and useful." It does not define the term "invention" other than to state that it means "invention or discovery." Many courts have tried to pass upon the degree of "genius" that must be displayed in the thing patented in order to amount to "invention." Some have said there must be a sudden inspiration, or a "flash of genius." In most cases, however, it has been regarded as sufficient if there is shown a degree of ingenuity beyond that to be expected of an average worker "skilled in the art."

The new Code tries to elucidate the matter by stating, Section 103, that a patent may not be granted "if the differences between the subject matter sought to be patented and the prior art are such that the subject matter as a whole would have been obvious at the time when the invention was made to a person having ordinary skill in the art to which said subject matter pertains."

Let us assume that an inventor has perceived a need or a possible use for something new falling within the statutory classes noted above. By careful study or by a "happy thought," he arrives at a way in which the desired object or result may be obtained or a mechanism may be constructed by which an improvement may be effected. So far, this may have been only a mental process and, if so, no matter how definite his idea or how certain he may be that he has a solution to the problem in hand, he has not "made an invention"

in the legal sense. He has only a "conception" and no means of proving even that.

If he then makes some sketches of the device or writes a description or both and signs and dates them, he now has available something in the nature of proof of the conception, but still no "invention." Furthermore, these documents need one or more witnesses who can testify that they saw the documents at a certain time. Accordingly, the cautious inventor will take the matter up with someone able to understand the device, explain it to him, and have the papers dated and signed. Now we have "corroboration," a highly important element in establishing an inventor's dates. These steps should be taken at the earliest possible time.

After "conception" the next step is to reduce the invention to practice. Without this the invention is not regarded as "completed." "Reduction to practice" may be accomplished in one of two ways, either by "actual" reduction, that is, by making and operating the structure and actual carrying out of a process, or by filing an application for patent thereon in the Patent Office. Such filing is regarded, by a sort of legal fiction, as fully equivalent to actual reduction and is termed "constructive" reduction to practice.

"Actual" reduction to practice requires successful use under substantially the same conditions as those for which the device is designed. As an example, a man had devised a stoplight for automobiles but his only test had been by mounting the mechanism on a bench and operating it by a lever. He was held not to have "reduced to practice" since the device was not used on an automobile. This may be an extreme case but it illustrates the principle.

In order to prove actual reduction to practice one should have witnesses and records similar to those required in proof of conception. The device used in demonstrating successful use should be preserved if possible.

32.2   APPLICATION FOR PATENTS.   Applications for patents must be made to the Commissioner of Patents. A complete application comprises: (1) a petition or request for a patent; (2) a specification, including a claim or claims; (3) an oath; (4) drawings, when

---

* This chapter was abstracted by permission from a paper by George A. Lovett, formerly Patent Attorney, General Motors Corporation.

necessary; (5) the prescribed filing fee.

32.3 SPECIFICATIONS. The specifications accompanying a patent petition should be arranged in the following order:

a. Title of the invention; or a preamble stating the name, citizenship, and residence of the applicant and the title of the invention may be used.
b. Brief summary of the invention.
c. Brief description of the several views of the drawing, if there are drawings.
d. Detailed description.
e. Claim or claims.
f. Signature.

32.4 DRAWINGS. The drawings required by the Patent Office differ somewhat from those used in engineering practice. Before beginning the drawings the inventor should secure a copy of "Rules of Practice of the United States Patent Office" from the Supt. of Documents, Washington 25, D. C. The cost is $.40. Stamps are not acceptable in payment. The drawings used for patents are made according to the usual rules of orthographic projection, but it is not necessary that they appear in projection with each other nor on one sheet. The following rules quoted verbatim from "Rules of Practice of the United States Patent Office" must be followed exactly. They are illustrated in Fig. 32.1.

Drawings required. The applicant for patent is required by statute to furnish a drawing of his invention whenever the nature of the case admits of it; this drawing must be filed with the application. Illustrations facilitating an understanding of the invention (for example, flow sheets in cases of processes, and diagrammatic views) may also be furnished in the same manner as drawings, and may be required by the Office when considered necessary or desirable.

Signature to drawing. The drawing must either be signed by the applicant in person or have the name of the applicant placed thereon followed by the signature of the attorney or agent as such.

Content of drawing. The drawing must show every feature of the invention specified in the claims. When the invention consists of an improvement on an old machine the drawing must when possible exhibit, in one or more views, the improved portion itself, disconnected from the old structure, and also in another view, so much only of the old structure as will suffice to show the connection of the invention therewith.

Standards for drawings. The complete drawing is printed and published when the patent issues, and a copy is attached to the patent. This work is done by the photolithographic process, the sheets of drawings being reduced about one-third in size. In addition, a reduction of a selected portion of the drawing of each application is published in the *Official Gazette*. It is therefore necessary for these and other reasons that the character of each drawing be brought as nearly as possible to a uniform standard of execution and excellence, suited to the requirements of the reproduction process and of the use of the drawings, to give the best results in the interest of inventors, of the Office, and of the public. The following regulations with respect to drawings are accordingly prescribed:

(*a*) *Paper and ink.* Drawings must be made upon pure white paper of a thickness corresponding to two-ply or three-ply Bristol board. The surface of the paper must be calendered and smooth and of a quality which will permit erasure and correction. India ink alone must be used for pen drawings to secure perfectly black solid lines. The use of white pigment to cover lines is not acceptable.

(*b*) *Size of sheet and margins.* The size of a sheet on which a drawing is made must be exactly 10 by 15 inches. One inch from its edges a single marginal line is to be drawn, leaving the "sight" precisely 8 by 13 inches. Within this margin all work and signatures must be included. One of the shorter sides of the sheet is regarded as its top, and, measuring down from the marginal line, a space of not less than 1¼ inches is to be left blank for the heading of title, name, number, and date, which will be applied subsequently by the Office in a uniform style.

(*c*) *Character of lines.* All drawings must be made with drafting instruments or by photolithographic process which will give them satisfactory reproduction characteristics. Every line and letter (signatures included) must be absolutely black. This direction applies to all lines however fine, to shading, and to lines representing cut surfaces in sectional views. All lines must be clean, sharp, and solid, and fine or crowded lines should be avoided. Solid black should not be used for sectional or surface shading. Free-hand work should be avoided wherever it is possible to do so.

(*d*) *Hatching and shading.* Hatching should be made by oblique parallel lines, which may be not less than about one-twentieth inch apart.

Heavy lines on the shaded side of the object should be used except where they tend to thicken the work and obscure reference characters. The light should come from the upper lefthand corner at an angle of 45°. Surface delineations should be shown by proper shading, which should be open.

(*e*) *Scale.* The scale to which a drawing is made ought to be large enough to show the mechanism without crowding when the drawing is reduced in reproduction, and views of portions of the mechanism on a larger scale should be used when necessary to show details clearly; two or more sheets should be used if one does not give sufficient room to accomplish this end, but the number of sheets should not be more than is necessary.

(*f*) *Reference characters.* The different views should be consecutively numbered figures. Reference numerals (and letters, but numerals are preferred) must be plain, legible and carefully formed, and not be encircled. They should, if possible, measure at least one-eighth of an inch in height so that they may bear reduction to one twenty-fourth of an inch; and they may be slightly larger when there is sufficient room. They must not be so placed in the close and complex parts of the drawing as to interfere with a thorough comprehension of the same, and therefore should rarely cross or mingle with the lines. When necessary grouped around a certain part, they should be placed at a little distance, at the closest point where there is available space, and connected by lines with the parts to which they refer. They should not be placed upon hatched or shaded surfaces but when necessary, a blank space may be left in the hatching or shading where the character occurs so that it shall appear perfectly distinct

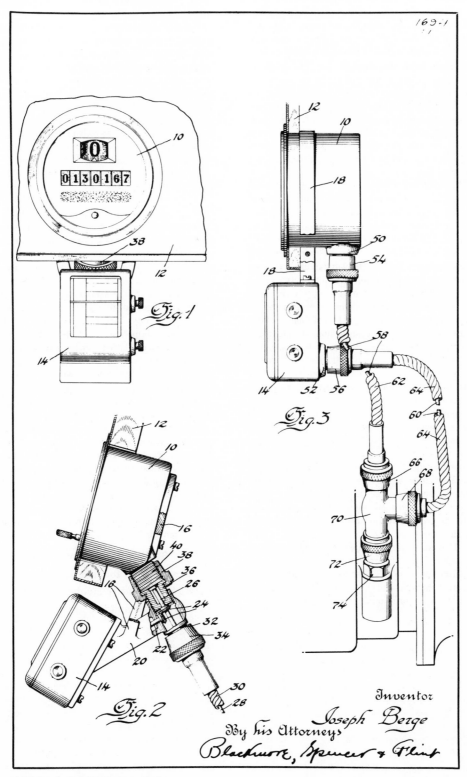

Fig. 32.1   Patent Office drawing.

and separate from the work. The same part of an invention appearing in more than one view of the drawing must always be designated by the same character, and the same character must never be used to designate different parts.

(*g*) *Symbols, legends.* Graphical drawing symbols for conventional elements may be used when appropriate, subject to approval by the Office. The elements for which such symbols are used must be adequately identified in the specification. While descriptive matter on drawings is not permitted, suitable legends may be used, or may be required in proper cases, as in diagrammatic views and flow sheets. The lettering should be as large as, or larger than, the reference characters.

(*h*) *Location of signature and names.* The signature of the applicant, or the name of the applicant and signature of the attorney or agent, should be placed in the lower right-hand corner of each sheet within the marginal line. Signatures of witnesses are not required. The title of the invention must not be placed on the drawing but may be written in pencil below the lower marginal line.

(*i*) *Views.* The drawing must contain as many figures as may be necessary to show the invention; the figures should be consecutively numbered if possible, in the order in which they appear. The figures may be plan, elevation, section, or perspective views, and detail views of portions or elements, on a larger scale if necessary may also be used. Exploded views, with the separated parts of the same figure embraced by a bracket to show the relationship or order of assembly of various parts, are permissible. When necessary a view of a large machine or device in its entirety may be broken and extended over several sheets if there is no loss of facility of understanding the view (the different parts should be identified by the same figure number but followed by the letters, *a, b, c,* etc., for each part). The plane upon which a sectional view is taken should be indicated on the general view by a broken line, the ends of which should be designated by numerals corresponding to the figure number of the sectional view and have arrows applied to indicate the direction in which the view is taken. A moved position may be shown by a broken line superimposed upon a suitable figure if this can be done without crowding, otherwise a separate figure must be used for this purpose. Modified forms of construction can only be shown in separate figures. Views should not be connected by projection lines nor should center lines be used.

(*j*) *Arrangement of views.* All views on the same sheet must stand in the same direction and should, if possible, stand so that they can be read with the sheet held in an upright position. If views longer than the width of the sheet are necessary for the clearest illustration of the invention, the sheet may be turned on its side. The space for a heading must then be reserved at the right and the signatures placed at the left, occupying the same space and position on the sheet as in

the upright views and being horizontal when the sheet is held in an upright position. One figure must not be placed upon another or within the outline of another.

(*k*) *Figure for Official Gazette.* The drawing should, as far as possible, be so planned that one of the views will be suitable for publication in the *Official Gazette* as the illustration of the invention.

(*l*) *Extraneous matter.* An agent's or attorney's stamp, or address, or other extraneous matter, will not be permitted upon the face of a drawing, within or without the marginal line, except that the title of the invention in pencil and identifying indicia, to distinguish from other drawings filed at the same tme, may be placed below the lower margin.

(*m*) *Transmission of drawings.* Drawings transmitted to the Office should be sent flat, protected by a sheet of heavy binder's board, or may be rolled for transmission in a suitable mailing tube; but must never be folded. If received creased or mutilated, new drawings will be required.

See rule 152 for design drawings, 165 for plant drawings, and 174 for reissue drawings.

Informal drawings. The requirements of rule 84 relating to drawings will be strictly enforced. A drawing not executed in conformity thereto may be admitted for the purpose of examination, but in such case the drawing must be corrected or a new one furnished, as required. The necessary corrections will be made by the Office upon applicant's request and at his expense. (See rule 21.)

Draftsman to make drawings. Applicants are advised to employ competent draftsmen to make their drawings.

The Office may furnish the drawings at the applicant's expense as promptly as its draftsmen can make them, for applicants who can not otherwise conveniently procure them. (See rule 21.)

Return of drawings. The drawings of an accepted application will not be returned to the applicant except for signature.

A photographic print is made of the drawing of an accepted application.

Use of old drawings. If the drawings of a new application are to be identical with the drawings of a previous application of the applicant on file in the Office, or with part of such drawings, the old drawings or any sheets thereof may be used if the prior application is, or is about to be, abandoned, or if the sheets to be used are cancelled in the prior application. The new application must be accompanied by a letter requesting the transfer of the drawings, which should be completely identified.

32.5 SYMBOLS. The symbols to be used on patent drawings may be found in the "Rules of Practice" quoted above. Other symbols may be used if their meaning is clear and unequivocal.

CHAPTER 33
Computer Graphics

NEW: Graphic I Console which enters and edits text material directly onto
programs. Inputs and corrections are made directly on computer's cathode
ray tube with a light pen. (Bell Telephone Laboratories)

OLD: Russian abacus (Philip Gendreau)

Chapter 33 Computer Graphics*

33.1 INTRODUCTION. This chapter discusses the preparation of drawings by automated means and describes the types of equipment that are available and their possible applications. It also touches briefly on the relationship of these new devices to the traditional drafting methods described in earlier chapters.

The term "computer graphics" is a rather broad one that encompasses not only the new devices and methods employed in automated drafting, but a new way of looking at the engineering functions. The reason for all this, of course, is the computer, which has brought about a new awareness of the interdependence of the roles played by designer, draftsman, manufacturer, and engineer. These roles are no longer regarded as isolated steps in the process, but as parts of a unified whole.

Preparing drawings by automated means, therefore, should be thought of as a natural development in the art of presenting engineering conceptions graphically. Computer graphics provides the means for a person to describe to a computer the picture in his mind's eye or the sketch or drawing he holds in his hand. It also provides the means for the computer to "draw" or display graphically the information that has been processed by the computer. The devices and techniques being employed today are themselves changing as engineering drafting keeps pace with the new computer technology.

The following paragraphs cover some of the basic types of devices by which drawings may be prepared today by automated means. The coverage is by no means exhaustive, but rather suggestive of the developments taking place in this field.

33.2 CHARACTERISTICS OF AUTOMATED DEVICES. Almost all devices used in computer graphics incorporate both mechanical and electrical features. The more sophisticated devices that are linked with computers are electronically operated. In almost all instances these machines must be monitored or directed by a design engineer or draftsman.

The foundation on which they are based is the fact

that engineering drawings, for the most part, consist of a series of lines and points that can be described in terms of *x-y* coordinates. This being so, machines have been developed that can "read off" the information on an engineering sketch and record it in a memory bank of a computer. These machines are generally referred to as *input devices,* and are most commonly represented by the *digitizer.*

The machines that are able, through directions or computer commands, to actually draw illustrations are generally referred to as *output devices.* They are most commonly represented by the *plotting machine* or *plotters,* as they are usually called.

The more advanced machines make use of both input and output devices in such a way as to become an integral part of the actual engineering process. Computer graphics provides a means by which the noncomputer specialist may conveniently communicate with the computer. He can, therefore, avail himself of the facility of the computer to assist in developing and analyzing his ideas.

33.3 INPUT DEVICES. These devices, the most representative of which is the digitizer (see Fig. 33.1) enable the operator to record automatically the coordinates of all points on an engineering sketch or drawing. These coordinates are recorded on either the familiar IBM cards, perforated paper tape, or magnetic tape.

The digitizer represents a significant contribution toward minimizing the input when preparing voluminous *x-y* coordinate data required to define pictorial or physical items. In using a digitizer, the operator places the drawing or design layout to be described on the surface of the digitizer table. He then positions a probe or cross hair to the location of each point and triggers a switch to record the coordinates. The digitizer permits the operator to record rapidly information directly into a machine-readable form depending on the complexity of the drawing and the precision required in positioning the probe.

Digitizers may include interpretive circuits in the hardware which directly produce the commands necessary to drive associated output devices. Some are equipped with automatic line-following devices that

* By Robert J. Tatem, The Engineering Information Department, Bell Telephone Laboratories, Whippany, N.J.

841

minimize operator guidance. Most of them can be equipped with special modifications to suit particular needs.

33.4 OUTPUT DEVICES. The *plotting machines* are the most familiar, but by no means the only, out-put devices. As the name indicates, these machines consist of a drafting table and a movable overhead arm that is used to plot and draw the lines of an illustration (see Fig. 33.2). They may be used separately or in conjunction with digitizers and computers. When

Fig. 33-1 Typical digitizer for recording *x-y* coordinate data. (Courtesy Bell Laboratories.)

Fig. 33-2 Typical automated drafting machine. (Courtesy Boeing Company.)

so combined, they are referred to as automatic drafting machines—ADM's. They may, moreover, be obtained in a variety of sizes and with a large selection of equipment options to suit the particular needs of the user. For the most part, these plotting machines are used to prepare conventional ink or pencil drawings of the block diagram, map, and electrical schematic types.

The operation is the reverse of that followed by the digitizer. The x-y coordinates are transferred from a storage device through the plotting arm onto an acceptable material in the form of a finished drawing. This is a simplified explanation but one sufficient to convey the basic idea.

In actual practice, the drawing instrument may be an ink pen, a ballpoint pen, a lead pencil, a cutting knife or scribe, a light beam, or a print head. Pens and pencils are available in various widths and colors, several of which may be mounted in a turret-type rotatable head for automatic selection. Moving the drawing head to a "down" position will produce a line, whereas retracting it to an "up" position will permit repositioning or changing of instruments. When equipped with a light beam, the operation must take place in the equivalent of a photographic darkroom. In this case, the focused beam of light produces a line on photosensitive paper or film equal in width to the diameter of the aperture through which the light is directed. Moving the head with the light "off" is analogous to operating the pen in an "up" position.

The materials on which information may be plotted and drawn may be paper, vellum, linen, metal, film, and scribe coat materials.

The light beam and knife instruments are employed extensively in the electronics industry to enscribe onto film the circuits used in the manufacture of printed wiring boards. For high precision work the use of these plotters is imperative. The pen and pencil implements, in a like manner, are effectively used in the preparation of manufacturing drawings, in the presentation of management data, in the making of maps, and so forth.

One of the faster types of plotting devices is the *microfilm recorder,* which permits the plotting and photographing onto microfilm of complex drawings in a very short time. As many as 40,000 points can be plotted and recorded each second. The device consists of a cathode ray tube (CRT) in which an electron beam is passed through a deflection system that directs and locates the beam as a spot or point in the face of the

tube. Lines are produced when the beam is swept across the tube. A camera records on microfilm the images portrayed on the tube. Although, in some applications, the relatively small plotting area of the tube may be restrictive, microfilm recorders currently provide the only means by which large volumes of material consisting of original drawings and revisions may be produced and conveniently stored.

33.5 INTEGRATED SYSTEMS. The more advanced equipment configurations consist of a group of input and output devices arranged in *an integrated system.* This system encompasses the electronic speeds of cathode ray tube (CRT) displays, the principles of the digitizer, the power of a time-shared computer system, and last, but most important, the judgement and creativity of man.

The equipment consists of a cathode ray tube display console that is equipped with a typewriter, an array of pushbottons, and a "light" pen, all of which are linked "on line" with a time-shared computer (see Fig. 33.3). The time-sharing permits a man to interact with the computer as if he were the only user. In reality, there may be many such consoles simultaneously linked with the same computer. When any one user calls upon the computer to perform some function, the microsecond processing speeds enable the apparent instantaneous display of his results on the CRT screen. Upon completion of each computation, the computer is automatically made available to another user.

The typewriter, pushbuttons, and light pen each provide a means by which the designer can communicate with the computer. The typewriter is generally used to insert any textual data likely to be associated with a drawing, such as component values, element names, titles, and figure and page numbers. Each pushbutton on the CRT console may direct the computer to perform a particular function or operation. The "light" pen is a pencil-like instrument used to point at any desired element of a picture or display on the CRT screen (see Fig. 33.4). Electronic circuitry, in conjunction with stored programs, determines the element at which the man is pointing.

Although the pushbuttons may be used to designate functions available to the operator, a technique referred to as the "light buttons" is considered more convenient to the user. In reality, "light buttons" are a set of predetermined commands or symbols which can be displayed by a program directly on the CRT screen in view of the user (see Fig. 33.5). They are generally

Fig. 33-3 Integrated system showing CRT console, light pen, typewriter, and pushbuttons. (Courtesy Bell Laboratories.)

Fig. 33-4 Light pen used in conjunction with CRT screen. (Courtesy Bell Laboratories.)

simple one-word commands such as "move," "delete," and "copy." The operator points the light pen to one of these terms and the program evaluates the specific command. Based on that interpretation, a new set of light button commands may be displayed to direct the user's next operation. This technique (1) insures that only these light buttons (functions) to be used at that instant in the processing are displayed, (2) provides a flexible and expandable number of functions, and (3) presents the light buttons in the field of vision.

For example, the light buttons displayed on the CRT screen could be standard electrical symbols and functions which the operator may use to describe a schematic (see Fig. 33.5). By pointing to a resistor symbol with the light pen, the user indicates his desire to locate a copy of the symbol at a desired posi-

tion. As he moves the light pen to position the resistor on the CRT screen, the interactive system responds by having the symbol follow the movement of the pen; when he withdraws the pen, the location of the symbol is fixed on the schematic. Pushbuttons or light buttons may also be used to indicate that the picture displayed on the CRT screen is to be plotted on one of the automatic drafting machines.

Once a schematic or layout drawing has been constructed or drawn on the CRT with the light pen, it may be analyzed by the computer and modified at the designer's command. Designs, therefore, can be interrupted at any point, analyzed, and changed before further work takes place. This type of interactive process is ideally suited to complex projects involving a multiplicity of interrelated design elements.

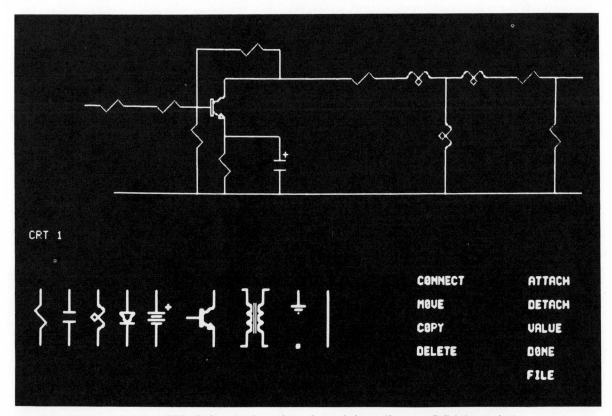

Fig. 33-5   Close-up of typical CRT display showing schematic symbology. (Courtesy Bell Laboratories.)

Figure 33.6 shows an operator using a light pen on a CRT in the design of a house. In this, the light pen actually draws the line on the CRT.

33.6 CONCLUSION. The development of these automated devices is continuing at a fairly rapid pace. They are being used increasingly in situations requiring high-speed production of large quantities of drawings and early visualization of ideas. That they have influenced the course of engineering drafting and have caused a shifting of emphasis are fairly evident facts. But these devices have neither diminished the importance of pictorial representation nor supplanted the traditional modes of portraying ideas. The inescapable fact is that the principles underlying manual methods pertain also to automated methods and must therefore be understood first before effective use of these new machines can be made.

As the material in this chapter touches only briefly on the subject, the reader is advised to supplement it with the following books and articles.

Fig. 33-6   Graphic input to an IBM System/360 computer using a light pen and an IBM 2250 graphic display unit. (Courtesy IBM.)

Bibliography for Further Study

System Analysis by Digital Computer, F. F. Kuo and J. F. Kaiser, John Wiley and Sons, New York, 1966.

"Technology and Manpower in Design and Drafting—1965–75," *Manpower Research Bulletin Number 12,* October 1966, U.S. Department of Labor, Manpower Administration.

"Sketchpad: A Man-machine Graphical Communication System," I. D. Sutherland, *Proceedings of the S.J.C.C.,* Volume 23, Spartan Books, Baltimore, 1963, pages 347–354.

"Graphic 1: A Remote Graphical Display Console System," W. H. Ninke, *Proceedings of the F.J.C.C.,* Volume 27, Spartan Books, Washington, D.C., 1965, pages 834–846.

"Graphic Data Processing," Machine Design, Volume 37, May 1965, pages 117–123.

Computer Graphics, F. Gruenberger (Ed.), Thompson Book Company, Washington, D.C., 1967.

"Computer Driven Displays and Their Use in Man Machine Interaction," Andries Van Dam in *Advances in Computers,* Volume 7, Academic Press, New York.

Appendix: Index of Tables

TABLE 1 GENERAL DIMENSIONS OF STRAIGHT SHANK TWIST DRILLS—SCREW MACHINE LENGTH WIRE GAGE SIZES, FRACTIONAL SIZES, LETTER SIZES, 0.040 TO 2.000 INCL.

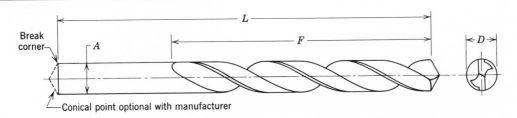

Conical point optional with manufacturer

Diameter of drill	Decimal equivalent	Overall length L	Flute length F	Diameter of drill	Decimal equivalent	Overall length L	Flute length F	Shank diameter A
60	0.040	1⅜	½	30	0.1285	1¹⁵⁄₁₆	¹⁵⁄₁₆	
59	0.041	1⅜	½	29	0.136	1¹⁵⁄₁₆	¹⁵⁄₁₆	
58	0.042	1⅜	½	28	0.1405	1¹⁵⁄₁₆	¹⁵⁄₁₆	
57	0.043	1⅜	½	⁹⁄₆₄	0.1406	1¹⁵⁄₁₆	¹⁵⁄₁₆	
56	0.0465	1⅜	½	27	0.144	2¹⁄₁₆	1	
³⁄₆₄	0.0469	1⅜	½	26	0.147	2¹⁄₁₆	1	
55	0.052	1⅝	⅝	25	0.1495	2¹⁄₁₆	1	
54	0.055	1⅝	⅝	24	0.152	2¹⁄₁₆	1	
53	0.0595	1⅝	⅝	23	0.154	2¹⁄₁₆	1	
¹⁄₁₆	0.0625	1⅝	⅝	⁵⁄₃₂	0.1562	2¹⁄₁₆	1	
52	0.0635	1¹¹⁄₁₆	¹¹⁄₁₆	22	0.157	2⅛	1¹⁄₁₆	
51	0.067	1¹¹⁄₁₆	¹¹⁄₁₆	21	0.159	2⅛	1¹⁄₁₆	
50	0.070	1¹¹⁄₁₆	¹¹⁄₁₆	20	0.161	2⅛	1¹⁄₁₆	
49	0.073	1¹¹⁄₁₆	¹¹⁄₁₆	19	0.166	2⅛	1¹⁄₁₆	
48	0.076	1¹¹⁄₁₆	¹¹⁄₁₆	18	0.1695	2⅛	1¹⁄₁₆	
⁵⁄₆₄	0.0781	1¹¹⁄₁₆	¹¹⁄₁₆	¹¹⁄₆₄	0.1719	2⅛	1¹⁄₁₆	
47	0.0785	1¾	¾	17	0.173	2³⁄₁₆	1⅛	
46	0.081	1¾	¾	16	0.177	2³⁄₁₆	1⅛	
45	0.082	1¾	¾	15	0.180	2³⁄₁₆	1⅛	
44	0.086	1¾	¾	14	0.182	2³⁄₁₆	1⅛	
43	0.089	1¾	¾	13	0.185	2³⁄₁₆	1⅛	
42	0.0935	1¾	¾	³⁄₁₆	0.1875	2³⁄₁₆	1⅛	
³⁄₃₂	0.0938	1¾	¾	12	0.189	2¼	1³⁄₁₆	
41	0.096	1¹³⁄₁₆	¹³⁄₁₆	11	0.191	2¼	1³⁄₁₆	
40	0.098	1¹³⁄₁₆	¹³⁄₁₆	10	0.1935	2¼	1³⁄₁₆	
39	0.0995	1¹³⁄₁₆	¹³⁄₁₆	9	0.196	2¼	1³⁄₁₆	
38	0.1015	1¹³⁄₁₆	¹³⁄₁₆	8	0.199	2¼	1³⁄₁₆	
37	0.104	1¹³⁄₁₆	¹³⁄₁₆	7	0.201	2¼	1³⁄₁₆	
36	0.1065	1¹³⁄₁₆	¹³⁄₁₆	¹³⁄₆₄	0.2031	2¼	1³⁄₁₆	
⁷⁄₆₄	0.1094	1¹³⁄₁₆	¹³⁄₁₆	6	0.204	2⅜	1¼	
35	0.110	1⅞	⅞	5	0.2055	2⅜	1¼	
34	0.111	1⅞	⅞	4	0.209	2⅜	1¼	
33	0.113	1⅞	⅞	3	0.213	2⅜	1¼	
32	0.116	1⅞	⅞	⁷⁄₃₂	0.2188	2⅜	1¼	
31	0.120	1⅞	⅞	2	0.221	2⁷⁄₁₆	1⁵⁄₁₆	
⅛	0.125	1⅞	⅞	1	0.228	2⁷⁄₁₆	1⁵⁄₁₆	

Shank diameter A: Same as nominal diameter of drill.

All dimensions are given in inches.

Courtesy USASI.

TABLE 1 *(Continued)* **GENERAL DIMENSIONS OF STRAIGHT SHANK TWIST DRILLS**

Diameter of drill	Decimal equivalent	Overall length L	Flute length F	Diameter of drill	Decimal equivalent	Overall length L	Flute length F	Shank diameter A
A	0.234	2⁷⁄₁₆	1⁵⁄₁₆	³⁷⁄₆₄	0.5781	4⅛	2⅝	
¹⁵⁄₆₄	0.2344	2⁷⁄₁₆	1⁵⁄₁₆	¹⁹⁄₃₂	0.5938	4⅛	2⅝	
B	0.238	2½	1⅜	³⁹⁄₆₄	0.6094	4¼	2¾	
C	0.242	2½	1⅜	⅝	0.6250	4¼	2¾	
D	0.246	2½	1⅜	⁴¹⁄₆₄	0.6406	4½	2⅞	
E & ¼	0.250	2½	1⅜	²¹⁄₃₂	0.6562	4½	2⅞	
F	0.257	2⅝	1⁷⁄₁₆	⁴³⁄₆₄	0.6719	4⅝	2⅞	
G	0.261	2⅝	1⁷⁄₁₆	¹¹⁄₁₆	0.6875	4⅝	2⅞	
¹⁷⁄₆₄	0.2656	2⅝	1⁷⁄₁₆	⁴⁵⁄₆₄	0.7031	4¾	3	
H	0.266	2¹¹⁄₁₆	1½	²³⁄₃₂	0.7188	4¾	3	
I	0.272	2¹¹⁄₁₆	1½	⁴⁷⁄₆₄	0.7344	5	3⅛	
J	0.277	2¹¹⁄₁₆	1½	¾	0.7500	5	3⅛	
K	0.281	2¹¹⁄₁₆	1½	⁴⁹⁄₆₄	0.7656	5⅛	3¼	
⁹⁄₃₂	0.2812	2¹¹⁄₁₆	1½	²⁵⁄₃₂	0.7812	5⅛	3¼	
L	0.290	2¾	1⁹⁄₁₆	⁵¹⁄₆₄	0.7969	5¼	3⅜	
M	0.295	2¾	1⁹⁄₁₆	¹³⁄₁₆	0.8125	5¼	3⅜	
¹⁹⁄₆₄	0.2969	2¾	1⁹⁄₁₆	⁵³⁄₆₄	0.8281	5⅜	3½	
N	0.302	2¹³⁄₁₆	1⅝	²⁷⁄₃₂	0.8438	5⅜	3½	
⁵⁄₁₆	0.3125	2¹³⁄₁₆	1⅝	⁵⁵⁄₆₄	0.8594	5½	3½	
O	0.316	2¹⁵⁄₁₆	1¹¹⁄₁₆	⅞	0.8750	5½	3½	
P	0.323	2¹⁵⁄₁₆	1¹¹⁄₁₆	⁵⁷⁄₆₄	0.8906	5⅝	3⅝	
²¹⁄₆₄	0.3281	2¹⁵⁄₁₆	1¹¹⁄₁₆	²⁹⁄₃₂	0.9062	5⅝	3⅝	
Q	0.332	3	1¹¹⁄₁₆	⁵⁹⁄₆₄	0.9219	5¾	3¾	
R	0.399	3	1¹¹⁄₁₆	¹⁵⁄₁₆	0.9375	5¾	3¾	
¹¹⁄₃₂	0.3438	3	1¹¹⁄₁₆	⁶¹⁄₆₄	0.9531	5⅞	3⅞	
S	0.348	3¹⁄₁₆	1¾	³¹⁄₃₂	0.9688	5⅞	3⅞	
T	0.358	3¹⁄₁₆	1¾	⁶³⁄₆₄	0.9844	6	4	
²³⁄₆₄	0.3594	3¹⁄₁₆	1¾	1	1.0000	6	4	
U	0.368	3⅛	1¹³⁄₁₆	1¹⁄₁₆	1.0625	6¼	4	1
⅜	0.375	3⅛	1¹³⁄₁₆	1⅛	1.1250	6⅜	4	1
V	0.377	3¼	1⅞	1³⁄₁₆	1.1875	6⅝	4¼	1
W	0.386	3¼	1⅞	1¼	1.2500	6¾	4⅜	1
²⁵⁄₆₄	0.3906	3¼	1⅞	1⁵⁄₁₆	1.3125	7	4⅜	1¼
X	0.397	3⁵⁄₁₆	1¹⁵⁄₁₆	1⅜	1.3750	7⅛	4½	1¼
Y	0.404	3⁵⁄₁₆	1¹⁵⁄₁₆	1⁷⁄₁₆	1.4375	7⅜	4¾	1¼
¹³⁄₃₂	0.4062	3⁵⁄₁₆	1¹⁵⁄₁₆	1½	1.5000	7½	4⅞	1¼
Z	0.413	3⅜	2	1⁹⁄₁₆	1.5625	7¾	4⅞	1½
²⁷⁄₆₄	0.4219	3⅜	2	1⅝	1.6250	7¾	4⅞	1½
⁷⁄₁₆	0.4375	3⁷⁄₁₆	2¹⁄₁₆	1¹¹⁄₁₆	1.6875	8	5⅛	1½
²⁹⁄₆₄	0.4531	3⁹⁄₁₆	2⅛	1¾	1.7500	8	5⅛	1½
¹⁵⁄₃₂	0.4688	3⅝	2⅛	1¹³⁄₁₆	1.8125	8¼	5⅜	1½
³¹⁄₆₄	0.4844	3¹¹⁄₁₆	2³⁄₁₆	1⅞	1.8750	8¼	5⅜	1½
½	0.500	3¾	2¼	1¹⁵⁄₁₆	1.9375	8½	5⅝	1½
³³⁄₆₄	0.5156	3⅞	2⅜	2	2.0000	8½	5⅝	1½
¹⁷⁄₃₂	0.5312	3⅞	2⅜					
³⁵⁄₆₄	0.5469	4	2½					
⁹⁄₁₆	0.5625	4	2½					

(Shank diameter A, upper rows: Same as nominal diameter of drill.)

All dimensions are given in inches.

Courtesy USASI.

TABLE 2   UNIFIED AND AMERICAN THREADS

Coarse-Threaded Series—UNC and NC (Basic Dimensions)

Sizes	Basic major diameter, D	Thds. per inch, n	Basic pitch diameter,* E	Minor diameter ext. thds. K_s	Minor diameter int. thds. K_n	Lead angle at basic pitch diameter, λ Deg	Min	Section at minor diameter at $D-2h_b$ Sq in.	Stress area† Sq in.	Tap drill number or size
	Inches		Inches	Inches	Inches	Deg	Min	Sq in.	Sq in.	
1(.073)	0.0730	64	0.0629	0.0538	0.0561	4	31	0.0022	0.0026	53
2(.086)	0.0860	56	0.0744	0.0641	0.0667	4	22	0.0031	0.0036	50
3(.099)	0.0990	48	0.0855	0.0734	0.0764	4	26	0.0041	0.0048	47
4(.112)	0.1120	40	0.0958	0.0813	0.0849	4	45	0.0050	0.0060	43
5(.125)	0.1250	40	0.1088	0.0943	0.0979	4	11	0.0067	0.0079	38
6(.138)	0.1380	32	0.1177	0.0997	0.1042	4	50	0.0075	0.0090	36
8(.164)	0.1640	32	0.1437	0.1257	0.1302	3	58	0.0120	0.0139	29
10(.190)	0.1900	24	0.1629	0.1389	0.1449	4	39	0.0145	0.0174	26
12(.216)	0.2160	24	0.1889	0.1649	0.1709	4	1	0.0206	0.0240	16
1/4	0.2500	20	0.2175	0.1887	0.1959	4	11	0.0269	0.0317	7
5/16	0.3125	18	0.2764	0.2443	0.2524	3	40	0.0454	0.0522	F
3/8	0.3750	16	0.3344	0.2983	0.3073	3	24	0.0678	0.0773	5/16
7/16	0.4375	14	0.3911	0.3499	0.3602	3	20	0.0933	0.1060	U
1/2	0.5000	13	0.4500	0.4056	0.4167	3	7	0.1257	0.1416	27/64
9/16	0.5625	12	0.5084	0.4603	0.4723	2	59	0.1620	0.1816	31/64
5/8	0.6250	11	0.5660	0.5135	0.5266	2	56	0.2018	0.2256	17/32
3/4	0.7500	10	0.6850	0.6273	0.6417	2	40	0.3020	0.3340	21/32
7/8	0.8750	9	0.8028	0.7387	0.7547	2	31	0.4193	0.4612	49/64
1	1.0000	8	0.9188	0.8466	0.8647	2	29	0.5510	0.6051	7/8
1⅛	1.1250	7	1.0322	0.9497	0.9704	2	31	0.6931	0.7627	63/64
1¼	1.2500	7	1.1572	1.0747	1.0954	2	15	0.8898	0.9684	1⁷⁄₆₄
1⅜	1.3750	6	1.2667	1.1705	1.1946	2	24	1.0541	1.1538	1¹³⁄₆₄
1½	1.5000	6	1.3917	1.2955	1.3196	2	11	1.2938	1.4041	1¹¹⁄₃₂
1¾	1.7500	5	1.6201	1.5046	1.5335	2	15	1.7441	1.8983	1⁹⁄₁₆
2	2.0000	4½	1.8557	1.7274	1.7594	2	11	2.3001	2.4971	1²⁵⁄₃₂
2¼	2.2500	4½	2.1057	1.9774	2.0094	1	55	3.0212	3.2464	2¹⁄₃₂
2½	2.5000	4	2.3376	2.1933	2.2294	1	57	3.7161	3.9976	2¼
2¾	2.7500	4	2.5876	2.4433	2.4794	1	46	4.6194	4.9326	2½

* British: Effective diameter.
† The stress area is the assumed area of an externally threaded part which is used for the purpose of computing the tensile strength.

TABLE 3   UNIFIED AND AMERICAN THREADS

Fine-Thread Series—UNF and NF (Basic Dimensions)

Sizes	Basic major diameter, D	Thds. per inch, n	Basic pitch diameter,* E	Minor diameter ext. thds. K_s	Minor diameter int. thds. K_n	Lead angle at basic pitch diameter, λ		Section at minor diameter at $D - 2h_b$	Stress area†	Tap drill number or size
	Inches		Inches	Inches	Inches	Deg	Min	Sq in.	Sq in.	
0(.060)	0.0600	80	0.0519	0.0447	0.0465	4	23	0.0015	0.0018	3/64
1(.073)	0.0730	72	0.0640	0.0560	0.0580	3	57	0.0024	0.0027	53
2(.086)	0.0860	64	0.0759	0.0668	0.0691	3	45	0.0034	0.0039	50
3(.099)	0.0990	56	0.0874	0.0771	0.0797	3	43	0.0045	0.0052	45
4(.112)	0.1120	48	0.0985	0.0864	0.0894	3	51	0.0057	0.0065	42
5(.125)	0.1250	44	0.1102	0.0971	0.1004	3	45	0.0072	0.0082	37
6(.138)	0.1380	40	0.1218	0.1073	0.1109	3	44	0.0087	0.0101	33
8(.164)	0.1640	36	0.1460	0.1299	0.1339	3	28	0.0128	0.0146	29
10(.190)	0.1900	32	0.1697	0.1517	0.1562	3	21	0.0175	0.0199	22
12(.216)	0.2160	28	0.1928	0.1722	0.1773	3	22	0.0226	0.0257	14
1/4	0.2500	28	0.2268	0.2062	0.2113	2	52	0.0326	0.0362	3
5/16	0.3125	24	0.2854	0.2614	0.2674	2	40	0.0524	0.0579	I
3/8	0.3750	24	0.3479	0.3239	0.3299	2	11	0.0809	0.0876	Q
7/16	0.4375	20	0.4050	0.3762	0.3834	2	15	0.1090	0.1185	25/64
1/2	0.5000	20	0.4675	0.4387	0.4459	1	57	0.1486	0.1597	29/64
9/16	0.5625	18	0.5264	0.4943	0.5024	1	55	0.1888	0.2026	33/64
5/8	0.6250	18	0.5889	0.5568	0.5649	1	43	0.2400	0.2555	37/64
3/4	0.7500	16	0.7094	0.6733	0.6823	1	36	0.3513	0.3724	11/16
7/8	0.8750	14	0.8286	0.7874	0.7977	1	34	0.4805	0.5088	13/16
1	1.0000	12	0.9459	0.8978	0.9098	1	36	0.6245	0.6624	59/64
1⅛	1.1250	12	1.0709	1.0228	1.0348	1	25	0.8118	0.8549	1³/₆₄
1¼	1.2500	12	1.1959	1.1478	1.1598	1	16	1.0237	1.0721	1¹¹/₆₄
1⅜	1.3750	12	1.3209	1.2728	1.2848	1	9	1.2602	1.3137	1¹⁹/₆₄
1½	1.5000	12	1.4459	1.3978	1.4098	1	3	1.5212	1.5799	1²⁷/₆₄

* British: Effective diameter.

† The stress area is the assumed area of an externally threaded part which is used for the purpose of computing the tensile strength.

Courtesy USASI

TABLE 4   SLOTTED HEAD MACHINE SCREWS (AMERICAN STANDARD)

Nominal size	Maximum Diameter	Threads per inch (coarse Series)	Maximum diameter of head			Maximum height of head			Maximum width of slot	Maximum depth of slot				Maximum height of the head	
			Flat and oval	Round	Fillister	Flat and oval	Round	Fillister		Flat	Round	Fillister	Oval	Oval	Fillister
	(D)		(A)	(A)	(A)	(H)	(H)	(H)	(J)	(T)	(T)	(T)	(T)	(F)	(F)
2	0.086	56	0.172	0.162	0.140	0.051	0.070	0.055	0.036	0.023	0.048	0.037	0.045	0.036	0.028
3	.099	48	.199	.187	.161	.059	.078	.063	.038	.027	.053	.043	.052	.038	.032
4	.112	40	.225	.211	.183	.067	.086	.072	.040	.030	.058	.048	.059	.040	0.35
5	.125	40	.252	.236	.205	.075	.095	.081	.043	.034	.062	.054	.067	.043	.039
6	.138	32	.279	.260	.226	.083	.103	.089	.045	.038	.067	.060	.074	.045	.043
8	.164	32	.352	.309	.270	.100	.119	.106	.050	.045	.076	.071	.088	.050	.050
10	.190	24	.385	.359	.313	.116	.136	.123	.055	.053	.086	.083	.103	.055	.057
12	.216	24	.438	.408	.357	.132	.152	.141	.059	.060	.095	.094	.117	.059	.064
1/4	.250	20	.507	.472	.414	.153	.174	.163	.066	.070	.108	.109	.136	.066	.074
5/16	.3125	18	.636	.591	.519	.192	.214	.205	.077	.088	.130	.137	.171	.077	.092
3/8	.375	16	.762	.708	.622	.230	.254	.246	.088	.106	.153	.164	.206	.088	.109

TABLE 5   SLOTTED AND HEXAGONAL-HEAD CAP SCREWS (AMERICAN STANDARD)

Nominal size	Maximum diameter	Threads per inch	Maximum diameter of head			Maximum height of head			Maximum width of slot	Maximum depth of slot			Maximum height of fillister head oval	Finished hexagonal-head cap screw		
			Flat	Round	Fillister	Flat (Nominal)	Round	Fillister		Flat	Round	Fillister		Maximum width across flats	Minimum width across corners	Maximum height
	(D)		(A)	(A)	(A)	(H)	(H)	(H)	(J)	(T)	(T)	(T)	(F)	(F)	(C)	(H)
1/4	0.2500	20	0.500	0.437	0.375	0.140	0.191	0.172	0.075	0.068	0.117	0.097	0.044	0.4375	0.488	0.163
5/16	0.3125	18	.625	.562	.437	.177	.245	.203	.084	.086	.151	.115	.050	0.5000	0.577	.211
3/8	0.3750	16	.750	.625	.562	.210	.273	.250	.094	.103	.168	.142	.064	0.5625	0.628	.243
7/16	0.4375	14	.813	.750	.625	.210	.328	.297	.094	.103	.202	.168	.071	0.6250	0.698	.291
1/2	0.5000	13	0.875	0.812	0.750	0.210	0.354	0.328	0.106	0.103	0.218	0.193	.084	0.7500	0.840	0.323
9/16	0.5625	12	1.000	0.937	0.812	0.244	0.409	0.375	0.118	0.120	0.252	0.213	.091	0.8125	0.910	0.371
5/8	0.6250	11	1.125	1.000	0.875	0.281	0.437	0.422	0.133	0.137	0.270	0.239	.099	0.8750	0.980	.403
3/4	0.7500	10	1.325	1.250	1.000	.352	.546	.500	0.149	.171	.338	.283	.112	1.0000	1.121	.483
7/8	0.8750	9	1.625		1.125	0.423		0.594	0.167	0.206		0.334	.126	1.1250	1.261	0.563
1	1.0000	8	1.875		1.312	0.494		0.656	0.188	0.240		0.371	.146	1.3125	1.473	0.627
1⅛	1.1250	7	2.062			0.529				.257				1.5000	1.684	.718
1¼	1.2500	7	2.312			0.600				.291				1.6875	1.896	.813

TABLE 6   DIMENSIONS OF HEXAGON AND SPLINE SOCKET HEAD CAP SCREWS (1960 SERIES)

AMERICAN STANDARD

Nominal size	D Body diameter		A Head diameter		H Head height		S Head side height	M Spline socket size	J Hexagon socket size	T Key engage-ment	G Wall thick-ness	F Fillet		K Chamfer or radius	Basic thread length
	Max	Min	Max	Min	Max	Min	Min	Nom	Nom	Min	Min	Max	Min	Max	
0	0.0600	0.0568	0.096	0.091	0.060	0.057	0.054	0.062	0.050	0.025	0.019	0.007	0.003	0.003	0.500
1	0.0730	0.0695	0.118	0.112	0.073	0.070	0.066	0.074	1⁄16	0.031	0.023	0.007	0.003	0.003	0.625
2	0.0860	0.0822	0.140	0.134	0.086	0.083	0.077	0.098	5⁄64	0.038	0.028	0.008	0.004	0.003	0.625
3	0.0990	0.0949	0.161	0.154	0.099	0.095	0.089	0.098	5⁄64	0.044	0.032	0.008	0.004	0.003	0.625
4	0.1120	0.1075	0.183	0.176	0.112	0.108	0.101	0.115	3⁄32	0.051	0.036	0.009	0.005	0.005	0.750
5	0.1250	0.1202	0.205	0.198	0.125	0.121	0.112	0.115	3⁄32	0.057	0.040	0.010	0.006	0.005	0.750
6	0.1380	0.1329	0.226	0.218	0.138	0.134	0.124	0.137	7⁄64	0.064	0.044	0.010	0.006	0.005	0.750
8	0.1640	0.1585	0.270	0.262	0.164	0.159	0.148	0.173	9⁄64	0.077	0.052	0.012	0.007	0.005	0.875
10	0.1900	0.1840	5⁄16	0.303	0.190	0.185	0.171	0.188	5⁄32	0.090	0.061	0.014	0.009	0.005	0.875
1⁄4	0.2500	0.2435	3⁄8	0.365	1⁄4	0.244	0.225	0.221	3⁄16	0.120	0.080	0.014	0.009	0.008	1.000
5⁄16	0.3125	0.3053	15⁄32	0.457	5⁄16	0.306	0.281	0.298	1⁄4	0.151	0.100	0.017	0.012	0.008	1.125
3⁄8	0.3750	0.3678	9⁄16	0.550	3⁄8	0.368	0.337	0.380	5⁄16	0.182	0.120	0.020	0.015	0.008	1.250
7⁄16	0.4375	0.4294	21⁄32	0.642	7⁄16	0.430	0.394	0.463	3⁄8	0.213	0.140	0.023	0.018	0.010	1.375
1⁄2	0.5000	0.4919	3⁄4	0.735	1⁄2	0.492	0.450	0.463	3⁄8	0.245	0.160	0.026	0.020	0.010	1.500
5⁄8	0.6250	0.6163	15⁄16	0.921	5⁄8	0.616	0.562	0.604	1⁄2	0.307	0.200	0.032	0.024	0.010	1.750
3⁄4	0.7500	0.7406	1 1⁄8	1.107	3⁄4	0.740	0.675	0.631	5⁄8	0.370	0.240	0.039	0.030	0.010	2.000
7⁄8	0.8750	0.8647	1 5⁄16	1.293	7⁄8	0.864	0.787	0.709	3⁄4	0.432	0.280	0.044	0.034	0.015	2.250
1	1.0000	0.9886	1 1⁄2	1.479	1	0.988	0.900	0.801	3⁄4	0.495	0.320	0.050	0.040	0.015	2.500
1 1⁄8	1.1250	1.1086	1 11⁄16	1.665	1 1⁄8	1.111	1.012	.....	7⁄8	0.557	0.360	0.055	0.045	0.015	2.812
1 1⁄4	1.2500	1.2336	1 7⁄8	1.852	1 1⁄4	1.236	1.125	.....	7⁄8	0.620	0.400	0.060	0.050	0.015	3.125
1 3⁄8	1.3750	1.3568	2 1⁄16	2.038	1 3⁄8	1.360	1.237	.....	1	0.682	0.440	0.065	0.055	0.015	3.437
1 1⁄2	1.5000	1.4818	2 1⁄4	2.224	1 1⁄2	1.485	1.350	.....	1	0.745	0.480	0.070	0.060	0.015	3.750
1 3⁄4	1.7500	1.7295	2 5⁄8	2.597	1 3⁄4	1.734	1.575	.....	1 1⁄4	0.870	0.560	0.080	0.070	0.015	4.375
2	2.0000	1.9780	3	2.970	2	1.983	1.800	.....	1 1⁄2	0.995	0.640	0.090	0.075	0.015	5.000
2 1⁄4	2.2500	2.2280	3 3⁄8	3.344	2 1⁄4	2.232	2.025	.....	1 3⁄4	1.120	0.720	0.100	0.085	0.031	5.625
2 1⁄2	2.5000	2.4762	3 3⁄4	3.717	2 1⁄2	2.481	2.250	.....	1 3⁄4	1.245	0.800	0.110	0.095	0.031	6.250
2 3⁄4	2.7500	2.7262	4 1⁄8	4.090	2 3⁄4	2.730	2.475	.....	2	1.370	0.880	0.120	0.105	0.031	6.875
3	3.0000	2.9762	4 1⁄2	4.464	3	2.979	2.700	.....	2 1⁄4	1.495	0.960	0.130	0.115	0.031	7.500
3 1⁄4	3.2500	3.2262	4 7⁄8	4.837	3 1⁄4	3.228	2.925	.....	2 1⁄4	1.620	1.040	0.140	0.125	0.031	8.125
3 1⁄2	3.5000	3.4762	5 1⁄4	5.211	3 1⁄2	3.478	3.150	.....	2 3⁄4	1.745	1.120	0.150	0.135	0.031	8.750
3 3⁄4	3.7500	3.7262	5 5⁄8	5.584	3 3⁄4	3.727	3.375	.....	2 3⁄4	1.870	1.200	0.160	0.145	0.031	9.375
4	4.0000	3.9762	6	5.958	4	3.976	3.600	.....	3	1.995	1.280	0.170	0.155	0.031	10.000

Courtesy USASI

TABLE 7   REGULAR SQUARE BOLTS

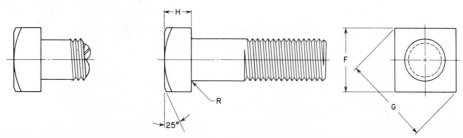

Nominal size or basic major diameter of thread		Body diam. Max.	Width across flats F			Width across corners G		Height H			Radius of fillet R
			Max (basic)		Min	Max	Min	Nom	Max	Min	Max
1/4	0.2500	0.260	3/8	0.3750	0.362	0.530	0.498	11/64	0.188	0.156	0.031
5/16	0.3125	0.324	1/2	0.5000	0.484	0.707	0.665	13/64	0.220	0.186	0.031
3/8	0.3750	0.388	9/16	0.5625	0.544	0.795	0.747	1/4	0.268	0.232	0.031
7/16	0.4375	0.452	5/8	0.6250	0.603	0.884	0.828	19/64	0.316	0.278	0.031
1/2	0.5000	0.515	3/4	0.7500	0.725	1.061	0.995	21/64	0.348	0.308	0.031
5/8	0.6250	0.642	15/16	0.9375	0.906	1.326	1.244	27/64	0.444	0.400	0.062
3/4	0.7500	0.768	1⅛	1.1250	1.088	1.591	1.494	1/2	0.524	0.476	0.062
7/8	0.8750	0.895	1⁵⁄₁₆	1.3125	1.269	1.856	1.742	19/32	0.620	0.568	0.062
1	1.0000	1.022	1½	1.5000	1.450	2.121	1.991	21/32	0.684	0.628	0.093
1⅛	1.1250	1.149	1¹¹⁄₁₆	1.6875	1.631	2.386	2.239	3/4	0.780	0.720	0.093
1¼	1.2500	1.277	1⅞	1.8750	1.812	2.652	2.489	27/32	0.876	0.812	0.093
1⅜	1.3750	1.404	2¹⁄₁₆	2.0625	1.994	2.917	2.738	29/32	0.940	0.872	0.093
1½	1.5000	1.531	2¼	2.2500	2.175	3.182	2.986	1	1.036	0.964	0.093
1⅝	1.6250	1.658	2⁷⁄₁₆	2.4375	2.356	3.447	3.235	1³⁄₃₂	1.132	1.056	0.125

TABLE 8   REGULAR SQUARE NUTS

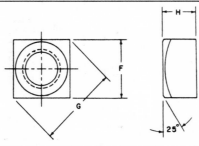

Nominal size or basic major diameter of thread		Width across flats F		Min	Width across corners G		Thickness H		
		Max (basic)		Min	Max	Min	Nom	Max	Min
1/4	0.2500	7/16	0.4375	0.425	0.619	0.584	7/32	0.235	0.203
5/16	0.3125	9/16	0.5625	0.547	0.795	0.751	17/64	0.283	0.249
3/8	0.3750	5/8	0.6250	0.606	0.884	0.832	21/64	0.346	0.310
7/16	0.4375	3/4	0.7500	0.728	1.061	1.000	3/8	0.394	0.356
1/2	0.5000	13/16	0.8125	0.788	1.149	1.082	7/16	0.458	0.418
5/8	0.6250	1	1.0000	0.969	1.414	1.330	35/64	0.569	0.525
3/4	0.7500	1⅛	1.1250	1.088	1.591	1.494	21/32	0.680	0.632
7/8	0.8750	1⁵⁄₁₆	1.3125	1.269	1.856	1.742	49/64	0.792	0.740
1	1.0000	1½	1.5000	1.450	2.121	1.991	7/8	0.903	0.847
1⅛	1.1250	1¹¹⁄₁₆	1.6875	1.631	2.386	2.239	1	1.030	0.970
1¼	1.2500	1⅞	1.8750	1.812	2.652	2.489	1³⁄₃₂	1.126	1.062
1⅜	1.3750	2¹⁄₁₆	2.0625	1.994	2.917	2.738	1¹³⁄₆₄	1.237	1.169
1½	1.5000	2¼	2.2500	2.175	3.182	2.986	1⁵⁄₁₆	1.348	1.276

TABLE 9 REGULAR HEXAGON BOLTS

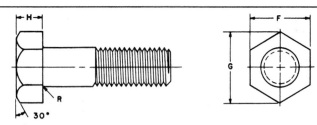

Nominal size or basic major diameter of thread		Body diam.	Width across flats *F*			Width across corners *G*		Height *H*			Radius of fillet *R*
		Max.	Max (basic)		Min	Max	Min	Nom	Max	Min	Max
1/4	0.2500	0.260	7/16	0.4375	0.425	0.505	0.484	11/64	0.188	0.150	0.031
5/16	0.3125	0.324	1/2	0.5000	0.484	0.577	0.552	7/32	0.235	0.195	0.031
3/8	0.3750	0.388	9/16	0.5625	0.544	0.650	0.620	1/4	0.268	0.226	0.031
7/16	0.4375	0.452	5/8	0.6250	0.603	0.722	0.687	19/64	0.316	0.272	0.031
1/2	0.5000	0.515	3/4	0.7500	0.725	0.866	0.826	11/32	0.364	0.302	0.031
5/8	0.6250	0.642	15/16	0.9375	0.906	1.083	1.033	27/64	0.444	0.378	0.062
3/4	0.7500	0.768	1 1/8	1.1250	1.088	1.299	1.240	1/2	0.524	0.455	0.062
7/8	0.8750	0.895	1 5/16	1.3125	1.269	1.516	1.447	37/64	0.604	0.531	0.062
1	1.0000	1.022	1 1/2	1.5000	1.450	1.732	1.653	43/64	0.700	0.591	0.093
1 1/8	1.1250	1.149	1 11/16	1.6875	1.631	1.949	1.859	3/4	0.780	0.658	0.093
1 1/4	1.2500	1.277	1 7/8	1.8750	1.812	2.165	2.066	27/32	0.876	0.749	0.093
1 3/8	1.3750	1.404	2 1/16	2.0625	1.994	2.382	2.273	29/32	0.940	0.810	0.093
1 1/2	1.5000	1.531	2 1/4	2.2500	2.175	2.598	2.480	1	1.036	0.902	0.093
1 3/4	1.7500	1.785	2 5/8	2.6250	2.538	3.031	2.893	1 5/32	1.196	1.054	0.125

Courtesy USASI

TABLE 10 REGULAR HEXAGON AND HEXAGON-JAM NUTS

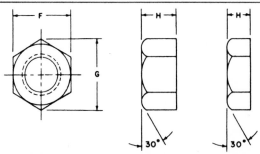

Nominal size or basic major diameter of thread		Width across flats *F*		Width across corners *G*		Thickness regular nuts *H*			Thickness regular jam nuts *H*		
		Max (basic)	Min	Max	Min	Nom	Max	Min	Nom	Max	Min
1/4	0.2500	7/16 0.4375	0.425	0.505	0.484	7/32	0.235	0.203	5/32	0.172	0.140
5/16	0.3125	9/16 0.5625	0.547	0.650	0.624	17/64	0.283	0.249	3/16	0.204	0.170
3/8	0.3750	5/8 0.6250	0.606	0.722	0.691	21/64	0.346	0.310	7/32	0.237	0.201
7/16	0.4375	3/4 0.7500	0.728	0.866	0.830	3/8	0.394	0.356	1/4	0.269	0.231
1/2	0.5000	13/16 0.8125	0.788	0.938	0.898	7/16	0.458	0.418	5/16	0.332	0.292
9/16	0.5625	7/8 0.8750	0.847	1.010	0.966	1/2	0.521	0.479	11/32	0.365	0.323
5/8	0.6250	1 1.0000	0.969	1.155	1.104	35/64	0.569	0.525	3/8	0.397	0.353
3/4	0.7500	1 1/8 1.1250	1.088	1.299	1.240	21/32	0.680	0.632	7/16	0.462	0.414
7/8	0.8750	1 5/16 1.3125	1.269	1.516	1.447	49/64	0.792	0.740	1/2	0.526	0.474
1	1.0000	1 1/2 1.5000	1.450	1.732	1.653	7/8	0.903	0.847	9/16	0.590	0.534
1 1/8	1.1250	1 11/16 1.6875	1.631	1.949	1.859	1	1.030	0.970	5/8	0.655	0.595
1 1/4	1.2500	1 7/8 1.8750	1.812	2.165	2.066	1 3/32	1.126	1.062	3/4	0.782	0.718
1 3/8	1.3750	2 1/16 2.0625	1.994	2.382	2.273	1 13/64	1.237	1.169	13/16	0.846	0.778
1 1/2	1.5000	2 1/4 2.2500	2.175	2.598	2.480	1 5/16	1.348	1.276	7/8	0.911	0.839

Courtesy USASI

TABLE 11   REGULAR SEMIFINISHED HEXAGON BOLTS

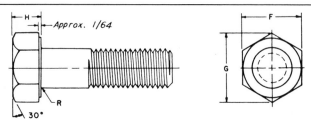

Nominal size or basic major diameter of thread		Body diam. Max.	Width across flats F			Width across corners G		Height H			Radius of fillet R	
			Max (basic)		Min	Max	Min	Nom	Max	Min	Max	Min
1/4	0.2500	0.260	7/16	0.4375	0.425	0.505	0.484	5/32	0.163	0.150	0.009	0.031
5/16	0.3125	0.324	1/2	0.5000	0.484	0.577	0.552	13/64	0.211	0.195	0.009	0.031
3/8	0.3750	0.388	9/16	0.5625	0.544	0.650	0.620	15/64	0.243	0.226	0.009	0.031
7/16	0.4375	0.452	5/8	0.6250	0.603	0.722	0.687	9/32	0.291	0.272	0.009	0.031
1/2	0.5000	0.515	3/4	0.7500	0.725	0.866	0.826	5/16	0.323	0.302	0.009	0.031
5/8	0.6250	0.642	15/16	0.9375	0.906	1.083	1.033	25/64	0.403	0.378	0.021	0.062
3/4	0.7500	0.768	1⅛	1.1250	1.088	1.299	1.240	15/32	0.483	0.455	0.021	0.062
7/8	0.8750	0.895	1⁵⁄₁₆	1.3125	1.269	1.516	1.447	35/64	0.563	0.531	0.031	0.062
1	1.0000	1.022	1½	1.5000	1.450	1.732	1.653	39/64	0.627	0.591	0.062	0.093
1⅛	1.1250	1.149	1¹¹⁄₁₆	1.6875	1.631	1.949	1.859	11/16	0.718	0.658	0.062	0.093
1¼	1.2500	1.277	1⅞	1.8750	1.812	2.165	2.066	25/32	0.813	0.749	0.062	0.093
1⅜	1.3750	1.404	2¹⁄₁₆	2.0625	1.994	2.382	2.273	27/32	0.878	0.810	0.062	0.093
1½	1.5000	1.531	2¼	2.2500	2.175	2.598	2.480	15/16	0.974	0.902	0.062	0.093
1¾	1.7500	1.785	2⅝	2.6250	2.538	3.031	2.893	1³⁄₃₂	1.134	1.054	0.078	0.125

Courtesy USASI

TABLE 12   REGULAR SEMIFINISHED HEXAGON AND HEXAGON-JAM NUTS

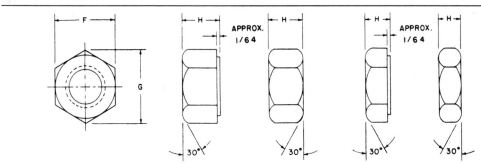

Nominal size or basic major diameter of thread		Width across flats F			Width across corners G		Thickness regular nuts H			Thickness regular jam nuts H		
		Max (basic)		Min	Max	Min	Nom	Max	Min	Nom	Max	Min
1/4	0.2500	7/16	0.4375	0.425	0.505	0.485	13/64	0.219	0.187	9/64	0.157	0.125
5/16	0.3125	9/16	0.5625	0.547	0.650	0.624	1/4	0.267	0.233	11/64	0.189	0.155
3/8	0.3750	5/8	0.6250	0.606	0.722	0.691	5/16	0.330	0.294	13/64	0.221	0.185
7/16	0.4375	3/4	0.7500	0.728	0.866	0.830	23/64	0.378	0.340	15/64	0.253	0.215
1/2	0.5000	13/16	0.8125	0.788	0.938	0.898	27/64	0.442	0.402	19/64	0.317	0.277
9/16	0.5625	7/8	0.8750	0.847	1.010	0.966	31/64	0.505	0.463	21/64	0.349	0.307
5/8	0.6250	1	1.0000	0.969	1.155	1.104	17/32	0.553	0.509	23/64	0.381	0.337
3/4	0.7500	1⅛	1.1250	1.088	1.299	1.240	41/64	0.665	0.617	27/64	0.446	0.398
7/8	0.8750	1⁵⁄₁₆	1.3125	1.269	1.516	1.447	3/4	0.776	0.724	31/64	0.510	0.458
1	1.0000	1½	1.5000	1.450	1.732	1.653	55/64	0.887	0.831	35/64	0.575	0.519
1⅛	1.1250	1¹¹⁄₁₆	1.6875	1.631	1.949	1.859	31/32	0.999	0.939	39/64	0.639	0.579
1¼	1.2500	1⅞	1.8750	1.812	2.165	2.066	1¹⁄₁₆	1.094	1.030	23/32	0.751	0.687
1⅜	1.3750	2¹⁄₁₆	2.0625	1.994	2.382	2.273	1¹¹⁄₆₄	1.206	1.138	25/32	0.815	0.747
1½	1.5000	2¼	2.2500	2.175	2.598	2.480	1⁹⁄₃₂	1.317	1.245	27/32	0.880	0.808
1⅝	1.6250	2⁷⁄₁₆	2.4375	2.356	2.815	2.686	1²⁵⁄₆₄	1.429	1.353	29/32	0.944	0.868
1¾	1.7500	2⅝	2.6250	2.538	3.031	2.893	1½	1.540	1.460	31/32	1.009	0.929

Courtesy USASI

TABLE 13   FINISHED HEXAGON BOLTS

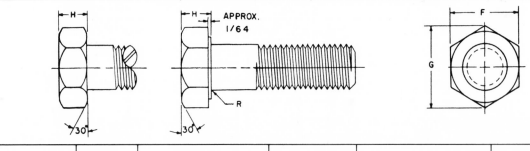

Nominal size or basic major diameter of thread		Body diameter min (maximum equal to nominal size)	Width across flats F			Width across corners G		Height H			Radius of fillet R	
			Max (basic)		Min	Max	Min	Nom	Max	Min	Min	Max
1/4	0.2500	0.2450	7/16	0.4375	0.428	0.505	0.488	5/32	0.163	0.150	0.009	0.023
5/16	0.3125	0.3065	1/2	0.5000	0.489	0.577	0.557	13/64	0.211	0.195	0.009	0.023
3/8	0.3750	0.3690	9/16	0.5625	0.551	0.650	0.628	15/64	0.243	0.226	0.009	0.023
7/16	0.4375	0.4305	5/8	0.6250	0.612	0.722	0.698	9/32	0.291	0.272	0.009	0.023
1/2	0.5000	0.4930	3/4	0.7500	0.736	0.866	0.840	5/16	0.323	0.302	0.009	0.023
9/16	0.5625	0.5545	13/16	0.8125	0.798	0.938	0.910	23/64	0.371	0.348	0.021	0.041
5/8	0.6250	0.6170	15/16	0.9375	0.922	1.083	1.051	25/64	0.403	0.378	0.021	0.041
3/4	0.7500	0.7410	1⅛	1.1250	1.100	1.299	1.254	15/32	0.483	0.455	0.021	0.041
7/8	0.8750	0.8660	1⁵⁄₁₆	1.3125	1.285	1.516	1.465	35/64	0.563	0.531	0.041	0.062
1	1.0000	0.9900	1½	1.5000	1.469	1.732	1.675	39/64	0.627	0.591	0.062	0.093
1⅛	1.1250	1.1140	1¹¹⁄₁₆	1.6875	1.631	1.949	1.859	11/16	0.718	0.658	0.062	0.093
1¼	1.2500	1.2390	1⅞	1.8750	1.812	2.165	2.066	25/32	0.813	0.749	0.062	0.093
1⅜	1.3750	1.3630	2¹⁄₁₆	2.0625	1.994	2.382	2.273	27/32	0.878	0.810	0.062	0.093
1½	1.5000	1.4880	2¼	2.2500	2.175	2.598	2.480	15/16	0.974	0.902	0.062	0.093
1¾	1.7500	1.7380	2⅝	2.6250	2.538	3.031	2.893	1³⁄₃₂	1.134	1.054	0.062	0.093

Note: Boldface indicates products unified dimensionally with British and Canadian Standards.

Courtesy USASI

TABLE 14 FINISHED HEXAGON AND HEXAGON-JAM NUTS

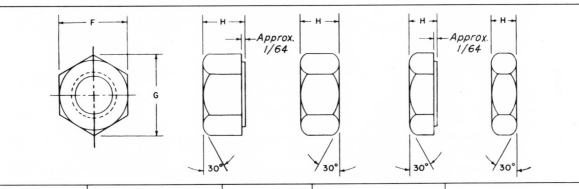

Nominal size or basic major diameter of thread		Width across flats F			Width across corners G		Thickness nuts H			Thickness jam nuts H		
		Max (basic)		Min	Max	Min	Nom	Max	Min	Nom	Max	Min
1/4	0.2500	7/16	0.4375	0.428	0.505	0.488	7/32	0.226	0.212	5/32	0.163	0.150
5/16	0.3125	1/2	0.5000	0.489	0.577	0.557	17/64	0.273	0.258	3/16	0.195	0.180
3/8	0.3750	9/16	0.5625	0.551	0.650	0.628	21/64	0.337	0.320	7/32	0.227	0.210
7/16	0.4375	11/16	0.6875	0.675	0.794	0.768	3/8	0.385	0.365	1/4	0.260	0.240
1/2	0.5000	3/4	0.7500	0.736	0.866	0.840	7/16	0.448	0.427	5/16	0.323	0.302
9/16	0.5625	7/8	0.8750	0.861	1.010	0.982	31/64	0.496	0.473	6/16	0.324	0.301
5/8	9.6250	15/16	0.9375	0.922	1.083	1.051	35/64	0.559	0.535	3/8	0.387	0.363
3/4	0.7500	1⅛	1.1250	1.088	1.299	1.240	41/64	0.665	0.617	27/64	0.446	0.398
7/8	0.8750	1⁵⁄₁₆	1.3125	1.269	1.516	1.447	3/4	0.776	0.724	31/64	0.510	0.458
1	1.0000	1½	1.5000	1.450	1.732	1.653	55/64	0.887	0.831	35/64	0.575	0.519
1⅛	1.1250	1¹¹⁄₁₆	1.6875	1.631	1.949	1.859	31/32	0.999	0.939	39/64	0.639	0.579
1¼	1.2500	1⅞	1.8750	1.812	2.165	2.066	1¹⁄₁₆	1.094	1.030	23/32	0.751	0.687
1⅜	1.3750	2¹⁄₁₆	2.0625	1.994	2.382	2.273	1¹¹⁄₆₄	1.206	1.138	25/32	0.815	0.747
1½	1.5000	2¼	2.2500	2.175	2.598	2.480	1⁹⁄₃₂	1.317	1.245	27/32	0.880	0.808
1¾	1.7500	2⅝	2.6250	2.538	3.031	2.893	1½	1.540	1.460	31/32	1.009	0.929

Note: Boldface indicates products unified dimensionally with British and Canadian Standards.

Courtesy USASI

TABLE 15   SQUARE HEAD SET SCREWS

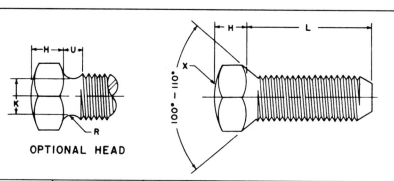

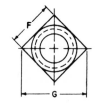

OPTIONAL HEAD

Nominal size		F Width across flats		G Width across corners	H Height of head			K Diameter of neck relief		X Radius of head	R Rad. of neck relief	U Width of neck relief
		Max	Min	Min	Nom	Max	Min	Max	Min	Nom	Max	Min
#10	0.190	0.1875	0.180	0.247	9/64	0.148	0.134	0.145	0.140	15/32	0.027	0.083
#12	0.216	0.216	0.208	0.292	5/32	0.163	0.147	0.162	0.156	35/64	0.029	0.091
1/4	0.250	0.250	0.241	0.331	3/16	0.196	0.178	0.185	0.170	5/8	0.032	0.100
5/16	0.3125	0.3125	0.302	0.415	15/64	0.245	0.224	0.240	0.225	25/32	0.036	0.111
3/8	0.3750	0.375	0.362	0.497	9/32	0.293	0.270	0.294	0.279	15/16	0.041	0.125
7/16	0.4375	0.4375	0.423	0.581	21/64	0.341	0.315	0.345	0.330	1 3/32	0.046	0.143
1/2	0.500	0.500	0.484	0.665	3/8	0.389	0.361	0.400	0.385	1 1/4	0.050	0.154
9/16	0.5625	0.5625	0.545	0.748	27/64	0.437	0.407	0.454	0.439	1 13/32	0.054	0.167
5/8	0.6250	0.625	0.606	0.833	15/32	0.485	0.452	0.507	0.492	1 9/16	0.059	0.182
3/4	0.750	0.750	0.729	1.001	9/16	0.582	0.544	0.620	0.605	1 7/8	0.065	0.200
7/8	0.875	0.875	0.852	1.170	21/32	0.678	0.635	0.731	0.716	2 3/16	0.072	0.222
1	1.000	1.000	0.974	1.337	3/4	0.774	0.726	0.838	0.823	2 1/2	0.081	0.250
1 1/8	1.125	1.125	1.096	1.505	27/32	0.870	0.817	0.939	0.914	2 13/16	0.092	0.283
1 1/4	1.250	1.250	1.219	1.674	15/16	0.966	0.908	1.064	1.039	3 1/8	0.092	0.283
1 3/8	1.375	1.375	1.342	1.843	1 1/32	1.063	1.000	1.159	1.134	3 7/16	0.109	0.333
1 1/2	1.500	1.500	1.464	2.010	1 1/8	1.159	1.091	1.284	1.259	3 3/4	0.109	0.333

All dimensions given in inches.

Threads shall be coarse-, fine-, or 8-thread series, class 2A; unless otherwise specified, coarse-thread series will be furnished. Square head set screws 1/4 in. size and larger are normally stocked in coarse thread series only.

Tolerance on screw length for sizes up to and including 5/8 in. shall be; minus 1/32 in. for lengths up to and including 1 in.; minus 1/16 in. for lengths over 1 in. to and including 2 in.; and minus 3/32 in. for lengths over 2 in. The tolerance shall be doubled for larger size screws of comparable length.

Square head set screws shall be made from alloy or carbon steel suitably hardened. Screws made from nonferrous material or corrosion-resisting steel shall be made from a material mutually agreed upon by manufacturer and user.

Courtesy USASI

TABLE 16   SQUARE HEAD SET SCREW POINTS

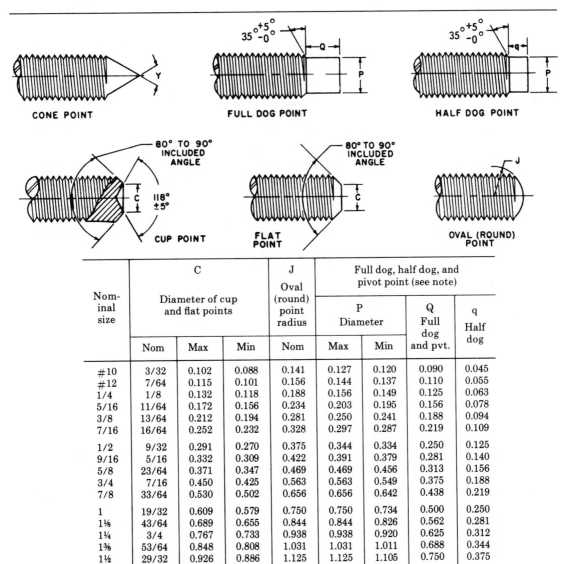

	C			J	Full dog, half dog, and pivot point (see note)			
Nom-inal size	Diameter of cup and flat points			Oval (round) point radius	P Diameter		Q Full dog and pvt.	q Half dog
	Nom	Max	Min	Nom	Max	Min		
#10	3/32	0.102	0.088	0.141	0.127	0.120	0.090	0.045
#12	7/64	0.115	0.101	0.156	0.144	0.137	0.110	0.055
1/4	1/8	0.132	0.118	0.188	0.156	0.149	0.125	0.063
5/16	11/64	0.172	0.156	0.234	0.203	0.195	0.156	0.078
3/8	13/64	0.212	0.194	0.281	0.250	0.241	0.188	0.094
7/16	16/64	0.252	0.232	0.328	0.297	0.287	0.219	0.109
1/2	9/32	0.291	0.270	0.375	0.344	0.334	0.250	0.125
9/16	5/16	0.332	0.309	0.422	0.391	0.379	0.281	0.140
5/8	23/64	0.371	0.347	0.469	0.469	0.456	0.313	0.156
3/4	7/16	0.450	0.425	0.563	0.563	0.549	0.375	0.188
7/8	33/64	0.530	0.502	0.656	0.656	0.642	0.438	0.219
1	19/32	0.609	0.579	0.750	0.750	0.734	0.500	0.250
1⅛	43/64	0.689	0.655	0.844	0.844	0.826	0.562	0.281
1¼	3/4	0.767	0.733	0.938	0.938	0.920	0.625	0.312
1⅜	53/64	0.848	0.808	1.031	1.031	1.011	0.688	0.344
1½	29/32	0.926	0.886	1.125	1.125	1.105	0.750	0.375

All dimensions are given in inches.

Pivot points are similar to full dog point except that the point is rounded by a radius equal to J.

Where usable length of thread is less than the nominal diameter, half-dog point shall be used.

When length equals nominal diameter or less, $Y = 118$ deg ± 2 deg; when length exceeds nominal diameter, $Y = 90$ deg ± 2 deg.

Courtesy USASI

TABLE 17　PROPORTIONS OF KEYS IN THE PRATT AND WHITNEY SYSTEM

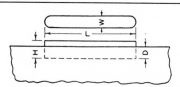

No. of key	L	W	H	D	No. of key	L	W	H	D
1	1/2	1/16	3/32	1/16	22	1⅜	1/4	3/8	1/4
2	1/2	3/32	9/64	3/32	23	1⅜	5/16	15/32	5/16
3	1/2	1/8	3/16	1/8	F	1⅜	3/8	9/16	3/8
4	5/8	3/32	9/64	3/32	24	1½	1/4	3/8	1/4
5	5/8	1/8	3/16	1/8	25	1½	5/16	15/32	5/16
6	5/8	5/32	15/64	5/32	G	1½	3/8	9/16	3/8
7	3/4	1/8	3/16	1/8	51	1¾	1/4	3/8	1/4
8	3/4	5/32	15/64	5/32	52	1¾	5/16	15/32	5/16
9	3/4	3/16	9/32	3/16	53	1¾	3/8	9/16	3/8
10	7/8	5/32	15/64	5/32	26	2	3/16	9/32	3/16
11	7/8	3/16	9/32	3/16	27	2	1/4	3/8	1/4
12	7/8	7/32	21/64	7/32	28	2	5/16	15/32	5/16
A	7/8	1/4	3/8	1/4	29	2	3/8	9/16	3/8
13	1	3/16	9/32	3/16	54	2¼	1/4	3/8	1/4
14	1	7/32	21/64	7/32	55	2¼	5/16	15/32	5/16
15	1	1/4	3/8	1/4	56	2¼	3/8	9/16	3/8
B	1	5/16	15/32	5/16	57	2¼	7/16	21/32	7/16
16	1⅛	3/16	9/32	3/16	58	2½	5/16	15/32	5/16
17	1⅛	7/32	21/64	7/32	59	2½	3/8	9/16	3/8
18	1⅛	1/4	3/8	1/4	60	2½	7/16	21/32	7/16
C	1⅛	5/16	15/32	5/16	61	2½	1/2	3/4	1/2
19	1¼	3/16	9/32	3/16	30	3	3/8	9/16	3/8
20	1¼	7/32	21/64	7/32	31	3	7/16	21/32	7/16
21	1¼	1/4	3/8	1/4	32	3	1/2	3/4	1/2
D	1¼	5/16	15/32	5/16	33	3	9/16	27/32	9/16
E	1¼	3/8	9/16	3/8	34	3	5/8	15/16	5/8

TABLE 18   WOODRUFF KEYS

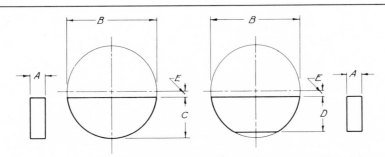

Woodruff Key Dimensions

Key* number	Nominal key size A × B	Width of key A		Diam. of key B		Height of key				Distance below center E
		Max	Min	Max	Min	C		D		
						Max	Min	Max	Min	
204	1/16 × 1/2	0.0635	0.0625	0.500	0.490	0.203	0.198	0.194	0.188	3/64
304	3/32 × 1/2	.0948	.0938	0.500	0.490	.203	.198	.194	.188	3/64
305	3/32 × 5/8	.0948	.0938	0.625	0.615	.250	.245	.240	.234	1/16
404	1/8 × 1/2	.1260	.1250	0.500	0.490	.203	.198	.194	.188	3/64
405	1/8 × 5/8	.1260	.1250	0.625	0.615	.250	.245	.240	.234	1/16
406	1/8 × 3/4	.1260	.1250	0.750	0.740	.313	.308	.303	.297	1/16
505	5/32 × 5/8	.1573	.1563	0.625	0.615	.250	.245	.240	.234	1/16
506	5/32 × 3/4	.1573	.1563	0.750	0.740	.313	.308	.303	.297	1/16
507	5/32 × 7/8	.1573	.1563	0.875	0.865	.375	.370	.365	.359	1/16
606	3/16 × 3/4	.1885	.1875	0.750	0.740	.313	.308	.303	.297	1/16
607	3/16 × 7/8	.1885	.1875	0.875	0.865	.375	.370	.365	.359	1/16
608	3/16 × 1	.1885	.1875	1.000	0.990	.438	.433	.428	.422	1/16
609	3/16 × 1⅛	.1885	.1875	1.125	1.115	.484	.479	.475	.469	5/64
807	1/4 × 7/8	.2510	.2500	0.875	0.865	.375	.370	.365	.359	1/16
808	1/4 × 1	.2510	.2500	1.000	0.990	.438	.433	.428	.422	1/16
809	1/4 × 1⅛	.2510	.2500	1.125	1.115	.484	.479	.475	.469	5/64
810	1/4 × 1¼	.2510	.2500	1.250	1.240	.547	.542	.537	.531	5/64
811	1/4 × 1⅜	.2510	.2500	1.375	1.365	.594	.589	.584	.578	3/32
812	1/4 × 1½	.2510	.2500	1.500	1.490	.641	.636	.631	.625	7/64

All dimensions given in inches.

* Note: Key numbers indicate the nominal key dimensions. The last two digits give the nominal diameter (B) in eighths of an inch and the digits preceding the last two give the nominal width (A) in thirty-seconds of an inch. Thus, 204 indicates a key ²⁄₃₂ × ⁴⁄₈ or ¹⁄₁₆ × ½ inches; 1210 indicates a key ¹²⁄₃₂ × ¹⁰⁄₈ or ⅜ × 1¼ inches.

Courtesy USASI

TABLE 19   PLAIN PARALLEL STOCK KEYS

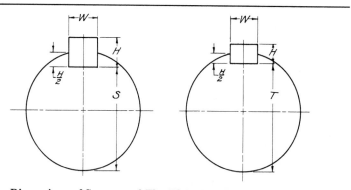

Dimensions of Square and Flat Plain Parallel Stock Keys

Shaft diameter	Square key W × H	Flat key W × H	Tolerance on W and H (−)	Bottom of keyseat to opposite side of shaft	
				Square key S	Flat key T
1/2	1/8 × 1/8	1/8 × 3/32	0.0020	0.430	0.445
9/16	1/8 × 1/8	1/8 × 3/32	.0020	0.493	0.509
5/8	3/16 × 3/16	3/16 × 1/8	.0020	0.517	0.548
11/16	3/16 × 3/16	3/16 × 1/8	.0020	0.581	0.612
3/4	3/16 × 3/16	3/16 × 1/8	.0020	0.644	0.676
13/16	3/16 × 3/16	3/16 × 1/8	.0020	0.708	0.739
7/8	3/16 × 3/16	3/16 × 1/8	.0020	0.771	0.802
15/16	1/4 × 1/4	1/4 × 3/16	.0020	0.796	0.827
1	1/4 × 1/4	1/4 × 3/16	.0020	0.859	0.890
1 1/16	1/4 × 1/4	1/4 × 3/16	.0020	0.923	0.954
1 1/8	1/4 × 1/4	1/4 × 3/16	.0020	0.986	1.017
1 3/16	1/4 × 1/4	1/4 × 3/16	.0020	1.049	1.081
1 1/4	1/4 × 1/4	1/4 × 3/16	.0020	1.112	1.144
1 5/16	5/16 × 5/16	5/16 × 1/4	.0020	1.137	1.169
1 3/8	5/16 × 5/16	5/16 × 1/4	.0020	1.201	1.232
1 7/16	3/8 × 3/8	3/8 × 1/4	.0020	1.225	1.288
1 1/2	3/8 × 3/8	3/8 × 1/4	.0020	1.289	1.351
1 9/16	3/8 × 3/8	3/8 × 1/4	.0020	1.352	1.415
1 5/8	3/8 × 3/8	3/8 × 1/4	.0020	1.416	1.478
1 11/16	3/8 × 3/8	3/8 × 1/4	.0020	1.479	1.542
1 3/4	3/8 × 3/8	3/8 × 1/4	.0020	1.542	1.605

TABLE 20   DIMENSIONS OF TAPER PINS

Number	7/0	6/0	5/0	4/0	3/0	2/0	0	1	2	3	4	5	6	7	8	9	10
Size (large end)	0.0625	0.0780	0.0940	0.1090	0.1250	0.1410	0.1560	0.1720	0.1930	0.2190	0.2500	0.2890	0.3410	0.4090	0.4920	0.5910	0.7060
Length, L																	
0.375	X	X															
0.500	X	X	X	X	X	X	X										
0.625	X	X	X	X	X	X	X										
0.750		X	X	X	X	X	X	X	X	X							
0.875					X	X	X	X	X	X							
1.000			X	X	X	X	X	X	X	X	X	X					
1.250						X	X	X	X	X	X	X	X				
1.500							X	X	X	X	X	X	X				
1.750								X	X	X	X	X	X				
2.000								X	X	X	X	X	X	X	X		
2.250									X	X	X	X	X	X	X		
2.500									X	X	X	X	X	X	X		
2.750										X	X	X	X	X	X	X	
3.000										X	X	X	X	X	X	X	
3.250													X	X	X	X	
3.500													X	X	X	X	X
3.750													X	X	X	X	X
4.000													X	X	X	X	X
4.250															X	X	X
4.500															X	X	X
4.750															X	X	X
5.000															X	X	X
5.250																X	X
5.500																X	X
5.750																X	X
6.000																X	X

All dimensions are given in inches.
Standard reamers are available for pins given above the line.
Pins Nos. 11 (size 0.8600), 12 (size 1.032), 13 (size 1.241), and 14 (1.523) are special sizes—hence their lengths are special.
To find small diameter of pin, multiply the length by 0.02083 and subtract the result from the large diameter.

TYPES	COMMERCIAL TYPE	PRECISION TYPE
Sizes	7/0 to 14	7/0 to 10
Tolerance on diameter	(+0.0013, −0.0007)	(+0.0013, −0.0007)
Taper	¼ in. per ft	¼ in. per ft
Length tolerance	(±0.030)	(±0.030)
Concavity tolerance	None	0.0005 up to 1 in. long
		0.001 1¹⁄₁₆ to 2 in. long
		0.002 2¹⁄₁₆ and longer

TABLE 21   RUNNING AND SLIDING FITS

Limits are in thousandths of an inch.
Limits for hole and shaft are applied algebraically to the basic size to obtain the limits of size for the parts.
Data in boldface are in accordance with ABC agreements.
Symbols H5, g5, etc., are Hole and Shaft designations used in ABC System.

Nominal size range inches over to	Class RC 1 Limits of Clearance	Class RC 1 Hole H5	Class RC 1 Shaft g4	Class RC 2 Limits of Clearance	Class RC 2 Hole H6	Class RC 2 Shaft g5	Class RC 3 Limits of clearance	Class RC 3 Hole H6	Class RC 3 Shaft f6	Class RC 4 Limits of clearance	Class RC 4 Hole H7	Class RC 4 Shaft f7
0.04–0.12	0.1 0.45	+0.2 0	−0.1 −0.25	0.1 0.55	+0.25 0	−0.1 −0.3	0.3 0.8	+0.25 0	−0.3 −0.55	0.3 1.1	+0.4 0	−0.3 −0.7
0.12–0.24	0.15 0.5	+0.2 0	−0.15 −0.3	0.15 0.65	+0.3 0	−0.15 −0.35	0.4 1.0	+0.3 0	−0.4 −0.7	0.4 1.4	+0.5 0	−0.4 −0.9
0.24–0.40	0.2 0.6	+0.25 0	−0.2 −0.35	0.2 0.85	+0.4 0	−0.2 −0.45	0.5 1.3	+0.4 0	−0.5 −0.9	0.5 1.7	+0.6 0	−0.5 −1.1
0.40–0.71	0.25 0.75	+0.3 0	−0.25 −0.45	0.25 0.95	+0.4 0	−0.25 −0.55	0.6 1.4	+0.4 0	−0.6 −1.0	0.6 2.0	+0.7 0	−0.6 −1.3
0.71–1.19	0.3 0.95	+0.4 0	−0.3 −0.55	0.3 1.2	+0.5 0	−0.3 −0.7	0.8 1.8	+0.5 0	−0.8 −1.3	0.8 2.4	+0.8 0	−0.8 −1.6
1.19–1.97	0.4 1.1	+0.4 0	−0.4 −0.7	0.4 1.4	+0.6 0	−0.4 −0.8	1.0 2.2	+0.6 0	−1.0 −1.6	1.0 3.0	+1.0 0	−1.0 −2.0
1.97–3.15	0.4 1.2	+0.5 0	−0.4 −0.7	0.4 1.6	+0.7 0	−0.4 −0.9	1.2 2.6	+0.7 0	−1.2 −1.9	1.2 3.6	+1.2 0	−1.2 −2.4
3.15–4.73	0.5 1.5	+0.6 0	−0.5 −0.9	0.5 2.0	+0.9 0	−0.5 −1.1	1.4 3.2	+0.9 0	−1.4 −2.3	1.4 4.2	+1.4 0	−1.4 −2.8
4.73–7.09	0.6 1.8	+0.7 0	−0.6 −1.1	0.6 2.3	+1.0 0	−0.6 −1.3	1.6 3.6	+1.0 0	−1.6 −2.6	1.6 4.8	+1.6 0	−1.6 −3.2
7.09–9.85	0.6 2.0	+0.8 0	−0.6 −1.2	0.6 2.6	+1.2 0	−0.6 −1.4	2.0 4.4	+1.2 0	−2.0 −3.2	2.0 5.6	+1.8 0	−2.0 −3.8
9.85–12.41	0.8 2.3	+0.9 0	−0.8 −1.4	0.8 0.9	+1.2 0	−0.8 −1.7	2.5 4.9	+1.2 0	−2.5 −3.7	2.5 6.5	+2.0 0	−2.5 −4.5

Nominal size range inches over to	Class RC 5 Limits of clearance	Class RC 5 Hole H7	Class RC 5 Shaft e7	Class RC 6 Limits of clearance	Class RC 6 Hole H8	Class RC 6 Shaft e8	Class RC 7 Limits of clearance	Class RC 7 Hole H9	Class RC 7 Shaft d8	Class RC 8 Limits of clearance	Class RC 8 Hole H10	Class RC 8 Shaft c9	Class RC 9 Limits of clearance	Class RC 9 Hole H11	Class RC 9 Shaft
0.04–0.12	0.6 1.4	+0.4 0	−0.6 −1.0	0.6 1.8	+0.6 0	−0.6 −1.2	1.0 2.6	+1.0 0	−1.0 −1.6	2.5 5.1	+1.6 0	−2.5 −3.5	4.0 8.1	+2.5 0	−4.0 −5.6
0.12–0.24	0.8 1.8	+0.5 0	−0.8 −1.3	0.8 2.2	+0.7 0	−0.8 −1.5	1.2 3.1	+1.2 0	−1.2 −1.9	2.8 5.8	+1.8 0	−2.8 −4.0	4.5 9.0	+3.0 0	−4.5 −6.0
0.24–0.40	1.0 2.2	+0.6 0	−1.0 −1.6	1.0 2.8	+0.9 0	−1.0 −1.9	1.6 3.9	+1.4 0	−1.6 −2.5	3.0 6.6	+2.2 0	−3.0 −4.4	5.0 10.7	+3.5 0	−5.0 −7.2
0.40–0.71	1.2 2.6	+0.7 0	−1.2 −1.9	1.2 3.2	+1.0 0	−1.2 −2.2	2.0 4.6	+1.6 0	−2.0 −3.0	3.5 7.9	+2.8 0	−3.5 −5.1	6.0 12.8	+4.0 0	−6.0 −8.8
0.71–1.19	1.6 3.2	+0.8 0	−1.6 −2.4	1.6 4.0	+1.2 0	−1.6 −2.8	2.5 5.7	+2.0 0	−2.5 −3.7	4.5 10.0	+3.5 0	−4.5 −6.5	7.0 15.5	+5.0 0	−7.0 −10.5
1.19–1.97	2.0 4.0	+1.0 0	−2.0 −3.0	2.0 5.2	+1.6 0	−2.0 −3.6	3.0 7.1	+2.5 0	−3.0 −4.6	5.0 11.5	+4.0 0	−5.0 −7.5	8.0 18.0	+6.0 0	−8.0 −12.0
1.97–3.15	2.5 4.9	+1.2 0	−2.5 −3.7	2.5 6.1	+1.8 0	−2.5 −4.3	4.0 8.8	+3.0 0	−4.0 −5.8	6.0 13.5	+4.5 0	−6.0 −9.0	9.0 20.5	+7.0 0	−9.0 −13.5
3.15–4.73	3.0 5.8	+1.4 0	−3.0 −4.4	3.0 7.4	+2.2 0	−3.0 −5.2	5.0 10.7	+3.5 0	−5.0 −7.2	7.0 15.5	+5.0 0	−7.0 −10.5	10.0 24.0	+9.0 0	−10.0 −15.0
4.73–7.09	3.5 6.7	+1.6 0	−3.5 −5.1	3.5 8.5	+2.5 0	−3.5 −6.0	6.0 12.5	+4.0 0	−6.0 −8.5	8.0 18.0	+6.0 0	−8.0 −12.0	12.0 28.0	+10.0 0	−12.0 −18.0
7.09–9.85	4.0 7.6	+1.8 0	−4.0 −5.8	4.0 9.6	+2.8 0	−4.0 −6.8	7.0 14.3	+4.5 0	−7.0 −9.8	10.0 21.5	+7.0 0	−10.0 −14.5	15.0 34.0	+12.0 0	−15.0 −22.0
9.85–12.41	5.0 9.0	+2.0 0	−5.0 −7.0	5.0 11.0	+3.0 0	−5.0 −8.0	8.0 16.0	+5.0 0	−8.0 −11.0	12.0 25.0	+8.0 0	−12.0 −17.0	18.0 38.0	+12.0 0	−18.0 −26.0

TABLE 22   CLEARANCE LOCATIONAL FITS

Limits are in thousandths of an inch.

Limits for hole and shaft are applied algebraically to the basic size to obtain the limits of size for the parts.

Data are in accordance with ABC agreements.

Symbols H6, h5, etc., are Hole and Shaft designations used in ABC System.

Nominal size range inches over to	Class LC 1			Class LC 2			Class LC 3			Class LC 4			Class LC 5		
	Limits of clearance	Standard limits		Limits of clearance	Standard limits		Limits of clearance	Standard limits		Limits of clearance	Standard limits		Limits of clearance	Standard limits	
		Hole H6	Shaft h5		Hole H7	Shaft h6		Hole H8	Shaft h7		Hole H9	Shaft h9		Hole H7	Shaft g6
0.04–0.12	0 0.45	+0.25 −0	+0 −0.2	0 0.65	+0.4 −0	+0 −0.25	0 1	+0.6 −0	+0 −0.4	0 2.0	+1.0 −0	+0 −1.0	0.1 0.75	+0.4 −0	−0.1 −0.35
0.12–0.24	0 0.5	+0.3 −0	+0 −0.2	0 0.8	+0.5 −0	+0 −0.3	0 1.2	+0.7 −0	+0 −0.5	0 2.4	+1.2 −0	+0 −1.2	0.15 0.95	+0.5 −0	−0.15 −0.45
0.24–0.40	0 0.65	+0.4 −0	+0 −0.25	0 1.0	+0.6 −0	+0 −0.4	0 1.5	+0.9 −0	+0 −0.6	0 2.8	+1.4 −0	+0 −1.4	0.2 1.2	+0.6 −0	−0.2 −0.6
0.40–0.71	0 0.7	+0.4 −0	+0 −0.3	0 1.1	+0.7 −0	+0 −0.4	0 1.7	+1.0 −0	+0 −0.7	0 3.2	+1.6 −0	+0 −1.6	0.25 1.35	+0.7 −0	−0.25 −0.65
0.71–1.19	0 0.9	+0.5 −0	+0 −0.4	0 1.3	+0.8 −0	+0 −0.5	0 2	+1.2 −0	+0 −0.8	0 4	+2.0 −0	+0 −2.0	0.3 1.6	+0.8 −0	−0.3 −0.8
1.19–1.97	0 1.0	+0.6 −0	+0 −0.4	0 1.6	+1.0 −0	+0 −0.6	0 2.6	+1.6 −0	+0 −1.0	0 5	+2.5 −0	+0 −2.5	0.4 2.0	+1.0 −0	−0.4 −1.0
1.97–3.15	0 1.2	+0.7 −0	+0 −0.5	0 1.9	+1.2 −0	+0 −0.7	0 3	+1.8 −0	+0 −1.2	0 6	+3 −0	+0 −3	0.4 2.3	+1.2 −0	−0.4 −1.1
3.15–4.73	0 1.5	+0.9 −0	+0 −0.6	0 2.3	+1.4 −0	+0 −0.9	0 3.6	+2.2 −0	+0 −1.4	0 7	+3.5 −0	+0 −3.5	0.5 2.8	+1.4 −0	−0.5 −1.4
4.73–7.09	0 1.7	+1.0 −0	+0 −0.7	0 2.6	+1.6 −0	+0 −1.0	0 4.1	+2.5 −0	+0 −1.6	0 8	+4 −0	+0 −4	0.6 3.2	+1.6 −0	−0.6 −1.6
7.09–9.85	0 2.0	+1.2 −0	+0 −0.8	0 3.0	+1.8 −0	+0 −1.2	0 4.6	+2.8 −0	+0 −1.8	0 9	+4.5 −0	+0 −4.5	0.6 3.6	+1.8 −0	−0.6 −1.8
9.85–12.41	0 2.1	+1.2 −0	+0 −0.9	0 3.2	+2.0 −0	+0 −1.2	0 5	+3.0 −0	+0 −2.0	0 10	+5 −0	+0 −5	0.7 3.9	+2.0 −0	−0.7 −1.9

Nominal size range inches over to	Class LC 6			Class LC 7			Class LC 8			Class LC 9			Class LC 10			Class LC 11		
	Limits of clearance	Standard limits		Limits of clearance	Standard limits		Limits of clearance	Standard limits		Limits of clearance	Standard limits		Limits of clearance	Standard limits		Limits of clearance	Standard limits	
		Hole H8	Shaft f8		Hole H9	Shaft e9		Hole H10	Shaft d9		Hole H11	Shaft c11		Hole H12	Shaft		Hole H13	Shaft
0.04–0.12	0.3 1.5	+0.6 −0	−0.3 −0.9	0.6 2.6	+1.0 −0	−0.6 −1.6	1.0 3.6	+1.6 −0	−1.0 −2.0	2.5 7.5	+2.5 −0	−2.5 −5.0	4 12	+4 −0	−4 −8	5 17	+6 −0	−5 −11
0.12–0.24	0.4 1.8	+0.7 −0	−0.4 −1.1	0.8 3.2	+1.2 −0	−0.8 −2.0	1.2 4.2	+1.8 −0	−1.2 −2.4	2.8 8.8	+3.0 −0	−2.8 −5.8	4.5 14.5	+5 −0	−4.5 −9.5	6 20	+7 −0	−6 −13
0.24–0.40	0.5 2.3	+0.9 −0	−0.5 −1.4	1.0 3.8	+1.4 −0	−1.0 −2.4	1.6 5.2	+2.2 −0	−1.6 −3.0	3.0 10.0	+3.5 +0	−3.0 −6.5	5 17	+6 −0	−5 −11	7 25	+9 −0	−7 −16
0.40–0.71	0.6 2.6	+1.0 −0	−0.6 −1.6	1.2 4.4	+1.6 −0	−1.2 −2.8	2.0 6.4	+2.8 −0	−2.0 −3.6	3.5 11.5	+4.0 −0	−3.5 −7.5	6 20	+7 −0	−6 −13	8 28	+10 −0	−8 −18
0.71–1.19	0.8 3.2	+1.2 −0	−0.8 −2.0	1.6 5.6	+2.0 −0	−1.6 −3.6	2.5 8.0	+3.5 −0	−2.5 −4.5	4.5 14.5	+5.0 −0	−4.5 −9.5	7 23	+8 −0	−7 −15	10 34	+12 −0	−10 −22
1.19–1.97	1.0 4.2	+1.6 −0	−1.0 −2.6	2.0 7.0	+2.5 −0	−2.0 −4.5	3.0 9.5	+4.0 −0	−3.0 −5.5	5 17	+6 −0	−5 −11	8 28	+10 −0	−8 −18	12 44	+16 −0	−12 −28
1.97–3.15	1.2 4.8	+1.8 −0	−1.2 −3.0	2.5 8.5	+3.0 −0	−2.5 −5.5	4.0 11.5	+4.5 −0	−4.0 −7.0	6 20	+7 −0	−6 −13	10 34	+12 −0	−10 −22	14 50	+18 −0	−14 −32
3.15–4.73	1.4 5.8	+2.2 −0	−1.4 −3.6	3.0 10.0	+3.5 −0	−3.0 −6.5	5.0 13.5	+5.0 −0	−5.0 −8.5	7 25	+9 −0	−7 −16	11 39	+14 −0	−11 −25	16 60	+22 −0	−16 −38
4.73–7.09	1.6 6.6	+2.5 −0	−1.6 −4.1	3.5 11.5	+4.0 −0	−3.5 −7.5	6 16	+6 −0	−6 −10	8 28	+10 −0	−8 −18	12 44	+16 −0	−12 −28	18 68	+25 −0	−18 −43
7.09–9.85	2.0 7.6	+2.8 −0	−2.0 −4.8	4.0 13.0	+4.5 −0	−4.0 −8.5	7 18.5	+7 −0	−7 −11.5	10 34	+12 −0	−10 −22	16 52	+18 −0	−16 −34	22 78	+28 −0	−22 −50
9.85–12.41	2.2 8.2	+3.0 −0	−2.2 −5.2	4.5 14.5	+5.0 −0	−4.5 −9.5	7 20	+8 −0	−7 −12	12 36	+12 −0	−12 −24	20 60	+20 −0	−20 −40	28 88	+30 −0	−28 −58

Courtesy USASI

TABLE 23 TRANSITION LOCATIONAL FITS

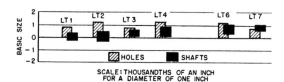

Limits are in thousandths of an inch.

Limits for hole and shaft are applied algebraically to the basic size to obtain the limits of size for the mating parts.

Data are in accordance with ABC agreements.

"Fit" represents the maximum interference (minus values) and the maximum clearance (plus values).

Symbols H8, j6, etc., are Hole and Shaft designations used in ABC System.

Nominal size range inches	Class LT 1			Class LT 2			Class LT 3			Class LT 4			Class LT 6			Class LT 7		
	Fit	Standard limits		Fit	Standard limits		Fit	Standard limits		Fit	Standard limits		Fit	Standard limits		Fit	Standard limits	
over to		Hole H7	Shaft j6		Hole H8	Shaft j7		Hole H7	Shaft k6		Hole H8	Shaft k7		Hole H8	Shaft m7		Hole H7	Shaft n6
0.04–0.12	−0.15 +0.5	+0.4 −0	+0.15 −0.1	−0.3 +0.7	+0.6 −0	+0.3 −0.1							−0.55 +0.45	+0.6 −0	+0.55 +0.15	−0.5 +0.15	+0.4 −0	+0.5 +0.25
0.12–0.24	−0.2 +0.6	+0.5 −0	+0.2 −0.1	−0.4 +0.8	+0.7 −0	+0.4 −0.1							−0.7 +0.5	+0.7 −0	+0.7 +0.2	−0.6 +0.2	+0.5 −0	+0.6 +0.3
0.24–0.40	−0.3 +0.7	+0.6 −0	+0.3 −0.1	−0.4 +1.1	+0.9 −0	+0.4 −0.2	−0.5 +0.5	+0.6 −0	+0.5 +0.1	−0.7 +0.8	+0.9 −0	+0.7 +0.1	−0.8 +0.7	+0.9 −0	+0.8 +0.2	−0.8 +0.2	+0.6 −0	+0.8 +0.4
0.40–0.71	−0.3 +0.8	+0.7 −0	+0.3 −0.1	−0.5 +1.2	+1.0 −0	+0.5 −0.2	−0.5 +0.6	+0.7 −0	+0.5 +0.1	−0.8 +0.9	+1.0 −0	+0.8 +0.1	−1.0 +0.7	+1.0 −0	+1.0 +0.3	−0.9 +0.2	+0.7 −0	+0.9 +0.5
0.71–1.19	−0.3 +1.0	+0.8 −0	+0.3 −0.2	−0.5 +1.5	+1.2 −0	+0.5 −0.3	−0.6 +0.7	+0.8 −0	+0.6 +0.1	−0.9 +1.1	+1.2 −0	+0.9 +0.1	−1.1 +0.9	+1.2 −0	+1.1 +0.3	−1.1 +0.2	+0.8 −0	+1.1 +0.6
1.19–1.97	−0.4 +1.2	+1.0 −0	+0.4 −0.2	−0.6 +2.0	+1.6 −0	+0.6 −0.4	−0.7 +0.9	+1.0 −0	+0.7 +0.1	−1.1 +1.5	+1.6 −0	+1.1 +0.1	−1.4 +1.2	+1.6 −0	+1.4 +0.4	−1.3 +0.3	+1.0 −0	+1.3 +0.7
1.97–3.15	−0.4 +1.5	+1.2 −0	+0.4 −0.3	−0.7 +2.3	+1.8 −0	+0.7 −0.5	−0.8 +1.1	+1.2 −0	+0.8 +0.1	−1.3 +1.7	+1.8 −0	+1.3 +0.1	−1.7 +1.3	+1.8 −0	+1.7 +0.5	−1.5 +0.4	+1.2 −0	+1.5 +0.8
3.15–4.73	−0.5 +1.8	+1.4 −0	+0.5 −0.4	−0.8 +2.8	+2.2 −0	+0.8 −0.6	−1.0 +1.3	+1.4 −0	+1.0 +0.1	−1.5 +2.1	+2.2 −0	+1.5 +0.1	−1.9 +1.7	+2.2 −0	+1.9 +0.5	−1.9 +0.4	+1.4 −0	+1.9 +1.0
4.73–7.09	−0.6 +2.0	+1.6 −0	+0.6 −0.4	−0.9 +3.2	+2.5 −0	+0.9 −0.7	−1.1 +1.5	+1.6 −0	+1.1 +0.1	−1.7 +2.4	+2.5 −0	+1.7 +0.1	−2.2 +1.9	+2.5 −0	+2.2 +0.6	−2.2 +0.4	+1.6 −0	+2.2 +1.2
7.09–9.85	−0.7 +2.3	+1.8 −0	+0.7 −0.5	−1.0 +3.6	+2.8 −0	+1.0 −0.8	−1.4 +1.6	+1.8 −0	+1.4 +0.2	−2.0 +2.6	+2.8 −0	+2.0 +0.2	−2.4 +2.2	+2.8 −0	+2.4 +0.6	−2.6 +0.4	+1.8 −0	+2.6 +1.4
9.85–12.41	−0.7 +2.6	+2.0 −0	+0.7 −0.6	−1.0 +4.0	+3.0 −0	+1.0 −1.0	−1.4 +1.8	+2.0 −0	+1.4 +0.2	−2.2 +2.8	+3.0 −0	+2.2 +0.2	−2.8 +2.2	+3.0 −0	+2.8 +0.8	−2.6 +0.6	+2.0 −0	+2.6 +1.4
12.41–15.75	−0.7 +2.9	+2.2 −0	+0.7 −0.7	−1.2 +4.5	+3.5 −0	+1.2 −1.0	−1.6 +2.0	+2.2 −0	+1.6 +0.2	−2.4 +3.3	+3.5 −0	+2.4 +0.2	−3.0 +2.7	+3.5 −0	+3.0 +0.8	−3.0 +0.6	+2.2 −0	+3.0 +1.6
15.75–19.69	−0.8 +3.2	+2.5 −0	+0.8 −0.7	−1.3 +5.2	+4.0 −0	+1.3 −1.2	−1.8 +2.3	+2.5 −0	+1.8 +0.2	−2.7 +3.8	+4.0 −0	+2.7 +0.2	−3.4 +3.1	+4.0 −0	+3.4 +0.9	−3.4 +0.7	+2.5 −0	+3.4 +1.8

Courtesy USASI

TABLE 24   INTERFERENCE LOCATIONAL FITS

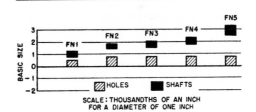

Limits are in thousandths of an inch.

Limits for hole and shaft are applied algebraically to the
   basic size to obtain the limits of size for the parts.

Data are in accordance with ABC agreements.

Symbols H7, p6, etc., are Hole and Shaft designations used in
   ABC System.

Nominal size range inches over to	Class LN 2			Class LN 3		
	Limits of interference	Standard limits		Limits of interference	Standard limits	
		Hole H7	Shaft p6		Hole H7	Shaft r6
0.04–0.12	0 0.65	+0.4 −0	+0.65 +0.4	0.1 0.75	+0.4 −0	+0.75 +0.5
0.12–0.24	0 0.8	+0.5 −0	+0.8 +0.5	0.1 0.9	+0.5 −0	+0.9 +0.6
0.24–0.40	0 1.0	+0.6 −0	+1.0 +0.6	0.2 1.2	+0.6 −0	+1.2 +0.8
0.40–0.71	0 1.1	+0.7 −0	+1.1 +0.7	0.3 1.4	+0.7 −0	+1.4 +1.0
0.71–1.19	0 1.3	+0.8 −0	+1.3 +0.8	0.4 1.7	+0.8 −0	+1.7 +1.2
1.19–1.97	0 1.6	+1.0 −0	+1.6 +1.0	0.4 2.0	+1.0 −0	+2.0 +1.4
1.97–3.15	0.2 2.1	+1.2 −0	+2.1 +1.4	0.4 2.3	+1.2 −0	+2.3 +1.6
3.15–4.73	0.2 2.5	+1.4 −0	+2.5 +1.6	0.6 2.9	+1.4 −0	+2.9 +2.0
4.73–7.09	0.2 2.8	+1.6 −0	+2.8 +1.8	0.9 3.5	+1.6 −0	+3.5 +2.5
7.09–9.85	0.2 3.2	+1.8 −0	+3.2 +2.0	1.2 4.2	+1.8 −0	+4.2 +3.0
9.85–12.41	0.2 3.4	+2.0 −0	+3.4 +2.2	1.5 4.7	+2.0 −0	+4.7 +3.5
12.41–15.75	0.3 3.9	+2.2 −0	+3.9 +2.5	2.3 5.9	+2.2 −0	+5.9 +4.5
15.75–19.69	0.3 4.4	+2.5 −0	+4.4 +2.8	2.5 6.6	+2.5 −0	+6.6 +5.0

Courtesy USASI

TABLE 25   FORCE AND SHRINK FITS

Limits are in thousandths of an inch.
Limits for hole and shaft are applied algebraically to the basic size to obtain the limits of size for the parts.
Data are in accordance with ABC agreements.
Symbols H7, s6, etc., are Hole and Shaft designations used in ABC System.

Nominal size range inches over to	Class FN 1 Limits of interference	Hole H6	Shaft	Class FN 2 Limits of interference	Hole H7	Shaft s6	Class FN 3 Limits of interference	Hole H7	Shaft t6	Class FN 4 Limits of interference	Hole H7	Shaft u6	Class FN 5 Limits of interference	Hole H7	Shaft x7
0.04–0.12	0.05	+0.25	+0.5	0.2	+0.4	+0.85				0.3	+0.4	+0.95	0.5	+0.4	+1.3
	0.5	−0	+0.3	0.85	−0	+0.6				0.95	−0	+0.7	1.3	−0	+0.9
0.12–0.24	0.1	+0.3	+0.6	0.2	+0.5	+1.0				0.4	+0.5	+1.2	0.7	+0.5	+1.7
	0.6	−0	+0.4	1.0	−0	+0.7				1.2	−0	+0.9	1.7	−0	+1.2
0.24–0.40	0.1	+0.4	+0.75	0.4	+0.6	+1.4				0.6	+0.6	+1.6	0.8	+0.6	+2.0
	0.75	−0	+0.5	1.4	−0	+1.0				1.6	−0	+1.2	2.0	−0	+1.4
0.40–0.56	0.1	+0.4	+0.8	0.5	+0.7	+1.6				0.7	+0.7	+1.8	0.9	+0.7	+2.3
	0.8	−0	+0.5	1.6	−0	+1.2				1.8	−0	+1.4	2.3	−0	+1.6
0.56–0.71	0.2	+0.4	+0.9	0.5	+0.7	+1.6				0.7	+0.7	+1.8	1.1	+0.7	+2.5
	0.9	−0	+0.6	1.6	−0	+1.2				1.8	−0	+1.4	2.5	−0	+1.8
0.71–0.95	0.2	+0.5	+1.1	0.6	+0.8	+1.9				0.8	+0.8	+2.1	1.4	+0.8	+3.0
	1.1	−0	+0.7	1.9	−0	+1.4				2.1	−0	+1.6	3.0	−0	+2.2
0.95–1.19	0.3	+0.5	+1.2	0.6	+0.8	+1.9	0.8	+0.8	+2.1	1.0	+0.8	+2.3	1.7	+0.8	+3.3
	1.2	−0	+0.8	1.9	−0	+1.4	2.1	−0	+1.6	2.3	−0	+1.8	3.3	−0	+2.5
1.19–1.58	0.3	+0.6	+1.3	0.8	+1.0	+2.4	1.0	+1.0	+2.6	1.5	+1.0	+3.1	2.0	+1.0	+4.0
	1.3	−0	+0.9	2.4	−0	+1.8	2.6	−0	+2.0	3.1	−0	+2.5	4.0	−0	+3.0
1.58–1.97	0.4	+0.6	+1.4	0.8	−1.0	+2.4	1.2	+1.0	+2.8	1.8	+1.0	+3.4	3.0	+1.0	+5.0
	1.4	−0	+1.0	2.4	−0	+1.8	2.8	−0	+2.2	3.4	−0	+2.8	5.0	−0	+4.0
1.97–2.56	0.6	+0.7	+1.8	0.8	+1.2	+2.7	1.3	+1.2	+3.2	2.3	+1.2	+4.2	3.8	+1.2	+6.2
	1.8	−0	+1.3	2.7	−0	+2.0	3.2	−0	+2.5	4.2	−0	+3.5	6.2	−0	+5.0
2.56–3.15	0.7	+0.7	+1.9	1.0	+1.2	+2.9	1.8	+1.2	+3.7	2.8	+1.2	+4.7	4.8	+1.2	+7.2
	1.9	−0	+1.4	2.9	−0	+2.2	3.7	−0	+3.0	4.7	−0	+4.0	7.2	−0	+6.0
3.15–3.94	0.9	+0.9	+2.4	1.4	+1.4	+3.7	2.1	+1.4	+4.4	3.6	+1.4	+5.9	5.6	+1.4	+8.4
	2.4	−0	+1.8	3.7	−0	+2.8	4.4	−0	+3.5	5.9	−0	+5.0	8.4	−0	+7.0
3.94–4.73	1.1	+0.9	+2.6	1.6	+1.4	+3.9	2.6	+1.4	+4.9	4.6	+1.4	+6.9	6.6	+1.4	+9.4
	2.6	−0	+2.0	3.9	−0	+3.0	4.9	−0	+4.0	6.9	−0	+6.0	9.4	−0	+8.0
4.73–5.52	1.2	+1.0	+2.9	1.9	+1.6	+4.5	3.4	+1.6	+6.0	5.4	+1.6	+8.0	8.4	+1.6	+11.6
	2.9	−0	+2.2	4.5	−0	+3.5	6.0	−0	+5.0	8.0	−0	+7.0	11.6	−0	+10.0
5.52–6.30	1.5	+1.0	+3.2	2.4	+1.6	+5.0	3.4	+1.6	+6.0	5.4	+1.6	+8.0	10.4	+1.6	+13.6
	3.2	−0	+2.5	5.0	−0	+4.0	6.0	−0	+5.0	8.0	−0	+7.0	13.6	−0	+12.0
6.30–7.09	1.8	+1.0	+3.5	2.9	+1.6	+5.5	4.4	+1.6	+7.0	6.4	+1.6	+9.0	10.4	+1.6	+13.6
	3.5	−0	+2.8	5.5	−0	+4.5	7.0	−0	+6.0	9.0	−0	+8.0	13.6	−0	+12.0
7.09–7.88	1.8	+1.2	+3.8	3.2	+1.8	+6.2	5.2	+1.8	+8.2	7.2	+1.8	+10.2	12.2	+1.8	+15.8
	3.8	−0	+3.0	6.2	−0	+5.0	8.2	−0	+7.0	10.2	−0	+9.0	15.8	−0	+14.0
7.88–8.86	2.3	+1.2	+4.3	3.2	+1.8	+6.2	5.2	+1.8	+8.2	8.2	+1.8	+11.2	14.2	+1.8	+17.8
	4.3	−0	+3.5	6.2	−0	+5.0	8.2	−0	+7.0	11.2	−0	+10.0	17.8	−0	+16.0
8.86–9.85	2.3	+1.2	+4.3	4.2	+1.8	+7.2	6.2	+1.8	+9.2	10.2	+1.8	+13.2	14.2	+1.8	+17.8
	4.3	−0	+3.5	7.2	−0	+6.0	9.2	−0	+8.0	13.2	−0	+12.0	17.8	−0	+16.0
9.85–11.03	2.8	+1.2	+4.9	4.0	+2.0	+7.2	7.0	+2.0	+10.2	10.2	+2.0	+13.2	16.0	+2.0	+20.0
	4.9	−0	+4.0	7.2	−0	+6.0	10.2	−0	+9.0	13.2	−0	+12.0	20.0	−0	+18.0
11.03–12.41	2.8	+1.2	+4.9	5.0	+2.0	+8.2	7.0	+2.0	+10.2	12.0	+2.0	+15.2	18.0	+2.0	+22.0
	4.9	−0	+4.0	8.2	−0	+7.0	10.2	−0	+9.0	15.2	−0	+14.0	22.0	−0	+20.0

TABLE 26 DIMENSIONS OF PLAIN WASHERS

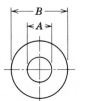

Screw or bolt size	Series	Inside diameter A Nom	Outside diameter B Nom	Thickness C Nom
5/16	Narrow		5/8	0.063
	Regular	0.344	7/8	0.063
	Wide		1 1/8	0.063
3/8	Narrow		47/64	0.063
	Regular	0.406	1	0.063
	Wide		1 1/4	0.100
7/16	Narrow		7/8	0.063
	Regular	0.480	1 1/8	0.063
	Wide		1 15/32	0.100
1/2	Narrow		1	0.063
	Regular	0.540	1 1/4	0.100
	Wide		1 3/4	0.100
9/16	Narrow		1 1/8	0.063
	Regular	0.604	1 15/32	0.100
	Wide		2	0.100
5/8	Narrow		1 1/4	0.100
	Regular	0.666	1 3/4	0.100
	Wide		2 1/4	0.160
3/4	Narrow		1 3/8	0.100
	Regular	0.812	2	0.100
	Wide		2 1/2	0.160
7/8	Narrow		1 15/32	0.100
	Regular	0.938	2 1/4	0.160
	Wide		2 3/4	0.160
1	Narrow		1 3/4	0.100
	Regular	1 1/16	2 1/2	0.160
	Wide		3	0.160
1 1/8	Narrow		2	0.100
	Regular	1 3/16	2 3/4	0.160
	Wide		3 1/4	0.160
1 1/4	Narrow		2 1/4	0.160
	Regular	1 5/16	3	0.160
	Wide		3 1/2	0.250

Screw or bolt size	Series	Inside diameter A Nom	Outside diameter B Nom	Thickness C Nom
1 3/8	Narrow		2 1/2	0.160
	Regular	1 7/16	3 1/4	0.160
	Wide		3 3/4	0.250
1 1/2	Narrow		2 3/4	0.160
	Regular	1 9/16	3 1/2	0.250
	Wide		4	0.250
1 5/8	Narrow		3	0.160
	Regular	1 3/4	3 3/4	0.250
	Wide		4 1/4	0.250
1 3/4	Narrow		3 1/4	0.160
	Regular	1 7/8	4	0.250
	Wide		4 1/2	0.250
1 7/8	Narrow		3 1/2	0.250
	Regular	2	4 1/4	0.250
	Wide		4 3/4	0.250
2	Narrow		3 3/4	0.250
	Regular	2 1/8	4 1/2	0.250
	Wide		5	0.250
2 1/4	Narrow		4	0.250
	Regular	2 3/8	5	0.250
	Wide		5 1/2	0.375
2 1/2	Narrow		4 1/2	0.250
	Regular	2 5/8	5 1/2	0.375
	Wide		6	0.375
2 3/4	Narrow		5	0.250
	Regular	2 7/8	6	0.375
	Wide		6 1/2	0.375
3	Narrow		5 1/2	0.375
	Regular	3 1/8	6 1/2	0.375
	Wide		7	0.375

Courtesy USASI

All dimensions are given in inches.
Inside and outside diameters shall be concentric within at least the inside diameter tolerance.
Washers shall be flat within 0.005 for outside diameters up to and including 7/8 inch, and 0.010 for outside diameters greater than 7/8 inch.
Tolerance on inside diameter 5/16 to 7/8 is −0.010.
Tolerance on inside diameter 1 to 3 is ±0.010.
Tolerance on outside diameter ±0.010.

TABLE 27 WF SHAPES

Dimensions for Detailing

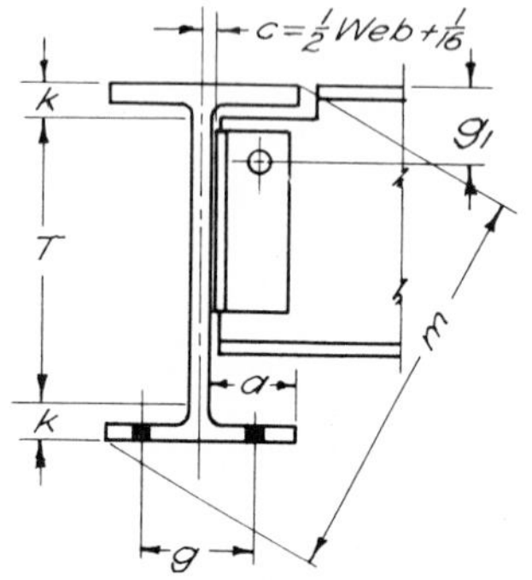

Nominal size	Weight per foot	Depth	Flange		Web		Distance						Usual gage g
			Width	Thick-ness	Thick-ness	Half thick-ness	a	T	k	m	g_1	c	
In.	Lb.	In.	In.	In.	In.	In.	In.	In.	In.	In.	In.	In.	In.
36 × 16½	230	35⅞	16½	1¼	3/4	3/8	7⅞	31⅛	2⅜	39½	3½	7/16	5½
36 × 12	150	35⅞	12	15/16	5/8	5/16	5⅝	32¼	1 13/16	37⅞	3	3/8	5½
33 × 15¾	200	33	15¾	1⅛	3/4	3/8	7½	28⅝	2 3/16	36⅝	3½	7/16	5½
33 × 11½	130	33⅛	11½	7/8	9/16	5/16	5½	29¾	1 11/16	35⅛	3	3/8	5½
30 × 15	172	29⅞	15	1 1/16	11/16	5/16	7⅛	25¾	2 1/16	33½	3¼	3/8	5½
30 × 10½	108	29⅞	10½	3/4	9/16	5/16	5	26⅞	1½	31⅝	2¾	3/8	5½
24 × 14	130	24¼	14	7/8	9/16	5/16	6¾	20¾	1¾	28	3	3/8	5½
24 × 12	100	24	12	3/4	1/2	1/4	5¾	20⅞	1 9/16	26⅞	2¾	5/16	5½
24 × 9	76	23⅞	9	11/16	7/16	1/4	4¼	21⅜	1¼	25⅝	2½	5/16	5½
21 × 13	112	21	13	7/8	9/16	1/4	6¼	17¾	1⅝	24¾	3	5/16	5½
21 × 9	82	20⅞	9	13/16	1/2	1/4	4¼	18	1 7/16	22¾	2¾	5/16	5½
21 × 8¼	62	21	8¼	5/8	3/8	3/16	4	18⅝	1 3/16	22⅝	2½	1/4	5½
18 × 11¾	96	18⅛	11¾	13/16	1/2	1/4	5⅝	15⅛	1½	21¾	2¾	5/16	5½
18 × 8¾	64	17⅞	8¾	11/16	7/16	3/16	4⅛	15⅜	1¼	20	2½	1/4	5½
18 × 7½	50	18	7½	9/16	3/8	3/16	3⅝	15⅞	1 1/16	19½	2¼	1/4	3½
16 × 11½	88	16⅛	11½	13/16	1/2	1/4	5½	13⅛	1½	19⅞	2¾	5/16	5½
16 × 8½	58	15⅞	8½	5/8	7/16	1/4	4	13⅜	1¼	18	2½	5/16	5½
16 × 7	36	15⅞	7	7/16	5/16	3/16	3⅜	14	15/16	17⅜	2¼	1/4	3½
14 × 12	78	14	12	11/16	7/16	1/4	5¾	11⅜	1 5/16	18½	2½	5/16	5½
14 × 10	61	13⅞	10	5/8	3/8	3/16	4¾	11⅜	1¼	17⅛	2½	1/4	5½
14 × 8	43	13⅝	8	1/2	5/16	3/16	3⅞	11⅜	1⅛	15⅞	2½	1/4	5½
12 × 10	53	12	10	9/16	3/8	3/16	4⅞	9¾	1 3/16	15⅝	2½	1/4	5½
12 × 8	40	12	8	1/2	5/16	3/16	3⅞	9¾	1⅛	14⅜	2½	1/4	5½
12 × 6½	27	12	6½	3/8	1/4	1/8	3⅛	10⅜	13/16	13⅝	2¼	3/16	3½
10 × 8	33	9¾	8	7/16	5/16	3/16	3⅞	7⅞	15/16	12⅝	2¼	1/4	5½
10 × 5¾	21	9⅞	5¾	5/16	1/4	1/8	2¾	8½	11/16	11½	2	3/16	2¾
8 × 6½	24	7⅞	6½	3/8	1/4	1/8	3⅛	6⅜	3/4	10¼	2¼	3/16	3½
8 × 5¼	17	8	5¼	5/16	1/4	1/8	2½	6¾	5/8	9⅝	2¼	3/16	2¾

Courtesy *AISC Manual*

TABLE 28   AMERICAN STANDARD I-BEAMS

Dimensions for Detailing

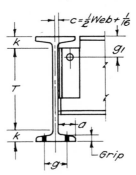

Depth of section	Weight per foot	Flange		Web		Distance					Grip	Max. flange rivet	Usual gage g
		Width	Mean thickness	Thickness	Half thickness	a	T	k	g_1	c			
In.	Lb.	In.	In.	In.	In.	In.	In.	In.	In.	In.	In.	In.	In.
24	79.9	7	7/8	1/2	1/4	3¼	20¾	1⅝	3	5/16	7/8	1	4
20	65.4	6¼	13/16	1/2	1/4	2⅞	16⅞	1 9/16	3	5/16	3/4	7/8	3½
18	54.7	6	11/16	1/2	1/4	2¾	15¼	1⅜	2¾	5/16	11/16	7/8	3½
15	42.9	5½	5/8	7/16	1/4	2½	12½	1¼	2¾	5/16	9/16	3/4	3½
12	31.8	5	9/16	3/8	3/16	2⅜	9¾	1⅛	2½	1/4	1/2	3/4	3
10	25.4	4⅝	1/2	5/16	3/16	2⅛	8	1	2½	1/4	1/2	3/4	2¾
8	18.4	4	7/16	5/16	1/8	1⅞	6¼	7/8	2¼	3/16	7/16	3/4	2¼
7	15.3	3⅝	3/8	1/4	1/8	1¾	5⅜	13/16	2	3/16	3/8	5/8	2¼
6	12.5	3⅜	3/8	1/4	1/8	1½	4½	3/4	2	3/16	5/16		
5	10.0	3	5/16	1/4	1/8	1⅜	3⅝	11/16	2	3/16	5/16	1/2	1¾
4	7.7	2⅝	5/16	3/16	1/8	1¼	2¾	5/8	2	3/16	5/16		
3	5.7	2⅜	1/4	3/16	1/8	1⅛	1⅞	9/16		3/16	1/4	3/8	1½

Courtesy AISC Manual

874 APPENDIX

TABLE 29 STANDARD GAGES FOR ANGLES (INCHES)

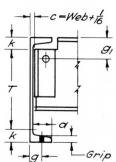

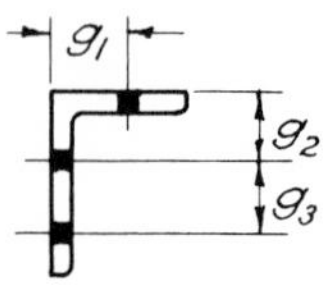

Leg	8	7	6	5	4	3½	3	2½	2	1¾	1½	1⅜	1¼	1	3/4
g_1	4½	4	3½	3	2½	2	1¾	1⅜	1⅛	1	7/8	7/8	3/4	5/8	1/2
g_2	3	2½	2¼	2											
g_3	3	3	2½	1¾											
Max. rivet	1⅛	1	7/8	7/8	7/8	7/8	7/8	3/4	5/8	1/2	3/8	3/8	3/8	1/4	1/4

Courtesy *AISC Manual*

TABLE 30 AMERICAN STANDARD CHANNELS

Dimensions for Detailing

Depth of section	Weight per foot	Flange		Web		Distance					Grip	Max. flange rivet	Usual gage g
		Width	Mean thickness	Thickness	Half thickness	a	T	k	g_1	c			
In.	Lb.	In.	In.	In.	In.	In.	In.	In.	In.	In.	In.	In.	In.
15	33.9	3⅜	5/8	7/16	3/16	3	12⅜	1⁵⁄₁₆	2¾	1/2	5/8	1	2
12	20.7	3	1/2	5/16	1/8	2⅝	9⅞	1¹⁄₁₆	2½	3/8	1/2	7/8	1¾
10	15.3	2⅝	7/16	1/4	1/8	2⅜	8⅛	15/16	2½	5/16	7/16	3/4	1½
9	13.4	2⅜	7/16	1/4	1/8	2¼	7¼	7/8	2½	5/16	3/8	3/4	1⅜
8	11.5	2¼	3/8	1/4	1/8	2	6⅜	13/16	2¼	5/16	3/8	3/4	1⅜
7	9.8	2⅛	3/8	1/4	1/8	1⅞	5⅜	13/16	2	5/16	3/8	5/8	1¼
6	8.2	1⅞	3/8	3/16	1/8	1¾	4½	3/4	2	1/4	5/16	5/8	1⅛
5	6.7	1¾	5/16	3/16	1/8	1½	3⅝	11/16	2	1/4	5/16	1/2	1⅛
4	5.4	1⅝	5/16	3/16	1/8	1⅜	2¾	5/8	2	1/4	1/4	1/2	1
3	4.1	1⅜	1/4	3/16	1/8	1¼	1¾	5/8		1/4	1/4		

Courtesy *AISC Manual*

TABLE 31   RIVET SPACING

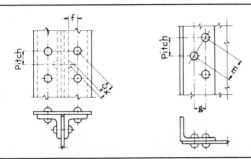

Minimum Pitch for Machine Riveting

Dia. of rivet	c	k	Distance, f, Inches													
			1⅛	1¼	1⅜	1½	1⅝	1¾	1⅞	2	2⅛	2¼	2⅜	2½	2¾	3
3/8	7/8	1³⁄₁₆	1/4	0												
1/2	1	1⅜	3/4	1/2	0											
5/8	1⅛	1⁹⁄₁₆	1⅛	1	3/4	3/8	0									
3/4	1¼	1¾	...	1¼	1⅛	1	3/4	0								
7/8	1⅜	2	...	...	1½	1⅜	1⅛	7/8	5/8	0						
1	1½	2³⁄₁₆	...	...	...	1⅝	1½	1⅜	1⅛	7/8	1/2	0				
1⅛	1⅝	2⅜	...	...	...	...	1¾	1⅝	1½	1⅜	1⅛	7/8	0			
1¼	1¾	2⅝	...	...	...	...	...	2	1⅞	1¾	1½	1¼	1	5/8	0	
1⅜	1⅞	2¹³⁄₁₆	...	...	...	...	...	...	2⅛	2	1⅞	1¾	1½	1¼	1/2	0
1½	2	3	...	...	...	...	...	...	...	2¼	2⅛	2	1⅞	1⅝	1⅛	0

Courtesy *AISC Manual*

TABLE 32   STANDARD BEAM CONNECTIONS—SERIES B, AISC MANUAL

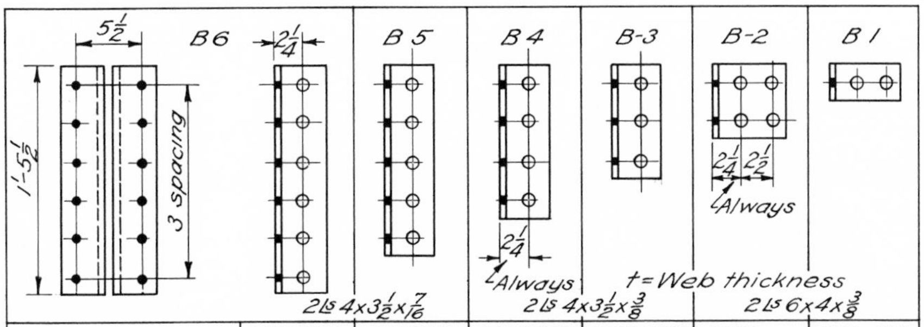

	B 6	B 5	B 4	B-3	B-2	B 1
BEAM SIZES	24WF160 to84, 76 24 I All	21WF142 to 73,68,62 20 I All	18WFto77 16WF 18T&15I	14WF, 12WF 12I	10WF 8WF 10I & 8I	7I, 6I 5I
RIVETS IN OUTSTANDING LEGS	12	10	8	6	4	2
SHEAR (OUTST'D LEG) (×1000 lbs)	79.5	66.3	53	39.8	26.5	13.3
BEARING IN WEB LEGS	180 t	150 t	120 t	90 t	120 t	60 t
MIN. SPAN IN FT. (LIGHT SECT. ONLY)	WF 14.8 I 14.6	WF 14.0 I 11.8	WF 13.8 &10.5 I 11.1 & 8.0	WF 11.5 &10.5 I 7.6	WF 5.4 &3.9 I 6.1 &3.6	I 5.2, 3.7 & 2.5
WEIGHT (SHOP RIV. ONLY)	34	28	20	14	13	7

TABLE 33 CLEARANCE DIMENSIONS FOR SKEWED-BEAM FRAMED CONNECTIONS—AISC MANUAL

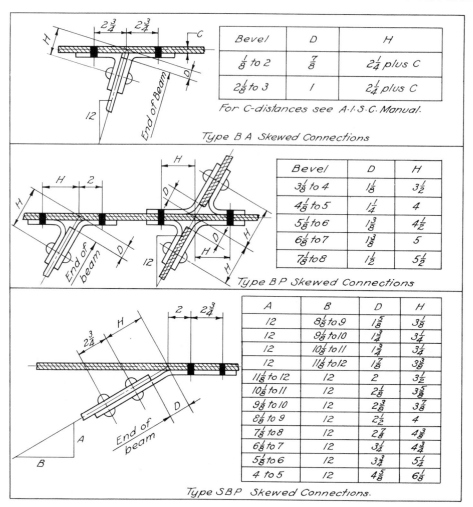

Bevel	D	H
$\frac{1}{8}$ to 2	$\frac{7}{8}$	$2\frac{1}{4}$ plus C
$2\frac{1}{8}$ to 3	1	$2\frac{1}{4}$ plus C

For C-distances see A.I.S.C. Manual.

Type BA Skewed Connections

Bevel	D	H
$3\frac{1}{8}$ to 4	$1\frac{1}{8}$	$3\frac{1}{2}$
$4\frac{1}{8}$ to 5	$1\frac{1}{4}$	4
$5\frac{1}{8}$ to 6	$1\frac{3}{8}$	$4\frac{1}{2}$
$6\frac{1}{8}$ to 7	$1\frac{3}{8}$	5
$7\frac{1}{8}$ to 8	$1\frac{1}{2}$	$5\frac{1}{2}$

Type BP Skewed Connections

A	B	D	H
12	$8\frac{1}{8}$ to 9	$1\frac{5}{8}$	$3\frac{1}{8}$
12	$9\frac{1}{8}$ to 10	$1\frac{3}{4}$	$3\frac{1}{4}$
12	$10\frac{1}{8}$ to 11	$1\frac{3}{4}$	$3\frac{1}{4}$
12	$11\frac{1}{8}$ to 12	$1\frac{7}{8}$	$3\frac{3}{8}$
$11\frac{1}{8}$ to 12	12	2	$3\frac{1}{2}$
$10\frac{1}{8}$ to 11	12	$2\frac{1}{8}$	$3\frac{5}{8}$
$9\frac{1}{8}$ to 10	12	$2\frac{3}{8}$	$3\frac{7}{8}$
$8\frac{1}{8}$ to 9	12	$2\frac{1}{2}$	4
$7\frac{1}{8}$ to 8	12	$2\frac{7}{8}$	$4\frac{3}{8}$
$6\frac{1}{8}$ to 7	12	$3\frac{1}{4}$	$4\frac{3}{4}$
$5\frac{1}{8}$ to 6	12	$3\frac{3}{4}$	$5\frac{1}{4}$
4 to 5	12	$4\frac{5}{8}$	$6\frac{1}{8}$

Type SBP Skewed Connections.

TABLE 34 MAXIMUM SPACING OF COLUMN TIES

Vertical bar size	Size and spacing of ties, in. Maximum spacing not to exceed least column dimension		
	#2	#3	#4
#5	10	10	10
#6	12	12	12
#7	12	14	14
#8	12*	16	16
#9	12*	18	18
#10	12*	18	20
#11	12*	18	22

* #2 ties are not recommended for #8 or larger verticals.

Courtesy ACI

TABLE 35   MAXIMUM NUMBER OF COLUMN BARS FOR ROUND COLUMNS

Diameter of column	Spiral size	Bar size						
		#5	#6	#7	#8	#9	#10	#11
14	3/8	12	11	10	9	7	6	
15	3/8	13	12	11	10	8	7	6
16	3/8	15	13	12	11	9	8	6
17	3/8	16	15	14	12	11	9	7
18	3/8	18	16	15	14	12	10	8
19	3/8	19	18	16	15	13	11	9
20	3/8	21	19	18	16	14	12	10
21	1/2	22	20	19	17	15	13	11
22	1/2	23	22	20	18	16	14	11
23	1/2	25	23	21	20	17	15	12
24	1/2	26	24	22	21	18	16	13

Courtesy ACI

TABLE 36   LAPPING OF BARS

Inches of lap corresponding to number of bar diameters (figured to next largest whole inch)

Number of diameters	Size of bar								
	#3	#4	#5	#6	#7	#8	#9	#10	#11
29	..	..	13	15	18	20	23	26	29
21	..	..	14	16	19	21	24	27	30
22	..	..	14	17	20	22	25	28	31
23	..	12	15	18	21	23	26	30	33
24	..	12	15	18	21	24	28	31	34
25	..	13	16	19	22	25	29	32	36
26	..	13	17	20	23	26	30	33	37
27	..	14	17	21	24	27	31	35	39
28	..	14	18	21	25	28	32	36	40
29	..	15	19	22	26	29	33	37	41
30	12	15	19	23	27	30	34	39	43
32	12	16	20	24	28	32	36	41	45
34	13	17	22	26	30	34	39	44	48
36	14	18	23	27	32	36	41	46	51
38	15	19	24	29	34	38	43	49	54
40	15	20	25	30	35	40	46	51	57

Minimum lap equals 12 in.   Courtesy ACI

TABLE 37   MINIMUM BEAM WIDTHS—ACI CODE

Size of bars	Number of bars in single layer of reinforcing							Add for each added bar
	2	3	4	5	6	7	8	
#4	5¾	7¼	8¾	10¼	11¾	13¼	14¾	1½
#5	6	7¾	9¼	11	12½	14¼	15¾	1⅝
#6	6¼	8	9¾	11½	13¼	15	16¾	1¾
#7	6½	8½	10¼	12¼	14	16	17¾	1⅞
#8	6¾	8¾	10¾	12¾	14¾	16¾	18¾	2
#9	7¼	9½	11¾	14	16¼	18½	20¾	2¼
#10	7¾	10¼	12¾	15¼	17¾	20¼	23	2⅝
#11	8	11	13¾	16½	19½	22¼	25	2⅞

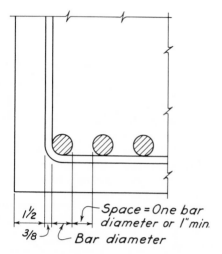

Table shows minimum beam widths when #3 stirrups are used; if no stirrups are required, deduct ¾ in. from figures shown.

For additional bars, add dimension in last column for each added bar.

For bars of different sizes, determine from table the beam width which would be required for the given number of smaller size bars, and then add last column figure for each larger bar used.

Clear space between bars should be at least 1⅓ times the maximum size of coarse aggregate, which often requires increased beam width when aggregate exceeds ¾ in.

Courtesy ACI

TABLE 38 ELECTRICAL SYMBOLS

USASI Z32.9-1943

Ceiling	Wall	GENERAL OUTLETS
◯	◯	Outlet.
Ⓑ	Ⓑ	Blanked Outlet.
Ⓓ	Ⓓ	Drop Cord.
Ⓔ	Ⓔ	Electrical Outlet; for use only when circle used alone might be confused with columns, plumbing symbols, etc.
Ⓕ	Ⓕ	Fan Outlet.
Ⓙ	Ⓙ	Junction Box.
Ⓛ	Ⓛ	Lamp Holder.
Ⓛ$_{PS}$	Ⓛ$_{PS}$	Lamp Holder with Pull Switch.
Ⓢ	Ⓢ	Pull Switch.
Ⓥ	Ⓥ	Outlet for Vapor Discharge Lamp.
Ⓧ	Ⓧ	Exit Light Outlet.
Ⓒ	Ⓒ	Clock Outlet. (Specify Voltage)

CONVENIENCE OUTLETS

Duplex Convenience Outlet.

Convenience Outlet other than Duplex. 1 = Single, 3 = Triplex, etc.

$_{WP}$ Weatherproof Convenience Outlet.

$_{R}$ Range Outlet.

$_{S}$ Switch and Convenience Outlet.

R Radio and Convenience Outlet.

Special Purpose Outlet. (Des. in Spec.)

Floor Outlet.

SWITCH OUTLETS

S — Single Pole Switch.

S_2 — Double Pole Switch.

S_3 — Three Way Switch.

S_4 — Four Way Switch.

S_D — Automatic Door Switch.

S_E — Electrolier Switch.

S_K — Key Operated Switch.

S_P — Switch and Pilot Lamp.

S_{CB} — Circuit Breaker.

S_{WCB} — Weatherproof Circuit Breaker.

S_{MC} — Momentary Contact Switch.

S_{RC} — Remote Control Switch.

S_{WP} — Weatherproof Switch.

S_F — Fused Switch.

S_{WF} — Weatherproof Fused Switch.

SPECIAL OUTLETS

◯ a, b, c, etc.

a, b, c, etc.

S a, b, c, etc.

Any Standard Symbol as given above with the addition of a lower case subscript letter may be used to designate some special variation of Standard Equipment of particular interest in a specific set of Architectural Plans.

When used they must be listed in the Key of Symbols on each drawing and if necessary further described in the specifications.

PANELS, CIRCUITS, AND MISCELLANEOUS

▮ Lighting Panel.

▨ Power Panel.

——— Branch Circuit; Concealed in Ceiling or Wall.

- - - Branch Circuit; concealed in Floor.

----- Branch Circuit; Exposed.

Home Run to Panel Board. Indicate number of Circuits by number of arrows. Note: Any circuit without further designation indicates a two-wire circuit. For a greater number of wires indicate as follows:

⫽ (3 wires) ⫽⫽ (4 wires), etc.

Feeders. Note: Use heavy lines and designate by number corresponding to listing in Feeder Schedule.

Underfloor Duct and Junction Box. Triple System. Note: For double or single systems eliminate one or two lines. This symbol is equally adaptable to auxiliary system layouts.

Ⓖ Generator.

Ⓜ Motor.

Ⓘ Instrument.

Ⓣ Power Transformer. (Or draw to scale.)

⊠ Controller.

▭ Isolating Switch.

AUXILIARY SYSTEMS

• Push Button.

Buzzer.

Bell.

◇ Annunciator.

◀ Outside Telephone.

⧓ Interconnecting Telephone.

⧓ Telephone Switchboard.

Ⓣ Bell Ringing Transformer.

D Electric Door Opener.

F Fire Alarm Bell.

F Fire Alarm Station.

✖ City Fire Alarm Station.

FA Fire Alarm Central Station.

FS Automatic Fire Alarm Device.

W Watchman's Station.

W Watchman's Central Station.

H Horn.

N Nurse's Signal Plug.

M Maid's Signal Plug.

R Radio Outlet.

SC Signal Central Station.

▭ Interconnection Box.

▥ Battery.

- - - Auxiliary System Circuits. Note: Any line without further designation indicates a 2-Wire System. For a greater number of wires designate with numerals in manner similar to --. --12-No. 18W-3/4"C., or designate by number corresponding to listing in Schedule.

▭ a, b, c Special Auxiliary Outlets. Subscript letters refer to notes on plans or detailed description in specifications.

Courtesy USASI

TABLE 39   AMERICAN STANDARD STEEL PIPE DATA

(All dimensions in inches. Weights in pounds.)

Nominal size	Actual outside diameter	Standard weight (40)*				Extra-strong (80)†			Double-extra strong‡		
		Inside diameter	Wall thickness	Weight per foot§		Inside diameter	Wall thickness	Weight per foot	Inside diameter	Wall thickness	Weight per foot
1/8	0.405	0.269	0.068	0.244		0.215	0.095	0.314	. . . . .	. . . . .	. . . . .
1/4	0.540	0.364	.088	0.424		0.302	.119	0.535	. . . . .	. . . . .	. . . . .
3/8	0.675	0.493	.091	0.567		0.423	.126	0.738	. . . . .	. . . . .	. . . . .
1/2	0.840	0.622	.109	0.850		0.546	.147	1.087	0.252	0.294	1.714
3/4	1.050	0.824	.113	1.130		0.742	.154	1.473	0.434	.308	2.440
1	1.315	1.049	.133	1.678		0.957	.179	2.171	0.599	.358	3.659
1¼	1.660	1.380	.140	2.272		1.278	.191	2.996	0.896	.382	5.214
1½	1.900	1.610	.145	2.717		1.500	.200	3.631	1.100	.400	6.408
2	2.375	2.067	.154	3.652		1.939	.218	5.022	1.503	.436	9.029
2½	2.875	2.469	.203	5.79		2.323	.276	7.66	1.771	.552	13.70
3	3.500	3.068	.216	7.58		2.900	.300	10.25	2.300	.600	18.58
3½	4.000	3.548	.226	9.11		3.364	.318	12.51	. . . . .	. . . . .	. . . . .
4	4.500	4.026	.237	10.79		3.826	.337	14.98	3.152	.674	27.54
5	5.563	5.047	.258	14.62		4.813	.375	20.78	4.063	.750	38.55
6	6.625	6.065	.280	18.97		5.761	.432	28.57	4.897	.864	53.16
8	8.625	7.981	.322	28.55		7.625	.500	43.39	6.875	.875	72.42
10	10.750	10.020	.365	40.48		9.750	.500	54.74	. . . . .	. . . . .	. . . . .
12	12.750	12.000	.375	49.56		11.750	.500	65.42	. . . . .	. . . . .	. . . . .

* Same as **USASI** B36.10—"Schedule 40" except 12-inch diameter.
† Same as **USASI** B36.10—"Schedule 80" except 10- and 12-inch diameter.
‡ Not identified with **USASI** Schedule number, but available as indicated.
§ Plain ends.

TABLE 40   AGA STANDARD CAST-IRON BELL-AND-SPIGOT PIPE DATA

(All dimensions in inches.   Approx. weights in pounds.)

Nominal size inside diameter	Outside diameter of pipe	Pipe wall thickness	Inside diameter of socket	Depth of socket	Thickness of joint	Weight per foot, 12-foot lengths*
4	4.80	0.40	5.80	4.00	0.50	19.5
6	6.90	0.43	7.90	4.00	.50	30.58
8	9.05	0.45	10.05	4.00	.50	42.42
10	11.10	0.49	12.10	4.00	.50	55.91
12	13.20	0.54	14.20	4.50	.50	73.83
16	17.40	0.62	18.40	4.50	.50	112.58
20	21.60	0.68	22.85	4.50	.63	153.83
24	25.80	0.76	27.05	5.00	.63	206.41
30	31.74	0.85	32.99	5.00	.63	284.00
36	37.96	0.95	39.21	5.00	.63	379.25
42	44.20	1.07	45.45	5.00	.63	497.66
48	50.50	1.26	51.75	5.00	.63	663.50

* Including bell-and-spigot bead.

TABLE 41   ASTM STANDARD BRASS AND COPPER PIPE DATA

(All dimensions in inches.   Weights in pounds.)

Nominal size	Outside diameter	Regular			Extra-strong		
		Wall thick-ness	Weight per foot		Wall thick-ness	Weight per foot	
			Red brass	Copper		Red brass	Copper
1/8	0.405	0.062	0.253	0.259	0.100	0.363	0.371
1/4	0.540	0.082	0.447	0.457	0.123	0.611	0.625
3/8	0.675	0.090	0.627	0.641	0.127	0.829	0.847
1/2	0.840	0.107	0.934	0.955	0.149	1.23	1.25
3/4	1.050	0.114	1.27	1.30	0.157	1.67	1.71
1	1.315	0.126	1.78	1.82	0.182	2.46	2.51
1¼	1.660	0.146	2.63	2.69	0.194	3.39	3.46
1½	1.900	0.150	3.13	3.20	0.203	4.10	4.19
2	2.375	0.156	4.12	4.22	0.221	5.67	5.80
2½	2.875	0.187	5.99	6.12	0.280	8.66	8.85
3	3.500	0.219	8.56	8.75	0.304	11.6	11.8
3½	4.000	0.250	11.2	11.4	0.321	14.1	14.4
4	4.500	0.250	12.7	12.9	0.341	16.9	17.3
5	5.562	0.250	15.8	16.2	0.375	23.2	23.7
6	6.625	0.250	19.0	19.4	0.437	32.2	32.9
8	8.625	0.312	30.9	31.6	0.500	48.4	49.5
10	10.750	9.365	45.2	46.2	0.500	61.1	62.4
12	12.750	0.375	55.3	56.5			

TABLE 42   ASTM STANDARD COPPER WATER TUBE DATA

(All dimensions in inches.   Weights in pounds.)

Nominal size	Outside diameter	Type K		Type L		Type M	
		Wall thick-ness	Weight per foot	Wall thick-ness	Weight per foot	Wall thick-ness	Weight per foot
1/8	0.250	0.032	0.085	0.025	0.068	0.025	0.068
1/4	0.375	0.032	0.134	0.030	0.126	0.025	0.107
3/8	0.500	0.049	0.269	0.035	0.198	0.025	0.145
1/2	0.625	0.049	0.344	0.040	0.285	0.028	0.204
5/8	0.750	0.049	0.418	0.042	0.362	0.030	0.263
3/4	0.875	0.065	0.641	0.045	0.455	0.032	0.328
1	1.125	0.065	0.839	0.050	0.655	0.035	0.465
1¼	1.375	0.065	1.04	0.055	0.884	0.042	0.682
1½	1.625	0.072	1.36	0.060	1.14	0.049	0.940
2	2.125	0.083	2.06	0.070	1.75	0.058	1.46
2½	2.625	0.095	2.93	0.080	2.48	0.065	2.03
3	3.125	0.109	4.00	0.090	3.33	0.072	2.68
3½	3.625	0.120	5.12	0.100	4.29	0.083	3.58
4	4.125	0.134	6.51	0.110	5.38	0.095	4.66
5	5.125	0.160	9.67	0.125	7.61	0.109	6.66
6	6.125	0.192	13.9	0.140	10.2	0.122	8.92
8	8.125	0.271	25.9	0.200	19.3	0.170	16.5
10	10.125	0.338	40.3	0.250	30.1	0.212	25.6
12	12.125	0.405	57.8	0.280	40.4	0.254	36.7

TABLE 43 AMERICAN STANDARD TAPER PIPE THREAD DATA

(All dimensions in inches. Weights in pounds.)

Nominal size	Outside diameter	Inside diameter	Threads per inch	Tap drill	Weight per foot thds. and couplings	Normal engagement by hand
1/8	0.405	0.269	27	11/32	0.245	0.180
1/4	0.540	0.364	18	7/16	0.425	0.200
3/8	0.675	0.493	18	37/64	0.568	0.240
1/2	0.840	0.622	14	23/32	0.852	0.320
3/4	1.050	0.824	14	59/64	1.134	0.339
1	1.315	1.049	11½	1⁵⁄₃₂	1.684	0.400
1¼	1.660	1.380	11½	1½	2.281	0.420
1½	1.900	1.610	11½	1⁴⁷⁄₆₄	2.731	0.420
2	2.375	2.067	11½	2⁷⁄₃₂	3.678	0.436
2½	2.875	2.469	8	2⅝	5.82	0.682
3	3.500	3.068	8	3¼	7.62	0.766
3½	4.000	3.548	8	3¾	9.20	0.821
4	4.500	4.026	8	4¼	10.89	0.844
5	5.563	5.047	8	5⁵⁄₁₆	14.81	0.937
6	6.625	6.065	8	6⁵⁄₁₆	19.18	0.958
8	8.625	7.981	8		29.35	1.063
10	10.750	10.020	8		41.85	1.210
12	12.750	12.000	8		51.15	1.360

TABLE 44 STANDARD FLANGED FITTINGS

(125 lb per sq in. pressure.)

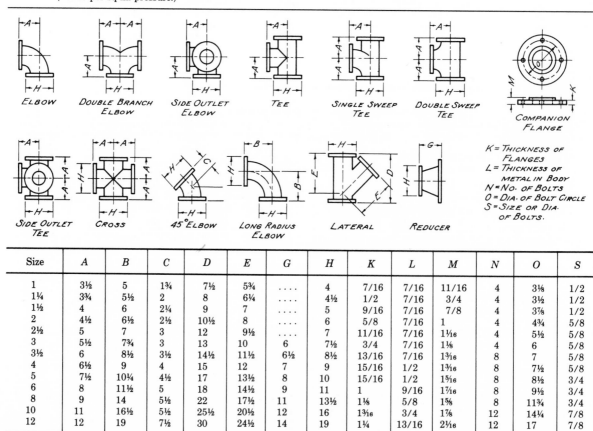

K = THICKNESS OF FLANGES
L = THICKNESS OF METAL IN BODY
N = NO. OF BOLTS
O = DIA. OF BOLT CIRCLE
S = SIZE OR DIA. OF BOLTS.

Size	A	B	C	D	E	G	H	K	L	M	N	O	S
1	3½	5	1¾	7½	5¾	....	4	7/16	7/16	11/16	4	3⅛	1/2
1¼	3¾	5½	2	8	6¼	....	4½	1/2	7/16	3/4	4	3½	1/2
1½	4	6	2¼	9	7	....	5	9/16	7/16	7/8	4	3⅞	1/2
2	4½	6½	2½	10½	8	....	6	5/8	7/16	1	4	4¾	5/8
2½	5	7	3	12	9½	....	7	11/16	7/16	1¹⁄₁₆	4	5½	5/8
3	5½	7¾	3	13	10	6	7½	3/4	7/16	1⅛	4	6	5/8
3½	6	8½	3½	14½	11½	6½	8½	13/16	7/16	1³⁄₁₆	8	7	5/8
4	6½	9	4	15	12	7	9	15/16	1/2	1³⁄₁₆	8	7½	5/8
5	7½	10¼	4½	17	13½	8	10	15/16	1/2	1⁵⁄₁₆	8	8½	3/4
6	8	11½	5	18	14½	9	11	1	9/16	1⁷⁄₁₆	8	9½	3/4
8	9	14	5½	22	17½	11	13½	1⅛	5/8	1⅝	8	11¾	3/4
10	11	16½	5½	25½	20½	12	16	1³⁄₁₆	3/4	1⅞	12	14¼	7/8
12	12	19	7½	30	24½	14	19	1¼	13/16	2¹⁄₁₆	12	17	7/8

TABLE 45 STANDARD CAST-IRON SCREW FITTINGS

(125 lb per sq in. pressure.)

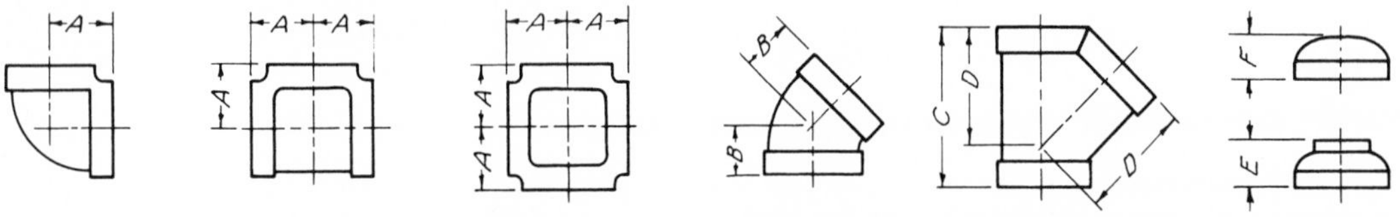

Size inches	Dimensions in inches					
	A	B	C	D	E	F
1/4	13/16	3/4				
3/8	15/16	13/16				
1/2	1 1/8	7/8	2 1/2	1 7/8		
3/4	1 5/16	1	3	2 1/4		
1	1 7/16	1 1/8	3 1/2	2 3/4		
1 1/4	1 3/4	1 5/16	4 1/4	3 1/4	2 1/8	
1 1/2	1 15/16	1 7/16	4 7/8	3 13/16	2 1/4	
2	2 1/4	1 11/16	5 3/4	4 1/4	2 7/16	
2 1/2	2 11/16	1 15/16	6 3/4	5 3/16	2 11/16	
3	3 1/8	2 3/16	7 7/8	6 1/8	2 15/16	
3 1/2	3 7/16	2 3/8	8 7/8	6 7/8	3 1/8	
4	3 3/4	2 5/8	9 3/4	7 5/8	3 3/8	2 1/16
5	7 7/16	3 1/16	11 5/8	9 1/4	3 7/8	2 3/8
6	5 1/8	3 7/16	13 7/16	10 3/4	4 3/8	2 5/8
8	6 1/2	4 1/4	16 15/16	13 5/8	5 1/4	3 1/8
10	8 1/16	5 3/16	20 11/16	16 3/4	6 3/16	3 5/8
12	9 1/2	6	24 1/8	19 5/8	7 1/8	4 1/4

Fractional dimensions are nominal. See **USASI** Bulletin for decimal dimensions.

TABLE 46 DIMENSIONS OF STANDARD GLOBE, ANGLE, AND CROSS VALVES

(All dimensions in inches.)

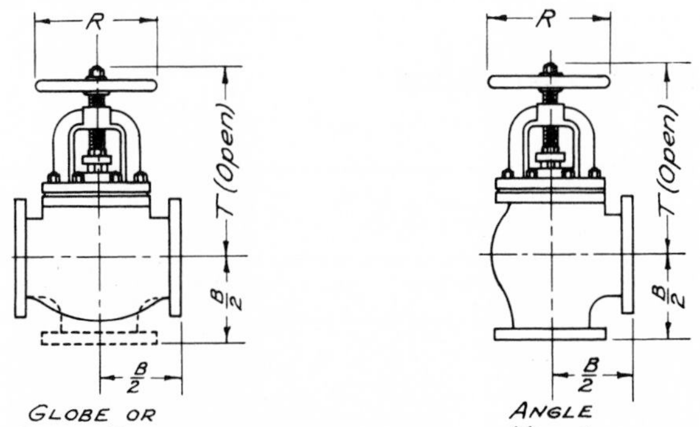

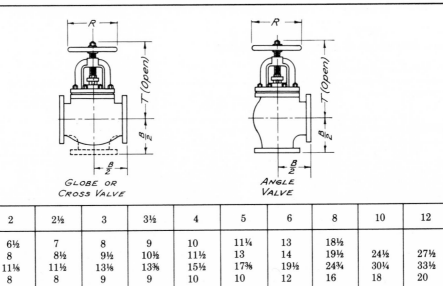

GLOBE OR CROSS VALVE

ANGLE VALVE

Size	2	2 1/2	3	3 1/2	4	5	6	8	10	12
A	6 1/2	7	8	9	10	11 1/4	13	18 1/2		
B	8	8 1/2	9 1/2	10 1/2	11 1/2	13	14	19 1/2	24 1/2	27 1/2
T	11 1/8	11 1/2	13 1/8	13 3/8	15 1/2	17 3/8	19 1/2	24 3/4	30 1/4	33 1/2
R	8	8	9	9	10	10	12	16	18	20

Substitute *A* for *B* for screw fittings.

TABLE 47   DIMENSIONS OF STANDARD LIFT AND SWING VALVES

(All dimensions in inches.)

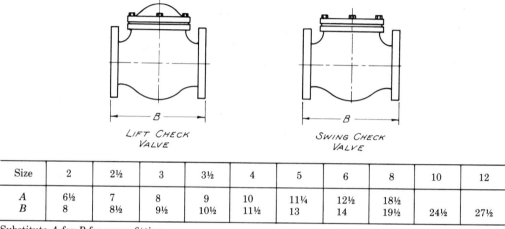

LIFT CHECK
VALVE

SWING CHECK
VALVE

Size	2	2½	3	3½	4	5	6	8	10	12
A	6½	7	8	9	10	11¼	12½	18½		
B	8	8½	9½	10½	11½	13	14	19½	24½	27½

Substitute *A* for *B* for screw fittings.

TABLE 48   DIMENSIONS OF STANDARD GATE VALVES

(All dimensions in inches.)

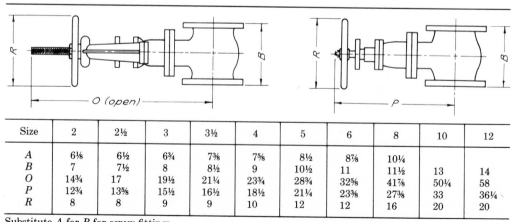

Size	2	2½	3	3½	4	5	6	8	10	12
A	6⅛	6½	6¾	7⅜	7⅝	8½	8⅞	10¼		
B	7	7½	8	8½	9	10½	11	11½	13	14
O	14¾	17	19½	21¼	23¾	28¾	32⅝	41⅞	50¼	58
P	12¾	13⅝	15½	16½	18½	21¼	23⅜	27⅞	33	36¼
R	8	8	9	9	10	12	12	16	20	20

Substitute *A* for *B* for screw fittings.

TABLE 49   USASI SYMBOLS FOR HEATING, VENTILATING, AND AIR CONDITIONING

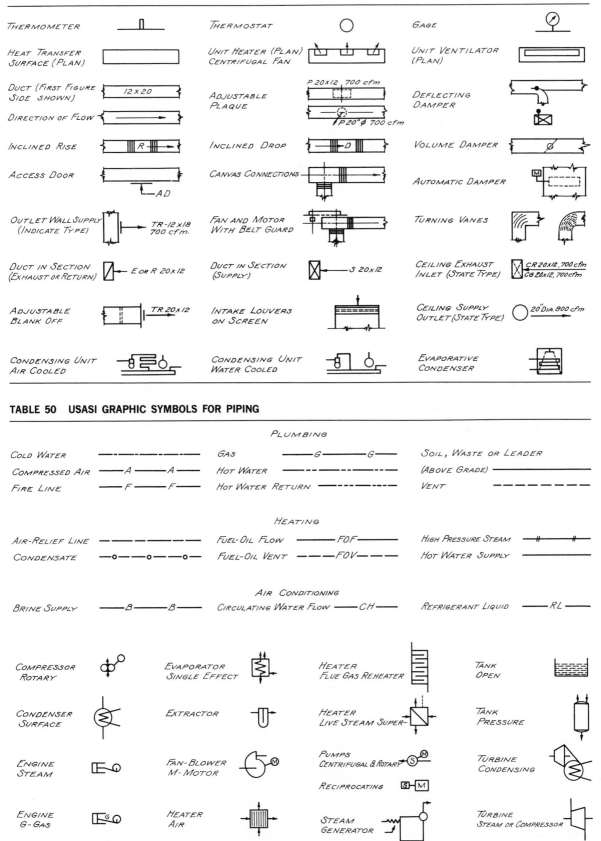

TABLE 50   USASI GRAPHIC SYMBOLS FOR PIPING

PLUMBING

COLD WATER

COMPRESSED AIR   A   A

FIRE LINE   F   F

GAS   G   G

HOT WATER

HOT WATER RETURN

SOIL, WASTE OR LEADER

(ABOVE GRADE)

VENT

HEATING

AIR-RELIEF LINE

CONDENSATE   o   o   o

FUEL-OIL FLOW   FOF

FUEL-OIL VENT   FOV

HIGH PRESSURE STEAM   #   #

HOT WATER SUPPLY

AIR CONDITIONING

BRINE SUPPLY   B   B

CIRCULATING WATER FLOW   CH

REFRIGERANT LIQUID   RL

COMPRESSOR
ROTARY

CONDENSER
SURFACE

ENGINE
STEAM

ENGINE
G-GAS

EVAPORATOR
SINGLE EFFECT

EXTRACTOR

FAN-BLOWER
M-MOTOR

HEATER
AIR

HEATER
FLUE GAS REHEATER

HEATER
LIVE STEAM SUPER-

PUMPS
CENTRIFUGAL & ROTARY   S   M

RECIPROCATING   S   M

STEAM
GENERATOR

TANK
OPEN

TANK
PRESSURE

TURBINE
CONDENSING

TURBINE
STEAM OR COMPRESSOR

TABLE 51 PLUMBING SYMBOLS

BATH (RECESSED)	BATH (ROLL RIM)	CLEANOUT	DISHWASHER	DRAIN	DRAIN (WITH VALVE)
DRINKING FOUNTAIN WALL TYPE	DRINKING FOUNTAIN PEDESTAL TYPE	DRINKING FOUNTAIN TROUGH TYPE	GAS OUTLET	GAS RANGE	GREASE SEPARATOR
HOSE BIBB	HOSE RACK	HOT WATER	LAUNDRY TRAY	LAVATORY (CORNER)	LAVATORY (DENTAL)
LAVATORY (MANICURE)	LAVATORY (PEDESTAL)	LAVATORY (WALL)	METER	OIL SEPARATOR	ROOF SUMP
PLAN ELEV. SHOWER (HEAD)	SHOWER (STALL)	SINK & DISHWASHER	SINK & LAUNDRY TRAY	SINK (KITCHEN)	SINK (KITCHEN) (WITH DRAINBOARDS)
SINK (SERVICE)	SINK (SERVICE) (FLOOR TYPE)	SINK (WASH) (FREE STANDING)	SINK (WASH) (WALL TYPE)	URINAL (STALL)	URINAL (TROUGH)
URINAL (WALL)	VACUUM OUTLET	WATER CLOSET (LOW TANK)	WATER CLOSET (NO TANK)	WASH FOUNTAIN (HALF CIRCULAR)	WATER HEATER

Courtesy Ramsey & Sleeper

TABLE 52 BALL BEARING DATA

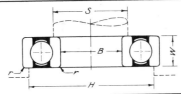

Brg. no.	Bore B	Dia. D	Width W	Balls Dia.	Balls No.	Rad. R	Shoulder dia. Shaft S	Shoulder dia. Housing H	Radial load at rpm 500	Radial load at rpm 1000	Radial load at rpm 2000
34	0.1575	0.6299	0.1969	1/8	6	0.016	0.222	0.550	99	83	66
35	0.1969	0.7480	.2362	9/64	6	.016	0.261	0.668	119	100	80
36	0.2362	0.7480	.2362	9/64	6	.016	0.300	0.668	119	100	80
37	0.2756	0.8661	.2756	5/32	7	.016	0.341	0.786	160	133	106
38	0.3150	0.8661	.2756	5/32	7	.016	0.379	0.786	160	133	106
39	0.3543	1.0236	.3150	3/16	7	.025	0.454	0.899	230	195	155
3L00	0.3937	1.0236	.3150	3/16	7	.016	0.500	0.920	230	195	155
3L01	0.4724	1.1024	.3150	3/16	8	.016	0.570	1.000	255	215	170
3L02	0.5906	1.2598	.3543	3/16	9	.016	0.690	1.15	275	230	185
3L03	0.6693	1.3780	.3937	3/16	10	.016	0.780	1.27	295	245	195
3L04	0.7874	1.6535	.4724	1/4	9	.025	0.940	1.50	505	425	340
3L05	0.9843	1.8504	.4724	1/4	10	.025	1.14	1.69	545	455	360
3L06	1.1811	2.1654	.5118	9/32	11	.040	1.37	1.94	750	630	500
3L07	1.3780	2.4409	.5512	5/16	11	.040	1.58	2.21	935	785	625
3L08	1.5748	2.6772	.5906	5/16	12	.040	1.78	2.44	990	835	665

Courtesy New Departure Division, General Motors Corp.

TABLE 53 DIMENSIONS OF SINGLE-ROW, STRAIGHT-BORE TYPE-S ROLLER BEARINGS

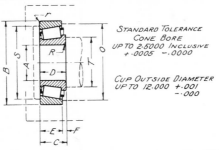

STANDARD TOLERANCE
CONE BORE
UP TO 2.5000 INCLUSIVE
+.0005 −.0000

CUP OUTSIDE DIAMETER
UP TO 12.000 +.001
−.000

Bore A	Outside dia. B	Width C	Rating at 500 rpm Radial lb	Rating at 500 rpm Thrust lb	Cone Radius R	Cone Length D	Cone Stand-out F	Cone Shoulder dia. T	Cup Radius R	Cup Length E	Cup Shoulder dia. S	Cup Shoulder dia. O
0.3750	1.2595	0.3940	255	205	3/64	0.4246	0.0815	1 1/16	3/64	0.3125	1	1 1/8
0.4720	1.2595	.3940	255	205	1/32	.4246	.0815	3/4	3/64	.3125	1	1 1/8
0.5000	1.3775	.4330	290	255	3/64	.4326	.0893	3/4	3/64	.3437	1 1/8	1 1/4
0.5900	1.3775	.4330	290	255	1/32	.4326	.0893	27/32	3/64	.3437	1 1/8	1 1/4
0.6250	1.5745	.4730	300	310	3/64	.4391	.0980	7/8	3/64	.3750	1 5/16	1 13/32
0.6690	1.5745	.4730	300	310	1/32	.4391	.0980	7/8	3/64	.3750	1 5/16	1 13/32
0.7500	1.5745	.4730	300	310	0.040	.4391	.0980	1	3/64	.3750	1 5/16	1 13/32
0.8125	1.9380	.7813	960	610	1/16	.7813	.1563	1 3/16	1/16	.6250	1 19/32	1 25/32
0.8750	1.9687	.5313	610	480	3/64	.5614	.1563	1 7/32	0.040	.3750	1 11/16	1 7/8
0.9375	2.2400	.7625	1010	610	1/32	.7810	.1375	1 1/4	3/64	.6250	1 15/16	1 31/32
1.000	2.2500	.6875	885	600	3/64	.6875	.1563	1 11/32	1/16	.5313	1 7/8	2 1/16
1.125	2.3750	.7813	1010	650	1/32	.7620	.1563	1 7/16	3/64	.6250	2	2 3/32
1.250	2.7500	.9375	1715	920	1/32	.9983	.1875	1 9/16	3/64	.7500	2 13/32	2 15/32

Courtesy Timken Roller Bearing Co.

TABLE 54 NATURAL TRIGONOMETRIC FUNCTIONS

Degrees	SINES							Cosines
	0′	10′	20′	30′	40′	50′	60′	
0	0.00000	0.00291	0.00582	0.00873	0.01164	0.01454	0.01745	89
1	.01745	.02036	.02327	.02618	.02908	.03199	.03490	88
2	.03490	.03781	.04071	.04362	.04653	.04943	.05234	87
3	.05234	.05524	.05814	.06105	.06395	.06685	.06976	86
4	.06976	.07266	.07556	.07846	.08136	.08426	.08716	85
5	.08716	.09005	.09295	.09585	.09874	.10164	.10453	84
6	.10453	.10742	.11031	.11320	.11609	.11898	.12187	83
7	.12187	.12476	.12764	.13053	.13341	.13629	.13917	82
8	.13917	.14205	.14493	.14781	.15069	.15356	.15643	81
9	.15643	.15931	.16218	.16505	.16792	.17078	.17365	80
10	.17365	.17651	.17937	.18224	.18509	.18795	.19081	79
11	.19081	.19366	.19652	.19937	.20222	.20507	.20791	78
12	.20791	.21076	.21360	.21644	.21928	.22212	.22495	77
13	.22495	.22778	.23062	.23345	.23627	.23910	.24192	76
14	.24192	.24474	.24756	.25038	.25320	.25601	.25882	75
15	.25882	.26163	.26443	.26724	.27004	.27284	.27564	74
16	.27564	.27843	.28123	.28402	.28680	.28959	.29237	73
17	.29237	.29515	.29793	.30071	.30348	.30625	.30902	72
18	.30902	.31178	.31454	.31730	.32006	.32282	.32557	71
19	.32557	.32832	.33106	.33381	.33655	.33929	.34202	70
20	.34202	.34475	.34748	.35021	.35293	.35565	.35837	69
21	.35837	.36108	.36379	.36650	.36921	.37191	.37461	68
22	.37461	.37730	.37999	.38268	.38537	.38805	.39073	67
23	.39073	.39341	.39608	.39875	.40142	.40408	.40674	66
24	.40674	.40939	.41204	.41469	.41734	.41998	.42262	65
25	.42262	.42525	.42788	.43051	.43313	.43575	.43837	64
26	.43837	.44098	.44359	.44620	.44880	.45140	.45399	63
27	.45399	.45658	.45917	.46175	.46433	.46690	.46947	62
28	.46947	.47204	.47460	.47716	.47971	.48226	.48481	61
29	.48481	.48735	.48989	.49242	.49495	.49748	.50000	60
30	.50000	.50252	.50503	.50754	.51004	.51254	.51504	59
31	.51504	.51753	.52002	.52250	.52498	.52745	.52992	58
32	.52292	.53238	.53484	.53730	.53975	.54220	.54464	57
33	.54464	.54708	.54951	.55194	.55436	.55678	.55919	56
34	.55919	.56160	.56401	.56641	.56880	.57119	.57358	55
35	.57358	.57596	.57833	.58070	.58307	.58543	.58779	54
36	.58779	.59014	.59248	.59482	.59716	.59949	.60182	53
37	.60183	.60414	.60645	.60876	.61107	.61337	.61566	52
38	.61566	.61795	.62024	.62251	.62479	.62706	.62932	51
39	.62932	.63158	.63383	.63608	.63832	.64056	.64279	50
40	.64279	.64501	.64723	.64945	.65166	.65386	.65606	49
41	.65606	.65825	.66044	.66262	.66480	.66697	.66913	48
42	.66913	.67129	.67344	.67559	.67773	.67987	.68200	47
43	.68200	.68412	.68624	.68835	.69046	.69256	.69466	46
44	.69466	.69675	.69883	.70091	.70298	.70505	.70711	45
Sines	60′	50′	40′	30′	20′	10′	0′	Degrees
	COSINES							

TABLE 54 *(Continued)*   **NATURAL TRIGONOMETRIC FUNCTIONS**

Degrees	COSINES							Sines
	0′	10′	20′	30′	40′	50′	60′	
0	1.00000	1.00000	0.99998	0.99996	0.99993	0.99989	0.99985	89
1	0.99985	0.99979	.99973	.99966	.99958	.99949	.99939	88
2	0.99939	0.99929	.99917	.99905	.99892	.99878	.99863	87
3	0.99863	0.99847	.99831	.99813	.99795	.99776	.99756	86
4	0.99756	0.99736	.99714	.99692	.99668	.99644	.99619	85
5	0.99619	0.99594	.99567	.99540	.99511	.99482	.99452	84
6	0.99452	0.99421	.99390	.99357	.99324	.99290	.99255	83
7	0.99255	0.99219	.99182	.99144	.99106	.99067	.99027	82
8	0.99027	0.98986	.98944	.98902	.98858	.98814	.98769	81
9	0.98769	0.98723	.98676	.98629	.98580	.98531	.98481	80
10	0.98481	0.98430	.98378	.98325	.98272	.98218	.98163	79
11	0.98163	0.98107	.98050	.97992	.97934	.97875	.97815	78
12	0.97815	0.97754	.97692	.97630	.97566	.97502	.97437	77
13	0.97437	0.97371	.97304	.97237	.97169	.97100	.97030	76
14	0.97030	0.96959	.96887	.96815	.96742	.96667	.96593	75
15	0.96593	0.96517	.96440	.96363	.96285	.96206	.96126	74
16	0.96126	0.96046	.95964	.95882	.95799	.95715	.95630	73
17	0.95630	0.95545	.95459	.95372	.95284	.95195	.95106	72
18	0.95106	0.95015	.94924	.94832	.94740	.94646	.94552	71
19	0.94552	0.94457	.94361	.94264	.94167	.94068	.93969	70
20	0.93969	0.93869	.93769	.93667	.93565	.93462	.93358	69
21	0.93358	0.93253	.93148	.93042	.92935	.92827	.92718	68
22	0.92718	0.92609	.92499	.92388	.92276	.92164	.92050	67
23	0.92050	0.91936	.91822	.91706	.91590	.91472	.91355	66
24	0.91355	0.91236	.91116	.90996	.90875	.90753	.90631	65
25	0.90631	0.90507	.90383	.90259	.90133	.90007	.89879	64
26	0.89879	0.89752	.89623	.89493	.89363	.89232	.89101	63
27	0.89101	0.88968	.88835	.88701	.88566	.88431	.88295	62
28	0.88295	0.88158	.88020	.87882	.87743	.87603	.87462	61
29	0.87462	0.87321	.87178	.87036	.86892	.86748	.86603	60
30	0.86603	0.86457	.86310	.86163	.86015	.85866	.85717	59
31	0.85717	0.85567	.85416	.85264	.85112	.84959	.84805	58
32	0.84805	0.84650	.84495	.84439	.84182	.84025	.83867	57
33	0.83867	0.83708	.83549	.83389	.83228	.83066	.82904	56
34	0.82904	0.82741	.82577	.82413	.82248	.82082	.81915	55
35	0.81915	0.81748	.81580	.81412	.81242	.81072	.80902	54
36	0.80902	0.80730	.80558	.80386	.80212	.80038	.79864	53
37	0.79864	0.79688	.79512	.79335	.79158	.78980	.78801	52
38	0.78801	0.78622	.78442	.78261	.78079	.77897	.77715	51
39	0.77715	0.77531	.77347	.77162	.76977	.76791	.76604	50
40	0.76604	0.76417	.76229	.76041	.75851	.75661	.75471	49
41	0.75471	0.75280	.75088	.74896	.74703	.74509	.74314	48
42	0.74314	0.74120	.73924	.73728	.73531	.73333	.73135	47
43	0.73135	0.72937	.72737	.72537	.72337	.72136	.71934	46
44	0.71934	0.71732	.71529	.71325	.71121	.70916	.70711	45

Cosines	60′	50′	40′	30′	20′	10′	0′	Degrees
				SINES				

TABLE 55   NATURAL TRIGONOMETRIC FUNCTIONS

Degrees	TANGENTS							Cotangents
	0′	10′	20′	30′	40′	50′	60′	
0	0.00000	0.00291	0.00582	0.00873	0.01164	0.01455	0.01746	89
1	.01746	.02036	.02328	.02619	.02910	.03201	0.03492	88
2	.03492	.03783	.04075	.04366	.04658	.04949	0.05241	87
3	.05241	.05533	.05824	.06116	.06408	.06700	0.06993	86
4	.06993	.07285	.07578	.07870	.08163	.08456	0.08749	85
5	.08749	.09042	.09335	.09629	.09923	.10216	0.10510	84
6	.10510	.10805	.11099	.11394	.11688	.11983	0.12278	83
7	.12278	.12574	.12869	.13165	.13461	.13758	0.14054	82
8	.14054	.14351	.14648	.14945	.15243	.15540	0.15838	81
9	.15838	.16137	.16435	.16734	.17033	.17333	0.17633	80
10	.17633	.17933	.18233	.18534	.18835	.19136	0.19438	79
11	.19438	.19740	.20042	.20345	.20648	.20952	0.21256	78
12	.21256	.21560	.21864	.22169	.22475	.22781	0.23087	77
13	.23087	.23393	.23700	.24008	.24316	.24624	0.24933	76
14	.24933	.25242	.25552	.25862	.26172	.26483	0.26795	75
15	.26795	.27107	.27419	.27732	.28046	.28360	0.28675	74
16	.28675	.28990	.29305	.29621	.29938	.30255	0.30573	73
17	.30573	.30891	.31210	.31530	.31850	.32171	0.32492	72
18	.32492	.32814	.33136	.33460	.33783	.34108	0.34433	71
19	.34433	.34758	.35085	.35412	.35740	.36068	0.36397	70
20	.36397	.36727	.37057	.37388	.37720	.38053	0.38386	69
21	.38386	.38721	.39055	.39391	.39727	.40065	0.40403	68
22	.40403	.40741	.41081	.41421	.41763	.42105	0.42447	67
23	.42447	.42791	.43136	.43481	.43828	.44175	0.44523	66
24	.44523	.44872	.45222	.45573	.45924	.46277	0.46631	65
25	.46631	.46985	.47341	.47698	.48055	.48414	0.48773	64
26	.48773	.49134	.49495	.49858	.50222	.50587	0.50953	63
27	.50953	.51320	.51688	.52057	.52427	.52798	0.53171	62
28	.53171	.53545	.53920	.54296	.54674	.55051	0.55431	61
29	.55431	.55812	.56194	.56577	.56962	.57348	0.57735	60
30	.57735	.58124	.58513	.58905	.59297	.59691	0.60086	59
31	.60086	.60483	.60881	.61280	.61681	.62083	0.62487	58
32	.62487	.62892	.63299	.63707	.64117	.64528	0.64941	57
33	.64941	.65355	.65771	.66189	.66608	.67028	0.67451	56
34	.67451	.67875	.68301	.68728	.69157	.69588	0.70021	55
35	.70021	.70455	.70891	.71329	.71769	.72211	0.72654	54
36	.72654	.73100	.73547	.73996	.74447	.74900	0.75355	53
37	.75355	.75812	.76272	.76733	.77196	.77661	0.78129	52
38	.78129	.78598	.79070	.79544	.80020	.80498	0.80978	51
39	.80978	.81461	.81946	.82434	.82923	.83415	0.83910	50
40	.83910	.84407	.84906	.85408	.85912	.86419	0.86929	49
41	.86929	.87441	.87955	.88473	.88992	.89515	0.90040	48
42	.90040	.90569	.91099	.91633	.92170	.92709	0.93252	47
43	.93252	.93797	.94345	.94896	.95451	.96008	0.96569	46
44	.96569	.97133	.97700	.98270	.98843	.99420	1.00000	45
Tangents	60′	50′	40′	30′	20′	10′	0′	Degrees

COTANGENTS

TABLE 55 *(Continued)* **NATURAL TRIGONOMETRIC FUNCTIONS**

Degrees	COTANGENTS							Tan-gents
	0′	10′	20′	30′	40′	50′	60′	
0	∞	343.77371	171.88540	114.58865	85.93979	68.75009	57.28996	89
1	57.28996	49.10388	42.96408	38.18846	34.36777	31.24158	28.63625	88
2	28.63625	26.43160	24.54176	22.90377	21.47040	20.20555	19.08114	87
3	19.08114	18.07498	17.16934	16.34986	15.60478	14.92442	14.30067	86
4	14.30067	13.72674	13.19688	12.70621	12.25051	11.82617	11.43005	85
5	11.43005	11.05943	10.71191	10.38540	10.07803	9.78817	9.51436	84
6	9.51436	9.25530	9.00983	8.77689	8.55555	8.34496	8.14435	83
7	8.14435	7.95302	7.77035	7.59575	7.42871	7.26873	7.11537	82
8	7.11537	6.96823	6.82694	6.69116	6.56055	6.43484	6.31375	81
9	6.31375	6.19703	6.08444	5.97576	5.87080	5.76937	5.67128	80
10	5.67128	5.57638	5.48451	5.39552	5.30928	5.22566	5.14455	79
11	5.14455	5.06584	4.98940	4.91516	4.84300	4.77286	4.70463	78
12	4.70463	4.63825	4.57363	4.51071	4.44942	4.38969	4.33148	77
13	4.33148	4.27471	4.21933	4.16530	4.11256	4.06107	4.01078	76
14	4.01078	3.96165	3.91364	3.86671	3.82083	3.77595	3.73205	75
15	3.73205	3.68909	3.64705	3.60588	3.56557	3.52609	3.48741	74
16	3.48741	3.44951	3.41236	3.37594	3.34023	3.30521	3.27085	73
17	3.27085	3.23714	3.20406	3.17159	3.13972	3.10842	3.07768	72
18	3.07768	3.04749	3.01783	2.98869	2.96004	2.93189	2.90421	71
19	2.90421	2.87700	2.85023	2.82391	2.79802	2.77254	2.74748	70
20	2.74748	2.72281	2.69853	2.67462	2.65109	2.62791	2.60509	69
21	2.60509	2.58261	2.56046	2.53865	2.51715	2.49597	2.47509	68
22	2.47509	2.45451	2.43422	2.41421	2.39449	2.37504	2.35585	67
23	2.35585	2.33693	2.31826	2.29984	2.28167	2.26374	2.24604	66
24	2.24604	2.22857	2.21132	2.19430	2.17749	2.16090	2.14451	65
25	2.14451	2.12832	2.11233	2.09654	2.08094	2.06553	2.05030	64
26	2.05030	2.03526	2.02039	2.00569	1.99116	1.97680	1.96261	63
27	1.96261	1.94858	1.93470	1.92098	1.90741	1.89400	1.88073	62
28	1.88073	1.86760	1.85462	1.84177	1.82907	1.81649	1.80405	61
29	1.80405	1.79174	1.77955	1.76749	1.75556	1.74375	1.73205	60
30	1.73205	1.72047	1.70901	1.69766	1.68643	1.67530	1.66428	59
31	1.66428	1.65337	1.64256	1.63185	1.62125	1.61074	1.60033	58
32	1.60033	1.59002	1.57981	1.56969	1.55966	1.54972	1.53987	57
33	1.53987	1.53010	1.52043	1.51084	1.50133	1.49190	1.48256	56
34	1.48256	1.47330	1.46411	1.45501	1.44598	1.43703	1.42815	55
35	1.42815	1.41934	1.41061	1.40195	1.39336	1.38484	1.37638	54
36	1.37638	1.36800	1.35968	1.35143	1.34323	1.33511	1.32704	53
37	1.32704	1.31904	1.31110	1.30323	1.29541	1.28764	1.27994	52
38	1.27994	1.27230	1.26471	1.25717	1.24969	1.24227	1.23490	51
39	1.23490	1.22758	1.22031	1.21310	1.20593	1.19882	1.19175	50
40	1.19175	1.18474	1.17777	1.17085	1.16398	1.15715	1.15037	49
41	1.15037	1.14363	1.13694	1.13029	1.12369	1.11713	1.11061	48
42	1.11061	1.10414	1.09770	1.09131	1.08496	1.07864	1.07237	47
43	1.07237	1.06613	1.05994	1.05378	1.04766	1.04158	1.03553	46
44	1.03553	1.02952	1.02355	1.01761	1.01170	1.00583	1.00000	45
Cotan-gents	60′	50′	40′	30′	20′	10′	0′	Degrees
	TANGENTS							

TABLE 56   COMMON LOGARITHMS

Number	0	1	2	3	4	5	6	7	8	9	Avg. diff.
1.0	0.0000	0043	0086	0128	0170	0212	0253	0294	0334	0374	
1.1	0414	0453	0492	0531	0569	0607	0645	0682	0719	0755	
1.2	0792	0828	0864	0899	0934	0969	1004	1038	1072	1106	
1.3	1139	1173	1206	1239	1271	1303	1335	1367	1399	1430	
1.4	1461	1492	1523	1553	1584	1614	1644	1673	1703	1732	
1.5	1761	1790	1818	1847	1875	1903	1931	1959	1987	2014	
1.6	2041	2068	2095	2122	2148	2175	2201	2227	2253	2279	
1.7	2304	2330	2355	2380	2405	2430	2455	2480	2504	2529	
1.8	2553	2577	2601	2625	2648	2672	2695	2718	2742	2765	
1.9	2788	2810	2833	2856	2878	2900	2923	2945	2967	2989	
2.0	0.3010	3032	3054	3075	3096	3118	3139	3160	3181	3201	21
2.1	3222	3243	3263	3284	3304	3324	3345	3365	3385	3404	20
2.2	3424	3444	3464	3483	3502	3522	3541	3560	3579	3598	19
2.3	3617	3636	3655	3674	3692	3711	3729	3747	3766	3784	18
2.4	3802	3820	3838	3856	3874	3892	3909	3927	3945	3962	17
2.5	3979	3997	4014	4031	4048	4065	4082	4099	4116	4133	17
2.6	4150	4166	4183	4200	4216	4232	4249	4265	4281	4298	16
2.7	4314	4330	4346	4362	4378	4393	4409	4425	4440	4456	16
2.8	4472	4487	4502	4518	4533	4548	4564	4579	4594	4609	15
2.9	4624	4639	4654	4669	4683	4698	4713	4728	4742	4757	15
3.0	0.4771	4786	4800	4814	4829	4843	4857	4871	4886	4900	14
3.1	4914	4928	4942	4955	4969	4983	4997	5011	5024	5038	14
3.2	5051	5065	5079	5092	5105	5119	5132	5145	5159	5172	13
3.3	5185	5198	5211	5224	5237	5250	5263	5276	5289	5302	13
3.4	5315	5328	5340	5353	5366	5378	5391	5403	5416	5428	13
3.5	5441	5453	5465	5478	5490	5502	5514	5527	5539	5551	12
3.6	5563	5575	5587	5599	5611	5623	5635	5647	5658	5670	12
3.7	5682	5694	5705	5717	5729	5740	5752	5763	5775	5786	12
3.8	5798	5809	5821	5832	5843	5855	5866	5877	5888	5899	11
3.9	5911	5922	5933	5944	5955	5966	5977	5988	5999	6010	11
4.0	0.6021	6031	6042	6053	6064	6075	6085	6096	6107	6117	11
4.1	6128	6138	6149	6160	6170	6180	6191	6201	6212	6222	10
4.2	6232	6243	6253	6263	6274	6284	6294	6304	6314	6325	10
4.3	6335	6345	6355	6365	6375	6385	6395	6405	6415	6425	10
4.4	6435	6444	6454	6464	6474	6484	6493	6503	6513	6522	10
4.5	6532	6542	6551	6561	6571	6580	6590	6599	6609	6618	10
4.6	6628	6637	6646	6656	6665	6675	6684	6693	6702	6712	10
4.7	6721	6730	6739	6749	6758	6767	6776	6785	6794	6803	9
4.8	6812	6821	6830	6839	6848	6857	6866	6875	6884	6893	9
4.9	6902	6911	6920	6928	6937	6946	6955	6964	6972	6981	9
5.0	0.6990	6998	7007	7016	7024	7033	7042	7050	7059	7067	9
5.1	7076	7084	7093	7101	7110	7118	7126	7135	7143	7152	8
5.2	7160	7168	7177	7185	7193	7202	7210	7218	7226	7235	8
5.3	7243	7251	7259	7267	7275	7284	7292	7300	7308	7316	8
5.4	7324	7332	7340	7348	7356	7364	7372	7380	7388	7396	8
5.5	7404	7412	7419	7427	7435	7443	7451	7459	7466	7474	8
5.6	7482	7490	7497	7505	7513	7520	7528	7536	7543	7551	8
5.7	7559	7566	7574	7582	7589	7597	7604	7612	7619	7627	8
5.8	7634	7642	7649	7657	7664	7672	7679	7686	7694	7701	7
5.9	7709	7716	7723	7731	7738	7745	7752	7760	7767	7774	7

TABLE 56 *(Continued)* COMMON LOGARITHMS

Number	0	1	2	3	4	5	6	7	8	9	Avg. diff.
6.0	0.7782	7789	7796	7803	7810	7818	7825	7832	7839	7846	7
6.1	7853	7860	7868	7875	7882	7889	7896	7903	7910	7917	7
6.2	7924	7931	7938	7945	7952	7959	7966	7973	7980	7987	7
6.3	7993	8000	8007	8014	8021	8028	8035	8041	8048	8055	7
6.4	8062	8069	8075	8082	8089	8096	8102	8109	8116	8122	7
6.5	8129	8136	8142	8149	8156	8162	8169	8176	8182	8189	7
6.6	8195	8202	8209	8215	8222	8228	8235	8241	8248	8254	7
6.7	8261	8267	8274	8280	8287	8293	8299	8306	8312	8319	6
6.8	8325	8331	8338	8344	8351	8357	8363	8370	8376	8382	6
6.9	8388	8395	8401	8407	8414	8420	8426	8432	8439	8445	6
7.0	0.8451	8457	8463	8470	8476	8482	8488	8494	8500	8506	6
7.1	8513	8519	8525	8531	8537	8543	8549	8555	8561	8567	6
7.2	8573	8579	8585	8591	8597	8603	8609	8615	8621	8627	6
7.3	8633	8639	8645	8651	8657	8663	8669	8675	8681	8686	6
7.4	8692	8698	8704	8710	8716	8722	8727	8733	8739	8745	6
7.5	8751	8756	8762	8768	8774	8779	8785	8791	8797	8802	6
7.6	8808	8814	8820	8825	8831	8837	8842	8848	8854	8859	6
7.7	8865	8871	8876	8882	8887	8893	8899	8904	8910	8915	6
7.8	8921	8927	8932	8938	8943	8949	8954	8960	8965	8971	6
7.9	8976	8982	8987	8993	8998	9004	9009	9015	9020	9025	5
8.0	0.9031	9036	9042	9047	9053	9058	9063	9069	9074	9079	5
8.1	9085	9090	9096	9101	9106	9112	9117	9122	9128	9133	5
8.2	9138	9143	9149	9154	9159	9165	9170	9175	9180	9186	5
8.3	9191	9196	9201	9206	9212	9217	9222	9227	9232	9238	5
8.4	9243	9248	9253	9258	9263	9269	9274	9279	9284	9289	5
8.5	9294	9299	9304	9309	9315	9320	9325	9330	9335	9340	5
8.6	9345	9350	9355	9360	9365	9370	9375	9380	9385	9390	5
8.7	9395	9400	9405	9410	9415	9420	9425	9430	9435	9440	5
8.8	9445	9450	9455	9460	9465	9469	9474	9479	9484	9489	5
8.9	9494	9499	9504	9509	9513	9518	9523	9528	9533	9538	5
9.0	0.9542	9547	9552	9557	9562	9566	9571	9576	9581	9586	5
9.1	9590	9595	9600	9605	9609	9614	9619	9624	9628	9633	5
9.2	9638	9643	9647	9652	9657	9661	9666	9671	9675	9680	5
9.3	9685	9689	9694	9699	9703	9708	9713	9717	9722	9727	5
9.4	9731	9736	9741	9745	9750	9754	9759	9763	9768	9773	5
9.5	9777	9782	9786	9791	9795	9800	9805	9809	9814	9818	5
9.6	9823	9827	9832	9836	9841	9845	9850	9854	9859	9863	4
9.7	9868	9872	9877	9881	9886	9890	9894	9899	9903	9908	4
9.8	9912	9917	9921	9926	9930	9934	9939	9943	9948	9952	4
9.9	9956	9961	9965	9969	9974	9978	9983	9987	9991	9996	4

$\log \pi = 0.4971$ $\log \pi/2 = 0.1961$ $\log \pi^2 = 0.9943$ $\log \sqrt{\pi} = 0.2486$ $\log e = 0.4343$ $\log (0.4343) = 0.6378 - 1$

These two pages give the common logarithms of numbers between 1 and 10, correct to four places. Moving the decimal point n places to the right (or left) in the number is equivalent to adding n (or $-n$) to the logarithm. Thus, $\log 0.017453 = 0.2419 - 2$, which may also be written $\bar{2}.2419$ or $8.2419 - 10$.

$$\log (ab) = \log a + \log b \qquad \log (a^N) = N \log a$$

$$\log \left(\frac{a}{b}\right) = \log a - \log b \qquad \log (\sqrt[N]{a}) = \frac{1}{N} \log a$$

Courtesy Mark's Handbook

TABLE 57 RADII OF RAILROAD AND HIGHWAY CURVES

Degree of curvature	Radius, feet	Degree of curvature	Radius, feet	Degree of curvature	Radius, feet
0° 0′	∞	5° 0′	1146.28	10° 0′	573.69
10	34377.5	10	1109.33	10	564.31
20	17188.8	20	1074.68	20	555.23
30	11459.2	30	1042.14	30	546.44
40	8594.42	40	1011.51	40	537.92
50	6875.55	50	982.64	50	529.67
1° 0′	5729.65	6° 0′	955.37	11° 0′	521.67
10	4911.15	10	929.57	10	513.91
20	4297.28	20	905.13	20	506.38
30	3819.83	30	881.95	30	499.06
40	3437.87	40	859.92	40	491.96
50	3125.36	50	838.97	50	485.05
2° 0′	2864.93	7° 0′	819.02	12° 0′	478.34
10	2644.58	10	800.00	30	459.28
20	2455.70	20	781.84		
30	2292.01	30	764.49	13° 0′	441.68
40	2148.79	40	747.89	30	425.40
50	2022.41	50	732.01		
				14° 0′	410.28
3° 0′	1910.08	8° 0′	716.78	30	396.20
10	1809.57	10	702.18		
20	1719.12	20	688.16	15° 0′	383.06
30	1637.28	30	674.69	30	370.78
40	1562.88	40	661.74		
50	1494.95	50	649.27	16° 0′	359.26
				30	348.45
4° 0′	1432.69	9° 0′	637.27		
10	1375.40	10	625.71	17° 0′	338.27
20	1322.53	20	614.56	30	328.68
30	1273.57	30	603.80		
40	1228.11	40	593.42	18° 0′	319.62
50	1185.78	50	583.38	30	311.06

Note. The degree of curvature is the angle subtended at the center of the arc by a chord of 100 feet. The length of a curve is the length measured in 100-feet chords plus fractional 100-feet chords at the ends from P.C. to P.T.

TABLE 58 METRIC CONVERSION TABLES

Inches to centimeters—1 in. = 2.540005 cm

Units tens	0	1	2	3	4	5	6	7	8	9
0		2.540	5.080	7.620	10.160	12.700	15.240	17.780	20.320	22.860
1	25.400	27.940	30.480	33.020	35.560	38.100	40.640	43.180	45.720	48.260
2	50.800	53.340	55.880	58.420	60.960	63.500	66.040	68.580	71.120	73.660
3	76.200	78.740	81.280	83.820	86.360	88.920	91.440	93.980	96.520	99.060
4	101.600	104.140	106.680	109.220	111.760	114.300	116.840	119.380	121.920	124.460
5	127.00	129.540	132.080	134.620	137.160	139.700	142.240	144.780	147.320	149.860
6	152.400	154.940	157.480	160.020	162.560	165.100	167.640	170.180	172.720	175.260
7	177.800	180.340	182.880	185.420	187.960	190.500	193.040	195.580	198.120	200.660
8	203.200	205.740	208.280	210.820	213.360	215.900	218.440	220.980	223.520	226.060
9	228.600	231.140	233.680	236.220	238.760	241.300	243.840	246.380	248.920	251.460

Centimeters to inches—1 cm = 0.3937 in.

Units tens	0	1	2	3	4	5	6	7	8	9
0		0.3937	0.7874	1.1811	1.5748	1.9685	2.3622	2.7559	3.1496	3.5433
1	3.9370	4.3307	4.7244	5.1181	5.5118	5.9055	6.2992	6.6929	7.0866	7.4803
2	7.8740	8.2677	8.6614	9.0551	9.4488	9.8425	10.2362	10.6299	11.0236	11.4173
3	11.8110	12.2047	12.5984	12.9921	13.3858	13.7795	14.1732	14.5669	14.9606	15.3543
4	15.7480	16.1417	16.5354	16.9291	17.3228	17.7165	18.1102	18.5039	18.8976	19.2913
5	19.6850	20.0787	20.4724	20.8661	21.2598	21.6535	22.0472	22.4409	22.8346	23.2283
6	23.6220	24.0157	24.4094	24.8031	25.1968	25.5905	25.9842	26.3779	26.7716	27.1653
7	27.5590	27.9527	28.3464	28.7401	29.1338	29.5275	29.9212	30.3149	30.7086	31.1023
8	31.4960	31.8897	32.2834	32.6671	33.0708	33.4645	33.8582	34.2519	34.6456	35.0393
9	35.4330	35.8267	36.2204	36.6141	37.0078	37.4015	37.7952	38.1889	38.5826	38.9763

TABLE 59 WIRE GAGES

There has come about, through lack of standardization, a great deal of confusion concerning wire gages to be specified on the engineer's drawings. Until wire manufacturers have agreed to some national standard it would be well to specify on the drawing the exact diameter of the wire wanted. In the case of steel wires, the Bureau of Standards at Washington has recommended that the American Steel and Wire Co.'s gage be adopted as the Steel Wire Gage. This gage is given in the table below in decimals of an inch, and is the same as the Washburn & Moen gage. When there is danger of confusion with the British gage, it should be called the United States Steel Wire Gage.

In the case of copper wire, the American Wire Gage is standard throughout the United States and is the same as the Brown & Sharpe gage. It is also given in the table below in decimals of an inch.

Sheet and Plate Metal Gage

Congress legalized the United States Standard Gage for sheet and plate iron and steel, March 3, 1893. The various gage sizes are given in decimals of an inch in the table below.

WIRE AND SHEET METAL GAGES

No. of gage	Steel wire gage	American copper or B. & S. wire gage	British imperial wire gage	U. S. St'd. gage for plate	No. of gage	Steel wire gage	American wire gage	British imperial wire gage	U. S. St'd. gage for plate
0000000	0.4900	.....	0.5000	0.5000	23	0.0258	0.0226	0.0240	0.0281
000000	0.4615	0.5800	0.4640	0.4688	24	0.0230	0.0201	0.0220	0.0250
00000	0.4305	0.5165	0.4320	0.4375	25	0.0204	0.0179	0.0200	0.0219
0000	0.3938	0.4600	0.4000	0.4063	26	0.0181	0.0159	0.0180	0.0188
000	0.3625	0.4096	0.3720	0.3750	27	0.0173	0.0142	0.0164	0.0172
00	0.3310	0.3648	0.3480	0.3438	28	0.0162	0.0126	0.0148	0.0156
0	0.3065	0.3249	0.3240	0.3125	29	0.0150	0.0113	0.0136	0.0141
1	0.2830	0.2893	0.3000	0.2813	30	0.0140	0.0100	0.0124	0.0125
2	0.2625	0.2576	0.2760	0.2656	31	0.0132	0.0089	0.0116	0.0109
3	0.2437	0.2294	0.2520	0.2500	32	0.0128	0.0080	0.0108	0.0102
4	0.2253	0.2043	0.2320	0.2344	33	0.0118	0.0071	0.0100	0.0094
5	0.2070	0.1819	0.2120	0.2188	34	0.0104	0.0063	0.0092	0.0086
6	0.1920	0.1620	0.1920	0.2031	35	0.0095	0.0056	0.0084	0.0078
7	0.1770	0.1443	0.1760	0.1875	36	0.0090	0.0050	0.0076	0.0070
8	0.1620	0.1285	0.1600	0.1719	37	0.0085	0.0045	0.0068	0.0066
9	0.1483	0.1144	0.1440	0.1563	38	0.0080	0.0040	0.0060	0.0063
10	0.1350	0.1019	0.1280	0.1406	39	0.0075	0.0035	0.0052	.....
11	0.1205	0.0907	0.1160	0.1250	40	0.0070	0.0031	0.0048	.....
12	0.1055	0.0808	0.1040	0.1094	41	0.0066	0.0028	0.0044	.....
13	0.0915	0.0720	0.0920	0.0938	42	0.0062	0.0025	0.0040	.....
14	0.0800	0.0641	0.0800	0.0781	43	0.0060	0.0022	0.0036	.....
15	0.0720	0.0571	0.0720	0.0703	44	0.0058	0.0020	0.0032	.....
16	0.0625	0.0508	0.0640	0.0625	45	0.0055	0.00176	0.0028	.....
17	0.0540	0.0453	0.0560	0.0563	46	0.0052	0.00157	0.0024	.....
18	0.0475	0.0403	0.0480	0.0500	47	0.0050	0.00140	0.0020	.....
19	0.0410	0.0359	0.0400	0.0438	48	0.0048	0.00124	0.0016	.....
20	0.0348	0.0320	0.0360	0.0375	49	0.0046	0.00099	0.0012	.....
21	0.0317	0.0285	0.0320	0.0344	50	0.0044	0.00088	0.0010	.....
22	0.0286	0.0253	0.0280	0.0313					

TABLE 60   DECIMAL EQUIVALENTS OF FRACTIONS OF AN INCH

1/32	1/64	Decimal	Fraction	1/32	1/64	Decimal	Fraction
	1	0.015625			33	0.515625	
1	2	.03125		17	34	0.53125	
	3	.046875			35	0.546875	
2	4	.0625	1/16	18	36	0.5625	9/16
	5	.078125			37	0.578125	
3	6	.09375		19	38	0.59375	
	7	.109375			39	0.609375	
4	8	.125	1/8	20	40	0.625	5/8
	9	.140625			41	0.640625	
5	10	.15625		21	42	0.65625	
	11	.171875			43	0.671875	
6	12	.1875	3/16	22	44	0.6875	11/16
	13	.203125			45	0.703125	
7	14	.21875		23	46	0.71875	
	15	.234375			47	0.734375	
8	16	.25	1/4	24	48	0.75	3/4
	17	.265625			49	0.765625	
9	18	.28125		25	50	0.78125	
	19	.296875			51	0.796875	
10	20	.3125	5/16	26	52	0.8125	13/16
	21	.328125			53	0.828125	
11	22	.34375		27	54	0.84375	
	23	.359375			55	0.859375	
12	24	.375	3/8	28	56	0.875	7/8
	25	.390625			57	0.890625	
13	26	.40625		29	58	0.90625	
	27	.421875			59	0.921875	
14	28	.4375	7/16	30	60	0.9375	15/16
	29	.453125			61	0.953125	
15	30	.46875		31	62	0.96875	
	31	.48375			63	0.984375	
16	32	.5	1/2	32	64	1	1

TABLE 61   AREAS AND VOLUMES

TRIANGLE — $Area = \frac{1}{2}bh = \frac{1}{2}ab\sin C$	**REGULAR RIGHT PRISMS** — $Surface\ Area = nah$, $n = number\ of\ sides$	**REGULAR RIGHT PRISMS** — $Volume = Bh$, $B = area\ of\ base$
RECTANGLE — $Area = bh$	**REGULAR RIGHT PYRAMIDS** — $Surface\ Area = \frac{1}{2}san$, $n = number\ of\ sides$, $s = h/\sin\alpha$	**REGULAR RIGHT PYRAMID** — $Volume = \frac{1}{3}Bh$
PARALLELOGRAM — $Area = bh = ab\sin C$	**RIGHT CIRCULAR CYLINDER** — $Surface\ Area = 2\pi rh$	**RIGHT CIRCULAR CYLINDER** — $Volume = \pi r^2 h$
TRAPEZOID — $Area = \frac{1}{2}(a+b)h$, $A = \frac{1}{2}d_1 d_2 \sin C$	**SEGMENT OF CYLINDER** — For Area of end segment see 1st Col.	**SEGMENT OF CYLINDER** — $Volume = Bl$, $B = area\ of\ segment$ see bottom of Col. 1.
ANY REGULAR POLYGON — $Area = \frac{1}{2}nbh$, $n = number\ of\ sides$, $h = (b/2)(\tan\alpha)$, $\alpha = (n-2)/2n)180°$		**HOLLOW CYLINDER** — $Volume = \pi l (R^2 - r^2)$
CIRCLE — $Circum. = \pi d = 2\pi r$, $Area = \pi r^2 = \frac{\pi}{4}d^2$	**RIGHT CIRCULAR CONE** — $Surface\ Area = \pi rs$	**RIGHT CIRCULAR CONE** — $Volume = \frac{1}{3}\pi r^2 h$
ANNULUS — $Area = \pi(R^2 - r^2) = \frac{\pi}{4}(D^2 - d^2)$	**FRUSTUM OF CONE** — $Surface\ Area = \pi s(R+r)$	**FRUSTUM OF CONE** — $Volume = \frac{1}{3}\pi h(R^2 + Rr + r^2)$
SECTOR OF CIRCLE — $Area = \frac{1}{2}rs = \pi r^2 (\alpha/360°)$, $s = 2\pi r(\alpha/360°)$	**SPHERE** — $Surface\ Area = 4\pi r^2$	**SPHERE** — $Volume = \frac{4}{3}\pi r^3$
SEGMENT OF CIRCLE — $Area = \frac{1}{2}[r(s-c)+ch]$, $c = 2r\sin\alpha$, $s = 4\pi r(\alpha/360°)$, $\cos\alpha = (r-h)/r$	**SPHERICAL SEGMENT** — $Surface\ Area = 2\pi rh$	**SPHERICAL SEGMENT** — $Volume = \frac{1}{6}\pi h(3a^2 + h^2)$, $a^2 = (h(2r-h))$

TABLE 62   STANDARD BEND RADII

Material thickness	Aluminum alloy							Magnesium alloy		Steel			
	2SO 3SO 52SO 53SO	2S½H 3S¼H 4SO 52S¼H 53S¼H	2S¾H 3S½H 4S¼H 52S½H 53S½H	3S¾H 4S½H 17SO 24SO 52S¾H 53S¾H 61SO	4S¾H 17ST 24ST 53ST 53SW 61ST 61SW	75SO	27ST 75ST			Low carbon X4130 annealed	Stainless		
								Cold formed	Hot formed		annealed	¼ Hard	½ Hard
0 through 0.013	0.031	0.031	0.031	0.031	0.062	0.031	0.062	0.062	0.031	0.031	0.031	0.062	0.062
0.014 through .017	.031	.031	.031	.031	.062	.031	0.062	0.062	.031	.031	.031	.062	.062
.018 through .022	.031	.031	.031	.031	.062	.062	0.094	0.094	.031	.031	.031	.062	.062
.023 through .027	.031	.031	.031	.062	.094	.062	0.125	0.125	.062	.031	.031	.062	.062
.028 through .035	.062	.062	.062	.062	.125	.062	0.156	0.156	.062	.031	.031	.062	.094
.036 through .044	.062	.062	.062	.062	.125	.094	0.219	0.219	.094	.062	.062	.094	.125
.045 through .054	.062	.062	.094	.094	.156	.125	0.250	0.250	.125	.062	.062	.094	.125
.055 through .068	.062	.094	.094	.125	.219	.125	0.312	0.312	.156	.062	.062	.125	.188
.069 through .075	.094	.094	.125	.125	.250	.156	0.375	0.375	.188	.062	.062	.125	.188
.076 through .084	.094	.094	.156	.125	.281	.188	0.406	0.406	.219	.094	.094	.156	.219
.085 through .097	.094	.094	.188	.125	.312	.188	0.469	0.469	.250	.094	.094	.188	.250
.098 through .113	.125	.125	.188	.156	.375	.219	0.531	0.625	.250	.125	.125	.219	.312
.114 through .139	.125	.156	.219	.188	.438	.281	0.688	0.750	.312	.125	.188		
.140 through .172	.156	.188	.250	.250	.562	.375	0.875	1.000	.375	.156	.188		
.173 through .219	.188	.250	.375	.312	.750	.438	1.062	1.250	.500	.188	.188		
.220 through .262	.250	.312	.500	.469	.938	.531	1.250	1.500	.625	.250	.250		

TABLE 63 FLAT PATTERN DEVELOPMENT

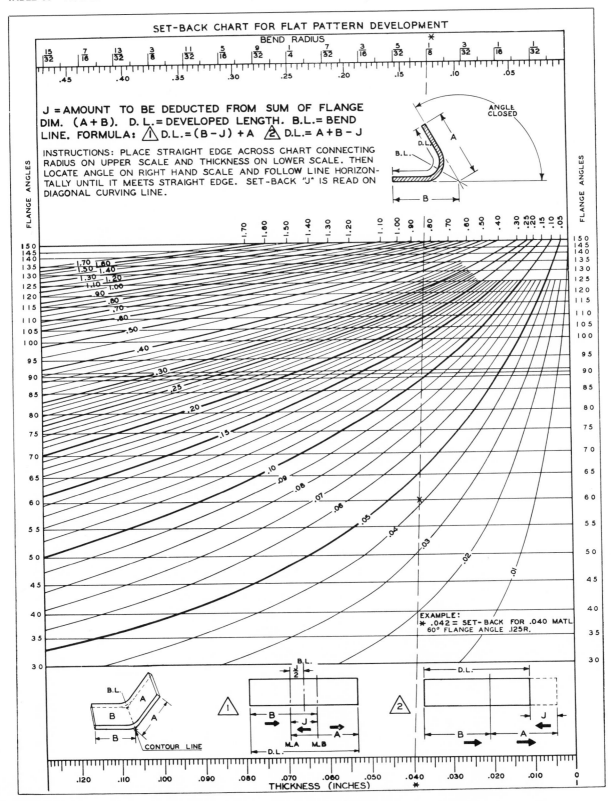

SET-BACK CHART FOR FLAT PATTERN DEVELOPMENT

BEND RADIUS

J = AMOUNT TO BE DEDUCTED FROM SUM OF FLANGE DIM. (A + B). D. L. = DEVELOPED LENGTH. B.L. = BEND LINE. FORMULA: △1 D.L. = (B − J) + A △2 D.L. = A + B − J

INSTRUCTIONS: PLACE STRAIGHT EDGE ACROSS CHART CONNECTING RADIUS ON UPPER SCALE AND THICKNESS ON LOWER SCALE. THEN LOCATE ANGLE ON RIGHT HAND SCALE AND FOLLOW LINE HORIZONTALLY UNTIL IT MEETS STRAIGHT EDGE. SET-BACK "J" IS READ ON DIAGONAL CURVING LINE.

ANGLE CLOSED

FLANGE ANGLES

FLANGE ANGLES

EXAMPLE:
* .042 = SET-BACK FOR .040 MATL
  60° FLANGE ANGLE .125R.

CONTOUR LINE

THICKNESS (INCHES)

TABLE 64   LIST OF COMMON ABBREVIATIONS

Adjust	ADJ	Grind	GRD
Allowance	ALLOW	Harden	HDN
Alteration	ALT	Head	HD
Aluminum	AL	Heat Treat	HT TR
American		High-Speed Steel	HSS
Standard	AMER STD	Hot Rolled Steel	HRS
American		Inside Diameter	ID
Wire Gage	AWG	Left Hand	
Approximate	APPROX	Thread	LH THD
Assemble	ASSEM	Locate	LOC
Assembly	ASSY	Lubricate	LUB
Auxiliary	AUX	Mild Steel	MS
Balance	BAL	Malleable Iron	MI
Base Line	BL	Material	MATL
Base Plate	BP	Maximum	MAX
Between Centers	BC	Micrometer	MIC
Bill of Materials	B/M	Minimum	MIN
Blueprint	B/P	National Coarse	NC
Bureau of		National Extra Fine	NEF
Standards	BU STD	National Fine	NF
Bushing	BUSH	National Special	NS
Carburize	CARB	On Center	OC
Cast Iron	CI	Outside Diameter	OD
Cast Steel	CS	Overall	OA
Center	CTR	Pattern	PATT
Center Line	CL	Piece	PC
Center to Center	C TO C	Place	PLC
Chamfer	CHF	Plate	PL
Cold Rolled Steel	CRS	Punch	PCH
Counterbore	C'BORE	Radius	R
Countersink	C'SINK	Ream	RM
Detail	DET	Reference	REF
Diameter	DIA	Required	REQD
Dimension	DIM	Right Hand	
Dowel	DWL	Thread	RH THD
Drawing	DWG	Rivet	RIV
Drill	DR	Screw	SCR
Drill Rod	DR RD	Section	SECT
Drop Forge	DF	Set Screw	SS
Eccentric	ECC	Shaft	SFT
Finish All Over	FAO	Socket Head	SOC HD
Fixture	FIX	Spotface	SF
Flat Ground Stock	FGS	Stainless Steel	SST
Flat Head	FH	Stock	STK
Forged Steel	FST	Taper	TPR
Forging	FORG	Temper	TEM
Foundry	FDRY	Threads Per Inch	TPI
Full Indicator		Tolerance	TOL
Reading	FIR	Tool Steel	TS
Gage	GA	Wrought Iron	WI

TABLE 65   USASI STANDARDS OF INTEREST TO DESIGNERS AND DRAFTSMEN

USA Standard Drafting Practices

Section 1 Size and Format.................Y14.1—1957

Section 2 Line Conventions, Sectioning and
  Lettering ....Y14.2—1957

Section 3 Projections...................Y14.3—1957

Section 4 Pictorial Drawing...............Y14.4—1957

Section 5 Dimensioning and Notes.........Y14.5—1966

Section 6 Screw Threads.................Y14.6—1957

Section 7 Gears, Splines and Serrations......Y14.7—1958

Section 8 Castings....................In Preparation

Section 9 Forgings......................Y14.9—1958

Section 10 Metal Stampings..............Y14.10—1959

Section 11 Plastics.....................Y14.11—1958

Section 12 Die Castings................In Preparation

Section 13 Springs, Helical and Flat.......In Preparation

Section 14 Mechanical Assemblies........Y14.14—1961

Section 15 Electrical Diagrams...........Y14.15—1960

Section 16 Tools, Dies and Gages........In Preparation

Section 17 Fluid Power Diagrams.........Y14.17—1966

Section 18 Drawings for Optical Parts.....In Preparation

Section 19 Engineering Drawings for
  Photographic Reproduction..........In Preparation

Graphical Symbols for:

  Metallizing Symbols ....Y32.12—1960

  Welding ....Y32.3—1959

  Plumbing ....Y32.4—1955

  Pipe Fittings, Valves and
    Piping.............Z32.2.3—1949 (Reaffirmed 1953)

  Heating, Ventilating and
    Air Conditioning....................Z32.2.4—1949

  Use on Railroad Maps and Profiles........Y32.7—1957

  Heat-Power
    Apparatus..........Z32.2.6—1950 (Reaffirmed 1956)

  Fluid Power Diagrams..................Y32.10—1958

  Process Flow Diagrams in Petroleum and
    Chemical Industries..................Y32.11—1961

  Nondestructive Testing Symbols.........Y32.17—1962

  Abbreviations for Use on Drawings........Z32.13—1950

Letter Symbols for:

  Hydraulics ....Y10.2—1958

  Rocket Propulsion ....Y10.14—1959

  Mechanics for Solid Bodies...............Z10.3—1948

  Structural Analysis.....................Z10.8—1949

  Heat and Thermodynamics...............Y10.4—1957

  Physics ....Z10.6—1948

  Aeronautical Sciences....................Y10.7—1954

  Radio ....Y10.9—1953

  Meteorology ....Y10.10—1953

  Acoustics ....Y10.11—1953 (Reaffirmed 1959)

  Chemical Engineering....Y10.12—1955 (Reaffirmed 1961)

  Petroleum Reservoir Engineering and
    Electric Logging ....Y10.15—1958

  Abbreviations for Scientific and Engineering
    Terms ....Z10.1—1941

  Guide for Selecting Greek Letters Used as
    Letter Symbols for Engineering
    Mathematics ....Y10.17—1961

  Shell Theory ....Y10.16—1964

TABLE 66 INTERNATIONAL, AMERICAN, BRITISH AND CANADIAN SYMBOLS FOR POSITIONAL AND FORM TOLERANCES

	DIFFERENCES IN SYMBOLIZATION FOR POSITIONAL AND FORM TOLERANCES			
Item	International ISO/TC 10 (Symbols mandatory)	American USASI Y14.5 (Symbols optional)	British BS 308 (No symbols-equivalent terms)	Canadian B 78.1
Straightness	—	—	STR TOL	STRAIGHT WITHIN
Roundness (circularity)	○	○	RD TOL	ROUND TOL
Profile of any line	⌒	⌒	Not specified	Not specified
Flatness	▱	▱	FLAT TOL	FLAT WITHIN
Cylindricity	⌭	⌭	CYL TOL	Not specified
Profile of any surface	⌓	⌓	TOL ZONE	TOL ZONE
Parallelism	//	||	PAR TOL	PARALLEL TO
Perpendicularity (squareness)	⊥	⊥	SQ TOL	SQUARE WITH
Angularity	∠	∠	ANG TOL	ANG TOL
Runout	↗	↗	Not specified	Not specified
True position	⊕	⊕	POSN TOL	LOCATE WITHIN
Concentricity	◎	◎	CONC TOL	CONCENTRIC TO
Symmetry	≡	≡	SYM TOL	SYMMETRICAL WITHIN
Datum feature	A	-A-	⟋ A	⟋ A
True position dimension	127	5.000	5.000 TP	5.000 (TP)
Maximum material condition	Ⓜ	Ⓜ	MMC	MMC
Regardless of feature size	Not specified	Ⓢ	Not specified	Not specified
Tolerance	Total value specified	Total value specified except where radial (half) value is an option.	Total value specified	Total value specified
Diameter	⌀	DIA	DIA or ⌀	DIA or ⌀
Shape of tolerance zone	Zone is a width in direction of leader arrow. ⌀ specified where zone is circular or cylindrical.	DIA, TOTAL, or R specified as applicable for positional tolerances. Otherwise, not specified and diameter or width implied as applicable.	DIA or WIDE specified as applicable.	FIM or DIA specified when considered necessary.
Sequence within geometric tolerance notation	1st-Geometric characteristic symbol 2nd-Tolerance value & modifier 3rd-Datum reference & modifier	1st-Geometric characteristic symbol 2nd-Datum reference & modifier 3rd-Tolerance value & modifier	1st-Geometric characteristic term 2nd-Tolerance value & modifier 3rd-Datum reference & modifier	1st-Geometric characteristic term 2nd-Datum reference & modifier 3rd-Tolerance value & modifier

TABLE 67   HEAVY-DUTY DIE SETS

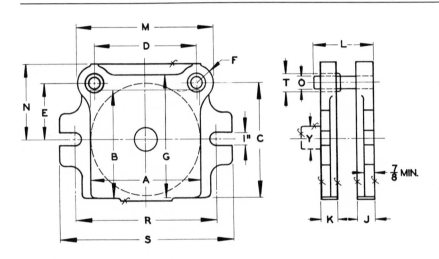

Commercial series, regular type.   Flanged Punch Holder and Die Holder Heavy Guide Posts

Die area		Thickness		Steel die holder Steel punch holder	General Dimensions										
A	B	Die holder	Punch holder		C	D	E	F	G	M	N	O	R	S	T
		J	K												
6	4	1½	1¼	939116	4¾	7½	2¾	1⅝	5¼	10¾	4½	1½	8¼	10¾	2
		2	1¾	939117											
8	6	1½	1¼	939118	6¾	9½	3¾	1⅝	7¼	12¾	5½	1½	10¼	12¾	2
		2	1¾	939119											
10	8	1¾	1½	939120	8⅞	11¾	4⅞	2	9⅝	15¾	7	1¾	12¼	14¾	2¼
		2¾	2	939121											
12	10	2	1¾	939122	10⅞	13¾	5⅞	2	11⅜	17¾	8	1¾	14¼	16¾	2¼
		3	2½	939123											
14	12	2¼	2	939124	13	16	7	2½	14	21	9⅝	2	16¼	18¾	2½
		3¼	2¾	939125											
16	14	2¼	2	939126	15	18	8	2½	16	23	10⅝	2	18¼	20¾	2½
		3½	2¾	939127											

Courtesy General Motors Corp.

TABLE 68 PRESS FIT WEARING BUSHINGS

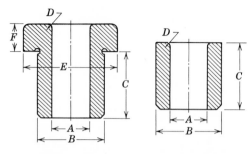

Press fit, head type   Press fit, headless type

Range of Hole Sizes A	Body Diameter B					Body Length C	Radius D	Head Dia E	Head Thickness F	Number
		Unfinished		Finished						
	Nom	Max	Min	Max	Min			Max	Max	
0.1406 To 0.1875	5/16	0.327	0.322	0.3141	0.3138	1/4	1/32	7/16	1/8	H-20-4
	5/16	0.327	0.322	0.3141	0.3138	5/16	1/32	7/16	1/8	H-20-5
	5/16	0.327	0.322	0.3141	0.3138	3/8	1/32	7/16	1/8	H-20-6
	5/16	0.327	0.322	0.3141	0.3138	1/2	1/32	7/16	1/8	H-20-8
	5/16	0.327	0.322	0.3141	0.3138	3/4	1/32	7/16	1/8	H-20-12
	5/16	0.327	0.322	0.3141	0.3138	1	1/32	7/16	1/8	H-20-16
0.189 To 0.2500	13/32	0.421	0.416	0.4078	0.4075	1/4	1/32	17/32	5/32	H-26-4
	13/32	0.421	0.416	0.4078	0.4075	5/16	1/32	17/32	5/32	H-26-5
	13/32	0.421	0.416	0.4078	0.4075	3/8	1/32	17/32	5/32	H-26-6
	13/32	0.421	0.416	0.4078	0.4075	1/2	1/32	17/32	5/32	H-26-8
	13/32	0.421	0.416	0.4078	0.4075	3/4	1/32	17/32	5/32	H-26-12
	13/32	0.421	0.416	0.4078	0.4075	1	1/32	17/32	5/32	H-26-16
	13/32	0.421	0.416	0.4078	0.4075	1 3/8	1/32	17/32	5/32	H-26-22
	13/32	0.421	0.416	0.4078	0.4075	1 3/4	1/32	17/32	5/32	H-26-28
0.2570 To 0.3125	1/2	0.520	0.515	0.5017	0.5014	5/16	3/64	5/8	7/32	H-32-5
	1/2	0.520	0.515	0.5017	0.5014	3/8	3/64	5/8	7/32	H-32-6
	1/2	0.520	0.515	0.5017	0.5014	1/2	3/64	5/8	7/32	H-32-8
	1/2	0.520	0.515	0.5017	0.5014	3/4	3/64	5/8	7/32	H-32-12
	1/2	0.520	0.515	0.5017	0.5014	1	3/64	5/8	7/32	H-32-16
	1/2	0.520	0.515	0.5017	0.5014	1 3/8	3/64	5/8	7/32	H-32-22
	1/2	0.520	0.515	0.5017	0.5014	1 3/4	3/64	5/8	7/32	H-32-28

Nominal Size of Hole	Maximum	Minimum
Above 0.0000 to 1/4 in. incl.	Nominal + 0.0004 in.	Nominal + 0.0001 in.
Above 1/4 to 3/4 in. incl.	Nominal + 0.0005 in.	Nominal + 0.0001 in.
Above 3/4 to 1-1/2 in. incl.	Nominal + 0.0006 in.	Nominal + 0.0002 in.
Above 1-1/2	Nominal + 0.0007 in.	Nominal + 0.0003 in.

The body diameter, B, for unfinished bushings is larger than the nominal diameter in order to provide grinding stock for fitting to jig plate holes. The grinding allowance is

0.005 to 0.010 in. for sizes 5/32, 13/64 and 1/4 in.,
0.010 to 0.015 in. for sizes 5/16 and 13/32 in., and
0.015 to 0.020 in. for sizes 1/2 in. and up.

Size and type of chamfer on lead end to be manufacturer's option.
The length, C, is the overall length for the headless type and length underhead for the head type.
The head design shall be in accordance with the manufacturer's practice.
Diameter "A" must be concentric to diameter "B" within 0.0005 T.I.V. on finish ground bushings.

TABLE 68 *(Continued)*

Range of Hole Sizes A	Body Diameter B				Body Length C	Radius D	Head Dia E Max	Head Thickness F Max	Number
	Nom	Unfinished Max	Min	Finished Max	Min					

Range of Hole Sizes A	Nom	Unfinished Max	Unfinished Min	Finished Max	Finished Min	Body Length C	Radius D	Head Dia E Max	Head Thickness F Max	Number
0.3160 To 0.4219	5/8	0.645	0.640	0.6267	0.6264	5/16	3/64	13/16	7/32	H-40-5
	5/8	0.645	0.640	0.6267	0.6264	3/8	3/64	13/16	7/32	H-40-6
	5/8	0.645	0.640	0.6267	0.6264	1/2	3/64	13/16	7/32	H-40-8
	5/8	0.645	0.640	0.6267	0.6264	3/4	3/64	13/16	7/32	H-40-12
	5/8	0.645	0.640	0.6267	0.6264	1	3/64	13/16	7/32	H-40-16
	5/8	0.645	0.640	0.6267	0.6264	1 3/8	3/64	13/16	7/32	H-40-22
	5/8	0.645	0.640	0.6267	0.6264	1 3/4	3/64	13/16	7/32	H-40-28
	5/8	0.645	0.640	0.6267	0.6264	2 1/8	3/64	13/16	7/32	H-40-34
0.4375 To 0.5000	3/4	0.770	0.765	0.7518	0.7515	1/2	1/16	15/16	7/32	H-48-8
	3/4	0.770	0.765	0.7518	0.7515	3/4	1/16	15/16	7/32	H-48-12
	3/4	0.770	0.765	0.7518	0.7515	1	1/16	15/16	7/32	H-48-16
	3/4	0.770	0.765	0.7518	0.7515	1 3/8	1/16	15/16	7/32	H-48-22
	3/4	0.770	0.765	0.7518	0.7515	1 3/4	1/16	15/16	7/32	H-48-28
	3/4	0.770	0.765	0.7518	0.7515	2 1/8	1/16	15/16	7/32	H-48-34
0.5156 To 0.6250	7/8	0.895	0.890	0.8768	0.8765	1/2	1/16	1 1/8	1/4	H-56-8
	7/8	0.895	0.890	0.8768	0.8765	3/4	1/16	1 1/8	1/4	H-56-12
	7/8	0.895	0.890	0.8768	0.8765	1	1/16	1 1/8	1/4	H-56-16
	7/8	0.895	0.890	0.8768	0.8765	1 3/8	1/16	1 1/8	1/4	H-56-22
	7/8	0.895	0.890	0.8768	0.8765	1 3/4	1/16	1 1/8	1/4	H-56-28
	7/8	0.895	0.890	0.8768	0.8765	2 1/8	1/16	1 1/8	1/4	H-56-34
	7/8	0.895	0.890	0.8768	0.8765	2 1/2	1/16	1 1/8	1/4	H-56-40
0.6406 To 0.7500	1	1.020	1.015	1.0018	1.0015	1/2	3/32	1 1/4	5/16	H-64-8
	1	1.020	1.015	1.0018	1.0015	3/4	3/32	1 1/4	5/16	H-64-12
	1	1.020	1.015	1.0018	1.0015	1	3/32	1 1/4	5/16	H-64-16
	1	1.020	1.015	1.0018	1.0015	1 3/8	3/32	1 1/4	5/16	H-64-22
	1	1.020	1.015	1.0018	1.0015	1 3/4	3/32	1 1/4		H-64-28
	1	1.020	1.015	1.0018	1.0015	2 1/8	3/32		5/16	H-64-34
	1	1.020	1.015	1.0018	1.0015	2 1/2	3/32	1 1/4	5/16	H-64-40
0.7656 To 1.0000	1 3/8	1.395	1.390	1.3772	1.3768	3/4	3/32	1 5/8	3/8	H-88-12
	1 3/8	1.395	1.390	1.3772	1.3768	1	3/32	1 5/8	3/8	H-88-16
	1 3/8	1.395	1.390	1.3772	1.3768	1 3/8	3/32	1 5/8	3/8	H-88-22
	1 3/8	1.395	1.390	1.3772	1.3768	1 3/4	3/32	1 5/8	3/8	H-88-28
	1 3/8	1.395	1.390	1.3772	1.3768	2 1/8	3/32	1 5/8	3/8	H-88-34
	1 3/8	1.395	1.390	1.3772	1.3768	2 1/2	3/32	1 5/8	3/8	H-88-40
1.0156 To 1.3750	1 3/4	1.770	1.765	1.7523	1.7519	1	3/32	2	3/8	H-112-16
	1 3/4	1.770	1.765	1.7523	1.7519	1 3/8	3/32	2	3/8	H-112-22
	1 3/4	1.770	1.765	1.7523	1.7519	1 3/4	3/32	2	3/8	H-112-28
	1 3/4	1.770	1.765	1.7523	1.7519	2 1/8	3/32	2	3/8	H-112-34
	1 3/4	1.770	1.765	1.7523	1.7519	2 1/2	3/32	2	3/8	H-112-40
	1 3/4	1.770	1.765	1.7523	1.7519	3	3/32	2	3/8	H-112-48
1.3906 To 1.7500	2 1/4	2.270	2.265	2.2525	2.2521	1	3/32	2 1/2	3/8	H-144-16
	2 1/4	2.270	2.265	2.2525	2.2521	1 3/8	3/32	2 1/2	3/8	H-144-22
	2 1/4	2.270	2.265	2.2525	2.2521	1 3/4	3/32	2 1/2	3/8	H-144-28
	2 1/4	2.270	2.265	2.2525	2.2521	2 1/8	3/32	2 1/2	3/8	H-144-34
	2 1/4	2.270	2.265	2.2525	2.2521	2 1/2	3/32	2 1/2	3/8	H-144-40
	2 1/4	2.270	2.265	2.2525	2.2521	3	3/32	2 1/2	3/8	H-144-48

All dimensions given in inches.

Tolerance on fractional dimensions where not otherwise specified shall be 0.010 inch, plus or minus.

Hole sizes are in accordance with the American Standard Twist Drill Sizes (USASI B5.12–1958).

The maximum and minimum values of the hole size, A, shall be as follows:

Index